# HANDBOOK OF PHASE CHANGE: BOILING AND CONDENSATION

# HANDBOOK OF PHASE CHANGE: BOILING AND CONDENSATION

*Editor-in Chief*
**Satish G. Kandlikar**

*Co-editors:*
**Masahiro Shoji**
**Vijay K. Dhir**

| | | |
|---|---|---|
| USA | Publishing Office: | TAYLOR & FRANCIS<br>325 Chestnut Street<br>Philadelphia, PA 19106<br>Tel: (215) 625-8900<br>Fax: (215) 625-2940 |
| | Distribution Center: | TAYLOR & FRANCIS<br>47 Runway Road, Suite G<br>Levittown, PA 19057-4700<br>Tel: (215) 269-0400<br>Fax: (215) 269-0363 |
| UK | | TAYLOR & FRANCIS<br>1 Gunpowder Square<br>London EC4A 3DE<br>Tel: +44 171 583 0490<br>Fax: +44 171 583 0581 |

**HANDBOOK OF PHASE CHANGE: Boiling and Condensation**

Copyright © 1999 Taylor & Francis. All rights reserved. Printed in the United States of America. Except as permitted under the United States Copyright Act of 1976, no part of this publication may be reproduced or distributed in any form or by any means, or stored in a database or retrieval system, without prior written permission of the publisher.

1 2 3 4 5 6 7 8 9 0

Printed by Edwards Brothers, Ann Arbor, MI, 1999.

A CIP catalog record for this book is available from the British Library.
⊗The paper in this publication meets the requirements of the ANSI Standard Z39.48-1984 (Permanence of Paper).

**Library of Congress Cataloging-in-Publication Data**
Handbook of phase change : boiling and condensation / Satish
    Kandlikar. Masahiro Shoji, Vijay K. Dhir. [editors]
       p. cm.
    Includes bibliographical references and index.
    ISBN 1-56032-634-4 (alk. paper)
      1.  Ebullition. 2. Condensation. I. Kandlikar, S. G. (Satish G.)
II. Shoji, Mansahiro.  III. Dhir, V.K.
QC307.H36 1999                                          99-26754
530.4'74--dc21                                            CIP

ISBN 1-56032-634-4 (case)

# CONTENTS

|  |  |  |
|---|---|---|
| Preface | | xiii |
| Nomenclature | | xix |
| Contributors | | xli |

**1 VAPOR LIQUID EQUILIBRIUM PROPERTIES** — 1
*Y. Fujita, S. G. Kandlikar*

| 1.1 | Thermodynamic Equilibrium—Pure Components | 1 |
| 1.2 | Thermodynamic Equilibrium—Binary and Multi-Component Mixtures | 11 |
| 1.3 | Thermodynamic and Transport Properties of Pure Substances and Multicomponent Mixtures | 34 |
| | References | 39 |

**2 REPRESENTATION OF SOLID-LIQUID-VAPOR PHASE INTERACTIONS** — 41
*M. Shoji, Y. Mori, S. Maruyama*

| 2.1 | Introduction of Solid-Liquid-Vapor Phase Interactions | 41 |
| 2.2 | Macroscopic Representation of Solid-Liquid-Vapor Phase Interactions | 44 |
| 2.3 | Microscopic Representation of Solid-Liquid-Vapor Interactions | 52 |
| | References | 59 |

**3 BOILING CURVE** — 63
*V. K. Dhir*

| 3.1 | Introduction | 63 |
| 3.2 | Pool Boiling | 63 |

| | | |
|---|---|---|
| 3.3 | Flow Boiling | 66 |
| | References | 69 |

| | | |
|---|---|---|
| **4** | **NUCLEATE BOILING** | **71** |
| | *V. K. Dhir, S. G. Kandlikar, Y. Fujita, Y. Iida, R. Heist* | |
| 4.1 | Introduction (VD) | 71 |
| 4.2 | Effect of System Variables on Nucleate Boiling (VD) | 74 |
| 4.3 | Nucleation Characteristics in Pool Boiling, Heterogeneous Nucleation (VD) | 79 |
| 4.4 | Bubble Dynamics and Heat Transfer (VD) | 85 |
| 4.5 | Nucleation Site Density (VD) | 89 |
| 4.6 | Heat Transfer in Nucleate Boiling (VD) | 93 |
| 4.7 | Pool Boiling in Binary Systems (SK, YF) | 99 |
| 4.8 | Homogeneous Nucleation of Liquids (YI, RH) | 109 |
| | References | 116 |

| | | |
|---|---|---|
| **5** | **ENHANCEMENT TECHNIQUES IN POOL BOILING** | **121** |
| | *A. Yabe, W. Nakayama, P. Di Marco* | |
| 5.1 | Introduction (AY, WN) | 121 |
| 5.2 | Basic Enhancement Mechanism in Pool Boiling (AY, WN) | 122 |
| 5.3 | Passive Methods of Pool Heat Transfer Enhancement (AY, WN) | 125 |
| 5.4 | Active Methods of Pool Boiling Enhancement (PD) | 133 |
| | References | 141 |

| | | |
|---|---|---|
| **6** | **CRITICAL HEAT FLUX IN POOL BOILING** | **145** |
| | *Y. Haramura* | |
| 6.1 | Critical Heat Flux in Saturated Pool Boiling of Pure Liquids | 145 |
| 6.2 | Mechanistic Models | 151 |
| 6.3 | Amount of Liquid Left in Macrolayer | 155 |
| 6.4 | Critical Heat Flux of Subcooled Pool Boiling for Single Component Liquid | 158 |
| 6.5 | Critical Heat Flux in Pool Boiling for Mixtures | 161 |
| | References | 163 |

| | | |
|---|---|---|
| **7** | **FILM AND TRANSITION BOILING** | **167** |
| | *S. Nishio, H. Auracher* | |
| 7.1 | Introduction (SN) | 167 |
| 7.2 | Film Pool Boiling (SN) | 168 |
| 7.3 | Transition Boiling (HA) | 181 |
| | References | 193 |

| 8 | INTRODUCTION AND BASIC MODELS | 197 |
|---|---|---|
| | *G. Hewitt* | |
| 8.1 | Introduction | 197 |
| 8.2 | Two-Phase Flow Systems | 198 |
| 8.3 | Flow Patterns | 200 |
| 8.4 | Modeling Two-Phase Flow Systems | 201 |
| 8.5 | Overview | 203 |

| 9 | FLUID MECHANICS ASPECTS OF TWO-PHASE FLOW | 205 |
|---|---|---|
| | *G. Hewitt, M. Kawaji* | |
| 9.1 | Flow Inside Circular Tubes (GH) | 205 |
| 9.2 | Flow In Other Geometries (MK) | 233 |
| | References | 254 |

| 10 | TWO-PHASE FLOW INSTABILITIES | 261 |
|---|---|---|
| | *M. Ozawa* | |
| 10.1 | Introduction | 261 |
| 10.2 | Problem Description and Classification | 261 |
| 10.3 | Basic Mathematical Modeling | 264 |
| 10.4 | Density Wave Oscillation | 268 |
| 10.5 | Non-Linear Dynamics and Chaos | 274 |
| | References | 278 |

| 11 | CRITICAL TWO PHASE FLOW | 279 |
|---|---|---|
| | *H. Nariai* | |
| 11.1 | Introduction | 279 |
| 11.2 | Equilibrium Critical Flow | 281 |
| 11.3 | Non-Equilibrium Critical Flow | 282 |
| 11.4 | Summary and Recommendation | 283 |
| | References | 283 |

| 12 | TWO-PHASE FLOW AND BOILING HEAT TRANSFER IN TUBE BUNDLES | 285 |
|---|---|---|
| | *R. Dowlati, M. Kawaji* | |
| 12.1 | Introduction | 285 |
| 12.2 | Flow Regimes | 289 |
| 12.3 | Void Fraction | 291 |
| 12.4 | Two-Phase Frictional Pressure Drop | 297 |

| | | |
|---|---|---|
| 12.5 | Two-Phase Heat Transfer Coefficient | 300 |
| | References | 307 |

| **13** | **EXTERNAL FLOW FILM BOILING** | **311** |
|---|---|---|
| | *L. Witte* | |
| 13.1 | Introduction | 311 |
| 13.2 | Physical/Mathematical Models for Flow Film Boiling | 311 |
| 13.3 | Data Correlation and Comparison to Theory | 320 |
| 13.4 | Concluding Remarks | 328 |
| | References | 329 |

| **14** | **AUGMENTATION TECHNIQUES AND EXTERNAL FLOW BOILING** | **331** |
|---|---|---|
| | *M. Monde, T. Ueda, Y. Koizumi, V. K. Dhir* | |
| 14.1 | Impinging Jets and Other Geometries (MM) | 331 |
| 14.2 | Falling Film Evaporation and Boiling (TU, YK) | 342 |
| 14.3 | Augmentation Techniques in External Flow Boiling (MM, VD) | 359 |
| | References | 363 |

| **15** | **FLOW BOILING IN CIRCULAR TUBES** | **367** |
|---|---|---|
| | *S. G. Kandlikar* | |
| | (with H. Nariai—15.2.4., 15.3.1–2, 15.3.7–8) | |
| 15.1 | Introduction | 367 |
| 15.2 | Subcooled Flow Boiling | 368 |
| 15.3 | Saturated Flow Boiling | 386 |
| | References | 399 |

| **16** | **FLOW BOILING IN ADVANCED GEOMETRIES AND APPLICATIONS** | **403** |
|---|---|---|
| | *W. Nakayama, A. Yabe, P. Kew, K. Cornwell, S. G. Kandlikar, V. K. Dhir* | |
| 16.1 | Flow Boiling in Narrow Channels for Thermal Management of Microelectronic Equipment (WN, AY) | 403 |
| 16.2 | Flow Boiling in Compact Heat Exchangers (PK, KC) | 412 |
| 16.3 | Flow Boiling of Binary Mixtures in Plain Tubes (SK) | 428 |
| 16.4 | Flow Boiling in Microgravity (VD) | 435 |
| | References | 436 |

| 17 | CHF AND POST-CHF (POST-DRYOUT) HEAT TRANSFER | 443 |
|---|---|---|
| | *G. P. Celata, A. Mariani* | |
| 17.1 | CHF in Subcooled Flow Boiling | 444 |
| 17.2 | CHF in Saturated Flow Boiling | 459 |
| 17.3 | Post-CHF Heat Transfer | 477 |
| | Appendix | 484 |
| | References | 486 |
| 18 | FLOW BOILING AUGMENTATION | 495 |
| | *S. G. Kandlikar, G. P. Celata, A. Mariani* | |
| 18.1 | Augmentation of Subcooled Boiling Heat Transfer (SK) | 495 |
| 18.2 | Augmentation of Saturated Flow Boiling Heat Transfer (SK) | 498 |
| 18.3 | Augmentation of CHF and Post-CHF Transfer (GC, AM) | 512 |
| | References | 518 |
| 19 | FILM CONDENSATION | 523 |
| | *J. Rose, H. Uehara, S. Koyama, T. Fujii* | |
| 19.1 | Laminar Film Condensation of Pure Vapors (JR) | 523 |
| 19.2 | Transition and Turbulent Film Condensation (HU) | 537 |
| 19.3 | Condensation on Tube Banks (HU) | 551 |
| 19.4 | Condensation of Mixtures (SK, TF) | 563 |
| | References | 575 |
| 20 | DROPWISE CONDENSATION | 581 |
| | *J. Rose, Y. Utaka, I. Tanasawa* | |
| 20.1 | Introduction | 581 |
| 20.2 | Promotion of Dropwise Condensation | 582 |
| 20.3 | Dropwise Condensation of Steam | 583 |
| 20.4 | Dropwise Condensation of Organic Vapors | 589 |
| 20.5 | Heat Transfer Theory | 590 |
| | References | 592 |
| 21 | DIRECT CONTACT CONDENSATION | 595 |
| | *I. Tanasawa, Y. Mori, Y. Utaka* | |
| 21.1 | Introduction | 595 |
| 21.2 | Case When a Low-Temperature Liquid Forms a Dispersed Phase | 596 |
| 21.3 | Case When a Vapor Forms a Dispersed Phase | 600 |
| | References | 603 |

## 22 AUGMENTATION TECHNIQUES IN EXTERNAL CONDENSATION  605
*H. Honda, J. Rose*

- 22.1 Vertical Fluted Tube  605
- 22.2 Horizontal Finned Tube  609
- 22.3 Electrohydrodynamic Augmentation Techniques  616
- 22.4 Other Techniques  618
- References  618

## 23 HEAT TRANSFER AND PRESSURE DROP IN INTERNAL FLOW CONDENSATION  621
*S. Koyama, J. Yu*

- 23.1 Introduction  621
- 23.2 Pressure Drop  622
- 23.3 Condensation Heat Transfer of Pure Vapors  624
- 23.4 Condensation Heat Transfer of Binary Mixtures  627
- 23.5 Condensation Heat Transfer of Multi-Component Mixtures  633
- 23.6 Future Research Needs  635
- References  635

## 24 AUGMENTATION TECHNIQUES AND CONDENSATION INSIDE ADVANCED GEOMETRIES  639
*M. H. Kim, V. Srinivasan, R. K. Shah*

- 24.1 Augmentation Techniques in Internal Flow Geometries (MK)  639
- 24.2 Condensation in Compact Heat Exchangers (VS, RS)  653
- References  675

## 25 INSTRUMENTATION IN BOILING AND CONDENSATION STUDIES  679
*J. Delhaye*
(with N. Takenaka—25.4.3 and D. Kenning—25.8)

- 25.1 Basic Definitions  680
- 25.2 Local Void Fraction Measurments  682
- 25.3 Line Void Fraction Measurements  687
- 25.4 Area Void Fraction Measurements  692
- 25.5 Mass Flow Rate Measurements  701
- 25.6 Volumetric Interfacial Area Measurements  709
- 25.7 Measurements of Other Quantities of Interest  711

| | | |
|---|---|---|
| 25.8 | Liquid Crystal Thermography in Boiling | 713 |
| 25.9 | Concluding Remarks | 716 |
| | References | 717 |

**CONVERSION FACTORS FOR COMMONLY USED QUANTITIES** — 725

**CONVERSION FACTORS IN DIFFERENT UNITS** — 726

**INDEX** — 729

# PREFACE

## INTRODUCTION

Phase change phenomena involving boiling and condensation have historically received sporadic attention. Boilers for motive steam generation, condensers in steam power plants, and applications in petrochemical, chemical, and automotive industries provided the necessary impetus. The nuclear industry and its safety concerns brought the focus to the critical heat flux and post-CHF heat transfer area. Energy conservation requirements opened up an entirely new area for research, and novel techniques were developed to augment the heat transfer performance. The small dimensional requirements associated with the cooling of electronic equipment produced new challenges at the micro-scale level and in the boiling and condensation field as well.

With so many diverse techniques and complex analytical methodologies being introduced in the area of boiling and condensation, it no longer remains a small subsection of the heat transfer compendium. With this background, it was only a matter of time before the need for a handbook dedicated to this important field of heat transfer was realized.

## AUTHORS OF THE HANDBOOK

Many universities, research laboratories, and industries worldwide are at the forefront of research in the field of boiling and condensation. To compile state-of-art information from these and other sources and present it in a timely fashion is an extremely arduous task for one person.

To best serve the readers, a group of international experts has been formed, and they constitute the authors of the present handbook. Each author is an expert in his field and has developed valuable insight through decades of research. We are indeed fortunate to have such a large number of internationally renowned researchers contribute to the handbook and present the results of their recent work.

## COVERAGE

The handbook consists of twenty-five chapters covering different aspects of boiling and condensation. Each chapter is subdivided into sections in which specific topics are covered in detail. The presentation is kept uniform throughout: first the specific topic or phenomenon is described, followed by a brief survey of previous work, a phenomenological model based on current understanding, and finally a set of recommended design equations or correlations. Areas for further research are also identified in the closing comments at the end of each section or chapter.

Chapter 1 introduces the vapor-liquid phase equilibrium properties, while Chapter 2 deals with the liquid and vapor phase interactions with a solid phase. This provides the basics of bubble and droplet behavior on a heater or a condenser surface at a microscopic level.

Chapters 3–7 cover different aspects of pool boiling, including the boiling curves, nucleate boiling of pure components and their mixtures, enhancement techniques, critical heat flux, and transition and film boiling. Recent developments in mixture boiling and enhancement techniques, which readers should find useful, have also been included.

Chapters 8–11 address various aspects of two-phase flow. The basic models and fluid mechanics aspects are introduced in Chapters 8 and 9. Chapter 10 and 11 deal with two-phase flow instabilities and critical two-phase flow. These chapters take the reader from an introductory level to the current state of design methodologies employed in complex systems.

The external flow boiling is covered in Chapters 12–14. Chapter 12 deals with heat transfer and pressure drop in tube bundles, a geometry that is employed extensively in nuclear power and process industries. With high heat fluxes employed in tube bundles under normal operation or in nuclear reactors experiencing near-accident conditions, external film flow boiling becomes important. This is covered in Chapter 13. Chapter 14 presents various techniques to enhance heat transfer in external flow boiling.

Internal flow boiling constitutes an important geometry in many applications. The recent impetus in refrigeration industry to improve performance as well as to find replacement refrigerants has fueled the research in this area. Chapter 15 covers the flow boiling of pure liquids in circular tubes and provides basic models that are extended to many other situations, such as flow boiling of binary mixtures. Chapter 16 covers these topics, along with the flow boiling in narrow channels, compact evaporators, and under microgravity conditions. Critical heat flux in subcooled and saturated flow boiling is covered in Chapter 17. Chapter 18 covers augmentation techniques in flow boiling under saturated and subcooled conditions, including the enhancements in nucleate boiling component, convective component, and CHF and post-CHF heat transfer.

Condensation heat transfer is covered in Chapters 19–24. Chapter 19 introduces the basic film condensation theories for laminar and turbulent film condensation of pure components and binary mixtures on external surfaces. Chapter 20 covers dropwise condensation, while direct contact condensation is covered in Chapter 21. Augmentation techniques in external condensation are covered in Chapter 22.

Internal flow condensation is covered in Chapter 23. Heat transfer and pressure drop theories and correlations are presented for in-tube condensation of pure and multi-component mixtures. Chapter 24 presents a detailed description of internal flow condensation in augmented tubes and compact condensers. Helpful comments are provided for designers in performing condenser design calculations.

The instrumentation specific to boiling and condensation is covered in Chapter 25. A number of modern instrumentation techniques are presented, along with a theoretical description of the principles and helpful remarks.

A detailed reference list at the end of each chapter provides the readers with publications important to pursuing further investigation in a specific field.

## NOMENCLATURE

While the handbook is written in parts by different authors, the continuity of the material and the uniformity in presentation have been of prime concern. To address these issues, the complete structure of the handbook was first formulated, and then experts were invited to write on specific topics. A common nomenclature is used to cover all chapters and is included at the beginning of the handbook. Any departures from the nomenclature are also clearly noted in the list. In the future, we plan to remove these deviations and move toward a truly unified nomenclature conforming to the internationally accepted terminology.

## ABOUT THE INTENDED READERS

The handbook is structured in such a way that it would be useful to a newcomer by providing detailed background information about specific topics and presenting a clear model describing the fundamental processes and related parameters. The literature survey and discussion of various methodologies provide the broad picture to the user. Finally, design correlations and methodologies are presented for use in equipment design or performance evaluation. The handbook therefore serves as (i) an introductory book in the field of boiling and condensation, (ii) a sourcebook for researchers and design engineers, and (iii) a textbook for graduate level courses. The handbook is also expected to serve as the basic reference material for short courses in this field.

## INDEX

To facilitate locating a topic and its related links, an exhaustive index has been developed. With some of the concepts being employed in different aspects of boiling and condensation phenomena, the index should prove useful in introducing the reader to additional possibilities, thus aiding creative endeavors.

## ACKNOWLEDGMENTS

The handbook is a joint effort of many individuals, with the authors generously sharing their expertise and writing in a unified handbook format. Their efforts in providing their manuscripts in a timely fashion and addressing various issues related to the production process in a patient manner are deeply appreciated. Also, I would like to thank the reviewers in helping us keep the appropriate focus and produce a fairly unbiased version. The staff at Taylor and Francis in the editorial, cover design, marketing, and production departments had a lion's share in improving the quality of the final product. My special thanks go to Susan Ciambrano, Amy Lorenzo, Kim Martin, Debbie Lovell, James Edwards, Lori Jean Baiocchi, Jim Reed, and many others at Taylor and Francis who made the task of coordinating the work with forty authors from eight countries possible.

My special thanks go to Professors Masahiro Shoji and Professor Yasunobu Fujita, who were instrumental in bringing the experts from Japan under the handbook umbrella. Also, I would like to thank co-editors Professors Masahiro Shoji and Vijay K. Dhir in bringing this unified concept for a handbook into reality.

Finally, I would like to extend my heartfelt appreciation to my wife Meera, who endured my more than occasional mental absence from the home scene over the last three years, my daughters Dipti and Jyoti, who happily shared what was rightfully their time with me, and all three of them for providing encouragement every step of the way.

## CLOSING REMARKS

We have made a conscious effort to produce a handbook with as few errors as possible. Given the breadth of the coverage and its diverse authorship, this seems to be an almost impossible task. The editors will very much appreciate receiving corrections and comments for further improvements in the handbook.

In the end, I look at the completed handbook with a sense of accomplishment for achieving such an international unification and dedicate it to the many friends, researchers, and industrial practitioners from all over the world.

*Satish G. Kandlikar*
Editor-in Chief
March 10, 1999
Rochester Institute of Technology
Rochester, NY 14623

# NOMENCLATURE

| | |
|---|---|
| A | flow area, interface area of an embryo, $m^2$, (4.8); Avogadro's number or atomic number, (7.1), (7.2); interface shape factor, (13); heated surface area, $m^2$, (17); multicomponent diffusion matrix defined by Eq. (19.4-35); total surface area, $m^2$, (22); cross-sectional area of fins, $m^2$, (24.2); cross-sectional area, $m^2$, (25) |
| $A_o$ | nominal surface area, $m^2$, (22) |
| $A_{12}$ | thermodynamic factor, (4.7) |
| $A_c$ | cross-sectional area, $m^2$, (10) |
| $A_f$ | fin surface area, $m^2$, (22) |
| $A_g/A_w$ | area fraction of vapor stems in the microlayer, (7.3) |
| $A_i$ | interfacial area, (25) |
| $A_n$ | constant in Eq. (21.2-6) |
| $A_r$ | fin root surface area, $m^2$, (20), (22) |
| $a$ | capillary constant defined by Eq. (2.2-4); thermal diffusivity, $m^2/s$, (23) |
| $a_1, a_2, a_3$ | dimensionless numerical factors in Eq. (21.3-1) |
| $a_{ij}$ | cross-coefficient, (1) |
| $a_{kl}$ | element of matrix **A** defined by Eq. (19.4-36) |
| $a_t$ | centrifugal acceleration (18.3) |
| B | coefficient in Eq. (4.8-6) |
| B | parameter in Eq. (9.1-52); transpiration parameter defined in Eq. (19.1-53); diagonal matrix derived from matrix **A** defined by Eq. (19.4-39) |

xix

| | |
|---|---|
| $Bo$ | Boiling number, $= \dot{q}/(\dot{m}\Delta h_{1g})$, dimensionless, (16.3), (18.2); Bond number, $= (\rho_l - \rho_v)gD_h^2/\sigma$, dimensionless, (24) |
| $b$ | exponent in Eq. (9.1-80); exponent, (12); flute pitch, also fin pitch, (22); fin height, m, (24.1) |
| $b_1, b_2$ | dimensionless numerical factors in Eq. (21.3-2) |
| $C$ | constant (7.1), (7.2), (11), (16.2), (18.2); flow coefficient, (25); constant in Eq. (12.4-4); constant in Eqs. (14.1-7) and (14.2-51); quantity defined in Eq. (19.1-14) |
| $C_1$ | constant in Eq. (6.2-1); constant in Eq. (12.3-4) |
| $C_2$ | constant in Eq. (12.3-4) |
| $C_5$ | Exponent for (25 $Fr_{lo}$), (18.2) |
| $C_D$ | drag coefficient, (14), (17); resistance coefficient, (19.3) |
| $C_F(Pr_V)$ | function of the vapor Prandtl number defined by Eq. (19.4-7) |
| $C_F(Sc_V)$ | function derived by replacing $Pr_V$ in Eq. (19.4-7) with $Sc_V$ |
| $C_L$ | geometry factor in Eq. (9.2-12) |
| $C_N(Pr_V)$ | function of the vapor Prandtl number defined by Eq. (19.4-23) |
| $C_N(Sc_V)$ | function derived by replacing $Pr_V$ in Eq. (19.4-23) with $Sc_V$ |
| $C_0$ | distribution parameter, (9), (10), (15.2), (15.3) |
| $C_p$ | pump characteristics (gradient of pump head against flow rate), (10) |
| $C_t$ | constant in Blasius-type friction factor, Eq. (9.2-12) |
| $Ca$ | capillary number, $\eta_l U/\rho_{1g}$, (2) |
| CHF | critical heat flux, W/m², (17), (18.3) |
| $Co$ | Confinement Number, (16.2); convection number, $= (\rho_G/\rho_L)^{0.5}((1-x)/x)^{0.8}$, (16.3) |
| $c$ | exponent in Eq. (12.3-1), contrast, defined by Eq. (25.3-6); fin spacing at fin tip, m, (22) |
| $c_f$ | coefficient of friction defined in Eq. (19.1-52) |
| $c_m$ | constant in Eq. (6.5-3) |
| $c_p$ | specific heat at constant pressure, J/(kg K); of mixture, J/kg K (19.4) |
| $c_{p,c}$ | specific heat capacity of continuous phase, (21) |
| $c_{pk}$ | specific isobaric heat of pure component $k$, J/(kg K), (19.4) |
| $c^*_{pknV}$ | dimensionless specific isobaric heat difference defined by Eq. (19.4-44) |
| $c^*_{pV}$ | dimensionless specific isobaric heat difference defined by Eq. (19.4-8) |

| | |
|---|---|
| $D$ | diameter, m; diameter of heated disk or tube, (14); departing drop diameter, mm, (20); mean distance between the nearest neighboring nucleation sites, m, (20); diffusion coefficient, m$^2$/s, (23) |
| $D_e$ | equi-periphery diameter ($=$ total wetted perimeter/$\pi$), m, (9.2) |
| $D_i$ | inner diameter of an annulus, m |
| $D_o$ | outer diameter of an annulus, m |
| $D_h$ | hydraulic diameter, m |
| $D_{ij}$ | diffusion coefficient of component i in mixture of i and j, m$^2$/s, (1) |
| $D_{kn}$ | diffusion coefficient of component k in mixture of k and n, m$^2$/s, (23) |
| $D^+$ | non-dimensional diameter, $= D/\lambda_0$, Eq. (7.2-20) |
| $D_{12}$ | diffusion coefficient of component 1 in mixture of 1 and 2, (4.7), (16.3) |
| $D_{12}^0$ and $D_{21}^0$ | diffusion coefficient of component 1 or 2 present in infinitely low concentration of liquid mixture, (4.7), (16.3) |
| $D_{12V}$ | mutual diffusivity between components 1 and 2, m$^2$/s, (19.4) |
| $D_{klV}$ | coefficient for diffusion defined by Eq. (19.4-38), m$^2$/s |
| $D_{klV}^M$ | diffusivity of the pair of components $k-l$ in n-component system, m$^2$/s, (19.4) |
| $D_{klV}^*$ | coefficient for diffusion defined by Eq. (19.4-37), m$^2$/s |
| DR | deposition rate, kg/s |
| $d$ | diameter, m; exponent in Eq. (12.3-1); distance between walls, (25); diameter of impinging jet, (14); equivalent specific diameter, m (21); tube diameter at fin tip, (22); inner diameter of tube, m, (23) |
| $d_B$ | departure bubble diameter, m |
| $d_e$ | hydraulic diameter, m; equivalent diameter of jet, m, (21) |
| $d_i$ | initial value of $d$, m, (21) |
| $d_0$ | outer diameter of a tube, m, (19.3) |
| $d_r$ | tube diameter at fin root, m, (22) |
| $E$ | parameter defined by Eq. (9.1-58); dimensional parameter, (19.3); strength of electric field, (22) |
| $EF$ | enhancement factor, (24.1) |
| $ER$ | entrainment rate, kg/m$^2$s, (17) |
| $E_{cb}$ | enhancement factor for convective boiling term, (18.2) |
| $E'_{cb}$ | modified enhancement factor, (18.2) |

| | |
|---|---|
| $E_m$ | dimensionless mixed-cup temperature, $= (T_m - T_i)/(T_v - T_i)$, (21) |
| $En_{max}$ | enhancement factor, dimensionless |
| $E_{nb}$ | enhancement factor for nucleate boiling term, (18.2) |
| $E'_{nb}$ | modified enhancement factor, (18.2) |
| $Eo$ | Eötvös number, generally defined by Eq. (2.2-2), given by $\rho_l g L^2 / \sigma_{lg}$ in case of liquid gas contact |
| $E_1$ and $E_2$ | parameter defined by Eqs. (9.1-71) and (9.1.72), respectively |
| $e$ | energy convected per unit mass of fluid, m²/s², (9); flute depth or fin height, m, (22); thickness (25) |
| $F$ | free energy of a given system, (2); parameter defined by Eq. (9.1-5); parameter defined by Eq. (9.1-59); fraction of liquid-solid contact, (7); two-phase enhancement factor in Eq. (12.5-1); Enhancement Factor, (16.2); dimensionless parameter, (19.3) |
| $F_b$ | component of gravitational acceleration; force on a bubble; N, (5.4) |
| $F_C$ | shape factor, (17) |
| $F_D$ | mass diffusion-induced suppression factor, $= \alpha/\alpha_{psc}$, (4.7), and (16.3) |
| $F_{Fl}$ | fluid-surface parameter, values listed in Table (15), (15), (16), (18.2) |
| $F_L$ | dimensionless quantity defined in Eq. (19.1-61) |
| $\vec{F}$ | force vector, (2.3) |
| $F^*$ | electrical bdy force, N/m³ |
| $F_1$ | fin parameter $= \lfloor \rho_l(\rho_l - \rho_v)gh_{lv}H^3 \rfloor/[k_1\mu_1(t_a - t_0)]$, dimensionless, (24.2) |
| $F_2$ | fin parameter $= (\delta_f k_f)/(2Hk_1)$ dimensionless, (24.2) |
| $Fr, Fr_L$ | Froude number, $U_\infty^2/gL$; defined by Eq. (9.1-61) in (9.1) |
| $(Fr_d)_n$ | Froude number of nth row of tube banks, (19.3) |
| $Fr_{LO}$ | Froude number with all flow as liquid, $G^2/(\rho_l^2 gD)$, (15, 16) |
| $f$ | fanning friction factor, (9), (15), (16.3), (17); fugacity, (1), (7); bubble departure frequency, s⁻¹, (4); fraction of area covered by drops, (17) |
| $f_1, f_2$ | areal fractions of solid and open portions, respectively, on a porous surface, Eq. (2.2-7); those of wetted and dry areas, respectively, each projected normal to a plane parallel to a given composite surface, Eq. (2.2-8), or those of higher and |

| | lower surface-energy portions, respectively, composing a heterogeneous surface, Eq. (2.2-9) |
|---|---|
| $G$ | mass flux, kg/(m²s); Gibbs function, (1); acceleration due to gravity, m/s², (2); dimensionless parameter defined in Eq. (19.1-56) |
| $G_l$ | dimensionless quantity, $= \rho_l g h_{lg} l^3 / \lambda_l \nu_l (T_s - T_w)$, (22) |
| $G_d$ | dimensionless quantity, $= \rho_l g h_{lg} d^3 / \lambda_l \nu_l (T_s - T_w)$, (22) |
| $G_d$ | dimensionless velocity of steam through maximum flow area, (19.3), kg/(m² s) |
| $Ga$ | Galileo number, $= g d_i^3 / \nu_c^2$, (21); $= g \rho_L^2 d^3 / \mu_L^2$, (23) |
| $Ga_{Lx}$ | Galileo number defined by Eq. (19.4-26) |
| $Gr$ | Grashof number, $= g \rho_{gf} (\rho_{1f} - \rho_{gf}) s^2 / \mu_{gf}^2$, (7.1), (7.2) |
| $Gr_d$ | dimensionless parameter defined in Eq. (19.1-41) |
| $Gr_L$ | dimensionless parameter defined in Eq. (19.1-20) |
| $Gr_{Vx}$ | Grashof number defined by Eq. (19.4-34) |
| $Gz$ | Graetz number, $= U d_e / (\kappa x)$, (21) |
| $g$ | acceleration due to gravity, m/s²; specific or molar Gibbs function, (1); $= (x_1 - x_{1,s})/(y_{1,s} - x_{1,s})$, defined by Eq. (4.7-23), (16.3) |
| $H$ | enthalpy, J/kg, (1); height of plate or width of a heater, m, (6); parameter defined by Eq. (9.1-60); channel height, m, (16.1); dimensionless parameter defined in Eq. (19.1-47); height of vapor space, m, (22); fin height projecting from base, (24.2); phase change number defined in Equation (24.1-10) |
| $h$ | specific enthalpy, J/kg; specific or molar enthalpy, J/kg or J/kg-mol, (1); height of passage, m, (16.2); distance between the upstream and throat pressure taps, (25) |
| $h^*$ | distance for a bubble to rise during a time period $t^*$, (21) |
| H-H | horizontal flow between horizontal flat plates, (9.2) |
| H-V | horizontal flow between vertical flat plates |
| $I$ | flow in an inclined channel, (9.2); intensity, photons/s over a certain time, (25) |
| I.D., O.D. | inlet and outlet diameter in annulus, (17), (18.3) |
| $J$ | rate of embryo formation, (4.8); current density, A/m², (5.4); volumetric flux, m/s, (10) |
| $\langle j \rangle$ | mixture mean velocity, m/s, (9), (12) |
| $j_G$ | superficial gas velocity, m/s |
| $j_G^*$ | modified superficial gas velocity, m/s, (9.2), dimensionless superficial gas velocity defined by Eq. (12.3-5) |

| | |
|---|---|
| $j_L$ | superficial liquid velocity, m/s |
| $j$ | Colburn modulus; local mass diffusion flux, (19-2) |
| $J$ | dimensionless parameter defined in Eqs. (19.1-19), (19.3-5) |
| $Ja$ | Jakob number, $[Ja = (\rho_l/\rho_g)(C_p \Delta T/h_{lg})]$, (14); $= \rho_c c_{p,c} \Delta T_i/(\rho_v h_{1g})$, (21) |
| $Ja_L$ | Jakob number of liquid, $\rho_l c_{pl} \Delta T / h'_{fg}$, where $h'_{fg} = h_{fg}(1 + \frac{0.4 c_p \Delta T_{sat}}{h_{fg}})^2$, (13) |
| $Ja_0$ | modified Jakob number, defined by Eq. (4.7-21) |
| $K$ | parameter defined by Eq. (9.1-4); resistance coefficient, (10); slip ratio, (12); constant, (20); defined in Eq. (19.1-63) |
| $Kc$ | gain constant of controller, W/m²K, (7.3) |
| $K_h$ | constant, (16.2); variable defined by Eq. (21.3-6) |
| $K_t$ | variable defined by Eq. (21.3-6) |
| $K_T$ | dimensional calibration constant for the turbine flowmeter, defined by Eq. (25.5-7). |
| $K_v$ | dimensional calibration constant for the Venturi meter, defined by Eq. (25.5-1) |
| $K_1$ | constant in Eq. (6.1-1); slope of boiling curve, W/m²K, (7.3) |
| $k$ | Boltzmann constant, (7); constant (14); thermal conductivity, W/m K, (12), (16.2); (24.2); wave number, (22) |
| $k_B$ | Boltzmann constant, (2.3) |
| $k_{ij}$ | binary interaction parameter, (1) |
| $L$ | characteristic length in a given system, m, (2); length of a heater, pitch of vapor stem, m, (6); length of heated surface (for impinging jet, distance from jet position to the edge), m, (14); horizontal dimension of module, m, (16.1); heated length, m, (17); height of vertical condensate surface, (19.1); fin length (perpendicular to the height H), m, (24.2); layer thickness, m, (25) |
| $L_s$ | saturated boiling length, m (14) |
| $l$ | length, m; length of fin, m, (16.2); effective length of test tube, (19.3); length of optical path in two-phase mixture, m, (25); tube length, m, (22), (23) |
| $l_b$ | boiling length, m, (17) |
| $M$ | molecular weight or molecular mass; thermodynamic property, (1); Morton number, $g\eta_l^4/(\rho_l \sigma_{lg}^3)$, (2); nondimensional number in Eq. (7.2-7), inertial mass, kg,/m² (10); |

| | |
|---|---|
| | vertical condensate flow rate, kg/s, (22); mass flow rate, kg/s, (25) |
| $Ma$ | Marangoni number, (6) |
| $M_k$ | molecular weight of component $k$, kg/kmol, (19.4) |
| $\dot{M}$ | mass flow rate, kg/s, (17), mass flow rate of vapor through maximum flow area, (19.3); vertical condensate flow rate, kg/s, (22) |
| $\dot{M}_{FL}$ | dimensionless condensation mass flux defined by Eq. (19.4-3) |
| $\dot{M}_{NL}$ | dimensionless condensation mass flux defined by Eq. (19.4-22) |
| $m$ | specific or molar thermodynamic property, (1); mass, kg, (2.3); friction factor parameter, (9), (12); mass flux, kg/(m$^2$ s), (12); mass flux, (13); condensation mass flux, kg/m$^2$s, (19); exponent defined by Eq. (19.4-12); fin parameter $= (2h/k_f \delta_f)^{1/2}$, m$^{-1}$, (24.2) |
| $m_{EB}$ | droplet entrainment rate, kg/s, (14) |
| $\dot{m}$ | mass flux, kg/m$^2$s; mass flow rate, kg/s, (16.2) |
| $\dot{m}_{lf}$ | liquid film mass flux, kg/m$^2$s, (17) |
| $\tilde{\dot{m}}_v$ | fraction of the mass of vapor reaching the liquid surface, (21) |
| $N$ | number density, (2.3); experimental parameter given by Eq. (11.3-3); number of nozzles, (14); drop distribution function, m$^{-3}$, (20); number of photons in Eq. (25.3-5); rotation Reynolds number in Eq. (25.5-6) |
| $N_l$ | number density of liquid molecules, (4.8) |
| $N_{pch}$ | phase change number, $= \rho_{lg} Q_B / (A_c h_{lg} \rho_g \rho_l u_{in0})$, (10) |
| $N_{sub}$ | subcooling number, $= \rho_{lg} \Delta h_{sub} / (h_{lg} \rho_g)$, (10), also see Sb |
| $N_X$ | number density of embryos containing X molecules, (4.8) |
| $Nu$ | Nusselt number; $\alpha D / \lambda$, or $\alpha s / \lambda_{gt}$ in (7.1), (7.2); $= \alpha D / k$, (24.2) |
| $Nu_d$ | Nusselt number based on diameter d, (22) |
| $\overline{Nu_l}$ | Nusselt number based on length $l$, (22) |
| $\overline{Nu}$ | mean Nusselt number for tube, (19.1) |
| $\overline{Nu}_L$ | mean Nusselt number for plate of height $L$, (19.1) |
| $Nu_{NU}$ | Nusselt number given by Nusselt theory, (19.1) |
| $(Nu_d)_m$ | Nusselt number of steam-air mixture for nth row of tube bank, (19.3) |
| $(Nu_d)_n$ | mean Nusselt number of nth row of tube banks, (19.3) |
| $(Nu_d)_0$ | Nusselt number of pure steam for nth row, (19.3) |
| $Nu_s$ | Nusselt's equation for a horizontal single tube, (19.3) |

| | |
|---|---|
| $Nu_x$ | local Nusselt number, $(= \alpha_x d_e/\lambda)$, (21) |
| $n$ | number of moles, (1); exponent in Eq. (9.1-52); Reynolds number exponent in convection heat transfer correlation, (12); rotational frequency, constant, (20); coordinate normal to interface, m, (22); rotational frequency, (25) |
| $\mathbf{P}$ | modal matrix defined by Eq. (19.4-41) |
| $P$ | pressure, Pa, (1), (9.2), (19.3), (20), (22); tube pitch, m, (12); fin perimeter, m, (24.2) |
| $P/D$ | pitch to diameter ratio in tube bundles, (12) |
| $P_w$ | wetted perimeter, m, (9.2) |
| $P_l$ | longitudinal tube pitch, m, (19.3) |
| $P_s$ | length of triple contact line, m, (6) |
| $P_{\text{slg}}$ | periphery of solid-liquid-gas contact line, m, (2) |
| $Pe$ | Pecelet number, Eq. (9.1-77) |
| $Ph$ | phase-change number; defined by Eq. (19.4-4); $= c_{\text{pL}}(T_{\text{sat}} - T_{\text{w}})/h_{\text{lg}}$, (23) |
| $Pr$ | Prandtl number, $= \eta c_p/\lambda$ or $= c_p\mu/\lambda$ |
| $p$ | pressure, Pa |
| $P_{kl}$ | element of matrix, (19.4) |
| $p_s$ | saturation pressure of the condensable vapor corresponding to the bulk temperature of the continuous phase, (21) |
| $p_v$ | vapor pressure, Pa, (19) |
| $p_\infty$ | system pressure, Pa, (21) |
| $p_{\text{sat}}(T)$ | saturation pressure at temperature $T$, Pa, (19) |
| $p'$ | constant, (16.2) |
| $Q$ | volumetric flow rate, m³/s, (25) |
| $Q$ | heat input, W, (10), heat transfer rate, W, (13), (22), (23), Volumetric flow rate, m³/s, (25) |
| $\dot{Q}$ | critical power, W, (18.3); heat input rate, W, (9.1-11); inverse matrix of matrix $\mathbf{P}$ defined by Eq. (19.4-40) |
| $Q_a$ | heat of adsorption, J, (7.1), (7.2) |
| $Q_l$ | heat loss to the environment, W, (19.3) |
| $QM$ | heat dissipation from module, (16.1) |
| $q, q''$ or $\dot{q}$ | heat flux, W/m²; average heat flux based on projected surface area, m², (22) |
| $\bar{q}$ | mean heat flux for tube, W/m², (19) |
| $q_B$ | boiling heat flux, W/m², (7.3) |
| $q_c$ | critical heat flux at subcooled condition or heat flux at film breakdown, W/m², (14) |

| | |
|---|---|
| $q_{co}$ | critical heat flux at saturated condition, W/m², (14) |
| $q_{ev}$ | heat flux component for evaporation, W/m², (7.1), (7.2) |
| $q_H$ | heating power per unit area, W/m², (7.3) |
| $q_{ic}$ | heat flux component at vapor-liquid interface by conduction, W/m², (7.1), (7.2) |
| $q_{lh}$ | heat flux component heating up liquid, W/m², (7.1), (7.2) |
| $q_{kl}$ | element of matrix, (19.4) |
| $q_L$ | local heat flux at bottom of plate of height $L$, W/m², (19) |
| $\bar{q}_L$ | mean heat flux for plate of height $L$, W/m², (19) |
| $q_V$ | heat loss per unit area, W/m², (7.3) |
| $q_v$ | volume heat flux, W/m³, (10) |
| $q_{vh}$ | heat flux component heating up vapor, W/m², (7.1), (7.2) |
| $q_{wc}$ | heat flux component by conduction, W/m², (7.1), (7.2) |
| $q_{wi}$ | heat flux at vapor-liquid interface, W/m², (7.1), (7.2) |
| $q_{wr}$ | heat flux component by radiation, W/m², (7.1), (7.2) |
| $\dot{q}_c$ | critical heat flux at saturation value, W/m², (6) |
| $\bar{q}_\theta$ | mean heat flux for surface of tube up to angle $\theta$, W/m², (19) |
| $R$ | radius; gas constant, (1); ratio of actual solid-surface area to its normal projection, (2); bubble radius, m, (5); gas constant in (7.1), (7.2), (19), (20); transfer function, (10); radius of cylindrical heater, m, (13); thermal resistance, °C/W, (16.1); radius, m, (17), (19), (20); $\rho-\mu$ ratio defined by Eq. (19.4-2); ratio of properties in equation (24.1-10); pipe radius, (25) |
| $R_g$ | specific ideal-gas constant, (19) |
| $R_{G1}$ | instantaneous line void fraction, defined by Eq. (25.1-2) |
| $\bar{R}_{G1}$ | time-averaged line void fraction, defined by Eq. (25.1-4) |
| $R_{G2}$ | instantaneous area void fraction, defined by Eq. (25.1-3) |
| $\bar{R}_{G2}$ | time-averaged area void fraction, defined by Eq. (25.1-5) |
| $R_i$ | coefficient, (25) |
| $R_v$ | fictitious void fraction at the Venturi meter, (25) |
| $R_T$ | fictitious void fraction at the turbine meter |
| $R_1, R_2$ | radii of curvature of fluid-liquid interface, (2) |
| $R'$ | dimensionless radius of a heater |
| $Ra$ | Rayleigh number = $Gr_g[D]Pr_{gf}/Sp^{**}$, derived by Eq. (7.2-18) |
| $Re$ | Reynolds number based on diameter d, $(=Gd/\eta)$; $(=UD/\nu_c)$, (21) |

| | |
|---|---|
| $\tilde{Re}_d$ | two-phase Reynolds number for tube defined in Eq. (19.1-70) |
| $Re_f$ | film Reynolds number, (14), (22) |
| $Re_G$, $Re_g$ | gas Reynolds number, (9), (14) |
| $Re_L$ | Reynolds number for liquid flowing alone in the entire flow cross section, $= \dot{m}(1-x)D/\eta$, dimensionless, Reynolds number for plate defined by Eq. (19.1-60) |
| $Re_{LO}$ | Reynolds number for total flow in the channel flowing as liquid, $= \dot{m}D/\eta$ dimensionless |
| $Re_{Lx}$ | two-phase Reynolds number defined by Eq. (19.4-9) |
| $Re_{Vx}$ | vapor Reynolds number defined by Eq. (19.4-20) |
| $Re_V$ | Reynolds number for vapor flowing alone in the entire cross section, dimensionless, $= \dot{m}xD/\eta$ |
| $Re_x$ | vapor Reynolds number for plate defined in Eq. (19.1-49) |
| $\tilde{Re}_x$ | two-phase Reynolds number for plate defined in Eq. (19.1-55) |
| $r$ | radial coordinate; intermolecular distance, m, (2.3); radius, (20), (21); radius of cavity, m, (5), (15); radius of curvature of liquid-vapor interface, m, (22) |
| $\dot{r}_a$ | growth rate of drops, m/s, (20) |
| $r_b$ | radius of curvature of thick film in flute (or fin) cross-section, m, (22) |
| $r_C$ | radius of the critical cluster, (4.8); radius of critical cavity, (5); radius of curvature of thick film in tube cross-section, m, (22) |
| $r_E$ | equivalent radius, m, (20) |
| $\dot{r}_e$ | substantial growth rate of drops, m/s, (20) |
| $r_h$ | hydraulic radius, $= D_h/4$, m, (24.2) |
| $r_o$ | radius of curvature at ridge of flute (or fin tip), m, (22) |
| $r_w$, | ratio of actually wetted surface area to its normal projection, (2); radius of curvature of flute (or fin) surface, m, (22) |
| $\vec{r}$ | position vector, (2.3) |
| $S$ | entropy, (1); parameter of Laplace transformation, (10); slip ratio between liquid and vapor phases, (11), (15.2), (15.3); bubble nucleation suppression factor in Eq. (12.5-1), non-dimensional parameter $= \lambda_1 v_1 z/(c_{pl} \rho_l g\, y_i^4)$, (14); suppression factor, (16.2); flow cross sectional area for steam, m$^2$, (19.3) |
| $\bar{S}$ | dimensionless parameter $(\bar{S}) = S/A$, (19.3) |

| | |
|---|---|
| $S_L$ | longitudinal pitch, m, (12) |
| $S_T$ | traverse pitch, m, (12) |
| Sb | subcooling number in (7.1), (7.2), $= c_{pl}\Delta T_{sub}/h_{lg}$, also see $N_{sub}$ |
| Sb* | nondimensional subcooling number in (7.1), (7.2), $=$ Sb/(1 + Sb/2) |
| Sc | Schmidt number $= \mu/(\rho D)$, (23) |
| $Sc_V$ | Schmidt number of binary vapor mixture defined by Eq. (19.4-11) |
| $Sc_{kV}$ | inverse of eigenvalue of the matrix **A** calculated from Eq. (19.4-79) |
| Sh | Sherwood number $(= \beta d/(\rho D))$, (23) |
| So | Soflata number, (19-2) |
| Sp | Superheat number, $= c_{p_{gf}}\Delta T/h_{lg}$, (7.1), (7.2) |
| Sp* | Sp/(1 + Sp/2) |
| Sp** | Sp/(1 + 0.375 Sp) |
| Sp*** | Sp/(1 + 0.34 Sp)$^2$ |
| s | specific or molar entropy, (1); representative length, m (7.1), (7.2); coordinate measured along flute (or fin) surface, m, (22) |
| s* | superheated layer, (17) |
| T | temperature, K; parameter defined by Eq. (9.1-5); period of oscillation, s, (10); time interval, s, (25) |
| $T^+$ | non-dimensional temperature difference defined by Eq. (14.2-15); dimensionless temperature, defined by Eq. (23.3-4) |
| $T_i^+$ | dimensionless temperature, defined by Eq. (23.3-4) |
| $T^*$ | reference temperature, see Eq. (19.1-71) |
| $T_C$ | critical temperature; temperature of saturated vapor in °C, (20) |
| $T_{c,bi}, T_{bi}$ | measured temperature for incipient nucleation on the heater film, K, (4.8) |
| $T_{c,w}, T_w$ | heater temperature, K, (4.8) |
| $T_i$ | initial temperature, K, (21) |
| $T_m$ | mixed-cup temperature, K, (21) |
| $T_s$ | saturation temperature, K; liquid surface temperature, K, (19) |
| $T_{sat}$ | saturation temperature, K |
| $T_v$ | vapor temperature, K, (21) |
| TTR | twisted tape ratio, (18.3) |

xxx NOMENCLATURE

| | |
|---|---|
| $t$ | time, s; time elapsed following the rapid heating of the film, s, (4.8); from bubble inception, s, (4.1-4.7); time, residence time, s, (10); fin thickness, m, (16.2), (22); thickness, m, (24.1) |
| $t_a$ | ambient temperature, K, (24.2) |
| $t_o$ | fin root temperature, K, (24.2) |
| $t_s$ | saturation temperature, K, (24.2) |
| $t_w$ | wall temperature, K, (24.2) |
| $t^*$ | time elapsed before a vapor bubble vanishes, s, Eq. (21.3-3) |
| $U$ | advancing speed of contact line on solid surface, m/s, (2); average velocity, (9), (21); average velocity of a rising bubble, m/s, (21); delayed step function, (10) |
| $U_{a,cr}, U_{r,cr}$ | critical values of $U$ at which $\phi$ arrives at 180° and 0°, respectively, Eq. (2.2-15) |
| $U_G$ | superficial vapor velocity, m/s |
| $U_L$ | superficial liquid velocity, m/s |
| $U_\infty$ | free-stream velocity of vapor, m/s, (19) |
| $u$ | velocity component of x direction, m/s; specific or molar internal energy, (1); velocity, (5), (16.2), (18.3), (19.3), (23) |
| $u_{gm}$ | gas velocity, m/s, (14) |
| $u_{mc}$ | average velocity of film at critical condition, m/s, (14) |
| $u_N$ | impinging jet velocity, m/s, (14) |
| $u_r$ | resultant water velocity, with twisted tape, (18.3) |
| $u_\tau$ | friction velocity, m/s, (17) |
| $u^+$ | non-dimensional velocity, (14) |
| $V$ | volume, m³, (1), (10), (25); cooling fluid velocity, m/s, (16.1); voltage, (22) |
| $\dot{V}$ | volume flow rate, m³/s |
| $V_n$ | vapor velocity normal to the interface into liquid, (13) |
| $V_g$ | volume of vapor in a nucleated embryo, (4.8) |
| $V_{gj}$ | mean drift velocity, m/s, (7), (9), (12), (14), (15.2), (15.3) |
| $V_1$ | volatility parameter, defined by Eq. (4.7-33), (16) |
| $V_\infty$ | free stream velocity in bulk liquid, m/s, (13) |
| V-D | vertical downward flow, (9) |
| V-U | vertical upward flow, (9) |
| $v$ | velocity component in y direction; specific molar volume, (1); volumetric growth rate of vapor mass, (6) |
| $\upsilon$ | specific volume, m³/kg, (1), (19), (20) |

| | |
|---|---|
| $v_g, v_l$ | specific volume of vapor and liquid condensate respectively, m³/kg, (19.1) |
| $v_{lg}$ | $= v_l - v_g$, (19.1) |
| $v_{m,1}, v_{m,2}$ | molar specific volumes of components 1 and 2 in liquid phase, m³/kg-mol, (4.7), (16.3) |
| $\dot{M}$ | mass flow rate, kg/s (23), (24.2), width of rectangular impinging jet, (14); channel width, (9) |
| $\langle W_G \rangle$ | area-averaged velocity of the gas phase, m, (25) |
| $\langle W_L \rangle$ | area-averaged velocity of the liquid phase, m, (25) |
| $W_X$ | minimum work to form an embryo with X molecules (4.8) |
| $W_{kR}$ | ratio of concentration in multi-component system defined by Eq. (19.4-46) |
| $W_R$ | ratio of concentration in binary system defined by Eq. (19.4-13) |
| $We$ | Weber number defined by Eqs. (9.1-62) and (9.1-73) |
| $We_l$ | Weber number for liquid phase, $= G^2(1-x)^2 D_h/(\sigma \rho_l)$, (24.2) |
| $We_v$ | Weber number for vapor phase, $= G^2 x^2 D_h/(\sigma \rho_v)$, (24.2) |
| $w$ | mass fraction in liquid, (1); width of passage, m, (16.2); condensate velocity in z-direction, m/s, (22) |
| $w_k$ | mass fraction of component $k$, (19.4) |
| $X$ | Martinelli parameter $= \{(dp/dz)_l/(dp/dz)_g\}^{1/2}$, dimensionless; number of molecules in embryos, (4.8); coordinate along the heater surface in the wake region, (13), mixture composition in the liquid phase, (17); parameter defined by Eq. (21.3-7); dimensionless quantity in Eq. (22.3-2) |
| $X_{eq}$ | thermodynamic quality, (25) |
| $X_o$ | bubble growth region defined by Eq. (12.5-3) |
| $X_{tt}$ | Martinelli parameter for both liquid and vapor phases in turbulent flow, dimensionless, $(=(\frac{1-x}{x})^{0.9}(\frac{\rho_V}{\rho_L})^{0.5}(\frac{\mu_L}{\mu_V})^{0.1})$ |
| $x$ | quality; mole fraction in liquid, (1, 6); coordinate, coordinate along the heater surface in the front region, (13); distance along condenser surface, m, (19); distance from nozzle exit, m, (21) |
| $x, y, z$ | coordinate axes, Cartesian coordinate measured from fin tip, (22) |
| $x_a$ | true quality at non-equilibrium condition, (11), (15.2) |
| $\tilde{x}_g$ | molar fraction of noncondensable gases, (21) |

| | |
|---|---|
| $x_1, x_2$ | mass fraction of components 1 and 2 in liquid phase, (4.7), (15.3), (23) |
| $\tilde{x}_1, \tilde{x}_2$ | mole fraction of components 1 and 2 in liquid phase, (4.7), (15.3) |
| $Y$ | parameter defined by Eq. (9.1-53); coordinate normal to the heater surface in the wake region, (13); parameter defined in Eq. (15.2-34); mixture composition in the vapor phase, (17) |
| $y$ | mole fraction in vapor; (1), (6); parameter defined by Eq. (9.1-70); dimensionless velocity, (10); coordinate normal to the heater surface in the front region, (13); distance from the axis of the pipe to the photon beam, m, (25), distance from the wall, (14); distance normal to condenser surface, (19); Cartesian coordinate measured from fin tip or coordinate measured outward normal to flute (or fin) surface, (22); coordinate normal to the heated/cooled surface, (23) |
| $y_b$ | base film thickness, m, (14) |
| $y_b^*$ | non-dimensional base film thickness, (14) |
| $y_i$ | distance from wall to interface, m, (14) |
| $y_m$ | mean thickness of falling liquid film, m, (14) |
| $y_m^*$ | non-dimensional mean film thickness, (14) |
| $y_{max}$ | maximum film thickness including wave height, m, (14) |
| $y_1, y_2$ | mass fraction of components 1 and 2 in vapor phase, (4.7), (15.3), (23) |
| $\tilde{y}_1, \tilde{y}_2$ | mole fraction of components 1 and 2 in vapor phase, (4.7) (15.3), (23) |
| $y^+$ | non-dimensional distance, (14, 23) |
| $Z$ | compressibility factor, (1) |
| $z$ | coordinate perpendicular to the interface, (2.3); distance from bubble interface in the liquid phase, m, (4.7); coordinate along tube axis, m, (14); distance along channel, m, (16.2); axial distance, m, (18); dimensionless film thickness defined in Eq. (19.1-25); cooling water pass, (19.3); distance measured vertically downward from top of vertical tube, also height of liquid-vapor interface at midpoint between adjacent fins, m, (22); coordinate along the heated/cooled surface from edge, (23) |
| $z_d$ | distance to bubble departure, m, (9) |
| $z_{eq}$ | distance to equilibrium conditions, m, (9) |
| $z_n$ | distance to onset of nucleate boiling, m, (9) |

## Greek Symbols:

| | |
|---|---|
| $\alpha$ | heat transfer coefficient, W/m² K; heat transfer coefficient in MW/m² K, (20); rate of gas molecules that strike a surface per unit area, (4.8); angle of inclination from horizontal, (9); liquid absorptivity, (13); average heat transfer coefficient, W/m² K, (22); Apex angle, degrees, (24.1) |
| $\alpha, \alpha_w$ | void fraction, vapor fraction on a heater, only in (6) |
| $\alpha_{conv}$ | convection heat transfer coefficient, W/m² K |
| $\alpha_G$ | local void fraction defined by Eq. (25.1-1) |
| $\alpha_i$ | interface heat transfer coefficient, W/m² K, (19.1) |
| $a_{kl}$ | element of matrix **A** defined by Eq. (19.4-36) |
| $\overline{\alpha_L}$ | mean heat-transfer coefficient for plate of height $L$, W/m² K, (19) |
| $\alpha_m$ | mean heat transfer coefficient for steam-air mixture, W/m² K, (19.3) |
| $(\alpha_m)_l$ | mean heat transfer coefficient for the first row, W/m² K, (19.3) |
| $\alpha_N$ | average heat transfer coefficient calculated from Nusselt equation, W/m² K, (22) |
| $\alpha_{nb}$ | nucleate boiling heat transfer coefficient, W/m² K |
| $\alpha_{pb}$ | pool boiling heat transfer coefficient, W/m² K |
| $\alpha_{psc}$ | heat transfer coefficient in pool boiling with pseudo-single component fluid having the same thermophysical properties as the mixture, W/m² K |
| $\alpha_s$ | mean heat transfer coefficient, W/m²K, (19.3) |
| $\alpha_x$ | local heat transfer coefficient at x. (21) |
| $\alpha_{2\phi}$ | flow boiling heat transfer coefficient, W/m² K |
| $\bar{\alpha}$ | mean heat-transfer coefficient for wall or tube, W/m² K, (14), (19) |
| $\beta$ | expansion coefficient in (7.1), (7.2); volumetric quality or homogeneous void fraction, (9); dimensionless parameter which expresses time-averaged velocity, (10); contact angle, (17); weighting factor, see Eq. (19.1-71); angle, (22); mass transfer coefficient, kg/(m²s); helix angle, deg, (24.1) |
| $\beta_0$ | equilibrium contact angle, rad |
| $\Gamma$ | film flow rate per unit width of wall, kg/m s, (14); volumetric interfacial area, Eq. (25.1-6) |
| $\Gamma_c$ | minimum wetting rate, kg/m s, (14) |

| | |
|---|---|
| $\gamma$ | activity coefficient, (1); function of $\zeta$, specific heat ratio, (20); angle measured from flute (or fin) tip, rad, (22); slip ratio, (25) |
| $\Delta$ | vapor boundary layer thickness, m, (19.4) |
| $\Delta_m$ | property change on mixing, (1) |
| $\Delta_m^{ex}$ | excess property of mixture, (1) |
| $\Delta h$ | enthalpy difference, J/kg ; specific or molar latent heat for phase change, (1); height of passage, m, (16.2); distance between the upstream and throat pressure taps, (25) |
| $\Delta h_{lg}, h_{fg}, h_{lg}, \Delta h_{LV}$ | latent heat of vaporization or condensation, J/kg |
| $\Delta l$ | length of one subsection, m, (23) |
| $\Delta P_{2\phi}$ | two-phase pressure drop, Pa, (12) |
| $\Delta p$ | pressure drop, Pa; pressure difference, Pa, (2) |
| $\Delta p_a$ | pressure drop due to acceleration, Pa, (10) |
| $\Delta p_f$ | pressure drop due to friction, Pa, (10) |
| $\Delta p_{gr}$ | pressure drop due to gravitation, Pa, (10) |
| $\Delta T$ | surface subcooling, K, (20), temperature difference, K, (17), (18.3); temperature difference across condensate film, K, (19) |
| $\Delta T_{bp}$ | boiling point range, difference between the dew point and bubble point temperatures, K, (4.7), (15.3) |
| $\Delta T_{id}$ | wall superheat for ideal mixture (evaluated using linear or reciprocal mole or mass fraction average of the pure component values), K |
| $\Delta T_s$ | $= (T_s - T_{sat})$, K |
| $\Delta T_{sub}$ | liquid, subcooling, difference between liquid temperature and its saturation temperature, K |
| $\Delta T_1, \Delta T_2$ | wall superheats for components 1 and 2 in pool boiling, (4.7) |
| $\overline{\Delta T_d}$ | mean value of $\Delta T$ for tube defined in Eq. (19.1-44) |
| $\overline{\Delta T_L}$ | mean value of $\Delta T$ for plate defined in Eq. (19.1-42) |
| $\Delta \rho$ | density difference, kg/m$^3$, (2); $\rho - \rho_g$, kg/m$^3$, (19) |
| $\delta$ | term in nucleation rate expression, in Eqs. (4.8-8), (4.8-9); thickness of heater, (6); macrolayer thickness, (6); thickness of vapor film, m, (7.1), (7.2); channel gap thickness, (9); small perturbation term, (10); thickness of vapor film layer, (13); film thickness, m, (16.2); liquid layer thickness, m, (17), local condensate film thickness, m, (19), liquid film thickness, m, (22) |
| $\delta_{kl}$ | Kronecker's delta, (19.4) |

| | |
|---|---|
| $\delta_l, \delta_L$ | boundary layer thickness of liquid |
| $\delta_m^*$ | thickness of mass diffusion boundary layer, m (4.7) |
| $\delta^+$ | $= \delta/\delta_1$ in (7.1), (7.2) |
| $\delta_0$ | initial macrolayer thickness, m, (7.3) |
| $\varepsilon$ | phase fraction; energy parameter of Lennard-Jones potential, (2.3); emissivity, (7), (13); void fraction, (9), (10), (12), (15.2), (15.3), (17); dielectric constant of vapor, (22); eddy diffusivity, m²/s, (14), (23) |
| $\varepsilon_E$ | absolute electrical permittivity, (F/m), (5.4) |
| $\varepsilon_H$ | homogeneous void fraction, (12) |
| $\varepsilon_h$ | eddy diffusivity for heat, m²/s, (23) |
| $\varepsilon_{sub}$ | correction factor for effect of subcooling on CHF, (14) |
| $\zeta$ | dimensionless parameter that controls van der Pol Equation, (10); angle measured from stagnation point, (13); ratio of maximum flow area, (19.3) |
| $\eta$ | dynamic viscosity, kg/m s; similarity variable, (13); fin efficiency, (22) |
| $\eta_A$ | enlargement ratio for heat transfer area, (23) |
| $\Theta$ | variable expressing the relation between dynamic contact angle and $\theta_s$, (2) |
| $\theta$ | contact angle, (6); angle of channel inclination from horizontal, (9.2); dimensionless temperature, (13); contact angle, (14); angle, (16.2); radial acceleration, (18.3); angle to vertical measured from top of tube, (19); fin half-tip angle, (22); Time interval, (25); angle, (25) |
| $\theta_a, \theta_A$ | advancing contact angle, rad, (2), (7.3), (14) |
| $\theta_r$ | retreating contact angle, rad, (2), (7.3) |
| $\theta_s$ | critical static contact angle, i.e., $\theta_a$ or $\theta_r$, rad, (2) |
| $\theta_Y, \theta_W, \theta_{CB}, \theta_{JD}, \theta_C$ | values of $\theta$ given by Eqs. (2.2-5), (2.2-6), (2.2-7), (2.2-8), and (2.2-9), respectively |
| $\vartheta$ | centrifugal acceleration (non dimensional), (18.3) |
| $\kappa$ | thermal diffusivity, m²/s |
| $\lambda$ | thermal conductivity, W/m K; characteristic dimension of roughness or heterogeneity on solid surface, (2); relaxation time, $(= \varepsilon_E/\sigma_E)$, s, (5.4); wavelength (6), (7.2) |
| $\lambda_n$ | Eigen-value (see Table 21) |
| $\mu$ | viscosity, kg/m s; (7.1), (7.2), (12), (15.2), (15.3), (16.2); chemical potential (molecule basis), (1); specific internal energy, m²/s², (9); linear absorption coefficient, Eq. (25.3-1) |

| | |
|---|---|
| $\mu^+$ | $= \mu_{gs}/\mu_{ls}$, (7.1), (7.2) |
| $\nu$ | kinematic viscosity, m²/s, void fraction, (16.2) |
| $\xi$ | coefficient for equivalent mass, (6); fitting constant of pressure drop characteristics, (10); dimensionless interphase mass transfer coefficient, Eq. (19.1-1); void fraction, (23) |
| $\xi_0$ | value of $\xi$ for $m \to 0$, (19) |
| $\pi$ | dimensionless parameter defined in Eq. (19.3-14) |
| $\rho$ | density, kg/m³; drop radius, m (20) |
| $\rho_c$ | density of continuous phase, kg/m³, (21) |
| $\rho_F$ | free charge density, C/m³, (5.4) |
| $\rho_l$ | density in the state of liquid or saturated liquid, kg/m³ |
| $\rho_T$ | momentum density in the turbine flowmeter, Eq. (25.5-7) |
| $\rho_v, \rho_g$ | density of vapor or gas in the saturated state, kg/m³, (15.2), (15.3), (19), (21); momentum density in the Venturi tube, defined by Eq. (25.5-2) |
| $(\rho V)_m$ | arithmetic mean density, kg/m³, (19.3) |
| $\sigma$ | surface tension; length parameter of Lennard-Jones potential, (2.3); condensation coefficient, (19) |
| $\sigma_E$ | electrical conductivity, $(\Omega \text{ m})^{-1}$ |
| $\sigma_s$ | intrinsic surface energy of solid, (2); Stefan-Boltzmann constant, (13) |
| $\tau$ | shear stress, Pa; time scale, s, (2.3); relaxation time, $(=\varepsilon_E/\sigma_E)$, s; dimensionless time, (10); dimensionless coordinate, (13); shear stress, Pa, (14), (23) |
| $\tau_d$ | hovering period of a vapor mass, (6); local shear stress at condensate surface, Pa, (19.1) |
| $\tau_W$ | frictional shear stress, N/m², (14) |
| $\Phi$ | potential, (2.3) |
| $\Phi$ | surface tension, N/m; condensation coefficient, (19) |
| $\Phi_l^2$ | two-phase friction multiplier $(= \Delta p_{fTP}/\Delta p_{fl})$, ratio of two-phase frictional pressure drop against frictional pressure drop of liquid flow, (9), (10), (24.2) |
| $\Phi_V$ | two-phase multiplier, defined by Eq. (23.2-3) |
| $\phi$ | fugacity coefficient, (1); angle of inclination of contact line with respect to the normal to the axis of its motion, (2); pair potential, (2.3); association parameter, (4.7); inclination angle of the heater in degrees, (6); two-phase multiplier, (9), (12), (15), (16.2); angle, function of $\zeta$ (13, 17); angle of plate to horizontal, (19); flow rate ratio of steam-air mixture, (19.3); angle measured from tube top, rad, (22) |

| | |
|---|---|
| $\phi_f$ | flooding angle, rad, (22) |
| $\phi_i$ | function for diffusion term in vapor energy equation defined by Eq. (19.4-43) |
| $\varphi$ | electrical potential, V, (5.4) |
| $\chi$ | exponent of Reynolds number for Nusselt number correlation, (16.1) |
| $\chi_{ki}$ | parameter of buoyancy force in multi-component system defined by Eq. (19.4-58) |
| $\chi_i$ | parameter of buoyancy force in binary system defined by Eq. (19.4-30) |
| $\chi_i^*$ | parameter of buoyancy force defined by Eqs. (19.4-24) or (19.4-54) |
| $\Psi$ | stream function, (13) |
| $\psi(\theta)$ | function defined in Eq. (19.1-32) |
| $\Omega_i$ | parameter of buoyancy force defined by Eqs. (19.4-25) or (19.4-55) |
| $\omega_T$ | parameter of buoyancy force due to temperature difference defined by Eq. (19.4-27) |
| $\omega_w$ | parameter of buoyancy force due to concentration difference in binary system defined by Eq. (19.4-28) |
| $\omega_{wk}$ | parameter of buoyancy force due to concentration difference in multi-component system defined by Eq. (19.4-56) |
| $\bar{\omega}$ | mass fraction of oil, dimensionless coordinate, (13) |

## Superscript

| | |
|---|---|
| overbar | average value; partial molar property, (1) |
| F | friction |

## Subscripts

| | |
|---|---|
| a | air, (9), (19.3); acceleration, (16.2); ambient, (24.2) |
| avg | average |
| B | binary mixture, (4.7), (16.3); blanket, (17), base, (20); gravity controlled, (23) |
| BL | boundary layer |
| b | bulk mean; bubble, (16.2); connecting point between thin and thick film regions, (22) |
| CBD | convective boiling dominant, (15), (16.3) |
| CHF | critical heat flux |

| | |
|---|---|
| c, cr | critical condition |
| c | contact, (13); continuous phase, (21); coolant, (24.2) |
| cal | calculated, (17) |
| D | mass diffusion; the most dangerous wavelength, (6) |
| DB | bubble departure point, (15.2) |
| d | saturated liquid state, (21) |
| dfb | departure from film boiling, (7.3) |
| *do* | dryout |
| E | in the presence of electric field |
| e | equilibrium, (9) |
| *eq* | equivalent |
| ex | excess, (1); exit, (10), (14), (17) |
| exp | experimental, (17) |
| F | frictional, (9); forced convective, (19.4) |
| f | frictional, (15.2), (15.3), (16.2), (23); film, (16.2); fin, (24.2) |
| fb | film boiling, (7.3) |
| $f_o$ | single-phase frictional, (15.2), (15.3) |
| front | front, (13) |
| G | gas, (9.2), (25) |
| Go | single phase flow at total mass flux with gas phase properties |
| GU | gas relative to mixture, Eq. (9.1-65) |
| g | gas or vapor; gravitational, (9); saturated vapor, (19) |
| gf | vapor at film temperature, (7.1), (7.2) |
| gr | gravitational |
| gs | saturated vapor, (7.1), (7.2) |
| H | Kelvin-Helmholtz instability, (6); homogeneous flow, (12) |
| h | heater (7.3); gravitational head, (16.2) |
| hn | homogeneous nucleation |
| IN | inlet |
| *i* | vapor-liquid interface; molecule index, (2.3); $i$th component in mixture, (1); inner, interface, (4.7), (13), (23), (25) |
| id | ideal, (4.7) |
| in | inlet; in-flow, (13) |
| KH | Kelvin-Helmholtz instability, (7.1), (7.2) |
| k | phase, (.2); component $k$ of multi-component mixture, (19.4), (23) |
| L, l | liquid |
| LO, Lo, lo | entire flow as liquid |
| lf | liquid at film temperature, (7.1), (7.2) |

| | |
|---|---|
| lg | latent quantity, vapor-liquid; liquid-gas interface, (2) |
| ls | saturated liquid, (7.1), (7.2) |
| M | denotes value at the condition of limiting superheat (Eq. (4.8-1)) |
| MHF | minimum heat flux of film boiling, $W/m^2$, (7) |
| m | mixture, (4.7), (6), (16.3); liquid-vapor mixture, (19.3); averaged value, (7.1), (7.2); |
| max | maximum measured, (25); mean, (14), (17), (19.3); momentum, (23) |
| min | minimum, (20) |
| N | normal direction, (2.3); natural convection condensation, (19.4) |
| NBD | nucleate boiling dominant, (15), (16.3) |
| Nu | given by Nusselt theory, (19) |
| NVG | point of net vapor generation |
| n | normal direction to vapor-liquid interface, (13) |
| nl | natural convection |
| *nb* | nucleate boiling, (12) |
| *npb* | nucleate pool boiling, (16.2) |
| nu | non uniform, (17) |
| *o* | outer, (24.2), fin root, (24.2), incident, (25) |
| out | out-flow, (13) |
| PB | pool boiling, (4.7) |
| p | wall, (25) |
| psc | pseudo-single component, (4.7) |
| *R* | reduced, (24.2) |
| RT | Rayleigh-Taylor instability |
| r | radiation, (7, 13), flow reversal point, (13), reduced property, (16.2); refrigerant, (24.2), mid-point between adjacent flutes (or fins), (22) |
| *ref* | reference, (24.2) |
| S | at surface, (2.3) |
| s | liquid-vapor interface of a bubble, (4.7); saturation at system pressure, (13); wall, (13); condensate surface, (19) |
| sat | saturation at system pressure |
| sg | solid-gas interface, (2) |
| sl | solid-liquid interface, (2) |
| st | smooth tube, (18.3) |
| sub | subcooled condition |
| T | tangential direction, (2.3); at constant temperature, (5); Rayleigh-Taylor instability, (6); turbine flowmeter (25) |

| | |
|---|---|
| TLS | thermodynamic limit of superheat, Eq. (4.8-1) |
| TP | two-phase |
| t, tot | total |
| tt | turbulent-turbulent; twisted tape, (18.3) |
| tv | turbulent-viscous, (9) |
| u | uniform, (17) |
| V | vapor; steam, (19.3); venturimeter (25) |
| v | vapor; bulk vapor, (19); saturated vapor state, (21) |
| vt | viscous-turbulent |
| vv | viscous-viscous |
| W, w | wall, heated surface |
| wake | wake, (13) |
| x | local value, (19) |
| Z | Zuber's value, (6) |
| 0 | without electric field, (5); original concentration, (6); steady state, (10), stagnation point, (11) |
| 1 | line, (25), subcooled region, (10) |
| 1, 2 | components of a binary system, 1-more volatile component, (4.7), (16.3), (23) |
| 2 | area, (25), boiling region, (10) |
| $\delta$ | surface of condensate film, (19) |
| $\phi$ | inclination |

## Index

| | |
|---|---|
| j | j = v (vapor); j = L (liquid), (13) |

# CONTRIBUTORS

H. Auracher
TU Berlin
Institut fur Energietechnik
Marchstr. 18, 10587 Berlin
Germany
E-mail: auracher@buran.fb10.tu-berlin.de

Gian Piero Celata
ENEA National Institute of Thermal-Fluid Dynamics
CR Casaccia, Via Anguillarese 301
I-00060 S.M. Galeria, Rome
Italy
E-mail: celata@casaccia.enea.it

Keith Cornwell
Director of Quality
Heriot-Watt University
Edinburgh EH14 4AS
United Kingdom
E-mail: K.Cornwell@hw.ac.uk

Jean–Marc Delhaye
Commissariat a l'Energie Atomique, Gernoble
Departement de Thermohydraulique et de Physique

CEA/Gernoble, DTP
38054 Gernoble Cedex 9
France
E-mail: delhaye@dtp.cea.fr

Vijay K. Dhir
Mechanical Engineering Department
School of Engineering
University of California, CA 90024, USA
E-mail: vdhir@seas.ucla.edu

Paolo Di Marco
Dipartimento di Energetica
Universita di Pisa
Via Diotisalvi 2, 56126 Pisa
Italy
E-mail: p.dimarco@ing.unipi.it

Ramin Dowlati
Department of Composites Product & Process Technology
Owens-Corning Science and Technology Center
Granville, OH 43023-1200, USA
E-mail: ramin.dowlati@owens-corning.com

Tetsu Fujii
Graduate School
University of East Asia
2-1 Ichinomiya-gakuen-machi, Shimonoseki 751-8503
Japan
E-mail: fujii@po.pios.cc.toua-u.ac.jp

Yasunobu Fujita
Department of Energy and Mechanical Engineering
Faculty of Engineering
Kyushu University
6-10-1 Hakozaki, Higashi-ku
Fukuoka, 812-81
Japan
E-mail: fujita@mech.kyushu-u.ac.jp

Yoshihiko Haramura
Kanagawa University

3-27-1 Rokkakubashi
Yokohama 221-8686
Japan
E-mail: bhthrm@cc.kanagawa-u.ac.jp

Richard Heist
University of Rochester
Rochester, NY 14620, USA
E-mail: rheist@rochester.edu

Geofferey F. Hewitt
Imperial College of Science, Technology, and Medicine
London, SW7 2AZ
United Kingdom
E-mail: g.hewitt@ic.ac.uk

Hiroshi Honda
Institute of Advanced Material Study
Kyushu University
6-1 Kasugakoen, 816-8580
Japan
E-mail: hhonda@cm.kyushu-u.ac.jp

Yoshihiro Iida
Department of Material Engineering
Yokohama National University
Yokohama, 240
Japan
E-mail: iida@chemeng.bsk.ynu.ac.jp

Satish G. Kandlikar
Mechanical Engineering Department
Rochester Institute of Technology
Rochester, NY 14623, USA
E-mail: sgkeme@rit.edu

Masahiro Kawaji
Department of Chemical Engineering and Applied Chemistry
University of Toronto
Toronto, Ontario M5S 3E5
Canada
E-mail: kawaji@ecf.utoronto.ca

David B. R. Kenning
Engineering Science Department
Oxford University
Oxford, OX13PJ
United Kingdom
E-mail: david.kenning@eng.ox.ac.uk

Peter Kew
Department of Mechanical and Chemical Engineering
Heriot-Watt University
Edinburgh EH14 4AS
United Kingdom
E-mail: p.a.kew@hw.ac.uk

Moo Hwan Kim
Pohang University of Science and Technology
Department of Mechanical Engineering
San 31, Hyoja Dong, Nam Gu
Pohang, Korea 790-784
Korea
E-mail: mhkim@vision.postech.ac.kr

Yasuo Koizumi
Department of Mechanical Engineering
Kogakuin University
2665-1, Nakano-machi, Hachioji-shi
Tokyo, 192
Japan
E-mail: at99534@ns.kogakuin.ac.jp

Shigeru Koyama
Institute of Advanced Material Study
Kyushu University
6-1 Kasuga-Koen, 816-8580
Japan
E-mail: koyama@cm.kyushu-u.ac.jp

Andrea Mariani
ENEA National Institute of Thermal-Fluid Dynamics
CR Casaccia, Via Anguillarese 301
I-00060 S.M. Galeria, Rome

Italy
E-mail: mariani_a@casaccia.enea.it

Shigeo Maruyama
Associate Professor
Department of Mechanical Engineering
The University of Tokyo
7-3-1 Hongo, Bunkyo-Ku, Tokyo 113-8656
Japan
E-mail: maruyama@photon.t.u-tokyo.ac.jp

Yasuhiko Mori
Department of Mechanical Engineering
Faculty of Science and Technology
Keio University
3-14-1 Hiyoshi, Kohoku-ku, Yokohama 223-8522
Japan
E-mail: yhmori@mech.keio.ac.jp

Wataru Nakayama
ThermTech International
920-7 Higashi Koiso, Oh-Iso Machi, Kanagawa 255-0004
Japan

Hideki Nariai
Institute of Engineering Mechanics
University of Tsukuba
Tsukuba, Ibaragi, 305
Japan
E-mail: nariai@kz.tsukuba.ac.jp

Shigefumi Nishio
Institute of Industrial Science
The University of Tokyo
7-22-1 Roppongi, Minato-ku
Tokyo, 106
Japan
E-mail: nishios@yari.iis.u-tokyo.ac.jp

Mamoru Ozawa
Department of Mechanical Engineering
Kansai University

3-3-35 Yamate-cho, Suita, Osaka 564-8680
Japan
E-mail: ozawa@kansai-u.ac.jp

John Rose
Department of Engineering
Queen Mary and Westfield College (University of London)
Mile End Road
London E1 4NS
United Kingdom
E-mail: J.W.Rose@qmw.ac.uk

Ramesh K. Shah
Delphi Harrison Thermal Systems, GM
Lockport, NY 14094-1896, USA
E-mail: rkshah@ibm.net

Masahiro Shoji
Department of Mechanical Engineering
The University of Tokyo
7-3-1 Hongo, Bunkyo-ku, Tokyo 113-8656
Japan
E-mail: shoji@ingram.mech.t.u-tokyo.ac.jp

Vijayaraghavan Srinivasan
Praxair Inc.
Tonawanda, NY 14150-7891, USA
E-mail: Vijay_Srinivasan@praxair.com

Nobuyuki Takenaka
Department of Mechanical Engineering
Kobe University
1-1 Rokkodai, Nada, Kobe, 657
Japan
E-mail: takenaka@mech.kobe-u.ac.jp

Ichiro Tanasawa
Tokyo University of Agriculture and Technology
2-24-16 Nakacho, Koganei, Tokyo 184-8588
Japan
E-mail: tanasawa@cc.tuat.ac.jp

CHAPTER
# ONE

# VAPOR LIQUID EQUILIBRIUM PROPERTIES

**Yasunobu Fujita**

*Kyushu University, Hakozaki, Fukuoka 812-8581, Japan*

**Satish G. Kandlikar**

*Rochester Institute of Technology, Rochester, NY 14623, USA*

The analysis of phase change heat transfer between liquid and vapor or the design of an evaporator or a condenser requires an understanding of the principles of two-phase equilibrium and an application of equilibrium data. Such phase equilibrium data are not fully compiled for any operating conditions expected in boiling and condensation of pure substances or multicomponent mixtures. An interpolation or extrapolation of available data to other conditions is inevitable. To facilitate this task, this chapter is intended to briefly present general aspects of vapor-liquid equilibrium of pure substances and binary and multicomponent mixtures.

## 1.1 THERMODYNAMIC EQUILIBRIUM—PURE COMPONENTS

### 1.1.1 Equilibrium Criteria

A system is stated to be in thermodynamic equilibrium if there are no macroscopically observable changes when the system is isolated from its surroundings. It is required for equilibrium that the temperature be uniform throughout the system and forces between parts of the system are balanced. The criterion for a system in a particular state to be in equilibrium is derived from the first and second laws of thermodynamics. It states that the Gibbs function of the system, $G$, has a minimum.

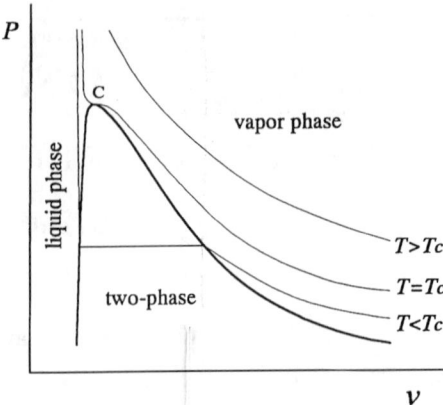

**Figure 1**  Pressure ($P$)-specific volume ($v$) diagram for a pure substance.

Thus,

$$dG\rfloor_{T,P} = 0 \qquad (1.1\text{-}1)$$

## 1.1.2 P-v-T Relationship

The $P$-$v$-$T$ relationship of a pure substance in thermodynamic equilibrium is usually indicated two-dimensionally on a $P$-$v$ plane, on which isotherms are drawn as parameters. Figure 1 shows such a diagram with three isotherms. Since no liquid phase can exist above the critical temperature, $T_c$, the volume at constant supercritical temperature decreases with increasing pressure in a monotonic fashion. In the subcritical region below the critical temperature, isotherms show discontinuous change at the two-phase envelope, i.e., at the saturated liquid and vapor curves that meet together at the critical point C. To the left of the envelope is the region of subcooled liquid where the isotherm is nearly vertical, showing only a slight change of volume with large changes in pressure. To the right of the envelope is the superheated vapor region.

The $P$-$v$-$T$ relationship is also indicated on a $P$-$T$ plane as shown in Figure 2. This vapor-pressure curve terminating at the critical point separates the state of single phase into the subcooled liquid region to the left of the curve and the superheated vapor region to the right. Two-phase mixtures of liquid and vapor exist on the curve. In Figure 2, the supercritical state is identified in the region where temperature and pressure are exceeding the respective critical values.

## 1.1.3 Equation of State

The functional relationship of $P$-$v$-$T$ data is expressed by an equation of state. All gases and vapors behave like ideal gas in an extreme situation when pressure

Tatsuhiro Ueda
Department of Mechanical Engineering
Kogakuin University
1-24-2 Nishi-shinjuku, Shinjuku-ku
Tokyo, 160
Japan

Haruo Uehara
Faculty of Science and Engineering
Saga University
Honjyo, Saga
Japan
E-mail: uehara@me.saga-u.ac.jp

Yoshio Utaka
Dept. of Mechanical Engineering & Materials Science,
Faculty of Engineering.
Yokohama National University
79-5 Tokiwadai, Hodogaya-ku, Yokohama 240-8501
Japan
E-mail: utaka@post.me.ynu.ac.jp

Larry C. Witte
Department of Mechanical Engineering
University of Houston
Houston, TX 77204-4792, USA
E-mail: witte@ch.edu

Akira Yabe
Mechanical Engineering Department
AIST, Min. Int. Trade & Industry of Japan
1-2, Namiki, Tsukuba, Ibaraki, 305-8564
Japan
E-mail: yabe@mel.go.jp

Jian Yu
Institute of Advanced Material Study
Kyushu University
6-1 Kasuga-Koen, 816-8580
Japan
E-mail: yujian@cm.kyushu-u.ac.jp

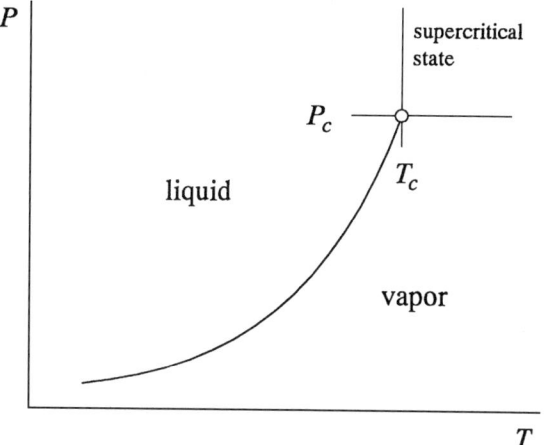

**Figure 2** Pressure ($P$)-temperature ($T$) diagram for a pure substance.

approaches zero and density becomes very low. In that case, their $P$-$v$-$T$ relationship follows the ideal gas equation of state.

$$Pv = RT \qquad (1.1\text{-}2)$$

Here, $v$ is the volume per unit amount of the substance. The number of moles being taken as a measure to express the amount, then $v$ is the molar volume. On the mass base, $v$ refers to the specific volume.

At higher densities, the $P$-$v$-$T$ relationship may deviate substantially from the ideal gas equation of state. Such an extent of deviation is expressed by the compressibility factor, $Z$, defined as

$$Z = \frac{Pv}{RT} \qquad (1.1\text{-}3)$$

Since $Z = 1$ for an ideal gas, the difference of $Z$ from unity becomes a measure of the deviation of actual behavior of a pure substance from the ideal gas behavior.

A virial equation of state can be theoretically derived from kinetic theory, and it is given in the form of a power series of reciprocal specific volume as

$$Z = 1 + \frac{B}{v} + \frac{C}{v^2} + \frac{D}{v^3} + \cdots \qquad (1.1\text{-}4)$$

Here, $B$, $C$, and $D$ are functions of temperature and are called the second, third, and fourth virial coefficients, which are related to the extent of interactions on the molecular level. In the limiting case of very low densities, i.e., very large molar volumes where the gas molecules are assumed to behave independently, the virial equation of state reduces to the ideal gas equation of state. Virial coefficients are calculable in principle if a model formulating the interaction forces between gas molecules is known. However, such calculations are successful at present only for the first two or three coefficients for gases with relatively simple molecules. As an alternative means, the first few virial coefficients are empirically determined by fitting $P$-$v$-$T$ data but with limited success. Such a truncated virial equation of state based on a single set of virial coefficients is unable to describe the $P$-$v$-$T$ relationship in the liquid and vapor phases simultaneously. Therefore, the $P$-$v$-$T$ behavior of pure substances at higher densities and in liquid phase is usually expressed by empirical equations of state. Such empirical equations range from relatively simple expressions (including a few arbitrary constants) to complex equations suitable only for computerized calculations and containing as many as twenty or more constants.

The van der Waals (1873) equation is the prototype for all equations of state with only two constants. It was presented as a semi-theoretical improvement over the ideal gas equation of state and runs as

$$P = \frac{RT}{v-b} - \frac{a}{v^2} \tag{1.1-5}$$

Here, $b$ is a constant to account for the finite volume occupied by molecules, and the term $a/v^2$ accounts for the attraction force between molecules.

Other widely used two-constant equations of state are those proposed separately by Berthelot, Dieterici, Redlich-Kwong, and Peng-Robinson. The last two are modifications of the van der Waals equation and are considered to be the best among the two-constant equations of state. Due to their simplicity, the Redlich-Kwong and the Peng-Robinson equations are frequently used to describe the $P$-$v$-$T$ relationship of multicomponent mixtures, from which mixture phase equilibrium diagrams are determined with reasonable success.

The Redlich-Kwong (1949) equation:

$$P = \frac{RT}{v-b} - \frac{a}{v(v+b)T^{1/2}} \tag{1.1-6}$$

The Peng-Robinson (1976) equation:

$$P = \frac{RT}{v-b} - \frac{a}{v^2 + 2bv - b^2} \tag{1.1-7}$$

Here, $a$ and $b$ are constants varying from substance to substance. Their values are different in the respective equations.

A more complex equation of state suitable for use at higher densities is that of Benedict et al. (1940):

$$P = RT/v + (BRT - A - C/T^2)/v^2 + (bRT - a)/v^3 + \alpha(a/v^6) \\ + (c/T^2 v^3)(1 + \gamma/v^2)\exp(-\gamma/v^2) \tag{1.1-8}$$

where $A$, $B$, $C$, $a$, $b$, $c$, $\alpha$, and $\gamma$ are constants. This equation is capable of representing both the liquid and vapor phases. The so-called modified versions (Nishiumi and Saito, 1975; Starling, 1971), including eleven or fifteen arbitrary constants, are proposed to fit $P$-$v$-$T$ data more accurately.

At present, no empirical or semi-empirical equation of state for pure substances is known that can describe the $P$-$v$-$T$ relationship with a fixed and single set of its constant values over a complete range of temperature and pressure. Thus, constants in any empirical equation of state are regarded as curve-fitting coefficients or accommodative constants, and their values clearly depend on the set of data used to determine such constants.

Any equation of state has to satisfy the constraints imposed at the critical point. That is, the critical isotherm passes through a point of inflection at the critical point and the slope is zero, both of which are expressed as

$$\left(\frac{\partial^2 P}{\partial v^2}\right)_T = 0 \quad \text{and} \quad \left(\frac{\partial P}{\partial v}\right)_T = 0 \tag{1.1-9}$$

These conditions are often used in determining constants in two-constant equations of state. For example, they are used to determine constants $a$ and $b$ in the van der Waals equation, Eq. (1.1-5), resulting in

$$a = \frac{9RT_c v_c}{8} \quad \text{and} \quad b = \frac{v_c}{3} \tag{1.1-10}$$

Then, the van der Waals equation is expressed in terms of reduced variables with respect to $P_c$, $T_c$, and $v_c$ at the critical point:

$$P_r = \frac{8T_r}{3v_r - 1} - \frac{3}{v_r^2} \tag{1.1-11}$$

This form of equation is applicable to all substances in principle because two arbitrary constants are absorbed in the dimensionless variables.

### 1.1.4 Two-Phase Equilibrium

For a two-phase system of a pure substance in equilibrium at temperature $T$ and pressure $P$, the Gibbs function is given by

$$G = f(T, P, n^l, n^v) \tag{1.1-12}$$

where $n$ denotes the number of moles, and the superscripts "$l$" and "$v$" indicate two phases. Forming the differential of $G$,

$$dG = \left(\frac{\partial G}{\partial T}\right)_{P,n} dT + \left(\frac{\partial G}{\partial P}\right)_{T,n} dP + \left(\frac{\partial G}{\partial n^l}\right)_{T,P,n^v} dn^l + \left(\frac{\partial G}{\partial n^v}\right)_{T,P,n^l} dn^v \tag{1.1-13}$$

Since the total amount of substance $n = n^l + n^v$ remains constant, the differential of $G$ under constant temperature and pressure becomes

$$dG]_{T,P} = \left(\frac{\partial G}{\partial n^l}\right)_{T,P,n^v} dn^l + \left(\frac{\partial G}{\partial n^v}\right)_{T,P,n^l} dn^v = g^l dn^l + g^v dn^v = (g^l - g^v) dn^l \quad (1.1\text{-}14)$$

where $g^l$ and $g^v$ are the molar Gibbs functions that are defined respectively as

$$g^l = \left(\frac{\partial G}{\partial n^l}\right)_{T,P,n^v} \quad \text{and} \quad g^v = \left(\frac{\partial G}{\partial n^v}\right)_{T,P,n^l} \quad (1.1\text{-}15)$$

At equilibrium, $dG]_{T,P} = 0$, as given by Eq. (1.1-1); thus, from Eq. (1.1-14),

$$g^l = g^v \quad (1.1\text{-}16)$$

This states that as a requirement of two-phase equilibrium of a pure substance, the molar Gibbs functions of each phase should be equal.

For two-phase equilibrium, the alternative and equivalent statement holds regarding the chemical potential, $\mu$, as well as the fugacity, $f$. That is,

$$\mu^l = \mu^v \quad (1.1\text{-}17)$$

$$f^l = f^v \quad (1.1\text{-}18)$$

Here, the chemical potential is identical to the molar Gibbs function, and the fugacity (Lewis, 1901) is related to the Gibbs function as

$$dg = d\mu = RT d(\ln f) \quad (1.1\text{-}19)$$

with the requirement as pressure approaches zero that

$$\lim_{P \to 0} (f/P) = 1 \quad (1.1\text{-}20)$$

The fugacity has units of pressure that may be considered as pseudo-pressure. The ratio of the fugacity to pressure defines another property, called the *fugacity coefficient*.

$$\phi = f/P \quad (1.1\text{-}21)$$

For an ideal gas, $f = P$, so that $\phi = 1$.

### 1.1.5 Clausius-Clapeyron Equation

Differentiation of Eq. (1.1-16) with respect to temperature yields

$$\left(\frac{\partial g^l}{\partial T}\right)_P + \left(\frac{\partial g^l}{\partial P}\right)_T \left(\frac{dP}{dT}\right) = \left(\frac{\partial g^v}{\partial T}\right)_P + \left(\frac{\partial g^u}{\partial P}\right)_T \left(\frac{dP}{dT}\right) \quad (1.1\text{-}22)$$

From the differential form of the Gibbs function $dg = v dP - s dT$,

$$\left(\frac{\partial g}{\partial P}\right)_T = v \quad \text{and} \quad \left(\frac{\partial g}{\partial T}\right)_P = -s \quad (1.1\text{-}23)$$

Thus, Eq. (1.1-22) becomes

$$-s^l + v^l \left(\frac{dP}{dT}\right) = -s^v + v^v \left(\frac{dP}{dT}\right) \qquad (1.1\text{-}24)$$

By noting that Eq. (1.1-16) means $h^l - Ts^l = h^v - Ts^v$,

$$\frac{dP}{dT} = \frac{h^v - h^l}{T(v^v - v^l)} = \frac{\Delta h}{T(v^v - v^l)} \qquad (1.1\text{-}25)$$

This is the Clapeyron equation that relates the pressure and temperature in two-phase equilibrium with the specific volumes and latent heat for phase change, $\Delta h$. When this relation is applied to the vapor-liquid equilibrium at low pressure, the specific volume of liquid, $v^l$, is negligible compared with the specific volume of vapor, $v^v$, and the further assumption of ideal gas behavior for vapor at low pressure results in replacing $v^v$ with $RT/P$. Then, Eq. (1.1-25) is reduced to the following Clausius-Clapeyron equation.

$$\frac{dP}{dT} = \frac{\Delta h P}{RT^2} \quad \text{or} \quad \frac{d \ln P}{dT} = \frac{\Delta h}{RT^2} \qquad (1.1\text{-}26)$$

### 1.1.6 Equation for Vapor Pressure

Integration of the Clausius-Clapeyron equation, Eq. (1.1-26), under an assumption of constant latent heat of evaporation $\Delta h$ gives

$$\ln P = A - \frac{\Delta h}{RT} \qquad (1.1\text{-}27)$$

where $A$ is a constant. This implies that a plot of $\ln P$ versus $1/T$ should be a straight line over the region where $\Delta h$ is constant. Such plots generally yield nearly a straight line over a certain range of temperature, suggesting the validity of the following form of vapor-pressure equation with two constants $A$ and $B$:

$$\ln P = A - \frac{B}{T} \qquad (1.1\text{-}28)$$

This type of equation is useful for many purposes, but it does not represent data sufficiently well to provide accurate values of derivatives.

The following so-called Antoine equation is more satisfactory to represent vapor pressure and has found wider use:

$$\ln P = A - \frac{B}{T + C} \qquad (1.1\text{-}29)$$

where $A$, $B$, and $C$ are constants.

When extensive vapor-pressure data of high accuracy are available, it is difficult for any simple equation to represent them faithfully. A more satisfactory equation has the form

$$\ln P = A - \frac{B}{T+C} + DT + E \ln T \tag{1.1-30}$$

With the flexibility afforded by five accommodative constants ($A$, $B$, $C$, $D$, and $E$), this equation should be capable of fitting vapor pressure data quite well, though the Antoine Equation is more widely employed.

All equations to represent vapor-pressure data are empirical, and there is no thermodynamic basis for the general form of vapor pressure curves. Equations faithfully representing vapor pressure and temperature data of pure substances are required to determine the phase equilibrium of their mixtures, as shown in the next section.

### 1.1.7 Metastable Equilibrium

On a $P$-$v$ diagram for a single pure substance (shown in Figure 3), an isotherm consists of three states of liquid (AB), two-phase mixture (BF), and vapor (FG). It is generally known that the specific volume of liquid can be increased along line BC; thus, it is possible to superheat the liquid above the saturation temperature in the absence of vapor nucleation. Similarly, the specific volume of vapor can be decreased along line FE, making it possible to subcool the vapor below the saturation temperature in the absence of droplet nucleation. The superheated

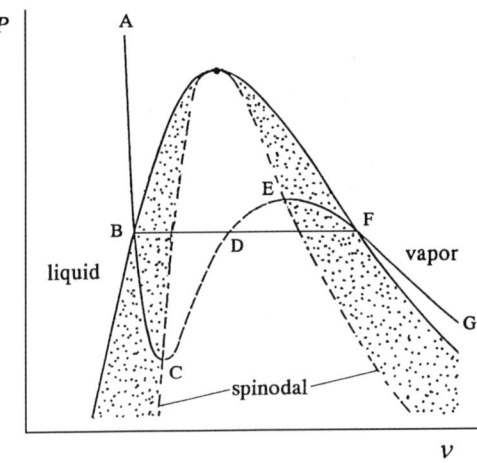

**Figure 3** Superheating of liquid, subcooling of vapor, and an isotherm predicted from the van der Waals equation of state.

liquid on line BC or subcooled vapor on line FE that is reached without any phase change occurring at points B or F is in metastable equilibrium because the criterion of mechanical stability, $(\partial P/\partial v)_T \leq 0$, is satisfied there. The state between points C and E violates the mechanical stability criterion and is therefore completely unstable and inaccessible in boiling and condensation. The locus of limiting points C and E where $(\partial P/\partial v)_T$ changes from negative to positive is named as the liquid and vapor spinodal, respectively.

If the van der Waals equation, Eq. (1.1-11), is assumed to be valid even for such nonequilibrium conditions, the line ABCDEFG and hence the spinodal curves are determined by differentiating Eq. (1.1-11) and setting $(\partial P/\partial v)_T = 0$.

### 1.1.8 Thermodynamic Equilibrium at a Curved Interface

The conditions of equilibrium at a curved liquid-vapor interface, as in the case of a spherical bubble or droplet shown in Figure 4, yield relations that are useful in predicting nucleation conditions in liquid or vapor. In equilibrium of a vapor bubble in liquid, the excess pressure of the vapor bubble above the surrounding liquid is given as

$$\Delta P_{v,l} = P_v - P_l = \frac{2\sigma}{R_b} \tag{1.1-31}$$

where $R_b$ is the bubble radius and $\sigma$ the surface tension. If the changes in Gibbs function in the vapor and liquid phases are equal against a change of bubble radius, the system remains in equilibrium. That is,

$$dg_v = dg_l \tag{1.1-32}$$

Since $dg = vdP - sdT$,

$$v_v dP_v - s_v dT_v = v_l dP_l - s_l dT_l \tag{1.1-33}$$

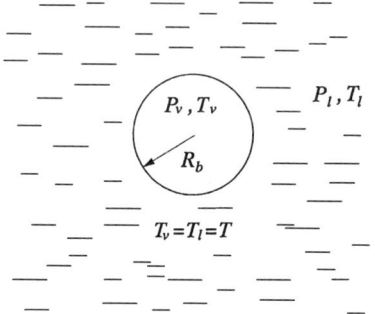

**Figure 4** A vapor bubble in equilibrium with liquid.

For a system at a uniform and constant temperature $T$,

$$v_v dP_v = v_l dP_l \tag{1.1-34}$$

Thus, for a change of bubble radius under the phase equilibrium condition,

$$d(\Delta P_{v,l}) = d\left(\frac{2\sigma}{R_b}\right) = dP_v - dP_l = \left(1 - \frac{v_v}{v_l}\right) dP_v \tag{1.1-35}$$

If the volume change in liquid is neglected and vapor is assumed as an ideal gas, the above equation becomes

$$d(\Delta P_{v,l}) = d\left(\frac{2\sigma}{R_b}\right) = dP_v - \left(\frac{RT}{v_l}\right)\frac{dP_v}{P_v} \tag{1.1-36}$$

Integration from the equilibrium state for a planar interface ($1/R = 0$), for which pressure is the saturation pressure $P_{sat,T}$ corresponding to $T$ and $\Delta P_{v,l} = 0$, yields

$$\Delta P_{v,l} = \frac{2\sigma}{R_b} = (P_v - P_{sat,T}) - \left(\frac{RT}{v_l}\right)\ln\frac{P_v}{P_{sat,T}} \tag{1.1-37}$$

In the case of small pressure difference $(P_v - P_{sat,T}) \ll P_{sat,T}$, Eq. (1.1-37) is simplified as

$$\Delta P_{v,l} = \frac{2\sigma}{R_b} = \left(1 - \frac{v_{v,sat}}{v_l}\right)(P_v - P_{sat,T}) \tag{1.1-38}$$

Thus, the vapor pressure for a spherical interface is related to the saturation pressure for a planar interface as

$$P_{sat,T} - P_v = \left(\frac{v_l}{v_{v,sat} - v_l}\right)\left(\frac{2\sigma}{R_b}\right) \tag{1.1-39}$$

Similarly, for the liquid pressure,

$$P_{sat,T} - P_l = \left(\frac{v_{v,sat}}{v_{v,sat} - v_l}\right)\left(\frac{2\sigma}{R_b}\right) \tag{1.1-40}$$

The last two relations state that for a spherical bubble in equilibrium with liquid at uniform temperature $T$, the vapor and liquid pressures $P_v$ and $P_l$ are less than the saturation pressure $P_{sat,T}$ for a planar phase interface at the same temperature $T$. At moderate pressure, apart from the critical point, the specific volume of liquid is negligibly small in comparison to vapor. Hence, Eqs. (1.1-39) and (1.1-40) become

$$P_v \cong P_{sat,T} \tag{1.1-41}$$

$$P_l \cong P_{sat,T} - \frac{2\sigma}{R_b} \tag{1.1-42}$$

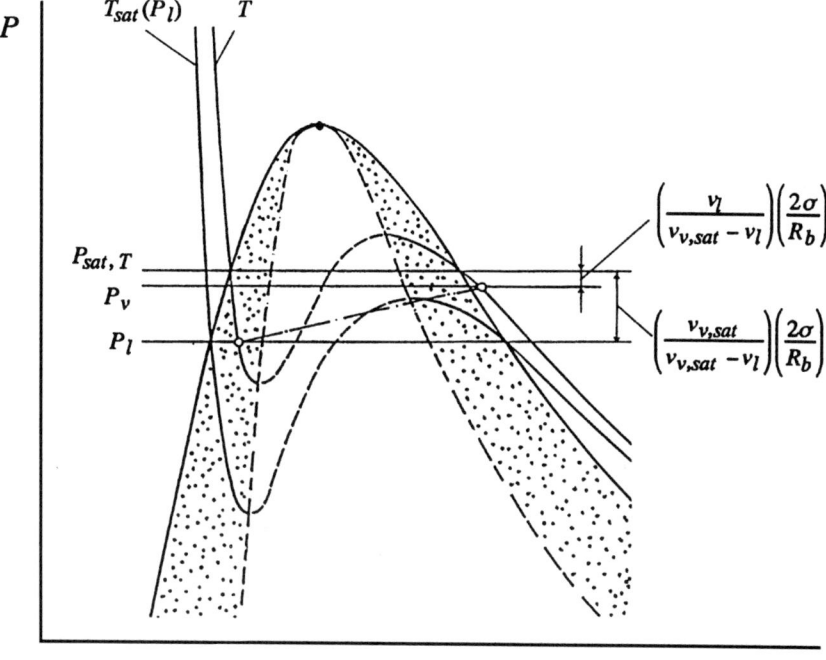

**Figure 5** Vapor-liquid equilibrium at a spherical interface.

The state points of vapor and liquid expressed by Eqs. (1.1-39) and (1.1-40) are shown in Figure 5. Thus, to maintain equilibrium of a bubble in liquid, the liquid must be superheated over the saturation temperature for a planar interface by the amount

$$\Delta T = T - T_{sat}(P_l) \qquad (1.1\text{-}43)$$

## 1.2 THERMODYNAMIC EQUILIBRIUM—BINARY AND MULTI-COMPONENT MIXTURES

### 1.2.1 Fugacity and Fugacity Coefficient of Pure Substance and Mixture

The fugacity and fugacity coefficient of mixtures (Lewis, 1901) are defined analogously to those for pure components. Thus, Eqs. (1.1-19)–(1.1-21) are valid for mixtures too, so their values are calculable if the equations of state or $P$-$v$-$T$ data are available for any mixture of interest.

For constant temperature and composition,

$$dg = -s\,dT + v\,dP + \sum \bar{g}_i\,dz_i = v\,dP \qquad (1.2\text{-}1)$$

where $\bar{g}_i$ is the partial molar Gibbs function of i-component, as defined later by Eq. (1.2-15). Combining this equation with Eq. (1.1-19) and using the definition of the compressibility factor $Z$ and relation of $\phi = f/P$, defined by Eq. (1.1-21), yield

$$d(\ln f) = \frac{v}{RT}dP = Z\frac{dP}{P} \qquad (1.2\text{-}2)$$

$$d(\ln \phi) = (Z-1)\frac{dP}{P} \qquad (1.2\text{-}3)$$

The integration of these two equations from zero-pressure where $f = P$ and $\phi = 1$ to an arbitrary pressure $P$ gives

$$\ln f = \ln P + \int_0^P (Z-1)\frac{dP}{P} \quad \text{(mixture at constant } T \text{ and concentration)}$$
$$(1.2\text{-}4)$$

$$\ln \phi = \int_0^P (Z-1)\frac{dP}{P} \quad \text{(mixture at constant } T \text{ and concentration)} \quad (1.2\text{-}5)$$

If $Z$ is explicit in $v$, then the variable of integration is changed from pressure to molar volume, creating the equivalent equations

$$\ln f = \ln\left(\frac{RT}{v}\right) + (Z-1) - \int_\infty^v (Z-1)\frac{dv}{v}$$
$$\text{(mixture at constant } T \text{ and concentration)} \quad (1.2\text{-}6)$$

$$\ln \phi = (Z-1) - \ln Z - \int_\infty^v (Z-1)\frac{dv}{v}$$
$$\text{(mixture at constant } T \text{ and concentration)} \quad (1.2\text{-}7)$$

These four relations commonly hold true for pure substances and mixtures. To distinguish them from each other, the fugacity and fugacity coefficient of pure substance "$i$" when it exists alone are denoted by adding the subscript "$i$" to the pertinent properties:

$$\ln f_i = \ln P + \int_0^P (Z_i - 1)\frac{dP}{P} \quad \text{(pure substance at constant } T\text{)} \quad (1.2\text{-}8)$$

$$\ln \phi_i = \int_0^P (Z_i - 1)\frac{dP}{P} \quad \text{(pure substance at constant } T\text{)} \quad (1.2\text{-}9)$$

or

$$\ln f_i = \ln\left(\frac{RT}{v_i}\right) + (Z_i - 1) - \int_{\infty}^{v_i} (Z_i - 1)\frac{dv_i}{v_i}$$
(pure substance at constant $T$) (1.2-10)

$$\ln \phi_i = (Z_i - 1) - \ln Z_i - \int_{\infty}^{v_i} (Z_i - 1)\frac{dv_i}{v_i}$$
(pure substance at constant $T$) (1.2-11)

## 1.2.2 Partial Molar Properties of Components in Mixtures

In considering phase equilibrium of multicomponent systems, the partial molar properties (Lewis and Randall, 1921) of each component in a mixture play an important role. For a pure substance in a single phase, any extensive thermodynamic property, designated collectively by $M$, is a function of two independent intensive properties and the amount of the substance. If temperature $T$ and pressure $P$ are selected as the independent properties and the number of moles $n$ as a measure to express the amount of the substance, then

$$M = f(T, P, n) \tag{1.2-12}$$

Likewise, any extensive property $M$ of a multicomponent mixture in a single phase is a function of temperature, pressure, and the number of moles of each component $n_1, n_2, \ldots n_j$. Thus, for a two-component mixture in a single phase, it becomes

$$M = f(T, P, n_1, n_2) \tag{1.2-13}$$

The differential of $M$ under constant temperature and pressure gives

$$dM]_{T,P} = \left(\frac{\partial M}{\partial n_1}\right)_{T,P,n_2} dn_1 + \left(\frac{\partial M}{\partial n_2}\right)_{T,P,n_1} dn_2 = \bar{m}_1 dn_1 + \bar{m}_2 dn_2 \tag{1.2-14}$$

where

$$\bar{m}_1 = \left(\frac{\partial M}{\partial n_1}\right)_{T,P,n_2} \quad \text{and} \quad \bar{m}_2 = \left(\frac{\partial M}{\partial n_2}\right)_{T,P,n_1} \tag{1.2-15}$$

Here, the subscript $n_j$ denotes that all $n$'s except $n_i$ are held constant during differentiation, and $\bar{m}_1$ and $\bar{m}_2$ are the partial molar properties of each component in the mixture. Since an extensive property is directly proportional to the amount of substance, Eq. (1.2-14) can be integrated at a specified temperature and pressure to give the molar property of the mixture as

$$m = M/n = z_1\bar{m}_1 + z_2\bar{m}_2 \tag{1.2-16}$$

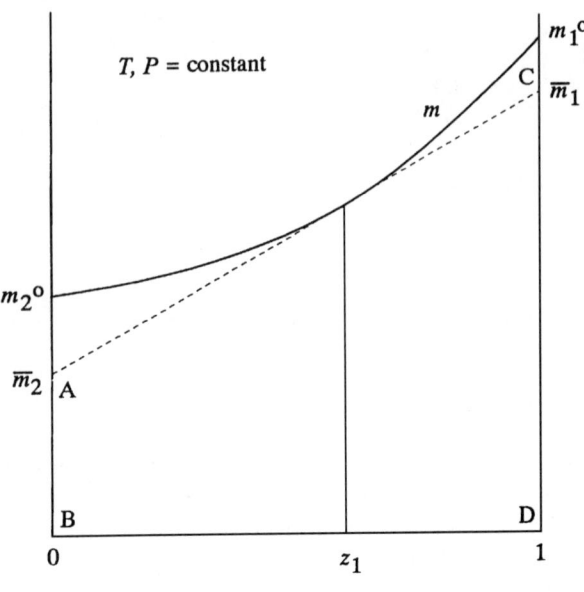

**Figure 6** Determination of the partial molar property from the molar property of a binary mixture.

Here, $z_1$ and $z_2$ are the mole fraction of each component. It is noted that $\bar{m}_i$ is not a property of the pure substance $i$ that exists alone but a property of component $i$ in a mixture; thus, $\bar{m}_i$ is not a function $f(T, P)$, but $f(T, P, z_1, z_2, \ldots, z_j)$. An overbar "$^-$" is used to distinguish the partial molar properties of component in a mixture from that of the corresponding pure component.

For a binary mixture, $\bar{m}_1$ and $\bar{m}_2$ can be determined from a data plot of the molar property $m$ of the mixture at constant temperature and pressure of interest versus the mole fraction $z_1$, as illustrated in Figure 6. From the differentiation of $M = n m = (n_1 + n_2)m$ in accordance with the definition of the molar property,

$$\bar{m}_1 = \left(\frac{\partial M}{\partial n_1}\right)_{T,P,n_2} = m + (n_1 + n_2)\left(\frac{\partial m}{\partial n_1}\right)_{T,P,n_2} \quad (1.2\text{-}17)$$

Since the mole fraction is given as $z_1 = n_1/(n_1+n_2)$ and $T$, $P$, and $n_2$ are constant,

$$\frac{dz_1}{dn_1} = \frac{n_2}{(n_1+n_2)^2} \quad \text{or} \quad \frac{n_1+n_2}{dn_1} = \left(\frac{n_2}{n_1+n_2}\right)\frac{1}{dz_1} = \frac{1-z_1}{dz_1} \quad (1.2\text{-}18)$$

Therefore,

$$\bar{m}_1 = m + (1-z_1)\left(\frac{\partial m}{\partial z_1}\right)_{T,P,n_2} = \overline{CD} \quad (1.2\text{-}19)$$

In the same way,

$$\bar{m}_2 = m - z_1 \left(\frac{\partial m}{\partial z_1}\right)_{T,P,n_1} = \overline{AB} \qquad (1.2\text{-}20)$$

Thus, $\bar{m}_1$ at a specified mixture concentration of $z_1$ is equal to the intercept at $z_1 = 1.0$ of the tangent to the $m$-curve at point $z_1$. Similarly, $\bar{m}_2$ is equal to the intercept at $z_1 = 0$ of the same tangent. For constant temperature and pressure, $\bar{m}_1$ and $\bar{m}_2$ vary with $z_1$ and are not equal, in general, to the molar specific properties of pure components 1 and 2, denoted as $m_1^o$ and $m_2^o$ on the vertical axes. The values of $m_1^o$ and $m_2^o$ are, of course, functions of temperature and pressure only. If $m$ would vary linearly with $z_1$, then $\bar{m}_1$ and $\bar{m}_2$ coincide with $m_1^o$ and $m_2^o$, respectively. This is the case with ideal mixtures, as mentioned later.

### 1.2.3 Partial Molar Gibbs Function and Fugacity of Components

The partial molar Gibbs function $\bar{g}_i$ of component $i$ in a mixture, which is equivalent to the partial molar chemical potential $\bar{\mu}_i$, is calculated from the Gibbs function of the mixture as

$$\bar{g}_i = \bar{\mu}_i = \left(\frac{\partial G}{\partial n_i}\right)_{T,P,n_k} = \left(\frac{\partial (ng)}{\partial n_i}\right)_{T,P,n_k} \qquad (1.2\text{-}21)$$

Here, $G$ is the Gibbs function of a mixture, $g$ is its molar value (i.e., $g = G/n$), and $n_i$ is the number of moles for component. The fugacity for the component, $\hat{f}_i$, is related to $\bar{g}_i$ as

$$d\bar{g}_i = d\bar{\mu}_i = RT d(\ln \hat{f}_i) \qquad (1.2\text{-}22)$$

with the requirement as pressure approaches zero that

$$\lim_{P \to 0} (\hat{f}_i / z_i P) = 1 \qquad (1.2\text{-}23)$$

The fugacity coefficient for the component is defined differently from those for pure substance and mixture as

$$\hat{\phi}_i = \hat{f}_i / z_i P \qquad (1.2\text{-}24)$$

so that from Eq. (1.2-23)

$$\lim_{P \to 0} \hat{\phi}_i = 1 \qquad (1.2\text{-}25)$$

Here, $z_i$ is the mole fraction of component $i$ in a mixture. When needed to distinguish the mole fraction for different phases, $y$ is used for the vapor or gaseous phase and $x$ for the liquid phase. Since the fugacity and fugacity coefficient of each component in a mixture are not related to the mixture fugacity and fugacity coefficient as partial molar properties, a carat (^) is used instead of an overbar (¯) on $\hat{f}_i$ and $\hat{\phi}_i$. As the limiting values of partial molar property, however, they become

$$\hat{f}_i = f_i^o \quad \text{and} \quad \hat{\phi}_i = \phi_i^o = f_i^o/P \quad \text{for } z_i = 1 \quad (1.2\text{-}26)$$

### 1.2.4 Two-Phase Equilibrium of Mixture

The Gibbs function of a multicomponent mixture in a single phase is expressed as $G(T, P, n_1, n_2, \ldots n_j)$, so that its differential becomes

$$\begin{aligned}
dG &= \left.\frac{\partial G}{\partial T}\right]_{P,n} dT + \left.\frac{\partial G}{\partial P}\right]_{T,n} dP + \sum \left(\frac{\partial G}{\partial n_i}\right)_{T,P,n_k} dn_i \\
&= \left.\frac{\partial G}{\partial T}\right]_{P,n} dT + \left.\frac{\partial G}{\partial P}\right]_{T,n} dP + \sum \bar{g}_i dn_i \quad (1.2\text{-}27)
\end{aligned}$$

The subscripts $n$ in the first two terms indicate that all n's are held constant during differentiation. This implies a fixed composition, resulting in

$$V = \left(\frac{\partial G}{\partial P}\right)_{T,n} \quad \text{and} \quad -S = \left(\frac{\partial G}{\partial T}\right)_{P,n} \quad (1.2\text{-}28)$$

Therefore, Eq. (1.2-27) becomes

$$dG = VdP - SdT + \sum \bar{g}_i dn_i \quad \text{or}$$

$$dg = d(G/n) = vdP - sdT + \sum \bar{g}_i dz_i \quad (1.2\text{-}29)$$

This expression for a mixture is the counterpart of the following equation for a single component system,

$$dg = vdP - sdT \quad (1.2\text{-}30)$$

A simple multicomponent and multiphase system is that composed of two components, "1" and "2," and two phases, "$l$" and "$v$," that are present at the same $T$ and $P$. For each phase of the two-component mixture, Eq. (1.2-29) is written at constant temperature and pressure as

$$dG^l]_{T,P} = \bar{g}_1^l dn_1^l + \bar{g}_2^l dn_2^l \quad (1.2\text{-}31)$$

$$dG^v]_{T,P} = \bar{g}_1^v dn_1^v + \bar{g}_2^v dn_2^v \quad (1.2\text{-}32)$$

Taking into account that the total amount of each component remaining constant, the differential of the Gibbs function for the mixture becomes

$$dG]_{T,P} = dG^l]_{T,P} + dG^v]_{T,P} = (\bar{g}_1^l - \bar{g}_1^v)dn_1^l + (\bar{g}_2^l - \bar{g}_2^v)dn_2^l \quad (1.2\text{-}33)$$

Since $n_1^l$ and $n_2^l$ can vary independently, it follows from an equilibrium condition, i.e., $dG]_{T,P} = 0$ (as given by Eq. [1.1-1]), that the terms in parentheses in Eq. (1.2-33) must be zero.

$$\bar{g}_1^l = \bar{g}_1^v \quad \text{and} \quad \bar{g}_2^l = \bar{g}_2^v \qquad (1.2\text{-}34)$$

This states that for equilibrium of a two-component and two-phase system, the partial molar Gibbs function of each component is the same in each phase. The above conditions are the counterparts of Eq. (1.1-16) for the two-phase equilibrium of a pure substance. Equation (1.2-34) is also expressed alternately in terms of the chemical potentials and the fugacities as

$$\bar{\mu}_1^l = \bar{\mu}_1^v \quad \text{and} \quad \bar{\mu}_2^l = \bar{\mu}_2^v \qquad (1.2\text{-}35)$$

$$\hat{f}_1^l = \hat{f}_1^v \quad \text{and} \quad \hat{f}_2^l = \hat{f}_2^v \qquad (1.2\text{-}36)$$

### 1.2.5 Gibbs Phase Rule

The above requirement for two-phase equilibrium of a two-component system can be extended with similar reasoning to an $m$-component and $\pi$-phase system, from which the Gibbs phase rule (Gibbs, 1876) is derived. For a system involving m components, there are at most $(m-1)$ independently variable mole fractions for each phase. For the total of $\pi$ phases, therefore, there are at most $\pi(m-1)$ independently variable mole fractions. Temperature and pressure, which are the same in each phase, are two further intensive properties, giving a maximum of $[\pi(m-1)+2]$ independently variable intensive properties for the system. Among these properties, there are $m(\pi-1)$ equilibrium conditions describing equality of Gibbs functions in each phase. Thus, the number of intensive properties that may be arbitrarily specified, i.e., the degrees of freedom $F$, becomes

$$F = \lfloor \pi(m-1) + 2 \rfloor - m(\pi - 1) = 2 + m - \pi \qquad (1.2\text{-}37)$$

This is referred to as the Gibbs phase rule, which imposes important limitations on various systems. For a single component system in a single phase, $m = 1$ and $\pi = 1$. Thus, $F = 2 + 1 - 1 = 2$. That is, two intensive properties, such as temperature and pressure, must be specified to fix the equilibrium state of this system. When two phases are present in a single component system, $\pi = 2$ and $m = 1$. Hence, $F = 2 + 1 - 2 = 1$. That is, the equilibrium state is determined by a single intensive property, for example, by specifying either temperature or pressure.

### 1.2.6 Phase Equilibrium Diagrams for Binary Mixtures

The Gibbs phase rule for a two component system ($m = 2$) yields the maximum number of intensive variables as three for the case when a single phase ($\pi = 1$)

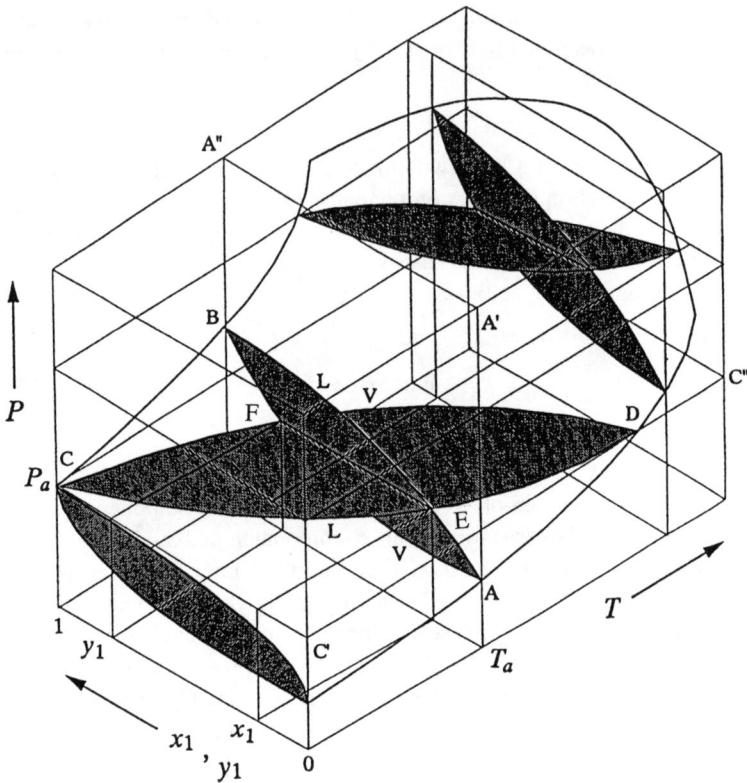

**Figure 7** Pressure-temperature-composition ($x_1$, $y_1$) diagram for a binary mixture.

exists in equilibrium. If the three intensive variables are chosen as $T$, $P$, and one of the mole fraction $z$, then the equilibrium state of the system is fixed. Thus, a single-phase state of liquid or vapor of binary mixtures can be represented in $T$-$P$-composition space, as shown in Figure 7. Within this space, the two phase ($\pi = 2$) equilibrium state defines surfaces because the phase rule yields two degrees of freedom, i.e., $F = 4 - 2 = 2$. The upper surface in Figure 7 represents the saturated liquid state, and the lower surface represents the saturated vapor state. The vapor and liquid mixtures exist in the area enveloped by these two surfaces. For two phases in equilibrium, temperature and pressure must be equal in both phases. Thus, the compositions of equilibrium vapor-liquid mixtures are determined as the intersection of an isothermal plane with an isobaric plane. In Figure 7, an isothermal vertical plane (A-A′-A″) corresponding to $T_a$ intersects the upper and lower surfaces to form the lens-shaped envelope ALBVA, and an isobaric horizontal plane (C-C′-C″) corresponding to $P_a$ intersects both surfaces to form the lens-shaped envelope CLDVC. The intersection of the two envelopes occurs in two places: on the upper surface for saturated liquid at point E and on the lower surface for saturated vapor at point F. These points represent values of the liquid composition $x_1$ and vapor composition $y_1$ that are in equilibrium at the temperature $T_a$ and pressure $P_a$. A horizontal line connecting points E and F is called a *tie line*, which determines the equilibrium liquid and vapor compositions at a given temperature and pressure.

Three-dimensional representation of the $T$-$P$-composition relationships illustrated in Figure 7 is usually projected on either one of the principal planes of constant pressure, constant temperature, or constant composition. Such two-dimensional phase diagrams are indicated in Figures 8 through 10. The envelopes on the $T$-$x$-$y$ and $P$-$x$-$y$ diagrams will cover the entire range of mole fractions from zero to unity when mixture temperature or pressure is less than the critical values of respective pure components. Unless equilibrium near the critical region is concerned, there is little use of the $P$-$T$ diagram shown in Figure 10. Curves CLD in Figure 8 and ALB in Figure 9 represent the state of saturated liquid, and they are referred to as the bubble-point curve. Curves CVD in Figure 8 and AVB in Figure 9 are the dew-point curves, representing the states of saturated vapor. These two curves converge to the pure-component saturation temperature or pressure at

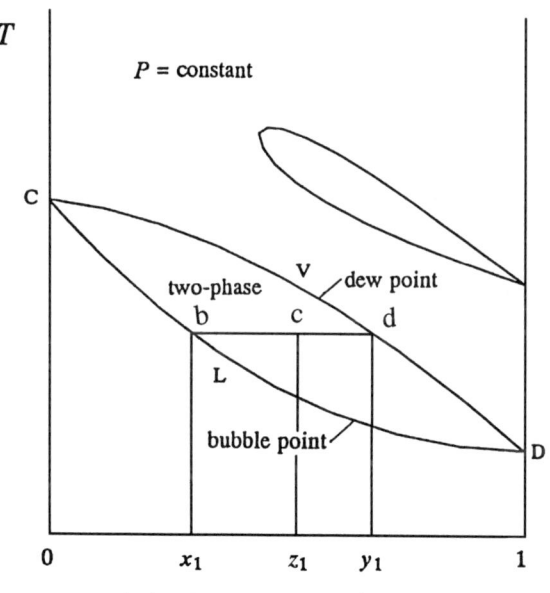

**Figure 8** Temperature-composition diagrams for a binary mixture at two constant pressures.

**20** HANDBOOK OF PHASE CHANGE: BOILING AND CONDENSATION

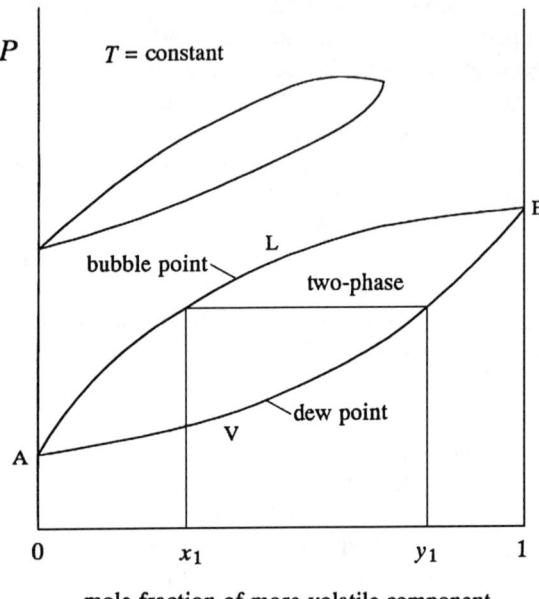

**Figure 9** Pressure-composition diagrams for a binary mixture at two constant temperatures.

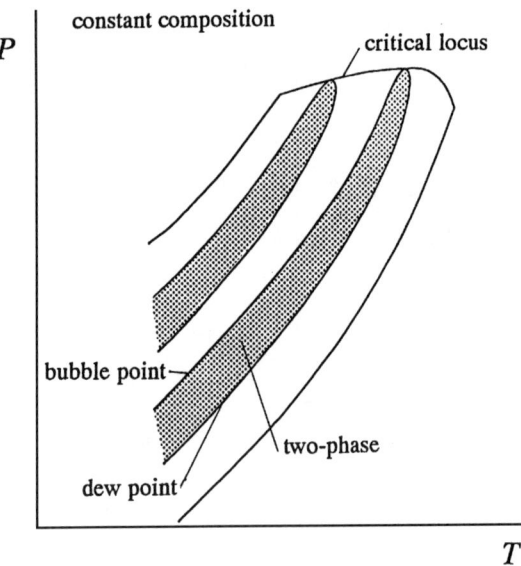

**Figure 10** Pressure-temperature diagrams for a binary mixture at two constant compositions.

the composition extremes of $x_1 = 0$ and $x_1 = 1$. The dew-point and bubble-point curves separate the mixture state into superheated vapor, vapor-liquid two-phase, and subcooled liquid, as shown in Figures 8 and 9.

### 1.2.7 Tie-Line

The $T$-$x$-$y$ diagram for a constant pressure is more widely used in considering heat transfer with phase change of multicomponent substance. The tie line bd in Figure 8 that goes through the point C at an overall concentration has a useful stoichiometric property. Let $n$ be the total number of moles of a mixture having a mole fraction $z_1$ for component 1. It separates into $n^l$ moles of liquid with a mole fraction $x_1$ and $n^v$ moles of vapor with a mole fraction $y_1$. A balance of overall mole number gives

$$n^l + n^v = n \tag{1.2-38}$$

while a mole number balance on component 1 yields

$$x_1 n^l + y_1 n^v = z_1 n \tag{1.2-39}$$

Solving these equations,

$$\frac{n^v}{n} = \frac{z_1 - x_1}{y_1 - x_1} = \frac{\overline{bc}}{\overline{bd}} \tag{1.2-40}$$

and

$$\frac{n^l}{n} = \frac{y_1 - z_1}{y_1 - x_1} = \frac{\overline{cd}}{\overline{bd}} \tag{1.2-41}$$

Thus, the ratio of the numbers of moles in the vapor and liquid phases is expressed by the ratio of the segment lengths of the tie line.

$$\frac{n^v}{n^l} = \frac{\overline{bc}}{\overline{cd}} \tag{1.2-42}$$

This lever principle is also true for mass units if the mass fraction is substituted for the mole fraction in the above equations.

### 1.2.8 Phase Change at Constant Pressure

If a binary mixture in a subcooled liquid state at point A in Figure 11 is heated in a vessel from an initial temperature $T_a$ under a quasi-equilibrium isobaric process, it will follow a vertical line, since the overall composition $x_{1a}$ remains constant during this heating process. When the temperature reaches the bubble-point temperature $T_b$ at point B, the first vapor bubble is formed. This vapor has the composition $y_{1b'}$

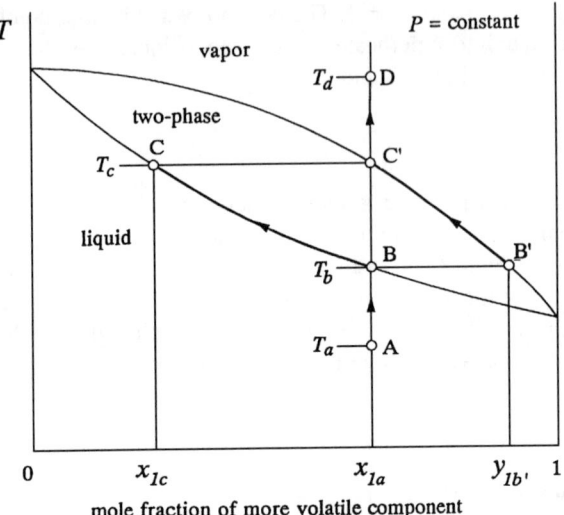

**Figure 11** State change of a binary mixture in a heating process at constant pressure.

corresponding to point B′. It is richer in the more volatile component than liquid, so the liquid becomes depleted of the more volatile component. As heating (and evaporation) continue, the amount of vapor increases and the amount of liquid decreases, and both $x_1$ and $y_1$ decrease with the states of vapor and liquid following the paths B′C′ and BC, respectively. Eventually, when the mixture reaches $T_c$ at point C, the last dew of liquid with the composition $x_{1c}$ corresponding to point C disappears. Further heating causes the system to go through the superheated vapor region to reach point D.

The cooling process of a binary mixture from a superheated vapor state to a subcooled liquid state follows the opposite path from point D to point A, shown in Figure 11. The above example is enough to indicate the substantial thermodynamic differences in the phase change process between binary mixture and pure fluid, namely that the saturation temperature and composition are not constant but are variable during the boiling and condensation processes of multicomponent mixtures. For a phase change process, such as shown in Figure 11, the boiling range is defined as the temperature difference between the dew point C′ and the bubble point B at the same overall composition as the mixture.

### 1.2.9 Azeotrope

Some binary mixtures form an azeotrope at an intermediate composition. Figures 12 and 13 illustrate phase equilibrium diagrams for such a binary mixture.

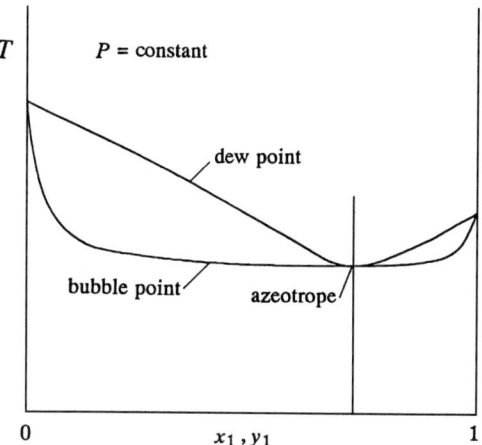

**Figure 12** Phase diagram at constant pressure for an azeotrope-forming binary mixture.

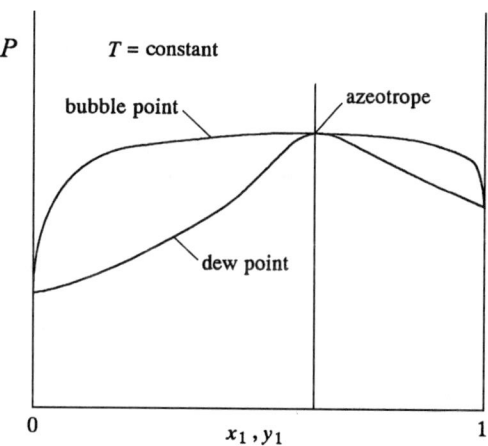

**Figure 13** Phase diagram at constant temperature for an azeotrope-forming binary mixture.

Liquid and vapor compositions are identical at the azeotrope, and hence the fluid behaves like a pure substance. The azeotropic state is special in that it possesses only one degree of freedom, rather than two as required for normal two-component and two-phase equilibrium of non-azeotropic mixtures. Thus, specification of any one of temperature, pressure, or composition fixes the other two for a binary azeotrope. A maximum or minimum occurs on both the bubble-point and dew-point curves at the azeotropic compositions and the respective pair of equations is satisfied:

$$\left(\frac{\partial T}{\partial x_1}\right)_{P,az} = \left(\frac{\partial T}{\partial y_1}\right)_{P,az} = 0 \qquad (1.2\text{-}43)$$

or

$$\left(\frac{\partial P}{\partial x_1}\right)_{T,az} = \left(\frac{\partial P}{\partial y_1}\right)_{P,az} = 0 \qquad (1.2\text{-}44)$$

The systems shown in Figures 12 and 13 have a minimum-temperature and a maximum-pressure azeotrope, respectively. Maximum-temperature and minimum-pressure azeotropes also exist. Azeotropes may also occur in mixtures containing more than two components.

### 1.2.10 Property Changes on Mixing

Property changes on mixing different pure substances, designated collectively by $\Delta M$ or $\Delta m$, are often introduced to calculate properties of multicomponent mixtures. They are defined as the difference between the actual mixture properties and the mole-fraction average of the properties of pure components.

The sum of any extensive property of pure components forming a mixture of a given composition at the same temperature $T$ and pressure $P$ as the mixture is given as

$$m_{comp} = M_{comp}/n = \sum z_i m_i^o \qquad (1.2\text{-}45)$$

where $m_i^o$ is the molar property of pure component $i$ at $T$ and $P$. The corresponding actual property of the mixture is expressed as

$$m = M/n = \sum z_i \bar{m}_i \qquad (1.2\text{-}46)$$

Thus, the property change on mixing of pure components to form the mixture is defined as

$$\Delta m = (M - M_{comp})/n = \sum z_i (\bar{m}_i - m_i^o) \qquad (1.2\text{-}47)$$

Selecting an extensive property $m$ to be volume, internal energy, enthalpy, entropy, or Gibbs function gives the respective change of molar property on mixing:

$$\Delta v = \sum z_i (\bar{v}_i - v_i^o), \quad \Delta u = \sum z_i (\bar{u}_i - u_i^o), \quad \Delta h = \sum z_i (\bar{h}_i - h_i^o)$$

$$\Delta s = \sum z_i (\bar{s}_i - s_i^o), \quad \Delta g = \sum z_i (\bar{g}_i - g_i^o) \quad (1.2\text{-}48)$$

The term $(\bar{g}_i - g_i^o)$ is replaced with an integration of Eq. (1.2-22) from the pure component state of $z_i = 1$ to the mixture composition $z_i$ as

$$\bar{g}_i - g_i^o = RT \ln(\hat{f}_i / f_i^o) \quad (1.2\text{-}49)$$

Substituting this relation for $\Delta g$ in Eq. (1.2-48) yields the change of Gibbs function on mixing in a dimensionless form as

$$\frac{\Delta g}{RT} = \sum z_i \ln(\hat{f}_i / f_i^o) \quad (1.2\text{-}50)$$

Similar dimensionless expressions can be derived for other property changes on mixing.

$$\frac{P \Delta v}{RT} = \sum z_i \left[ \frac{\partial \ln(\hat{f}_i / f_i^o)}{\partial \ln P} \right]_{T,z} \quad (1.2\text{-}51)$$

$$\frac{\Delta h}{RT} = -\sum z_i \left[ \frac{\partial \ln(\hat{f}_i / f_i^o)}{\partial \ln T} \right]_{P,z} \quad (1.2\text{-}52)$$

$$\frac{\Delta s}{R} = -\sum z_i \ln(\hat{f}_i / f_i^o) - \sum z_i \left[ \frac{\partial \ln(\hat{f}_i / f_i^o)}{\partial \ln T} \right]_{P,z}$$

$$= -\sum z_i \ln(\hat{f}_i / f_i^o) + \frac{\Delta h}{RT} \quad (1.2\text{-}53)$$

Thus, all property changes on mixing can be related to the fugacity ratio $\hat{f}_i / f_i^o$ and its temperature or pressure derivatives. Provided that the fugacity ratio $\hat{f}_i / f_i^o$ is known as a function of temperature, pressure, and composition, an arbitrary mixture property $m$ of given composition can be obtained from the pure component properties $m_i^o$ on the basis of the corresponding equations. For example, the molar volume and enthalpy of a mixture are given by:

$$v = \frac{V}{n} = v_{comp} + \Delta v = \sum z_i v_i^o + \frac{RT}{P} \sum z_i \left[ \frac{\partial \ln(\hat{f}_i / f_i^o)}{\partial \ln P} \right]_{T,z} \quad (1.2\text{-}54)$$

$$h = \frac{H}{n} = h_{comp} + \Delta h = \sum z_i h_i^o - RT \sum z_i \left[ \frac{\partial \ln(\hat{f}_i / f_i^o)}{\partial \ln T} \right]_{P,z} \quad (1.2\text{-}55)$$

## 1.2.11 Ideal Mixture

An ideal mixture is defined as that for which the fugacity of every component in a mixture $\hat{f}_i$ is expressed over the entire composition range as the product of its mole fraction $z_i$ and the fugacity of pure component $f_i^o$ in the same phase and at the same temperature and pressure as the mixture. That is,

$$\hat{f}_i / f_i^o = z_i \qquad (1.2\text{-}56)$$

Here, $f_i^o$ is often referred to the standard-state fugacity of pure component $i$. Substitution of this relationship into Eqs. (1.2-50) through (1.2-53) gives

$$\Delta g = RT \sum z_i \ln z_i, \quad \Delta v = 0, \quad \Delta h = 0, \quad \Delta s = -R \sum z_i \ln z_i \qquad (1.2\text{-}57)$$

As consequences of an ideal mixture (though $\Delta g$ and $\Delta s$ are not zero), the volume and enthalpy changes on mixing are zero. Hence, the volume, enthalpy, and internal energy of an ideal mixture can be calculated as a mole fraction average of pure component properties:

$$v = V/n = \sum z_i \bar{v}_i = \sum z_i v_i^o, \quad u = U/n = \sum z_i \bar{u}_i = \sum z_i u_i^o,$$
$$h = H/n = \sum z_i \bar{h}_i = \sum z_i h_i^o, \qquad (1.2\text{-}58)$$

## 1.2.12 Phase Equilibrium Equations for Mixtures

The basic equation for calculation of $\pi$-phase equilibrium of an m-component mixture is given by an extension of Eq. (1.2-36) as

$$\hat{f}_i^l = \hat{f}_i^v = \cdots = \hat{f}_i^\pi \quad (i = 1, 2, \ldots, m) \qquad (1.2\text{-}59)$$

This states that the fugacity $\hat{f}_i$ of each component $i$ in mixture must be the same in all phases. The same form of equality in each phase holds true equivalently regarding the Gibbs function $\bar{g}_i$ or the fugacity coefficient $\hat{\phi}_i$ too.

For equilibrium between the vapor and liquid phases, Eq. (1.2-59) runs

$$\hat{f}_i^v = \hat{f}_i^l \quad (i = 1, 2, \ldots, m) \qquad (1.2\text{-}60)$$

The fugacities of component $i$ in the vapor and liquid phases are respectively expressed as

$$\hat{f}_i^v = \hat{\phi}_i (y_i P) \qquad (1.2\text{-}61)$$
$$\hat{f}_i^l = \hat{\gamma}_i (x_i f_i^o) \qquad (1.2\text{-}62)$$

Therefore, Eq. (1.2-47) becomes

$$y_i \hat{\phi}_i P = x_i \hat{\gamma}_i f_i^o \quad (i = 1, 2, \ldots, m) \qquad (1.2\text{-}63)$$

Here, $\hat{\phi}_i$ is the fugacity coefficient in the vapor phase, $\hat{\gamma}_i$ is the activity coefficient in the liquid phase that denotes the deviation from an ideal liquid mixture, and $y_i$ and $x_i$ are the mole fractions in the vapor and liquid phase, respectively. $f_i^o$ is the fugacity of pure component $i$ in the liquid phase at the same $T$ and $P$ as the mixture, and it is written formally as

$$f_i^o = f_i(P) = P_i^{sat} \times \left(\frac{f_i^{sat}(P_i^{sat})}{P_i^{sat}}\right) \times \left(\frac{f_i(P)}{f_i^{sat}(P_i^{sat})}\right) \tag{1.2-64}$$

Here, $P_i^{sat}$ is the saturation vapor pressure of pure substance $i$ corresponding to the mixture temperature $T$, and $f_i^{sat}(P_i^{sat})$ is the fugacity of pure $i$ at $P_i^{sat}$, the values of which are equal in the liquid and vapor phases as required by Eq. (1.1-18). As shown below, the first ratio on the right-hand side of Eq. (1.2-64) is evaluated from the equation of the state of pure $i$ in the vapor phase, and the second ratio is calculable from the equation of the state in the liquid phase.

For a pure substance at constant temperature, Eq. (1.1-19) is written as

$$d(\ln f) = \frac{dg}{RT} = \frac{v}{RT} dP = Z \frac{dP}{P} \tag{1.2-65}$$

This equation is integrated in the vapor phase of pure substance $i$ from zero-pressure to the saturation pressure $P_i^{sat}$ and then from $P_i^{sat}$ to $P$ in the liquid phase, giving

$$\frac{f_i^{sat}(P_i^{sat})}{P_i^{sat}} = \exp\left[\int_0^{P_i^{sat}} (Z_i - 1) \frac{dP}{P}\right] \quad \text{(constant } T\text{)} \tag{1.2-66}$$

and

$$\frac{f_i(P)}{f_i^{sat}(P_i^{sat})} = \exp\left[\frac{1}{RT} \int_{P_i^{sat}}^{P} v_i dP\right] \quad \text{(constant } T\text{)} \tag{1.2-67}$$

respectively, where $Z_i$ is the vapor-phase compressibility factor of pure component $i$ and $v_i$ is the liquid-phase molar volume. Substitution of these two expressions for $f_i^o$ into Eq. (1.2-63) yields

$$y_i \hat{\phi}_i P = x_i \hat{\gamma}_i P_i^{sat} \exp\left[\int_0^{P_i^{sat}} (Z_i - 1) \frac{dP}{P} + \frac{1}{RT} \int_{P_i^{sat}}^{P} v_i dP\right]$$
$$(i = 1, 2, \ldots, m) \tag{1.2-68}$$

This is a general form of equation that should be satisfied for the phase equilibrium of multicomponent mixtures. Simplifications are usually adopted to this equation as follows.

(1) An ideal vapor mixture, i.e., $Z_i = 1$ and $\hat{\phi}_i = 1$, and an incompressible liquid, leading to

$$y_i P = x_i \hat{\gamma}_i P_i^{sat} \exp\left[\frac{v_i^{l,sat}(P - P_i^{sat})}{RT}\right] \quad (1.2\text{-}69)$$

(2) An ideal vapor mixture, i.e., $Z_i = 1$ and $\hat{\phi}_i = 1$, and a negligible liquid molar volume $v_i \cong 0$ or a small pressure deviation from the saturation pressure $P \cong P_i^{sat}$, resulting in

$$y_i P = x_i \hat{\gamma}_i P_i^{sat} \quad (1.2\text{-}70)$$

(3) Ideal mixtures in both the liquid and vapor phases. That is, $\hat{\gamma}_i = 1$ is added to the simplification (2) above, leading to

$$y_i P = x_i P_i^{sat} \quad (1.2\text{-}71)$$

This last equation is the statement of Raoult's law, which represents the simplest vapor-liquid behavior of ideal mixtures.

### 1.2.13 Calculation of Phase Equilibrium for Mixture

**Ideal mixture.** For an ideal mixture that follows Raoult's law, equilibrium diagrams between the liquid and vapor phases can be determined from a knowledge of the vapor pressures of pure components as a function of temperature. For a binary mixture, for example, applying Raoult's law to each component, 1 and 2, gives

$$y_1 P = x_1 P_1^{sat}(T) \quad (1.2\text{-}72)$$

$$y_2 P = x_2 P_2^{sat}(T) \quad (1.2\text{-}73)$$

The mole fraction in each phase totals to unity

$$x_1 + x_2 = 1, \quad y_1 + y_2 = 1 \quad (1.2\text{-}74)$$

This set of four equations can be uniquely solved for four unknown equilibrium compositions, resulting in

$$x_1 = \frac{P - P_2^{sat}(T)}{P_1^{sat}(T) - P_2^{sat}(T)} = \frac{\overline{BM}}{\overline{BC}} \quad (1.2\text{-}75)$$

$$y_1 = \frac{x_1 P_1^{sat}(T)}{P} = \frac{\overline{BM}}{\overline{BC}} \times \frac{\overline{AC}}{\overline{AM}} \quad (1.2\text{-}76)$$

Thus, for a given pressure $P$, the composition $x_1$ in the liquid phase is readily determined as a function of temperature $T$ between the saturation temperatures

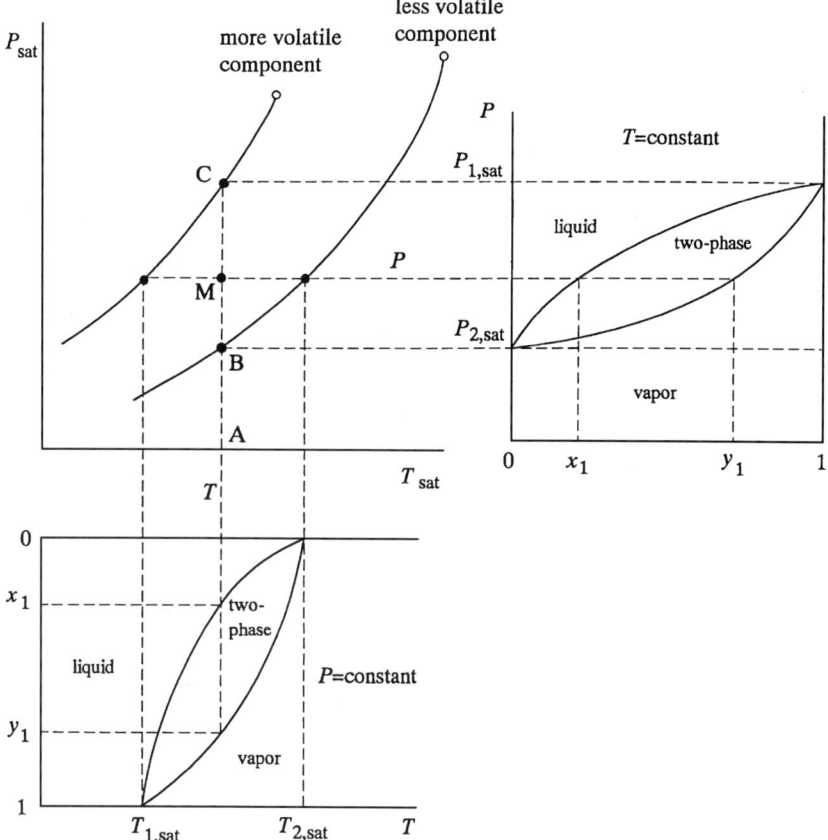

**Figure 14** Determination of phase diagrams of an ideal mixture from the vapor-pressure curves for pure components.

$T_1^{sat}(P)$ and $T_2^{sat}(P)$ for two pure components, as shown in Figure 14. Then the corresponding equilibrium composition $y_1$ in the vapor phase is calculated from Eq. (1.2-76). In this way, the $T$-$x$-$y$ phase diagram of an ideal binary mixture following the Raoult's law is obtained only if the vapor pressure data of pure components are available as a function of temperature.

**Non-ideal mixture.** At moderate pressure where Eq. (1.2-70) holds true, the liquid and vapor compositions of a binary mixture in equilibrium are determined as

$$x_1 = \frac{P - \hat{\gamma}_2 P_2^{sat}(T)}{\hat{\gamma}_1 P_1^{sat}(T) - \hat{\gamma}_2 P_2^{sat}(T)} \tag{1.2-77}$$

$$y_1 = \frac{\hat{\gamma}_1 x_1 P_1^{sat}(T)}{P} \tag{1.2-78}$$

If the activity coefficients in the liquid phase are estimated (as shown below) using empirical expressions for the excess Gibbs function, the phase diagram then will be obtained.

### 1.2.14 Excess Property and Activity Coefficient

An excess property (Scatchard and Raymond, 1938) of a mixture is defined as the difference between the actual mixture property and that which would be obtained under an assumption of an ideal mixture at the same temperature, pressure, and composition. Thus

$$\Delta m^{ex} = m - m^{id} = (m - m_{comp}) - (m^{id} - m_{comp}) = \Delta m - \Delta m^{id} \quad (1.2\text{-}79)$$

Here, the superscript "$ex$" denotes an excess property. If the Gibbs function is selected as $m$, the molar excess Gibbs function is expressed as

$$\frac{(\Delta g)^{ex}}{RT} = \frac{(\Delta h)^{ex} - T(\Delta s)^{ex}}{RT} = \sum z_i \ln\left(\frac{\hat{f}_i}{f_i^o}\right) - \sum z_i \ln z_i$$

$$= \sum z_i \ln\left(\frac{\hat{f}_i}{z_i f_i^o}\right) = \sum z_i \ln \hat{\gamma}_i \quad (1.2\text{-}80)$$

$$\hat{\gamma}_i = \hat{f}_i / z_i f_i^o \quad (1.2\text{-}81)$$

Here, $\hat{\gamma}_i$ is the activity coefficient, defined as a property useful in particular for liquid mixtures, which represents the deviation of an actual mixture from an ideal one when $\hat{f}_i = z_i f_i^o$ holds. For an ideal mixture, $\hat{\gamma}_i = 1$ and $(\Delta g)^{ex} = 0$.

It is clear from Eq. (1.2-80) that $\ln \hat{\gamma}_i$ is related to $(\Delta g)^{ex}/RT$ as a partial molar property. That is,

$$\ln \hat{\gamma}_i = \left[\frac{\partial [n(\Delta g)^{ex}/RT]}{\partial n_i}\right]_{T,P,n} = \left[\frac{\partial [(\Delta g)^{ex}/RT]}{\partial z_i}\right]_{T,P,z} \quad (1.2\text{-}82)$$

If the excess Gibbs function $(\Delta g)^{ex}$ of a mixture is known as a function of $T$, $P$, and composition $z_i$, then both the activity and fugacity coefficients are determined, making the calculation of the mixture properties possible, as exemplified by the molar volume and enthalpy in Eqs. (1.2-54) and (1.2-55). Thus, equations of $(\Delta g)^{ex}$ play the important role in mixture thermodynamics analogous to equations of state for pure substances. Needless to say, if an equation of state with accurate mixing rules is known for a mixture, then $(\Delta g)^{ex}$ and other mixture properties are directly calculable from the equation of state, as described before. This approach, ordinarily taken for pure substances, is adopted for gas mixtures up to moderate pressures. For liquid mixtures, however, equations of state with accurate mixing rules are rarely available so that empirical equations for $(\Delta g)^{ex}$ are used as an alternate means to calculate the mixture properties.

Many equations have been proposed to express the composition dependence of $(\Delta g)^{ex}$. Some such equations for binary mixtures are given in the following form as

$$\frac{(\Delta g)^{ex}}{z_1 z_2 RT} = A_0 + A_1(z_1 - z_2) + A_2(z_1 - z_2)^2 + \cdots \quad (1.2\text{-}83)$$

$$\frac{z_1 z_2 RT}{(\Delta g)^{ex}} = A'_0 + A'_1(z_1 - z_2) + A'_2(z_1 - z_2)^2 + \cdots \quad (1.2\text{-}84)$$

where the parameters A's are functions of $T$ and $P$ but not $z$. The two-parameter Margules and van Laar equations for $\ln \hat{\gamma}_i$ are based on the above expressions, with only the first two terms being taken into account. The parameters in the above equations are changed in both equations as below, giving respective expressions of the activity coefficient.

The Margules equation:

$$A_0 = \frac{A_{12} + A_{21}}{2} \quad \text{and} \quad A_1 = \frac{A_{21} - A_{12}}{2} \quad (1.2\text{-}85)$$

then

$$\ln \hat{\gamma}_1 = z_2^2 [A_{12} + 2z_1(A_{21} - A_{12})] \quad (1.2\text{-}86)$$

$$\ln \hat{\gamma}_2 = z_1^2 [A_{21} + 2z_2(A_{12} - A_{21})] \quad (1.2\text{-}87)$$

The van Laar (1935) equation:

$$A'_0 = \frac{1}{2}\left(\frac{1}{B_{12}} + \frac{1}{B_{21}}\right) \quad \text{and} \quad A'_1 = -\frac{1}{2}\left(\frac{1}{B_{12}} - \frac{1}{B_{21}}\right) \quad (1.2\text{-}88)$$

then

$$\ln \hat{\gamma}_1 = \frac{B_{12}}{[1 + (B_{12}z_1/B_{21}z_1)]^2} \quad (1.2\text{-}89)$$

$$\ln \hat{\gamma}_2 = \frac{B_{21}}{[1 + (B_{21}z_1/B_{12}z_1)]^2} \quad (1.2\text{-}90)$$

The coefficients in the above equations must satisfy the requirements in the extremes of composition.

$$A_{12}, B_{12} = \lim_{z_1 \to 1}(\ln \hat{\gamma}_1) = \ln \gamma_1^o \quad (1.2\text{-}91)$$

$$A_{21}, B_{21} = \lim_{z_2 \to 1}(\ln \hat{\gamma}_2) = \ln \gamma_2^o \quad (1.2\text{-}92)$$

The Wilson (1964) equation:

$$\frac{(\Delta g)^{ex}}{RT} = -[z_1 \ln(z_1 + G_{12}z_2) - z_2 \ln(z_2 + G_{21}z_1)] \quad (1.2\text{-}93)$$

then

$$\ln \hat{\gamma}_1 = -\ln(z_1 + G_{12}z_2) + z_2 \left( \frac{G_{12}}{z_1 + G_{12}z_2} - \frac{G_{21}}{z_2 + G_{21}z_1} \right) \quad (1.2\text{-}94)$$

$$\ln \hat{\gamma}_2 = -\ln(z_2 + G_{21}z_1) + z_1 \left( \frac{G_{12}}{z_1 + G_{12}z_2} - \frac{G_{21}}{z_2 + G_{21}z_1} \right) \quad (1.2\text{-}95)$$

Since each set of the above equations for $\ln \hat{\gamma}_1$ and $\ln \hat{\gamma}_2$ contains only two parameters A's, B's, or G's, a minimum of one vapor-liquid equilibrium data, $T$, $P$, $x_1$, and $y_1$, is sufficient to determine them. These data allow the calculation of the activity coefficients $\hat{\gamma}_1$ and $\hat{\gamma}_2$ from Eq. (1.2-69) or (1.2-70) in a case when these equations hold true. Thereafter, the calculated activity coefficients are substituted together with the values of $x_1$ and $y_1$ into the respective set of above equations to determine the two parameters A's, B's, or G's. If many vapor-liquid equilibrium data are available in the full range of concentration, the accuracy in determining the parameters will be improved.

The Wilson equation for $m$-component mixtures is given as

$$\frac{(\Delta g)^{ex}}{RT} = -\sum_{i=1}^{m} z_i \ln \left( \sum_{j=1}^{m} G_{ij} z_j \right) \quad (1.2\text{-}96)$$

and then

$$\ln \hat{\gamma}_i = 1 - \ln \left( \sum_{i=1}^{m} G_{ij} z_j \right) - \sum_{j=1}^{m} \left( G_{ij} z_j \bigg/ \sum_{k=1}^{m} G_{jk} z_k \right) \quad (1.2\text{-}97)$$

Here, G's are those coefficients that apply to binary mixtures. Thus, it should be possible to calculate activity coefficients in a ternary mixture from G's determined for the 1-2, 1-3, and 2-3, respective binary mixtures. While the Wilson equation is more difficult to manipulate, it has been recommended as superior to the Margules or van Laar equation for many multicomponent systems.

### 1.2.15 Approach Based on Equations of State

For m-component mixtures, the following empirical mixing rules are employed to evaluate the constants in two-constant equations of state, such as the van der Waals equation, Eq. (1.1-5), the Redlich-Kwong equation, Eq. (1.1-6), or the Peng-Robinson equation, Eq. (1.1-7).

$$a = \sum_{i=1}^{m} \sum_{j=1}^{m} z_i z_j a_{ij} \quad (1.2\text{-}98)$$

$$b = \sum_{i=1}^{m} z_i b_i \quad (1.2\text{-}99)$$

The mole fraction of component, $z_i$, is replaced by $x_i$ for the liquid phase and by $y_i$ for the vapor phase. The cross coefficients in Eq. (1.2-98) are usually assumed to follow the combination rule (De Santis et al., 1976).

$$a_{ij} = \sqrt{a_i a_j} \quad \text{or} \quad a_{ij} = (1 - k_{ij})\sqrt{a_i a_j} \tag{1.2-100}$$

Here, $a_i$ and $b_i$ are constants for pure component $i$ in the equation of state, Eqs. (1.1-5) through (1.1-7). The binary interaction parameter, $k_{ij}$, is determined so as to fit the equation of state to experimental phase equilibrium data.

If any equation of state following the mixing rules is able to reasonably represent the $P$-$v$-$T$ data of mixtures, the phase equilibrium calculation will be performed on the basis of the original equation, Eq. (1.2-68), which describes the condition of phase equilibrium of mixtures. In this process, the fugacity and fugacity coefficient of the mixture are at first evaluated from the pertinent equations.

$$\ln f = \ln P + \int_0^P (Z - 1) \frac{dP}{P} \tag{1.2-4}$$

$$\ln \phi = \int_0^P (Z - 1) \frac{dP}{P} \tag{1.2-5}$$

Then for each component in the mixture, the fugacity or the fugacity coefficient in the vapor phase and the activity coefficient in the liquid phase are determined from the following equations.

$$\ln\left(\frac{\hat{f}_i}{z_i}\right) = \left[\frac{\partial(n \ln f)}{\partial n_i}\right]_{T,P,n_j} \tag{1.2-101}$$

$$\ln \hat{\phi}_i = \left[\frac{\partial(n \ln \phi)}{\partial n_i}\right]_{T,P,n_j} \tag{1.2-102}$$

$$\ln \bar{\gamma}_i = \left[\frac{\partial(n \ln f)}{\partial n_i}\right]_{T,P,n_j} - \ln f_i^o \tag{1.2-103}$$

where $f_i^o$ is the fugacity of pure component $i$ at the saturated state, the values of which are equal for the saturated vapor and liquid as described by Eq. (1.1-18).

For the Redlich-Kwong equation of state, Eq. (1.1-6), with the above mixing rule, the fugacity is determined as

$$RT \ln \frac{\hat{f}_i}{z_i} = \frac{b_i}{b}\left[\frac{bRT}{v-b} - \frac{a}{(v+b)T^{1/2}}\right] - RT \ln\left(\frac{v-b}{RT}\right)$$

$$- \frac{a}{bT^{1/2}}\left[\frac{2\sum z_j \sqrt{a_i a_j}}{a} - \frac{b_i}{b}\right] \ln\left(\frac{v+b}{v}\right) \tag{1.2-104}$$

For the Benedict-Webb-Rubin equation of state, Eq. (1.1-8), it becomes

$$RT \ln \frac{\hat{f}_i}{z_i} = RT \ln(RT/v) + \frac{1}{v}[(B + B_i)RT - 2(AA_i)^{1/2} - 2(CC_i)^{1/2}/T^2]$$

$$+ \frac{3}{2v^2}[RT(b^2 b_i)^{1/3} - (a^2 a_i)^{1/3}] + \frac{3}{5v^5}[a(\alpha^2 \alpha_i)^{1/3} + \alpha(a^2 a_i)^{1/3}]$$

$$+ \frac{3(c^2 c_i)^{1/3}}{v^2 T^2} \left\{ [1 - \exp(-\gamma/v^2)]\left(\frac{v^2}{\gamma}\right) - \frac{1}{2}\exp(-\gamma/v^2) \right\}$$

$$- \frac{2c}{v^2 T^2}\left(\frac{\gamma_i}{\gamma}\right)^{1/2} \left\{ [1 - \exp(-\gamma/v^2)]\left(\frac{v^2}{\gamma}\right) \right.$$

$$\left. - \exp(-\gamma/v^2) - \frac{\gamma}{2v^2}\exp(-\gamma/v^2) \right\} \qquad (1.2\text{-}105)$$

where the mixing rules are

$$A = \sum\sum z_i z_j A_{ij}, \quad B = \sum\sum z_i z_j A_{ij}, \quad C = \sum\sum z_i z_j C_{ij} \quad (1.2\text{-}106)$$

$$a = \left(\sum z_i a_i^{1/3}\right)^3, \quad b = \left(\sum z_i b_i^{1/3}\right)^3, \quad c = \left(\sum z_i c_i^{1/3}\right)^3 \quad (1.2\text{-}107)$$

$$\alpha = \left(\sum z_i \alpha_i^{1/3}\right)^3, \quad \gamma = \left(\sum z_i \gamma_i^{1/2}\right)^3 \qquad (1.2\text{-}108)$$

## 1.3 THERMODYNAMIC AND TRANSPORT PROPERTIES OF PURE SUBSTANCES AND MULTICOMPONENT MIXTURES

### 1.3.1 Thermodynamic Properties

Thermodynamic properties of both pure substances and multicomponent mixtures are determined consistently from their respective $P$-$v$-$T$ relationship or equation of state. Calculation of some properties is based on the following equations:

$$u = \int_v^\infty \left[ P - T\left(\frac{\partial P}{\partial T}\right)_{v,n_i} \right] dv + \sum z_i u_i^o \qquad (1.3\text{-}1)$$

$$h = u + Pv \qquad (1.3\text{-}2)$$

$$s = \int_v^\infty \left[ \frac{R}{v} - \left(\frac{\partial P}{\partial T}\right)_{v,n_i} \right] dv + R \sum z_i \ln \frac{v}{RT} + \sum z_i s_i^o \qquad (1.3\text{-}3)$$

$$g = h - Ts \qquad (1.3\text{-}4)$$

$$c_p = \left(\frac{\partial h}{\partial T}\right)_P \qquad (1.3\text{-}5)$$

$$c_v = \left(\frac{\partial u}{\partial T}\right)_V \qquad (1.3\text{-}6)$$

Here, $u_i^o$ and $s_i^o$ are the internal energy and entropy for pure component $i$, the values of which are specified at a certain reference state. For pure substances, $z_i = 1$ is substituted in the above equations.

## 1.3.2 Transport Properties of Mixtures

Transport properties of pure substances and multicomponent mixtures in the vapor and liquid phases have a large influence on heat and mass transfer processes in boiling and condensation. When necessary property data are unavailable or not compiled in the form of convenient use, we have to resort to any possible means for their prediction or estimation, as done for example by Kandlikar et al. (1975a, 1975b). Reid, Prausnitz, and Poling (1987) critically reviewed various predictive methods and correlations for a limited number of properties of liquids and vapors for pure substances and their mixtures.

For pure substances, the transport property data are extensively measured, and correlating equations for those data are well established. Since all measurements of transport properties of interest are impossible for many mixtures, their estimation or prediction on the basis of the properties of pure components are very important. A small change in mixture composition sometimes results in a large change in mixture properties, especially diffusion coefficient, surface tension, thermal conductivity, and viscosity. Furthermore, the property variations with compositions are nonlinear in nature, causing mixture properties to deviate from the mole fraction or mass fraction average values of pure component properties. There are a few recommended methods in predicting transport properties of liquid mixtures essential to phase change phenomena, though the predicted results should be verified solely in reference to measured data.

**Thermal conductivity of liquid mixtures.** Thermal conductivities of organic liquid mixtures are in general less than either the mole or mass average values of the thermal conductivities for pure components. Since the deviations are usually small, many prediction methods have been developed to compensate for the deviations from such an interpolated value. Here are two methods suitable respectively for binary and multicomponent mixtures.

A correlation for binary mixtures (Chen et al. 1987):

$$\lambda = w_1\lambda_1 + w_2\lambda_2 - (C - |\lambda_1/\lambda_2 - 0.5|)w_1w_2(\lambda_2 - \lambda_1), \quad \lambda_2 \geq \lambda_1 \quad (1.3\text{-}7)$$

where $\lambda_1$ and $\lambda_2$ are thermal conductivity of pure components, $w_1$ and $w_2$ are mass fraction of each components, and $C$ is a mixture constant. An optimum value of $C$ was determined separately for 159 different mixtures, and their values are given in a table. An average constant value of $C = 0.375$ provides a good fit to the 90%

of the reference data with an error less than 3%. However, this method cannot be extended to multicomponent mixtures.

A method for multicomponent mixtures (Li, 1977):

$$\lambda = \sum_i \sum_j \phi_i \phi_j \lambda_{ij} \quad \text{with}$$

$$\lambda_{ij} = \frac{2}{1/\lambda_i + 1/\lambda_j} \quad \text{and} \quad \phi_i = \frac{x_i V_i}{\sum_i x_i V_i} \tag{1.3-8}$$

where $\lambda_{ij}$ is a parameter characterizing the interactions of thermal conductivities between i and j components. The harmonic average in the above equation is found superior to an arithmetic or geometric average after an extensive investigation. $\phi_i$ is the superficial volume fraction and $V_i$ is the molar volume of pure components.

**Viscosity of liquid mixtures.** Liquid mixture viscosities are usually estimated on the basis of the viscosities of the pure components comprising the mixture. In addition to pure component data, most such interpolating methods require some experimental data of mixture viscosity to determine adjustable constants included in their correlations. Teja and Rice (1981) include a single parameter, and their method is usable irrespective of nonpolar-nonpolar, nonpolar-polar, polar-polar, and aqueous mixtures.

$$\ln(\eta \varepsilon) = x_1 \ln(\eta_1 \varepsilon_1) + x_2 \ln(\eta_2 \varepsilon_2) \tag{1.3-9}$$

Here $\varepsilon$ and $\varepsilon_i$ are parameters defined for the mixture and for the pure components respectively as

$$\varepsilon = \frac{V_c^{2/3}}{(MT_c)^{1/2}} \tag{1.3-10}$$

$$\varepsilon_i = \frac{V_{ci}^{2/3}}{(M_i T_{ci})^{1/2}} \tag{1.3-11}$$

The viscosity values for the components $\eta_1$ and $\eta_2$ are to be evaluated not at the mixture temperature $T$ but at the reference temperatures equal to $T(T_{c1}/T_c)$ and $T(T_{c2}/T_c)$. The mixture parameters are defined by

$$M = \sum_i x_i M_i \tag{1.3-12}$$

$$V_c = \sum_i \sum_j x_i x_j V_{cij} \tag{1.3-13}$$

$$T_c = \frac{\sum_i \sum_j x_i x_j T_{cij} V_{cij}}{V_c} = \frac{\sum_i \sum_j \psi_{ij} x_i x_j (T_{ci} T_{cj} V_{ci} V_{cj})^{1/2}}{V_c} \quad (1.3\text{-}14)$$

$$V_{cij} = \frac{\left(V_{ci}^{1/3} + V_{cj}^{1/3}\right)^3}{8} \quad (1.3\text{-}15)$$

where $M_i$, $T_{ci}$, and $V_{ci}$ are molecular mass, critical temperature, and critical molar volume of pure component $i$, respectively. $\psi_{ij}$ in Eq. (1.3-14) is an interaction parameter that is assumed invariant with composition and must be determined from experimental data of mixture viscosity.

**Diffusion coefficient in liquid mixtures.** There is no single correlation satisfactory for estimating the mutual diffusion coefficient in binary mixtures as a function of mixture concentration. The well-tested and easily-applicable Vignes method is widely recommended.

An empirical correlation (Vignes, 1966):

$$D_{12} = (D_{12}^\circ)^{x_2} (D_{21}^\circ)^{x_1} \alpha \quad (1.3\text{-}16)$$

where $\alpha$ is a thermodynamic correction factor related to the activity, $a_i$, or activity coefficient, $\hat{\gamma}_i$, defined in Eq. (1.2-62) for the liquid phase as

$$\alpha = \left(\frac{\partial \ln a_i}{\partial \ln x_i}\right)_{T,P} = \left(\frac{\partial \ln x_i \hat{\gamma}_i}{\partial \ln x_i}\right)_{T,P} = 1 + \left(\frac{\partial \ln \hat{\gamma}_i}{\partial \ln x_i}\right)_{T,P} \quad (1.3\text{-}17)$$

According to the Gibbs-Duhem equation for a binary mixture, $\alpha$ is to be the same for each component. $D_{12}^\circ$ is the diffusion coefficient of an infinitely dilute component 1 diffusing in a medium consisting essentially of 2. Several methods for an evaluation of $D_{12}^\circ$ at infinite dilution are developed. A correlation by Wilke and Chang (1955) is widely utilized. It gives $D_{12}^\circ$ in cm$^2$/s as

$$D_{12}^\circ = \frac{7.4 \times 10^{-8} (\varphi_2 M_2)^{1/2} T}{\eta_2 (V_1)^{0.6}} \quad (1.3\text{-}18)$$

Here, $M$ is molecular mass in g/mol, $\varphi$ association factor, $T$ temperature in K, $V$ molar volume in cm$^3$/mol at its normal boiling temperature, and $\eta$ viscosity in cP.

**Surface tension of liquid mixtures.** The composition liquid mixture on the surface is not always the same as that of the bulk, though the surface concentration is not easily amenable to measurement. Thus, the surface tension of a mixture is unpredictable as a function of the surface tensions of pure components. Compared to a mole fraction or mass fraction average of the surface tensions of pure components, surface tension of a mixture is lower in many cases, while it becomes higher for other mixtures. Nonlinear characteristics of surface tension against the composition variation is more pronounced in aqueous mixtures of organic substances.

Meissner and Michaels (1949) put forth a correlation for infinitely dilute aqueous mixtures:

$$\sigma = \sigma_w \left[ 1 - 0.411 \log \left( 1 + \frac{x_o}{a} \right) \right] \quad (1.3\text{-}19)$$

where $\sigma_w$ is surface tension of water, $x_o$ is mole fraction of organic component, and $a$ is a constant characteristic of organic component, the values of which are evaluated for twenty five compounds and range from $26 \times 10^{-4}$ for propyl alcohol to $2.5 \times 10^{-7}$ for n-decanoic acid. For mixtures containing more than one mole percent of organic compounds, Eq. (1.3-9) is no longer applicable.

Tamura, Kurata, and Odani (1955) proposed a method for aqueous mixtures of organic substances:

$$\sigma^{1/4} = \psi_w^\sigma (\sigma_w)^{1/4} + \psi_o^\sigma (\sigma_o)^{1/4} \quad (1.3\text{-}20)$$

$$\psi_w^\sigma + \psi_o^\sigma = 1 \quad (1.3\text{-}21)$$

where the subscripts $w$ and $o$ represent water and the organic component, and $\psi^\sigma$ is the superficial volume fraction in the surface layer. The surface volume fractions $\psi_w^\sigma$ and $\psi_o^\sigma$ are determined under an assumption of equilibrium between the surface and bulk phases from the following set of equations:

$$B \equiv \log \frac{(\psi_w)^q}{\psi_o} \quad (1.3\text{-}22)$$

$$C \equiv \log \frac{(\psi_w^\sigma)^q}{\psi_o^\sigma} \quad (1.3\text{-}23)$$

$$W \equiv 0.441 \frac{q}{T} \left( \frac{\sigma_o V_o^{2/3}}{q} - \sigma_w V_w^{2/3} \right) \quad (1.3\text{-}24)$$

$$C = B + W \quad (1.3\text{-}25)$$

Here, $T$ is in K, and $q$ is a constant depending on the type and size of organic component. Its numerical value is specified as the number of carbon atoms for fatty acids and alcohols, the number of carbon atoms minus one for ketone, and the number of carbon atoms times the ratio of molal volume of halogen derivative to parent fatty acid for halogen derivatives of fatty acids. $\psi$ is the superficial bulk volume fraction, i.e.,

$$\psi_w = \frac{x_w V_w}{x_w V_w + x_o V_o} \qquad (1.3\text{-}26)$$

$$\psi_o = \frac{x_o V_o}{x_w V_w + x_o V_o} = 1 - \psi_w \qquad (1.3\text{-}27)$$

where $V$ is molal volume.

Macleod and Sugden's correlation (Reid et al., 1987) for nonaqueous mixtures:

$$\sigma^{1/4} = \sum_i [P_i](\rho_l x_i - \rho_v y_i) \qquad (1.3\text{-}28)$$

where $\rho_l$ and $\rho_v$ are mixture densities in the liquid and vapor phases, respectively, and $[P_i]$ is a temperature-independent constant of pure component $i$, which is called the *parachor*. The value of parachor is determined from surface tension data, if they are available; otherwise, it is estimated from an additive method of structural contributions of the molecule.

# REFERENCES

Benedict, M., Webb, G. B., and Rubin, L. C. 1940. An Empirical Equation for Thermodynamic Properties of Light Hydrocarbons and Their Mixtures. *J. Chem. Phys.* 8:334–345.

Chen, Z. S., Fujii, T., Fujii, M., and Ge, X. S. 1987. An Equation for Predicting Thermal Conductivity of Binary Liquid Mixtures. *Reports of Research Institute of Industrial Science, Kyushu Univ.* 82: 159–171.

De Santis, R., Gironi, F., and Marrelli, L. 1976. Vapor-Liquid Equilibrium from a Hard-Sphere Equation of State. *Ind. Eng. Chem. Fundamentals.* 15:183–189.

Gibbs, J. W. 1876. On the Equilibrium of Heterogeneous Substances. *Trans. Connecticut Acad.* 3:108–248.

Kandlikar, S. G., Bijlani, C. A., and Sukhatme, S. P. 1975a. Predicting the Properties of R-22 and R-12 Mixtures—Thermodynamic Properties. *ASHRAE Trans.* 81:266–284.

Kandlikar, S. G., Bijlani, C. A., and Sukhatme, S. P. 1975b. Predicting the Properties of R-22 and R-12 Mixtures—Transport Properties. *ASHRAE Trans.* 81:285–294.

Lewis, G. N. 1901. The Law of Physico-Chemical Change. *Proc. Am. Acad. Arts Sci.* 37:46–69.

Lewis, G. N. and Randall, M. 1921. The Activity Coefficient of Strong Electrolytes. *J. Am. Chem. Soc.* 43:1112–1154.

Li, C. C. 1976. Thermal Conductivity of Liquid Mixtures. *AIChE J.* 22:927–929.

Meissner, H. P. and Michaels, A. S. 1949. Surface Tensions of Pure Liquids and Liquid Mixtures. *Ind. Eng. Chem.* 41:2782–2787.

Nishiumi, H. and Saito, S. W. 1975. An Improved Generalized BWR Equation of State Applicable to Low Reduced Temperatures. *J. Chem. Eng. Japan.* 8:356–360.

Peng, D. Y. and Robinson, D. B. 1976. A New Two-Constant Equation of State. *Ind. Eng. Chem. Fundamentals.* 15:59–64.

Redlich, O. and Kwong, J. N. S. 1949. On the Thermodynamics of Solution. *Chem. Rev.* 44:233–244.

Reid, R. C., Prausnitz, J. M., and Poling, B. E. 1987. *The Properties of Gases and Liquids*, 4th ed., New York: McGraw-Hill.

Scatchard, G. and Raymond, C. L. 1938. Vapor-Liquid Equilibrium. II. Chloroform-Ethanol Mixtures at 35, 45 and 55°C. *J. Am. Chem. Soc.* 60:1278–1287.

Starling, K. E. 1971. Thermo Data Refined for LPG. Part 1: Equation of State and Computer Prediction. *Hydrocarbon Processing.* 3:101–104.

Tamura, M., Kurata, M., and Odani, H. 1955. Practical Method for Estimating Surface Tensions of Solutions. *Bull. Chem. Soc. Japan.* 28:83–88.

Teja, A. S. and Rice, P. 1981. The Measurement and Prediction of the Viscosities of Some Binary Liquid Mixtures Containing n-Hexane. *Chem. Eng. Sci.* 36:7–10.

van der Waals, J. D. 1873. Over de Continuiteit van den Gas en Vloeist of Toestand. Diss., Univ. Leiden.

van Laar, J. J. 1935. *Die Thermodynamik Einheitlicher Stoffe und Binärer Gemische.* Groningen: Verlag von P. Noordhoff N.V.

Vignes, A. 1966. Diffusion in Binary Solutions. Variation of Diffusion Coefficient with Composition. *Ind. Eng. Chem. Fundamentals* 5:189–199.

Wilke, C. R. and Chang, P. 1955. Correlation of Diffusion Coefficients in Dilute Solutions. *AIChE J.*, 1:264–270.

Wilson, G. M. 1964. Vapor-Liquid Equilibrium. XI. A New Expression for the Excess Free Energy of Mixing. *J. Am. Chem. Soc.* 86:127–130.

CHAPTER
# TWO

## REPRESENTATION OF SOLID-LIQUID-VAPOR PHASE INTERACTIONS

**Masahiro Shoji**

*The University of Tokyo, 7-3-1 Hongo, Bunkyo-ku, Tokyo 113-8656, Japan*

**Yasuhiko H. Mori**

*Keio University, 3-14-1 Hiyoshi, Kohoku-ku, Yokohama 223-8522, Japan*

**Shigeo Maruyama**

*The University of Tokyo, 7-3-1 Hongo, Bunkyo-ku, Tokyo 113-8656, Japan*

## 2.1 INTRODUCTION OF SOLID-LIQUID-VAPOR PHASE INTERACTIONS

Solid-liquid-vapor interaction phenomena play a very important role in phase-change heat transfer. Except for the cases of direct contact heat transfer, most practical phase-change heat-transfer systems involve the solid surface as a heater or condenser. The importance of the liquid wettability to the surface is apparent in dropwise condensation, boiling heat transfer, and capillary liquid film evaporation. Actually, the heat transfer coefficient of dropwise condensation for surfaces with low wettability is much larger than that of film condensation. The thin liquid film on the partly wet surface can contribute considerably to the overall heat transfer, since the thermal resistance of the liquid film due to heat conduction is inversely proportional to the thickness of the liquid film. In this section, fundamental liquid-solid contact phenomena are considered from the traditional macroscopic and microscopic representations.

The mechanistic and thermodynamic treatments of the traditional macroscopic approach yield many practical concepts and empirical correlation equations. However, it is sometimes essential to understand the phenomena from the microscopic point of view. The contact line is a singular point in the macroscopic sense, since the non-slip condition of fluid dynamics at the surface simply denies the movement of the contact line. The "monolayer liquid film" considered in some macroscopic theories needs further examination. Thus, a brief overview of the microscopic techniques and the molecular dynamics simulations is presented, and illustrative examples of simulations for a simple molecular system follow in the succeeding sections.

In both macroscopic and microscopic representations, the approach starts from the liquid-vapor interaction and the surface tension. The well-known Young-Laplace equation [Eq. (2.2-1)] relates the curvature of liquid-vapor interface and surface tension to the pressure difference called capillary pressure. From the equation, it is possible to obtain the geometry of the interface once the pressure term is prescribed. The microscopic representation of the Young-Laplace equation is used in the next section for the evaluation of the surface tension, which should be the kinetic property derived from the molecular parameters. Another example of the capability of the macroscopic representation is the gravitational deformation of a liquid droplet or a curved interface. The effect of gravity can be expressed using the capillary length $a$. When the system size is much smaller than $a$, the gravitational effect is negligible. No counterpart of the microscopic representation is possible, since the system size that the molecular dynamics method can handle is too small to show the effect, or, in other words, the system length scale L is always much smaller than the capillary length. In relation to the macroscopic representation, one of the hot arguments in molecular dynamics study is the determination of the condensation coefficient, which will be discussed here.

As is well-known, the contact angle is introduced to represent the degree of the partial wettability of a solid surface. The well-known Young's equation [see Eq. (2.2-5)] relates the contact angle to the balance of surface energies. This equation can be understood from the mechanical balance of forces or the thermodynamic concept of minimizing the Helmholtz free energy. Since it is usually difficult to independently measure the surface energy between solid and vapor and between liquid and solid, Young's equation is still somewhat conceptual. Furthermore, the definition of the contact angle seems to be controversial if the thin liquid film exists over the "dry" surface. The microscopic representation discusses this point by the simulation of molecular dynamics method. There are debates whether or not Young's equation could be verified if each surface energy can be calculated. There are interesting features of liquid structure near the contact line: layered liquid structure (order of the size of a molecule) and the spread of the first molecular layer. Regardless of such special structure, it seems that Young's equation still holds beyond the structured area.

In macroscopic treatments, the effective contact angle is introduced for the practical solid surface, which is not perfectly smooth and defect-free. The conceptual and statistical equations representing the effect of roughness (Wenzel equation) and chemically heterogeneous surface are surveyed, and the multiplicity of the contact angle (metastable angle) is described. The phase change heat transfer occurs through the evaporation or the condensation process, which usually accompanies the moving of the contact line: the decay of liquid by evaporation or the growth of liquid by condensation. Hence, the non-equilibrium feature of the moving contact line is crucial for the heat transfer. Furthermore, reliable techniques to measure the contact angle involve the movement of the contact line. It is well known that the contact angle is a function of the velocity of the contact line U. We define the advancing condition (U > 0) when the contact line is moving in the direction from liquid to vapor and the receding condition (U < 0) for the opposite. It is very interesting that the limit of U = 0 for advancing condition (called advancing contact angle) and that for receding conditions (receding contact angle) do not coincide. The contact angle remembers its moving history (called *contact angle hysteresis*).

From the extensive macroscopic studies surveyed here, it is believed that the moving contact line shows the range of angles between advancing and receding due to the metastable contact angle directly related to the surface conditions, such as roughness and chemical heterogeneity. However, the relation between the apparent contact angle (dynamic contact angle) to the moving velocity is not well established in the macroscopic correlation techniques. On the other hand, there are reports of molecular dynamics calculations that insist on the reproduction of the dynamic contact angle, even though the surface is perfectly smooth and chemically homogeneous. This contradiction is still open to question. One possibility is that the microscopic result indicates a new breakthrough for the concept of the dynamic contact angle. However, the system size of typical molecular dynamics simulation is so small that the crystal of solid molecules may be felt as the periodically rough potential field. As a result, some analogous or similarity discussions to the macroscopic dynamic contact angle may be possible in the microscopic representation. Even though such an analogy might help to understand the real microscopic phenomena to some extent, readers should be careful that *it might simply be an analogy*.

When the contact-line speed is increased for advancing condition, the dynamic contact angle generally increases until it reaches 180°. Further increase in the advancing speed beyond this critical speed $U_{a,cr}$ induces a macroscopic saw-tooth instability of the contact line. The same instability is observed for the receding condition after the contact angle is decreased to 0°. It seems that the shape of the contact-line is adjusted so that the velocity component normal to the curved contact line is kept at the critical speed $U_{a,cr}$. Such instability must be genuine macroscopic phenomena, and no counterpart in the microscopic representation exists. If you force the similar condition in the microscopic molecular dynamics simulation, you may find another kind of instability, which is never experienced in the macroscopic system.

## 2.2 MACROSCOPIC REPRESENTATION OF SOLID-LIQUID-VAPOR PHASE INTERACTIONS

### 2.2.1 The Young-Laplace Equation

Consider two fluid phases in contact with each other. One of the phases is a liquid, and the other may be its own vapor, a mixture of the vapor and air, or another immiscible liquid. The interface between the two phases may be flat or curved. We can arbitrarily select two planes, say plane 1 and plane 2, that are perpendicular to each other and whose intersection crosses the interface at right angles (see Figure 1). Let $R_1$ and $R_2$ denote the radii of curvature at the cross point, one on plane 1 and the other on plane 2. If the interface is in mechanical equilibrium, the pressure difference, $\Delta p$, across the interface at that point is related to $R_1$ and $R_2$ through the so-called Young-Laplace equation as

$$\Delta p = \sigma \left( \frac{1}{R_1} + \frac{1}{R_2} \right) \qquad (2.2\text{-}1)$$

where $\sigma$ is the interfacial tension between the two phases. The interphase pressure difference $\Delta p$ thus related to the interface curvature is called the *capillary pressure*. For the derivation of Eq. (2.2-1), readers can consult a textbook written by Adamson (1990).

In the absence of any forces other than those due to the interfacial tension and gravity, the geometry of the interface can be determined by substituting an appropriate expression for the hydrostatic head, between each point on the interface and some reference level in each phase, into the Young-Laplace equation (thereby eliminating $\Delta p$ from the Young-Laplace equation) and then by integrating it analytically, if possible, or numerically. A comprehensive survey of such a solution

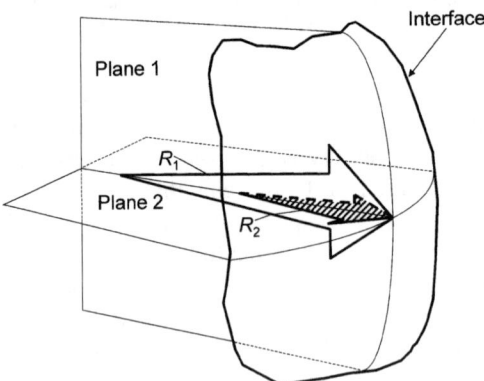

**Figure 1** Illustration of an arbitrary curved interface between two fluid phases.

procedure for equilibrium interfaces is given by Princen (1969). Details of the solution procedure and extensive solution tables for axisymmetric interfaces are given in a monograph by Hartland and Hartley (1976).

### 2.2.2 The Capillary Constant

The interface between two fluid phases in a gravitational field can be exactly spherical only when $\Delta\rho$, the density difference between the two phases, is zero. Nevertheless, we know empirically that tiny liquid drops or vapor bubbles are nearly spherical irrespective of the magnitude of $\Delta\rho$, while larger drops and bubbles are generally deformed to greater extents. An index for a possible gravity-induced deformation from sphericity of drops, bubbles, or other curved interfaces is a dimensionless modulus known as Eötvös (or Bond) number:

$$\text{Eo} = \Delta\rho g L^2 / \sigma \qquad (2.2\text{-}2)$$

where $L$ is the characteristic length in a given system, such as the volume-equivalent diameters of drops or bubbles. Note that Eo expresses the ratio of an interphase-differential hydrostatic head, $\Delta\rho g L$, to a capillary pressure, $\sigma/L$. Eo may alternatively be viewed as an index of the ratio of $L$ to a certain reference scale $a$, which depends merely on the fluid substances composing the system and on $g$, namely

$$\text{Eo} = 2(L/a)^2 \qquad (2.2\text{-}3)$$

where $a$, the scale termed *capillary constant*[1] (or *capillary length*), is defined as

$$a = \left(\frac{2\sigma}{\Delta\rho g}\right)^{1/2} \qquad (2.2\text{-}4)$$

The effect of gravity on the interface geometry should be negligible if $\text{Eo} \ll 1$ or $L \ll a$.

### 2.2.3 Wettability and Contact Angle—Some Introductory Remarks on Liquid-Solid Contact

Suppose a drop of a liquid is brought into contact, in the ambience of air, with a solid surface that is mechanically rigid, smooth to molecular scale, chemically homogeneous and isotropic, and horizontally oriented to face upward. After the

---

[1] Readers should be cautious about the non-unique usage of the term "capillary constant" in literature. The term may be used to express some quantities other than $a$, though related to it. For example, $a/\sqrt{2}$ and $2/a^2$ are actually called the *capillary constant* in some major publications.

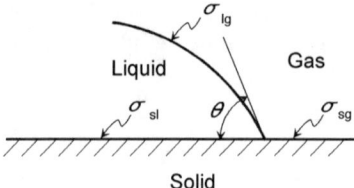

**Figure 2** Three phases in mutual contact—a schematic of a cross section normal to the three-phase contact line.

contact, the drop may spread over the surface until it becomes a uniform film (if the surface is wide enough, the film may be thinned to a monomolecular layer) or may be deformed into a sessile drop that lies on a limited area of the surface, leaving the rest of the surface apparently dry (see Figure 2). These two possible modes of liquid-solid contact are generally called *complete wetting* and *partial wetting*, respectively. The degree of the partial wetting may be evaluated in terms of the *contact angle* $\theta$, a plane angle measured through the liquid phase from the solid surface, at which the interface between the liquid and gas (air + vapor) phases meets the solid surface. Once an equilibrium state is established, we can assume that $\theta$ is related to the solid-gas, solid-liquid, and liquid-gas interfacial tensions—denoted by $\sigma_{sg}$, $\sigma_{sl}$, and $\sigma_{lg}$, respectively—as

$$\sigma_{lg} \cos \theta = \sigma_{sg} - \sigma_{sl} \qquad (2.2\text{-}5)$$

(Note that $\sigma_{sg}$ may be significantly lower than the intrinsic surface energy of the solid, $\sigma_s$, because the solid-gas interface is likely to be covered with a monolayer of the liquid-forming substance. The higher the vapor pressure of the liquid-forming substance, the denser the adsorbed molecules in the monolayer.) The above equation is called Young's equation or the Young-Dupré equation in the literature. This equation may be regarded, as conceived by Young (1805) himself, as a horizontal force balance at the three-phase contact line. It is better founded, however, on a thermodynamic basis, which was discussed first by Gauss (1829), then by Gibbs (1875–1878), and more comprehensively by Johnson (1959). Johnson (1959) derived Young's equation as the solution of a variational problem for minimizing the Helmholtz free energy of the drop-on-solid system. This means that the contact angle given by Young's equation, which is designated as $\theta_Y$ hereafter, is a *unique* thermodynamic property of the system.

## 2.2.4 Equilibrium Contact Angles on Rough and Heterogeneous Surfaces

The concept of a thermodynamics-based contact angle may be extended to nonideal surfaces. For a chemically homogeneous surface with a finite roughness, Wenzel (1936) proposed the following expression for $\theta_W$, the contact angle macroscopically observed at the geometrically averaged level of the rough surface, simply by taking into account an increase in the actual liquid-solid contact area due to the roughness:

$$\cos\theta_W = r\cos\theta_Y \quad (2.2\text{-}6)$$

where $r$ is the ratio of actual to apparent (or normally projected) area of the surface and $\theta_Y$ is the Young contact angle given by Eq. (2.2-5). A thermodynamic derivation of the above Wenzel equation is shown later by Good (1952).

Cassie and Baxter (1944) extended Wenzel's treatment to porous surfaces, such as meshes or screens. When an apparent surface is composed of a solid and open area occupying fractions $f_1$ and $f_2$, respectively, the contact angle observed on the surface, $\theta_{CB}$, can be estimated by the Cassie-Baxter equation:

$$\cos\theta_{CB} = f_1 \cos\theta_Y - f_2 \quad (2.2\text{-}7)$$

where $\theta_Y$ is the Young contact angle for the solid area.

The Cassie and Baxter equation may be modified to make it applicable to the rough surfaces on which each *apparent* liquid-solid contact area forms a so-called *composite surface*, a mosaic of actually wetted protuberances and dry cavities or hollows (see Figure 3). In general, surfaces having steep roughness and/or low $\sigma_s$ values tend to form composite surfaces, particularly when brought into contact with high surface-tension liquids. If the fractions of the actually wetted and dry areas, each projected normal to a plane parallel to a given composite surface, are $f_1$ and $f_2$, respectively, the contact angle macroscopically observed on the surface, $\theta_{JD}$, may be given (as suggested by Johnson and Dettre [1964]) as

$$\cos\theta_{JD} = r_w f_1 \cos\theta_Y - f_2 \quad (2.2\text{-}8)$$

where $r_w$ denotes the ratio of actually wetted area to its projection.

For a smooth, chemically heterogeneous surface composed of two surface-components, one having a higher surface energy (e.g., a clean metal surface) and

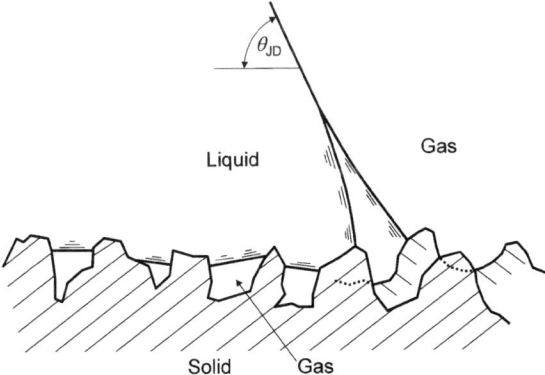

**Figure 3** A composite surface formed on a solid surface with a steep roughness.

the other having a lower surface energy (e.g., a metal surface covered with a monolayer of an organic substance), Cassie (1948) derived an expression for the apparent contact angle $\theta_C$:

$$\cos\theta_C = f_1 \cos\theta_{Y1} + f_2 \cos\theta_{Y2} \qquad (2.2\text{-}9)$$

where $f_1$ and $f_2$ are the fractions of the higher and the lower energy surface-components, respectively, and $\theta_{Y1}$ and $\theta_{Y2}$ are the Young contact angles on those components. (Note that Eq. [2.2-9] reduces to Eq. [2.2-7] at $\theta_{Y2} \rightarrow 180°$.)

It is very important to note that the applicability of Eqs. (2.2-6)–(2.2-9) is limited to the surfaces having random roughness or heterogeneity whose characteristic dimension $\lambda$ is much smaller than $L$, the characteristic length of the system, such as the length of the three-phase contact line or the diameter $d$ of a liquid drop resting on the surface. This is due to the fact that the free energy of a given system, $F$, is not a continuous function of the apparent contact angle $\theta$ but has multiple (generally numerous) minima over a finite (sometimes significantly wide) range in $\theta$. If the system is not such that $\lambda \ll L$, or if the solid surface in the system has a highly oriented surface texture (e.g., parallel or concentric grooves or stripewise heterogeneity parallel to the contact line), the energy barrier between successive minima may be so high as to prevent $\theta$ from relaxing from some *metastable* angle corresponding to one of the $F$ minima to the *stable* angle corresponding to the lowest $F$ minimum, i.e., the angle that may be approximated by some of Eqs. (2.2-6)–(2.2-9). More details of thermodynamic analysis of the above issue are given in Neumann (1974) and Marmur (1994). An alternative mechanistic analysis of the same issue is developed by Huh and Mason (1977).

### 2.2.5 Contact-Angle Hysteresis

Figure 4 illustrates two representative and reliable methods of contact-angle measurement. In one, a liquid is steadily supplied to or drained from a horizontally-oriented test surface through a small hole drilled on it. An axially symmetric sessile

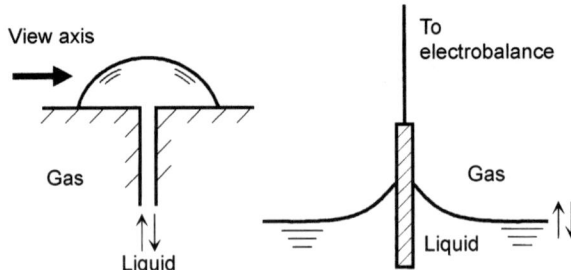

**Figure 4** Two representative methods of contact-angle measurement.

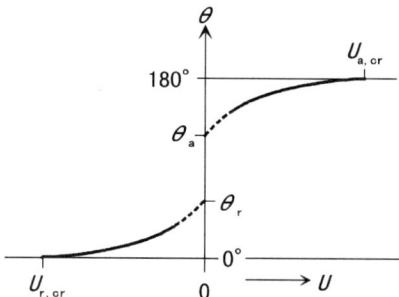

**Figure 5** Typical variation of contact angle $\theta$ with the speed of contact-line motion. In the region $U > 0$, the liquid phase through which $\theta$ is measured is advancing; in the region $U < 0$, it is receding. The solid curves represent the $\theta$–$U$ relations actually observable with contact lines in steady motion. The dashed curves indicate the extrapolations of those $\theta$–$U$ relations to $U = 0$.

drop is grown or contracted, causing a macroscopically circular contact line to advance or recede on the surface. The instantaneous contact angles can be determined by recording and processing the horizontal projections (Li et al., 1992) or simultaneous horizontal and vertical projections (Mori et al., 1982) of the drop. In the other method, a solid sample, preferably having the form of a cylindrical fiber or a thin rectangular plate, is suspended at a fixed position from an electrobalance, and a liquid container is moved up and down at a constant speed by means of a precise hydraulic drive (Okagawa and Mason, 1978). If the surface tension of the liquid, $\sigma_{lg}$, is known, the contact angle $\theta$ is calculated from the force detected by the balance, $P_{slg}\,\sigma_{lg}\cos\theta$, where $P_{slg}$ is the periphery of the three-phase contact line. These methods enable us to obtain contact angle data at various speeds of advancing ($U > 0$) or receding ($U < 0$) of the contact line on each sample surface. A typical $\theta$–$U$ plot will be in such form, as illustrated in Figure 5. The $\theta$ extrapolated to $U = 0$ from the positive $U$ side is called the *advancing contact angle*, $\theta_a$, while that extrapolated from the negative $U$ side is called the *receding contact angle*, $\theta_r$. (It is believed that $\theta_a[\theta_r]$ is actually obtained by stopping an advancing [receding] motion of a contact line, then leaving the liquid near the contact line relaxing until the system is mechanically equilibrated.) $\theta_a$ and $\theta_r$ are the possible maximum and minimum, respectively, of the *static* contact angle. In other words, $\theta$ in an equilibrium state may take any value between $\theta_r$ and $\theta_a$, depending on the "history" of the liquid-solid contact in each given system. This nonuniqueness, or multiplicity, in the static contact angle is referred to as *contact-angle hysteresis* in the literature, and it is reasonably ascribable to the multiplicity of the free-energy minima caused by surface roughness and/or heterogeneity. A mechanistic explanation of the hysteresis is given in Huh and Mason (1977).

It appears to be logical to assume that the hysteresis is lost, i.e., $\theta_a = \theta_r = \theta_Y$, only on ideally smooth and homogeneous surfaces that are actually unavailable. In practice, however, liquids may "see" actual surfaces as smooth and homogeneous, if the characteristic dimensions of the roughness and the heterogeneity on them are quite small. This is because the liquid surfaces are accompanied with thermal fluctuations and, at the same time, subjected more or less to some mechanical disturbances propagated from the environment. Such fluctuations and/or disturbances may be enough to make contact lines move, clearing energy barriers that should be lower with smaller scale roughness and heterogeneity. Some experimental results (Mori et al., 1982) indicate that liquids no longer "sense" roughness $\sim$10 nm or smaller in height.

### 2.2.6 Dynamic Contact Angles and Contact-Line Instability

In general, $\theta$ measured at a contact line tends to increase (decrease) with an increase in the speed of the advancing (receding) of the contact line. Various attempts have been made to express $\theta$ as a function of $U$ and some system properties, but none of them have succeeded in presenting a $\theta$–$U$ correlation with comprehensive utility due to the complex nature of the problem. Dimensional analysis can provide some insight into this issue, which is outlined below.

First, we limit our consideration to the case that one liquid phase is displacing, or is displaced by, a gaseous phase. There are two versions in counting the variables relevant to dynamic wetting processes: one includes a system-characteristic length $L$ and the other does not. The first version leads alternatively to two dimensionless functional forms (Esmail and Ghannam, 1990; Gutoff and Kendrick, 1982):

$$\Theta = \mathrm{fn}_1(\mathrm{Re}, \mathrm{Fr}, \mathrm{We}) \qquad (2.2\text{-}10)$$

$$\Theta = \mathrm{fn}_2(\mathrm{Ca}, \mathrm{Eo}, \mathrm{M}) \qquad (2.2\text{-}11)$$

where $\mathrm{Re} \equiv UL\rho_l/\eta_l$, $\mathrm{Fr} \equiv U^2/Lg$, $\mathrm{We} \equiv U^2 L \rho_l/\sigma_{lg}$, $\mathrm{Ca} \equiv \eta_l U/\sigma_{lg}$, $\mathrm{Eo} \equiv \rho_l g L^2/\sigma_{lg}$, $\mathrm{M} \equiv g\eta_l^4/(\rho_l \sigma_{lg}^3)$, $\rho_l$ and $\eta_l$ are the density and the viscosity, respectively, of the liquid, and $\Theta$ denotes a dynamic-to-static contact angle relation. Possible forms of $\Theta$ are $\theta/\theta_s$, $\theta - \theta_s$, $\cos\theta_s - \cos\theta$, etc., where $\theta_s$ denotes either of $\theta_a(U>0)$ or $\theta_r(U<0)$. The second version yields the following (Burley and Jolly, 1984; Gutoff and Kendrick, 1982):

$$\Theta = \mathrm{fn}_3(\mathrm{Ca}, \mathrm{M}) \qquad (2.2\text{-}12)$$

In the case that one liquid is displacing another liquid, it might be necessary to rewrite Eq. (2.2-12) as

$$\Theta = \mathrm{fn}_4\left(\mathrm{Ca}, \mathrm{M}, \frac{\eta_{1,2}}{\eta_{1,1}}, \frac{\rho_{1,2}}{\rho_{1,1}}, \frac{\rho_{1,1}-\rho_{1,2}}{\rho_{1,1}}\right) \qquad (2.2\text{-}13)$$

where the subscripts 1 and 2 are used to distinguish the two liquids from each other, and Ca and M are based on the properties of either liquid through which $\theta$ is measured (Gutoff and Kendrick, 1982).

Most of the empirical correlations for dynamic contact angle are given in the above-listed functional forms or their truncated versions. Such correlations were prepared individually, each to fit a particular set of data typically from a single source (Burley and Jolly, 1984; Cazabat, 1990; Chen and Wada, 1992; Esmail and Ghannam, 1990; Gutoff and Kendrick, 1982; Hopf and Geidel, 1987; Jiang et al., 1979; Martynov et al., 1983; Petrov and Petrov, 1991; Rillaerts and Joos, 1980). Any of them should not be used for quantitative contact-angle predictions unless a good similarity is confirmed between the system of current interest and that once used to obtain the experimental data to which the very correlation is fitted.

The critical contact-line speeds, $U_{a,cr}$ and $U_{r,cr}$, at which $\theta$ arrives at 180° and 0°, respectively, may be predicted by extrapolating some of the above-mentioned $\theta$–$U$ correlations. For liquids displacing a gas phase, it is easier to use empirical correlations that were prepared to explicitly express $U_{a,cr}$, a quantity of industrial importance as the critical speed for stable liquid coating (Burley and Jolly, 1984; Burley and Kennedy, 1976; Esmail and Ghannam, 1990; Gutoff and Kendrick, 1982). Esmail and Ghannam (1990) compare various correlations for $U_{a,cr}$ with experimental data from several different sources. Exemplified below is a correlation prepared by Burley and Kennedy (1976) based on their *plunging plane tape* experiments:

$$U_{a,cr} = 67.7 \left[ \eta_l \left( \frac{g}{\rho_l \sigma_{lg}} \right)^{1/2} \right]^{-0.67} \quad (2.2\text{-}14)$$

where $U_{a,cr}$ and $\eta_l(g/\rho_l\sigma_{lg})^{1/2}$ are to be given in the unit of cm/s. The above correlation may be used for roughly estimating $U_{a,cr}$ in the range 1 cm/s $\lesssim \eta_l(g/\rho_l\sigma_{lg})^{1/2} \lesssim$ 100 cm/s.

At contact-line speeds outside the range between $U_{a,cr}$ and $U_{r,cr}$, the contact line is no longer kept macroscopically smooth and normal to the direction of its motion. Instead, the contact line adopts, as schematically illustrated in Figure 6, a saw-tooth configuration composed of straight-line segments, each slanted from the smooth *reference line* about which the contact line spatially fluctuates by a finite angle $\phi$ (Blake and Ruschak, 1979; Burley and Kennedy, 1976). The number of segments through the entire contact line is not fixed definitely, and it may change from time to time. The lengths of individual segments are usually irregular. Nevertheless, $\phi$ is the same for all the segments, and it is invariable while $U$ is held constant (Blake and Ruschak, 1979). It seems that $\phi$ is so adjusted that the component of the contact-line velocity vector normal to each contact-line segment has a magnitude equal to $U_{a,cr}$ or $|U_{r,cr}|$; i.e.,

$$\begin{aligned} U \cos\phi &= U_{a,cr} \ (U > U_{a,cr}) \\ U \cos\phi &= U_{r,cr} \ (U < U_{r,cr}). \end{aligned} \quad (2.2\text{-}15)$$

The contact angle measured on a plane normal to each segment is held at 180° (when $U > U_{a,cr}$) or 0° (when $U < U_{r,cr}$). Tiny gas bubbles ($U > U_{a,cr}$) or liquid

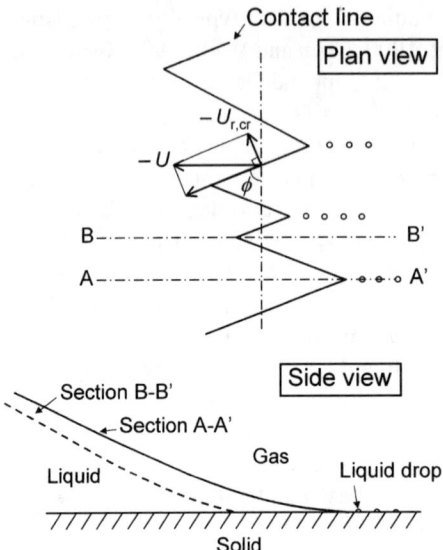

**Figure 6** Schematic illustration of sawtooth contact line obtained when $U < U_{r,cr}$. Liquid drops are broken off from the trailing vertices of the contact line and left on the solid surface.

drops ($U < U_{r,cr}$) are broken off from each trailing vertex of the contact line, where two neighboring segments apparently intersect, and are entrained into the liquid or the gas phase.

## 2.3 MICROSCOPIC REPRESENTATION OF SOLID-LIQUID-VAPOR INTERACTIONS

The microscopic aspects of solid-liquid-vapor interactions are usually crucial when we consider theories of phase change phenomena, such as nucleation of bubbles and droplets and the heat transfer at the three-phase interface. For a microscopic system, we need to start from the verification of the well-known Young-Laplace equation (Eq. 2.2-1) and Young's equation (Eq. 2.2-5) for the contact angle. In addition, for the reliable theory of the dropwise condensation, the determination of the condensation coefficient would be necessary. Furthermore, the oxidation layer on the solid surface or the surfactant layer in the gas-liquid interface, which may have a thickness of only a molecular monolayer, will drastically change the surface phenomena. In general, experimental assignments of such problems are usually extremely difficult since the scale is too small to access, so the individual measurement of surface energy is almost impossible. Thus, in this section, the molecular dynamics studies are discussed in order to understand such molecular scale phenomena.

## 2.3.1 Molecular Dynamics Method and Force Between Molecules

Knowledge of statistical gas dynamics has been very helpful to understand the relationship between molecular motion and macroscopic gas dynamics phenomena. Recently, a direct simulation method using the Monte Carlo technique (DSMC) developed by Bird (1994) has been widely used for the practical simulations of rarefied gas dynamics. In the other extreme, statistical treatment of solid state matters has been well developed as solid state physics (e.g., Kittel, 1996). However, when we need to take care of liquid or inter-phase phenomena (which are inevitable for phase-change phenomena), the gas-dynamics or solid-state statistics are no longer valid at all.

The most powerful tool for the investigation of the microscopic phenomena of solid-liquid-vapor interaction is the molecular dynamics method (e.g., Allen and Tildesley, 1987), where the classical equations of motion (Newton's equations) are solved for a set of molecules.

$$m_i \frac{d^2 \vec{r}_i}{dt^2} = \vec{F}_i = -\frac{\partial \Phi}{\partial \vec{r}_i} \qquad (2.3\text{-}1)$$

where $m_i$, $\vec{r}_i$, and $\vec{F}_i$ are mass, position vector, and force vector of molecule i, respectively. For many kinds of molecule systems, the potential $\Phi(\vec{r}_1, \vec{r}_2, \ldots \vec{r}_N)$ can be assumed to be the sum of effective pair potential $\phi(r_{ij})$ as

$$\Phi = \sum_i \sum_{j>i} \phi(r_{ij}) \qquad (2.3\text{-}2)$$

where $r_{ij}$ is the distance of molecules i and j. Once the intermolecular potential is obtained, one is able to numerically solve Eq. (2.3-1). In principle, Eq. (2.3-1) can be solved for any gas, liquid, solid, or inter-phase phenomena without the knowledge of "thermo-physical properties," such as thermal conductivity, viscosity, latent heat, saturation temperature, and surface tension. It should be noticed, however, that the validity of Eq. (2.3-2) should be questioned when the density of molecules varies in a wide range.

An example of the pair potential is the well-known Lennard-Jones (12-6) potential, expressed as

$$\phi(r) = 4\varepsilon[(\sigma/r)^{12} - (\sigma/r)^6] \qquad (2.3\text{-}3)$$

where $\varepsilon$ and $\sigma$ are energy and length scales and $r$ is the intermolecular distance, as shown in Figure 7. The intermolecular potentials of inert monatomic molecules such as Ar and Xe are known to be reasonably well expressed by this function. Moreover, many computational and theoretical studies are performed with this potential in order to investigate the general features of molecular dynamics. Here, the equation of motion can be non-dimensionalized by choosing $\sigma$, $\varepsilon$, and m as

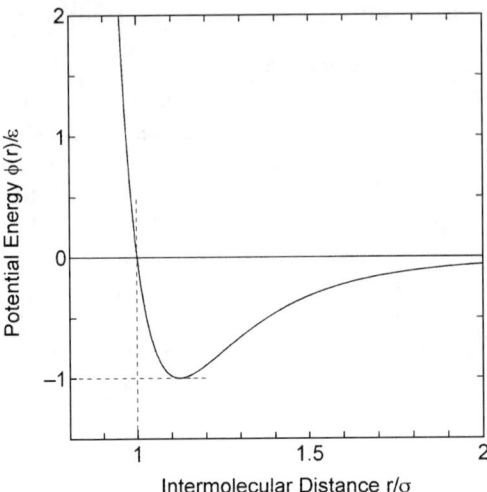

**Figure 7** Lennard-Jones potential.

length, energy, and mass scale: $r^* = r/\sigma$, $t^* = t/\tau$ ($\tau = \sigma(m/\varepsilon)^{1/2}$), $\phi^* = \phi/\varepsilon$, pressure $p^* = p\sigma^3/\varepsilon$, number density $N^* = N\sigma^3$, density $\rho^* = \sigma^3\rho/m$, and temperature $T^* = k_B T/\varepsilon$, where $k_B$ is the Boltzmann constant. In order to illustrate the physical quantities, we can use the argon properties as $\sigma = 3.4$ Å, $\varepsilon = 1.67 \times 10^{-21}$ J ($\cong 120$ K), $m = 40$ amu, and $\tau = 2.2 \times 10^{-12}$ s. Typical time step of the numerical integration of Eq. (2.3-1) is about 0.005 $\tau$ or 10 fs.

In order to simulate practical molecules, the determination of the potential function is very important. For example, many intermolecular potential functions have been proposed for water. The simple classical form of ST2 potential proposed by Stillinger and Rahman (1974) still has an advantage in computer task and physical simplicity. The CC potential by Carravetta and Clementi (1984) that was constructed by fitting to the ab initio molecular orbital calculations certainly has better accuracy. Recently, the simple and well-tuned SPC/E potential by Berendsen et al. (1987) has been found to have superior characteristics for liquid-vapor interface phenomena (Alejandre et al., 1995).

## 2.3.2 Liquid-Vapor Interface (Surface Tension and Young-Laplace Equation)

After solving the motion of each molecule, we need to average the molecular motion to obtain the macroscopic properties, such as surface tension and condensation coefficient. Figure 8 shows examples of liquid-vapor interfaces of (a) liquid slab and (b) liquid droplet surrounded by its vapor (Maruyama et al., 1994a, 1994b). In

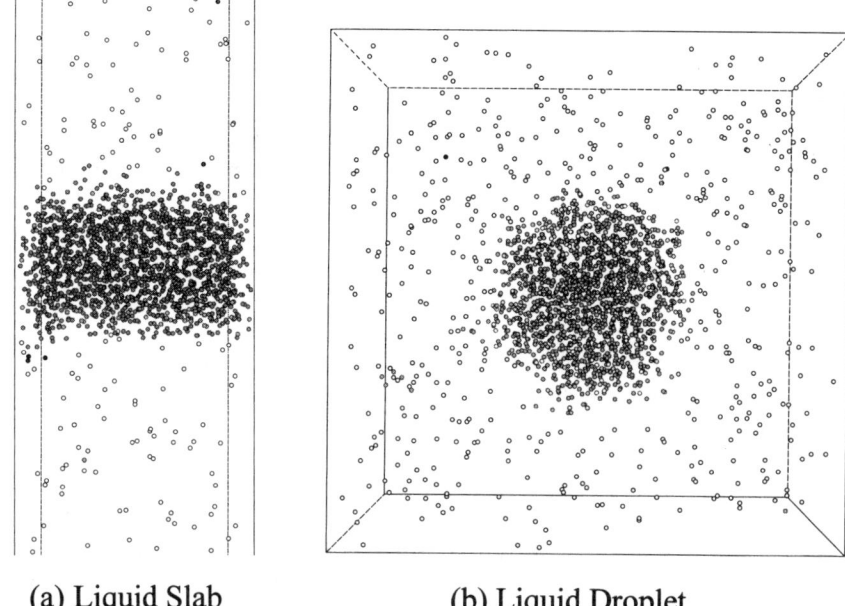

**(a) Liquid Slab**   **(b) Liquid Droplet**

**Figure 8** Snapshots of argon liquid slab and droplet. (a) Liquid slab and vapor made of 1944 molecules saturated at 100 K in 5.5 × 5.5 × 12 nm box. (b) Liquid droplet and vapor made of 2048 molecules saturated at 95 K in a 12 nm cubic box.

both cases, calculation region had periodic boundary conditions for all six boundaries. Starting from a crystal of argon and continuing over side boundaries, the liquid slab with flat liquid-vapor interface in Figure 8(a) was realized after 2 ns molecular dynamics simulation. Considering the periodic boundary conditions, this liquid slab can be regarded as an infinitely wide thin liquid film. During the simulation, the number of molecules, volume, and total energy of the system were conserved except for the early temperature control period. The vapor, interface, and liquid molecules are distinguished by the potential felt by each molecule. By taking a time average, the density profile (just counting the number of molecules in a finite volume), pressure tensor (calculating the virial function based on the statistical description), and surface tension can be reasonably predicted. The quite accurate prediction of surface tension has been demonstrated for Lennard-Jones fluid (Nijmeijer et al., 1988) and water (Alejandre et al., 1995) by integrating the difference of normal $p_N(z)$ and tangential $p_T(z)$ components of pressure tensor across the surface as

$$\sigma_{lg} = \int_{z_l}^{z_g} [p_N(z) - p_T(z)]\,dz \qquad (2.3\text{-}4)$$

where z is the coordinate perpendicular to the interface. Here, $p_N$ and $p_T$ equal the thermodynamic pressure $p$ in bulk vapor position $z_g$ or bulk liquid position $z_l$. In the case of liquid slab (as shown in Figure 8[a]), the integration between two vapor regions results in $2\sigma_{lg}$, since there are two liquid-vapor interfaces.

On the other hand, the liquid droplet shown in Figure 8(b) was obtained when the initial argon crystal was placed at the center of the cubic region. This is regarded as an isolated liquid droplet floating in its vapor. For a liquid droplet, the Young-Laplace equation

$$\sigma_{lg} = \frac{(p_l - p_g)R_s}{2} \quad (2.3\text{-}5)$$

should be used to calculate the surface tension. We can evaluate the pressure variation through the liquid and vapor interface in order to obtain $p_l$ and $p_g$ as asymptotic values. However, the rigorous definition of the dividing radius $R_s$ (which must be the surface of tension) is not straightforward, since the size of the droplet is normally very small and the liquid-vapor interface cannot be simply defined. This is seen from the interfacial molecules shown in Figure 8(b), which have different potential energy from liquid or vapor. Detailed discussions about the estimation of surface tension of small liquid droplet can be found in the literature (Haye and Bruin, 1994; Nijmeijer et al., 1992; Thompson et al., 1984; Townsend and Rice, 1991). Roughly a thousand molecules are enough to calculate the reasonable value of the bulk surface tension for argon (Maruyama et al., 1994a).

## 2.3.3 Condensation Coefficient

The determination of the condensation coefficient by the molecular dynamics simulations is a very fascinating task, as described in a review by Tanasawa (1994). The condensation coefficient has been simply defined as the ratio of the condensation rate to the rate of molecules incident at the interface. Through detailed studies of the liquid-vapor inter-phase phenomena of argon, water, and methanol, Matsumoto (1996) and Matsumoto et al. (1995b) pointed out that this macroscopic concept cannot be directly converted to the molecular scale concept. They stressed the importance of an "exchange" process: a molecule condensed into the liquid phase lets another liquid molecule to vaporize. By excluding those molecules from the number of condensing molecules, they had shown a good agreement with experiments. On the other hand, Tsuruta et al. (1996) had reported a significant dependence of the trapping rate on the normal velocity of incident molecules. They sought the connection to the classical gas dynamics theory for the calculation of the condensation process. Since there are significant differences in these two approaches, a new microscopic definition of the condensation coefficient that is physically plausible and useful for the further connection to the macroscopic theories may be necessary.

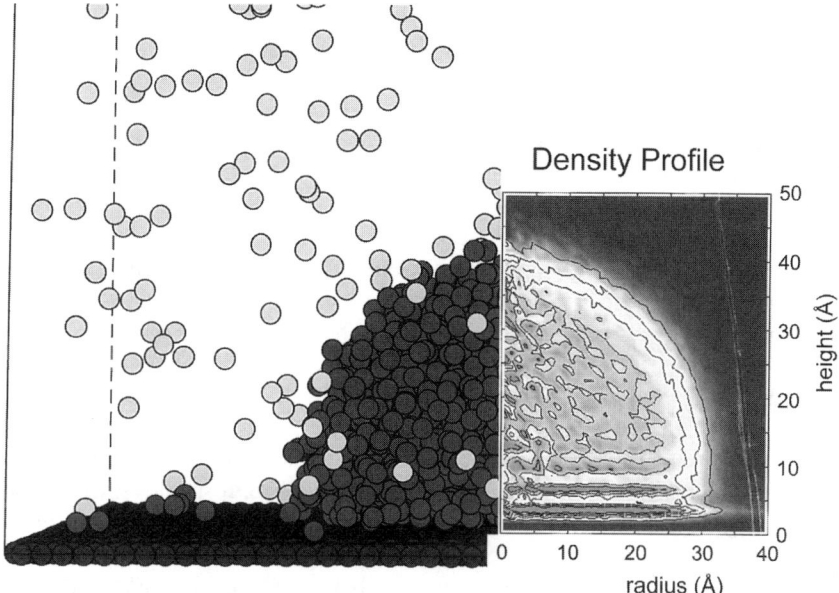

**Figure 9** The molecular representation of a liquid droplet in contact with solid surface compared with the two-dimensional density profile.

## 2.3.4 Solid-Liquid-Vapor Interactions (Contact Angle)

The contact phenomena of liquid to the solid surface are a critical issue of phase change heat transfer. The efficiency of evaporation and condensation near the three-phase interface sometimes rules the macroscopic heat transfer rate. Figure 9 compares a snapshot of the liquid droplet in contact with a solid wall and a two-dimensional density distribution. Simulation conditions are similar to our previous report (Matsumoto et al., 1995a; Maruyama et al., 1998), but 1944 argon molecules are included and about 1600 molecules constitute the liquid droplet surrounded by the saturated vapor. Solid molecules are located as three layers of fcc (111) surfaces with harmonic potential (only the surface layer is shown in Figure 9 for simplicity). The interaction potential between argon and solid molecule expressed by L-J potential is chosen so that the apparent contact angle becomes about $90°$. Except for the two or three liquid layers near the surface, the average shape of the liquid droplet is close to semi-spherical. In order to measure the contact angle, we can fit a circle to the density contour, disregarding the two layers of liquid near the solid surface. The layered structure is commonly observed for liquid-solid interfaces and explained as due to the solvation force (Israelachvili, 1985). With stronger interaction potential, the spread of the first layer of liquid film is much more pronounced (Matsumoto et al., 1995a). Controversially enough, the cosine of measured contact angle or the average shape of the droplet far from the surface was linearly dependent on the strength of the surface potential.

Dussan (1979), and recently Koplik and Banavar (1995), presented good reviews of the connection between microscopic and macroscopic views of the wetting phenomena. Saville (1977) has claimed that Young's equation is not satisfied from his molecular dynamics results. He enclosed a liquid slab and coexisting vapor between two parallel surfaces represented by the one-dimensional potential function. Using 255 to 1205 L-J molecules at about the triplet temperature, he measured the meniscus of the liquid-vapor interface and compared it with the calculated surface tensions $\sigma_{lg}$ and $\sigma_{sl} - \sigma_{sg}$. However, Nijmeijer et al. (1990) showed a good agreement of the observed contact angle and the contact angle calculated from Young's equation. Sikkenk et al. (1988) and Nijmeijer et al. (1990) used slightly different configurations with 8500 fluid molecules and 2904 solid molecules, and the difficulty of the calculation of surface tension term $\sigma_{sl} - \sigma_{sg}$ was also overcome. Later, Thompson et al. (1993) further supported the soundness of Young's equation and even discussed the dynamic contact angle. Here, it should be noted that in addition to the accuracy of the calculation of surface energies, the definition of apparent contact angle has not been clear. It seems that the increase in the number of molecules resulted in more attention to the bulk structure, disregarding the few special layers. Anyway, the contact angle measurement by the molecular dynamics simulation as in Figure 9 can be useful to predict the wettablitiy of realistic molecules on a realistic surface (Fan and Cagin, 1995).

## 2.3.5 Future Directions

The sound understanding of molecular level phenomena are anticipated in a variety of phase-change theories, such as nucleation of dropwise condensation, atomization, and homogeneous and heterogeneous nucleation of vapor bubbles in cavitation and boiling. Moreover, heat transfer right at the three-phase interface, which is a singular point in the macroscopic sense, should be considered for evaporation in micro-channel and for micro- and macro-layer of boiling. The upper limit of heat flux of phase-change must be clarified since recent advanced technologies, such as intense laser light or electron beam, easily achieve a very high heat flux. Phase change phenomena involved in the thin film manufacturing process and laser manufacturing are often out of the range of the conventional approach. Other examples are surfactant effect in liquid-vapor interface and surface treatment effect of a solid surface.

Even though the molecular dynamics method is a powerful tool, the reader should notice its shortcoming—that the spatial and temporal scale of the system that can be handled is usually too small to directly compare with the macroscopic phenomena. Even with the rapid advances of computer technology in the future, most macroscopic problems cannot be handled by directly solving each motion of molecules. Then, the ensemble technique of the molecular motion and the treatment of boundary condition must be improved for the connection to macroscopic phenomena.

Moreover, the determination of potential function for molecules in a real application is not straightforward, and the assumption of classical potential fails when the effect of electrons is not confined in the potential form. For example, even a simple heat conduction in metal cannot be easily handled due to free electrons. Quantum feature of electrons must be considered when electrons are excited by laser light, electromagnetic waves, or certain chemical reactions.

# REFERENCES

Adamson, A. W. 1990. *Physical Chemistry of Surfaces*, 5th ed. New York: Wiley, pp. 7–9.

Alejandre, J., Tildesley, D. J., and Chapela, G. A. 1995. Molecular Dynamics Simulation of the Orthobaric Densities and Surface Tention of Water. *J. Chem. Phys.*, 102(11):4574–4583.

Allen, M. P. and Tildesley, D. J. 1987. *Computer Simulation of Liquids*. New York: Oxford University Press.

Berendsen, H. J. C., Grigera, J. R., and Straatsma, T. P. 1987. The Missing Term in Effective Pair Potentials. *J. Phys. Chem.* 91(24):6269–6271.

Bird, G. A. 1994. *Molecular Gas Dynamics and the Direct Simulation of Gas Flow*. New York: Oxford University Press.

Blake, T. D. and Ruschak, K. J. 1979. Maximum Speed of Wetting. *Nature* 282:489–491.

Burley, R. and Jolly, R. P. S. 1984. Entrainment of Air into Liquids by a High Speed Continuous Solid Surface. *Chem. Engng. Sci.* 39:1357–1372.

Burley, R. and Kennedy, B. S. 1976. An Experimental Study of Air Entrainment at a Solid/Liquid/Gas Interface. *Chem. Engng. Sci.* 31:901–911.

Carravetta, V. and Clementi, E. 1984. Water-Water Interaction Potential: An Approximation of the Electron Correlation Contribution by a Function of the SCF Density Matrix. *J. Chem. Phys.* 81(6):2646–2651.

Cassie, A. B. D. 1948. Contact Angles. *Discuss. Faraday Soc.* 3:11–16.

Cassie, A. B. D. and Baxter, S. 1944. Wettability of Porous Surfaces. *Trans. Faraday Soc.* 40:546–551.

Cazabat, A.-M. 1990. Statics and Dynamics of Wetting. *Mol. Cryst. Liq. Cryst.* 179:99–107.

Chen, J.-D. and Wada, N. 1992. Edge Profiles and Dynamic Contact Angles of a Spreading Drop. *J. Colloid Interface Sci.* 148:207–222.

Dussan, V. E. B. 1979. On the Spreading of Liquids on Solid Surfaces: Static and Dynamic Contact Lines. *Ann. Rev. Fluid Mech.* 11:371–400.

Esmail, M. N. and Ghannam, M. T. 1990. Air Entrainment and Dynamic Contact Angles in Hydrodynamics of Liquid Coating. *Can. J. Chem. Engng.* 68:197–203.

Fan, C. F. and Cagin, T. 1995. Wetting of Crystalline Polymer Surfaces: A Molecular Dynamics Simulation. *J. Chem. Phys.* 103(20):9053–9061.

Gauss, K. F. 1829. Principia Generalia Theoriae Figurae Fluidorum in Statu Aequilibrii. Reproduced in: *Carl Friedrich Gauss Werke*, Volume 5, pp. 287–292. Hidesheim, Germany: Olms, 1973.

Gibbs, J. W. 1875–1878. On the Equilibrium of Heterogeneous Substances. Reproduced in: *The Scientific Papers of J. Willard Gibbs*, Volume 1, pp. 55–353. New York: Dover, 1960.

Good, R. J. 1952. A Thermodynamic Derivation of Wenzel's Modification of Young's Equation for Contact Angles: Together with a Theory of Hysteresis. *J. Am. Chem. Soc.* 74:5041–5042.

Gutoff, E. B. and Kendrick, C. E. 1982. Dynamic Contact Angles. *AIChE J.* 28:459–466.

Hartland, S. and Hartley, R. 1976. *Axisymmetric Fluid-Liquid Interfaces*. Amsterdam: Elsevier.
Haye, M. J. and Bruin, C. 1994. Molecular Dynamics Study of the Curvature Correction to the Surface Tension. *J. Chem. Phys.* 100(1):556–559.
Hopf, W. and Geidel, T. 1987. The Dynamic Contact Angle I. Dependence of the Receding Contact Angle on Velocity in the Surfactant-Containing Three-Phase System. *Colloid Polymer Sci.* 265:1075–1084.
Huh, C. and Mason, S. G. 1977. Effects of Surface Roughness on Wetting (Theoretical). *J. Colloid Interface Sci.* 60:11–38.
Israelachvili, J. N. 1985. *Intermolecular and Surface Forces*. London: Academic Press.
Jiang, T.-S., Oh, S.-G., and Slattery, J. C. 1979. Correlation for Dynamic Contact Angle. *J. Colloid Interface Sci.* 69:74–77.
Johnson, R. E., Jr. 1959. Conflicts Between Gibbsian Thermodynamics and Recent Treatments of Interfacial Energies in Solid-Liquid-Vapor Systems. *J. Phys. Chem.* 63:1655–1658.
Johnson, R. E. and Dettre, R. H. 1964. Contact Angle Hysteresis. I. Study of an Idealized Rough Surface. In: *Contact Angle, Wettability, and Adhesion*. Advances in Chemistry Series 43, pp. 112–135. Washington, D.C.: Am. Chem. Soc.
Kittel, C. 1996. *Introduction to Solid State Physics*, 7th ed. New York: John Wiley & Sons.
Koplik, J. and Banavar, J. R. 1995. Continuum Deductions from Molecular Hydrodynamics. *Ann. Rev. Fluid Mech.* 27:257–292.
Li, D., Cheng, P., and Neumann, A. W. 1992. Contact Angle Measurement by Axisymmetric Drop Shape Analysis (ADSA). *Adv. Colloid Interface Sci.* 39:347–382.
Marmur, A. 1994. Thermodynamic Aspect of Contact Angle Hysteresis. *Adv. Colloid Interface Sci.* 50:121–141.
Martynov, G. A., Malev, V. V., and Gribanova, E. V. 1983. Kinetics of Capillary Rise of Liquids. *Colloid J. USSR.* 45:205–209.
Maruyama, S., Kurashige, T, Matsumoto, S., Yamaguchi, Y., and Kimura, T. 1998. Liquid Droplet in Contact with a Solid Surface. *Microscale Thermophysical Engineering.* 2(1): 49–62.
Maruyama, S., Matsumoto, S., and Ogita, A. 1994a. Surface Phenomena of Molecular Clusters by Molecular Dynamics Method. *Thermal Science & Engineering.* 2(1):77–84.
Maruyama, S., Matsumoto, S., Shoji, M., and Ogita, A. 1994b. A Molecular Dynamics Study of Interface Phenomena of a Liquid Droplet. *Proc. 10th International Heat Transfer Conf.*, Volume 3. Brighton, pp. 409–414. Washington DC: Taylor and Francis.
Matsumoto, M. 1996. Molecular Dynamics Simulation of Interphase Transport at Liquid Surfaces. *Fluid Phase Equilibria.* 125:195–203.
Matsumoto, M., Yasuoka, K., and Kataoka, Y. 1995b. Molecular Mechanism of Evaporation and Condensation. *Thermal Science and Engineering.* 3(3):27–31.
Matsumoto, S., Maruyama, S., and Saruwatari, H. 1995a. A Molecular Dynamics Simulation of a Liquid Droplet on a Solid Surface. *Proc. ASME / JSME Thermal Engng*, Volume 2. Joint Conf., Maui, pp. 557–562.
Mori, Y. H., van de Ven, T. G. M., and Mason, S. G. 1982. Resistance to Spreading of Liquid by Sharp Edged Microsteps. *Colloids Surf.* 4:1–15.
Neumann, A. W. 1974. Contact Angles and Their Temperature Dependence: Thermodynamic Status, Measurement, Interpretation, and Application. *Adv. Colloid Interface Sci.* 4:105–191.
Nijmeijer, M. J. P., Bakker, A. F., Bruin, C., and Sikkenk, J. H. 1988. A Molecular Dynamics Simulation of the Lennard-Jones Liquid-Vapor Interface. *J. Chem. Phys.* 89(6):3789–3792.
Nijmeijer, M. J. P., Bruin, C., and Bakker, A. F. 1990. Wetting and Drying of an Inert Wall by a Fluid in a Molecular-Dynamics Simulation. *Physical Rev. A* 42(10):6052–6059.
Nijmeijer, M. J. P., Bruin, C., van Woerkom, A. B., and Bakker, A. F. 1992. Molecular Dynamics of the Surface Tension of a Drop. *J. Chem. Phys.* 96(1):565–576.

Okagawa, A. and Mason, S. G. 1978. Capillarography: A New Surface Probe. In: *Fibre-Water Interactions in Papermaking (Proceedings of the 6th Fundamental Research Symposium, Oxford, 1977)*, Technical Section, British Paper and Board Industry Federation, London, pp. 581–586.

Petrov, P. G. and Petrov, J. G. 1991. Comparison of the Static and Dynamic Contact Angle Hysteresis at Low Velocities of the Three-Phase Contact Line. *Colloids Surfaces.* 61:227–240.

Princen, H. M. 1969. The Equilibrium Shape of Interfaces, Drops, and Bubbles. Rigid and Deformable Particles at Interfaces. In: *Surface and Colloid Science*, Volume 2. Ed. E. Matijević. pp. 1–84. New York: Wiley.

Rillaerts, E. and Joos, P. 1980. The Dynamic Contact Aangle. *Chem. Engng. Sci.* 35:883–887.

Saville, G. 1977. Computer Simulation of the Liquid-Solid-Vapor Contact Angle. *J. Chem. Soc. Faraday Trans. 2.* 73:1122–1132.

Sikkenk, J. H., Indekeu, J. O., van Leeuwen, J. M. J., Vossnack, E. O., and Bakker, A. F. 1988. Simulation of Wetting and Drying at Solid-Fluid Interfaces on the Delft Molecular Dynamics Processor. *J. Statistical Physics*, 52(1/2):23–44.

Stillinger, F. H. and Rahman, A. 1974. Improved Simulation of Liquid Water by Molecular Dynamics. *J. Chem. Phys.* 60(4):1545–1557.

Tanasawa, I. 1994. Recent Advances in Condensation Heat Transfer, Volume 1. *Proc. 10th International Heat Transfer Conf.*, Brighton, pp. 297–312. Washington DC: Taylor and Francis.

Thompson, P. A., Brickerhoff, W. B., and Robbins, M. O. 1993. Microscopic Studies of Static and Dynamic Contact Angle. *J. Adhesion Sci Technol.* 7(6):535–554.

Thompson, S. M., Gubbins, K. E., Walton, J. P. R. B., Chantry, R. A. R., and Rowlinson, J. S. 1984. A Molecular Dynamics Study of Liquid Drops. *J. Chem. Phys.* 81(1):530–542.

Townsend, R. M. and Rice, S. A. 1991. Molecular Dynamics Studies of the Liquid-Vapor Interface of Water. *J. Chem. Phys.* 94(3):2207–2218.

Tsuruta, T., Tanaka, H., Tamashima, K., and Masuoka, T. 1997. Condensation Coefficient and Interphase Mass Transfer. *International Symposium on Molecular and Microscale Heat Transfer in Materials Processing and Other Applications*. Eds. I. Tanasawa and S. Nishio, pp. 229–240. New York: Begell House.

Wenzel, R. N. 1936. Resistance of Solid Surfaces to Wetting by Water. *Ind. Eng. Chem.* 28:988–994.

Young, T. 1805. An Essay on the Cohesion of Fluids. *Phil. Trans. Roy. Soc. Lond.* 95:65–87.

CHAPTER
# THREE

## BOILING CURVE

**Vijay K. Dhir**

*University of California, Los Angeles, CA 90024, USA*

## 3.1 INTRODUCTION

Boiling is a phase change process in which vapor bubbles are formed either on a heated surface and/or in a superheated liquid layer adjacent to the heated surface. It differs from evaporation at predetermined vapor/gas-liquid interfaces, as it also involves creating these interfaces at discrete sites on the heated surface. Boiling (nucleate) is a very efficient mode of heat transfer, and it is utilized in various energy conversion and heat exchange systems and in cooling of high energy density electronic components. Pool boiling refers to boiling under natural convection conditions, whereas in forced flow boiling, liquid flow over the heater surface is imposed by external means. Forced flow boiling is subdivided into external and internal flow boiling. In external boiling, liquid flow occurs over unconfined heated surfaces, whereas internal flow boiling refers to flow inside tubes.

## 3.2 POOL BOILING

Figure 1 shows, qualitatively, the boiling curve, i.e., dependence of the wall heat flux $\dot{q}$ on the wall superheat on a surface submerged in a pool of saturated liquid. The wall superheat, $\Delta T$, is defined as the difference between the wall temperature and the saturation temperature of the liquid at the system pressure. The plotted curve is for a flat plate or a horizontal wire to which the heat input rate is controlled.

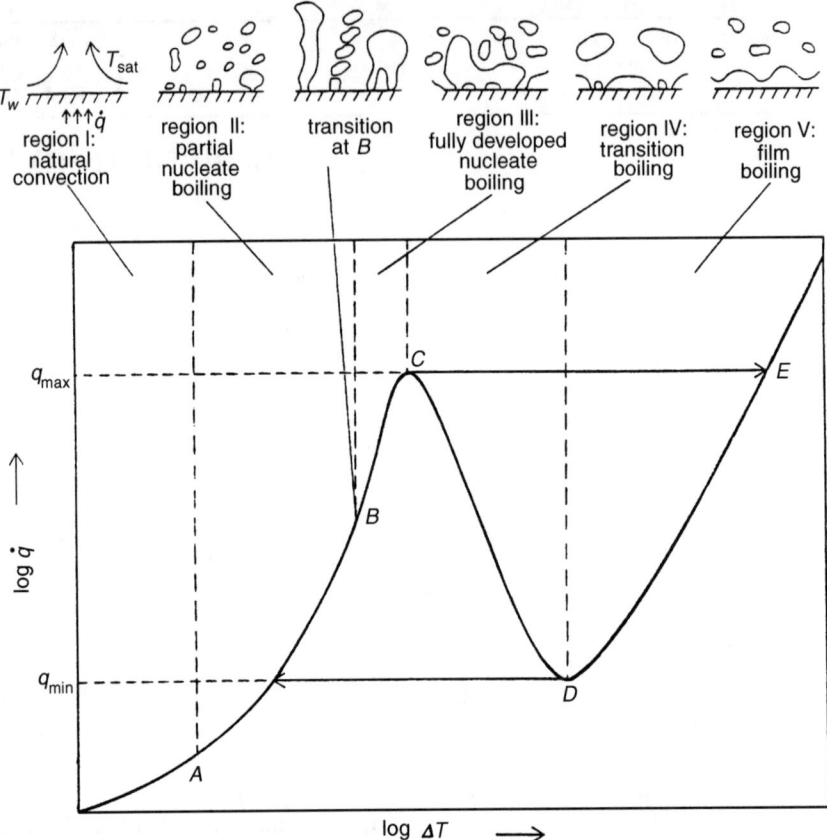

**Figure 1** Typical boiling curve, showing qualitatively the dependence of the wall heat flux $\dot{q}$ on the wall superheat $\Delta T$, defined as the difference between the wall temperature $T_w$ and the saturation temperature $T_{sat}$ of the liquid. Schematic drawings show the boiling process in regions I–V. These regions and the transition points A–E are discussed in the text.

As the heat-input rate to the surface is increased, the first mode of heat transfer to appear in a gravitational field is natural convection. At a certain value of the wall superheat (Point A), vapor bubbles appear on the heater surface. This is the onset of nucleate boiling. The bubbles form on cavities or scratches on the surface that contain pre-existing gas/vapor nuclei. In liquids that wet the surface well, the onset of nucleation may be delayed. For these liquids, a sudden activation of a large number of cavities at an increased wall superheat causes a reduction in the surface temperature while the heat flux remains constant. This behavior is not observed when the boiling curve is obtained by reducing the heat flux; thus, hysteresis results. After inception, a dramatic increase in the slope of the boiling curve is observed. In partial nucleate boiling, corresponding to region II (curve AB) in Figure 1, discrete bubbles are released from randomly located active sites on the heater surface. The density of active sites and the frequency of bubble release increase with heat flux or wall superheat. The transition from isolated bubbles to fully developed nucleate boiling (region III) occurs when bubbles at a given site begin to merge in the vertical direction. Vapor appears to leave the heater in the form of jets. The condition of the formation of jets also coincides (approximately) with the merger of vapor bubbles at the neighboring sites. After lateral merger, vapor structures appear like mushroom type bubbles with several stems (Gaertner, 1965). Figure 2 shows a photograph of a large vapor structure supported by several smaller bubbles (stems). A small change in the slope of the boiling curve can occur upon transition from partial to fully developed nucleate boiling. The heat flux on polished surfaces varies with wall superheat roughly as

$$\dot{q} \sim \Delta T^m \tag{3.2-1}$$

where m has a value between 3 and 4.

The maximum, peak, or critical heat flux, $\dot{q}_{max}$, sets the upper limit of fully developed nucleate boiling or safe operation of equipment. After the occurrence of the maximum heat flux condition, most of the surface is very rapidly covered with

**Figure 2** Photograph of fully developed nucleate boiling of saturated water at 1 atm. Pressure $q = 25$ W/cm², $\Delta T = 12.5$ K.

vapor. As such, the surface becomes nearly insulated, and the surface temperature rises quickly. When the heat input rate to the heater is controlled, the heater surface will very rapidly pass through regions IV and V in Figure 1 and stabilize at point E. If the temperature at E exceeds the melting temperature of the heater material, the heater will fail (burn out). The curve ED (region V) represents stable film boiling, and the system can be made to follow this curve by reducing the heat flux. In stable film boiling, the surface is totally covered with vapor film, and liquid does not contact the solid. On a horizontal surface, the vapor release pattern is governed by Taylor instability of the vapor-liquid interface. With a reduction of heat flux in film boiling, a condition is reached when a stable vapor film on the heater can no longer be sustained. Heat flux and wall superheat corresponding to the condition at which vapor film collapse occurs are referred to as $\dot{q}_{min}$ and $\Delta T_{min}$, respectively.

Upon collapse of the vapor film, the surface very rapidly goes through regions IV, III, and II and settles in nucleate boiling. Region IV, falling between nucleate and film boiling, is called *transition boiling*. It is a mixed mode of boiling that has features of both nucleate and film boiling. Transition boiling is very unstable since it is accompanied by a reduction in the heat flux with an increase in the wall superheat. As a result, it is very difficult to obtain steady state data in transition boiling, except when the heater surface temperature is controlled. Transient transition boiling data can be obtained either by quenching or accessing from the nucleate boiling side when heat input to the heater is controlled.

## 3.3 FLOW BOILING

A boiling curve similar to that in pool boiling is obtained when flow occurs over the heater surface (external boiling) or inside a heated tube (internal boiling). In internal flow boiling, the vapor/liquid flow configurations change due to the addition of vapor along the flow direction. Figure 3 shows a typical forced flow boiling curve for a tube in which subcooled liquid enters the tube. The curve is drawn for a fixed total flow rate and system pressure. The first mode of heat transfer as subcooled liquid enters the tube is forced convection. The magnitude of the heat transfer coefficient increases with flow velocity. Since the heat transfer coefficient depends very weakly on the wall superheat in single phase forced convection, the heat flux linearly with wall superheat. After inception, a marked improvement in heat transfer coefficient occurs as wall superheat is increased. The region A'B', spanning wall superheats from inception to fully developed nucleate boiling, is termed partial nucleate boiling. In this region, bubbles are formed discretely on the heated surface, and both single phase convection and phase change heat transfer contribute to the total heat transfer rate. As such, the functional dependence of heat

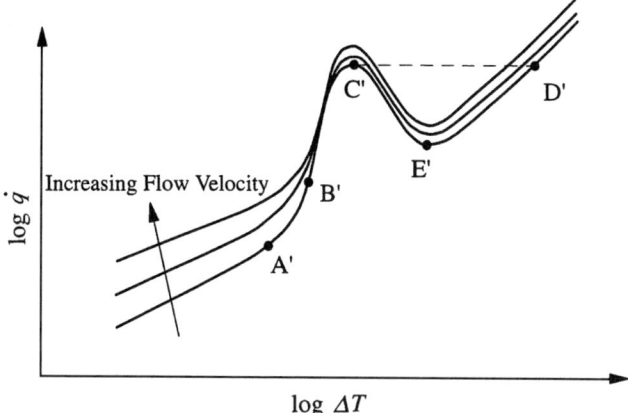

**Figure 3** Flow boiling curve.

flux on wall superheat is stronger than that for forced convection, but it is weaker than that for fully developed nucleate boiling.

Fully developed nucleate boiling curves (B'C') at different velocities generally overlap each other, suggesting the dominance of the heat removal by phase change. In fully developed nucleate boiling, bubble merger occurs at the heated surface. However, the phasic structure is influenced by the flow regime that exists in the bulk. Possible flow regimes are bubbly, slug, and annular. In annular flows, when liquid film on the wall becomes very thin, nucleate boiling may be suppressed. Now, the heat removal is through evaporation at the liquid vapor interface of the thin film. The heat transfer coefficient in very thin film annular flow may exceed that given by extension of the pool boiling curve. As a result, for a fixed heat flux, the wall superheat in very thin film flow may become smaller than that for fully developed nucleate boiling.

Under low flow/heat flux conditions, the critical heat flux occurs when the thin liquid film in annular flow dries out. Such a heat flux is called *dryout heat flux*, and this condition generally occurs in steam generators. However, under high flow/heat flux conditions, the critical heat flux occurs under conditions similar to those for pool boiling, i.e., sufficient liquid is available away from the wall or in the bulk. The critical heat flux condition results when vapor removal rate from the heater surface falls short of the vapor generation rate or liquid at the heater surface is not replenished fast enough to compensate for the evaporation rate. In the literature, critical heat flux condition has also been referred to as a departure from nucleate boiling, boiling crisis, and burnout heat flux. The magnitude of the critical heat flux depends on the local quality, mass velocity, and system pressure.

For a surface subjected to axially uniform heat flux, the critical heat flux condition will first occur at the exit where the local quality is the highest. After occurrence of the critical heat flux, the temperature (for a heat flux controlled surface) rises very rapidly, and after passing through regions C'D' and D'E', the surface settles down in film boiling at E'. As for pool boiling, in forced flow a vapor film separates the heater surface from the liquid core. This flow configuration is called *inverse annual flow boiling*. If the liquid film dries (dryout heat flux), the surface will be cooled by forced flow of vapor. Some liquid droplets may be entrained in the vapor, and single phase forced convection correlations modified to account for the presence of droplets can be applied to determine the post dryout wall temperature.

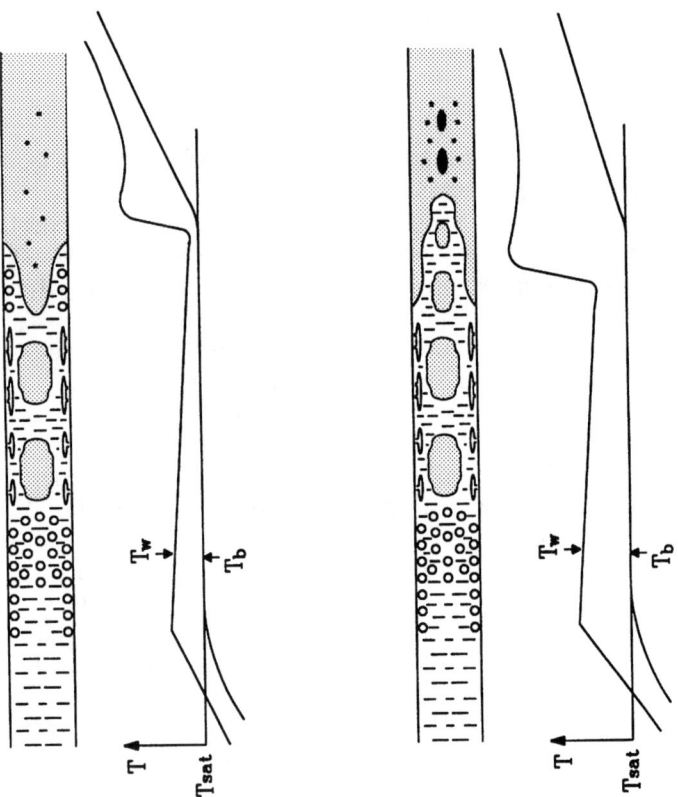

Low Heat Flux/Low Flow Rate     High Heat Flux/High Flow Rate

**Figure 4** Flow regimes during flow boiling in a tube.

In the transition boiling region (C'D'), partial contact of the liquid with the solid occurs. As in pool boiling, this mode of boiling is unstable, and it is difficult to obtain steady state transition boiling data on a heat flux controlled surface. If the dryout front in a low flow/low heat flux case oscillates, the surface in the vicinity of the dryout front will be alternately wet and dry. As such, large variation in temperature will occur as the surface transitions from totally wet to totally dry conditions. Figure 4 shows, qualitatively, the flow regimes and variations in tube wall temperature for low flow/low heat flux and high flow/high heat flux conditions.

## REFERENCE

Gaertner, R. F. 1965. Photographic Study of Nucleate Pool Boiling on a Horziontal Surface. *J. Heat Transfer* 97:17–29.

CHAPTER
# FOUR

## NUCLEATE BOILING

**4.1–4.6   Vijay K. Dhir**

*University of California, Los Angeles, CA 90024, USA*

**4.7   Satish G. Kandlikar**

*Rochester Institute of Technology, Rochester, NY 14623, USA*

**4.7   Yasunobu Fujita**

*Kyushu Unversity 36, Fukuoka 812-81, Japan*

**4.8   Yoshihiro Iida**

*Yokohama National University, Yokohama 240, Japan*

**4.8   Richard Heist**

*University of Rochester, Rochester, NY 14620, USA*

## 4.1 INTRODUCTION

The onset of nucleate boiling on a heater submerged in a pool of liquid is characterized by the appearance of vapor bubbles at discrete locations on the heater surface. These bubbles form on surface imperfections, such as cavities and scratches. The gas/vapor trapped in these imperfections serves as nuclei for the bubbles. After inception, the bubbles grow to a certain size and depart from the surface. A certain time elapses before a new bubble is formed on the same active site. The onset of nucleate boiling is marked by an increase in the slope of the heat flux, $\dot{q}$, versus the wall superheat, $\Delta T_w$, curve. With an increase in heat flux or wall superheat, the number of active sites and the frequency of release of bubbles from these randomly located sites increase. As such, in a pool of saturated liquid, a state is reached when bubbles released from a given site merge in the vertical direction (on an upward facing horizontal surface). The merger of bubbles in the vertical direction causes the vapor to leave the heater in the form of jets. Due to the increase in number density of active sites with the increase in wall superheat, bubbles at neighboring sites also begin to merge. This lateral merger of bubbles leads to formation of mushroom-type bubbles. These bubbles appear to be attached to the heater surface via several vapor stems. Gaertner (1965) called this condition of the formation of vapor jets and mushroom-type bubbles *first transition*, and it marks the shift from partial to fully developed nucleate boiling. Thus, wall superheat or wall heat flux are important parameters that determine the structure of the vapor phase near the heated surface. Moissis and Berenson (1963) obtained a semi-theoretical expression for Gaertner's first transition as

$$\dot{q} = 0.11\sqrt{\phi}\rho_v h_{\ell g} \left[ \frac{\sigma g}{(\rho_\ell - \rho_v)} \right]^{1/4} \quad (4.1\text{-}1)$$

where $\phi$ is the contact angle in degrees.

With continued increase in wall superheat in fully developed nucleate boiling, most of the heater area is covered with large mushroom type of bubbles. As heat flux is further increased, vapor stems start to merge, and dry patches form on the heater surface. Gaertner called this condition *second transition*. The vapor structures in nucleate boiling, as identified by Gaertner, are shown in Figure 1.

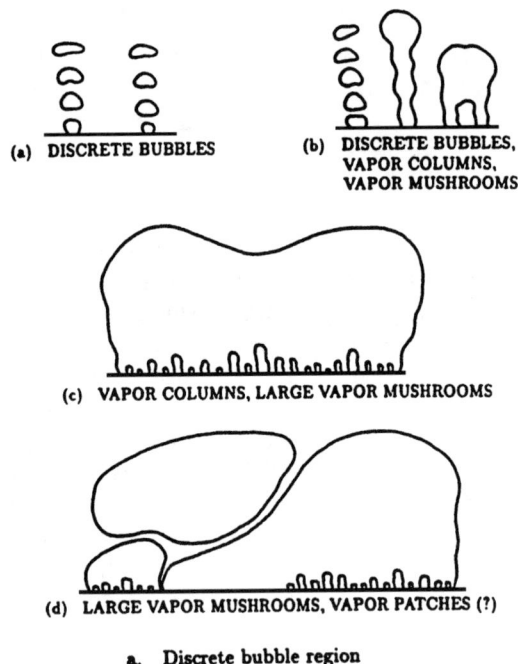

a. Discrete bubble region
b. First transition
c. Vapor mushroom region
d. Second transition region

**Figure 1** Gaertner's (1965) identification of vapor structures in nucleate boiling.

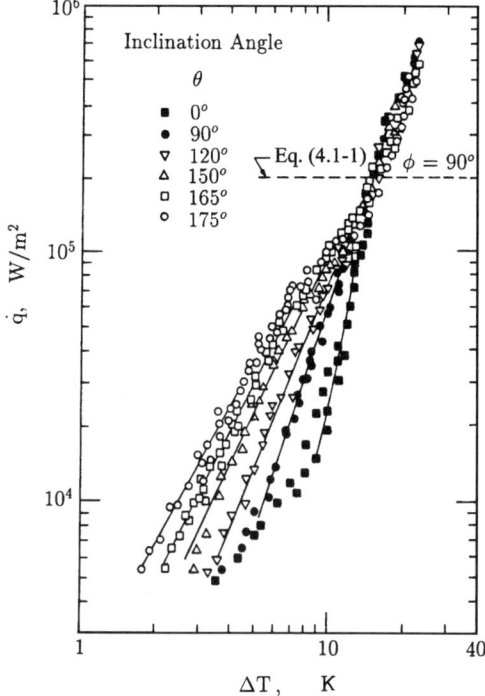

**Figure 2** Nucleate boiling data of Nishikawa et al. (1984) on plates oriented at different angles to be horizontal.

Figure 2 shows nucleate boiling data obtained by Nishikawa et al. (1984) on plates inclined at different angles with the horizontal. The data plotted in Figure 2 are for saturated water at one atmosphere pressure and were taken on polished copper plates. In partial nucleate boiling, the angle of inclination of the surface is seen to influence the dependence of nucleate boiling heat flux on wall superheat. However, at higher heat fluxes or in fully developed nucleate boiling, all of the boiling curves merge into a single curve. In Figure 2, the prediction from Eq. (4.1-1) for transition from partial to fully developed nucleate boiling is also plotted when the contact angle, $\phi$, is assumed to be 90°. It is seen that, though Eq. (4.1-1) was developed for a horizontal surface, it generally describes the transition from partial to fully developed nucleate boiling for all of the surfaces studied in the experiments of Nishikawa et al. In nucleate boiling, the relation between wall heat flux and wall superheat can be written as

$$\dot{q} = C \Delta T^m \quad (4.1\text{-}2)$$

For the data plotted in Figure 2, the exponent $m$ is found to lie approximately between 2 and 4 for partial nucleate boiling and between 3.3 and 4.3 for fully developed nucleate boiling. The value of exponent $m$ is not only affected by the orientation of the surface but by other variables as well, such as heater geometry, surface roughness, and system pressure, etc. Similarly, the proportionality constant $C$ is influenced by surface wettability, surface contamination, heater geometry, system pressure, etc. Often, in developing a correlation such as Eq. (4.1-2), a distinction between partial and fully developed nucleate boiling is not made, and the same values are assigned to $C$ and $m$ in both regimes. Various system variables affect the nucleate boiling curves, and some of these effects are described here.

## 4.2 EFFECT OF SYSTEM VARIABLES ON NUCLEATE BOILING

### 4.2.1 Surface Finish

The effect of increased surface roughness is to shift the nucleate boiling curve to the left. This, in turn, corresponds to a higher heat flux at a given wall superheat for a rougher surface. Figure 3 shows boiling curves obtained by Bui and Dhir (1985) on a clean mirror finish and on an emery 600 finish vertical surface made of copper.

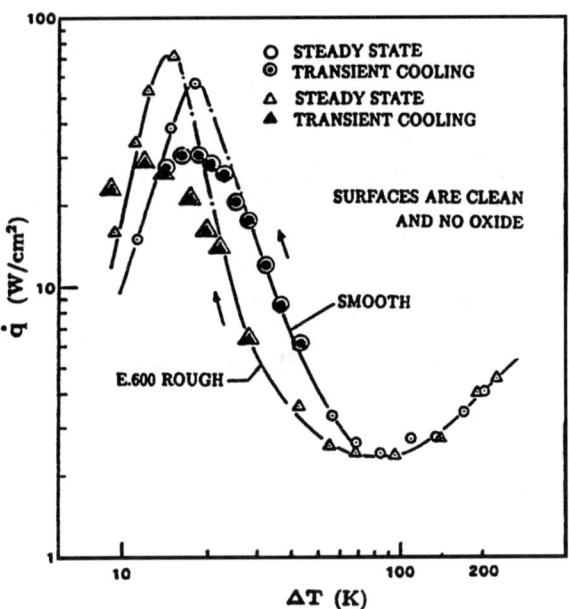

**Figure 3** Effect of surface roughness on nucleate and transition boiling.

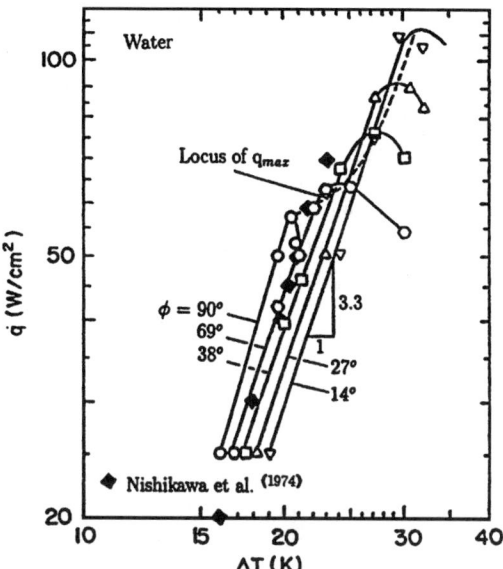

**Figure 4** Effect of surface wettability on nucleate boiling heat fluxes.

The curves were obtained during boiling of saturated water at one atmosphere pressure. It is noted that both the proportionality constant $C$ and exponent $m$ increase with roughness. Similar results have been reported by Berenson (1962) for a horizontal surface.

## 4.2.2 Surface Wettability

With an increase in surface wettability, the nucleate boiling curves shift to the right. Figure 4 shows the saturated water data of Liaw and Dhir (1989), obtained on vertical surfaces having different static contact angles. The plotted data are for fully developed nucleate boiling and include the data of Nishikawa et al. for a vertical surface. It is noted that although the boiling curves shifts to the right with an increase in the wettability of the surface (decreasing contact angle), the value of exponent $m$ on wall superheat remains nearly unchanged, i.e., $m = 3.3$. It is interesting to note that maximum heat flux increases as the surface wettability improves.

For liquids that wet the surface well (contact angle approaching zero), an overshoot is observed in the nucleate boiling curve. For these liquids, the convective heat removal process continues to persist up to a high superheat. Upon inception, a large reduction in wall superheat is observed at the imposed heat flux. Thereafter, the wall superheat increases with heat flux as for a liquid that only partially wets the surface.

### 4.2.3 Heater Geometry

As noted from the data of Nishikawa et al. (1984), the partial nucleate boiling heat flux at a given wall superheat is sensitive to the orientation of the surface with respect to the direction of gravitational acceleration. Partial nucleate boiling heat fluxes are generally higher on a downward facing surface. The higher heat transfer is probably caused by the cyclic disruption of the thermal layer by bubbles moving along the heater surface. On a horizontal cylinder, data of Cornwell and Einarsson (1989) show that under partial nucleate boiling conditions, the heat transfer coefficient is highest near the lower stagnation point and is lowest at the top. However, the heat transfer coefficient remains fairly constant over most of the periphery of the cylinder.

### 4.2.4 Surface Contamination

Physicochemical changes on a boiling surface can take place in several ways: deposition of inert matter contained in the host liquid, slow chemical reaction of the surface with gases dissolved in the liquid or with vapor, and strong chemical reaction of the metal with concentrated solutions of electrolytes. The latter two processes, if continued over a long period of time, can lead to loss of material or corrosion of the surface. Corrosion can also result from repeated collapse of vapor bubbles subjected to subcooled liquid and repeated collisions with the surface of bubbles entrained in liquid. The presence of foreign material on the surface can affect its nucleation behavior by deactivating some cavities, providing new nucleation sites, and changing the wettability of the surface. Generally, the wettability is increased, and as a result, the nucleate boiling curve shifts slightly to the right.

The presence of oxygen in the host liquid leads to contamination of the surface via slow chemical reactions. The process, if continued over a long period, can lead to the aging of the surface and a resulting permanent change in its boiling characteristics. The metal ions combine with oxygen to form metal oxides that precipitate around the mouth of the cavities or at the base of bubbles, where high heat and mass transfer gradients exist. The effect of contamination of the surface is similar to that of improved wettability, i.e., to push the nucleate boiling curve to the right or to increase the wall superheat for a given heat flux.

From corrosion studies (see Ross, 1967) performed during long term boiling on iron, copper, and aluminum surfaces, it is found that mass loss rate increases with an increase in the concentration of oxygen in water. At low heat fluxes, the mass loss rate is independent of heat flux, but at high heat fluxes, a reduction in mass loss rate is observed as the heat flux is increased. When sodium chloride (electrolyte) is dissolved in water, the mass loss rate curves show a local minima, because at low heat fluxes, the mass loss rate decreases with heat flux, whereas at high heat fluxes, an opposite trend is observed. It has been suggested that minima in mass loss rate may be due to competing effects of oxygen and chloride ions at the surface.

### 4.2.5 System Pressure

With an increase in system pressure, the incipience superheat decreases and the nucleate boiling curve is shifted to the left. Gorenflo et al. (1986) have correlated nucleate boiling heat transfer coefficient data for Freon-12, Freon-22, and propane, obtained at reduced pressure $p^*(p/p_c)$, up to 0.93 as

$$\frac{\alpha}{\alpha_0} = \left(\frac{\dot{q}}{\dot{q}_0}\right)^n \cdot F(p^*) \tag{4.2-1}$$

where

$$F(p^*) = 2.1 p^{*0.27} + \left(4.4 + \frac{1.8}{1-p^*}\right) p^* \tag{4.2-2}$$

and

$$n(p^*) = 0.9 - 0.3 p^{*0.3} \tag{4.2-3}$$

The values of the reference heat transfer coefficient, $\alpha_0$, at the reference heat flux, $\dot{q}_0 = 2 \times 10^4$ W/m², and the reference pressure, $p_0^* = 0.03$, for these liquids are:

| Liquid | R-12 | R-22 | $C_3H_8$ | |
|--------|------|------|----------|---|
| $\alpha_0$ | 2300 | 2200 | 2100 | W/m² K |

### 4.2.6 Liquid Subcooling

The rate of the convective heat transfer increases with liquid subcooling. As a result, liquid subcooling influences the inception and partial nucleate boiling regions of the boiling curve. On the wall heat flux versus wall superheat plots, convective and partial nucleate boiling heat fluxes lie higher than those for saturated boiling. However, at high nucleate boiling heat fluxes, the subcooled and saturated boiling curves almost overlap. At present, no criterion such as that developed by Moissis and Berenson (Eq. 4.1-1) for saturated boiling on a horizontal upward facing plate exists for the transition from partial to fully developed nucleate boiling under subcooled conditions.

## 4.2.7 Gravity

The magnitude and direction of the gravitational acceleration with respect to the heater surface influence the convective hydrodynamic and thermal boundary layers and bubble trajectory. In partial nucleate boiling, heat transfer by convection represents a major fraction of the total heat transfer rate. Thus, gravity plays an important role in this mode of boiling. Merte (1988) reported nucleate boiling data of liquid nitrogen at one atmosphere pressure but at different levels of gravity. The high gravity data were taken in a centrifuge, the near zero gravity data in a drop tower, and the data obtained on a downward-facing horizontal disk were considered to be $-1$ g data. All of the data were taken under transient boiling conditions. At low heat fluxes, the effect of increased levels of gravity is to increase the convective and partial nucleate boiling. However, the heat fluxes associated with zero and $-1$ g are found to be higher than those obtained on a surface subjected to large accelerations. On a downward-facing surface, the bubbles move along the surface and thereby enhance the heat removal by disrupting the thermal layer over a larger area. At zero gravity, the bubbles in the transient experiments probably persisted over the heater for long periods and thereby enhanced the evaporative contribution to total heat transfer rate. However, at higher heat fluxes, boiling data obtained at different levels of gravity merge on a single curve. In recent experiments conducted at low gravity, Zell et al. (1989) also found no distinct effect of magnitude of gravity at higher nucleate boiling heat fluxes. It is still not known if steady state nucleate boiling heat fluxes are at all possible under microgravity conditions; if so, their magnitudes are not known.

## 4.2.8 Mode of the Tests

The boiling curve can be affected by the manner in which the heat flux is imposed on the surface—steady state or transient. The early experiments of Johnson (1971), in which thin metallic heaters submerged in water were heated electrically and to which power was increased exponentially, show that for exponential periods greater than 5 ms, the transient nucleate boiling process including incipience can be described by a steady state process. The studies of Sakurai and Shiotsu (1977a, 1977b) on platinum wires submerged in a pool of water show that for exponential periods varying from 5 ms to 1 s, the incipience heat fluxes increase as the exponential time decreases. In nucleate boiling, the transient heat transfer coefficients are generally found to be lower than those obtained under steady state. The ratio of the transient and steady state heat fluxes depends on the magnitude of the heat flux, but this ratio can be as low as 0.5.

In many industrial applications, a hot solid is quenched in a saturated or subcooled liquid. The thermal stresses induced in the solid depend on the rate of cooling. To circumvent the difficulties associated with carrying out steady state boiling experiments in certain geometries and to facilitate acquisition of data in transition boiling, quenching (transient cooling) has also been used as an experimental technique for carrying out boiling studies. In quenching experiments, the time-dependent temperature history in the solid is used to recover the surface heat flux. The transient nucleate boiling data obtained during quenching experiments generally do not overlap the steady state data. Although no quantitative basis exists in the literature for the displacement of the transient nucleate boiling curve, the magnitude of displacement is affected by several of the variables described above, as well as by the thickness and thermal properties of the heater material.

## 4.3 NUCLEATION CHARACTERISTICS IN POOL BOILING, HETEROGENEOUS NUCLEATION

Nucleation is a process in which finite size clusters of molecules encompassing properties of the second phase appear in the host liquid. This can be the initiation of bubble formation during boiling or cavitation or crystal formation during solidification. The nucleation process is generally subdivided into two categories: homogeneous nucleation and heterogeneous nucleation. The homogeneous nucleation refers to the formation of a vapor-liquid interface (bubble) in superheated liquid in the absence of any pre-existing gas/vapor nuclei and not on any solid surfaces. The heterogeneous nucleation is a process in which bubbles form discretely at pits, scratches, and grooves on a heated surface submerged in a pool of liquid. In this section, we discuss only heterogeneous nucleation. Homogeneous nucleation is discussed later.

### 4.3.1 Pre-Existing Gas Nuclei

The early work of Bankoff (1958) has shown that superheats associated with heterogeneous nucleation are much smaller than those associated with homogeneous nucleation. The reason for lower inception superheat can be easily rationalized if one considers that the cavities generally trap air or other non-condensable vapor and have radii that are much larger than the critical radius of the cluster of activated molecules. The volume of air trapped in a cavity depends on the magnitude of surface tension, the contact angle, the shape of the cavity, and the experimental conditions, such as system pressure, liquid temperature, and temperature of the heated surface. The wall temperature at which nucleate boiling begins strongly depends on the availability of cavities with trapped gas (unflooded cavities). Thus, as cavities become fewer and fewer and their size decreases, the nucleation temperatures will approach homogeneous nucleation temperature.

The trapped gas not only promotes nucleation by providing pre-existing interfaces, but it also reduces the superheat required for nucleation. Using Dalton's law, the pressure in the bubble nucleus can be written as

$$p_b = p_v + p_g \qquad (4.3\text{-}1)$$

Since the pressure difference between vapor and liquid across the interface is reduced by $p_g$ for a fixed pressure in the bubble, the liquid superheat for thermal equilibrium between vapor and liquid is also reduced accordingly:

$$T_\ell - T_{\text{sat}} \simeq \frac{\left[\dfrac{2\sigma}{R} - p_g\right] T_{\text{sat}}}{\rho_v h_{\ell g}} \qquad (4.3\text{-}2)$$

Bankoff (1958) also provided a criterion for the entrapment of gas in a wedge-shaped cavity. According to his criterion, if the contact angle[1] $\phi$ is greater than the wedge angle $2\beta$, an advancing liquid front will fill the upper portion of the cavity while trapping gas underneath. An advancing gas or vapor front, however, will not be able to displace the liquid if $\phi < \pi - 2\beta$. A liquid-filled cavity is not conducive to nucleation. In a subsequent work, Ward and Forest (1976) analyzed the relation between platelet adhesion and roughness of a synthetic material and have shown that the gas/vapor nucleus in a long narrow fissure is stable if

$$\phi > \frac{\pi}{2} + \beta \qquad (4.3\text{-}3)$$

where $\beta$ is the half wedge angle. Thus, according to Eq. (4.3.3), conical cavities present on a hydrophilic surface will not trap gas.

In a more recent work, Wang and Dhir (1993a) have developed the gas/vapor entrapment criterion by minimizing the Helmholtz free energy of a system involving the liquid-gas interface in a cavity. According to this criterion, a cavity will trap gas if

$$\phi > \psi_{\min} \qquad (4.3\text{-}4)$$

where $\psi_{\min}$ is the minimum cavity side angle of a spherical, conical, or sinusoidal cavity. For spherical and conical cavities, $\psi_{\min}$ occurs at the mouth of the cavity and is equal to the cavity mouth angle, $\psi_m$. For a sinusoidal cavity, the minimum side angle, $\psi_{\min}$, occurs at a location where the radius of the cavity is equal to half of the cavity mouth radius. It should be noted that for a conical cavity, the criterion given by Eq. (4.3-4) is the same as that given by Eq. (4.3-3) of Ward and Forest (1976), and liquids with a contact angle less than 90° will not provide a stable/gas vapor embryo for nucleation.

According to Eq. (4.3-4), hardly any pre-existing gas/vapor nuclei are possible for well wetting liquids, such as R-113 and FC-72. Thus, for these liquids, the wall superheat at nucleation can approach the homogeneous nucleation temperature. The observed inception superheats for these liquids, though much higher than those observed for partially wetting liquids, are much smaller (see Barthau, 1992) than those corresponding to homogeneous nucleation temperature. It is possible that

---

[1] A distinction must be made between an advancing and receding contact angle. See Chapter 2. However, in the discussion presented here, a static contact angle, $\phi$, is used.

gases dissolved in these liquids serve to initiate the nucleation and, as a result, the observed superheat is smaller than the homogeneous nucleation. After inception, the bubbles at active sites can momentarily displace the liquid from the neighboring cavities that are flooded, or the flooded cavities simply dry out during the bubble growth period. Subsequently, these latter cavities become active nucleation sites and remain so, as long as sufficient wall superheat is maintained. The sudden activation of many additional sites leads to improvement in heat transfer and, in turn, to reduction in wall temperature at a fixed heat flux (hysteresis).

## 4.3.2 Inception

Griffith and Wallis (1960) proposed that incipient superheat for boiling from pre-existing nuclei corresponds to the minimum radius of curvature of the interface. The minimum radius of curvature of the interface was assumed to be equal to the radius of the cavity mouth. By replacing the pressure difference between the vapor bubble (no gas) and liquid with the liquid superheat through the use of the Clausius-Clapeyron equation, they obtained an expression for inception superheat as

$$\Delta T = \frac{4\sigma \, T_{\text{sat}}}{\rho_v h_{\ell g} D_c} \qquad (4.3\text{-}5)$$

where $D_c$ is the cavity mouth diameter. It should be noted that Eq. (4.3-5) includes neither the effect of contact angle on inception superheat nor the effect of temperature gradient that exists near a heated wall. Subsequently, Hsu (1962) studied the effect of temperature profile adjacent to the heated surface on the minimum superheat needed for nucleation. In developing his model, Hsu proposed that the top of a bubble embryo should be covered with warm liquid before it can grow. Since vapor in the embryo must be at saturation temperature corresponding to the pressure of vapor in the bubble (which is higher than the pool pressure by $2\sigma/R$), the liquid surrounding the bubble must be superheated to maintain the thermal equilibrium. If the required superheat does not exist, the heat transfer to colder liquid will cause the bubble embryo to shrink. Because heat is transferred from the wall, the liquid temperature decreases with distance from the wall, and the above criterion is satisfied everywhere around the embryo, if the temperature of the liquid at the tip of the embryo is equal to the saturation temperature corresponding to pressure in the bubble.

Figure 5 shows how the criterion can be satisfied for a bubble embryo when the wall heat flux is gradually increased. In plotting the temperature, a fictitious film thickness, $\delta$, is defined, which with a linear temperature profile gives the same heat flux at the wall as the actual thermal layer, $\delta_{th}$. Also, it is assumed that $\delta$ is independent of the temperature difference across the layer. During natural convection this is not a correct assumption. However, in natural convection, the dependence of film thickness on temperature difference is weak. The temperature profile traced by the solid line marks the wall heat flux at which Hsu's criterion is

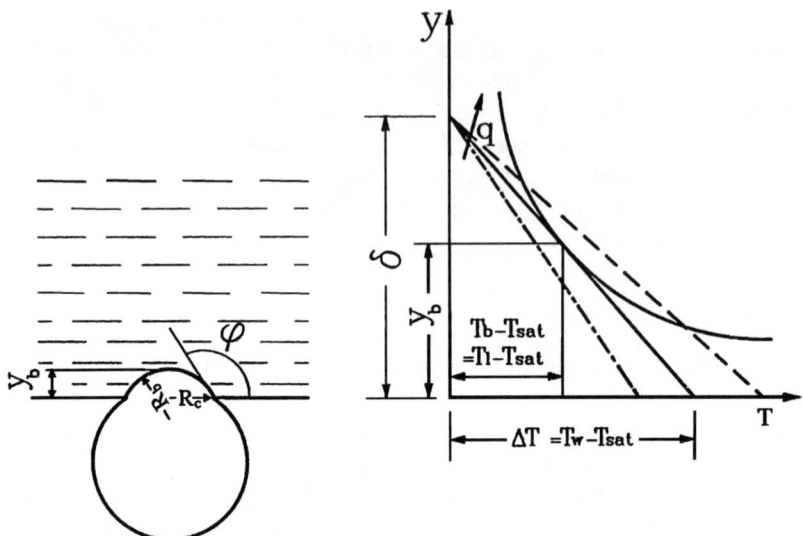

**Figure 5** Hsu's criterion for inception of a heated surface.

just satisfied. If the cavity for which the criterion is satisfied is available on the surface (i.e., is not completely filled with liquid), this cavity will be the first one to nucleate. The lowest superheat at which nucleation is possible can be determined from the expressions for the temperature distribution in the film and the liquid temperature determined from the equilibrium considerations. If the bulk liquid is saturated, the temperature profile in the liquid film is given by

$$T_\ell - T_{sat} = (T_w - T_{sat})(1 - y/\delta) \tag{4.3-6}$$

The vapor bubble thermal equilibrium condition is written as

$$T_\ell - T_{sat} = \frac{2\sigma T_{sat}}{R_b \rho_v h_{\ell g}} \tag{4.3-7}$$

If the vapor-liquid interface of the vapor bubble embryo just occupying the mouth of the cavity is considered to be part of a sphere, the interface radius of curvature and the height of the bubble tip can be written as

$$R_b = f_1 R_c \quad \text{and} \quad y_b = f_2 R_c / f_1 \tag{4.3-8}$$

when $f_1$ and $f_2$ are functions of the contact angle, $\phi$. Differentiating Eqs. (4.3-6) and (4.3-7), with respect to the distance, $y$, normal to the heater surface, and equating the two derivatives $dT_\ell/dy$, we obtain the radius of the nucleating cavity as

$$R_c \equiv \frac{D_c}{2} = \left[ \frac{2 f_1^2 \sigma T_{sat} \delta}{f_2 \rho_v h_{\ell g} (T_w - T_{sat})} \right]^{1/2} \tag{4.3-9}$$

If the wall superheat is replaced with wall heat flux, the expression for the cavity diameter, $D_c$, becomes

$$D_c = \left[\frac{8f_1^2\sigma T_{sat}\lambda_\ell}{f_2\rho_v h_{\ell g}\dot{q}}\right]^{1/2} \quad (4.3\text{-}10)$$

Upon substitution for $R_b$ in terms of the diameter of the nucleating cavity given by Eq. (4.3-10) into Eq. (4.3-7) and elimination of the liquid temperature $T_\ell$ between Eqs. (4.3-6) and (4.3-7) after $y$ is replaced by $y_b$ in Eq. (4.3-6), an expression for the minimum wall superheat for nucleation is obtained as

$$\Delta T \equiv T_w - T_{sat} = \frac{8f_2\sigma T_{sat}}{\rho_v h_{\ell g}\delta} \quad (4.3\text{-}11)$$

For $f_2$ equal to 1, a comparison of wall superheats given by Eqs. (4.3-5) and (4.3-11) suggests that the cavity diameter corresponds to half the thermal layer thickness. An expression for the heat flux corresponding to the wall superheat given by Eq. (4.3-11) is obtained as

$$\dot{q} = \frac{h_{\ell g}\rho_v \lambda_\ell}{8f_2\sigma T_{sat}}(\Delta T)^2 \quad (4.3\text{-}12)$$

To determine the range of cavities that can nucleate if the wall superheat exceeds the minimum wall superheat for nucleation, elimination of liquid temperature between Eqs. (4.3-6) and (4.3-7) yields a quadratic equation in terms of the diameter of the cavity as

$$D_c^2 - \frac{2f_1}{f_2}\delta D_c + \frac{8f_1^2\sigma T_{sat}\delta}{f_2\rho_v h_{\ell g}\Delta T} = 0 \quad (4.3\text{-}13)$$

or

$$D_{c_{1,2}} = \frac{f_1\delta}{f_2}\left[1 \pm \sqrt{1 - \frac{8f_2\sigma T_{sat}}{\rho_v h_{\ell g}\Delta T\delta}}\right] \quad (4.3\text{-}14)$$

In Figure 5, the intercepts of the dotted line representing temperature distribution in the thermal layer represent the range of cavities between $D_{c1}$ and $D_{c2}$ that can nucleate. In terms of the heat flux, Eq. (4.3-13) can be written as

$$\dot{q} = \frac{2f_1\lambda_\ell \Delta T}{f_2} - \frac{8f_1^2\sigma T_{sat}\lambda_\ell}{f_2\rho_v h_{\ell g}D_c^2} \quad (4.3\text{-}15)$$

For a given $D_c$, Eq. (4.3-15) represents an equation in two unknowns, namely $q$ and $\Delta T$. To solve explicitly for both, another relation between $q$ and $\Delta T$ is needed. This relation is provided by the correlations for single phase natural convection or forced convection that may be present on the heater surface prior to inception. In terms of the wall superheat, Eq. (4.3-13) can also be written as

$$\Delta T = \frac{\frac{4 f_1 \sigma T_{sat}}{\rho_v h_{\ell g} D_c}}{\left[1 - \frac{f_2 D_c}{f_1 2\delta}\right]} \quad (4.3\text{-}16)$$

For $D_c$ much smaller than $\delta$, the size of a nucleating cavity varies inversely with wall superheat, as was the case for Eq. (4.3-5).

As an alternative to Hsu's criterion, Mizukami (1975), Nishio (1985), and more recently, Wang and Dhir (1993a), have proposed that the instability of vapor nuclei in a cavity determines the inception superheat. The vapor nucleus is stable if the curvature of the interface increases with an increase in vapor volume or if it decreases with a decrease in vapor volume. Otherwise, the vapor bubble embryo or nucleus is unstable. If $K$ is the nondimensional modified curvature of interface, the stability criterion is written as

$$\frac{dK}{dV^*} > 0 \quad (4.3\text{-}17)$$

where $V^*$ is the dimensionless volume of the embryo. The minimum wall superheat required for nucleation will correspond to the value of $K$ for which the interface is unstable.

Figure 6 shows, for a spherical cavity with mouth angle of 30°, the nondimensional modified curvature of the interface as a function of the non-dimensional volume of the vapor bubble nucleus. The plotted results are for different contact angles and in the absence of any non-condensable gas. The curvature of the liquid-vapor interface is negative for $V^*$ just less than that corresponding to point A and is positive for $V^*$ larger than that for point A. The metastable position of entrapped vapor-liquid interface for a contact angle larger than the cavity mouth angle is represented by point A. The volume of trapped vapor is equal to the volume of the cavity $V_c$, so that $V^*$ corresponding to point A is equal to 1. Outside of the cavity, the interface is in stable equilibrium from point A to point D because $K$ increases with $V^*$. The maximum value of K occurs at points B, C, and D for contact angles of 150°, 120° and for a contact angle equal to or less than 90°, respectively. The values of $K_{max}$ can be determined from the geometric shapes shown for cases (1) and (2) in the inset of Figure 4 and can be expressed as

$$\begin{aligned} K_{max} &= 1 \quad \text{for } \phi < 90° \\ &= \sin \phi \quad \text{for } \phi > 90° \end{aligned} \quad (4.3\text{-}18)$$

Nucleation occurs beyond the point where the non-dimensional modified curvature

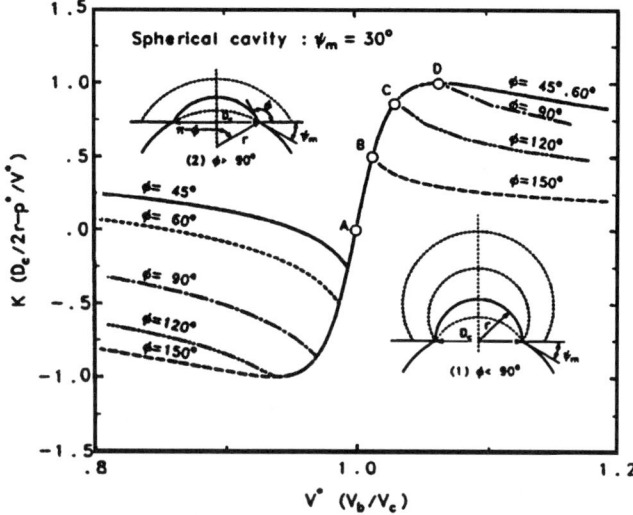

**Figure 6** Dimensionless modified curvature as a function of dimensionless volume of vapor bubble nucleus in a spherical cavity.

has its maximum value. As such, the incipient superheat is obtained as

$$\Delta T = \frac{4\sigma T_{\text{sat}}}{\rho_v h_{\ell g} D_c} K_{\max} \qquad (4.3\text{-}19)$$

The above expression of wall superheat at nucleation is obtained under the assumption that cavity diameter, $D_c$, is much smaller than the thermal layer thickness. Thus, in this limit, Eq. (4.3-16) suggests that $f_1$ is unity for $\phi < 90°$ and is equal to $\sin \phi$ for $\phi \geq 90°$. Or, for non-wetted surfaces, the required superheat is smaller than that given by Eq. (4.3-5) of Griffith and Wallis. Wang and Dhir (1993a), from their experiments on surfaces with different contact angles, have shown the general validity of Eq. (4.3-19).

## 4.4 BUBBLE DYNAMICS AND HEAT TRANSFER

After inception, a bubble continues to grow (in a saturated liquid) until forces causing it to detach from the surface exceed those pushing the bubble against the wall. After departure, liquid from the bulk fills the space vacated by the bubble, and the thermal layer at and around the nucleation site reforms (transient conduction). When the required superheat is attained at the tip of the vapor bubble embryo or the interface instability criterion is met, a new bubble starts to form at the same nucleation site, and the process repeats. Wall heat transfer in nucleate boiling results from natural convection on the heater surface areas not occupied by bubbles and from transient conduction and evaporation at and around nucleation sites.

### 4.4.1 Bubble Dynamics

Bubble dynamics includes the processes of bubble growth, bubble departure, and reformation of the thermal layer (waiting period). In the following, each one of these processes is described separately.

**4.4.1.1 Bubble growth.** Generally, two points of view with respect to the growth of a bubble on a heated surface have been put forth in the literature. One group of investigators has proposed that the growth of a bubble occurs as a result of evaporation all around the bubble interface. The energy for evaporation is supplied from the superheated liquid layer that surrounds the bubble since its inception. Bubble growth models similar to that proposed for growth of a vapor bubble in a sea of superheated liquid, such as that of Plesset and Zwick (1954), have been proposed. The bubble growth process on a heater surface, however, is more complex because the bubble shape continuously changes during the growth process, and superheated liquid is confined to only a thin region around the bubble. Mikic et al. (1970) used a geometric factor to relate the shape of a bubble growing on a heated surface to a perfect sphere, properly accounted for the thermal energy stored in the liquid layer prior to bubble inception, and obtained an analytical solution for the bubble growth rate. Their expression for the growth rate is

$$\frac{dD^*}{dt^*} = 2\left[t^* + 1 - \theta\left(\frac{t^*}{t^* + t_w^*}\right)^{1/2}\right]^{1/2} - t^{*1/2} \qquad (4.4\text{-}1)$$

where

$$D^* = \left(\frac{b\rho_v \Delta T\, h_{\ell g}}{\rho_\ell T_{\text{sat}}}\right)^{1/2}\left(\frac{\pi D}{12\kappa_\ell J_a^2}\right) \qquad (4.4\text{-}2)$$

$$t^* = \frac{b\rho_v \Delta T\, h_{\ell g}}{\rho_\ell T_{\text{sat}}}\left(\frac{\pi t}{12\kappa_\ell J_a^2}\right) \qquad (4.4\text{-}3)$$

$$\theta = \frac{T_w - T_b}{\Delta T} \qquad (4.4\text{-}4)$$

and

$$J_a = \frac{\rho_\ell c_{p\ell} \Delta T}{\rho_v h_{\ell g}} \qquad (4.4\text{-}5)$$

In Eq. (4.4-4), $T_b$ is the liquid bulk temperature, and in Eqs. (4.4-2) and (4.4-3), $b$ is a geometric parameter that has a value of 2/3 for a perfect sphere. A value of $\pi/7$ for $b$ has been suggested by Mikic et al. for a bubble attached to the heater surface.

The second point of view is that most of the evaporation occurs at the base of the bubble, in that the micro-layer between the vapor-liquid interface and the heater surface plays an important role. Snyder and Edwards (1956) were the first to propose this mechanism for evaporation. Subsequently, Moore and Mesler (1961) deduced the existence of a microlayer under the bubble from the oscillations in the temperature measured at the bubble release site. Cooper and Lloyd (1969) further confirmed the existence of the micro-layer. Using the lubrication theory for the liquid flow in the micro-layer, they deduced the average thickness of the microlayer underlying a bubble as

$$\delta = 0.8\sqrt{\nu_\ell t}$$

The contribution of the micro-layer to the total heat transfer rate depends on the area occupied by the micro-layer. As such, the empirical constant in the above equation for the average micro-layer thickness may not be realistic for bubbles formed on surfaces with widely varying contact angles. A complete theoretical treatment of the evolution of the micro-layer during bubble growth still does not exist in the literature.

**4.4.1.2 Bubble departure.** The diameter to which a bubble grows before departing is dictated by the balance of forces acting on the bubble. These forces are associated with the inertia of the liquid and vapor, liquid drag on the bubble, buoyancy, and surface tension.

Fritz (1935) correlated the bubble departure diameter by balancing buoyancy, which acts to lift the bubble from the surface, with the surface tension force, which tends to hold the bubble to the wall, so that

$$D_d = 0.0208\phi\sqrt{\frac{\sigma}{g(\rho_\ell - \rho_g)}} \qquad (4.4\text{-}6)$$

where $\phi$ is the contact angle measured in degrees. Though significant deviations of the bubble diameter at departure with respect to the above equation have been reported in the literature (especially at high pressures), Eq. (4.4-6) does provide a correct length scale for the boiling process. Several other expressions that are obtained either empirically or analytically by involving various forces acting on a bubble have been reported in the literature for bubble diameter at departure. These expressions (see, e.g., Hsu and Graham, 1976), however, are not always consistent with each other. Some investigators report an increase in bubble diameter at departure with wall superheat, whereas others find the bubble diameter at departure to be insensitive to or decrease with an increase in wall superheat. One reason for this discrepancy could be the merger of bubbles that occurs at high heat fluxes. Cole and Rohsenow (1969) correlated the bubble diameter at departure at low pressures as

$$D_d = 1.5 \times 10^{-4} \sqrt{\frac{\sigma}{g(\rho_\ell - \rho_v)}} Ja^{*5/4} \text{ for water} \qquad (4.4\text{-}7)$$

and

$$D_d = 4.65 \times 10^{-4} \sqrt{\frac{\sigma}{g(\rho_\ell - \rho_v)}} Ja^{*5/4} \text{ for other liquids} \qquad (4.4\text{-}8)$$

where

$$Ja^* = \frac{\rho_\ell c_{p\ell} T_{\text{sat}}}{\rho_v h_{\ell g}} \qquad (4.4\text{-}9)$$

Gorenflo et al. (1986) have proposed an expression for bubble diameter at departure at high heat fluxes as

$$D_d = C_1 \left( \frac{Ja^4 \lambda_\ell^2}{g} \right)^{1/3} \left[ 1 + \left( 1 + \frac{2\pi}{3Ja} \right)^{1/2} \right]^{4/3} \qquad (4.4\text{-}10)$$

Different values of the proportionality constant were suggested for different liquids.

Knowing the growth rate and the diameter to which a bubble grows before departing, the growth time, $t_g$, can be calculated. After bubble departure, cooler bulk liquid fills the space vacated by the bubble. Schlieren pictures by Hsu and Graham (1976) show that an area, about two times the bubble diameter at departure, is influenced by bubble motion. As a result, the thermal layer reforms over an area of a circle of diameter $2D_d$ surrounding the nucleation site. A new bubble at this location will now grow until the superheated liquid layer is reestablished and the inception criterion is satisfied. The time taken by the thermal layer to develop prior to inception is termed the *waiting period*. Han and Griffith (1965) obtained an analytical expression for the waiting period by assuming the liquid layer to be semi-infinite and by substituting the expression for the thermal layer thickness in Eq. (4.3-16) as

$$t_w = \left[ \frac{f_2 D_c}{2\sqrt{\pi \kappa_\ell} f_1 \left[ 1 - \frac{4 f_1 \sigma T_{\text{sat}}}{\Delta T \rho_v h_{\ell g} D_c} \right]} \right]^2 \qquad (4.4\text{-}11)$$

It is seen from Eq. (4.4-11) that the waiting time will first decrease and then increase with cavity size. However, it will continuously decrease as the wall superheat is increased.

**4.4.1.3 Bubble release frequency.** Conceivably, a theoretical evaluation of the bubble release frequency can be made from expressions for the waiting time, $t_w$, and the growth time, $t_g$ (the growth time can be determined by knowing the growth rate and bubble diameter at departure). In fact, such an approach meets with little success when a comparison is made with the data. Some of the reasons for the discrepancy are the following:

1. Evaporation takes place at the base and at the surface of the bubbles, and the growth models reported in the literature generally do not account for both.
2. Generally, large cavities yield large bubbles. This in turn drastically alters the growth time from cavity to cavity.
3. Bubble activity, heat transfer, and fluid motion in the vicinity of an active site can influence the growth pattern as well as the waiting period.
4. Bubble shape continuously changes during the growth period.

Thus, correlations have been reported in the literature that include both the bubble diameter at departure and the bubble release frequency. One of the most comprehensive correlations of this type is given by Malenkov (1971). According to this correlation, the product of bubble release frequency, $f$, and diameter at departure are correlated as

$$f D_d = \frac{V_d}{\pi \left(1 - \dfrac{1}{1 + V_d \rho_v h_{\ell g}/\dot{q}}\right)} \qquad (4.4\text{-}12)$$

where

$$V_d = \left[\frac{D_d g(\rho_\ell - \rho_v)}{2(\rho_\ell + \rho_v)} + \frac{2\sigma}{D_d(\rho_\ell + \rho_v)}\right]^{1/2} \qquad (4.4\text{-}13)$$

## 4.5 NUCLEATION SITE DENSITY

As the wall superheat or heat flux is increased, the number density of sites that become active increases. Since adding new nucleation sites influences the rate of heat transfer from the surface, knowledge of nucleation site density as a function of wall superheat is necessary if a credible model for prediction of nucleate boiling is to be developed. In the earlier studies, listed by Hsu and Graham (1976), it was noted that the density of active nucleation sites increases approximately as the square of the heat flux or as the 4th to 6th power of wall superheat. In the listed studies, no attempt was made to relate either the proportionality constant or the exponent with the surface characteristics.

Kocamustafagoullari and Ishii (1983) have correlated the cumulative nucleation site density reported by various investigators for water boiling on a variety of surfaces at pressures varying from 1–198 atm as

$$N_a^* = \left[D_c^{*-4.4} F(\rho^*)\right]^{1/4.4} \qquad (4.5\text{-}1)$$

where

$$N_a^* = N_a D_d^2; \qquad D_c^* = D_c/D_d \qquad (4.5\text{-}2)$$

and

$$F(\rho^*) = 2.157 \times 10^{-7} \rho^{*-3.2} (1 + 0.0049\rho^*)^{4.13} \qquad (4.5\text{-}3)$$

In the above equations, $D_d$ is the bubble diameter at departure and is obtained by multiplying Eq. (4.4-6) of Fritz (1935) by $0.0012(\rho^*)^{0.9}$. The parameters $\rho^*$ and $D_c$ are defined as

$$\rho^* = \frac{\rho_\ell - \rho_v}{\rho_v} \qquad (4.5\text{-}4)$$

$$D_c = 4\sigma[1 + (\rho_\ell/\rho_v)]/p_\ell \cdot \{\exp[h_{fg}(T_v - T_{\text{sat}})/(R_v T_v T_{\text{sat}})] - 1\} \qquad (4.5\text{-}5)$$

In Eq. (4.5-5), $T_v$ is the temperature of vapor, $p_l$ is the liquid pressure, and $R_v$ is the gas constant for vapor. At moderate pressures, Eq. (4.5-5) reduces to Eq. (4.3-16), when cavity diameter is assumed to be much smaller than the thickness of the thermal layer.

Cornwell and Brown (1978) have made a systematic study of active nucleation sites on copper surfaces during the boiling of water at 1 atm pressure. Their study was limited to low heat fluxes and to surface conditions ranging from a smooth to a scratched rough surface. From their work, it was concluded that the active site density varied with wall superheat as

$$Na \sim \Delta T^{4.5} \qquad (4.5\text{-}6)$$

The proportionality constant in Eq. (4.5-6) was found to increase with surface roughness, but the exponent on $\Delta T$ was independent of surface roughness. Mikic and Rohsenow (1969a) have proposed that on commercial surfaces, the cumulative number of active sites per unit heater area can be assumed to vary in partial nucleate boiling as

$$Na \sim \left(\frac{D_s}{D_c}\right)^m \qquad (4.5\text{-}7)$$

where $D_s$ is the diameter of the largest active cavity present on the surface and $m$ is an empirical constant. The size, $D_c$, of a cavity that nucleates at a wall superheat $\Delta T$ is obtained from Eq. (4.3-5). Bier et al. (1978), on the other hand, have deduced an expression for active site density from heat transfer data as

$$\ell n N_a = \ell n N_{\max} \left[1 - \left(\frac{D_c}{D_s}\right)^m\right] \qquad (4.5\text{-}8)$$

In Eq. (4.5-8), $N_{\max}$ is the maximum value of $N_a$, which occurs at $D_c = 0$. The value of $m$ was found to depend on the manner in which a surface was prepared.

With Freon 115 or Freon 11 boiling on a chemically etched copper surface and on a turned surface, values of 0.42 and 0.26, respectively, have been noted for $m$. This observation is not consistent with the conclusion of Cornwell and Brown (1978). In the heat transfer experiments, the reduced pressure was varied from 0.0037 to 0.9. It was found that to correlate the data at low and high saturation pressures, some changes in the functional form of Eq. (4.5-8) are necessary.

Wang and Dhir (1993a, 1993b) have studied the effect of surface wettability during boiling of saturated water at one atm pressure on mirror finish copper surfaces. They have also provided a mechanistic approach for relating the cavities that are present on the surface to the cavities that actually nucleate.

The number density of all types of cavities was found to correlate as

$$N_s \text{(sites/cm}^2\text{)} = \begin{array}{ll} 9.0 \times 10^3 D_c^{-2.0} & D_c \geq 5.8 \ \mu\text{m} \\ 10.3 + 2.4 \times 10^6 D_c^{-5.2} & 3.5 \leq D_c \leq 5.8 \ \mu\text{m} \\ 2214 + 1.0 \times 10^6 D_c^{-5.4} & D_c \leq 3.5 \ \mu\text{m} \end{array} \quad (4.5\text{-}9)$$

In Eq. (4.5-9), $D_c$ is measured in $\mu$m.

From these expressions, the cumulative number density of reservoir cavities (these were cavities that were proposed to nucleate) with mouth angle, $\psi_m$, less than 90° was correlated as

$$N_{as} \text{(sites/cm}^2\text{)} = 5.8 \times 10^5 D_c^{-5.4} \quad (4.5\text{-}10)$$

Wang and Dhir (1993a, 1993b) have also noted that for spherical cavities, the number density of cavities with mouth angle less than $\psi_m^\circ$ can be approximately written as

$$N_{as} = (\psi_m^\circ) = \frac{1 - \cos \psi_m^\circ}{2} N_s \quad (4.5\text{-}11)$$

Since for cavities to trap gas/vapor, the cavity mouth angle $\psi_m$ should be less than the contact angle, the cumulative number density of cavities that become active can be written as

$$N_a(\phi) = P_{as}(\phi, \psi_m^\circ) N_{as}(\psi_m^\circ) \quad (4.5\text{-}12)$$

where

$$P_{as}(\phi, \psi_m^\circ) = \frac{1 - \cos \phi}{1 - \cos \psi_m^\circ} \quad (4.5\text{-}13)$$

To obtain the cumulative number density of active sites as a function of wall superheat, Eq. (4.5-12) must be corrected to

$$N_a(\phi, \Delta T) = \frac{N_a(\phi)}{K_{max}} \quad (4.5\text{-}14)$$

where $K_{max}$ is given by Eq. (4.3-18). According to Eq. (4.5-10), the active nucleation site density should vary as $\Delta T^{5.4}$. Figure 7 shows a comparison of the

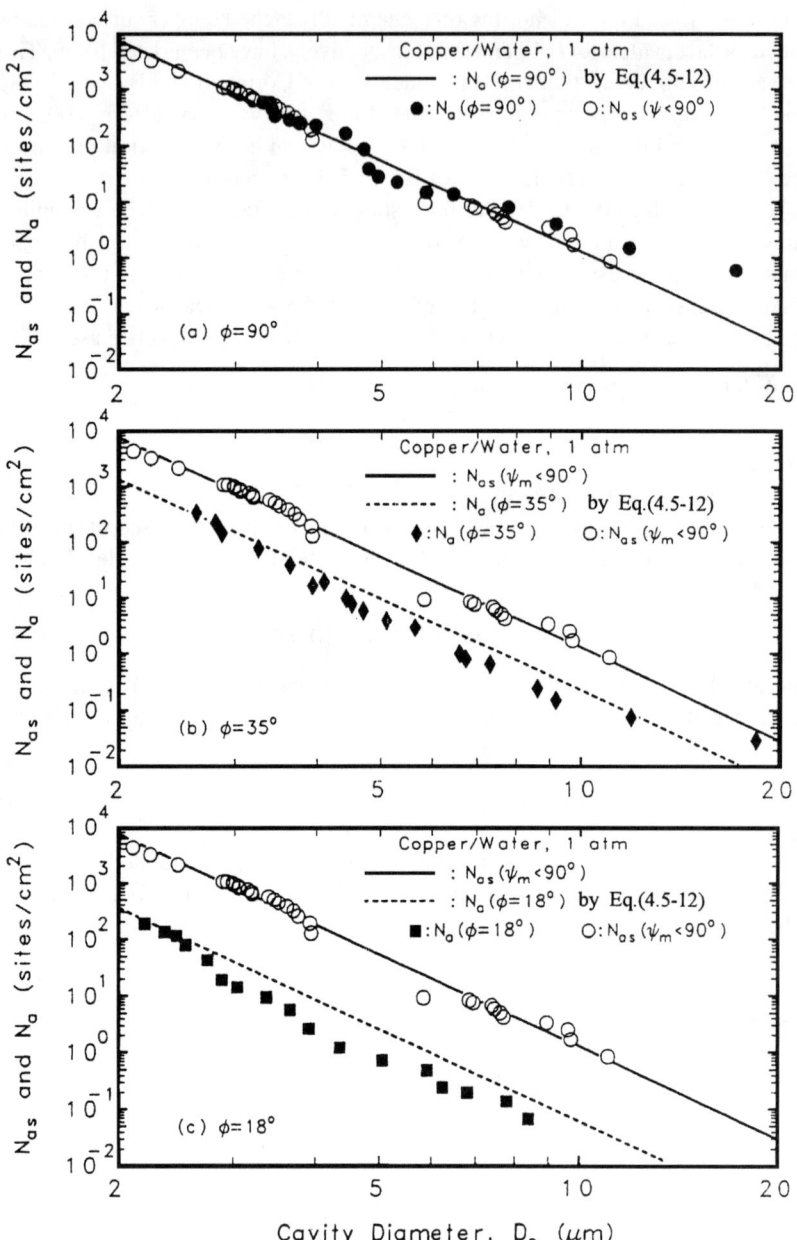

**Figure 7** Comparison of the predicted and the measured active site density for contact angles of 90, 35, and 18°.

measured and predicted number density of active sites for different contact angles. Wang and Dhir have also found the average nearest neighbor distance, $\ell$, to correlate with nucleation site density as

$$\ell = \frac{0.84}{\sqrt{N_a}} \tag{4.5-15}$$

## 4.6 HEAT TRANSFER IN NUCLEATE BOILING

### 4.6.1 Mechanistic Models

In partial nucleate boiling or the isolated bubble regime, transient conduction into liquid adjacent to the wall is probably the most important mechanism for heat removal from an upward facing horizontal surface. After bubble inception, the superheated liquid layer is pushed outward and mixes with the bulk liquid. The bubble acts like a pump in removing hot liquid from the surface and replacing it with cold liquid. This mechanism was originally proposed by Forster and Greif (1959). Combining the contribution of transient conduction on and around nucleation sites, micro-layer evaporation underneath the bubbles, and natural convection on inactive areas of the heater, an expression for partial nucleate boiling heat flux is obtained as

$$\dot{q} = \frac{K_1^2}{2} \sqrt{\pi(\lambda \rho c_p)_\ell f} \, D_d^2 N_a \Delta T + \left(1 - \frac{K_1^2}{2} N_a \pi D_d^2\right) \bar{\alpha}_{nc} \Delta T$$
$$+ \bar{\alpha}_{ev} \Delta T N_a \frac{\pi}{4} D_d^2 \tag{4.6-1}$$

Only the first two terms in the above equation were included in the original model proposed by Mikic and Rohsenow (1969a). The evaporation at the bubble boundary is included in the first term, which represents the transient conduction in the liquid. The addition of the last term on the right hand side of Eq. (4.6-1) was suggested by Judd and Hwang (1976). This term accounts for the microlayer evaporation at the base of bubbles. For Eq. (4.6-1) to serve as a predictive tool, the following must be known: the bubble diameter at departure, $D_d$; bubble release frequency, $f$; the proportionality constant, $K_1$, for the bubble area of influence; number density, $N_a$, of active sites; and average heat transfer coefficients, $\bar{\alpha}_{nc}$ and $\bar{\alpha}_{ev}$, for natural convection and microlayer evaporation, respectively. Using empirical correlations for several of these parameters, Mikic and Rohsenow (1969a) justified the validity of Eq. (4.6-1) when the third term on the right hand side was not included. Judd and Hwang (1976), in matching the heat fluxes predicted from Eq. (4.6-1) with those observed in experiments in which dichloromethane was boiled on a glass surface, relied on the measured values of micro-layer thickness to evaluate $\bar{\alpha}_{ev}$ and on the assumption that $K_1^2$ had a value of 1.8. Additionally, experimentally

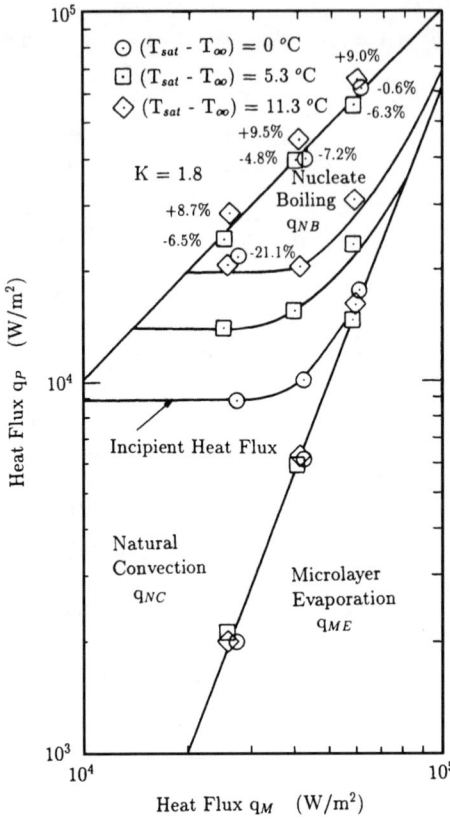

**Figure 8** Relative contribution of various mechanisms to nucleate boiling heat flux (Judd and Hwang, 1976).

measured values of active nucleation site density and bubble release frequency were used in the model. Figure 8 shows their data and predictions. It is seen that at the total measured heat flux of 6 w/cm$^2$, about one third of the energy is dissipated through evaporation at the bubble base.

The data plotted in Figure 8 show that at high heat fluxes or in fully developed nucleate boiling, most of the energy from the heater is removed by evaporation. A similar observation can be made from the measurement of Paul and Abdel-Khalik (1983) and Ammerman et al. (1996) on horizontal cylinders. The results of all of these studies are in general agreement with the findings of Gaertner (1965)—that after the first transition, evaporation is the dominant mode of heat transfer. According to Gaertner, most evaporation occurs at the periphery of vapor stems. Energy for the phase change is supplied by the superheated liquid layer in which the stems are implanted. Thus, the boiling heat flux can be calculated if the fractional area occupied by the vapor stems and the thickness of the thermal layer are known. The heater area fraction occupied by the vapor stems is equal to the product of the number density of stems and the area occupied by one stem. Alternatively, the heat flux can also be calculated if the vaporization rate per stem and number density of active sites are known. Lay and Dhir (1994) have used the latter approach to predict the fully developed nucleate boiling heat flux. By assuming that the duration for which vapor stems exist on the heater is much larger than the time needed to form the stems, Lay and Dhir have carried out a quasi-static analysis to determine the maximum diameter of vapor stems as a function of wall superheat. The shape of the vapor stem was found to depend on the value that was chosen for the Hamaker constant. From the analysis, the vaporization rate per stem could be calculated as a function of wall superheat. Using the data of Wang and Dhir (1993a, 1993b) for density of active sites, they found the predicted heat fluxes to show good agreement with the data. This approach needs to be verified with data from other sources.

## 4.6.2 Correlations

The augmented version of the model by Mikic and Rohsenow requires the use of several empirical constants, and it is not in a form that it can be readily used to predict nucleate boiling heat flux as a function of wall superheat. Instead, the earlier correlation of Rohsenow (1952), which involves the use of three empirical constants, has enjoyed wide popularity. According to this correlation, the functional dependence of partial nucleate boiling heat flux on wall superheat can be written as

$$\frac{\dot{q}\sqrt{\frac{\sigma}{g(\rho_\ell - \rho_v)}}}{\mu_\ell h_{\ell g}} = C_s^{-3} \left(\frac{c_{p\ell}\Delta T}{h_{\ell g}}\right)^3 \left(\frac{\mu_\ell c_{p\ell}}{\lambda_l}\right)^{n_1} \quad (4.6\text{-}2)$$

where $C_s$ depends on heater material and fluid combination. The exponent, $n_1$, has a value of 3.0 for water and 5.1 for all other liquids. It should be noted that since gravity did not vary in the data that was used to develop Eq. (4.6-2), the parameter, $g$, should be considered as a dimensional constant. Also, in arriving at the correlation (Eq. [4.6-2]), no attempt was made to relate the values of $C_s$ to surface conditions (e.g., roughness or cleanliness), but the correlation was shown to be applicable at different system pressures. Table 1 gives values of $C_s$ for different fluid-solid combinations.

From Eq. (4.6-2), it can be seen that the magnitude of heat flux at a given wall superheat is very sensitive to the values of $C_s$. A factor of about two change in $C_s$ can cause almost an order of magnitude change in heat flux. As such, the values given in Table 1 must be considered as a guide and, for a particular application, it is

**Table 1 Values of constant $C_s$ in Rohsenow's correlation**

| Fluid | Solid | $C_s$ |
| --- | --- | --- |
| Water | Nickel | 0.006 |
| Water | Platinum | 0.013 |
| Water | Copper | 0.013 |
| Water | Brass | 0.006 |
| Benzene | Chromium | 0.010 |
| Carbon tetrachloride | Copper | 0.013 |
| Ethanol | Chromium | 0.0027 |
| Isopropanol | Copper | 0.0025 |
| n-Butanol | Copper | 0.003 |
| N-pentane | Chromium | 0.015 |

always wise to determine the value of constant $C_s$ experimentally for conditions of particular interest. Although the correlation was derived for partial nucleate boiling, it has generally been successfully extended to fully developed nucleate boiling. Liaw and Dhir (1989) have systematically studied the effect of wettability of a polished copper surface on nucleate boiling of saturated water at one atmosphere pressure. Their data show that the empirical constant $C_s$ is a function of the contact angle, and it increases with a decrease in contact angle. Table 2 gives the values of constant $C_s$ for different static contact angles.

Recently, Stephan and Abdelsalam (1980) have developed a comprehensive correlation for saturated nucleate pool boiling of different liquids. In developing these correlations, they have divided the liquids into four groups: (i) water, (ii) hydrocarbons, (iii) cryogenic liquids, and (iv) refrigerants. In these correlations, dimensionless heat transfer coefficients (Nusselt numbers) were written in terms of several dimensionless parameters that depend on fluid and solid properties. The important fluid property groups were identified through regression analysis, and the values of exponents of the property groups were obtained by matching predictions with the data. In developing the correlations, data from different heater

**Table 2 Dependence of $C_s$ on contact angle**

| Contact angle | $C_s$ |
| --- | --- |
| 14° | 0.0209 |
| 27° | 0.0202 |
| 38° | 0.0194 |
| 69° | 0.0186 |
| 90° | 0.0172 |

geometries (such as flat plates, horizontal cylinders, vertical cylinders, etc.) were used. Also, a mean surface roughness of 1 mm was assumed for the heaters. Their correlations for different liquids are:

Water:
$$Nu = 2.46 \times 10^6 \cdot X_1^{.673} \cdot X_4^{-1.58} \cdot X_3^{1.26} \cdot X_8^{5.22} \quad (4.6\text{-}3)$$
for $\quad 10^{-4} \leq p/p_c \leq 0.886 \quad \text{and} \quad \phi = 45°$

Hydrocarbons:
$$Nu = 0.0546 \left(X_5^{0.5} \cdot X_1\right)^{0.67} \cdot X_8^{4.33} \cdot X_4^{0.248} \quad (4.6\text{-}4)$$
for $\quad 5.7 \times 10^{-3} \leq p/p_c \leq 0.9 \quad \text{and} \quad \phi = 35°$

Cryogenic Liquids:
$$Nu = 4.82 X_1^{0.624} \cdot X_7^{0.117} \cdot X_5^{0.257} \cdot X_3^{0.374} \cdot X_4^{-0.329} \quad (4.6\text{-}5)$$
for $\quad 4.0 \times 10^{-3} \leq p/p_c \leq 0.97 \quad \text{and} \quad \phi = 1°$

Refrigerants:
$$Nu = 207 X_1^{0.745} \cdot X_5^{0.581} \cdot X_6^{0.533} \quad (4.6\text{-}6)$$
for $\quad 3.0 \times 10^{-3} \leq p/p_c \leq 0.78 \quad \text{and} \quad \phi = 35°$

All of the above equations correlate the data within ±15% mean absolute error. The Nusselt number and various dimensionless groups $X_1 \ldots X_8$ are defined as

$$Nu = \frac{\dot{q} D_d}{\Delta T \lambda_\ell}$$

$$X_1 = \frac{\dot{q} D_d}{\lambda_\ell T_{\text{sat}}} \qquad X_5 = \frac{\rho_v}{\rho_\ell}$$

$$X_2 = \frac{\kappa_\ell^2 \rho_\ell}{\sigma D_d} \qquad X_6 = \frac{\nu_\ell}{\kappa_\ell}$$

$$X_3 = \frac{c_{p\ell} T_{\text{sat}} D_d^2}{\kappa_\ell^2} \qquad X_7 = \frac{(\rho c_p \lambda)_s}{(\rho c_p \lambda)_\ell}$$

$$X_4 = \frac{h_{\ell g} D_d^2}{\kappa_\ell^2} \qquad X_8 = \frac{\rho_\ell - \rho_v}{\rho_\ell}$$

Stephan and Abdelsalam have also given a generalized correlation that is applicable to all liquids, but has a larger mean absolute error:
$$N_u = 0.23 X_1^{0.674} \cdot X_5^{0.297} \cdot X_4^{0.371} \cdot X_8^{-1.73} \cdot X_2^{0.35} \quad (4.6\text{-}7)$$
It should be noted that all of these correlations suggest that $q \sim \Delta T^{3 \text{ to } 4}$.

More recently, Cooper (1984) has proposed a much simpler correlation for saturated nucleate pool boiling. His correlation employs reduced pressure, molecular weight, and surface roughness as the correlating parameters. This correlation for a flat plate can be written as

$$\frac{(\dot{q})^{1/3}}{\Delta T} = 55.0 \left(\frac{p}{p_c}\right)^{0.12-0.21\log_{10} R_p} \cdot \left(-\log_{10} \frac{p}{p_c}\right)^{-0.55} \cdot M^{-0.50} \quad (4.6\text{-}8)$$

In the above equation, the roughness, $R_p$, is measured in microns, and $M$ is the molecular weight, $\Delta T$ is measured in degrees $K$, and $q$ is given in W/m². Cooper suggests that for application of the correlation to horizontal cylinders, the lead constant on the right hand side should be increased to 95. It should be noted that correlation Eq. (4.6-8) accounts for roughness but does not account for the variations in degree of surface wettability. Similarly, Eqs. (4.6-3) to (4.6-6) are for a specific contact angle and for an assumed value of roughness. Also, while Eq. (4.6-8) accounts for geometry of the heater, Eqs. (4.6-3) to (4.6-6) are independent of the heater geometry. Equation (4.6-8) is easy to use and is recommended. However, any of the equations should be used with caution, as large derivations between actual data and predictions from these equations can occur when the conditions under which the data used in developing the correlation are not duplicated.

### 4.6.3 Future Research Needs

The correlations described earlier are useful in providing dependence of nucleate boiling heat fluxes on wall superheat over the range of parameters that has formed the basis of these correlations. However, the utility of these correlations diminishes as we apply them to situations involving parameters that go beyond the range used in the correlations. As a result, there is a significant impetus to develop mechanistic models for nucleate boiling. The mechanistic models developed in the literature have not progressed much in the past because they themselves have employed parameters that have an empirical basis. These models have also excluded the interactions that occur between simultaneously occurring processes. It is believed that significant further progress in predicting nucleate boiling heat fluxes can be made by using complete numerical simulation of bubble growth, departure and merger processes, and associated heat transfer in the vicinity of an active nucleation site. Also, mechanistic models need to be incorporated for the prediction of density of active nucleation sites. The models of physical processes, such as the formation of a micro-layer underneath the bubbles, shape of advancing and receding interfaces, heat transfer around an evolving interface, and heat transfer on the unpopulated areas of the heater as influenced by the flow field created by bubble growth/departure, need to be verified with detailed experimental measurements. It should be stressed that a macroscopic model need not only describe macroscopic data, but it should also be verifiable at the sub-model/ microscale level.

## 4.7 POOL BOILING IN BINARY SYSTEMS

### 4.7.1 Introduction

Boiling of binary and multi-component mixtures constitutes an important process in chemical, process, air-separation, refrigeration, and many other industrial applications. Reboilers feeding the vapors to distillation columns and flooded evaporators generally employ pool boiling, while the in-tube evaporation process involves flow boiling. Although the multi-component boiling is of greater interest from a process standpoint, a fundamental understanding can be obtained first through a study of pool boiling heat transfer with binary mixtures.

The vapor-liquid equilibrium phase diagram introduced earlier in Chapter 1 provides an insight into the associated concentration gradient and changes in saturation temperature around a growing bubble in nucleate boiling for binary mixtures. Nucleation criterion for pure components may be applied to mixtures; however, there is no work reported on this aspect in literature. As a bubble grows, the more volatile component evaporates preferentially at the liquid-vapor interface, setting up a concentration gradient in the liquid surrounding the interface. This additional mass transfer resistance along with the associated rise in interface temperature causes deterioration in heat transfer with mixtures. A summary of available literature and recommended model and correlations are presented in this section.

### 4.7.2 Heat Transfer Correlations

There are a number of correlating schemes proposed in literature for predicting pool boiling heat transfer coefficient for binary mixtures. Success of a purely theoretical treatment has been limited, and many investigators have generally resorted to empirical methods. A detailed review of these correlations is provided by Kandlikar (1998).

Calus and Rice (1972) incorporated the diffusion resistance term derived by Scriven (1959) and Van Stralen (1966, 1967) and developed a widely known correlation modifying the single-phase convection equation. Calus and Leonidopoulos (1974) effectively employed a linear mass fraction averaged heat transfer coefficient of the pure components and modified it with the diffusion resistance term. Although this term affects the heat transfer rate, its effect on heat transfer was not clearly derived. Calus and Leonidopoulos' equation is given below.

$$\Delta T = (x_1 \Delta T_1 + x_2 \Delta T_2) \left[ 1 + \left( \frac{\kappa}{D_{12}} \right) \left( \frac{c_p}{\Delta h_{1g}} \right) \frac{dT}{dx} \right] \quad (4.7\text{-}1)$$

Equation (4.7-1) is seen to underpredict the results considerably. Stephan and Körner (1969) recognized the importance of the term $|y_1 - x_1|$, representing the difference between the liquid and vapor phase mass concentrations in the reduction of binary heat transfer. Schlünder (1982) introduced the difference between the saturation temperatures of the pure components at the same pressure as a parameter in his correlating scheme. He also introduced the convective mass transfer coefficient at the interface. In the absence of any reliable method to predict this coefficient, it was treated as an empirical constant specific to a system. Thome (1983) recognized the need to account for the rise in the saturation temperature at the liquid-vapor interface of a bubble. He introduced the boiling range (difference between the dew point and bubble point temperatures at a given composition) as a parameter in reducing the available temperature difference. Later, Thome and Shakir (1987) introduced the mass transfer correction factor proposed by Schlünder (1982). Wenzel et al. (1995) followed a similar approach, but set out to obtain the actual value of the interface concentration by applying the mass transfer equation at the bubble boundary. This approach required knowledge of the mass transfer coefficient at the interface. It was empirically determined to be $10^{-4}$ m/s. The interface concentration was then used to determine the interface temperature.

Fujita et al. (1996) developed an empirical correlation from their own experimental data on methanol/water, ethanol/water, methanol/ethanol, ethanol/n-butanol, methanol/benzene, benzene/n-heptane, and water/ethylene glycol systems. It incorporates several key features of earlier correlations, and is reproduced below.

$$\alpha = \frac{(\tilde{x}_1/\alpha_1 + \tilde{x}_2/\alpha_2)^{-1}}{1 + \left\{1 - \exp\left[-2.8\dfrac{\tilde{x}_1\Delta T_1 + \tilde{x}_2\Delta T_2}{T_{sat,2}|_p - T_{sat,1}|_p}\right]\right\}\left\{\dfrac{T_{dp} - T_{bp}}{\tilde{x}_1\Delta T_1 + \tilde{x}_2\Delta T_2}\right\}} \quad (4.7\text{-}2)$$

$\alpha_1$, $\alpha_2$, and $\Delta T_1$, $\Delta T_2$ are the heat transfer coefficients and wall superheat values of the pure components, respectively, and $T_{sat,1}|_p$ and $T_{sat,2}|_p$ refer to saturation temperatures of the pure components at the system pressure. Component 1 is the more volatile component with a lower boiling point. $T_{dp}$ and $T_{bp}$ are the dew point and bubble point temperatures, respectively. Equation (4.7-2) predicts the parent data sets within less than 20%, but larger deviations are observed with the refrigerant mixture data from Jungnickel et al. (1979) for R-22/R-12 and R23/R-12 systems.

The theoretical model presented by Kandlikar (1998) first defines a pseudo single-component heat transfer coefficient for mixtures. The effect of mass diffusion and changes in saturation temperature are considered by obtaining the interface concentration under diffusion-controlled bubble growth conditions. This approach eliminates the need for an empirical value for mass transfer coefficient in the liquid near the interface as used by the previous investigators (e.g., Schlünder,

### 4.7.3 Pseudo-Single Component Heat Transfer Coefficient, $\alpha_{PSC}$

Differences in pool boiling of mixtures and pure components arise due to (i) the changes in thermodynamic and thermophysical properties of the mixtures, and (ii) the presence of a mass transfer resistance to the more volatile component diffusing to the interface of a nucleating bubble. To account for the property effects before introducing the mass transfer resistance, many investigators have employed an ideal heat transfer coefficient for the mixture, $\alpha_{id}$. It is calculated from a pure component pool boiling correlation with the mixture properties. Alternatively, when the pure component pool boiling data is available, a mole-fraction or mass-fraction averaged value of pure component coefficients is emplyoed for $\alpha_{id}$. One widely used equation is the reciprocal mole fraction averaged $\alpha$ for the pure components at the same temperature or pressure:

$$\alpha_{id} = \left( \frac{\tilde{x}_1}{\alpha_1|_{p \text{ or } T}} + \frac{\tilde{x}_2}{\alpha_2|_{p \text{ or } T}} \right)^{-1} \tag{4.7-3}$$

Calus and Leonidopoulos (1974) employed the mass-fraction average value in defining $\alpha_{id}$.

The "ideal" coefficient, $\alpha_{id}$, does not incorporate actual mixture properties. To overcome this difficulty, Kandlikar (1998) proposed a pseudo single-component coefficient, $\alpha_{PSC}$, which utilizes an averaging equation between the pure component values, further modified by a property correction factor derived from the Stephan and Abdelsalem (1980) correlation. The final form of the equation for $\alpha_{PSC}$ is as follows:

$$\alpha_{PSC} = \alpha_{avg} \left( \frac{T_{sat,m}}{T_{sat,avg}} \right)^{-0.674} \left( \frac{\Delta h_{LG,m}}{\Delta h_{LG,avg}} \right)^{0.371} \left( \frac{\rho_{G,m}}{\rho_{G,avg}} \right)^{0.297}$$

$$\times \left( \frac{\sigma_m}{\sigma_{avg}} \right)^{-0.317} \left( \frac{\lambda_{L,m}}{\lambda_{L,avg}} \right)^{0.284} \tag{4.7-4}$$

where $\alpha_{avg}$ is obtained from the following equation,

$$\alpha_{avg} = 0.5 \left[ (x_1 \alpha_1 + x_2 \alpha_2) + \left( \frac{x_1}{\alpha_1} + \frac{x_2}{\alpha_2} \right)^{-1} \right] \tag{4.7-5}$$

The subscript m in the individual properties, $\Delta h_{LG}$, $\rho_G$, $\sigma$, and $\lambda_L$, refers to the actual mixture properties, while the subscript avg refers to mass fraction averaged properties. Thus,

$$\Delta h_{LG,avg} = x_1 \Delta h_{LG,1} + x_2 \Delta h_{LG,2} \tag{4.7-6}$$

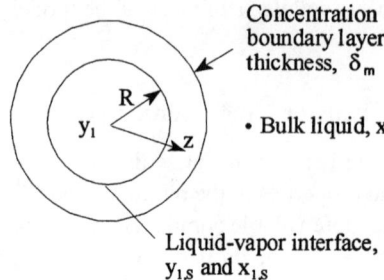

**Figure 9** Schematic representation of concentrations around a bubble growing in a binary mixture.

Similar equations are obtained for $\rho_{G,avg}$, $\rho_{avg}$, and $\lambda_{L,avg}$. One major advantage of using $\alpha_{PSC}$ is that the actual property variations are taken into account, and a sudden change in a property, such as surface tension, with the addition of the second component is reflected in the heat transfer coefficient through Eq. (4.7-4). The effect of adding a surfactant on the heat transfer coefficient is therefore seen through the negative exponent of $-0.317$ in the surface tension ratio. However, if the property variations do not deviate far from a linear mass-fraction average value or as a first approximation, $\alpha_{PSC}$ may be assumed to be equal to $\alpha_{avg}$ without applying any correction given in (4.7-4).

### 4.7.4 Theoretical Analysis for Pool Boiling Heat Transfer with Binary Mixtures

Consider a control volume surrounding a spherical bubble (the analysis is equally applicable to a truncated bubble shape), as shown in Figure 9. Applying the mass conservation equation around the bubble within the boundary layer thickness $\delta_m$ and the vapor inside, the average concentration in the boundary layer is obtained.

$$x_{1,BL,avg} = x_1 - \frac{1}{3}\frac{R}{\delta_m}\frac{\rho_G}{\rho_L}(y_{1,s} - x_1) \qquad (4.7\text{-}7)$$

The concentration gradient in the boundary layer is obtained following the 1-D analysis by Mikic and Rohsenow (1969b) under the assumption of a planar interface.

$$\frac{x_{1,z} - x_{1,s}}{x_1 - x_{1,s}} = erf\left[\frac{z}{2\sqrt{D_{12}t}}\right] \qquad (4.7\text{-}8)$$

The boundary layer thickness is estimated as $\delta_m = (\pi D_{12} t)^{1/2}$. Introducing $\delta_m$ in Eq. (4.7-8) and integrating over the boundary layer, the average concentration is obtained as

$$\frac{x_{1,BL,avg} - x_1}{x_{1,s} - x_1} = 0.313 \qquad (4.7\text{-}9)$$

Comparing Eqs. (4.7-7) and (4.7-9), $x_{1,s}$ is obtained.

$$x_{1,s} = x_1 - 1.06 \frac{R}{\delta_m} \frac{\rho_G}{\rho_L}(y_{1,s} - x_1) \tag{4.7-10}$$

The ratio $R/\delta_m$ reaches an asymptotic value and is given by Van Stralen (1975) as

$$\frac{R}{\delta_m} = \frac{2}{\pi} Ja_0 \left(\frac{\kappa}{D_{12}}\right)^{1/2} \tag{4.7-11}$$

Combining Eqs. (4.7-10) and (4.7-11), the interface concentration is obtained.

$$x_{1,s} = x_1 - \frac{2.13}{\pi} Ja_0 \left(\frac{\kappa}{D_{12}}\right)^{1/2} \frac{\rho_G}{\rho_L}(y_{1,s} - x_1) \tag{4.7-12}$$

where

$$Ja_0 = \frac{T_w - T_{sat}}{\frac{\rho_G}{\rho_L}\left[\frac{\Delta h_{LG}}{c_{p,L}} + \left(\frac{\kappa}{D_{12}}\right)^{1/2} \frac{\Delta T_s}{g}\right]} \tag{4.7-13}$$

$$\Delta T_s = T_{sat,s} - T_{sat} \tag{4.7-14}$$

and

$$g = \frac{x_1 - x_{1,s}}{y_{1,s} - x_{1,s}} \tag{4.7-15}$$

The subscript s refers to the interface condition. The instantaneous heat transfer rate at the interface in the absence of mass diffusion is obtained from the transient heat conduction equation

$$\dot{q}_s = \frac{\lambda_L(T_w - T_{sat})}{(\pi \kappa t)^{1/2}} \tag{4.7-16}$$

The resulting mass flux is obtained as

$$\dot{m}_s = \frac{\dot{q}_s}{\Delta h_{LG}} = \frac{1}{\Delta h_{LG}} \frac{T_w - T_{sat}}{(\pi \kappa t)^{1/2}} \tag{4.7-17}$$

The instantaneous mass transfer rate of component 1 at the interface can be similarly obtained as

$$\dot{m}_{1,s} = \frac{\rho_L D_{12}(x_1 - x_{1,s})}{(\pi D_{12} t)^{1/2}} \tag{4.7-18}$$

The total evaporation $\dot{m}_{s,D}$ at the interface is obtained by dividing Eq. (4.7-18) with $(y_{1,s} - x_1)$.

$$\dot{m}_{s,D} = \frac{\dot{m}_{1,s}}{y_{1,s} - x_1} = \left[\frac{\rho_L D_{12}}{(\pi D_{12} t)^{1/2}}\right]\left[\frac{x_1 - x_{1,s}}{y_{1,s} - x_1}\right] \tag{4.7-19}$$

The heat transfer rate may be assumed to be proportional to the evaporation rate at the interface. The reduction due to mass diffusion effects are then given by a mass diffusion factor $F_D$, which is the ratio of the mass transfer rates given by Eqs. (4.7-19) and (4.7-17). Incorporating Eqs. (4.7-12) and (4.7-13) and simplifying, we get

$$F_D = \frac{\dot{m}_{s,D}}{\dot{m}_s} = 0.678 \left[ 1 + \frac{c_{p,L}}{\Delta h_{LG}} \left( \frac{\kappa}{D_{12}} \right)^{1/2} \left( \frac{\Delta T_s}{g} \right) \right]^{-1} \quad (4.7\text{-}20)$$

The heat transfer coefficient for binary mixture is then obtained by incorporating $F_D$ in $\alpha_{PSC}$.

$$\alpha = \alpha_{PSC} F_D \quad (4.7\text{-}21)$$

The expression for $F_D$ is further modified to account for the fact that when the diffusion effects are negligible, $F_D$ approaches 1. These effects are quantified by a new volatility parameter $V_1$, which is obtained by simplifying the bracketed term in Eq. (4.7-20) with $y_{1,s} = y_1$ and assuming the bubble point curve to be linear in the region.

$$V_1 = \left( \frac{c_{p,L}}{\Delta h_{LG}} \right) \left( \frac{\kappa}{D_{12}} \right) (x_1 - y_1) \frac{dT}{dx_1} \quad (4.7\text{-}22)$$

After comparing with experimental data, the final form of the equation for $F_D$ is obtained.

$$F_D = \begin{cases} 1 & \text{for } V_1 \leq 0.03 \\ 1 - 64 V_1 & \text{for } 0.03 < V_1 \leq 0.2 \\ 0.678 \left[ 1 + \frac{c_{p,L}}{\Delta h_{LG}} \left( \frac{\kappa}{D_{12}} \right)^{1/2} \frac{\Delta T_s}{g} \right]^{-1} & \text{for } V_1 > 0.2 \end{cases}$$

$$(4.7\text{-}23)$$

The binary pool boiling heat transfer coefficient is given by Eq. (4.7-21) in conjunction with Eqs. (4.7-22) and (4.7-23). $\Delta T_s$ and g are obtained from Eqs. (4.7-14) and (4.7-15), and the interface concentration is obtained from Eq. (4.7-12), with $Ja_0$ from Eq. (4.7-13). An iterative procedure is needed to find $x_{1,s}$ and $\alpha$. The following procedure is recommended:

1. Calculate $T_{sat}$ corresponding to the bulk liquid concentration and system pressure.
2. Assume $x_{1,s}$. Determine $T_{sat,s}$ and $y_{1,s}$ from the thermodynamic property data for the mixture.
3. Assume $\alpha$ and calculate $T_w = T_{sat} + \dot{q}/\alpha$.
4. Calculate g, $\Delta T_s$, and $Ja_0$ from Eqs. (4.7-13)–(4.7-15).
5. Calculate $x_{1,s}$ from Eq. (4.7-12).

6. Calculate $V_1$ from Eq. (4.7-22).
7. Calculate $F_D$ from Eq. (4.7-23) and $\alpha$ from Eq. (4.7-21).
8. Iterate steps 2 through 7 until $x_{1,s}$ and $\alpha$ are converged.

The diffusion coefficients in the above equations are calculated by the Vignes (1971) correlation given below.

$$D_{12} = \left(D_{12}^0\right)^{\tilde{x}_2} \left(D_{21}^0\right)^{\tilde{x}_1} A_1 \qquad (4.7\text{-}24)$$

This correlation was found to be very suitable for non-ideal mixtures. $D_{12}^0$ and $D_{21}^0$ in the above equation are respective diffusion coefficients for dilute solutions given by the Wilke-Chang (1955) correlation

$$D_{12}^0 = 1.1782 \times 10^{-16} (\phi M_2)^{1/2} T / (\eta_{L,2} v_{m,1}) \qquad (4.7\text{-}25)$$

$A_{12}$ is the thermodynamic factor to account for the non-ideality of the mixture. As discussed by Kandlikar et al. (1975), $A_{12}$ is assumed to be 1.0, since the error introduced is quite small. $\phi$ is the association factor for the solvent (2.26 for water, 1.9 for methanol, 1.5 for ethanol, and 1.0 for unassociated solvents; Taylor and Krishna, 1993), $\eta_L$ is the liquid viscosity, and $v_{m,1}$ is the molar specific volume of component 1.

### 4.7.5 Comparison with Experimental Data

Figures 10 and 11 show the comparison of experimental data, with the Kandlikar (1998) model given by Eqs. (4.7-22) for methanol/water data by Fujita et al. (1996) and R-22/R-12 by Jungnickel et al. (1979). Also shown are predictions from

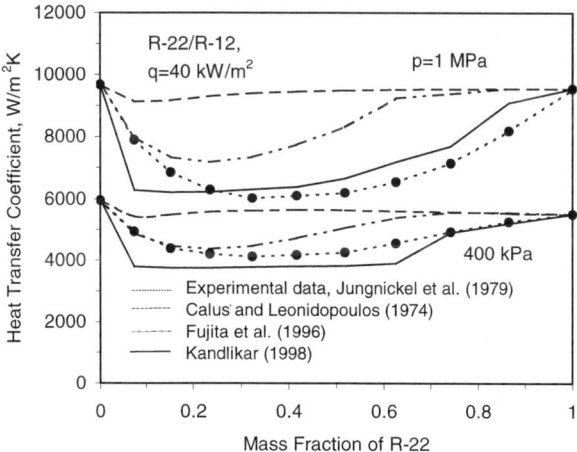

**Figure 10** Comparison of Jungnickel et al.'s R-22/R-12 data with correlations.

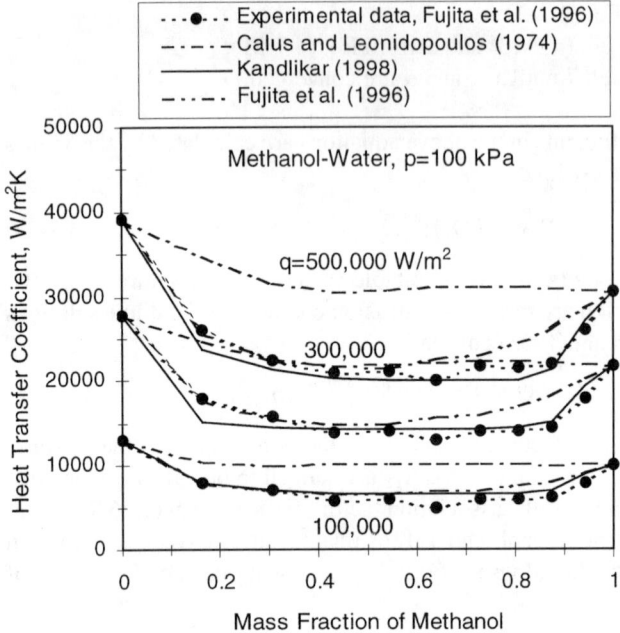

**Figure 11** Comparison of methanol/water data of Fujita et al. with correlations.

Eqs. (4.7-1) and (4.7-2) by Calus and Leonidopoulos (1974) and Fujita et al. (1997). An additional comparison is presented by Kandlikar (1998) for different binary systems. Since there are no empirical constants introduced in the formulation, the Kandlikar (1998) model is expected to be applicable to other binary systems as well. Although Eq. (4.7-21) represents the data quite well, further research is needed near the low concentration region.

Extensive phase equilibrium properties are needed in applying many of the correlations in pool boiling of binary mixtures. Sources such as HYSIM (1996) and NIST (1995) provide such data in a computerized form and are recommended.

### 4.7.6 Effect of Surfactants on Pool Boiling Heat Transfer

Surfactants are surface active substances that significantly alter the surface tension of a liquid even at very low concentrations. Although the surface tension is altered considerably, its effect on heat transfer is not clear. A comprehensive summary of some of the important work in this area is given in Table 3 as reported by Kandlikar and Alves (1998). They also presented results indicating a slight increase in the heat transfer coefficient with 1–2% (mass basis) solution of ethylene glycol in water.

Table 3  Summary of some important studies on surface tension effects on boiling

| Author/Year | Mixtures/composition | Results | Comments |
|---|---|---|---|
| Lowery and Westwater (1957) | Methanol with additives | Heat transfer increased, though the surface tension remained unchanged with additives. | Rate of nucleation on the heating surface was affected by the presence of additives |
| Jontz and Myers (1960) | Water and Aerosol and Targitol of different concentrations | Volumetric study with air indicated that dynamic surface tension changed for Targitol solutions but not for aerosol solutions. Heat transfer increased by 50% with Targitol and 400% with Aerosol. | Initiation of nucleation was identified as another parameter being affected by surface tension besides the departure bubble volume. |
| Dunskus and Westwater (1961) | Isopropanol with additives | Bubble frequency increased with additives; surface viscosity with higher molecular weight additives was identified as a factor. | Changes in contact angle and surface viscosity are believed to affect the heat transfer rates. |
| Roll and Myers (1964) | Water and five surfactants | Bubble volume at departure and bubble growth rates were obtained experimentally. Bubble volume, growth time, and delay time decrease with surface tension; bubble frequency increased by an order of magnitude. | The complex influence of surfactants on heat transfer through bubble growth, departure size, and frequency was identified. |
| Kochaphakdee and Williams (1970) | Water and polymeric additives | Polymeric additives with long chain molecules improved heat transfer. Although the viscosity was not affected, the heat transfer was improved due to the same factors as those responsible for reducing turbulent drag for these mixtures in pipe flow. | Surface viscosity with high molecular weight additives retards bubble coalescence, leading to increase in heat transfer rate. |
| Shah and Darby (1973) | Water with commercial surfactant | In the falling film experiments, heat transfer improved due to the increased foaming under nucleate boiling conditions. | Foaming results as the bubbles do not coalesce. This behavior is due to the reduction in surface tension. |
| Yang and Maa (1983) | Water with two different surfactants | As surface tension of the mixture decreased, the heat transfer coefficient increased. | The localized increase in surface tension during the growth of a bubble inhibits coalescence. |

(Continued)

**Table 3 (Continued)**

| Author/Year | Mixtures/composition | Results | Comments |
|---|---|---|---|
| Tzan and Yang (1990) | Water with SLS surfactant | Heat transfer improved with addition of surfactant. The bubble density also increased on the heater surface. | The photographs show the increased bubble activity with smaller bubbles as the surface tension decreased. |
| Wang and Hartnett (1994) | Water with surfactants | Heat transfer with SLS and Tween surfactants in water was same or lower than water, though the surface tension was lower. | The results are contradictory to other studies. The reasons are not clear. |
| Straub (1993) | Water and refrigerant under regular and microgravity | The presence of bubble on a surface induced microconvection, which improved heat transfer with refrigerant but not for water. Role of surface tension through flow around bubble explained. | Photographic results under saturated conditions should be used with caution as the camera speed was low at 100 fpm. Presence of smaller bubbles improved heat transfer against the formation of dry spots with large bubbles. |
| Malyshenko, (1994) | Argon | The experimental values of superheat prior to nucleation are lower than calculated values. | For small bubbles, the curvature effect on surface tension needs to be considered. |
| Ammerman and You (1996) | Water and FC-72 with SLS surfactant | The heat transfer rate increased with the addition of surfactant. The convection component increased while the latent component decreased. | The system is similar to Wang and Hartnett (1992) for water, but the heat transfer improved with addition of surfactant. Increased nucleation with surfactants caused agitation of liquid. |
| Wozniak, Wozniak, and Bergelt (1996) | Water under regular and microgravity | Surface tension driven flow becomes important in the absence of buoyancy circulation caused by gravity. | Role of surface tension becomes more important in micro-gravity. |
| Kandlikar and Alves (1998) | Water and ethylene glycol | Slight increase in heat transfer observed at low concentration of ethylene glycol in water | Effect of contact angles and other parameters affecting bubble characteristics needs to be studied. |

The reduction in surface tension causes the bubbles to become smaller and prevents their coalescence. The heating surface is covered by a larger number of smaller bubbles. The contact angle is also affected by the addition of surfactants, though their trends are not clearly established. The nucleate boiling heat transfer depends on the nucleation, bubble growth rates, bubble departure sizes, and contact angle, which may all be affected by the addition of surfactants. Further research is needed to establish the effect of surfactants on these parameters and the resulting influence on the pool boiling heat transfer.

## 4.8 HOMOGENEOUS NUCLEATION OF LIQUIDS

The boiling of a pure liquid normally occurs when the liquid is in contact with its vapor and the equilibrium vapor pressure at the temperature of the liquid is equal to the ambient pressure. If, however, the extent of the vapor contact is limited to microscopic regions located within surface irregularities of the container (or in the surface structure of impurities within the liquid, e.g., motes), then the temperature at which the liquid boils increases, and the liquid can become superheated. The extent of such superheating often ranges from a few tenths of a degree to several tens of degrees, depending upon the liquid, the nature of the container, the volume of liquid, the rate of heating, and the purity of the liquid, among other things. The superheated liquid is often localized in a thin layer adjacent to the heating surface. In the limiting case of no vapor (or surface) contact whatsoever, it is possible to achieve remarkably large degrees of superheat before the liquid is observed to boil—usually with explosive force. In fact, it is just this latter type of explosive boil that is believed to be responsible for a number of rather devastating industrial accidents resulting in severe damage to property and loss of life (Reid, 1978).

The limit of superheat is the maximum temperature to which a liquid can be heated before it homogeneously nucleates (spontaneously vaporizes). The limit of superheat can be determined thermodynamically, based upon stability considerations, as the spinodal curve for the liquid that is the locus of minima in the $P$-$V$ isotherms satisfying the conditions $(\partial P/\partial V)_T = 0$ and $(\partial^2 P/\partial V^2)_T > 0$. A typical liquid spinodal is illustrated in Figure 12 as the line C-C'-Critical point. In Figure 12, the thermodynamic determined limit of superheat at pressure $p_s$ is $T_l$. The shaded area between the liquid spinodal and the two-phase boundary (the line B - Critical point) represents the metastable, superheated fluid. The calculated value of the spinodal generally depends upon the equation of state used for the analysis (Eberhart, 1976). There have been a number of attempts to use equations of state to accurately predict the thermodynamic limit of superheat (e.g., Eberhart, [1976] and Lienhard [1976]). One example of a particularly simple relation is

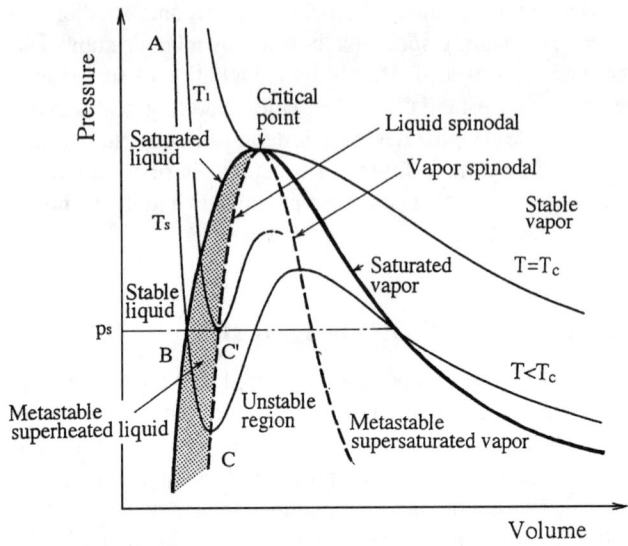

**Figure 12** Volume-pressure chart of fluid and the range of metastable superheated liquid.

given by Lienhard (1976):

$$\left\{\frac{(T_{TLS} - T_S)}{T_C}\right\}_M = 0.905 - \left(\frac{T_S}{T_C}\right) + 0.095\left(\frac{T_S}{T_C}\right)^8 \qquad (4.8\text{-}1)$$

where $T_C$ is the critical temperature, $T_S$ is the saturation temperature, and the subscript $M$ denotes the value at the condition of limiting superheat.

The process of boiling in liquids is analogous to the condensation of vapors. The condensation process begins with the nucleation of vapor molecules forming embryos of the condensed phase that can either grow to become macroscopic segments of the new phase or decay to molecules of the vapor. Similarly, the boiling process begins with the nucleation of vapor embryos. If the vapor embryo grows to a size sufficient to be in unstable equilibrium with the liquid (the so-called critical nucleus), it can grow to macroscopic size (boil). If not, the tendency is to decay to the liquid. If an interface or foreign surface is involved, the process is called *heterogeneous nucleation* and generally occurs at low supersaturation (vapors) or smaller degrees of superheat (liquids). If not, the process is called *homogeneous nucleation*.

We note that the homogeneous nucleation of vapors has been studied extensively in the laboratory, and in spite of a rather long history of investigation, there is much not yet understood. This is reflected in the results of recent investigations into the effects of background gases on the nucleation process, as well as other related investigations into the nucleation of vapors using thermal diffusion cloud chambers. Details of these studies are available elsewhere and will not be reproduced here (see Bertelsmann and Heist, 1997a, 1997b; Bertelsmann et al., 1996; Heist, 1995; Heist and He, 1994; and Heist et al., 1994a, 1994b).

The limit of superheat can also be determined kinetically, based upon nucleation theory, as the temperature at which homogenous nucleation (spontaneous vaporization) occurs (Blander and Katz, 1975; Carey, 1992; Frenkel, 1995; Skripov, 1974). In this regard, we consider the rate of embryo formation from embryos of size $X$ (containing $X$ molecules) to size $(X+1)$. In nucleation theory, this rate of formation is expressed as the difference between the rate of growth from size $X$ to $X+1$ (by evaporation from the embryo surface) and the rate of decay from size $X+1$ to $X$ (by condensation on the embryo surface). At steady state (constant flux of embryos through size space), the rate of embryo formation, $J$, per unit volume per time can expressed as (Skripov, 1974):

$$J = \frac{\alpha}{\int (AN_X)^{-1} dX} \qquad (4.8\text{-}2)$$

where $\alpha$ is the vaporization rate from the surface of the embryo (usually taken to be the same as the condensation rate from the vapor, i.e., $p_v/(2\pi mkT)^{1/2}$, where $p_v$ is the vapor pressure, $m$ is the molecular mass, and $k$ is the Boltzmann constant), $A$ is the interface area of the embryo, and $N_x$ is the number density of embryos containing $X$ molecules. The number density of embryos is generally taken to be of the form

$$N_X = N_1 \exp(-W_X/kT) \qquad (4.8\text{-}3)$$

where $N_1$ is the number density of liquid molecules. $W_X$ is the work required to form an embryo with $X$ molecules and involves the work necessary to form the interface separating the two phases and the work required to vaporize the gas to a volume $V_g$ at a pressure $p_g$. According to Skripov (1974), $W_X$ can be expressed as:

$$W_X = \sigma A - (p_g - p_l) V_g + X(\mu_g - \mu_l) \qquad (4.8\text{-}4)$$

where $\sigma$ is the surface tension, $p_l$ is the pressure in the superheated liquid phase, and $\mu$ is the chemical potential (on a molecule basis) given by $d\mu = (V/X) dp$. When mechanical and chemical equilibrium apply, the embryo is the critical cluster, and the Laplace equation holds:

$$p_g = p_v = p_l + \frac{2\sigma}{r_C} \qquad (4.8\text{-}5)$$

where $r_C$ is the radius of the critical cluster (also called a bubble nucleus).

## Table 4 Limit of superheat and nucleation rate in water at atmosheric pressure

| T (K) | J [1/(cm³s0] | Waiting time |
|---|---|---|
| 560 | $2.7 \times 10^{-76}$ | $12 \times 10^{68}$ yr |
| 570 | $8.5 \times 10^{-20}$ | $3.7 \times 10^{11}$ yr |
| 575 | $5.7 \times 10^{-3}$ | $1.8 \times 10^{2}$ s |
| 580 | $4.3 \times 10^{9}$ | $2.3 \times 10^{-10}$ s |
| 590 | $4.3 \times 10^{23}$ | $2.3 \times 10^{-24}$ s |

Non-ideal gas effects have been included by Katz and Blander (1973) in deriving the work of formation of the critical cluster, giving

$$W_X \cong \frac{4\pi\sigma r_C^2}{3} - 4\pi\sigma(r-r_C)^2 B \qquad (4.8\text{-}6)$$

where

$$B \cong 1 - \frac{\left(1 - \frac{p_l}{p_v}\right)}{3} \approx \frac{2}{3} \quad \text{for } p_l \ll p_v \qquad (4.8\text{-}7)$$

The work required to form an embryo—Eq. (4.8-4) or, alternatively, Eq. (4.8-6)—increases to a maximum at $r = r_C$ and then decreases as the bubble size increases past the critical radius. Thus, bubbles with radii larger than the critical radius (continue to) grow spontaneously.

With reasonable approximations, Eq. (4.8-2) has been rewritten by Debenedetti (1996) as:

$$J = N_{tot} \sqrt{\frac{2\sigma}{\pi MB}} \exp\left[-\frac{16\pi}{3kT} \cdot \frac{\sigma^3}{\delta^2 (p_v - p_l)^2}\right] \qquad (4.8\text{-}8)$$

where $N_{tot}$ is the total number density in the superheated liquid, M is the molecular mass, and

$$\delta = 1 - \frac{p_v v}{kT} \qquad (4.8\text{-}9)$$

where $v$ is the specific molecular volume of the liquid. All other symbols in Eqs. (4.8-8) and (4.8-9) have already been defined.

The value of $J$ obtained using Eq. (4.8-8) varies dramatically as a function of temperature. In Table 4, the value of $J$ obtained using Eq. (4.8-8) is shown as a function of temperature for superheated water at one atmosphere pressure (Avedisian, 1985). The "waiting time" (essentially, the reciprocal of the rate) is also shown for comparison. At a calculated rate of $J = 1$ bubble/cm³/sec, the waiting (expected) time for the nucleation of one bubble in one cm³ of water is one second. These data suggest that bubble nucleation is a rare event at temperatures less than 570 K under these conditions. At higher temperatures, the rate (expected time) increases (decreases) dramatically—approximately $10^2$–$10^3$ times for each increase in temperature of one degree. Thus, it is apparent that the kinetically determined value of the superheat temperature is a function of the nucleation rate (actually, the embryo or bubble flux through the critical nucleus size) and increases slowly as that rate (bubble flux) increases. The thermodynamically determined limit, however, must be the larger value, since thermodynamics provides an upper limit on the (meta)stability of the superheated state. At the maximum possible bubble flux, the kinetically and thermodynamically determined limits of superheat should agree. It has been estimated that the maximum possible bubble flux is approximately $10^{30}$ nuclei/cm$^3$/sec$^2$. In fact, there is evidence that if the thermodynamic value of the limit of superheat is taken to be the kinetic limit of superheat at a nuclei flux of $10^{30}$ nuclei/cm$^3$/sec, the measured kinetic limit of superheat temperatures at various nuclei flux appear to be reasonably consistent with that value (Eberhart, 1976).

The limit of liquid superheat has been determined by experimental methods in which the test liquid is heated slowly with no vapor phase contact and by methods in which it is heated rapidly so as to avoid the effects of pre-existing nuclei. These methods include the isobatic heating of a small volume of liquid within a capillary tube or an immiscible liquid, the isothermal decompression technique utilizing a bubble chamber, and the rapid heating of the test liquid by a small heater immersed in the liquid. In this latter method, the heating rate is maintained sufficiently fast so as to avoid heterogeneous boiling caused by pre-existing nuclei on the heater surface. Results from these investigations indicate that the temperatures at which spontaneous boiling occur agree well with the predictions of homogeneous nucleation theory for organic liquids and low-boiling point liquids.

Skripov (1974) has confirmed the limit of superheat for a variety of liquids and has studied the kinetics of bubble nucleation using rapidly heated fine wires. Iida et al. (1994) have immersed a small film heater (0.1 mm × 0.25 mm) in test liquids and heated the film using a narrow pulse of current. They have been able to attain heating rates up to approximately $10^8$ K/sec. Figure 13 shows data from these experiments for the measured onset of bubble formation in ethanol. These authors have determined that the generation of one bubble on the heater in this system corresponds to a nucleation rate (nuclei flux) of approximately $10^{14}$ nuclei/cm$^3$/sec. The data are presented by Iida et al. (1993, 1994) as the measured temperature, $T_{c,bi}$, for incipient nucleation on the heater film at various heating rates for three different pressures. The measured temperatures are also presented in reduced form, $T_{c,bi}/T_c$. Note that $T_{c,bi}$ increases with the heating rate and approaches a constant value for heating rates of approximately 5–10 × $10^6$ K/sec and above. These constant values of the nucleation temperatures shown in Figure 13 agree with the limit of

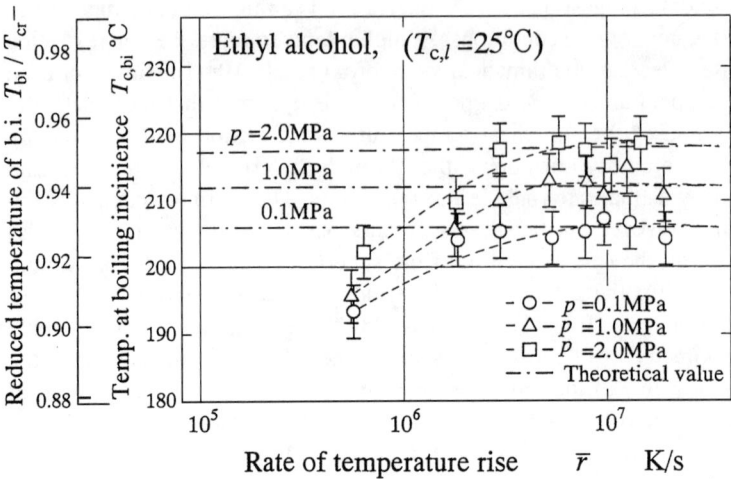

**Figure 13** Measured temperature at boiling incipience versus the rate of temperature rise of a film heater immersed in ethyl alcohol at $p = 0.1$, 1.0, and 2.0 Mpa, respectively.

superheat temperatures obtained from homogeneous nucleation theory (obtained using Eq. (4.8-8) with $J = 10^{14}$ nuclei/cm$^3$/sec and shown as dash-dot lines in the figure). The drop-off of the nucleation temperatures at lower heating rates is believed to be due to heterogeneous nucleation. At these constant values of the nucleation temperature, the number of bubbles formed on the heater increases dramatically with time following the formation of the first bubble. It should be noted, however, that similar experiments by these authors using water as the test liquid resulted in measured limit of superheat temperatures at atmospheric pressure (analogous to the constant values shown in Figure 13) that were 19 K lower than that predicted using homogeneous nucleation theory.

In Figure 14, four successive pictures of bubbles obtained by Iida et al. (1996) are shown as they are formed on the surface of the film heater immersed in ethanol at 1.0 MPa and heated at a rate of $9.7 \times 10^6$ K/sec. The value of $t$ indicated below each picture is the time elapsed following the rapid heating of the film, and the value, $T_{c,w}$, is the heater temperature. The temperature of the test liquid prior to heating is 25°C, and the exposure time for the picture was 10 ns. In the first picture (labeled 1 in Figure 14), only a few, small bubbles are observed on the heater surface. In the second picture (labeled 2 in Figure 14), taken 0.1 μs later, a rather large number of bubbles of comparable diameter are observed on the heater surface. In the third and fourth pictures, the number of bubbles has increased dramatically and abruptly over a short period of time. Note that there is an area with no bubble generation. This may be due to an inhomogeneous temperature

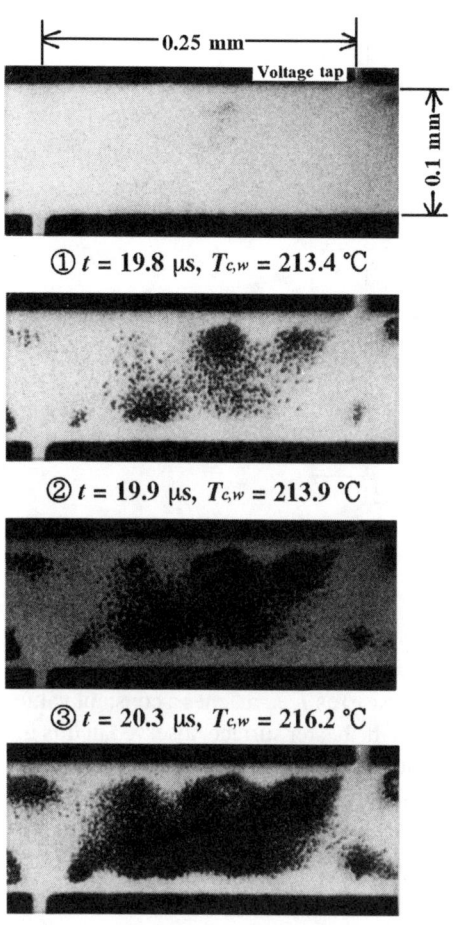

**Figure 14** Four successive shots of spontaneous bubble generation on a rapidly heated film heater (ethyl alcohol, $p = 1.0$ Mpa, $T_{c,1} = 25°C$, $r = 9.7 \times 10^6$ K/s, exposure time $=10$ ns).

field over the surface of the heater caused by edge effects and/or slight variations in the thickness of the film.

In Figure 15, the measured numbers of bubbles, formed at different film temperatures and at different heating rates for a pressure of 0.1 MPa, are plotted by Iida et al. (1997). Also included (as solid line plots) are the predictions of homogeneous nucleation theory for two different heating rates. The data obtained from experiments utilizing the slower heating rates are seen to be at considerably lower temperatures than predicted by nucleation theory. However, reasonable agreement

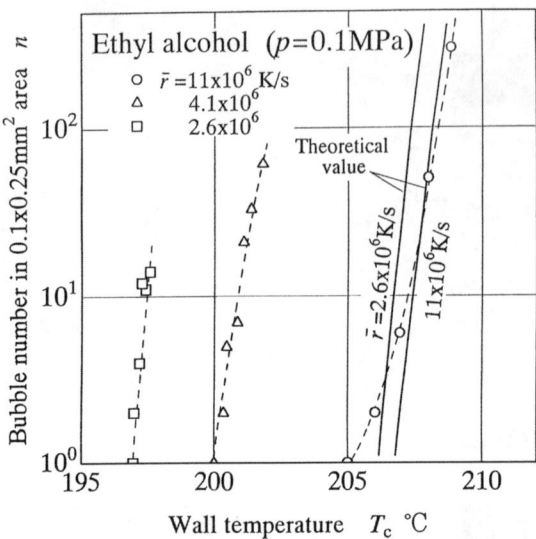

**Figure 15** Comparison of the number of bubbles on a rapidly heated film heater with those predicted by the homogeneous nucleation theory.

with nucleation theory is obtained with the data from the experiments using the faster heating rates ($1.1 \times 10^7$ K/sec, in this case) as $T_{c,bi}$ reaches a constant value. The maximum number density of bubbles on the heater surface observed in this investigation was approximately $7 \times 10^{10}$ bubbles/m², measured during the ethanol experiments with a pressure of 2.0 MPa and a heating rate of $2.0 \times 10^7$ K/sec. These many small bubbles generated on the surface of the heater quickly aggregate, forming a large bubble that then undergoes film boiling (Iida et al., 1997).

## REFERENCES

Ammerman, C. N. and You, S. M. 1996. Determination of the Boiling Enhancement Mechanism Caused by Surfactant Addition to Water. *J. Heat Transfer* 118:429–435.

Ammerman, C. N., You, S. M., and Hong, Y. S. 1996. Identification of Pool Boiling Heat Transfer from a Wire Immersed in Saturated FC-72 Using a Simple/LDA Method. *J. Heat Transfer* 118:117–123.

Avedisian, C. T. 1985. The Homogeneous Nucleation Limits of Liquids. *J. Phys. Chem. Ref. Data* 14(3):695–729.

Bankoff, S. G. 1958. Entrapment of Gas in the Spreading of Liquid over a Rough Surface. *AIChE Journal* 4:24–26.

Barthau, G. 1992. Active Nucleation Site Density and Pool Boiling Heat Transfer—An Experimental Study. *Int'l. J. Heat Mass Transfer* 33:271–278.

Berenson, P. J. 1962. Experiments On Pool Boiling Heat Transfer. *International Journal of Heat and Mass Transfer* 5:985–999.

Bertelsmann, A. and Heist, R. H. 1997a. Two Dimensional Transport and Wall Effects in the Thermal Diffusion Cloud Chamber, Part I: Analysis and Operations Criteria. *J. Chem. Phys.* 106:610–623.
Bertelsmann, A. and Heist, R. H. 1997b. Two-Dimensional Transport and Wall Effects in the Thermal Diffusion Cloud Chamber, Part II: *J. Chem. Phys.* 106:624–634.
Bertelsmann, A., Stuczynski, R., and Heist, R. H. 1996. The Effects of Background Gases on the Homogeneous Nucleation of Vapors, III. *J. Phys. Chem.* 100:9762–9773.
Bier, K., Gorenflow, D., Salem, M., and Tanes, Y. 1978. Pool Boiling Heat Transfer and Size of Active Nucleation Centers for Horizontal Plates with Different Surface Roughness, Volume 1. *Proc. 6th Int'l. Heat Transfer Conf.*, Toronto, Ontario, Canada, pp. 151–156.
Blander, M. and Katz, J. L. 1975. Bubble Nucleation in Liquids. *AIChE J.* 21(5):833–848.
Bui, T. D. and Dhir, V. K. 1985. Transition Boiling Heat Transfer on a Vertical Surface. *ASME Journal of Heat Transfer* 107:756–763.
Calus, W. F. and Leonidopoulos, D. J. 1974. Pool Boiling—Binary Liquid Mixtures. *Int. J. Heat Mass Transfer* 17:249–256.
Calus, W. F. and Rice, P. 1972. Pool Boiling—Binary Liquid Mixtures. *Chem. Engng. Sci* 27:1687–1697.
Carey, V. P. 1992. *Liquid-Vapor Phase-Change Phenomena.* Washington, DC: Hemisphere Publications.
Cole, R. and Rohsenow, W. M. 1969. Correlations for Bubble Departure Diameters for Boiling of Saturated Liquids. *Chem. Engr. Prog.* 65:211–213.
Cooper, M. G. 1984. Saturation Nucleate Pool Boiling—A Simple Correlation. *IChemE Symposium Series* 86:786–793.
Cooper, M. G. and Lloyd, A. J. P. 1969. The Microlayer in Nucleate Pool Boiling. *Int. J. Heat Mass Transfer* 12:895–913.
Cornwell, K. and Brown, R. D. 1978. Boiling Surface Topography, Volume 1. *Proc. 6th Int'l. Heat Transfer Conf.*, Toronto, Ontario, Canada, pp. 157–161.
Cornwell, R. and Einarsson, J. G. 1989. The Influence of Fluid Flow on Nucleate Boiling from a Tube. *Proceedings of European Seminar, No. 8: On Advances in Pool Boiling Heat Transfer.* University of Paderborn, May 11–12, 1989, Paderborn, Germany, pp. 28–41.
Debenedetti, P. G. 1996. Metastable Liquids—Concepts and Principles. Princeton, NJ: Princeton University Press.
Dunskus., T. and Westwater, J. W. 1961. The Effect of Trace Additives on the Heat Transfer to Boiling Isopropanol. *Chem. Engng. Prog. Symp., Ser. No. 32* 57:173–181.
Eberhart, J. G. 1976. The Thermodynamic and the Kinetic Limits of Superheat of a Liquid. *J. Colloid and Interface Science* 56(2):262–269.
Forster, D. E. and Greif, R. 1959. Heat Transfer to a Boiling Liquid—Mechanism and Correlation. *J. Heat Transfer* 81:43–53.
Frenkel, J. 1955. Kinetic Theory of Liquids. New York: Dover Publications.
Fritz, W. 1935. Maximum Volume of Vapor Bubbles. *Physik Zeitschr.* 36:379–384.
Fujita, Y., Bai, Q., and Tsutsui, M. 1996. Heat Transfer of Binary Mixtures in Nucleate Pool Boiling. *2nd Eur. Therml. Sci. and 14th UIT Nat. Heat Trans. Conf.* Eds. Celata, G. P., Di Marco, P., and Mariani, A., pp. 1639–1646.
Gaertner, R. F. 1965. Photographic Study of Nucleate Pool Boiling on a Horizontal Surface. *ASME Journal of Heat Transfer* 87:17–29.
Gorenflo, D., Knabe, V., and Beiling, V. 1986. Bubble Density on Surfaces with Nucleate Boiling—Its Influence on Heat Transfer and Burnout Heat Flux at Elevated Saturation Pressures. *Proceedings of the 8th International Heat Transfer Conference*, Volume 4, August 1986. San Francisco, CA, pp. 1995–2000. Washington, DC: Hemisphere Publishing Corp.

Griffith, P. and Wallis, J. D. 1960. The Role of Surface Conditions in Nucleate Boiling. *Chemical Engineering Proj. Symposium, Ser. 56* 30:49–63.

Han, C. Y. and Griffith, P. 1965. The Mechanism of Heat Transfer in Nucleate Pool Boiling. Part I, Bubble Initiation, Growth, and Departure. *International Journal of Heat and Mass Transfer* 8:887–904.

Heist, R. H. 1995. Homogeneous Nucleation of Vapors: Critical Supersaturation Measurements for Methanol, Ethanol, 1-Propanol, 2-Propanol. *J. Phys. Chem.* 99:16792–16799.

Heist, R. H. and He, H. 1994. Review of Vapor to Liquid Homogeneous Nucleation Experiments from 1968 to 1992. *J. Phys. Chem. Ref. Data.* 23:781–805.

Heist, R. H., Ahmed, J., and Janjua, M. 1994. The Effects of Background Gases on the Homogeneous Nucleation of Vapors, II. *J. Phys. Chem.* 99:375–383.

Heist, R. H., Janjua, M., and Ahmed, J. 1994. The Effects of Background Gases on the Homogeneous Nucleation of Vapors, I. *J. Phys. Chem.* 98:4443–4453.

Hsu, Y. Y. 1962. On the Size Range of Active Nucleation Sites on a Heating Surface. *J. Heat Transfer* 84:207–216.

Hsu, Y. Y. and Graham, R. W. 1976. *Transport Processes in Boiling and Two Phase Systems.* Washington, DC: Hemispheric Publishing Corp.

HYSIM. Version 6. 1996. Calgary, Alberta, Canada: Hyprotech Ltd.

Iida, Y., Okuyama, K., Endou, T., and Kanda, K. 1996. Effect of Ambient Pressure on the Dynamics of Bubble Formation by Fluctuation Nucleation on a Platinum Film Rapidly Heated to the Limit of Liquid Superheat. Volume I. *Proceedings of the 3rd KSME-JSME Thermal Engineering Conference,* pp. 373–378.

Iida, Y., Okuyama, K., and Nishizawa, T. 1997. Heat Transfer During Boiling Initiated by Fluctuation Nucleation on a Platinum Film Rapidly Heated to the Limit of Liquid Superheat. First Report. *Trans. JSME, B* 63(613):3048–3054.

Iida, Y., Okuyama, K., and Sakurai, K. 1993. Peculiar Bubble Generation on a Film Heater Subjected to Extremely Rapid Heating. *Int. J. Heat Mass Transfer* 36–10:2699–2701.

Iida, Y., Okuyama, K., and Sakurai, K. 1994. Boiling Nucleation on a Very Small Film Heater Subjected to Extremely Rapid Heating. *Int. J. Heat Mass Transfer* 37–17:2771–2780.

Johnson, H. A. 1971. Transient Boiling Heat Transfer to Water. *International Journal of Heat and Mass Transfer* 14:67–82.

Jontz, P. D. and Myers, J. E. 1960. The Effect of Dynamic Surface Tension on Nucleate Boiling Coefficients. *AIChE J.* 6(1):34–38.

Judd, R. L. and Hwang, K. S. 1976. A Comprehensive Model for Nucleate Boiling Heat Transfer Including Microlayer Evaporation. *J. Heat Transfer* 98:623–629.

Jungnickel, H., Wassilew, P., and Kraus, W. E. 1979. Investigation on the Heat Transfer of Boiling Binary Refrigerant Mixtures. *Proc. XVth Int. Cong. Refrig.* II:525–536.

Kandlikar, S. G. 1998. Boiling Heat Transfer in Binary Systems, Part I—Pool Boiling. HTD-Vol. 342, *ASME Proceedings of the 32nd National Heat Transfer Conference,* Baltimore, MD, Vol. 4, pp. 19–26. Also published in *J. Heat Transfer* 120:380–387.

Kandlikar, S. G. and Alves, L. 1998. Effects of Surface Tension and Binary Diffusion on Pool Boiling of Dilute Solutions—An Experimental Assessment. Paper presented at the ASME National Heat Transfer Conference, Albuquerque, NM, June.

Kandlikar, S. G., Bijlani, C. A., and Sukhatme, S. P. 1975. Predicting the Properties of R-22 and R-12 Mixtures—Transport Properties. *ASHRAE Trans.* 81:285–294.

Katz, J. L. and Blander, M. 1973. Condensation and Boiling: Corrections to Homogeneous Nucleation Theory for Nonideal Gases. *J. Colloid and Interface Science* 42(3):496–502.

Kocamustafagoullari, G. and Ishii, M. 1983. Interfacial Area and Nucleation Site Density in Boiling Systems. *Int'l. J. Heat Mass Transfer* 26:1377–1387.

Kochaphakdee, P. and Williams, M. C. 1970. Enhancement of Nucleate Pool Boiling with Polymeric Additives. *Int. J. Heat and Mass Transfer* 13:835–848.

Lay, J. H. and Dhir, V. K. 1994. A Nearly Theoretical Model for Fully Developed Nucleate Boiling of Saturated Liquids, Volume 5. *Proc. 10th Int'l. Heat Transfer Conference*, Brighton, England, pp. 105–110.

Liaw, S. P. and Dhir, V. K. 1989. Void Fraction Measurement During Saturated Pool Boiling of Water on Partially Wetted Vertical Surfaces. *ASME Journal of Heat Transfer* 111:731–738.

Lienhard, J. H. 1976. Correlation for the Limiting Liquid Superheat. *CES 31-9-H*:847–849.

Lowery, A. J. and Westwater, J. W. 1957. Heat Transfer to Boiling Methanol—Effect of Added Agents. *Ind. and Eng. Chem.* 49:1445–1448.

Malyshenko, S. P. 1994. Effect of a Curved Phase Boundary on Surface Tension and Kinetics of Nucleation in Liquids. *High Temperature* 32(5):671–678.

Malenkov, I. G. 1971. Detachment Frequency as a Function of Size of Vapor Bubbles. Translated. *Inzh. Fiz. Zhur.* 20:99.

Merte, H. 1988. Nucleate Pool Boiling: High Gravity to Reduced Gravity, Liquid Metals to Cryogenics. *Trans. 5th Symposium on Space Nuclear Power Systems*, University of New Mexico, January 11–14, 1988, Albuquerque, NM, pp. 437–442.

Mikic, B. B. and Rohsenow, W. M. 1969a. A New Correlation of Pool Boiling Data, Including the Effect of Heating Surface Characteristics. *Journal of Heat Transfer* 9:245–250.

Mikic, B. B. and Rohsenow, W. M. 1969b. Bubble Growth Rates in Non-Uniform Temperature Field. *Progress in Heat and Mass Transfer*, Volume II, pp. 283–293.

Mikic, B. B., Rohsenow, W. M., and Griffith, P. 1970. On Bubble Growth Rates. *Int'l. J. Heat Mass Transfer* 13:647–666.

Mizukami, K. 1975. Entrapment of Vapor in Re-Entrant Cavities. *Letters in Heat and Mass Transfer* 2:279–284.

Moissis, R. and Berenson, P. J. 1963. On the Hydrodynamic Transitions in Nucleate Boiling. *ASME Journal of Heat and Mass Transfer* 27:221–229.

Moore, F. D. and Mesler, R. B. 1961. The Measurement of Rapid Surface Temperature Fluctuations During Nucleate Boiling of Water. *AICHE Journal* 7:620–624.

Nishikawa, K., Fujita, Y., and Ohta, H. 1984. Effect of Surface Configuration on Nucleate Boiling Heat Transfer. *International Journal of Heat and Mass Transfer* 27:1559–1571.

Nishio, A. 1990. Seiken Seminar Text (Course 159), in Japanese. NIST 1995. *REFPROP*. Washington, D.C: National Institute for Science and Technology.

Nishio, S. 1985. Stability of Pre-Existing Vapor Nucleus in Uniform Temperature Field. *Trans. JSME*, Series B 54–503:1802–1807.

Paul, D. D. and Abdel-Khalik, S. I. 1983. A Statistical Analysis of Saturated Nucleate Boiling Along a Pleated Wire. *Int'l. J. Heat Mass Transfer* 26:509–519.

Plesset, M. S. and Zwick, S. A. 1954. Growth of Vapor Bubbles in Superheated Liquids. *Journal Appe. Phys.* 25:493–500.

Reid, R. C. 1978. Superheated Liquids—A Laboratory Curiosity and, Possibly, an Industrial Curse. *Chemical Engineering Education*. Spring, 60–87; Summer, 108–129; Fall, 194–206.

Rohsenow, W. M. 1952. A Method of Correlating Heat Transfer Data for Surface Boiling of Liquids. *Trans. ASME* 74:969–976.

Roll, J. B. and Myers, J. M. 1964. The Effect of Surface Tension on Factors in Boiling Heat Transfer. *AIChE J.* 10(4):530–534.

Ross, T. K. 1967. Corrosion and Heat Transfer Review. Ed. Corros, J. Volume 2, pp. 131–142.

Sakurai, A. and Shiotsu, M. 1977a. Transient Pool Boiling Heat Transfer, Part 1: Incipience Boiling Superheat. *Journal of Heat Transfer* 99:547–553.

Sakurai, A. and Shiotsu, M. 1977b. Transient Pool Boiling Heat Transfer, Part 2: Boiling Heat Transfer and Burnout. *Journal of Heat Transfer* 99:554–560.

Schlünder, E. U. 1982. Heat Transfer in Nucleate Pool Boiling of Mixtures. *Proc. 7th Int. Heat Transfer Conf.* 4:2073–2079.

Scriven, L. E. 1959. On the Dynamics of Phase Growth. *Chem. Engng. Sci.* 10, 1–13.

Shah, B. T. and Darby, R. 1973. The Effect of Surfactant on Evaporative Heat Transfer in Vertical Film Flow. *Int. J. Heat Mass Transfer* 16:1889–1903.

Skripov, V. P. 1974. *Metastable Liquids*. New York: John Wiley and Sons.

Snyder, N. R. and Edwards, D. K. 1956. Summary of Conference On Bubble Dynamics and Boiling Heat Transfer. Memo 20-137, Jet Propulsion Laboratory, Pasadena, CA:14–15.

Stephan, K. and Abdelsalam, M. 1980. Heat Transfer Correlation for Natural Convection Boiling. *Int'l. J. Heat Mass Transfer* 23:73–87.

Straub, J. 1993. The Role of Surface Tension for Two-Phase Heat and Mass Transfer in the Absence of Gravity. *Experimental Heat Transfer, Fluid Mechanics, and Thermodynamics*. Ed. Kelleher, M. D., Elsevier Science Publishers.

Taylor, R. and Krishna, P. 1993, *Multicomponent Mass Transfer*. New York: John Wiley & Sons, Inc.,

Thome, J. R. 1983. Prediction of Binary Mixture Boiling Heat Transfer Coefficients Using Only Phase Equilibrium Data. *Int. J. Heat Mass Transfer* 26:965–974.

Thome, J. R. and Shakir, S. 1987. A New Correlation for Nucleate Pool Boiling of Binary Mixtures. *AIChE Symp. Ser.* 83:46–51.

Tzan, Y. L. and Yang, Y. M. 1990. Experimental Study of Surfactant Effects on Pool Boiling Heat Transfer. *Journal of Heat Transfer* 112:207–212.

Van Stralen, S. 1966, 1967. The Mechanism of Nucleate Boiling in Pure Liquids and Binary Mixtures. *Int. J. Heat Mass Transfer*, I–IV: 995–1046, 1469–1498.

Van Stralen, S. 1979. Growth Rate of Vapor and Gas Bubbles. *Boiling Phenomena*, Chapter 7. Eds. Van Stralen, S. and Cole, R. Washington, DC: Hemisphere Publishing Corp.

Vignes, A. 1966. Diffusion in Binary Solutions. *Ind. Eng. Chem. Fundam.* 5:189–199.

Wang, C. H. and Dhir, V. K. 1993a. On the Gas Entrapment and Nucleation Site Density During Pool Boiling of Saturated Water. *Journal of Heat Transfer* 115:670–679.

Wang, C. H. and Dhir, V. K. 1993b. Effect of Surface Wettability on Active Nucleation Site Density During Pool Boiling of Saturated Water. *Journal of Heat Transfer* 115:659–669.

Wang, T. A. A. and Hartnett, J. P. 1994. Pool Boiling of Heat Transfer from a Horizontal Wire to Aqueous Surfactant Solutions. *Heat Transfer 1994, Proceedings of $10^{th}$ International Heat Transfer Conference*. Brighton, Institute of Chemical Engineers/Institute of Mechanical Engineers, pp. 177–182.

Ward, C. A. and Forest, T. W. 1976. On the Relation Between Platelet Adhesion and the Roughness of a Synthetic Biomaterial. *Annals of Biomedical Engineering* 4:184–207.

Wenzel, U., Balzer, F., Jamialahmadi, M., and Müller-Steinhagen, H. 1995. Pool Boiling Heat Transfer Coefficients for Binary Mixtures of Acetone, Isopropanol, and Water. *Heat Tr. Engng.* 16:36–43.

Wilke, C. R. and Chang, P. 1955. Correlation of Diffusion Coefficients in Dilute Solutions. *AIChE J.* 1:264–270.

Wozniak, G., Wozniak, K., and Berglet, H. 1996. On the Influence of Buoyancy on the Surface Tension Driven Flow Around a Bubble on a Heater Wall. *Experiments in Fluids* 21:181–186.

Yang, Y. M. and Maa, J. R. 1983. Pool Boiling of Dilute Surfactant Solutions. *Journal of Heat Transfer, Trans. ASME* 105:190–192.

Zell, M., Straub, J., and Vogel, B. 1989. Pool Boiling Under Microgravity. *Proceedings of European Seminar, No. 8 On Advances in Pool Boiling Heat Transfer*. Paderborn, Germany, pp. 70–74.

CHAPTER
# FIVE

## ENHANCEMENT TECHNIQUES IN POOL BOILING

**5.1–5.3   Akira Yabe**

*AIST, Min. Int. Trade & Industry of Japan, Namiki, Tsukuba, Ibaraki, Japan*

**5.1–5.3   Wataru Nakayama**

*ThermTech International 920-7 Higashi Koiso, Oh-Iso Machi, Kanagawa, Japan*

**5.4   Paolo Di Marco**

*Università di Pisa, Via Diotisalvi 2, 56126 Pisa, Italy*

## 5.1 INTRODUCTION

Enhancement of boiling heat transfer is utilized in many advanced engineering fields, including (a) energy conservation technologies, such as various types of heat pump systems and waste heat recovery systems, (b) power plants, such as geothermal energy plants, and (c) electronics cooling systems.

In many cases, the targets of utilizing enhancement techniques of boiling heat transfer are as follows:

- To decrease the temperature difference between the heat transferring media for realizing the higher thermal cycle performance at the constant volume of heat exchangers.
- To increase the heat flux at a constant temperature difference for realizing compact heat exchangers with higher heat transfer coefficients and smaller surface area.

Since the required temperature difference in advanced heat pump systems would be limited below 1 or 2 degrees for realizing the higher coefficients of performance (COP), the enhancement techniques of heat transfer would become more important.

The applications of boiling heat transfer enhancement have been utilized so far for mainly organic heat transferring media, which were used for thermal cycles of air conditioning, heat recovery, and other small temperature difference thermal cycles. For the case of water, the application field would be limited to the small temperature difference cases of thermal cycles such as the absorption heat pump systems, since the nucleate boiling heat flux of water is originally much larger than that of organic liquids even without any enhancement method.

Among the heat transfer enhancement techniques for various types of heat transfer phenomena, the pool boiling enhancement techniques have been applied typically to the evaporators of the turbine compressor type heat pump systems, which have utilized flooded type shell and tube heat exchangers. As for electronic cooling, pool boiling has been studied for cooling the chips of super computers by organic dielectric liquid. Furthermore, the mechanism of the pool boiling heat transfer enhancement has been considered as the fundamental phenomenon applicable to various kinds of boiling heat transfer enhancement techniques.

Therefore, in this chapter, the basic enhancement mechanism in pool boiling and the key factors for promoting it are explained in detail as the fundamental step for creating the advanced enhancement techniques.

## 5.2 BASIC ENHANCEMENT MECHANISM IN POOL BOILING

The important aspects of the pool boiling heat transfer enhancement mechanisms can be described as follows:

(1) To generate repeatable boiling cavities for increasing the nucleation site density and the associated latent heat flux while decreasing the wall superheat.
(2) To increase the total area of thin liquid film under the boiling bubbles and inside the cavities for promoting the latent heat flux.
(3) To increase the forced convection heat transfer between the boiling surface and the heat transfer liquid for increasing the accumulated sensible superheat in liquid.

Figure 1 shows the schematic of the pool boiling phenomenon and the above mechanisms involved in enhancing pool boiling heat transfer.

A typical method of increasing the nucleation site density that is related to the second enhancement mechanism mentioned above is by making reentrant cavities, as shown in Figure 1. Many interesting ideas have been presented so far for making the reentrant cavities, and they have had substantial enhancement effects. There are mainly two categories of making reentrant cavities. The first one is to use the mechanically manufactured structured surfaces. The second one is to make the

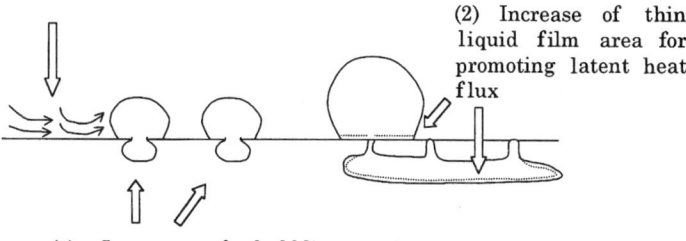

Figure 1  Mechanism of pool boiling heat transfer enhancement.

porous structure by sintered coating of metal particles, plating, or metal-sprayed coating.

The special method of increasing the thin liquid film area for promoting latent heat flux, which is related to the second enhancement mechanism mentioned above, is realized by the tunnel structure of the reentrant cavities or the electrohydrodynamic (EHD) effect, as shown in Figure 2. The total surface of the boiling heat transfer is increased by the amount of the tunnel structure of the reentrant cavities. The applied electric field, which is specific to the weak electrical conducting heat transfer media, influences the shape of the bubble, increasing the thin liquid film area under the bubble by up to nearly ten times. The buoyancy force is balanced by the electrostatic force around the bubble. The electrostatic force flattens out the bubbles at the base longitudinally and increases the liquid film area.

An effective method of increasing the forced convection heat flux to increase the accumulated sensible superheat in liquid near the heat transfer surface, which is related to the third enhancement mechanism mentioned above, is the generation of the forced convection effects as shown in Figure 2. The forced convection would be generated by utilizing bulk flow, impinging jets, inserted ribbons, electric field induced convection, etc.

The pool boiling heat transfer enhancement would be generated by one of the three enhancement mechanisms and their combination. There are various methods of pool boiling heat transfer enhancement that are frequently categorized into either passive methods or active methods. The characteristics of passive methods are using some kinds of structured heat transfer surface without any external power. The active methods are characterized by utilizing some kind of external power, such as electric fields, ultrasonic, and vibration. Passive and active techniques of pool boiling heat transfer enhancement are explained in the following sections.

**(1)-1**

**(1)-2**

Porous structure

**(2)-1**

Boiling surface area increase by reentrant cavities

**(2)-2**

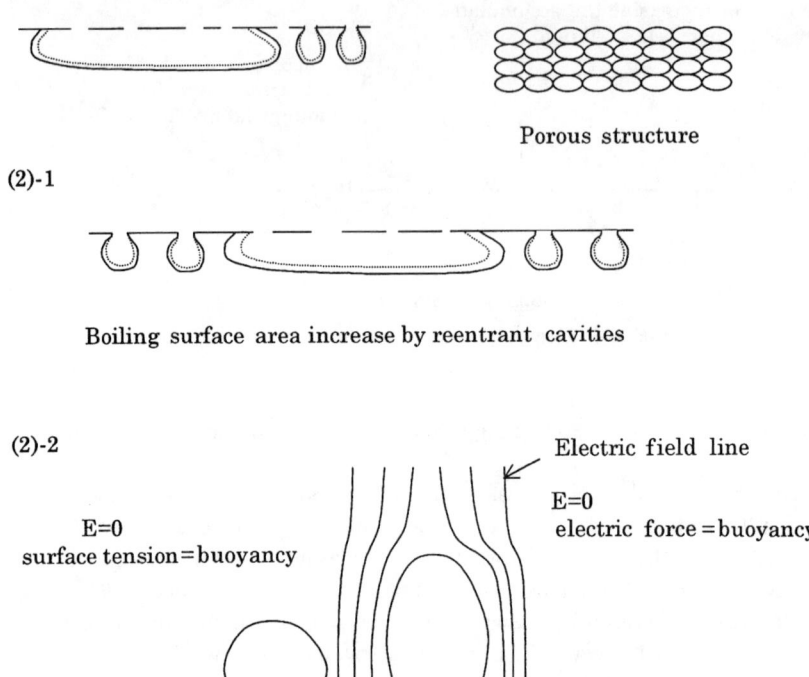

$E=0$
surface tension = buoyancy

Electric field line

$E\neq0$
electric force = buoyancy

Larger thin liquid film area

Electric field effect

**(3)**

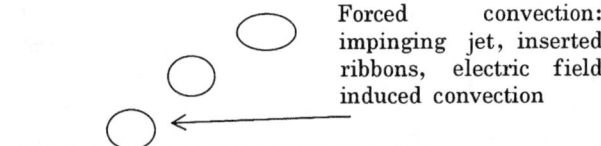

Forced convection: impinging jet, inserted ribbons, electric field induced convection

**Figure 2** Methods of pool boiling heat transfer enhancement.

## 5.3 PASSIVE METHODS OF POOL BOILING HEAT TRANSFER ENHANCEMENT

As fundamental techniques common to many passive methods of pool boiling heat transfer, the structure and characteristics of the reentrant cavities are discussed, and the enhancement effects are reviewed in this section.

### 5.3.1 Reentrant Cavities

The generally applicable reentrant cavity should have the hole or tunnel structure with the sharp enlargement of the inlet mouth, as shown in Figure 3a. The enlargement angle $\phi$ should be equal to or greater than 90 degrees in order to be applicable

(a) Reentrant Cavity Structure
    (Ideal Example)

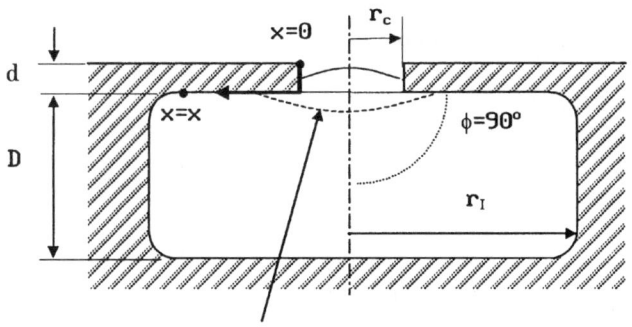

(b) Required Liquid Superheat

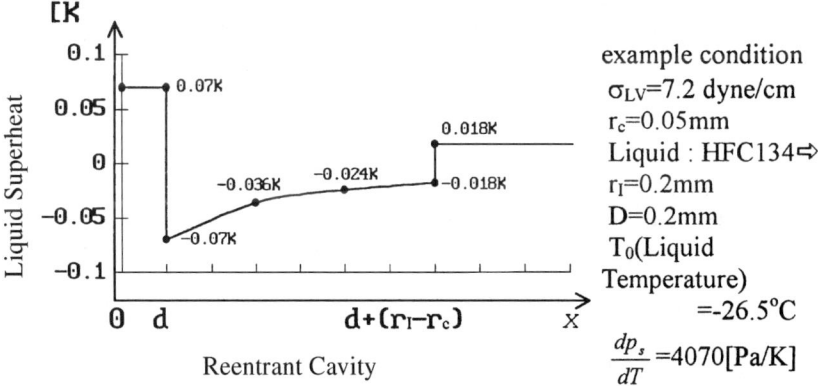

**Figure 3** Structure and required liquid superheat.

for any kind of liquids. If the contact angle of the liquid is larger, the necessary enlargement angle becomes smaller. The equilibrium liquid superheat required to nucleate the reentrant cavity is shown in Figure 3b. The equilibrium liquid superheat along the wall of the reentrant cavity shows that the liquid-vapor interface is stable even in the subcooled condition between $x = \delta$ and $x = \delta + (r_I - r_C)$. The required liquid superheat is of the order of 0.1 K.

The above reentrant cavities have the following characteristics.

1. The stability of the liquid-vapor interface in the subcooled condition means that the vapor can be trapped in the cavity during the whole boiling process to produce bubbles repeatedly.
2. For the typical reentrant cavity shown in Figure 3a, the liquid would not be able to enter into the cavity across the sharp enlargement. This means that the evaporation to make bubbles occurs only at the inlet mouth of the reentrant cavity and that the evaporation does not occur on the internal wall surface of the reentrant cavity. From this point of view, the smaller volume of the reentrant cavity would be estimated to have the higher performance, especially in the higher heat flux region.
3. In case of subsurface tunnel structure, many reentrant cavities with the connected tunnel can divide the role of the liquid sink and the vapor release (Nakayama et al., 1980).
4. Bubble nucleation is possible for low wall superheat values of the order of 0.1 K.
5. The structure of the reentrant cavities or similar shapes can be manufactured by machining, sintering of metal particles, composite structure of metal fibers, and covered perforated metal sheet, abrasive treatment, etching of the surface, attached wires or screen, etc.
6. In the case where the structure of the reentrant cavities is the limiting factor for the entering of the liquid and ejecting of the vapor, the critical heat flux of the boiling would be decreased. Furthermore, in the case where the evaporation rate of the liquid is not the limiting factor of the heat transfer, the structure of the reentrant cavity would not be effective. One example is the evaporation of the non-azeotropic mixtures.

Most of the enhanced surfaces for boiling heat transfer have the structure of the reentrant cavities for increasing nucleation sites. The size of the reentrant cavities is varied from visible scale to a few micrometers. One example is the mechanically manufactured surface shown in Figure 4, which was manufactured by the following process. At first, the outer surface of the tube was deformed to make the low fin tube. Then, the top surface of the low fin tube was cut out. Finally, the fins were bent to form reentrant cavities with small spaced holes, as shown in Figure 4b.

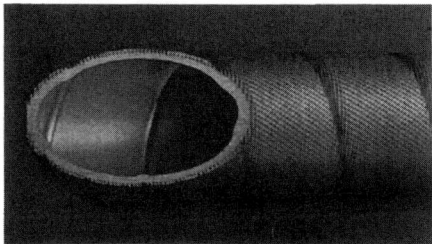

(a) THERMO-EXCEL, HEC

(b) Surface structure

**Figure 4 (a and b)** Thermo-Excel, HEC tube and its surface structure (from the Catalog of Hitachi Cable Co., Ltd.).

As for the enhancement effect of the other structured tubes (such as low fin tubes), the fundamental mechanism of the enhancement would be the same. Therefore, in the case of the low-fin tube, some points along the base of the fin would be effective as micro-scale reentrant cavities.

### 5.3.2 Enhancement Data of Passive Techniques

A large number of experimental studies have been reported in the literature on various chlorofluorocarbons (CFCs) (Nishikawa and Fujita, 1990). Since the usage of CFCs was already regulated for protecting the global environment, the data for CFCs are not practical today. As for CFC alternatives, which include HFC (hydrofluorocarbons) and some HCFC (hydrochlorofluorocarbons) and organic refrigerants, they have thermophysical properties similar to those of CFCs. Therefore, the enhancement data for various kinds of enhanced surfaces for CFCs would be useful in predicting the enhancement effect for CFC alternatives.

Concerning the enhancement data of the structured surfaces, the typical data for isopropyl alcohol at 101 kPa and p-xylene at 101 kPa (Yilmaz and Westwater, 1981)

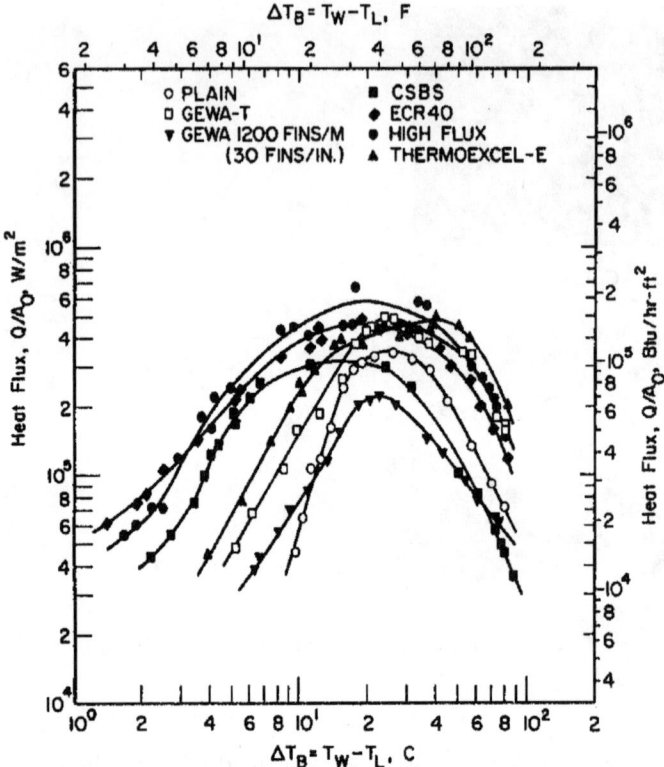

**Figure 5a**  Heat flux and temperature difference [isopropyl alcohol] (Yilmaz and Westwater, 1981).

and for water at atmospheric pressure (Nishikawa and Fujita, 1990) are shown in Figures 5a–c. From these figures, it is seen that a ten-fold enhancement is achieved for decreasing wall superheat. Therefore, by selecting the appropriate enhanced surfaces, it is feasible to enhance the nucleate pool boiling heat transfer coefficients by a factor of ten. As for the figures, CSBS is the copper-metal sprayed surface, Br350-0.94 means sintered surface with metal particles of 300 $\mu$m sintered to the thickness of 0.94 mm, and M3-0.4 means the copper structured surface mechanically machined with the fin height of 0.4 mm. THERMOEXCEL, HIGH FLUX, GEWA-T, GEWA 1200FINS/m, and ECR40 are the names of commercially available structured enhancement surfaces.

As for the enhancement effects of the sintered porous metal surface, one attempt was conducted to correlate the various enhancement data for obtaining the empirical correlation (Nishikawa and Ito, 1982). The empirical correlation is

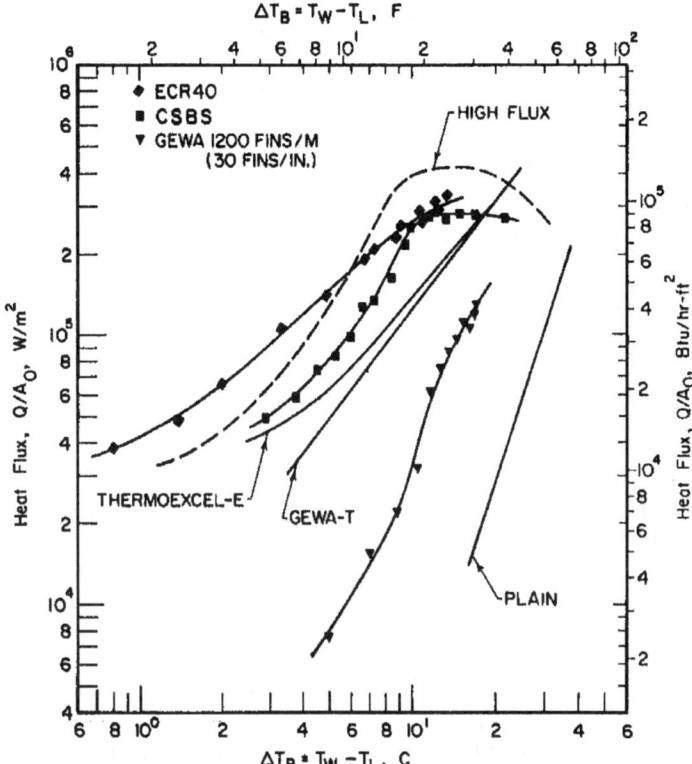

**Figure 5b** Heat flux and temperature difference [p-xylene] (Yilmaz and Westwater, 1981).

shown below:

$$\frac{q\delta}{\lambda_m \Delta T} = 1.00 \times 10^{-3} \left(\frac{\sigma^2 L}{q^2 \delta^2}\right)^{0.0284} \left(\frac{\delta}{d}\right)^{0.560} \left(\frac{qd}{\varepsilon L \mu_V}\right)^{0.593}$$

$$\times \left(\frac{\lambda_m}{\lambda_L}\right)^{-0.708} \left(\frac{\rho_L}{\rho_V}\right)^{1.67} \quad (5.3\text{-}1)$$

$$\lambda_m = \varepsilon \lambda_L + (1 - \varepsilon) \lambda_P \quad (5.3\text{-}2)$$

The applicable range of parameters are as follows:

0.1 mm $< d <$ 1 mm, 1.6 $< \delta/d <$ 20, 0.38 $< \varepsilon <$ 0.71, and 61 W/m/K $< \lambda p <$ 372 W/m/K, where $\delta$ is the thickness of the sintered porous metal, $\varepsilon$ the porosity of the sintered metal, $L$ the latent heat of refrigerating medium, $\lambda$ the thermal conductivity, $\mu$ the viscosity, $\rho$ the density, $\sigma$ the surface tension at the vapor-liquid interface, and subscripts $L$, $V$, $p$, and $m$ denote liquid, vapor, particle, and

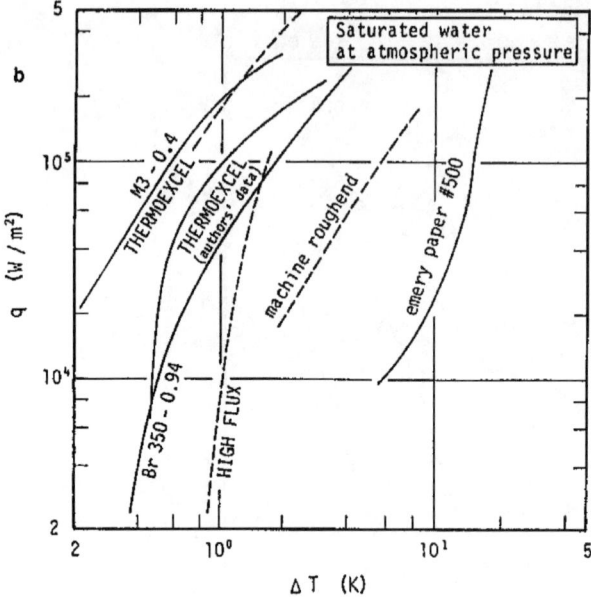

**Figure 5c** Nucleate boiling heat transfer with saturated water (Nishikawa and Fujita, 1990).

the apparent value for the sintered metal filled with the boiling liquid, respectively. The left-hand side of Eq. (5.3-1) represents the Nusselt number. The first and the third non-dimensional variables of the right-hand side represent the effect of the surface tension and the Reynolds number of vapor flow if it would fill up voids of sintered metal. The above correlation was compared with the data for benzene, CFC-11, and CFC-113 at the atmospheric pressure and agreed within less than 30% for the sintered particles of bronze and copper.

As for the necessity of diminishing the hysteresis effects of pool boiling, which had been researched so far for increasing the reliability to control the electronics cooling, some structured surfaces for promoting the holding characteristics of bubbles inside the cavities have been proposed. The forced convection effects also decrease the hysteresis; furthermore, the restriction of the usage range of heat flux to realize the repeatable boiling curves would be effective (Bar-Cohen, 1992).

### 5.3.3 Dynamic Models and Future Work of Passive Enhancement Techniques

In the dynamic model of the boiling phenomenon for the structured surfaces, it is important to optimize the surface structure, such as the reentrant cavity size and the diameter of the openings. The successful dynamic model of the structured pool

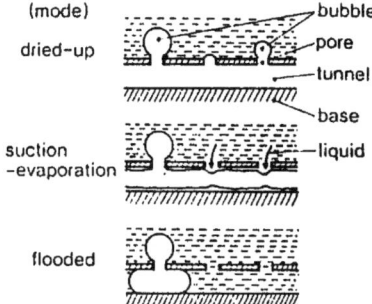

**Figure 6** Heat transfer modes in tunnels of structured surface (Nakayama et al., 1982).

boiling surfaces, which has the subsurface tunnel, is explained here (see Chien and Webb, 1998; Nakayama et al., 1980, 1982; Webb, 1994).

Figure 6 shows the heat transfer modes in subsurface tunnels for one kind of structured surface proposed on the basis of the fundamental visualization research. There would be three possible evaporation modes in the tunnel. The "flooded mode" occurs at low heat flux, where most of the tunnel space is occupied by liquid and some active pores act as isolated reentrant cavities. At the higher heat flux region, the "suction-evaporation mode" occurs, where liquid is sucked in the tunnel space through inactive pores by pumping actions of bubbles growing at active pores. The sucked liquid then spreads along the subsurface tunnels and evaporates from some pores of the tunnel. This mode means that some pores work for the suction of the liquid, while other pores work for the evaporation of the bubbles to compose the systematic enhancement effect. In the higher wall superheat region near the critical heat flux, the "dried-up mode" occurs, where the subsurface tunnel space is nearly filled with vapor, and vaporization into bubbles takes place on the heated wall outside of the tunnels.

One advantage of the structured surface with subsurface tunnels is the higher enhancement effects based on the "suction-evaporation mode" described above. Therefore, many dynamic models based on the suction-evaporation mode have been proposed in the literature (Webb, 1994). The fundamental model to predict the boiling characteristics assumes the bubble cycles categorized into three phases as shown in Figure 7 (Nakayama et al., 1980):

1. Phase I (Pressure Build-up): Evaporation of liquid in the tunnel causes the internal vapor pressure to increase until the vapor nuclei located at the pores along the tunnel attain a hemispherical shape, protruding outward into the external liquid pool.
2. Phase II (Pressure-Reduction): The vapor nuclei become active and grow into bubbles at some pores. The number of the active pores would depend on the

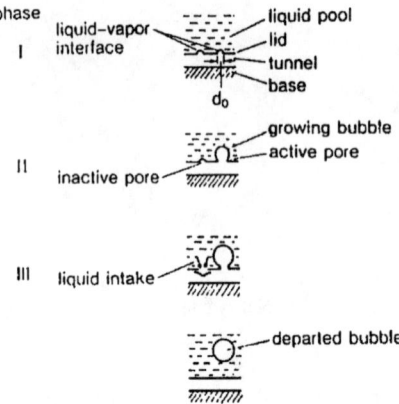

**Figure 7** Basis of dynamic boiling model in the tunnels of structured surface (Nakayama et al., 1980).

evaporation rate, which is equivalent to the heat flux. Initially, the bubbles grow as a result of the increased internal pressure, which reduces the internal pressure in the tunnel as the vapor flows into the bubbles. The bubbles would continue to grow as a result of the inertial force imparted to the surrounding liquid.

3. Phase III (Liquid-Intake): During the inertial stage of bubble growth, the pressure inside the tunnel is reduced to less than that of the external liquid pool. When the internal pressure becomes lower than the critical pressure for the liquid intake to reentrant cavities (which would be determined by the shape of the cavity), liquid is drawn into the tunnel mainly through inactive pores. At the end of this phase, the bubbles depart, all pores are closed by liquid menisci, and the liquid spreads along the angled corners of the tunnel by capillary forces. The cycle then repeats to Phase I.

This dynamic model was used for predicting the best pore diameter of the structured surfaces.

As for the dynamic model of a single reentrant cavity, it is difficult to model the liquid intake period, during which the liquid intake into the cavity takes place by the effect of the liquid inertial force. Furthermore, the reentrant cavity volume would disturb the enhancement effect near the critical heat flux region. Therefore, the dynamic model for the optimum reentrant cavity shape should be tried as an important future topic related to the enhancement of pool boiling heat transfer. This problem would be important to realize the enhanced electronics cooling at the higher heat flux region near the critical heat flux.

Furthermore, the resistivity against fouling and the deterioration characteristics of the pool boiling enhancement surface should be researched for the long-term operation. The advanced structured enhanced surface, which would be strong against the fouling of the surface during the long-term operation and have the higher enhancement performance, should be developed to realize its wider application to the contaminated heat transfer media.

## 5.4 ACTIVE METHODS OF POOL BOILING ENHANCEMENT

### 5.4.1 Active Enhancement Techniques

In heat transfer enhancement, techniques requiring an external activator or power supply are generally labeled "active enhancement techniques." Various methodologies have been tested: fluid or surface vibration, mechanical aids (centrifugal forces), and electrohydrodynamic (EHD) enhancement. As a result of a literature survey, only electrohydrodynamic (EHD) and, to a far lesser extent, vibration have been systematically applied to pool boiling enhancement.

### 5.4.2 Surface and Fluid Vibration

It is generally agreed that the application of vibration to the fluid or the heated surface can improve natural convection and film boiling; thus, Iida & Tsutsui (1992) suggest an application in enhancing quenching processes. Some improvement has been detected in subcooled nucleate boiling, while saturated nucleate boiling and critical heat flux are almost unaffected (Serizawa et al., 1994). Bonekamp & Bier (1996) found a higher improvement (around 50% in heat transfer coefficient) in pool boiling of binary mixtures, though it decreased with increasing heat flux. Both high frequency (ultrasound) and sonic vibrations were tested. Navruzov et al. (1992) point out that the amplitude of vibrations is a governing parameter. Vibrations have a beneficial effect in reducing or suppressing the boiling hysteresis at ONB.

Some significant works in this field are reported in Table 1. The reported power consumption is generally quite high. The mechanism of enhancement is yet unclear: Serizawa et al. (1994) suggest that acoustically induced streams that bring bulk fluid close to the heated surface could improve heat transfer, while the formation of cavitation bubbles seems to be a secondary effect.

### 5.4.3 Electric Field

The effect of an electric field (EF) on pool boiling has been evidenced since 1916 (Chubb, 1916). However, the era of applying this technique to boiling started in the 1960s by Bochirol et al. (1960). Now, several techniques and patents for electrically enhanced evaporators and condensers are available, and EF enhancement is widely

**Table 1  Overview on experimental activities on vibration enhanced pool boiling**

| Reference | Heater geometry | Type of vibration | Fluid | Notes |
|---|---|---|---|---|
| Iida & Tsutsui, 1992 | horizontal wire 0.2 mm dia. | ultrasound 28 kHz | water, ethyl alchool | increase (20%) in CHF detected; increase in minimum film boiling heat flux detected |
| Navruzov at al., 1992 | horizontal plate | 20–40 Hz | ethyl alchool | increase in pool boiling heat transfer; hysteresis detected |
| Serizawa et al., 1994 | plate 20 mm dia. | ultrasound 28 kHz | water | various orientations tested |
| Bonekamp & Bier, 1996 | horizontal tube 8 mm dia. | ultrasound 42–85 kHz | R-23 R134a mixture | |
| Zitko & Afgan, 1994; Zitko & Afgan, 1996 | plate 60 mm$^2$ | horizontally or vertically vibrating surface 0–70 Hz | water | little improvement detected at low heat flux for horizontal vibration; improvement of 25% detected for vertical vibration |

recognized as the most promising active technique of boiling enhancement in dielectric or slightly conductive fluids for refrigeration, power, and process industry. Furthermore, it can also be intended as a technique to "modulate" heat transfer performance by varying the applied voltage. A further field of application may be boiling in microgravity, where the electrical forces can replace the ones lacking gravity (Di Marco & Grassi, 1996). Both ac and dc power supplies were tested in laboratory configurations: the latter is preferred for technological application to avoid problems connected with the electrical impedance of the system, though the risk of electrostaic fouling may be increased. The major drawback lies in the potentially dangerous high voltages required: indicatively, values from 3 to 30 kV were adopted. However, these values are of the same order as those commonly involved in electrostatic separators for particulate or in cathode-ray tubes. Furthermore, the electrical current is in most cases negligible (usually some $\mu$A, maximum reported 1–2 mA), making EHD safe and operationally inexpensive; besides, no moving parts are needed. Several reviews on the subject are available (Allen & Karayiannis, 1995; Di Marco & Grassi, 1993; Jones, 1978; Yabe et al., 1995).

The modeling of EF action in boiling is very complex, due to the fact that the fluid-dynamics conservation equations are coupled with Maxwell's and Ohm's laws and that they have to be solved together. The actual field configuration is continuously altered by the phase distribution changes: this may lead to a field configuration very different from the single-phase one, which is generally assumed as reference. Recently, quite simple configurations were analyzed with computer aid (Karayiannis & Xu, 1998a; Ogata & Yabe, 1993).

**The electrical forces and their effects on bubbles and interfaces.** The electrical body force $\mathbf{F}^*$ can be expressed as (Landau & Lifshitz, 1963)

$$\mathbf{F}^* = \rho_F \mathbf{E} - \frac{1}{2}\varepsilon_E E^2 \operatorname{grad} \varepsilon_E + \frac{1}{2}\operatorname{grad}\left[\varepsilon_E E^2 \rho \left(\frac{\partial \varepsilon_E}{\partial \rho}\right)_T\right] \quad (5.4\text{-}1)$$

where $E$ is the electric field intensity and $\varepsilon_E$ is the absolute permittivity of the medium. The first term is the well known Coulomb (or electrophoretic) force, due to the presence of free charge. When free charge is present, this term dominates over the remaining two. The second term is the force due to the spatial variation of $\varepsilon_E$ (induced by changes in temperature and density). The third term comprises the dielectrophoretic and electrostrictive forces, due to the nature of $E$ and $\varepsilon_E$ and their spatial distribution. The last two terms in R.H.S. can be defined as polarization forces, since they act on polarization charges; they are independent of field polarity. The third term is irrotational and has also been interpreted as an "electric pressure." The force $\mathbf{F}^*$ must be added to the right-hand side of the Navier-Stokes equation to study electroconvective problems.

Other relevant electrodynamic equations to be included in the problem are

$$\operatorname{div}(\varepsilon_E \mathbf{E}) = \rho_F \quad (5.4\text{-}2)$$

$$\mathbf{E} = -\operatorname{grad}\varphi \quad (5.4\text{-}3)$$

$$\operatorname{div}\mathbf{J} = 0 \quad (5.4\text{-}4)$$

where $\rho_F$ is the free charge density, $\varphi$ is the electric potential, and $\mathbf{J}$ is the current density, which in turn is given by

$$\mathbf{J} = \rho_F \mathbf{u} + \sigma_E \mathbf{E} + \frac{\partial(\varepsilon_E \mathbf{E})}{\partial t} \quad (5.4\text{-}5)$$

where charge convection, Ohm's law, and displacement current are accounted for, respectively. As the electrical current is always quite low, magnetic field effects can be neglected. The most relevant coupling mechanisms among the flow, temperature, and electrostatic fields are free charge convection, electrical body force $\mathbf{F}^*$, and variations of $\varepsilon_E$ and $\sigma_E$ with temperature. Furthermore, the presence and displacement of vapor masses may substantially alter the electrostatic field distribution.

The coupling of mass and electric charge continuity in a medium generates as an important consequence the so-called charge relaxation equation:

$$\frac{D\rho_F}{Dt} + \frac{1}{\tau}(\rho_F - \sigma_E E \cdot \operatorname{grad}\tau) = 0 \quad (5.4\text{-}6)$$

where $\sigma_E$ is the ohmic conductivity of the medium. The equation shows that the charge relaxation time, $\tau = \varepsilon_E/\sigma_E$, is an important parameter in determining the electric coupling, as first made clear by Jones (1978). Free electric charge buildup may take place if the characteristic times in the system are less than $\tau$; among them, the period of the electric field (if it is alternate) and the mechanical oscillations of the interfaces or bubble detachment are the most significant ones. As a consequence, the presence of free charge should be evaluated not only with mere reference to the electrical properties of the fluid, but also taking into account the characteristics of the whole system. To give an order of magnitude, relaxation time is about 1.3 s for R-11 and $9 \times 10^{-3}$ s for R-123 (Ogata & Yabe, 1993). Bubble detachment times are generally of the order of 10 ms.

The dielectrophoretic force acting on a spherical bubble is given by Pohl (1958):

$$\mathbf{F}_b = 2\pi R^3 \frac{\varepsilon_{Eg} - \varepsilon_{El}}{\varepsilon_{Eg} + 2\varepsilon_{El}} \varepsilon_{El} \text{ grad } E^2 \qquad (5.4\text{-}7)$$

The approximations involved in the former relationship are thoroughly discussed by Jones (1979). The force $F_b$ tends to push the vapor (of lower electrical permittivity, $\varepsilon_{Eg} < \varepsilon_{El}$) towards zones of weaker electric field and can also be interpreted as a "electric buoyancy" force.

When the EF is present across a vapor-liquid interface, an interfacial stress (Maxwell stress) appears, and the Rayleigh-Taylor instability mechanism is electrohydrodynamically coupled. As a result, liquid-vapor interfaces are generally destabilized by an externally applied electric field (Jones, 1978; Melcher and Smith 1969). This leads to an increase of critical heat flux and can reverse film boiling to nucleate boiling. Possible variations in the physical properties (e.g., bubble contact angle) induced by the application of EF have yet to be fully documented.

**Effect of EF in pool boiling.** The EF has been recognized as an effective means in enhancing single-phase natural convection (Jones, 1978); this, of course, is equally important for the non-boiling component of boiling heat transfer.

All the experimental works are in agreement in evidencing a reduction of temperature overshoot at the onset of nucleate boiling. Conversely, due to the enhancement of single-phase convection, the heat flux at ONB generally increases with applied voltage. It has been also reported that a single high voltage pulse can trigger the ONB at lower wall superheat (Allen & Cooper, 1987). This may have important applications in establishing boiling where a limited temperature difference is available.

The effect of EF on nucleate boiling depends on geometrical configuration: strong enhancement is generally reported for plate and tube configurations, while on thin wires, little enhancement or even slight degradation generally takes place. It is universally agreed that the enhancing effect is reduced with increasing heat flux; this could be attributed either to the reduction of the electric field intensity due to the increasing presence of vapor or to the reduced role played by enhanced single-phase convection among bubbles. The size of the bubbles is in any case reduced, and their detachment frequency is increased with increasing electric field.

Contrary to evidence from early EHD works, it was found that field configurations resulting in a force that pushes the bubbles against the heated surface are more effective in nucleate boiling enhancement. Even an electric field established between flat plates that is uniform if the fluid is homogeneous exerts such an action due to its alteration by the bubbles themselves. The enhancement is likely due to the reduction in microlayer thickness under the bubble and to the "sliding bubble" mechanism (Cornwell, 1990). At present, no reliable and widely applicable heat transfer correlation for EHD nucleate pool boiling is available in the open literature, though Cooper (1992) modified Rohsenow's correlation with partial success.

Critical heat flux is always increased by EF. The increase is a function of the applied voltage, and values up to 5 times the zero-field once were reported in pool boiling applications. This significantly improves the safety margin against the boiling crisis. Correlations of the type

$$\frac{q''_{CHF,E}}{q''_{CHF,0}} = f\left(\frac{\varepsilon_E E^2}{\sqrt{(\rho_l - \rho_g)\sigma g}}\right) \quad (5.4\text{-}8)$$

can predict with success the enhancement in CHF, provided that $\varepsilon$ is correctly estimated (Di Marco & Grassi, 1993; Zaghdoudi & Lallemand, 1997).

Although the film boiling regime is seldom adopted as the operational one, it can be consistently enhanced by the application of an EF. Experimental data are available only for wires: the enhanced film boiling regime cannot be sustained indefinitely and reverts to a conventional one for sufficiently high wall superheat (Carrica et al., 1996).

**Practical applications.** In the following, references will be made to EHD enhancement of external pool boiling heat transfer on tubes and tube bundles, i.e., the most significant configurations for practical application. Several electrode layouts resulting in different field distributions were tested. Evaluations showed possible savings in heat transfer surface from 10% to 30%.

In selecting geometry, the target should be pursued to generate electric forces that may assist the maximum number of bubbles in sliding on the heated surface. Furthermore, a simple geometry should be selected, making sure the other design parameters (e.g., hydraulic resistance, tube density, serviceability, fouling) are as unaltered as possible. Although a non-uniform electric field is needed, excessive non-uniformity should be avoided to prevent local fluid disruption resulting in dangerous discharges. Computer assisted calculation methods start to be developed (Karayiannis & Xu, 1998a; Ogata & Yabe, 1993) that generally make use of finite element techniques and account for the actual thermal field and vapor configuration that modifies the field distribution.

The most widely applied configuration consists of a set of rods parallel to the tubes that is quite straightforward to set up. The number and the position of the rods may vary: very recently, Karayiannis & Xu (1998b) compared different rod layouts. Typical enhancements in heat transfer coefficient up to 5-fold and more with an applied voltage of 10–15 kV were easily obtained in this way. Circumferential wire meshes coaxial to the tube are generally more efficient, though they are weaker and less simple to implement in real system of tube bundles.

Other tested geometries range from perforated plates, rod-plate combinations, and different wire configurations: straight wires, helical coil, rings, and wire mesh. Some of them were compared by Cooper (1992). An overview of the main experimental activities in this field is given in Table 2. Allen & Karayiannis (1995) have compiled a literature survey, also including other geometries. The maximum encountered enhancement factor, $En_{max}$, though indicative, should not be considered as an absolute figure of merit: it varies considerably with heat flux and configuration. It was also noted that sometimes a further increase in applied voltage may lead to saturation or, in some cases, reduction of enhancement (Seyed-Yagoobi et al., 1996). In every case, a progressive decrease of boiling hysteresis was encountered. In some cases, for the higher values of applied voltage, hysteresis completely disappeared. The maximum reported EHD power consumption was 5% of the heat transfer rate. Several authors tested the effect of oil contaminants: although the heat transfer coefficient was reduced, the EHD enhancement factor was not impaired. Conversely, contaminant altering the relaxation time, like ethanol in R11, may have a strong impact (Ogata et al., 1992).

Yabe et al. (1992) reported EHD enhancement also for non-azeotropic boiling mixtures.

**EHD application on enhanced surfaces.** The action of EF was also associated with an enhanced surface. This is sometimes referred to as "compound enhancement." The improvement in heat transfer (with respect to the zero-field one) was found to be greater than on a smooth surface, presumably due to the intensification of the gradient of EF in the proximity of grooves. Several configurations were tested, as detailed in Table 3. It was found that finned surfaces (like Thermoexcel, lo-fin, and others) generally benefit with the application of an electric field, thus combining passive and active enhancements. Conversely, porous or deeply finned surfaces give less or no improvement, presumably because the EF penetration inside the cavities is lower. Additionally, it was found that the comparative

Table 2  Overview on experimental activities on EHD enhanced pool boiling on smooth tubes

| Reference | Heater geometry | Electrode geometry | Applied Voltage | Fluid | $E\eta_{max}$ | Notes |
|---|---|---|---|---|---|---|
| Papar et al., 1993 | Horizontal tube 12.7 mm O.D. | straight wires helical wire wire mesh | 5–20 kV | R-123 R-123/oil | 5 (R-123) | wire mesh performs better |
| Ohadi et al., 1992 | Horizontal tube 12.7 mm O.D. | straight wires | | R-123 R-11 | 1.7 (R11) 4.5 (R-123) | oil contamination tested |
| Seyed-Yagoobi et al., 1996 | Horizontal tube 26.5 O.D. | straight wires rings | 5–15 kV | R-123 | 2 (wires) 1.7 (rings) | best enhancement at 5–10 kV |
| Ogata et al., 1992 | Horizontal tube bundles, 22 mm O.D. | straight rods | 5–25 kV | R-11 R-123 | 7 | ethanol contamination tested |
| Kawahira et al., 1990 | Horizontal tube 22 mm O.D. | straight rods | 5–25 kV | R-11 | 3 | negative dc, positive dc and ac field tested |
| Yabe et al., 1992 | Horizontal tube | perforated coaxial cylinder | 7 kV | mixture R-123/ R-134a | 3 | non-azeotropic mixtures tested |
| Karayiannis, 1998 | Horizontal tube bundle, 19 mm O.D. | straight rods | 0–25 kV | R-11 R-123 | 1.05 (R11) 9.3 (R123) | effect of pressure tested |

Table 3  Overview on experimental activities on EHD enhanced pool boiling on enhanced tubes

| Reference | Heater geometry | Electrode geometry | Voltage | Fluid | $En_{max}$ | Notes |
|---|---|---|---|---|---|---|
| Salehi et al., 1997 | grooved channels, 1 mm hydraulic diameter | plate to plate (external pipe grounded) | 5–15 kV | R-134a | 10 | smooth and enhanced surfaces tested |
| Cheung et al., 1996 | lo-fin horizontal tube bundle, 19 mm O.D | Wire mesh or parallel pipe rods | 0–3 kV | R-134a | 4 (mesh) 2 (wire) | field polarity tested |
| Yan and Neve, 1996 Yan et al., 1996 | single horizontal tube, ~19 mm O.D. | Circumferential wire mesh | 10–30 kV | R-114 | 3.4 | various surfaces (Thermoexcel HE, Thermoexcel C, Gewa-T, lo-fin, smooth) compared |
| Al-Dadah et al., 1997 | horizontal lo-fin tube bundle 16 mm O.D. | plate-rod arrangement | 10–27 kV | R-12 R-12/oil | | oil contamination tested |
| Damiadinis et al., 1992 | Horiz. tube bundle Horiz. single tube | plate-rod arrangement | 10–30 kV | R-114 | 2.4 | smooth and lo-fin surfaces tested |
| Allen & Cooper, 1987 Cooper, 1990 | Single lo-fin horizontal tube | wire mesh | 10–27 kV | R-114 | | |
| Singh et al., 1995 | Horizontal finned tubes, 19 mm O.D. | straight wire wire mesh | 5–20 kV | R-123 | 11.5 | wire mesh performs better |

performance of different surfaces varied with the applied voltage (Yan et al., 1996). This suggests that the EHD effect is strongly dependent on geometry and that the optimum field-surface coupling has still to be identified; a better performance might be achieved with a surface geometry specifically designed for use with EHD.

## REFERENCES

Al-Dadah, R. K., Chaer, I., and Karayiannis, T. G. 1997. EHD Enhanced Heat Transfer in the Evaporator of a Refrigeration Plant. *Proc. Experimental Heat Transfer, Fluid Mechanics and Thermodynamics 1997*. Ed. Giot, M., Mayinger, F., and Celata, G. P. Bruxelles. Pisa: ETS, 1:1929–1939.

Allen, P. H. G. and Cooper, P. 1987. The Potential of Electrically Enhanced Evaporators. *Proc. 3rd Int. Symp on the Large Scale Application of Heat Pumps*, Oxford, pp. 221–229.

Allen, P. H. G. and Karayiannis, T. G. 1995. Electrohydrodynamic Enhancement of Heat Transfer and Fluid Flow. *Heat Recovery Systems & CHP* 15:389–423.

Bar-Cohen, A. 1992. Hysteresis Phenomena at the Onset of Nucleate Boiling. In: *Pool and External Flow Boiling*. Eds. V. J. Dhir and A. E. Bergeles, pp. 1–14. Proceedings of the Engineering Foundation Conference, Santa Barbara, CA. New York: ASME.

Bochirol, L., Bonjour, E., and Weil, L. 1960. Etude de L'Action de Champs Electriques sur les Transfert de Chaleur dans les Liquides Bouillants. *C. R. Hebd. Seances Acad. Sci.* 250:76–78.

Bonekamp, S. and Bier, K. 1996. Influence of Ultrasound on Pool Boiling Heat Transfer to Mixtures of the Refrigerants R-23 and R-134a. *Proc. of Eurotherm Seminar 48*. Eds. D. Gorenflo, D. Kenning, C. Marvillet, and D. Paderborn. Pisa: ETS, 1:227–238.

Carrica, P., Di Marco, P., and Grassi, W. 1996. Electric Field Effects on Film Boiling on a Wire. *Experimental Heat Transfer* 11–27.

Cheung, K., Ohadi, M. M., and Dessiatoun, S. V. 1996. Boiling Heat Transfer Enhancement of R-134a in a Tube Bundle Utilizing the EHD Technique. *Journal of Enhanced Heat Transfer* 3:301–309.

Chien, L. H., and Webb, R. L. 1998. A Nucleate Boiling Model for Structured Enhanced Surfaces. *Int. J. Heat Mass Transfer* 41(14):2183–2195.

Chubb, L. W. 1916. Improvements Relating to Methods and Apparatus for Heating Liquids. UK Patent 100796.

Cooper, P. 1990. EHD Enhancement of Nucleate Boiling. *ASME J. Heat Transfer* 112:458–464.

Cooper, P. 1992. Practical Design Aspects of EHD Heat Transfer Enhancement in Evaporators. *ASHRAE Transactions* 98:445–454.

Cornwell, K. 1990. The Role of Sliding Bubbles in Boiling on Tube Bundles. *Proc 9th International Heat Transfer Conference*, Volume 3. Jerusalem, Israel. New York: Hemisphere Publishing Corp., pp. 455–460.

Damianidis, C., Karayiannis, T. G., Al-Dadah, A., James, R. W., Collins, M. W., and Allen, P. H. G. 1992. EHD Boiling Enhancement in Shell-and-Tube Evaporators and Its Application in Refrigeration Plants. *ASHRAE Transactions* 98:462–472.

Di Marco, P. and Grassi, W. 1993. Saturated Pool Boiling Enhancement by Means of an Electric Field. *J. Enhanced Heat Transfer* 1:99–114.

Di Marco, P. and Grassi, W. 1996. Nucleate Pool Boiling in the Presence of an Electric Field and in a Variable Gravity Field: Results of Experiments in Parabolic Flight. *Proc. of Eurotherm Seminar 48*. Eds. D. Gorenflo, D. Kenning, C. Marvillet, and D. Paderborn. Pisa: ETS, 1:255–264.

Iida, Y. and Tsutsui, K. 1992. Effects of Ultrasonic Waves on Natural Convection, Nucleate Boiling, and Film Boiling Heat Transfer from a Wire to Saturated Liquid. *Experimental Thermal and Fluid Science* 5:108–115.

Jones, T. B. 1978. Electrohydrodynamically Enhanced Heat Transfer in Liquids—A Review. *Advances in Heat Transfer* 14:107–148.

Jones, T. B. 1979. Dielectrophoretic Force Calculation. *J. Electrostatics* 6:69–82.

Karayiannis, T. G. 1998. EHD Boiling Heat Transfer Enhancement of R-123 and R-11 on a Tube Bundle. *J. of Applied Thermal Engineering*, in press.

Karayiannis, T. G. and Xu, Y. 1998a. Electric Field Effect in Pool Boiling Heat Transfer. Part A: Simulation of the Electric Field and Electric Forces. *J. of Enhanced Heat Transfer* 5(4):217–229.

Karayiannis, T. G. and Xu, Y. 1998b. Electric Field Effect in Pool Boiling Heat Transfer. Part B: Electrode Geometry. *J. of Enhanced Heat Transfer* 5(4):231–247.

Kawahira, H., Kubo, Y., Yokoyama, T., and Ogata, J. 1990. Effect of an Electric Field on Boiling Heat Transfer of Refrigerant-11—Boiling on a Single Tube. *IEEE Transactions on Industry Applications* 26:359–365.

Landau, L. D. and Lifshitz, E. M. 1963. *Electrodynamics of Continuous Media*. New York: Pergamon, p. 68.

Melcher, J. R. and Smith, C. V. 1969. EHD Charge Relaxation and Interfacial Perpendicular Field Instability. *Physics of Fluids* 12:778–790.

Nakayama, W., Daikoku, T., and Nakajima, T., 1982. Effects of Pore Diameters and System Pressure on Saturated Pool Nucleate Boiling Heat Transfer from Porous Surfaces. *Journal of Heat Transfer* 104:286–291.

Nakayama, W., Daikoku, T. Kuwahara, H., and Nakajima, T., 1980. Dynamic Model of Enhanced Boiling Heat Transfer on Porous Surfaces. Part I: Experimental Investigation. Part II: Analytical Modeling. *ASME Journal of Heat Transfer* 102(3):445–456.

Navruzov, Y. V., Mamontov, P. V., and Stoychev, A. V. 1992. Subcooled Liquid Pool Boiling Heat Transfer on a Vibrating Heating Surface. *Heat Transfer Research* 24:771–776.

Nishikawa, K. and Fujita, Y. 1990. Nucleate Boiling Heat Transfer and Its Augmentation. *Advances in Heat Transfer* 20:1–82.

Nishikawa, K. and Ito, T. 1982. Augmentation of Nucleate Boiling Heat Transfer by Prepared Surfaces. In: *Heat Transfer in Energy Problems*. Eds. T. Mizushina and W. J. Yang, pp. 111–118. New York: Hemisphere Publishing Corp.

Ogata, J. and Yabe, A. 1993. Basic Study on the Enhancement of Nucleate Boiling Heat Transfer by Applying Electric Fields. *Int. J. Heat Mass Transfer* 36:775–782.

Ogata, J., Iwafuji, Y., Shimada, Y., and Yamazaki, T. 1992. Boiling Heat Transfer Enhancement in Tube-Bundle Evaporators Utilizing Electric Field Effects. *ASHRAE Transactions* 98:435–444.

Ohadi, M. M., Papar, R. A., Ng, T. L., Faani, M. A., and Radermacher, R. 1992. EHD Enhancement of Shell-Side Boiling Heat Transfer Coefficients of R-123/Oil Mixture. *ASHRAE Transactions* 98:427–434.

Papar, R. A., Ohadi, M. M., Kumar, A., and Ansari, A. I. 1993. Effect of Electrode Geometry on EHD-Enhanced Boiling of R-123/Oil Mixture. *ASHRAE Transactions* 99:1237–1243.

Pohl, H. A. 1958. Some Effects of Non-Uniform Fields on Dielectrics. *J. of Applied Physics*. 29:1182–1189.

Salehi, M., Ohadi, M. M., and Dessiatoun, S. 1995. EHD, Enhanced Convective Boiling of R-134a in Grooved Channels—Application to Subcompact Heat Exchangers. *ASME Journal of Heat Transfer* 119:805–809.

Serizawa, A., Mukai, M., Aoki, N., Takahashi, O., Kawara, Z., Mishima, K., and Michiyoishi, I. 1994. Effect of Ultrasonic Emission on Boiling and Non-Boiling Heat Transfer in Natural and Forced Circulation Systems. *Proc. of the X International Heat Transfer Conference*, Brighton, Volume 6. Ed. G. F. Hewitt, pp. 97–102.

Seyed-Yagoobi, J., Geppert, C. A., and Geppert, L. M., 1996. Electrohydrodynamically Enhanced Heat Transfer in Pool Boiling. *ASME J. Heat Transfer* 118:233–237.

Singh, A., Ohadi, M. M., and Dessiatoun, S. 1995. EHD-Enhanced Boiling of R-123 over Commercially Available Enhanced Tubes. *ASME Journal of Heat Transfer* 117:1070–1073.

Webb, R. L. 1994. *Principles of Enhanced Heat Transfer*, Chap.11. New York: John Wiley and Sons.

Yabe, A., Mori, Y., and Hijikata, K. 1995. Active Heat Transfer Enhancement by Utilizing Electric Fields. In *Annual Review of Heat Transfer*, Volume 7. Begell House, pp.193–244.

Yabe, A., Taketani, T., Maki, H., Takahashi, K., and Nakadai, Y. 1992. Experimental Study of Electro-Hydrodynamically (EHD) Enhanced Evaporator for Nonazeotropic Mixtures. *ASHRAE Transactions* 98:455–460.

Yan, Y. Y. and Neve, R. S. 1996. EHD Augmentation of Nucleate Boiling at a Gewa-T Surface. *Journal of Enhanced Heat Transfer* 3:211–219.

Yan, Y. Y., Neve, R. S., Karayiannis, T. G., Collins, M. W., and Allen, P. H. G. 1996. EHD Effects on Nucleate Boiling at Passive Enhanced Surfaces. *Int. J. of Experimental Heat Transfer* 9:195–211.

Yilmaz, S. and Westwater, J. W. 1981. Effect of Commercial Enhanced Surfaces on the Boiling Heat Transfer Curve. In: *Advances in Enhanced Heat Transfer.* Eds. R. L. Webb, T. C. Carnavos, E. F. Park, Jr., and K. M. Hostetler, pp.73–92. ASME Symposium, HTD-Volume 18. New York: ASME.

Zaghdoudi, M. C. and Lallemand, M. 1997. Study of EHD Effect on Heat Transfer with Boiling Dielectric Fluids. *Proc. Int. Symp. on the Physics of Heat Transfer in Boiling and Condensation*, Moscow, May 21–24, 1997, pp. 335–340.

Zitko, V. and Afgan, N. 1994. Boiling Heat Transfer from Oscillating Surface. *Journal of Enhanced Heat Transfer* 1:191–196.

Zitko, V. and Afgan, N. 1996. Boiling Heat Transfer from Horizontally Oscillating Surface. *Proc. $2^{nd}$ European Thermal Sciences and $14^{th}$ UIT National Conference*. Eds. G. P. Celata, P. Di Marco, and A. Mariani. Rome, pp. 183–187.

CHAPTER
# SIX

## CRITICAL HEAT FLUX IN POOL BOILING

Yoshihiko Haramura

*Kanagawa University, 3-27-1 Rokkakubashi, Yokohama 221-8686, Japan*

## 6.1 CRITICAL HEAT FLUX IN SATURATED POOL BOILING OF PURE LIQUIDS

As the surface temperature of a heater is increased in nucleate boiling, heat flux increases and reaches a maximum. If we heat the surface with the heat flux beyond the maximum, transition from nucleate boiling to film boiling takes place. The maximum heat flux that can be obtained with nucleate boiling is called as critical heat flux (CHF). In most practical systems, the temperature of the film boiling corresponding to CHF is so high that heater surface is damaged and sometimes melts down. CHF is therefore sometimes called *burn-out heat flux*.

### 6.1.1 Primary Factors Affecting Critical Heat Flux

Test liquid, system pressure, and gravity level are the primary factors that govern CHF. Using dimensional analysis, Kutateladze (1952) derives the expression for CHF as

$$\dot{q}_c = K_1 \rho_g h_{lg} \left[ \sigma g (\rho_l - \rho_g) / \rho_g^2 \right]^{1/4} \qquad (6.1\text{-}1)$$

From the fitting to CHF data, Kutateladze employed $K_1 = 0.16$, whereas Zuber (1959) recommended $K_1 = 0.131$. Figure 1 shows the correlation of CHF data by Eq. (6.1-1). The data in Figure 1 were obtained on a horizontal flat plate surface

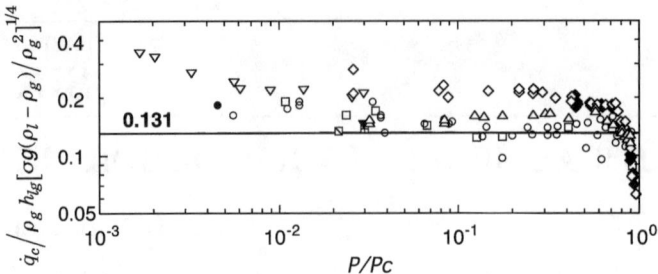

**Figure 1** Critical heat flux on horizontal flat surfaces.

for various liquids under various system pressures, the experimental conditions of which are listed in Table 6.1-1. It may be seen from Figure 1 that CHF is fairly well correlated by Eq. (6.1-1). The deviation of helium data and R-113 data at low pressures indicated a larger value of $K_1$ than that given by Kutateladze or Zuber.

The effect of gravity level on CHF was investigated by Merte and Clark (1964), who conducted a transient cooling test in liquid nitrogen at reduced gravity using a copper sphere with 25.4 mm diameter. Sun and Lienhard (1970) carried out the experiment for a cylindrical surface using the centrifugal systems. The results of both studies for large heaters were well explained by Eq. (6.1-1).

### 6.1.2 Secondary Factors Affecting Critical Heat Flux

In high heat flux nucleate boiling, evaporation from the part of triple contact line at the nucleation sites plays an important role in heat transfer. Surface roughness, wettability, and thermal properties of the heater affect CHF. There are other secondary factors of CHF that connect to the fluid motion, i.e., the size and the

**Table 1** Experimental condition of data in Figure 1

| Symbol | Liquid | Diameter (mm) | Pressure (MPa) | Surface finish or roughness | Source |
|---|---|---|---|---|---|
| □ | ethanol | 95.3 | 0.069–5.9 | — | Cichelli & Bonilla (1945) |
| ○ | water | 10 | 0.12–20 | — | Kazakova (1952) |
| ● | water | 50.8 | 0.10 | Emery 4/0 | Gaertner (1965) |
| ▽ | R-113 | 59 | 0.0058–0.1 | 0.7–2 $\mu$m | Abuaf & Staub (1983) |
| ⊠ | acetone | 63.5 | 0.10 | Emery 80 | Ramilison & Lienhard (1987) |
| ⊞ | n-pentane | 63.5 | 0.10 | Emery 80 | Ramilison & Lienhard (1987) |
| ▼ | R-113 | 63.5 | 0.10 | Emery 80 | Ramilison & Lienhard (1987) |
| ◇ | helium | 25 | 0.019–0.22 | Emery F9 | Bewilogua et al. (1975) |
| △ | nitrogen | 19 | 0.1–3.0 | Emery F9 | Bewilogua et al. (1975) |
| ◆ | helium | 30 × 30 square | 0.1–0.22 | $R_z = 0.08$–$0.3$ $\mu$m | Deev et al. (1977) |

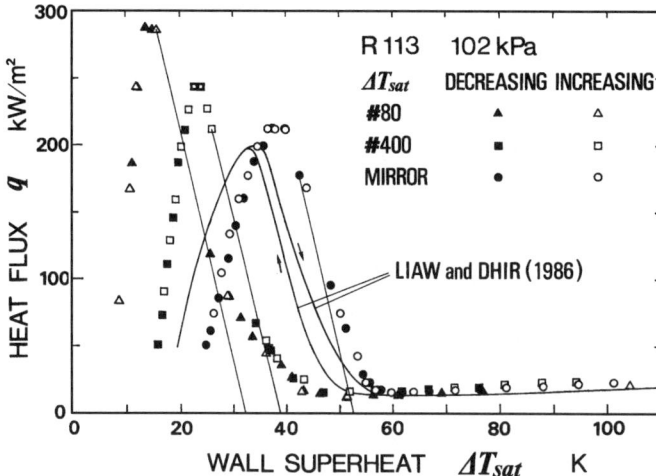

**Figure 2** Effects of surface finish (Haramura, 1991).

geometry of the heater. These factors are not involved explicitly in Eq. (6.1-1), and the effects are usually evaluated by comparing the CHF value with Eq. (6.1-1).

**Surface Roughness.** Nucleate boiling heat transfer is strongly affected by surface roughness. The surface roughness effect on CHF has been extensively investigated from the early stage of boiling research. Berenson (1960) conducted boiling tests in n-pentane, showing that the roughest surface (polished with #60 Emery paper) gives the highest CHF, and that the mirror finished surface gives about 20% lower CHF than that for the roughest surface. Ramilison and Lienhard (1987) and Haramura (1991) also show that surface roughness enhances CHF by 25–35%. Typical data showing the roughness effects on CHF is given in Figure 2.

**Surface Wettability.** Costello and Frea (1965) and others reported the reduction of CHF on a poor wetting surface. Contact angle is a usual representative parameter of surface wettability. The retreating contact angle is often employed to correlate CHF because the surface comes to dry at the CHF condition. When we control the surface wettability by coating the material to the surface, thermal resistance of the coated film becomes important to wall superheat. If the thickness of the coated film is 1 $\mu$m and the thermal conductivity of it is 1 W/mK (this is the case for ceramics, while it is several times greater than that for resins), the local temperature drop across the coated film could exceed 1 K. Liaw and Dhir (1986) proposed an ingenious way to control wettability. They kept copper surface at a certain temperature for 10 to 60 minutes to oxidize the surface. Contact angle was found to be a function of the copper temperature, ranging from 20° to 70°

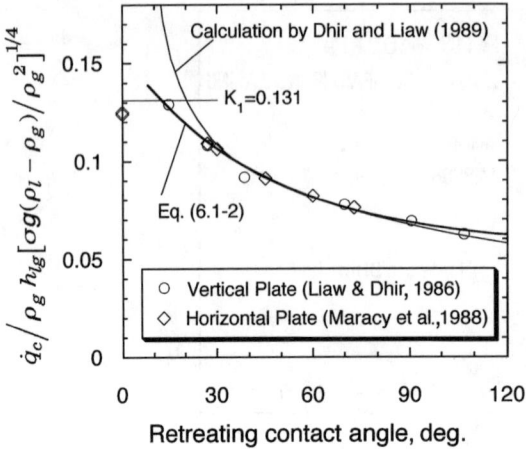

**Figure 3**  Effect of contact angle on CHF.

for water. Maracy and Winterton (1988) changed the contact angle by repeated heating and cooling of the surface between nucleate and film boiling. Figure 3 shows the dependency of CHF on the contact angle they obtained, in which two data of Liaw and Dhir are also involved that were obtained at large contact angles on a surface coated with fluoro-silicone sealant deposit. The best fit curve of the data in Figure 3 is expressed by

$$\dot{q}_c / \rho_g h_{lg} \left[ \sigma g (\rho_l - \rho_g) / \rho_g^2 \right]^{1/4} = 0.1 \exp(-\theta/45°) + 0.055 \quad (6.1\text{-}2)$$

**Heat Capacity of a Heater.** The thermal property of a heater is one of the non-hydrodynamic factors that affects boiling heat transfer. Ivey and Morris (1962) reported scattered data of CHF on a thin heater. Houchin and Lienhard (1966) and Tachibana et al. (1967) correlated data as a function of heat capacity per unit area of the heater $\rho c \delta$, as shown in Figure 4. It is clear that CHF is suppressed for very thin heaters. The heater employed by Houchin and Lienhard was a strip glued on a horizontal wooden block. It was 5.8–7.9 mm wide and surrounded by vertical walls on all four sides. Tachibana et al. used an 8 mm-wide strip suspended vertically. In both experiments, the surface was also heated using AC current, and the reduction of CHF is pronounced when compared with the case of DC current.

**Size of a Heater.** Dependence of heater size on CHF has often been examined using a horizontal cylinder as a test surface. Sun and Lienhard (1970) measured CHF in various liquids and acceleration (gravity) fields by widely varying the heater size. Bakhru and Lienhard (1972) obtained the data for smaller cylinders. Their

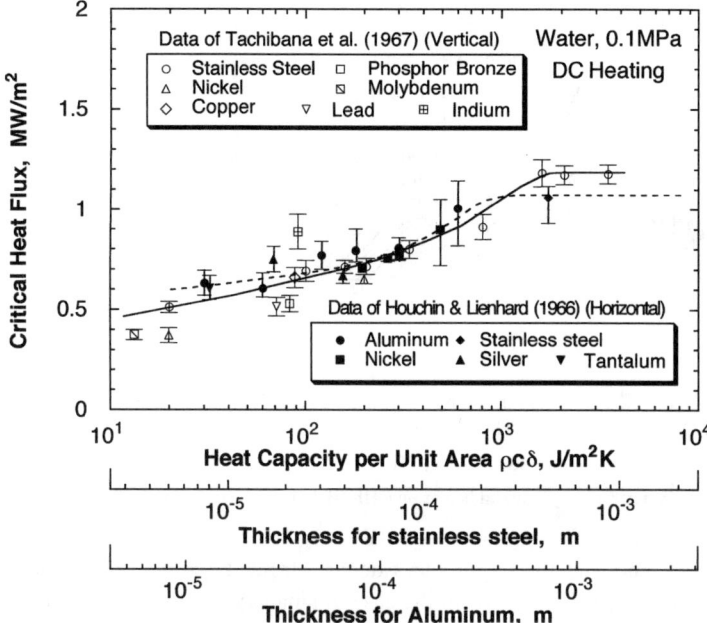

**Figure 4** Effects of thermal capacity of a heater on CHF.

CHF data are plotted against dimensionless radius $R' = (d/2)/\sqrt{\sigma/g(\rho_l - \rho_g)}$, as shown in Figure 5. Sun and Lienhard (1970) correlated about 900 data in the range of $0.15 < R' < 3.5$ by the following equation:

$$\frac{q_c}{q_{c,z}} = 0.89 + 2.27 \exp\left(-3.44\sqrt{R'}\right) \quad (6.1\text{-}3)$$

where $q_{c,z}$ is the CHF value given by Eq. (6.1-1) with $K_1 = 0.131$. It is found in Figure 5 that as the diameter of the heater becomes smaller, CHF increases once and then decreases.

Shoji et al. (1993) investigated the effects of heater width on CHF using a rectangular ribbon made of stainless steel stuck on a resin block and set horizontally in water. Their results show that for the narrow surface less than 4 mm ($[H/2]/\sqrt{\sigma/g[\rho_l - \rho_g]} = 0.8$), CHF increases with decreasing heater width in a form of $1/\sqrt{H}$ and the CHF value attained for 0.2 mm-wide heater is about four times that on a flat surface of sufficient width.

The different tendency of size effect on CHF between a cylinder system and a ribbon system may come from the different mechanisms of bubble departure from the heater, as pointed out by Shoji et al. (1993). In cases of large cylinders, it is possible that bubbles and even vapor masses stay along the periphery of the

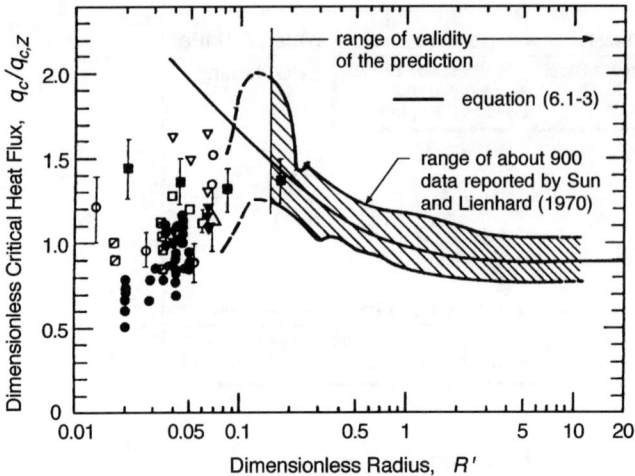

**Figure 5** Effect of diameter of a cylindrical heater on CHF (Bakhru and Lienhard, 1972).

cylindrical surface and that the vapor mass departs from the surface subjected mainly to buoyancy force. Contrarily, in the case of small cylinders, every bubble usually covers the cylindrical surface, and the bubble departure is governed by buoyancy force as well as the attaching force to the cylinder. Thus, the departure frequency differs between the two cases. The similar characteristics concerning bubble departure frequency has been observed by Kumada et al. (1995). In cases of a narrow ribbon heater stuck on a plate, the situation is similar to the large cylinder mentioned above.

The size effects of the flat plate were summarized by Lienhard and Dhir (1973). They showed that CHF on a large plate is given well by Eq. (6.1-1) with $K_1 = 0.149$. The terminology of "large" here means that the size of the heater is two to three times larger than the most dangerous wave length of Rayleigh-Taylor instability, $\sqrt{3} \times 2\pi \sqrt{\sigma/g(\rho_l - \rho_g)}$.

**Orientation of Heater Surface.** Critical heat flux on a flat surface changes with the inclination angle of the surface. In general, CHF is reduced on an inclined surface when compared with that on an upward facing horizontal surface, while the heat transfer coefficient is enhanced under some conditions. Bewilogua et al. (1975) measured CHF of helium on a copper disk (4.9 cm$^2$ surface area) for various inclination angles. They correlated data as a function of inclination angle $\phi$ ($\phi = 0°$ for upward facing horizontal surface) as

$$q_{c,\phi}/q_{c,0} = [1 - \phi/190°]^{0.5} \quad \text{for } 0° \leq \phi \leq 165° \qquad (6.1\text{-}4)$$

Recently, Chang and You (1996) proposed the following correlation based on their data for FC-72:

$$q_{c,\phi}/q_{c,0} = 1 - 0.00120\phi \tan(0.414\phi) - 0.122 \sin(0.318\phi) \qquad (6.1\text{-}5)$$

Most of the existing data fall within the range of values given by Eqs. (6.1-4) and (6.1-5).

## 6.2 MECHANISTIC MODELS

Mechanistic studies of nucleate boiling were actively done in 1950s and 1960s. In this early stage of boiling research, observation of boiling phenomena was also precisely made. Gaertner (1965) revealed that vapor departs from the surface in massive bubbles and that numerous columnar stems of vapor exist in the liquid film at the base of the massive vapor. Katto and Yokoya (1968) observed that a liquid layer exists under the massive bubbles where vigorous nucleation takes place and that at the critical condition, the layer dries out in the vapor mass hovering period. The layer is often called a *macrolayer*. Since the middle 1980s, mechanistic study has again become one of the most important activities in boiling research.

In high heat flux nucleate boiling, heat is transferred from the surface to the liquid-vapor interface by thermal diffusion; liquid then evaporates to generate vapor, which escapes from the surface. It is possible to assume that the CHF condition is initiated when either evaporation or vapor escape is restricted. The model that the vapor escape limit yields CHF was proposed by Zuber (1959) and then developed by Sun and Lienhard (1970) and Lienhard and Dhir (1973). We call this model the *vapor escape path instability model*. The other model comes from the limit of evaporation, in which the large scale dry patch is assumed to suppress the evaporation. Katto and Yokoya (1968) proposed such a type of model, and Haramura and Katto (1983) proposed the mechanism of how the supply of liquid to the surface is restricted. We call this the *macrolayer dry-out model*. On the other hand, Dhir and Liaw (1989) considered that the triple (three phase) contact line around nucleation sites plays an important role in liquid evaporation, proposing a model in which the triple contact line is shortened by merging vapor stems on the surface. We call this model the *vapor stem merging model*.

### 6.2.1 Vapor Escape Path Instability Model

The interface between liquid and vapor becomes unstable when the relative velocity of two phases becomes large beyond a certain critical value. Zuber (1959) proposed a model in which the instability of vapor liquid interface yields CHF. He assumed steady columnar escape paths in high heat flux pool boiling. Each escape path was assumed to have a diameter $\lambda_T/2$, located $\lambda_T$ in pitch. The pitch is assumed to be determined by Rayleigh-Taylor instability as follows:

$$\lambda_T = C_1 \times 2\pi \sqrt{\sigma/g(\rho_l - \rho_g)}, \quad \text{where } C_1 = 1 \text{ to } \sqrt{3} \qquad (6.2\text{-}1)$$

Since the increase in heat flux makes vapor escape velocity higher, the vapor-liquid interface of the path becomes unstable at a critical heat flux. The permissible maximum velocity of the vapor $u_g$ in the path is determined from the Kelvin-Helmholtz instability as a function of wave length $\lambda_H$ as

$$u_g = \left[\frac{2\pi\sigma}{\rho_g \lambda_H}\right]^{1/2} \left[\frac{\rho_l}{\rho_l + \rho_g}\right]^{1/2} \qquad (6.2\text{-}2)$$

He assumed that the wave length $\lambda_H$ is equal to the critical length of columnar interface (with a diameter $\lambda_T/2$) with sufficiently low relative velocity, $\pi \times \lambda_T/2$. After a small adjustment of the constant value, he reached the following expression for CHF:

$$\dot{q}_c = 0.131 \, \rho_g \, h_{lg} \left[\sigma g(\rho_l - \rho_g)/\rho_g^2\right]^{1/4} \left[\frac{\rho_l}{\rho_l + \rho_g}\right]^{1/2} \qquad (6.2\text{-}3)$$

The last term in Eq. (6.2-3) is close to unity because the density of liquid is much larger than that of vapor, and so it is frequently omitted from the expression.

Lienhard and co-workers extended Zuber's model to the critical heat flux of finite bodies, such as horizontal cylinders and a vertical plate with low height and spheres.

## 6.2.2 Macrolayer Dry-out Model

Katto and Yokoya (1968) proposed a preliminary model of the macrolayer dry out. Later, Haramura and Katto (1983) completed the model by proposing the mechanism of macrolayer formation. Katto and his co-workers have assumed the periodic process of macrolayer formation and consumption as shown in Figure 6. As also shown in Figure 7, small bubbles generated on the surface merge to make massive bubbles, which grow with accumulating vapor supplied by the macrolayer evaporation. The macrolayer thickness at the initial stage of vapor mass formation is $\delta_c$, and its thickness decreases with time during the hovering period of massive

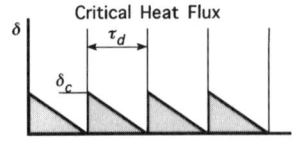

**Figure 6** Schematic of time-history of macrolayer consumption at CHF (Macrolayer dry out model).

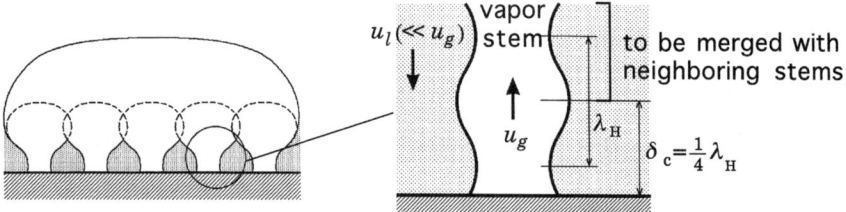

**Figure 7** Hydrodynamic instability of a vapor stem and vapor mass formation.

bubbles, $\tau_d$. The time required for the macrolayer to dry out depends on the value of heat flux. Thus, the heat flux would become maximum when the macrolayer evaporates completely at the end of the hovering period, which gives CHF. At this condition, the equation of heat balance yields

$$\rho_l h_{lg}(1-\alpha)\delta_c = \dot{q}_c \tau_d \qquad (6.2\text{-}4)$$

where $\alpha$ is the vapor fraction in the macrolayer.

On the other hand, the motion of vapor mass is determined from the balance between inertia and buoyancy force. If we assumed that a vapor mass grows at a constant volumetric growth rate, $v_1$, the hovering period $\tau_d$ is given from the bubble dynamics as follows:

$$\tau_d = \left(\frac{3}{4\pi}\right)^{1/5}\left[\frac{4(\xi\rho_l+\rho_g)}{g(\rho_l-\rho_g)}\right]^{3/5} v_1^{1/5} \qquad (6.2\text{-}5)$$

where $\xi$ is a coefficient to give the equivalent mass of the bubble. For a vapor bubble growing on a horizontal plate, it is adequate to put $\xi = 11/16$. If it is assumed that a single vapor mass grows from being fed with vapor from square area (the side length of which is the most dangerous wave length of Rayleigh-Taylor instability, $\lambda_{TD}$), the following equation is obtained for the volumetric growth rate $v_1$:

$$v_1 = \lambda_{TD}^2 \frac{\dot{q}}{\rho_g h_{lg}} = \frac{12\pi^2\sigma}{g(\rho_l-\rho_g)}\frac{\dot{q}}{\rho_g h_{lg}} \qquad (6.2\text{-}6)$$

As shown in Figure 7, the small bubbles on the surface grow vertically to form long stems. The long vapor stem would become unstable due to the Kelvin-Helmholtz instability, resulting in the lateral coalescence of the vapor stems that pushes away liquid above a certain distance from the surface; thus, the liquid film remains on the heated surface. This is the mechanism of macrolayer formation that Haramura and Katto (1983) have postulated. They assumed that the occurrence of the instability restricts the length of the interface of vapor stem to 1/4 of the critical wavelength and derived the following expression:

$$\delta_c = \frac{1}{4}\lambda_H = \frac{\pi}{2}\frac{\sigma}{\rho_g u_g^2}, \qquad (6.2\text{-}7)$$

where the velocity $u_g$ of vapor inside the vapor stem is given from heat balance for the prescribed heat flux $\dot{q}$ as

$$u_g = \dot{q}/(\alpha \rho_g h_{lg}). \qquad (6.2\text{-}8)$$

From Eqs. (6.2-4)–(6.2-8), Haramura and Katto expressed CHF in the following form:

$$\frac{\dot{q}_c}{\rho_g h_{lg}} \bigg/ \left[\sigma g(\rho_l - \rho_g)/\rho_g^2\right]^{1/4} = func(\rho_g/\rho_l, \alpha). \qquad (6.2\text{-}9)$$

By putting $func(\rho_g/\rho_l, \alpha) = 0.131$ they also derived the equation for macrolayer thickness as

$$\frac{\delta_c(\dot{q}/h_{lg})^2}{\sigma \rho_g} = 0.00536 \left(\frac{\rho_g}{\rho_l}\right)^{0.4} \left(1 + \frac{\rho_g}{\rho_l}\right) \qquad (6.2\text{-}10)$$

Equation (6.2-10) holds not only at critical heat flux but also at any heat flux, as long as the vapor mass is formed.

As for the macrolayer formation, a few different views and mechanisms have been proposed by many researchers. Bhat et al. (1983) postulated a merging of the rising bubbles over the heated surface. Shoji et al. (1992) and Kumada and Sakashita (1995) postulated the merging of adjacent spherical bubbles on the heater. They all consider that the liquid trapped between the bubbles due to bubble merging remains on the heated surface as macrolayer.

### 6.2.3 Vapor Stem Merging Model

As heat flux is increased in nucleate boiling, the pitch and the size of the vapor stems become smaller. If the pitch decreases more quickly, vapor stems merge with one another on the solid wall. It reduces the length of the triple contact line per unit area. Dhir and Liaw (1989) have proposed a model on this basis. They postulated a steady shape of interface around the bottom of vapor stem. The stem was assumed to be circular, having the diameter, $d$, distributed with spacing, $L$. The liquid was assumed to contact the surface with an angle $\theta$. Temperature within the liquid was assumed to be governed only by the heat conduction with the liquid surface condition of non-equilibrium evaporation—molecular effusion. Thus, the heat transfer rate is determined by the values of $d$, $L$, $\theta$, and wall superheat, $\Delta T_{sat}$. As $\Delta T_{sat}$ increases, the length of triple contact line per unit area and the heat transfer increase rapidly, while $d/L$ increases slowly and finally reaches unity. At high heat flux, $d/L$ finally reaches unity, and the vapor stems merge with each other. Figure 8 shows that stem periphery (that is, the length of triple contact line $P_s$) first increases and then decreases with increasing heat flux. Heat transfer rate

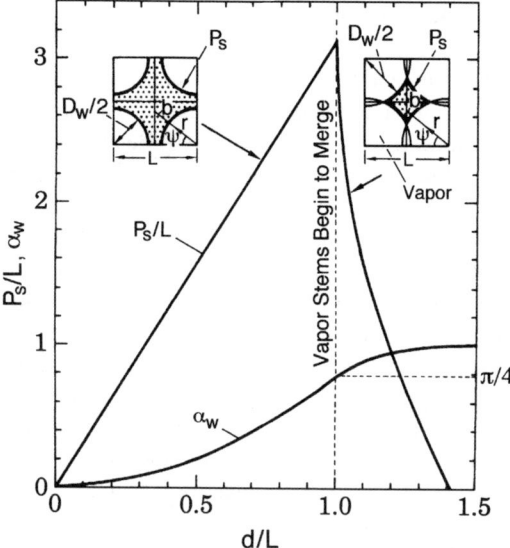

**Figure 8** Void fraction and stem diameter-to-stem periphery relation.

therefore reaches the maximum value when $d/L$ is unity. So, according to their model, critical condition takes place when the void fraction $\alpha_w$ is $\frac{\pi}{4}$.

Dhir and Liaw (1989) assumed further that the nucleation site density is proportional to the heat flux to the power of 1.5 and calculated CHF for various contact angles $\theta$, as shown in Figure 3. As the authors pointed out, this model is not applicable to liquid-solid combinations with a small contact angle.

## 6.3 AMOUNT OF LIQUID LEFT IN MACROLAYER

It may be stated that the macrolayer dry out model is a simple and probable model. In the model, the thickness of the macrolayer plays an important role, so it will be discussed in more detail below. It should be noted here that the contribution of microlayer, not of macrolayer, becomes important for CHF at low pressures.

### 6.3.1 Measurements of Macrolayer Thickness

There are several methods to measure the macrolayer thickness: photographic observation, void detection using electrical resistance probes or optical probes, void fraction measurement with $\gamma$-ray absorption, direct measurement from the electrical resistance of liquid, and estimation from heat consumption during the vapor mass hovering period.

Gaertner (1965) measured the diameter and length of vapor stems (macrolayer thickness) from the side-view photographs. He plotted the diameter against heat flux and found that the length to the diameter ratio is a constant 0.6. He also found that vapor stem occupies about 9% of the surface area, independent of heat flux, in the high heat flux region.

Using an electric resistance probe, Iida and Kobayashi (1970) measured the void fraction over the boiling surface. From the data, they defined the average thickness of macrolayer, $\bar{\delta}$, as a height where the spatial standard deviation of void fraction settles to a nearly constant value, independent of the distance from the heated surface. With a similar electric probe, Bhat et al. (1986) and Rajvanshi et al. (1992) measured the frequency of vapor-phase-passing frequency at every height from the boiling surface. The frequency gradually increased and then suddenly decreased as the probe approached the surface. So they defined the macrolayer thickness as a height where the frequency reaches the maximum value. Shoji (1992) showed that the signal of an electric resistance probe drastically changes, depending on the height from the boiling surface. When the tip of the probe is located at a certain height, the signal goes up and down with a high frequency. When it is located close to the boiling surface, however, the signal is steady and uniform. From the range where the characteristics of the signal are apparent, Shoji determined the maximum and the minimum of macrolayer thickness. Tomiyama et al. (1993) detected vapor and liquid phases from the difference of reflectance at the wedge-shaped tip of optical fiber to find that the results are similar to those of Iida and Kobayashi (1970) and Bhat et al. (1986).

Macrolayer thickness $\delta$ may be estimated from the heat balance equation,

$$\rho_l h_{lg}(1 - \alpha)\delta = \int_0^{\tau_d} \dot{q}\, dt \qquad (6.3\text{-}1)$$

if the macrolayer completely dries out within the hovering time of the vapor mass. In other words, the macrolayer thickness can be determined if the hovering period of the vapor mass, void fraction $\alpha$ in the macrolayer, and heat transfer rate are specified. Employing this method, Haramura (1989, 1990) conducted a boiling test to measure the heat flux time-history and took high speed photographs to simultaneously detect the hovering period. He neglected the void fraction and estimated the thickness of macrolayer. Haramura and Takeno (1997) discussed and estimated the macrolayer thickness more precisely using statistical methods. They concluded that the estimated thickness is not a gross average but an average for fewer cases when the layer is thin enough to dry out. They calculated the gross average by taking into account the statistical variances of the thickness and the hovering period. The gross average was found to be 5–40% thicker than that for the dried out cases.

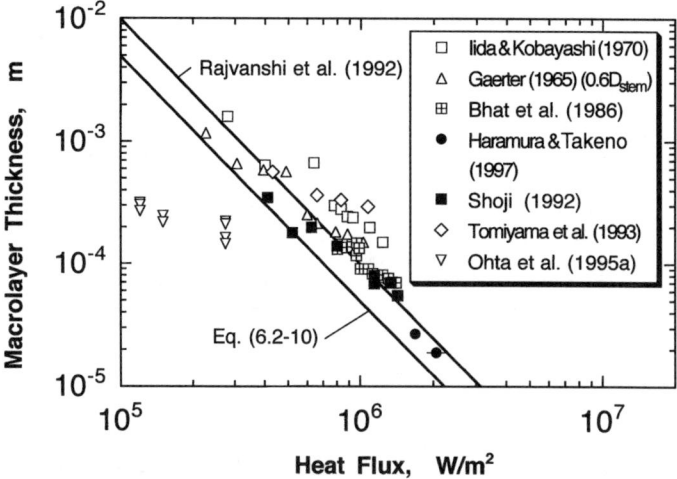

**Figure 9** Experimental data of macrolayer initial thickness.

When a liquid film exists in a narrow space between two electrodes, the electric resistance between the electrodes becomes a function of the film thickness. Ohta et al. (1995a, 1995b) used a couple of concentric electrodes with a 5 mm gap to measure the thickness in boiling of water under reduced gravity (of the order of 1/100 of normal gravity) to find the thickness of the thin liquid film. Liaw and Dhir (1989) measured void fraction over a boiling surface, utilizing $\gamma$-ray absorption. The detector window was 0.2 mm high (vertical direction against the surface) and 1.16 mm wide, with a shape surrounded by two arcs. This method has potential in the measurement of macrolayer thickness.

### 6.3.2 Measured Macrolayer Thickness

Figure 9 summarizes the available data of macrolayer thickness in pool boiling of water at atmospheric pressure; the configuration of the heater surfaces and other conditions are listed in Table 2. Most data show that the thickness of the macrolayer decreases with 1.5–2 power of heat flux. Data of Bhat et al. (1986), Shoji (1992), and Haramura and Takeno (1997) coincide fairly well with each other. It is especially noted here that the heat balance method employed by Haramura and Takeno may be regarded as an inspection of heat transfer in detail near CHF and that the macrolayer detected using electrical resistance probes seems to control CHF. The thickness can be correlated with Eq. (6.2-10) with a doubled coefficient (0.0107 instead of 0.00536), as pointed out by Rajvanshi et al. (1992) and Haramura and Takeno (1997).

**Table 2** Conditions for measurements in Figure 9

| Symbol | Surface | Surface finish | Method |
|---|---|---|---|
| □ | Copper $d = 29$ mm | Emery 4/0 | Electric resistance probe |
| △ | Copper $d = 50.8$ mm | Emery 4/0 | Photographic observation |
| ⊞ | Copper $d = 42$ mm | Emery 4/0 | Electric resistance probe |
| ●̶ | Nickel foil $4 \times 4$ mm$^{2*1}$ | Emery 4/0 | Heat balance |
| ● | Copper $d = 15$ mm | Emery #400 | Heat balance |
| ■ | Copper $d = 10$ mm | Emery #600 | Electric resistance probe |
| ◇ | Copper $d = 20$ mm, 30 mm | Emery #500 | Optical fiber |
| ▽ | Sapphire $d = 55$ mm$^{*2}$ | *3 | Electric resistance of water film |

*1 The center of 12 mm-diameter copper disk. Ceramic substrate is under the nickel foil.
*2 ITO heater film. It is located at the center of 76 mm diameter sapphire glass plate.
*3 Bare sapphire glass and vacuum evaporated platinum film.

## 6.4 CRITICAL HEAT FLUX OF SUBCOOLED POOL BOILING FOR SINGLE COMPONENT LIQUID

Boiling heat transfer and CHF are greatly enhanced in subcooled liquid. In the past, a number of studies on subcooled pool boiling have been made, but reliable data are limited because it is difficult to keep the bulk liquid temperature constant. The effects of non-condensable gas are also marked.

Ivey and Morris (1966) carried out an experiment for horizontal wires (1.22–2.67 mm diameter) in water. They found that CHF increases with subcooling as

$$\frac{\dot{q}_{c,sub}}{\dot{q}_{c,sat}} = 1 + 0.1(\rho_g/\rho_l)^{1/4}\frac{\rho_l c_p \Delta T_{sub}}{\rho_g h_{lg}} \qquad (6.4\text{-}1)$$

where $\dot{q}_{c,sub}$ and $\dot{q}_{c,sat}$ are CHF for subcooling and for saturation, respectively. Elkassabgi and Lienhard (1988) carried out experiment for horizontal wires (0.81–1.52 mm diameter) in iso-propanol, methanol, R-113, and acetone for a wide range of subcoolings. Their data of CHF are shown in Figure 10, in which they found that CHF increases almost linearly with subcooling but reaches an asymptotic value at $\Delta T_{sub} = 40\text{--}60$ K. Then Elkassabgi and Lienhard classified the region into three subcooling regions where the bubble behavior and the characteristics of CHF are different from each other. Their data of CHF at low subcooling region are well correlated by

$$\frac{\dot{q}_{c,sub}}{\dot{q}_{c,sat}} = 1 + 4.28 \frac{\rho_l c_p \Delta T_{sub}}{\rho_g h_{lg}} \left[\frac{\kappa_l [g(\rho_l - \rho_g)]^{1/4} \rho_g^{1/2}}{\sigma^{3/4}}\right]^{1/4} \qquad (6.4\text{-}2)$$

Critical heat flux at high subcooling region was explained by the evaporation limit due to molecular effusion. Shoji and Yoshihara (1991) carried out an experiment

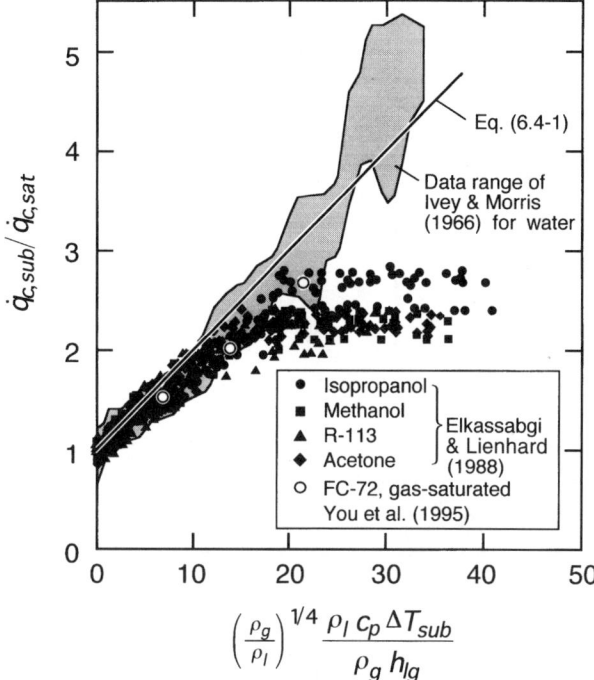

**Figure 10** Effects of subcooling on CHF on a horizontal cylinder.

for a horizontal wire (0.05–0.2 mm diameter) in water. They carefully evacuated gases and supplied a low temperature liquid from the lower side to the test wire at a velocity less than 6 mm/s to keep the bulk temperature at a constant subcooling. Their CHF data are plotted in Figure 11, in which they, like Elkassabgi and Lienhard (1988), found that CHF reaches a ceiling at a certain subcooling. However, the authors' CHF value is about five times higher than that predicted by Elkassabgi and Lienhard. Elkassabgi and Lienhard observed in their photographs (Figure 7-d in their article) that the bubble at high subcooling does not shrink so much, whereas bubbles at low and moderate subcooling shrink rapidly due to condensation as they rise. In contrast, Shoji and Yoshihara (1991) observed completely different bubble behaviors. They observed very small bubbles of the order of 0.1 mm in diameter attached to the wire, and numerous tiny bubbles smaller than 20 $\mu$m emitting from the wire just as smoke. This type of boiling is known as *micro-bubble emission boiling*. Both Elkassabgi and Lienhard (1988) and Shoji and Yoshihara (1991) observed characteristics suggesting that there exists a saturation limit of CHF in subcooled boiling, though the mechanism of the limit seems to be different between the two. The limit detected by Elkassabgi and Lienhard

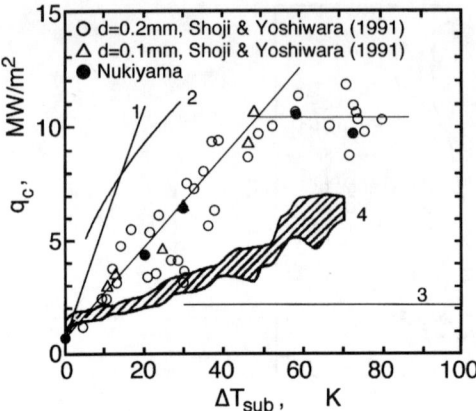

1-3. Equations of Elkassabgi and Lienhard (1988)
1. low subcooling (Eq. 6.4-2)
2. intermediate subcooling
3. high subcooling
4. Range of data of Ivey and Morris (1966)

**Figure 11** Effects of subcooling on CHF on a horizontal cylinders (Shoji and Yoshihara, 1991).

is probably caused by non-condensable gasses, while the limit detected by Shoji and Yoshihara may be caused from the evaporation limit due to molecular effusion or from some instability relating to the Marangoni convection. As for the micro-bubble emission boiling, refer also to the paper of Kubo and Kumagai (1994).

Recently, experiments on the effect of non-condensable gases have been extensively carried out in which the non-condensable gas is positively dissolved into the liquid to increase nucleate boiling heat transfer. For instance, You et al. (1995) measured CHF on a horizontal wire of 0.51 mm-diameter in FC-72; O'Connor et al. (1996) measured CHF on horizontal flat surface ($5 \times 18$ mm rectangle) in FC-72. Both the data of CHF for gas-saturated conditions are correlated in the same form as Eq. (6.4-1), but the coefficients employed in the equation by You et al. (see Figure 10 for data) and O'Connor et al. are 0.077 and 0.057, respectively, against 0.13 in Eq. (6.4-1). Dissolved gases entering vapor bubbles enhance vapor phase volumetric growth without heat removal. This tends to decrease CHF. On the other hand, temperature difference along the liquid-vapor interface induces the Marangoni convection. Since the vapor more likely condenses at the cold interface rather than on the interface at the saturation temperature, temperature difference along the interface is reduced when the liquid is free of non-condensable gases. In cases in which large amounts of gases are dissolved, gases are accumulated on the condensing side of the interface and act as a diffusive resistance, resulting in larger temperature difference along the interface and significant convection. Thus, although it is reported that non-condensable gases reduce CHF, more systematic experiments are required to understand their quantitative effects.

## 6.5 CRITICAL HEAT FLUX IN POOL BOILING FOR MIXTURES

The first key to evaluate CHF for mixtures is the correlation developed for pure liquid, which involves the properties of liquid and vapor, such as densities, latent heat, and surface tension. However, simple interpolation on mole fractions between two pure liquids or using properties of mixture does not lead to a simple correlation. Several causes have been pointed out. The less volatile component is concentrated in the liquid phase near the evaporating surface; more volatile components have to diffuse through this region. The first hypothesis, supported by Van Stralen and Cole (1979) and Yang (1987), among others, regards the diffusion resistance as the primary factor. It reduces bubble growth rate and the departure diameter of bubbles, resulting in the enhancement of critical heat flux. Yang correlated data in terms of the concentration difference $y_B - x_A$ between vapor mixture and bulk liquid. The notations are defined in Figure 12. The second hypothesis was suggested by McEligot (1964) and Reddy and Lienhard (1989), who directed their attention to local subcooling. Boiling temperature of concentrated liquid is higher than that of the original mixture; therefore, bulk liquid was considered to be under a subcooled condition. They correlated critical heat flux data in terms of the Jacob number, defined as $\rho_l c_p (T_C - T_A)/\rho_g h_{lg}$.

The third hypothesis was first suggested by Hovestreijdt (1963) and developed by Fujita et al. (1995) and McGillis and Carey (1996). They considered the Marangoni convection induced by the surface tension difference due to concentration difference. When the surface tension of the mixture increases with the fraction of less volatile liquid (so-called positive mixture), the surface tension is greater at the interface in the neighborhood of the triple contact line, where more

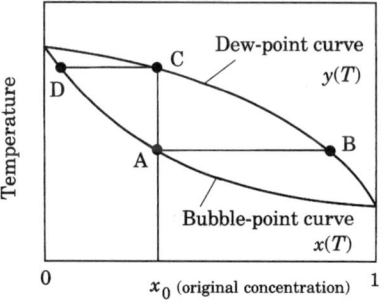

**Figure 12** Schematic of a phase-equilibrium diagram for binary non-azeotropic mixture.

evaporation takes place. The Marangoni convection is therefore induced to irrigate such an area, which results in higher critical heat flux. Fujita et al. employed the Marangoni number defined by

$$Ma = \frac{\sigma_D - \sigma_A}{\rho_l \nu_l^2}[\sigma/g(\rho_l - \rho_g)]^{1/2} Pr \qquad (6.5\text{-}1)$$

as a predominant parameter and correlated data with

$$\dot{q}_{cm} = \dot{q}_{cm,Z}[1 \pm 4.18 \times 10^{-4}|Ma|^{0.68}] \qquad (6.5\text{-}2)$$

where a double sign follows the sign of $Ma$ and $\dot{q}_{cm,Z}$ is the critical heat flux calculated from Eq. (6.1-1) with $K_1 = 0.131$, using properties of mixture at original concentration. McGillis and Carey (1996) introduced the concentration at the evaporating interface $x_i$ and employed the parameter $(1/\sigma)(\partial\sigma/\partial x)(x_i - x_D)$. Then they replaced $(x_i - x_D)$ with const. $\times (y_B - x_A)$ and finally correlated data as

$$\dot{q}_{cm} = \dot{q}_{cm,Z}\left[1 + c_m \frac{1}{\sigma}\frac{\partial\sigma}{\partial x}(y_B - x_A)\right]^{1/4} \qquad (6.5\text{-}3)$$

with empirical constant $c_m$.

Figures 13 and 14 show examples of phase equilibrium diagram, the variation of surface tension, and CHF with mole fraction. The phase equilibrium diagrams for methanol/water and for ethanol/n-butanol bear a great resemblance to each other. However, we find that the variation in $T_C - T_A$ with mole fraction is a little different for the two mixtures. Refer to Figure 12 for the location of A and C. The difference of critical heat flux tendency is quite remarkable, as shown by

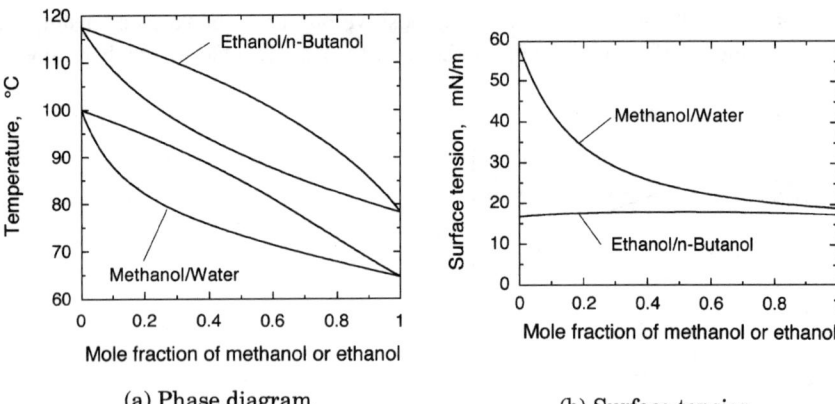

(a) Phase diagram  (b) Surface tension

**Figure 13** Phase diagram and surface tension of methanol/water and ethanol/n-butanol mixtures.

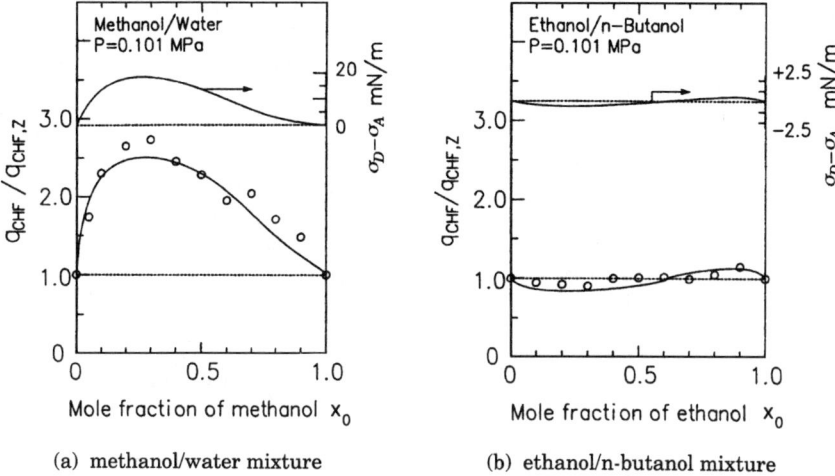

**Figure 14** Critical heat flux of mixtures (Fujita et al., 1995).

Figure 14a. It seems impossible to explain this difference from the phase diagram itself. On the other hand, the variation of surface tension is quite different as shown in Figure 13b. For a methanol/water mixture, surface tension markedly decreases with methanol mole fraction, especially for small mole fractions. It remains nearly constant for ethanol/n-butanol mixture. Moreover, variation of critical heat flux against mole fraction bears quite a resemblance to that of $\sigma_D - \sigma_A$. Refer to Figure 12 for the location of $A$ and $D$. This reveals that the Marangoni convection plays a great role in CHF for mixtures. Thome and Shock (1984) provide an extensive review of the literature on mixtures.

## REFERENCES

Abuaf, N. and Staub, F. W. 1983. Low Pressure Pool Boiling and Critical Heat Flux Limits for R-113. *AIChE Symposium Series* 79(225):35–40.

Bakhru, N. and Lienhard, J. H. 1972. Boiling From Small Cylinders. *International Journal of Heat and Mass Transfer* 15:2011–2025.

Berenson, P. 1960. Transition Boiling Heat Transfer from a Horizontal Surface. Ph.D. dissertation, Massachusetts Institute of Technology.

Bewilogua, L., Knoener, R., and Vinzelberg, H. 1975. Heat Transfer in Cryogenic Liquids Under Pressure. *Cryogenics* 15(3):121–125.

Bhat, A. M., Prakash, P., and Saini, J. S. 1983. On the Mechanism of Macrolayer Formation in Nucleate Pool Boiling at High Heat Flux. *International Journal of Heat and Mass Transfer* 26:735–740.

Bhat, A.M., Saini, J. S., and Prakash, R. 1986. Role of Macrolayer Evaporation in Pool Boiling at High Heat Flux. *International Journal of Heat and Mass Transfer* 29:1953–1961.

Chang, J. Y. and You, S. M. 1996. Heater Orientation Effect on Pool Boiling of Micro-Porous- Enhanced Surface in Saturated FC-72. *Journal of Heat Transfer* 118:937–943.

Cichelli, M. T. and Bonilla, C. F. 1945. Heat Transfer to Liquids Boiling Under Pressure. *Transaction of AIChE* 41:755.

Costello, C. P. and Frea, J. W. 1965. A Salient Nonhydrodynamic Effect on Pool Boiling Burnout of Small Semicylindrical Heaters. *Chemical Engineering Progress Symposium Series* 61(57):258–268.

Deev, V. I., Keilin, V. E., Kondratenko, I. A., and Petrovichev, V. I. 1977. Nucleate and Film Pool Boiling Heat Transfer to Saturated Liquid Helium. *Cryogenics* 17(10):557–562.

Dhir, V. K. and Liaw, S. P. 1989. Framework for a Unified Model for Nucleate and Transition Pool Boiling. *Journal of Heat Transfer* 111:739–746.

Elkassabgi, Y. and Lienhard, J. H. 1988. Influences of Subcooling on Burnout of Horizontal Cylindrical Heaters. *Journal of Heat Transfer* 110:479–486.

Fujita, Y., Bai, Q., and Tsutsui, M. 1995. Critical Heat Flux of Binary Mixtures in Pool Boiling. Volume 2. *Proceedings of ASME/JSME Thermal Engineering Joint Conference 1995*, 193–200.

Gaertner, R. F. 1965. Photographic Study of Nucleate Pool Boiling on a Horizontal Surface. *Journal of Heat Transfer* 87:17–29.

Haramura, Y. 1989. Measurement of Thickness of Liquid Film Formed on a Heated Surface in High Heat Flux Saturation Boiling. *Transaction of JSME, Ser. B*, 55:1392–1396 (in Japanese).

Haramura, Y. 1990. Characteristics of Pool Boiling Heat Transfer in the Vicinity of the Critical Heat Flux (Relations Between Bubble Motion and Heat Flux Fluctuations). *Heat Transfer Japanese Research*. 18(3):18–31.

Haramura, Y. 1991. Steady State Pool Transition Boiling Heated With Condensing Steam. *Proceedings of ASME/JSME Thermal Engineering Joint Conference 1991*, Volume 2. ASME, pp. 59–64.

Haramura, Y. and Katto, Y. 1983. New Hydrodynamic Model of Critical Heat Flux Applicable Widely to Both Pool and Forced Convection Boiling on Submerged Bodies in Saturated Liquids. *International Journal of Heat and Mass Transfer* 26:379–399.

Haramura, Y. and Takeno, H. 1997. Statistical Characteristics of Parameters Affecting Pool Boiling CHF. *Proceedings of Convective Flow and Pool Boiling Conference*, Paper No. X-1.

Houchin, W. R. and Lienhard, J. H. 1966. Boiling Burnout in Low Thermal Capacity Heater. *Proceedings of ASME Winter Annual Meeting 1966 (Heat Transfer)*, pp. 1–8.

Hovestreijdt, J. 1963. The Influence of the Surface Tension Difference on Boiling of Mixtures. *Chemical Engineering Science* 18:631–639.

Iida, Y. and Kobayashi, K. 1970. An Experimental Investigation on the Mechanism of Pool Boiling Phenomena by a Probe Method. *Proceedings of 4th International Heat Transfer Conference*, Paper No. B1.3.

Ivey, H. J. and Morris, D. J. 1962. The Effect of Test Section Parameters on Saturation Pool Boiling Burnout at Atmospheric Pressure. *AIChE Reprints* No. 160, Chicago.

Ivey, H. J. and Morris, D. J. 1966. Critical Heat Flux of Saturation and Subcooled Pool Boiling in Water at Atmospheric Pressure. *Proceedings of 3rd International Heat Transfer Conference*, Volume III, pp. 129–142.

Katto, Y. and Yokoya, S. 1968. Principal Mechanism of Boiling Crisis in Pool Boiling. *International Journal of Heat and Mass Transfer* 11:993–1002.

Kazakova, E. A. 1952. Maximum Heat Transfer to Boiling Water at High Pressure. *Engineer's Digest* 12:81–85.

Kubo, R. and Kumagai, S. 1994. Occurrence and Stability of Microbubble Emission Boiling—Stormy and Calm Regimes. *Symposium Series* 135(5):99–104.

Kumada, T., Sakashita, H., and Yamagishi, H. 1995. Pool Boiling Heat Transfer—I. Measurement

and Semi-Empirical Relations of Detachment Frequency of Coalesced Bubbles. *International Journal of Heat and Mass Transfer* 38:969–977.
Kumada, T. and Sakashita, H. 1995. Pool Boiling Heat Transfer—II. Thickness of Liquid Macrolayer Formed Beneath Vapor Masses. *International Journal of Heat and Mass Transfer* 38:979–987.
Kutateladze, S. S. 1952. Heat Transfer in Condensation and Boiling. USAEC Rept. AECU-3770.
Liaw, S. P. and Dhir, V. K. 1986. Effect of Surface Wettability on Transition Boiling Heat Transfer from a Vertical Surface. *8th International Heat Transfer Conference* 4:2031–2036.
Liaw, S. P. and Dhir, V. K. 1989. Void Fraction Measurements During Saturated Pool Boiling of Water on Partially Wetted Vertical Surface. *Journal of Heat Transfer* 111:731–738.
Lienhard, J. H. and Dhir, V. K. 1973. Hydrodynamic Prediction of Peak Pool-Boiling Heat Transfer from Finite Bodies. *Journal of Heat Transfer* 95:152–158.
Maracy, M. and Winterton, R. H. S. 1988. Hysteresis and Contact Angle Effects in Transition Boiling of Water. *International Journal of Heat and Mass Transfer* 31:1443–1449.
McEligot, D. M. 1964. Generalized Peak Heat Flux for Dilute Binary Mixtures. *AIChE Journal* 10:130–131.
McGillis, W. R. and Carey, V. P. 1996. On the Role of the Marangoni Effects on the Critical Heat Flux for Pool Boiling of Binary Mixture. *Journal of Heat Transfer* 118:103–109.
Merte, J., Jr. and Clark, J. A. 1964. Boiling Heat Transfer With Cryogenic Fluid at Standard and Near-Zero Gravity. *Journal of Heat Transfer* 86:351–359.
O'Conner, J. P., You, S. M., and Chang, J. Y. 1996. Gas-Saturated Pool Boiling Heat Transfer From Smooth and Microporous Surfaces in FC-72. *Journal of Heat Transfer* 118:662–667.
Ohta, H., Inoue, K., Yamada, Y., Yoshida, S., Tomobe, T., and Okada, S. 1995a. Microgravity Pool Boiling from a Transparent Heating Surface (2nd Report, Results of Aircraft Experiment). *Proceedings of 32nd National Heat Transfer Symposium of Japan*. ASME, pp. 547–548 (in Japanese).
Ohta, H., Yamada, Y., Inoue, K., Yoshida, S., Tomobe, T., and Okada, S. 1995b. Microgravity Pool Boiling from a Transparent Heating Surface (1st Report, Experimental Apparatus). *Proceedings of 32nd National Heat Transfer Symposium of Japan*, pp. 545–546 (in Japanese).
Rajvanshi, A. K., Saini, J. S., and Prakash, R. 1992. Investigation of Macrolayer Thickness in Nucleate Pool Boiling at High Heat Flux. *International Journal of Heat and Mass Transfer* 35:343–350.
Ramilison, J. M. and Lienhard, J. H. 1987. Transition Boiling Heat Transfer and Film Transition Regime. *Journal of Heat Transfer* 109:746–752.
Reddy, R. P. and Lienhard, J. H. 1989. The Peak Heat Flux in Saturated Ethanol-Water Mixtures. *Journal of Heat Transfer* 111:480–486.
Shoji, M. 1992. Study of Steady Transition Boiling of Water (Experimental Verification of Macrolayer Evaporation Model). *Proceedings of the Engineering Foundation Conference on Pool and External Flow Boiling*, Santa Barbara CA, March 22–27, 1992. ASME, pp. 237–242.
Shoji, M. and Kuroki, H. 1994. A Model of Macrolayer Formation in Pool Boiling. *Heat Transfer 1994*. Washington DC: Taylor and Francis, 5:147–152.
Shoji, M. and Yoshihara, M. 1991. Burnout Heat Flux of Water on a Thin Wire (Effect of Diameter and Subcooling). *Proceedings of 28th National Heat Transfer Symposium of Japan*, pp. 121–123 (in Japanese).
Shoji, M., Suganuma, H., and Wakamatsu, K. 1993. *Burnout Heat Flux and Thermodynamics*. Ed. Kelleher, M. D. Elsevier Science Publishers, 2:1291–1297.
Sun, K. H. and Lienhard, J. H. 1970. The Peak Pool Boiling Heat Flux on Horizontal Cylinders. *International Journal of Heat and Mass Transfer* 13:1425–1439.
Tachibana, F., Akiyama, M., and Kawamura, H. 1967. Non-Hydrodynamic Aspects of Pool Boiling Burnout. *Journal of Nuclear Science and Technology* 4:121–130.

Thome, J. R. and Shock, A. W. 1984. Boiling of Multicomponent Liquid Mixtures. *Advances in Heat Transfer*, Volume 16. New York: Academic Press Inc., pp. 59–156.

Tomiyama, Y., Kamoshida, J., Isshiki, N., Satoh, K., and Kataoka, K. 1993. High Heat Flux Pool Boiling of Water/Lithium Salts Solutions. *Proceedings of 30th National Heat Transfer Symposium of Japan*, pp. 451–453 (in Japanese).

Van Stralen, S. J. and Cole, R. 1979. Boiling Phenomena. Volume 1. Washington DC: Hemisphere Publishing Corp., pp. 33–65.

Yang, Y. M. 1987. An Estimation of Pool Boiling Critical Heat Flux for Binary Mixture. *Proceeding of ASME/JSME Thermal Engineering Joint Conference 1987*, Volume 5. ASME, pp. 439–446.

You, S. M., Simon, T. W., Bar-Cohen, A., and Hong, Y. S. 1995. Effect of Dissolved Gas Content on Pool Boiling of a Highly Wetting Fluid. *Journal of Heat Transfer* 117:687–692.

Zuber, N. 1959. Hydrodynamic Aspects of Boiling Heat Transfer. AEC Report. AECU-4439.

CHAPTER
# SEVEN

## FILM AND TRANSITION BOILING

**7.1, 7.2  Shigefumi Nishio**

*The University of Tokyo, Tokyo, 106 Japan*

**7.3  H. Auracher**

*Institut fur Energietechnik, Marchstr 18, 10587 Berlin, Germany*

## 7.1 INTRODUCTION

In most cases, the so-called boiling curve is used to describe the time- and spatially-averaged characteristics of pool-boiling heat transfer. Usually the boiling curves have the following three characteristic points: the incipience of nucleate boiling, the critical heat flux (CHF), and the minimum heat flux (MHF) points. Based on these characteristic points, boiling heat transfer is divided into the following four regions: the non-boiling, nucleate boiling, transition boiling, and film boiling regions. The transition boiling region is defined as the surface-superheat region between the critical and minimum heat flux points, and the film boiling region is the surface-superheat region beyond the minimum heat flux point.

From the viewpoint of two-phase structures, however, the pool boiling phenomena can be divided into the following two typical modes—nucleate and film boiling modes. The liquid phase keeps perfect contact with the boiling surface except at the base areas of bubbles in the nucleate boiling mode, and it is perfectly separated from the boiling surface by a vapor layer in the film boiling mode. A combination of the nucleate and film boiling modes is observed, at least in the transition boiling region. The fraction of liquid-solid contact, F, is used as a measure of the contribution of the nucleate boiling mode to the averaged heat flux in this region. The fraction decreases rapidly with the increase of the surface superheat in the transition boiling region, but in general $F > 0$, even at low superheats in the film boiling region. The film boiling region can be subdivided therefore into the low-superheat film-boiling region, accompanied by liquid-solid contact, and the high-superheat film-boiling region, where the liquid phase is completely separated from the boiling surface.

Considering heat conduction through a vapor film, it is understood that the heat transfer coefficient of the film boiling mode, $\alpha$, is given as

$$\alpha_{\text{fb}} = \text{const.} \lambda_g / \delta \qquad (7.1\text{-}1)$$

where $\delta$ is the thickness of the vapor film. Since the vapor film is thicker than the microlayer existing under primary bubbles and the thermal conductivity of vapor is lower than that of liquid, the heat transfer coefficient of the film boiling mode is much lower than that of the nucleate boiling mode. The increase in surface superheat brings about a rapid decrease of the fraction of liquid-solid contact and also an increase in heat flux of the film boiling mode. Such conflicting effects result in the occurrence of the minimum heat flux point.

The contribution of liquid-solid contact to the averaged heat flux depends on spreading rates of the liquid. Heat fluxes in the transition boiling and low-superheat film-boiling regions therefore depend on the wettability of the boiling surface. In addition, the combination of the nucleate and film boiling modes causes remarkable fluctuation and distribution in surface superheat. Heat fluxes in these regions depend on thermal characteristics of the boiling surface. The minimum heat flux point also depends on these surface parameters because it is located at the boundary between the transition boiling and low-superheat film-boiling regions.

## 7.2 FILM POOL BOILING

If the contribution of liquid-solid contact can be neglected, heat transfer in the film boiling region is the same as the film boiling mode. In this section, heat transfer of the film boiling mode is simply called as "film-boiling heat transfer." Regarding film-boiling heat transfer, intensive reviews have been published by Jordan (1969), Kalinin et al. (1975), and Sakurai (1990). Therefore, attention is focused on the fundamental principles, ideas, and new information relating to film boiling.

### 7.2.1 Introduction and Application Areas

Figure 1 shows a schematic of film pool boiling on a vertical plate. Equation (7.1-1) indicates that the most important parameter in film-boiling heat transfer is the thickness of the vapor film, $\delta$. The thickness is influenced by the production rate of vapor at the liquid-vapor interface and also the velocity distribution in the vapor film.

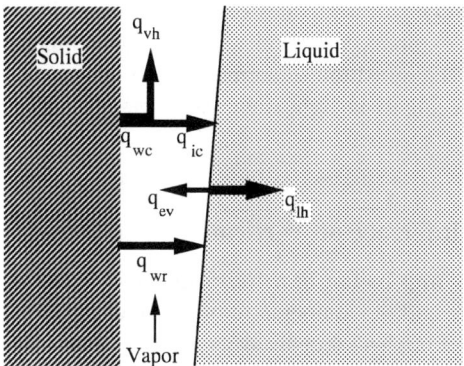

**Figure 1** Heat flow in film-boiling heat transfer.

The production rate of vapor depends on the heat flux reaching the interface, $q_{wi}$. The heat flux is composed of the components by conduction and radiation through the vapor film. Regarding the component conducted from the boiling surface, $q_{wc}$, a part of it is spent to heat up the vapor flow in the vapor film, $q_{vh}$, and the rest reaches the interface, $q_{ic}$. As for the component emitted from the boiling surface, $q_{wr}$, it directly reaches the interface because the vapor film is usually thin and hence the attenuation from the surface is very small. As a result,

$$q_{wi} = q_{ic} + q_{wr} \quad (7.2\text{-}1)$$

A part of the heat flux reaching the interface, $q_{lh}$, is conducted to the liquid phase if it is subcooled, and the rest, $q_{ev}$, goes in vapor production.

As for the velocity distribution in the vapor film, it can be analyzed in a manner similar to single-phase natural convection by using the well-known boundary layer equations. Since the vapor flow induces a liquid flow near the interface, the boundary layer equations for the vapor phase should be solved together with those for the liquid phase by using the boundary conditions and the matching conditions at the interface. This set of equations is called the *two-phase boundary-layer equations*.

Film boiling is regarded as technologically less important than nucleate boiling, but heat transfer processes accompanied by film boiling are encountered widely in such fields as energy, cryogenic, metallurgical, and space technologies. For example, solid walls such as rocket nozzles and combustion chambers exposed to high temperature gases must be cooled to keep their temperature below the permitted value, and film boiling is encountered if they are cooled by a liquid. In metallurgical processes such as the quenching of solid products of steel and rapid solidification of melt, their initial temperature is above the minimum heat flux point of water, and hence the quenching process relates closely to film-boiling heat transfer and the minimum heat flux point. Film boiling is also encountered inevitably in some accidents, such as the transition to normal state of superconducting conductors, loss-of-coolant accidents in light water reactors, and vapor explosions.

### 7.2.2 Film Boiling with Smooth Interface on Vertical Surface

Similar to the single-phase heat transfer, film-boiling heat transfer is also influenced by the geometry of the boiling surface and the temperature of the liquid. In this section, the physical aspects of film-boiling heat transfer is reviewed focusing on film boiling from a vertical surface kept at a uniform temperature, $T_w$.

**Fundamental equations and boundary conditions.** The following assumptions are employed to describe the hydrodynamics and heat transfer in film boiling of a single component liquid.

(1) The liquid and vapor phases at the interface are at saturation temperature corresponding to the system pressure. This assumption implies that the rate of evaporation at the liquid-vapor interface is much smaller than the maximum evaporation rate (Carey, 1992), and thus the non-equilibrium effect is negligible. Heat fluxes in film boiling are usually much lower than the heat flux corresponding to the maximum evaporation rate.
(2) The so-called boundary layer approximations are applicable for momentum and energy equations of each phase. This assumption indicates that the radius of curvature of the liquid-vapor interface is much larger than the vapor film thickness. This assumption is expected to be valid because the vapor film thickness is usually the order of 0.1 mm.

With these assumptions, the hydrodynamics and heat transfer in film boiling are described by the following equations. For the vapor phase,

$$\frac{\partial u_g}{\partial x} + \frac{\partial v_g}{\partial y} = 0$$

$$u_g \frac{\partial u_g}{\partial x} + v_g \frac{\partial u_g}{\partial y} = \left(\frac{\rho_{lf}}{\rho_{gf}} - 1\right) F_b[x] + v_g \frac{\partial^2 u_g}{\partial y^2} \qquad (7.2\text{-}2)$$

$$u_g \frac{\partial T_g}{\partial x} + v_g \frac{\partial T_g}{\partial y} = \kappa_g \frac{\partial^2 T_g}{\partial y^2}$$

and for the liquid phase,

$$\frac{\partial u_l}{\partial x} + \frac{\partial v_l}{\partial y} = 0$$

$$u_l \frac{\partial u_l}{\partial x} + v_l \frac{\partial u_l}{\partial y} = \rho_l \beta F_b[x](T_l - T_\infty) + v_l \frac{\partial^2 u_l}{\partial y^2} \tag{7.2-3}$$

$$u_l \frac{\partial T_l}{\partial x} + v_l \frac{\partial T_l}{\partial y} = \kappa_l \frac{\partial^2 T_l}{\partial y^2}$$

where $u$ and $v$ are velocity components in the $x$ and $y$ directions, and $F_b[x]$ is the component of gravity in the vapor flow direction ($F_b[x] = g$ for a vertical surface). The boundary and matching conditions are,

$$y = 0; \quad u_g = v_g = 0$$
$$T_g = T_w$$
$$y = \delta; \quad u_g = u_l$$
$$\rho_{gs}\left(v_g - u_g \frac{d\delta}{dx}\right) = \rho_{ls}\left(v_l - u_l \frac{d\delta}{dx}\right)$$
$$\mu_{gs} \frac{\partial u_g}{\partial y} = \mu_{ls} \frac{\partial u_l}{\partial y} \tag{7.2-4}$$
$$T_g = T_l = T_{sat}$$
$$-\lambda_{gs} \frac{\partial T_g}{\partial y} + \dot{q}_{wr} = -\rho_{gs}\left(v_g - u_g \frac{d\delta}{dx}\right) - \lambda_{ls} \frac{\partial T_l}{\partial x}$$
$$y = \infty; \quad u_l = v_l = 0$$
$$T_l = T_\infty$$

where the subscripts "gs" and "ls" denote the properties of each phase at the saturation temperature. Alternatively, we can use a set of the two-phase boundary-layer equations of integral type instead of Eqs. (7.2-2)–(7.2-4).

**Analytical results neglecting radiation contribution.** The total heat-transfer coefficient for a gas can be expressed simply as the algebraic sum of the convective and radiation heat-transfer coefficients. In the case of film boiling, however, radiation from the boiling surface changes the vapor film thickness, which relates closely to the convective heat transfer, as seen from Eq. (7.1-1). The heat transfer coefficient of film boiling therefore cannot be expressed by a simple summation. In addition, as reported first by Hsu and Westwater (1960), the liquid-vapor interface is smooth in some cases but wavy in others. Furthermore, it is questionable whether the variation of properties in the vapor film can be ignored because the temperature difference in the vapor film is very large. These problems make it difficult to rigorously examine the hydrodynamic and heat transfer processes in film boiling.

Most of early analytical works on film boiling, e.g., Bromley (1950), employed the following additional assumptions: laminar vapor flow, smooth interface, constant properties for each phase, and no contribution of radiation from the boiling surface. With such additional assumptions, Nishikawa and Ito (1966) numerically solved the two-phase boundary-layer equations after transforming them to a set of ordinary differential equations using a similarity transformation. Nishikawa et al. (1976) numerically solved the two-phase boundary-layer equations to examine the influence of the assumption of constant property. They showed that except at high system pressures, the solution with constant property at the film temperature was in reasonable agreement with the exact solution, taking into account the actual temperature dependence of the properties.

On the other hand, the integral method originating from Bromley (1950) is very useful in obtaining a physical understanding of film-boiling heat transfer. For example, using all the additional assumptions stated above, Nishio and Ohtake (1993) solved the two-phase boundary-layer equations of integral type, and they obtained the following non-dimensional equation for the averaged Nusselt number, $Nu_m[s]$, which is independent of the velocity profile in the boundary layer of the liquid phase.

$$Nu_m[s] = C_{FB,s} \left( \frac{Gr_g[s] \Pr_{gf}}{Sp^*} \right)^{1/4} \left( \frac{1 + \dfrac{3 + Sp}{1 + \dfrac{Sp}{2}} a_g}{1 - 2 \dfrac{\Pr_{gf}}{\Pr_{lf}} \dfrac{Sb \delta^+}{Sp \mu^+}} \right)^{1/4} \quad (7.2\text{-}5)$$

where $C_{FB,s}$ is a constant depending on the geometry of the boiling surface, $a_v$ is a constant related to the velocity at the interface, the subscripts "gf" and "lf" denote the properties of each phase at the respective film temperatures, and s is the representative size of the boiling surface, e.g., $s = H$ for film boiling on a vertical plate ($H$ is the height of the plate). The constant $C_{FB,s}$ is 0.667 for a vertical plate ($s = H$), 0.586 for a sphere ($s = D$), and 0.515 for a horizontal cylinder ($s = D$). The non-dimensional numbers in eq. (7.2-5) are defined as

$$Nu_m[s] \equiv \frac{\alpha s}{\lambda_{gf}}, \qquad Gr_g[s] \equiv \frac{g\rho_{gf}(\rho_{lf} - \rho_{gf})s^3}{\mu_{gf}^2}$$

$$Sp \equiv \frac{c_{pgf}\Delta T_{sat}}{h_{lg}}, \qquad Sp^* \equiv \frac{Sp}{1 + Sp/2}, \qquad Sb \equiv \frac{c_{plf}\Delta T_{sub}}{h_{lg}} \quad (7.2\text{-}6)$$

$$\delta^+ \equiv \frac{\delta}{\delta_l}, \qquad \mu^+ \equiv \frac{\mu_{gs}}{\mu_{ls}}$$

where $\delta_l$ is the boundary layer thickness of the liquid phase. Following Nishikawa and Ito (1966), the assumption of $a_g = 0$ does not result in a serious deviation from the exact numerical solution of the two-phase boundary layer equations for saturated film boiling. If this assumption is used, the heat transfer coefficient of saturated film boiling can be calculated from Eq. (7.2-5) without determining the values of $\delta^+$ and $\mu^+$. For subcooled film boiling, however, the values of $a_g$, $\delta^+$, and $\mu^+$ should be determined to calculate the heat transfer coefficient from Eq. (7.2-5) (see Nishio and Ohtake, 1993). For example, assuming negligible effect of buoyancy on the flow in the liquid boundary layer, Sakurai et al. (1990a) obtained the following approximate solution.

$$Nu_m[H] = 0.793 \left\{ \left( \frac{Gr_g[H] \Pr_{gf}}{Sp^*} \right) \left( \frac{E^3}{1 + \frac{E \Pr_{gf}}{Sp^* \Pr_{lf}}} \right) \times \left( \frac{\Pr_{gf}}{\sqrt{\rho^+ \mu^+} Sp^* \Pr_{lf}} \right)^2 \right\}^{1/4}$$

$$= 0.793 M^{1/4} \qquad (7.2\text{-}7)$$

Here, the non-dimensional numbers in this equation are

$$E \equiv \left( A + C\sqrt{B} \right)^{1/3} + \left( A - C\sqrt{B} \right)^{1/3} + \frac{Sb^*}{3}, \qquad Sb^* \equiv \frac{Sb}{1 + Sb/2}$$

$$A \equiv \frac{Sb^{*3}}{27} + \frac{\rho^+ \mu^+ Sp^* Sb^* \Pr_{lf}}{3 \Pr_{gf}} + \frac{\rho^+ \mu^+ Sp^{*2} \Pr_{lf}^2}{4 \Pr_{gf}^2},$$

$$C \equiv \frac{\rho^+ \mu^+ Sp^* \Pr_{lf}}{2 \Pr_{gf}} \qquad (7.2\text{-}8)$$

$$B \equiv -\frac{4 Sb^{*2}}{27} + \frac{2 Sp^* Sb^* \Pr_{lf}}{3 \Pr_{gf}} - \frac{32 \rho^+ \mu^+ Sp^* \Pr_{lf}}{27 \Pr_{gf}} + \frac{Sp^{*2} \Pr_{gf}^2}{4 \Pr_{gf}^2} + \frac{2 Sb^{*3}}{27 \rho^+ \mu^+}$$

**Analytical results for contribution of radiation.** As for the contribution of radiation from the boiling surface, the following approximate equation was derived by Bromley (1950).

$$\alpha_t = \alpha \left( \frac{\alpha}{\alpha_t} \right)^{1/3} + \alpha_r \approx \alpha + 0.75 \alpha_r \qquad (7.2\text{-}9)$$

where $\alpha_t$ is the total heat-transfer coefficient, $\alpha$ is the convective component neglecting radiation, and $\alpha_r$ is the radiation component given as

$$\alpha_r = \frac{\sigma_{SB} T_w^4 - T_{sat}^4}{\left( \frac{1}{\varepsilon_w} + \frac{1}{\varepsilon_l} - 1 \right) (T_w - T_{sat})} \qquad (7.2\text{-}10)$$

Here, $\sigma_{SB}$ in this equation is the Stefan-Boltzman constant, and in most cases, the emissivity of the liquid is $\varepsilon_l = 1$. Srinivasan and Rao (1984) solved the finite difference form of the two-phase boundary-layer equations by the false-transient method, taking into account the variation of properties and the contribution of radiation. Sakurai et al. (1990b) examined the validity of Eq. (7.2-9) with numerical solutions of the two-phase boundary-layer equations, and they recommended the following correlation.

$$\alpha_t = \alpha + \left\{ Fs + \frac{(1-F)}{1+1.4\dfrac{\alpha}{\alpha_r}} \right\} \alpha_r$$

$$Fs = \text{Max}\left[0.19, \left(1 - \frac{\exp\left[-0.13\dfrac{Sp}{Pr_{gf}}\right]}{4}\right) \exp\left[-0.64 \frac{Sb^{1.1} Pr_{gf}^{0.73}}{\rho^+ \mu^{+0.3} Pr_{lf}^{0.45} Sp^{0.73}}\right]\right]$$

(7.2-11a)

**Heat transfer correlations.** Regarding film boiling with a smooth interface on vertical surfaces, while it is difficult to obtain experimental data of the heat transfer coefficient because the interface tends to be wavy, the following equation is recommended here as the heat transfer correlation developed by Sakurai et al. (1990a, b).

$$Nu_m[D] = 0.793 M^{*1/4} \qquad (7.2\text{-}11b)$$

where $M^*$ is given by $M$ in Eq. (7.2-7), except that the modified subcooling number $Sb^+ = 0.93\, Pr_{lf}^{0.22}\, Sb^*$ is used instead of $Sb^*$.

### 7.2.3 Film Boiling with Wavy Interface on Vertical Surface

**Analytical models.** Hsu and Westwater (1960) reported experimental results in which the liquid-vapor interface exhibited wave motion in saturated film boiling on a long vertical surface. They assumed that such wave motion resulted from transition of the laminar to turbulent vapor flow, and they developed a heat transfer model taking into account the turbulent vapor flow. Suryanarayana and Merte (1972) developed a more detailed model for turbulent film boiling of saturated liquids.

On the other hand, Andersen (1976) developed another model, taking into account the wave motion. He assumed that the vapor flow remained laminar but the wave motion resulted from the Kelvin-Helmholtz instability (Chandrasekhar, 1961) due to a high vapor velocity. Andersen calculated the most dangerous wavelength simply by using the maximum vapor velocity as the relative velocity between the liquid and vapor phases, $\lambda_{KH}$, and he proposed to take $s = \lambda_{KH}$ in such an analytical solution of laminar film boiling as Eq.(7.2-5). Bui and Dhir (1985a) developed a more sophisticated model from this point of view. In these models, it is assumed that the interfacial instability forms vapor domes, and the vapor domes act as vapor sinks so that vapor generated in the region preceding a dome is fed into that dome. As a result, the vapor film is renewed at intervals of the wavelength. Such models are here named as the vapor-film-unit model. Nishio and Ohtake (1993) proposed the following approximate equation, estimating $\lambda_{KH}$ for saturated film boiling, and they reported that in usual cases the value of $\lambda_{KH}$ was near that of $\lambda_{RT}$, where $\lambda_{RT}$ is the critical wavelength of the Rayleigh-Taylor instability.

$$\lambda_{KH} = 16.2 \left( \frac{Pr_{gf}^3}{Sp^{*3} Gr_g \lambda_0} \right)^{1/11}, \quad \lambda_0 = \sqrt{\frac{\sigma}{g(\rho_l - \rho_g)}} \qquad (7.2\text{-}12)$$

Leonard et al. (1976) compared their experimental data of film-boiling heat-transfer coefficient of saturated water with the turbulent and vapor-film-unit models. The results indicate that the turbulent model developed by Hsu and Westwater overestimates the heat transfer coefficient, but the vapor film unit model taking $s = \lambda_{RT}$ is in good agreement with their data. Figure 2 shows experimental data of the local heat-transfer coefficient of film boiling on a vertical surface (Nishio and Ohtake, 1993). The curves marked by "TPBL" are the predictions from the two-

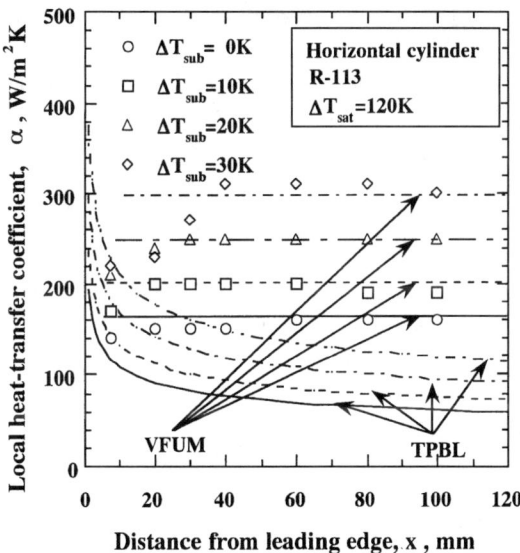

**Figure 2** Effect of liquid subcooling on local heat transfer coefficient of film boiling on vertical surfaces.

phase boundary-layer theory, assuming a smooth interface, and those marked by "VFUM" are those from Eq.(7.2-5), taking $s = \lambda_{KH}$. This figure indicates that the liquid-vapor interface is considered smooth near the leading edge of the vapor film but becomes wavy at a height due to the instability of the interface. In addition, it is found that the critical height at which the wave motion develops fully increases with an increase in liquid subcooling.

**Heat transfer correlations.** The following correlations developed by Nishio and Ohtake (1993) are recommended for film-boiling heat transfer on long vertical surfaces. For saturated liquids,

$$Nu_m \lambda_{KH} = 0.74 \left( \frac{Gr_g \lambda_{KH} \Pr_{gf}}{Sp^*} \right)^{1/4} \quad (7.2\text{-}13)$$

and for subcooled liquids,

$$\alpha_{sub} = \alpha_{sat} + 0.067 \left( \frac{\lambda_{gf}}{\lambda_{KH}} \right) \left\{ \frac{\Pr_{lf}^{0.21}}{\rho^+ \mu^{+0.23}} \right\} (Gr_g \lambda_{KH} \Pr_{lf})^{1/4} \frac{\Delta T_{sub}}{\Delta T_{sat}} \quad (7.2\text{-}14)$$

where $\alpha_{sat}$ is given by Eq.(7.2-13). Equation (7.2-14) was derived based on Eq.(7.2-16). Figure 3 shows a comparison of experimental data with this correlation for saturated liquids.

### 7.2.4 Film Boiling on Surfaces of Other Geometries

**Film boiling on horizontal flat plate and inclined surfaces.** The liquid-vapor interface exhibits wave motion in the case of film boiling on horizontal flat plates

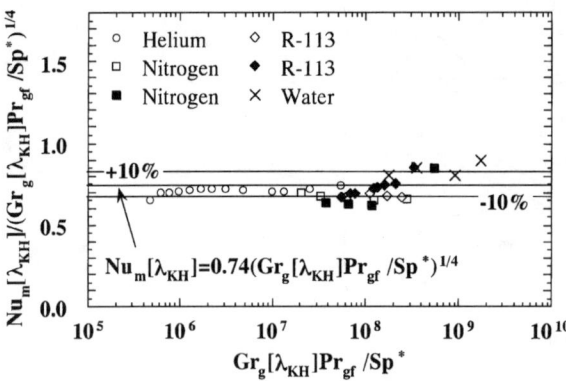

**Figure 3** Heat transfer correlation for saturated film boiling on vertical surfaces.

due to the Rayleigh-Taylor instability. Assuming that the Rayleigh-Taylor instability subdivides the vapor film into individual vapor cells and the size of the cells are given by the most dangerous wavelength, Berenson developed an analytical model similar to the vapor-film-unit model for film boiling on a vertical surface. His analytical result for film boiling of saturated liquids is given by

$$Nu_m \lambda_0 = 0.425 \left( \frac{Gr_g \lambda_0 \Pr_{gf}}{Sp^*} \right)^{1/4} \quad (7.2\text{-}15)$$

Hamill and Baumeister (1967) proposed an analytical model taking into account the effects of radiation and liquid subcooling. They reported the following results:

$$\alpha_t = \alpha_{sat} + 0.12\alpha_{nl} \left( \frac{\Delta T_{sub}}{\Delta T_{satt}} \right) + 0.88\alpha_r, \quad \text{for} \left| \frac{\alpha_r}{\alpha_t} - \left( \frac{\alpha_{nl}}{\alpha_{sat}} \right) \left( \frac{\Delta T_{sub}}{\Delta T_{sat}} \right) \right| < 0.5 \quad (7.2\text{-}16)$$

where $\alpha_{nl}$ is the heat transfer coefficient of liquid at the interface. Sauer and Ragsdell (1971) proposed to replace the constant in Eq. (7.2-15) by 0.512, and Sakurai (1990) developed another heat transfer correlation based on Eq. (7.2-7). Klimenko (1981) developed a set of heat transfer correlations for saturated film boiling on horizontal plates of small and large diameters. There is, however, no reliable data for film boiling of subcooled liquids.

As long as the interface is smooth, Eqs. (7.2-5) and (7.2-7) are applicable even for inclined surfaces if g is replaced by $g \sin \theta$. Here, $\theta$ is the inclination angle measured from the horizontal plane. Nishio et al. (1991) extended the vapor-film-unit model to film boiling of saturated liquids with a wavy interface on inclined surfaces. Based on Eqs. (7.2-5) and (7.2-12), Nishio and Ohtake (1993) proposed the following heat transfer correlation for film boiling of saturated liquids from inclined surfaces:

$$\alpha[\theta] = \alpha[\theta = 90 \text{ degree}] \sin^{3/8} \theta, \quad \text{for } 30 < \theta < 180 \text{ degree} \quad (7.2\text{-}17)$$

In the case of film boiling from a flat plate facing downward, vapor generated at the interface can escape only from the outer edge of the boiling surface. Film-boiling heat transfer is affected in this case by the geometry of the insulating part surrounding the boiling surface. Shigechi et al. (1989) numerically solved the two-phase boundary-layer equations, including the effect of radiation from the surface. Barron and Dergham (1987) solved the equations of integral type, and they obtained the following equation for film boiling of saturated liquids:

$$Nu_m D = \left( \frac{0.325}{1 + 1.486 \times 10^6 Ra_g D^{-1/2}} \right) Ra_g D^{1/5},$$

$$Ra_g D \equiv \frac{Gr_g D \, Pr_{gf}}{Sp^{**}}, \quad Sp^{**} \equiv \frac{Sp}{1 + 0.375 Sp} \quad (7.2\text{-}18)$$

**Film boiling on horizontal cylinders and spheres.** Film-boiling heat transfer of saturated liquids on a horizontal cylinder was first analyzed by Bromley (1950). He employed the integral method, assuming the laminar vapor film, the smooth interface, and constant properties. His analytical result is:

$$Nu_m[D] = 0.62 \left( \frac{Gr_g[D] \, Pr_{gf}}{Sp^{***}} \right)^{1/4}, \quad Sp^{***} = \frac{Sp}{(1 + 0.34 Sp)^2} \quad (7.2\text{-}19)$$

As for subcooled film boiling, analytical results such as Eq. (7.2-5) can be obtained. For example, Sakurai et al. (1990a) reported their analytical results in which the constant was replaced by 0.612 in Eq. (7.2-7).

Breen and Westwater (1962) compared Eq. (7.2-19) with experimental data and found that Eq. (7.2-19) was only applicable for film boiling from horizontal cylinders of middle diameters, and that it underestimated the heat transfer coefficient for large and small diameters. In the case of horizontal cylinders of very large diameter, it is considered that the liquid-vapor interface is wavy on the upper portion due to the Rayleigh-Taylor instability and on the other portion due to the Kelvin-Helmholtz instability. Assuming such a situation, Nishio and Ohtake (1993) extended the vapor-film-unit model to film boiling on horizontal cylinders of large diameter. As for horizontal wires of small diameter, there seems to be two possible reasons causing the deviation from the analyses based on the assumptions of laminar vapor flow and smooth interface. One is the violation of the boundary layer approximation, as pointed out first by Bromley (1950), because the vapor film around fine wires is not small compared with the radius of curvature of the interface. The other results from the effects of the interfacial instability. As pointed out first by Baumeister and Hamill (1967), the Rayleigh-Taylor instability at the liquid-vapor interface generates vapor bubbles surrounding the wire at axial intervals of the wavelength. The bubbles act as vapor sinks so that an axial component appears in the vapor flow. Baumeister and Hamill (1967) analyzed film boiling of saturated liquids from horizontal wires, and they obtained the following equation:

$$Nu_m[D] = 0.373 \left\{ 1 + \frac{9}{\sqrt{6} D^+} + \frac{8}{\sqrt{54} \, D^{+3}} \right\} \left( \frac{Gr_g[D] \, Pr_{gf}}{Sp^{***}} \right)^{1/4}, \quad D^+ = \frac{D}{\lambda_0}$$

$$(7.2\text{-}20)$$

There are a number of heat transfer correlations for film boiling from horizontal cylinders. Here, the following equations are recommended. For saturated film boiling,

$$Y = 0.22 + 0.15X + 0.0058X^2$$

$$X \equiv \log\left[\left(\frac{Gr_g[D]\Pr_{gf}}{Sp\left\{\frac{(\Pr_{gf}+1.33)Sp + 3.33Sp}{(Sp+3.33)^2 \Pr_{gf}}\right\}}\right)^{1/4}\right], \quad Y \equiv \log[Nu_m[D]]$$

(7.2-21)

and for film boiling of saturated and subcooled liquids other than liquid metals,

$$\frac{Nu_m[D]}{1 + 2/Nu_m[D]} = \{0.57 - 0.041\log[D^+] + 0.19(\log[D^+])^2\}(M^*)^{1/4}$$

(7.2-22)

where $M^*$ is given by $M$ in Eq.(7.2-21), except that the modified subcooling number $Sb^+ = 0.93\Pr_{lf}^{0.22} Sb^*$ is used instead of $Sb^*$. Equation (7.2-21) was developed by Nishikawa et al. (1972), and Eq.(7.2-22) by Sakurai et al. (1990a, 1990b).

For film boiling from spheres, Hendricks and Baumeister (1969) proposed an analytical model taking into account the Rayleigh-Taylor instability on the upper portion of the sphere and proposed the following results for saturated liquids:

$$Nu_m[D] = 3 + \left\{0.177 + \frac{0.71}{D^{+1/4}}\right\}\left(\frac{Gr_g[D]\Pr_{gf}}{Sp^*}\right)^{1/4}, \quad \text{for } D^+ \to 0$$

$$Nu_m\lambda_0 = 0.35\left(\frac{Gr_g[D]\Pr_{gf}}{Sp^*}\right)^{1/4}, \quad \text{for } D^+ \to \infty$$

(7.2-23)

Grigoriev et al. (1982) reported a set of heat transfer correlations for saturated film boiling from spheres of wide range in diameter.

### 7.2.5 Transient Film Boiling

Transient film boiling occurs under either quenching or rapid heating conditions. Payayopanakul and Westwater (1978) conducted quenching experiments with flat plates and reported that heat fluxes in transient film boiling were lower than those in steady-state film boiling if the plate was very thin.

Inoue and Bankoff (1981) and Inoue et al. (1981) investigated transient film boiling after passage of a shock wave. They indicated analytically and experimentally that the arrival of a pressure shock markedly enhanced film-boiling heat transfer. Jackson and Yen (1970) proposed an analytical model for transient film boiling around a horizontal wire under large power input by assuming that the primary mode of heat transfer through the vapor film was by conduction. Kim and Corradini (1986) extended a general Rayleigh equation to transient film boiling.

### 7.2.6 Minimum Heat Flux Point

As mentioned earlier, heat transfer in the transition boiling and low-superheat film-boiling regions is affected by wettability and thermal characteristics of the boiling surface. The minimum heat flux point, which is given by the surface superheat $\Delta T_{MHF}$ and heat flux $q_{MHF}$, is therefore influenced by such factors. At the present time, however, it is impossible to predict the condition at the minimum heat flux point, taking into account such factors in actual systems.

**Analytical models.** Zuber (1959) argued that as long as more vapor was being generated than required to sustain the natural rate of growth of unstable disturbances, the disturbances would collapse and release bubbles periodically. Following such an idea, Berenson (1961) developed an analytical model of $q_{MHF}$ for saturated film boiling on a horizontal flat plate:

$$q_{MHF} = 0.09 \rho_{gf} h_{lg} \sqrt{\frac{g(\rho_l - \rho_g)}{\rho_l + \rho_g}} \left\{ \frac{\sigma}{g(\rho_l - \rho_g)} \right\}^{1/4} \quad (7.2\text{-}24)$$

This model was extended to $q_{MHF}$ for horizontal cylinders by Lienhard and Wong (1964). Gunnerson and Cronenberg (1980) proposed a more detailed model, taking into account the contribution of liquid-solid contact.

On the other hand, Spiegler et al. (1963) proposed the so-called *foam limit model*, in which $\Delta T_{MHF}$ was assumed equal to the maximum superheat of the liquid. Segev and Bankoff (1980) developed another model based on the adsorption characteristics of the boiling system. In their model, $T_{MHF}$ is assumed to be the temperature at which only one monolayer exists on the surface.

$$T_{MHF} = \frac{T_{mw} + \sqrt{(\lambda \rho c_p)_l / (\lambda \rho c_p)_w} T_l}{1 + \sqrt{(\lambda \rho c_p)_l / (\lambda \rho c_p)_w}} \quad (7.2\text{-}25)$$

where $T_{mw}$ is the temperature at $\eta = 0.9$. $\eta$ is given by

$$\eta = \frac{1}{\frac{\sqrt{2\pi MRT}\,\Gamma_0}{A\rho\tau} + 1}, \quad \tau = \tau_0 \exp\exp\left[\frac{Q_a}{RT}\right] \quad (7.2\text{-}26)$$

where $Q_a$ is the heat of adsorption, $R$ is the gas constant, $M$ is the molecular weight, A is Avogadro's number, $\Gamma_0$ is the number of adsorbed molecules per unit area that form a monolayer, and $\tau$ is a residential time in the adsorbed state.

**Correlations.** Nikolayev and Skripov (1970) developed the following correlation for the effect of the system pressure on $q_{MHF}$.

$$q_{MHF} p = 1.67 \left(\frac{p}{p_{cr}}\right)^{0.24} \left(1 - \frac{p}{p_{cr}}\right)^{0.61} \qquad q_{MHF} p = 0.9 p_{cr} \qquad (7.2\text{-}27)$$

Baumeister and Simon (1973) developed the following correlation for $T_{MHF}$ based on the maximum superheat of the liquid.

$$T_{MHF}^* = \frac{27}{32} T_{cr} \left\{ 1 - \exp\left[-0.52\left(\frac{10^4 (\rho/A)^{4/3}}{\sigma}\right)^{1/3}\right]\right\} \qquad (7.2\text{-}28)$$

where $T_{MHF}^*$ is the temperature at the minimum heat flux point on an isothermal solid, and A is the atomic number of the material of the boiling surface. Nishio (1987) pointed out that the dominant value for the minimum heat flux point must be $T_{MHF}$ but not $q_{MHF}$ because experimental values of $T_{MHF}$ were independent of the geometry and size of the boiling surface, and he presented a set of correlations of $T_{MHF}$.

## 7.3 TRANSITION BOILING

### 7.3.1 Introduction and Application Areas

The upper end of the transition boiling regime is limited by the critical heat flux (CHF), and the lower one is limited by the minimum heat flux of film boiling (MHF). However, it seems, preferable to call the limits "critical boiling point" and "minimum film boiling point," since the limiting temperatures $T_{CHF}$ and $T_{MHF}$ also play an important role. Transition boiling is the most complex and least understood of all the boiling regimes. On the one hand, this is because transition boiling is regarded as technologically less important than nucleate boiling; on the other, it is due to its complicated mechanism and the difficulties encountered in experimental studies. Transition boiling therefore represents a challenge for future research as its application is not limited to the modeling of reactor cooling during hypothetical accidents. All quenching processes, e.g., in material techniques, imply the same boiling problem. Furthermore, prediction methods for the upper region of transition boiling heat transfer are required to design high-performance evaporators heated by a liquid or a condensing fluid. If such heat exchangers are operated around the critical boiling point, there is no danger of an instability because the heat transfer is temperature controlled.

### 7.3.2 Stability in Transition Boiling and Temperature Uniformity on the Heating Surface

Due to its negative slope, the transition region of a boiling curve is only accessible if the heating surface is temperature-controlled or in a transient process. Steady-state stable operation can only be achieved in one of the following ways: passive stabilization by means of fluid heating, active stabilization by adjusting the energy input of an electrical heat source according to some control law, or a combination of the two.

Blum et al. (1996) carried out a rigorous stability analysis of boiling systems based on linear stability analysis of general distributed parameter systems. Figure 4 presents a characteristic result for a cylindrical copper heater of radius $r = 17.5$ mm and length $l = 10$ mm. In the cases of electrical heating, it was assumed that the controller was purely proportional (gain constant $K_c$), the thermocouples measure the wall temperature at $z_l = l$ with no lag, and there are no filter elements in the control loop.

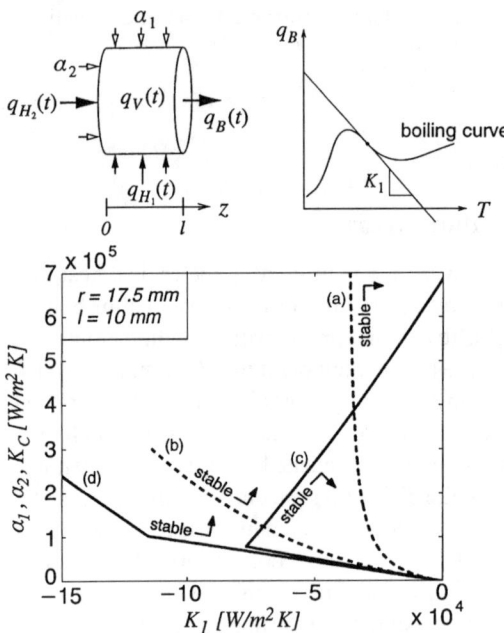

**Figure 4** Stability bound for passive and active stabilization: (a) stabilizing fluid at $z = 0$ ($\alpha_1 = 0$, $\alpha_2 \neq 0$) and (b) along the perimeter ($\alpha_1 \neq 0$, $\alpha_2 = 0$); temperature control by (c) indirect electrical heating and (d) direct electrical heating (Blum et al. 1996).

Figure 4 shows the stability limits in the $K_1/\alpha - [(a)\ and\ (b)]$ and the $K_1/K_c - [(c)\ and\ (d)]$ parameter planes. Clearly, the most favorable method of stabilizing is temperature control by direct electrical heating (d). In contrast, temperature control via indirect heating (c) reveals an upper stability limit due to limit cycle oscillations of the controlled wall temperature for high control gains. If stabilizing fluids are used (a, b), heating along the curved surface is preferable. If the stabilizing fluid is interfacing the heater at its backside opposite the boiling surface (z = 0), the bound for operable boiling curve slopes $K_1$ is relatively low.

The stability condition for the use of stabilizing fluids is

$$K_1 = -\lambda \left[ \frac{\alpha_2 + \left(\frac{2\alpha\lambda}{r}\right)^{1/2} \tanh\left[\left(\frac{2\alpha}{r\lambda}\right)^{1/2} l\right]}{\lambda + \alpha_2 \left(\frac{r\lambda}{2\alpha}\right)^{1/2} \tanh\left[\left(\frac{2\alpha}{r\lambda}\right)^{1/2} l\right]} \right] \quad (7.2\text{-}1)$$

It includes the stability limit for $\alpha_1 = 0$ derived by Stephan (1965). In stabilizing systems with electrical heating, a PI-type controller, a filter in the control loop, and the finite time constant of the control thermocouple reduce the stability bounds. These effects are also quantified by Blum et al. (1996). The above results are only valid for uniform boiling on the heated surface. On very thin heaters, heterogeneous temperature profiles may occur in temperature controlled experiments with wires or heated foils, well-known as "two-mode" boiling (e.g., coexistence of nucleate boiling and film boiling).

### 7.3.3 Experimental Results and Parametric Trends

Due to the complex nature of transition boiling and its dependency on numerous parameters, our present knowledge is not sufficient to present prediction methods with a satisfactory degree of reliability and a wide validity range. For a better understanding of how heat transfer in the transition region could nevertheless be estimated, typical results are summarized here. Much more comprehensive studies of this kind were presented by Kalinin et al. (1987), Dhir (1990), Auracher (1990, 1992), and Adiutori (1991).

**Hysteresis in steady-state and transient experiments.** There is a contradiction in the literature about the existence of a hysteresis in transition boiling. Some authors obtained different transition boiling curves for experiments performed in the direction of increasing heater surface temperatures and vice versa. Experiments by others showed no evidence of two boiling curves. Recently, Ungar and Eichhorn (1996) presented steady-state transition boiling data and comprehensively summarized this contradicting situation. Therefore, the following presents only some key-results of former studies and focuses the emphasis on recent findings.

*Steady-state experiments* Based on the experiments of Berenson (1962) and data obtained from quenching of small spheres, Witte and Lienhard (1982) suggested the existence of two transition boiling curves: the *transitional nucleate boiling curve*, occurring as the heater surface temperature increases from nucleate boiling, and, with lower heat fluxes, the *transitional film boiling curve*, occurring as the temperature decreases from film boiling. Ramilison and Lienhard (1987) rebuilt Berenson's horizontal flat plate apparatus to improve the access to the steep sections of the transition curve. They conjecture that "jumps" from film-transition to nucleate-transition boiling occur because the control of the process is shifted from the advancing contact angle $\theta_a$ to the retreating one, $\theta_r$. The authors did not observe the jumps in their experiments (see Figure 5) and explained it by the loss of accessibility to these steep parts of the boiling curve. Only for acetone on a teflon-coated surface, where both contact angles represent almost perfect wetting, was a complete and single boiling curve measured. This was explained by a direct jump from the film boiling to the transitional nucleate boiling curve.

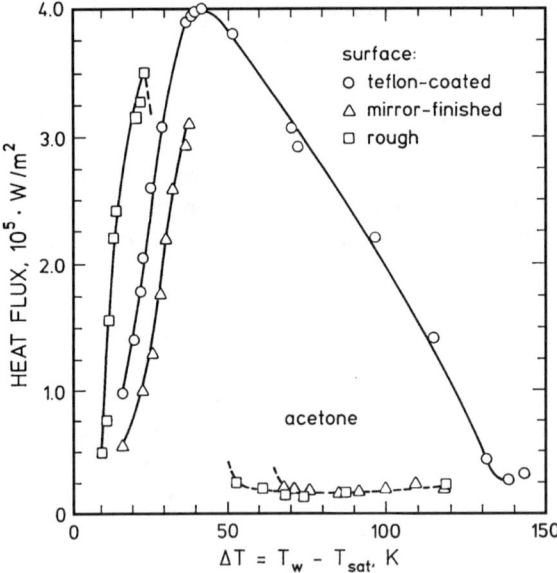

**Figure 5** Steady-state boiling curves of acetone boiling on teflon-coated, mirror-finished, and rough copper surfaces (Ramilison and Lienhard, 1987).

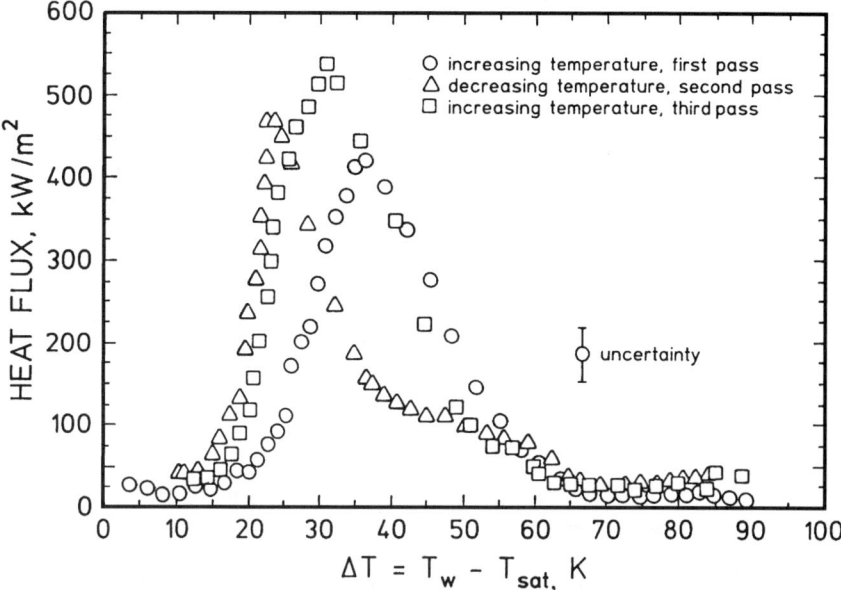

**Figure 6** Steady-state boiling curves of saturated methanol (Ungar and Eichhorn, 1996).

Ungar and Eichhorn (1996) used a horizontal 3.18 mm-diameter thin walled brass tube, heated by an internal high-speed flow of ethylene glycol and found in experiments with methanol two transtion boiling curves for increasing temperatures step by step starting from nucleate boiling and vice versa (see Figure 6). Methanol has a small positive contact angle with the brass surface used in the experiments. The discrepancies in the nucleate boiling results and the critical heat flux between the different passes are explained by the building-up of a thin black powdery coating on the tube during the eight-hours experiment. The jumps reported by Ramilison and Lienhard were not observed in the above experiments.

Hohl et al. (1996) measured entire boiling curves for FC-72 ($C_6F_{14}$) under steady-state and transient conditions. They used an electrically heated feedback-controlled horizontal flat copper plate of 34-mm diameter and 10-mm thickness with a 20-$\mu$m nickel layer on the heating surface. Figure 7 shows a typical curve measured three times with increasing and decreasing wall superheat, respectively, in a steady-state procedure. No hysteresis was observed. This confirms similar results with R113 for a smaller heater with 11.3 mm diameter obtained by Auracher (1992). Ungar and Eichhorn (1996) assumed that the disagreement in their experiments concerning the hysteresis problem was due to the similarity of heater diameter and Taylors' most dangerous wavelength for R113 ($\lambda_d = 10.9$ mm). The more recent experiments by Hohl et al. (1996, 1997) support the assumption

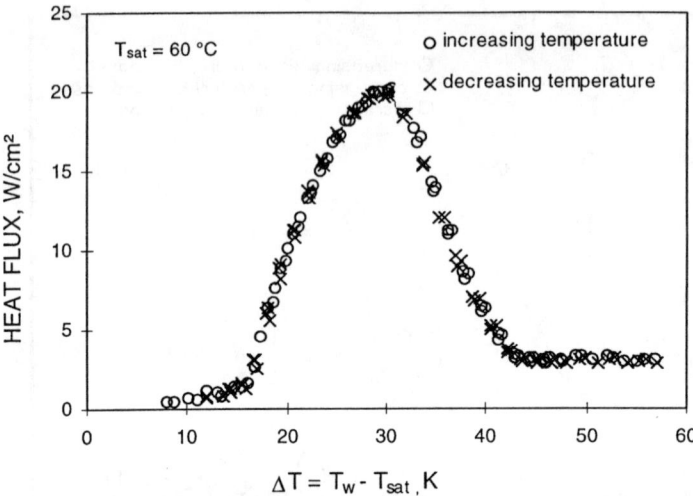

**Figure 7** Steady-state boiling curves of saturated FC 72 (Hohl et al. 1996).

that this is not the explanation for the hysteresis-discrepancy, since in their experiments, the heater diameter was 4.3-times larger than the most dangerous Taylor wavelength ($\lambda_d = 7.94$ mm for FC-72 at 60°C).

At present, there is no convincing explanation for the different results in the transition boiling behavior. A reason could be the different geometrical configurations and control systems. Contamination also plays a crucial role. In the experiments by Hohl et al. (1996, 1997), the surface remained very clean due to the thermal stability of FC-72. Other experiments with the same system but with some contamination on the heater yielded no reproducibility of the boiling curves. Finally, the effect of contact angle needs to be studied further. FC-72 and nickel have a small contact angle. At present, it is not clear whether hysteresis would occur in the experiments by Hohl et al. if larger contact angles are encountered.

***Transient experiments*** Several pool and flow boiling studies prove that different transition boiling curves are obtained for transient cooling, transient heating, and steady-state-experiments. The study by Bui and Dhir (1985b), shown in Figure 8, with saturated water boiling on a vertical copper surface (103 mm high, 63 mm wide) may serve as an example. It shows typical trends as observed in other studies: smaller heat flux in the transition region in transient cooling than in transient heating experiments. With the feedback controlled horizontal flat plate apparatus mentioned above, Hohl et al. (1996) also carried out systematic experiments on the influence of temperature transients on the boiling curve. By the control system, fixed temperature/time transients along the entire boiling could be measured:

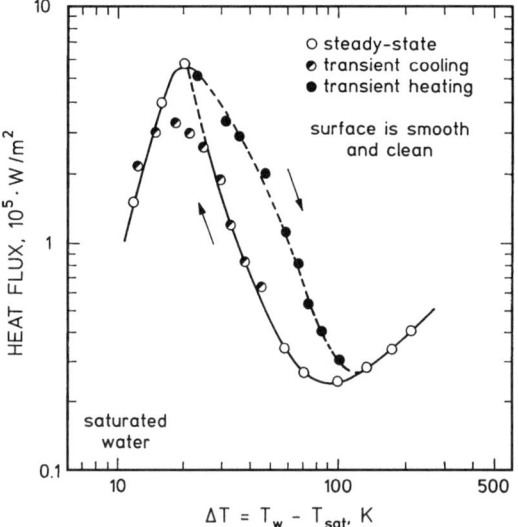

**Figure 8** Boiling curves on a smooth clean copper-surface during heating and cooling modes (Bui and Dhir, 1985).

heating transients up to $\Delta T/\Delta t = 10$ K/s were performed, while cooling transients were limited by the thermal inertia of the heater (Figure 9). The trends mentioned above have been confirmed. Moreover, it is obvious that transient heating yields higher critical heat fluxes than steady-state experiments (in contrast, e.g., to the results in Figure 8). Experiments with smaller temperature/time-rates reveal that steady-state data are approached for $\Delta T/\Delta t \to 0$.

## Surface effects and the effects of heater size and subcooling

### Surface effects

**Wettability, contact angle, coatings** Wettability has a strong influence on heat transfer in transition boiling. Heat transfer is improved with better wetting, i.e., smaller contact angles. Various contact angles can be achieved by different surface finishes, oxidation, or coatings, as typically shown in Figure 5. The increase in heat flux with decreasing contact angle includes both the critical boiling point and the minimum film boiling point. In particular, the temperature difference at MHF shifts to higher values. Coatings have not only an influence on the contact angle, but their thickness and thermal properties may also have a strong effect on the transition boiling curve (Chandratilleke et al., 1989). All these qualitative results hold for both steady-state and transient processes.

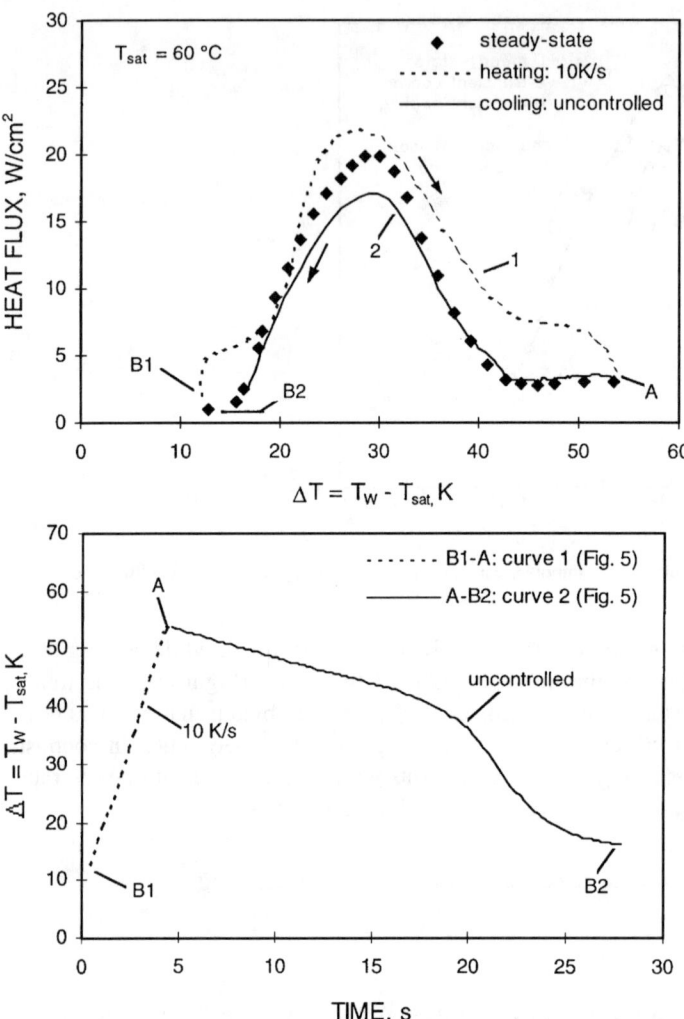

**Figure 9** Boiling curves for FC 72 under steady-state conditions, and for heating and cooling transients with the corresponding temperature/time characteristic (Hohl et al. 1996).

**Cleanliness** This effect is involved in the results shown in Figure 6. During the experiments, the authors observed an increasing contamination of the heating surface, resulting in a shift to higher heat fluxes in nucleate boiling and in the upper region of transition boiling (third pass). More typical data have been presented by Bui and Dhir (1985b), who carried out experiments with water as the deposits accumulated on the heating surface. The results clearly show that an increase in deposit has an effect similar to that with improved wettability.

**Roughness** The effect of roughness is typically shown in Figure 5. In steady-state experiments, the heat transfer coefficient in nucleate boiling is improved with increasing roughness. Also CHF is higher and shifted to lower temperature differences. The same holds for the minimum film boiling point. Hence, heat transfer in transition boiling, which is always anchored between these two limiting points, decreases with increasing roughness. The latter also holds in transient cooling. However, the effect on CHF is ambiguous. Bui and Dhir (1985b) found that CHF is not significantly affected by the roughness, and Shoji et al. (1990) found that the CHF of water even decreases with increasing roughness.

*Effect of heater size* According to the few studies available, this effect does not seem to be significant. Abassi et al. (1989) carried out transient cooling experiments with methanol as well as steady-state measurements with water on a horizontal upward-facing heater. The diameters of the heaters employed were comparable to the most dangerous wavelength for disturbance of the liquid-vapor interface. No significant effect on the heat flux in transition boiling was observed.

*Effect of subcooling* All results presented in the open literature clearly show that subcooling has a strong influence on the entire boiling curve. Both the CHF- and the MHF-points are raised with increasing subcooling. MHF in particular is shifted towards higher superheats. Hence, the transition boiling heat flux is shifted to higher values for a given wall superheat as subcooling increases.

### 7.3.4 The Mechanism of Transition Boiling and Prediction Methods

Most of the modeling approaches for transition boiling follow the assumption by Berenson (1962) that transition boiling is a combination of unstable nucleate boiling and unstable film boiling, each of which alternately exists at any given location on the heating surface. The heat flux at a given overall wall superheat is consequently expressed as the sum of a component due to liquid contact and a film boiling component,

$$q = Fq_l + (1 - F)q_g \qquad (7.2\text{-}2)$$

where $q_l$ and $q_g$ are the average heat fluxes during the liquid and vapor contact, respectively. It is reasonable to assume that $q_g = q_{\text{MHF}}$. Further, $q_l$ is time-dependent. During the local wetting lifetime, it is characterized by a sequence of transient conduction, nucleation, and dryout. $F$ denotes the average statistical proportion $(A_l/A_{tot})$ of the heating wall in contact with liquid at a given moment. If the process is ergodic, F also represents the local liquid contact time-fraction according to

$$F = \frac{A_l}{A_{tot}} \approx \frac{t_l}{t_{tot}}$$

where $t_l$ denotes the liquid contact time sampled for a statistical sufficient total time $t_{tot}$ at a point on the surface.

As examples for modeling approaches of this type, the contributions of Pan and Lin (1991) and Nishio and Nagai (1992) are quoted. Both models are mainly based on the theory by Katto and Yokoya (1970) of macrolayer formation, which will be discussed later in the text. The procedures to calculate the heat flux in transition boiling are still quite preliminary and include assumptions that have not been verified by experiments. Moreover, not all relevant parameters for transition boiling have been included in the analysis. We are therefore dependent on the few experimental data for the quantities in Eq. (7.3-2) to provide us with at least an estimate for $q(\Delta T_{sat})$ in the transition region.

In Figure 10, $F$-factors are depicted from different experimental studies. It is notable that regardless of the very different system conditions (see Auracher, 1992,

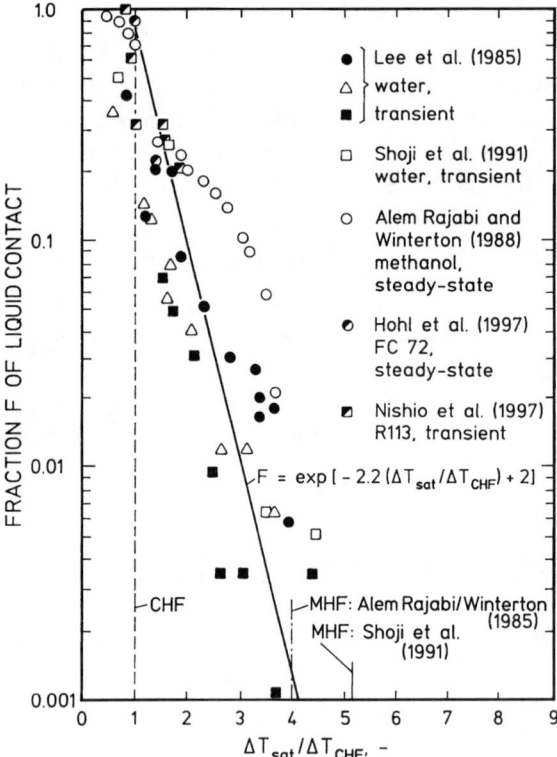

**Figure 10** Fraction of liquid contact as a function of surface superheat.

for details), F is below unity at CHF, indicating that at the critical boiling point, the surface is already covered by some vapor. It is further noted that F decreases rapidly with increasing wall superheat. The data in Figure 10 can be correlated by

$$F = \exp[-2.2(\Delta T_{sat}/\Delta T_{CHF}) + 2] \qquad (7.2\text{-}3)$$

to provide an estimate for F in Eq. (7.3-2). Note that Eq. (7.3-3) cannot be used to determine $\Delta T_{MHF}$.

Taking the few data sets available in the literature for the quantities $q(\Delta T_{sat})$, $q_{CHF}$, $q_{MHF}$, and $\Delta T_{CHF}$ of transition boiling, the time-averaged heat flux $q_l$ during a wetting period can be determined as a function of $\Delta T_{sat}$. The resulting correlation

$$\frac{q_l}{q_{CHF}} = \frac{1 - 0.18\,(q_{MHF}/q_{CHF})}{0.82\,(\Delta T_{sat}/\Delta T_{CHF})} \qquad (7.2\text{-}4)$$

can be used together with Eq. (7.3-3) to estimate $q(\Delta T_{sat})$ in the transition region if $q_g = q_{MHF}$ is assumed. More reliable measurements are required to improve correlations (7.3-3) and (7.3-4), respectively.

An experimental study by Shoji (1992) attempted to verify the Katto and Yokoya (1970) theory of macrolayer formation, which is often the basis of modeling approaches to transition boiling. In this theory, it is assumed that a liquid sublayer (macrolayer) penetrated by small vapor stems is formed on the heater surface beneath a vapor bubble. The heat transfer characteristic is determined by the competition of two time intervals, namely, the hovering time of the vapor bubble ($\tau$) above the macrolayer and the evaporation time (t) of this layer. The transition region is modeled under the assumption that $\tau > t$. In his study on steady-state transition boiling of water, Shoji presents a revised version of the basic equation derived from macrolayer theory

$$q = \rho_l h_{lg} \delta_0 (1 - A_g/A_w) f \qquad (7.2\text{-}5)$$

where $\rho_l$ denotes the liquid density, $h_{lg}$ the latent heat of evaporation, $\delta_0$ the initial macrolayer thickness, $A_g/A_w$ the area fraction of vapor stems in the macrolayer, and $f = 1/\tau$ the bubble departure frequency. Shoji was able to measure, or at least estimate, the a priori unknown quantities $\delta_0$, $A_g/A_w$, and f, and found a good agreement with his transition boiling heat transfer data. It should be noted, however, that at present no correlations with a wider range of validity are available for the above mentioned quantities. The heat transfer models based on the macrolayer theory suffer from various assumptions that need to be refined, and additional data are needed to study the parametric effects as mentioned earlier.

Another phenomenological model to predict transition boiling heat transfer has been recommended by Ramilison and Lienhard (1987) based on their experiments with different fluids and surface finishes (see, e.g., Figure 5). The following correlation can be used to predict film boiling and the so-called transitional film boiling.

$$\dot{q}_{fb} = 3.74 \cdot 10^{-6} \left[ \frac{\lambda_h^2 g^3 (\rho_l - \rho_g)}{\kappa_h \sigma} \right] \frac{\lambda_l/\kappa_l^{1/2}}{\lambda_l/\kappa_l^{1/2} + \lambda_h/\kappa_h^{1/2}} Ja^{*2} \Delta T_{sat} + \dot{q}_{fb} \quad (7.2\text{-}6)$$

where

$$Ja^* = \frac{\rho_h c_{ph}(T_{dfb} - T_w)}{\rho_g h_{lg}} \quad (7.2\text{-}7)$$

where index h denotes: heater and $q_{fb}$ is the heat flux of film boiling at the wall superheat $\Delta T_{sat}$. The authors used the turbulent film boiling correlation (Eq. 15 for Ja > 0.5) by Klimenko (1981) but modified his empirical constant of 0.0086 (0.0057 for Freon 113 and n-pentane, 0.0066 for acetone, and 0.0154 for benzene). $T_{dfb}$ is the temperature at which the first liquid contact occurs (MHF-point). The graphical correlation for $T_{dfb}$ given by Ramilison and Lienhard is well approximated (see Carey, 1992) by

$$\frac{T_{dfb} - T_{sat}}{T_{hn} - T_{sat}} = 0.97 \exp\left(-0.0006 \theta_a^{1.8}\right) \quad (7.2\text{-}8)$$

where $\theta_a$ is the advancing contact angle in degrees. $T_{hn}$ denotes the homogeneous nucleation temperature, which the authors determine by

$$T_{hn} = \left[ 0.932 + 0.077 \left( \frac{T_{sat}}{Tc} \right)^9 \right] Tc \quad (7.2\text{-}9)$$

Tc is the critical temperature of the boiling liquid. Values for $\theta_a$ are summarized by Ramilison and Lienhard in their Table 2: at 5°C, $\theta_a = 5°$ for acetone on a teflon-coated surface; the other $\theta_a$-values are between 25° and 50°, depending on the combination of surface finish and fluid. This prediction method provides a reasonable fit to the data for the fluids already quoted above and the different surface finishes (see Figure 5) as well as to data by Berenson (1962).

All modeling approaches suffer from the fact that on one hand, numerous effects have an influence on transition boiling, and on the other, few experimental results are available. Hereby, it should not be forgotten that all these effects may have a different impact under steady-state and transient conditions. Therefore, if no specific data for a given problem are available, it is recommended to predict heat transfer in transition boiling by using the two anchor points, namely, the CHF-point and the MHF-point. In a first approximation, if it can be assumed that a linear relationship exists in a log/log-plot between the two limiting points, then

$$\frac{\ln(q/q_{MHF})}{\ln(q_{CHF}/q_{MHF})} = \frac{\ln(\Delta T_{MHF}/\Delta T_{sat})}{\ln(\Delta T_{MHF}/\Delta T_{CHF})}. \qquad (7.2\text{-}10)$$

With $q = \alpha \Delta T_{sat}$, one of the quantities, $q$ or $\Delta T_{sat}$, may be replaced by the heat transfer coefficient $\alpha$. Prediction methods for the limiting quantities $q_{CHF}/\Delta T_{CHF}$ and $q_{MHF}/\Delta T_{MHF}$ are presented in chapters 6 and 7.

## REFERENCES

Abassi, A., Alem Rajabi, A. A., and Winterton, R. H. S. 1989. Effect of Confined Geometry on Pool Boiling at High Temperatures. *Exp. Thermal and Fluid Sci.* 2:127–133.

Adiutori, E. F. 1991. Thermal Behavior in the Transition Region Between Nucleate and Film Boiling. *Proc. ASME/JSME Thermal Eng. Joint Conf.*, Volume 2. Reno, NV, pp. 51–58.

Alem Rajabi, A. A. and Winterton, R. H. S. 1988. Liquid-Solid Contact in Steady-State Transition Pool Boiling. *Int. J. Heat Fluid Flow* 9:215–219.

Andersen, J. G. M. 1976. Low-Flow Boiling Heat Transfer on Vertical Surfaces, Part I:Theoretical Model. *AIChE Symp. Ser.* 164:2–6.

Auracher, H. 1990. Transition Boiling. *Proc. 9th Int. Heat Transfer Conf.*, Jerusalem, Volume 1, pp. 69–90.

Auracher, H. 1992. Transition Boiling in Natural Convection Systems. *Pool and External Flow Boiling*, Eds. V. K. Dhir and A. E. Bergles. Engineering Foundation, pp. 219–236.

Barron, R. F. and Dergham, A. R. 1987. Film Boiling to a Plate Facing Downward. *Adv. Cryogn.Eng.*, Volume 33, pp. 355–362. New York: Plenum Press.

Baumeister, K. J. and Hamill, T. D. 1967. Laminar Flow Analysis of Film Boiling from a Horizontal Wire. NASA, TN D-4035.

Baumeister, K. J. and Simon, F. F. 1973. Leidenfrost Temperature—Its Correlation for Liquid Metals, Cryogens, Hydrocarbons, and Water. *ASME J. Heat Transfer* 95(2):166–173.

Berenson, P. J. 1961. Film Boiling Heat Transfer from a Horizontal Surface. *ASME J. Heat Transfer* 83(3):351–358.

Berenson, P. J. 1962. Experiments on Pool-Boiling Heat Transfer. *Int. J. Heat Mass Transfer* 5: 985–999.

Blum, J., Marquardt, W., and Auracher, H. 1996. Stability of Boiling Systems. *Int. J. Heat Mass Transfer* 39:3021–3033.

Breen, B. P. and Westwater, J. W. 1962. Effect of Diameter of Horizontal Tube on Film Boiling Heat Transfer. *Chem. Eng. Progr.* 58(7):67–72.

Bromley, L. A. 1950. Heat Transfer in Stable Film Boiling. *Chem. Eng. Progr.* 46(5):221–227.

Bui, T. D. and Dhir, V. K. 1985a. Film Boiling Heat Transfer on an Isothermal Vertical Surface. *ASME J. Heat Transfer* 107(4):764–771.

Bui, T. D. and Dhir, V. K. 1985b. Transition Boiling Heat Transfer on a Vertical Surface. *J. Heat Transfer* 107:756–763.

Carey, V. P. 1992. *Liquid-Vapor Phase-Change Phenomena*. Washington, DC: Taylor and Francis, pp. 120–124, 291.

Chandrasekhar, S. 1961. *Hydrodynamic and Hydromagnetic Stability*. New York: Dover, pp. 428–514.

Chandratilleke, G. R., Nishio, S., and Ohkubo, H. 1989. Pool Boiling Heat Transfer to Saturated Liquid Helium From Coated Surface. *Cryogenics* 129:588–592.

Dhir, V. K. 1990. Nucleate and Transition Boiling Heat Transfer Under Pool and External Flow Conditions. *Proc. 9th Int. Heat Transfer Conf.* 1:129–155.

Grigoriev, V. A, Klimenko, V. V., and Shelepen, A. G. 1982. Pool Film Boiling from Submerged Spheres. *Proc.7th Int. Heat Transfer Conf.* 1:387–392.

Gunnerson, F. S. and Cronenberg, A. W. 1980. On the Minimum Film Boiling Conditions for Spherical Geometries. *ASME J. Heat Transfer* 102:335–341.

Hamill, T. D. and Baumeister, K. J. 1967. Effect of Subcooling and Radiation on Film-Boiling Heat Transfer from a Flat Plate. NASA, TN D-3925.

Hendricks, R. C. and Baumeister, K. J. 1969. Film Boiling From Submerged Spheres. NASA, TN D-5124.

Hohl, R., Auracher, H., Blum, J., and Marquardt, W. 1996. Pool Boiling Heat Transfer Experiments with Controlled Wall Temperature Transients. *2nd European Thermal Science and 14th UIT Nat. Heat Transfer Conf.*, Rome, pp. 1647–1652.

Hohl, R., Auracher, H., Blum, J., and Marquardt, W. 1997. Identification of Liquid-Vapor Fluctuations Between Nucleate and Film Boiling In Natural Convection. *Proc. Int. Engng. Foundation Conf.: Convective Flow and Pool Boiling*, Eds. Celata, G. P., DiMarco, P., and Mariani, A. Irsee, May 18–23. Pisa: Edizoni ETS.

Hsu, Y. Y. and Westwater, J. W. 1960. Approximate Theory for Film Boiling on Vertical Surface. *Chem. Eng. Progr. Symp. Ser.* 30:15–24.

Inoue, A. and Bankoff, S. G. 1981. Destabilization of Film Boiling Due to Arrival of a Pressure Shock. Part I: Experiments. *ASME J. Heat Transfer* 103(3):459–464.

Inoue, A., Ganguli, A., and Bankoff, S. G. 1981. Destabilization of Film Boiling Due to Arrival of a Pressure Shock. Part II: Analytical. *ASME J. Heat Transfer* 103(3):465–471.

Jackson, T. W. and Yen, H. H. 1970. A Simplified Solution for Transient Film Boiling with Constant Heat Flux. *Heat Transfer 1970* V:B3.8.

Jordan, D. P. 1969. Film and Transition Boiling. *Adv. Heat Transfer*. Eds. T. F. Irvine and J. P.Hartnett, pp. 55–128. New York: Academic Press.

Kalinin, E. K., Berlin, I. I., and Kostyuk, V. V. 1975. Film-Boiling Heat Transfer. *Adv. Heat Transfer*, Volume 11, pp. 51–197. New York: Academic Press.

Kalinin, E. K., Berlin, I. I., and Kostyuk, V. V. 1987. Transition Boiling Heat Transfer. In: *Advances in Heat Transfer*, Volume 18, pp. 241–323.

Katto, Y. and Yokoya, S. 1970. Mechanism of Boiling Crisis and Transition Boiling on Pool Boiling. *Proc. $4^{th}$ Int. Heat Transfer Conf.*, Vol. B3.2.

Kim, B. J. and Corradini, M. L. 1986. Recent Film Boiling Calculations: Implication of Fuel-Coolant Interactions. *Int. J. Heat and Mass Transfer* 29(8):1159–1167.

Klimenko, V. V. 1981. Film Boiling on a Horizontal Plate—New Correlation. *Int. J. Heat and Mass Transfer* 24(1):69–79.

Lee, L. Y. W., Chen, J. C., and Nelson, R. A. 1985. Liquid-Solid Contact Measurements Using a Surface Thermocouple Temperature Probe in Atmospheric Pool Boiling Water. *Int. J. Heat Mass Transfer* 28:1415–1423.

Leonard, J. E., Sun, K. H., and Dix, G. E. 1976. Low Flow Film Boiling Heat Transfer on Vertical Surface, Part II: Empirical Formulations and Application to BWR-LOCA Analysis. *AIChE Symp. Ser.* 164:7–13.

Lienhard, J. H. and Wong, P. T. Y. 1964. The Dominant Unstable Wavelength and Minimum Heat Flux During Film Boiling on a Horizontal Cylinder. *ASME J. Heat Transfer* 86(2):220–226.

Nikolayev, G. P. and Skripov, V. P. 1970. Experimental Investigation of Minimum Heat Fluxes at Submerged Surface in Boiling. *Heat Transfer—Soviet Research* 2(3):122–127.

Nishikawa, K. and Ito, T. 1966. Two-Phase Boundary-Layer Treatment of Free-Convection Film Boiling. *Int. J. Heat and Mass Transfer* 9(1):103–115.

Nishikawa, K., Ito, T., Kuroki, T., and Matsumoto, K. 1972. Pool Film Boiling Heat Transfer from a Horizontal Cylinder to Saturated Liquids. *Int. J. Heat and Mass Transfer* 15:853–862.

Nishikawa, K., Ito, T., and Matsumoto, K. 1976. Investigation of Variable Thermophysical Property Problem Concerning Pool Film Boiling from Vertical Plate with Prescribed Uniform Temperature. *Int. J. Heat and Mass Transfer* 19(10):1173–1181.

Nishio, S. 1987. Prediction Technique for Minimum-Heat-Flux (MHF)-Point Condition of Saturated Pool Boiling. *Int. J. Heat and Mass Transfer* 30:2045–2057.

Nishio, S. and Nagai, N. 1992. A Model Predicting Transition-Boiling Heat Transfer. *Pool and External Flow Boiling*. Eds. V. K. Dhir and A. E. Bergles, pp. 271–276. New York: ASME, Engineering Foundation.

Nishio, S. and Ohtake, H. 1993. Vapor-Film-Unit Model and Heat Transfer Correlation for Natural-Convection Film Boiling with Wave Motion Under Subcooled Conditions. *Int. J. Heat and Mass Transfer* 36(10):2541–2552.

Nishio, S., Gotoh, T., and Nagai, N. 1997. Observation of Boiling Structures. *Proc. Int. Engng. Foundation Conf., "Convective Flow and Pool Boiling."* Irsee, May 18–23.

Pan, C. and Lin, T. L. 1991. Predictions of Parametric Effects on Transition Boiling Under Pool Boiling Conditions. *Int. J. Heat Mass Transfer* 34:1355–1370.

Payayopanakul, W. and Westwater, J. W. 1978. Evaluation of the Unsteady-State Quenching Method for Determining Boiling Curves. *Int. J. Heat and Mass Transfer* 21(11):1437–1445.

Ramilison, J. M. and Lienhard, J. H. 1987. Transition Boiling Heat Transfer and the Film Transition Regime. *J. Heat Transfer* 109:746–752.

Sakurai, A. 1990. Film Boiling Heat Transfer. *Proc. 9th Int. Heat Transfer Conf.*, Volume 1, pp.157–186.

Sakurai, A., Shiotsu, M., and Hata, K. 1990a. A General Correlation for Pool Film Boiling Heat Transfer from a Horizontal Cylinder to Subcooled Liquid. Part 1-A: Theoretical Pool Film Boiling Heat Transfer Model Including Radiation Contributions and Its Analytical Solution. *ASME J. Heat Transfer* 112(2):430–441.

Sakurai, A., Shiotsu, M., and Hata, K. 1990b. A General Correlation for Pool Film Boiling Heat Transfer from a Horizontal Cylinder to Subcooled Liquid. Part 2: Experimental Data for Various Liquids and Its Correlation. *ASME J. Heat Transfer* 112(2):441–450.

Sauer, H. J., Jr. and Ragsdell, K. M. 1971. Film Pool Boiling of Nitrogen from Flat Surfaces. *Adv. Cryogenic Eng.*, Volume 16, pp. 412–415. New York: Plenum Press.

Segev, A. and Bankoff, S. G. 1980. The Role of Adsorption in Determining the Minimum Film Boiling Temperature. *Int. J. Heat and Mass Transfer* 23:637–642.

Shigechi, T., Kawae, N., Tokita, Y., and Yamada, T. 1989. Film Boiling Heat Transfer from a Horizontal Circular Plate Facing Downward. *JSME Int. J., Series II* 32(4):646–651.

Shoji, M. 1992. A Study of Steady Transition Boiling of Water: Experimental Verification of Macrolayer Evaporation Model. *Pool and External Flow Boiling*. Eds. V. K. Dhir and A. E. Bergles, pp. 237–242. New York: ASME, Engineering Foundation.

Shoji, M., Witte, L. C., Yokoya, S., Kawakami, M., and Kuroki, H. 1991. Measurement of Liquid-Solid Contact Using Micro-Thermocouples in Pool Transition Boiling of Water on a Horizontal Copper Surface. *Proc. ASME/JSME Thermal Eng. Joint. Conf.*, Volume 2. Reno, NV, pp. 333–338.

Shoji, M., Witte, L. C., Yokoya, S., and Ohshima, M. 1990. Liquid-Solid Contact and Effects of Surface Roughness and Wettability in Film and Transition Boiling on a Horizontal Large Surface. *Proc. 9th Int. Heat Transfer Conf.* 2:135–140.

Spiegler, P., Hopenfeld, J., Silberberg, M., Bumpus, Jr., C. F., and Norman, A. 1963. Onset of Stable Film Boiling and the Foam Limit. *Int. J. Heat and Mass Transfer* 6:987–989.

Srinivasan, J. and Rao, N. S. 1984. Numerical Study of Heat Transfer in Laminar Film Boiling by the Finite-Difference Method. *Int. J. Heat Mass Transfer* 27(1):77–84.

Stephan, K. 1965. Stabilität beim Sieden. *Brennst.-Wärme-Kraft* 17:571–578.
Suryanarayana, N. V. and Merte, H., Jr. 1972. Film Boiling on Vertical Surfaces. *ASME J. Heat Transfer* 90(4):377–384.
Ungar, E. K. and Eichhorn, R. 1996. Transition Boiling Curves in Saturated Pool Boiling from Horizontal Cylinders. *J. Heat Transfer* 118:654–661.
Witte, L. C. and Lienhard, J. H. 1982. On the Existence of Two Transition Boiling Curves. *Int. J. Heat Mass Transfer* 25:771–779.
Zuber, N. 1959. Hydrodynamic Aspects of Boiling Heat Transfer. *Atomic Energy Commission Report No.AECU-4439, Physics and Mathematics*.

CHAPTER
# EIGHT

## INTRODUCTION AND BASIC MODELS

**Geofferey F. Hewitt**

*Imperial College of Science, Technology and Medicine, London, SW7 2AZ, United Kingdom*

## 8.1 INTRODUCTION

The next four chapters of this handbook are concerned with the important topic of two-phase flow. The objective is to provide a brief but fundamental exposition on two-phase flow that can serve as a basis for estimating flow characteristics in phase change processes, particularly evaporation (boiling) and condensation. This present chapter gives a general introduction to the topic of two-phase flow systems and Chapter 9 deals with the fluid mechanics of such systems, covering both flow inside circular tubes and flow in other geometries, such as heat exchangers. Two-phase flows are often fluctuating in nature but, superimposed on these fluctuations, gross excursions and oscillations in flow may occur due to system instability; these phenomena are discussed in more detail in Chapter 10. Another important characteristic of two-phase flows is the relatively low sound speeds (much less than those for gases and liquids) that can occur due to the combination in these systems of high compressibility and high density. Thus, the maximum rate at which two-phase fluids may be discharged through, say, relief systems, is limited, and the maximum ("critical") rate is of crucial importance in two-phase system design. The important topic of two-phase critical flow is discussed in more detail in Chapter 11.

As is well known, true predictions of even single-phase turbulent flows are not possible except for very low Reynolds numbers, close to the transition from laminar flow. In two-phase flows with deformable interfaces (i.e., gas-liquid and liquid-liquid flows), the interfacial configuration is also usually unpredictable in detail; when we combine this with the fact that such flows are more often than not turbulent in nature, then it becomes obvious that (as in single-phase turbulent flows), fundamental analytical predictions of two-phase flows are not readily achievable. In this part of the handbook, we are concerned primarily with gas-liquid flows, and here, there is a further complication, namely, the compressibility of the gas phase. This is of course an all important feature in the case of critical two-phase flows (as discussed in Chapter 11). Despite the formidable difficulties in treating two-phase flows, their practical importance dictates that methodologies have to be developed to deal with them. It should not be surprising to the reader, however, that such methodologies contain a very large element of empiricism; as a consequence, extrapolation to a range of conditions outside those for which the empirical relationships were developed is often uncertain at best!

The main objective of this chapter is to explore on a relatively qualitative basis the types of approaches that have been followed in treating two-phase gas-liquid flows. Section 8.2 discusses the types of system (adiabatic, phase change, etc.) that may be encountered and reviews the important topic of *equilibrium*. Much better models for two-phase flows may be obtained by classifying the types of interfacial distribution into generic types called *flow patterns or flow regimes*. The general background to such classifications is given in Section 8.3. Modelling methods for two-phase flow are classified in Section 8.4, and the chapter closes with a brief overview (Section 8.5). It should be stressed that the present chapter is introductory in nature; many of the topics will be explored in much more detail in Chapter 9.

## 8.2 TWO-PHASE FLOW SYSTEMS

Much of the work carried out on gas-liquid flows has been done with *adiabatic* systems, that is, systems without heat transfer to or from the flowing two-phase mixture. Archetypically, such experiments are done with the most convenient fluids, namely, air and water. Though adiabatic flows have significant industrial importance (for instance, in the transport of oil/natural gas mixtures in petroleum recovery systems), the main applications of the data are in fact in predicting *diabatic* systems, where heat is added or removed from the system, causing evaporation and condensation, respectively. Such diabatic systems are the main focus of this handbook. In Chapter 9, a more detailed discussion of two-phase flow in diabatic systems will be given. However, in the context of the present introductory chapter, it is worth noting the importance of *non-equilibrium effects*. These effects can lead to situations in which the application of adiabatic data and correlations to phase change systems can lead to considerable errors in prediction. Non-equilibrium effects can be classified under several headings, as follows.

## 8.2.1 Hydrodynamic Non-Equilibrium

In single-phase turbulent flows, the flow parameters (particularly pressure gradient) become invariant with distance after only a short distance (typically 10 diameters) from the entrance of the flow channel. However, for gas-liquid flows, many hundreds of diameters may be required to reach invariant conditions (hydrodynamic equilibrium). Examples here are the development of bubbly flows (described in more detail in Chapter 9) as a result of bubble coalescence and the development of annular flows as a result of entrainment of the liquid film into the gas core. Bearing in mind that these departures from hydrodynamic equilibrium occur in adiabatic flows, it is not surprising that they are even more dominant in diabatic flows, where the flow rates of the respective phases are changing along the channel. A prime example of the effects of departure from hydrodynamic equilibrium is that of the occurrence of *dryout* in evaporating annular flows. Here, the liquid film on the wall dries out, while at the same time, a large proportion of the original liquid flow is still flowing in the channel in the form of droplets. In an adiabatic situation, such dryout of course would not occur. The presence of the liquid film has a dramatic effect on the pressure gradient, and it is clearly inappropriate to use adiabatic correlations for pressure gradient under dryout or near-dryout conditions (though this does not stop such correlations from being built into the most widely used computer codes for predicting phase change systems!). Conversely, in annular flow condensation, there is often much less entrainment at a given quality than for the adiabatic or evaporation cases. This implies that the pressure gradient is much higher at a given quality in condensation than for adiabatic or evaporating flows.

## 8.2.2 Thermodynamic Non-Equilibrium

In evaporating and condensing systems, the assumption is often made that there exists *thermodynamic equilibrium* between the two phases. Thus, the phases are assumed to co-exist at their *saturation temperature*. Even though it is usually a good approximation to assume that local thermodynamic equilibrium applies at the vapor-liquid interfaces, temperature gradients within the respective phases can give rise to situations in which, on average, the flow departs grossly from equilibrium. One example of such a non-equilibrium situation is that of the occurrence of vapor bubbly flow in the presence of a sub-cooled liquid; on average, the fluid enthalpy may be less than that for saturation, but nevertheless, a two-phase flow is occurring. This situation arises due to sub-cooled boiling. Another example is the co-existence of liquid droplets and highly super-heated vapors such, as that which occurs in the post-dryout region. Here, droplets may persist in the flow even though the bulk enthalpy is greater than that for the saturated vapor.

### 8.2.3 Component Non-Equilibrium

Many of the phase change situations encountered in practice involve multi-component rather than single-component fluids. For example, in the process industry, reboilers and condensers associated with distillation processes always (by definition) have to deal with mixtures of fluids, such as hydrocarbon mixtures. Again, a common assumption in calculating such systems is that vapor-liquid equilibrium persists in a bulk sense, which dictates the fractions of the components in the vapor and liquid phases, respectively. However, in phase change systems, complex heat and mass transfer processes are taking place, which means that component equilibrium is not maintained.

The above types of non-equilibrium effects are not mutually exclusive and can occur simultaneously. For instance, in annular flow evaporation of multi-component mixtures, the liquid compositions in the liquid film and the entrained droplets may be different; this can have a profound effect on the heat transfer behavior.

In dealing with phase change systems, it is important to be aware of these potential non-equilibrium effects. Unfortunately, they are largely ignored in many of the methodologies developed for prediction of phase change systems!

## 8.3 FLOW PATTERNS

In a gas-liquid flow, since the interfaces are deformable, there are in principle an infinite number of ways in which the interfaces can be distributed within the flow. Fortunately, however, there are a number of characteristic types of interfacial distribution, which is a considerable aid in developing models for gas-liquid flows. The types of interfacial distribution are termed *flow patterns* or *flow regimes*. The classification of flow patterns still depends largely on visual observation, and a bewildering variety of types of flow pattern have been defined in the literature. However, a consensus is gradually developing, which is described in more detail in Chapter 9. Flow patterns can be classified into three broad types as follows.

### 8.3.1 Dispersed

Here, elements (roughly spherical) of one of the phases are dispersed in the other. This type of flow pattern would include *bubbly flows* where bubbles of the gas (vapor) are dispersed in a liquid continuum. In *drop flow*, the liquid phase is dispersed as droplets in the gas phase. Drop flows are difficult to obtain in adiabatic systems since there is a natural tendency to form a wall film characteristic of annular flow. However, they are an important type of flow in diabatic systems, where the wall film has been evaporated.

## 8.3.2 Separated Flows

Here, the two phases flow in separate regions of the channel while still interacting at the interface between the regions. Examples here are *stratified flow* in horizontal pipes, in which the liquid flows in a layer at the bottom of the pipe with the gas above it, and *annular flow*, in which the liquid flows as a film on the periphery of the channel.

## 8.3.3 Intermittent Flows

Though nearly all two-phase flows are fluctuating in nature, there exist several flow patterns where gross intermittency occurs. These include slug (or plug) flows in vertical channels and slug and semi-slug flows in horizontal channels.

The feature of flow patterns in gas-liquid flows that makes for additional difficulties is that they often cannot be classified into the above three categories, but rather have features of two or more of the categories. Thus, in annular flow, part of the liquid is dispersed in the gas core of the flow, making the flow simultaneously dispersed and separated. Similarly, gas bubbles are entrained into the liquid slugs in slug flow, making the flow simultaneously intermittent and dispersed. Further details of such flow patterns are given in Chapter 9.

## 8.4 MODELING TWO-PHASE FLOW SYSTEMS

In the modeling of two-phase flow systems, the most important objectives are to predict the *pressure gradient* and the *in situ phase fractions*. The in-situ phase fractions are commonly known as the *void fraction* for the gas phase and the *liquid hold-up* for the liquid phase. In general, the in situ phase fractions are different from the volumetric phase fractions on a flow basis. This is because the velocities of the two phases may be different (the ratio of the mean gas and liquid velocities is known as the *slip ratio*). In considering phase change, other hydrodynamic parameters, such as wall shear stress, frequency characteristics of intermittency, extent of liquid entrainment in annular flow, etc., may be important. However, the main traditional focus has been on pressure gradient and phase fraction. The pressure gradient is usually regarded as the sum of three components, namely the *accelerational, gravitational*, and *frictional* pressure gradients. Further details of this categorization are given in Chapter 9. The accelerational component of the pressure gradient arises from changes in the momentum flux of the mixture along the channel. Accelerational pressure gradients are particularly important in phase change systems, where the vapor velocity is increasing or decreasing as a result of evaporation or condensation. It should be noted that the accelerational pressure gradient can be negative in the case of condensation systems where the momentum flux decreases along the channel. The gravitational component of pressure gradient is related to the in situ mean density of the mixture and, hence, to the phase fraction. Finally, the frictional pressure gradient is related to the wall shear stress and is normally negative. However, in vertical slug flows, the mean wall shear stress may be negative, giving rise to a positive frictional pressure gradient (though not, of course, to a positive total pressure gradient). All of these features are discussed in more detail in Chapter 9. Here, we will categorize the models that are commonly used for predicting these system variables as follows.

### 8.4.1 Homogeneous Model

Here, the phases are assumed to be intimately mixed such that the mixture can be assigned a density corresponding to the total mass rate of flow divided by the total volume rate of flow. The velocity of the two phases is considered to be equal, and the flow can be treated by analogy with single phase flow. The accelerational and gravitational components of pressure drop can be calculated directly from the independent variables, and a correlation is required only for the friction term. Often, this term is calculated on the basis of single-phase flow correlations using an appropriate mean viscosity.

### 8.4.2 Separated Flow Model

Here, the two phases are considered to be flowing in separate regions and with different velocities. However, the equations describing the flow (continuity, momentum, and energy) are in a combined form. To solve for the accelerational and gravitational pressure gradients, a correlation is required for phase fraction (void fraction or liquid hold-up), and for frictional pressure gradient, a separate correlation is required. Thus, while the method is usually more accurate than the homogeneous model, more empirical correlations are needed.

### 8.4.3 Two-Fluid Model

Here, separate continuity, momentum, and energy equations are written for the two phases (making 6 equations in all—hence the name *six-equation model* is often given to this type of modeling). In this type of modeling, relationships are required for the transfer of mass, momentum, and energy across the interfaces, and also for the wall shear stresses for the respective phases. Thus, the need for empiricism is not avoided by using the two-fluid model; the argument is that the empirical relationships developed for the interface and wall terms are more general than those that can be achieved by merely correlating wall friction and hold-up, as in the separated flow model.

### 8.4.4 Phenomenological Models

Experimental observations of the phenomena occurring in gas-liquid two-phase flows can sometimes give a better indication of the form of model to be adopted. Examples here are the modeling of slug flow, taking account of correlations for such parameters as slug frequency, liquid shedding rate behind slugs, etc., and models of annular flow, which take detailed account of the entrainment and deposition processes. Such *phenomenological* models go further than the two-fluid model in representing the detailed processes. However, it is possible sometimes to represent the flows by extending the two-fluid model to a multi-fluid representation; an example here is that of representing the droplets in annular flow as a separate "field," for which a further three equations are added, making nine in total. However, this approach is often not suitable for intermittent flows such as slug flow, since a fundamental difficulty occurs in averaging the quantities.

### 8.4.5 Computational Fluid Dynamics (CFD) Models

In single-phase flows, it is becoming increasingly prevalent to seek solutions using modern CFD codes. Though there are serious deficiencies in modeling of the turbulent flows that occur in most practical systems (even for single-phase flow), the use of CFD codes is now widely adopted for prediction methods for commercial applications. For two-phase flows, due to the complications arising from the interfacial structure, CFD is much less useful for direct calculations. However, it can often be helpful in developing an understanding of the phenomena occurring.

Therefore, two-phase flows present particular challenges, especially when linked to phase change. The type of model selected would depend on the desire for accuracy and detail, but it should be stressed that none of the current modeling techniques can be relied on to produce accurate results.

## 8.5 OVERVIEW

In this chapter, a brief qualitative description has been made of the general nature of two-phase flows and of the way in which they are structured and modeled. Two-phase flow is still a rich area for research, and a more detailed understanding is gradually developing. When designing two-phase flow systems, it is important to remember that calculations are necessarily inaccurate. The design should take account of this uncertainty.

CHAPTER
# NINE

# FLUID MECHANICS ASPECTS OF TWO-PHASE FLOW

**9.1 Geofferey F. Hewitt**

*Imperial College of Science, Technology and Medicine, London, SW7 2AZ, United Kingdom*

**9.2 Masahiro Kawaji**

*University of Toronto, Toronto, Ontario M5S 3E5, Canada*

## 9.1 FLOW INSIDE CIRCULAR TUBES

### 9.1.1 Introduction

Two-phase flow in circular tubes is found in a wide range of industrial applications, including oil/gas pipelines and systems with evaporation (such as thermosyphon reboilers in the process industry and water-tube boilers in the power generation industry) and condensation (in-tube condensation in shell-and-tube heat exchangers and air-cooled heat exchangers, for instance). This industrial importance is reflected in the vast amount of work that has been done in the area. In this chapter (for which the objective is to give an introduction to the subject together with a selection of hopefully useful relationships), it would be impossible to even list this literature! To further reduce the attempted coverage of the chapter, the following restrictions have been imposed:

(1) The tubes dealt with are assumed to be *straight*, and two-phase flow in bends, coils, and other singularities are not dealt with. Flows in singularities, such as orifices, bends, venturies, etc., are reviewed by, for instance, Hewitt (1984) and Chisholm (1983), and work on coiled tubes is typified by the papers of Banerjee et al. (1969) and Hewitt and Jayanti (1992).

(2) Only *co-current* flows will be considered. Static systems such as bubble columns and counter-current flows (such as those that occur in reflux condensers) are not dealt with. Typical of studies of two-phase flow in bubble columns is the work of Ohnuki et al. (1995), and studies of counter-current flows in falling film systems are typified by that of Govan et al. (1991).

Though only straight pipes are considered, the *orientation* of the pipe is an important parameter. Quite different behaviors are observed in horizontal, inclined, and vertical tubes, respectively.

We shall first discuss types of interfacial structure (namely, flow patterns) and then present the basic equations. This is followed by a discussion of prediction methods for pressure drop and void fraction.

### 9.1.2 Flow Patterns

**9.1.2.1 Flow patterns in vertical upflow.** The flow regimes in vertical upflow are illustrated in Figure 1 and are defined as follows:

(1) Bubble flow. Here, the liquid phase is continuous, and a dispersion of bubbles flows within the liquid continuum.
(2) Slug or plug flow. At higher gas flows, bubble coalescence occurs, and the bubble diameter approaches that of the tube. Large characteristically bullet-shaped bubbles (often referred to as Taylor bubbles) are formed, which may be separated by regions containing dispersions of smaller bubbles.
(3) Churn Flow. With increasing gas velocity, a breakdown of the slug flow bubbles leads to an unstable flow regime called *churn flow*. Near the point of breakdown of slug flow, periodic bridging of the pipe occurs, as illustrated in Figure 1.

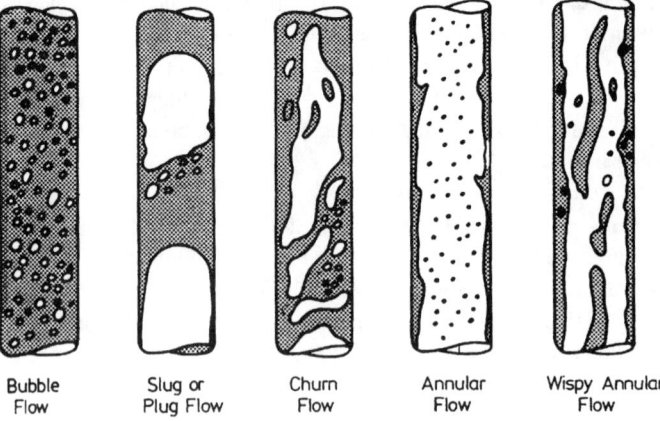

**Figure 1** Flow regimes in vertical upflow (from Hewitt, 1982, with permission).

However, as the gas flow rate is increased, the flow behavior is different; large waves are swept up the surface of the tube with liquid films between them, which flow initially upwards and then reverse in direction (Hewitt et al., 1985).
(4) *Annular Flow.* Here, the liquid flows on the wall of the tube as a film and the gas phase flows in the center. Usually, some of the liquid phase is entrained as droplets in the gas core.
(5) *Wispy Annular Flow.* As the liquid flow rate is increased, the concentration of drops in the gas core increases. Ultimately, coalescence and other processes lead to the formation of large agglomerates (wisps) of liquid in the gas core, characterizing the wispy annular flow regime. A more detailed discussion of this regime is presented by Hewitt (1997).

It should be emphasized that the description of flow patterns is essentially qualitative in nature, and the classification of flow patterns is therefore rather subjective. More detailed discussion of flow pattern determination is given by Hewitt (1982).

As was discussed earlier, the identification of flow patterns is important as a basis for the development of more phenomenological models. Data for flow patterns are often represented in terms of *flow pattern maps*, which are of two types:

(1) *Specific Flow Pattern Maps.* Here, data for a particular set of conditions (i.e., given tube diameter, orientation, and fluid physical properties) are presented in terms of variables such as phase superficial velocities or mass flux and quality. An example of a specific flow pattern map for vertical upflow is shown in Figure 2 (showing data for high pressure steam-water mixtures).

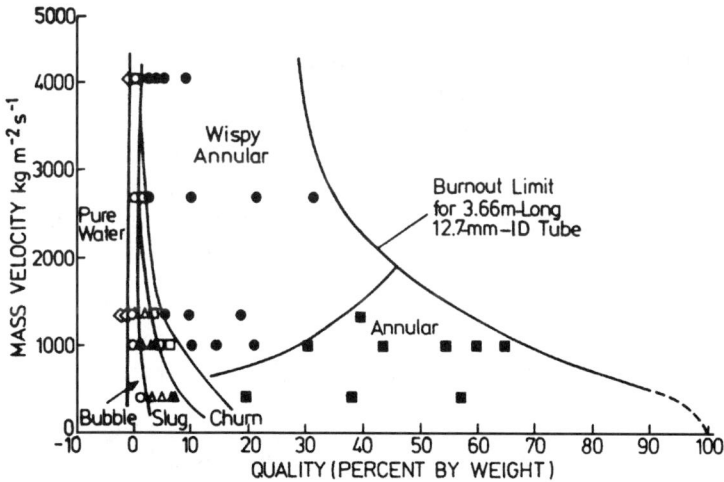

**Figure 2** Flow pattern data obtained by Bennett et al. (1965) for steam water flow at 6.8 MPa pressure (from Hewitt, 1982, with permission).

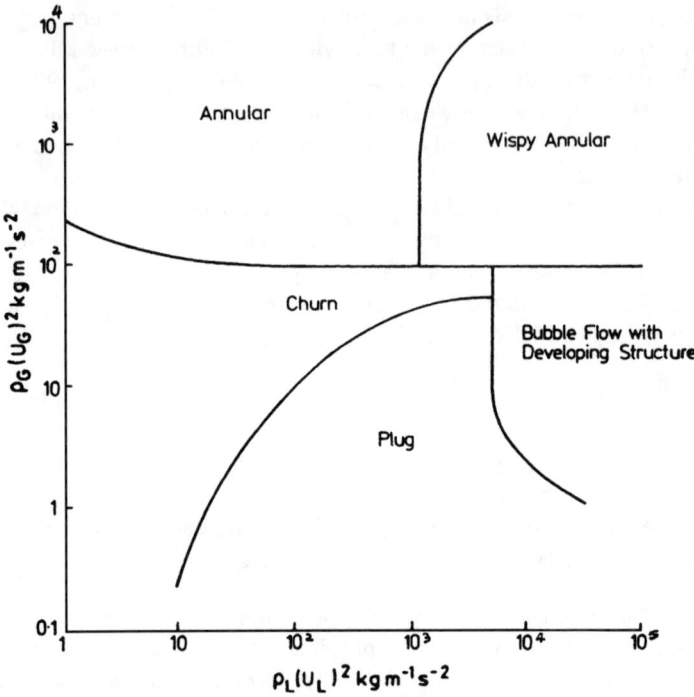

**Figure 3** Flow pattern map obtained by Hewitt and Roberts (1969) for vertical upward two-phase upward flow (from Hewitt, 1982, with permission).

(2) *General Flow Pattern Maps.* A general flow pattern map is one in which the flow pattern transitions can be represented for a wide range of fluid physical properties, tube diameters, etc. Such maps are typified by that of Hewitt and Roberts (1969), as illustrated in Figure 3. Here, the flow patterns for a wide range of fluid conditions could be represented in terms of the superficial momentum fluxes $\rho_G(U_G)^2$ and $\rho_L(U_L)^2$ where $\rho_G$ and $\rho_L$ are the gas and liquid densities, and $U_G$ and $U_L$ are the superficial velocities of the gas and liquid phases (volume flow rates of the phases per unit cross sectional area of the channel). More recent generalized maps for vertical flows are presented by Taitel et al. (1980) and Weisman and Kang (1981).

Much work has been done on the individual transitions between regimes. It is beyond the scope of this chapter to review these in detail, but the work is exemplified by the following:

(1) *Bubble-slug transition.* The transition between bubbly flow and slug flow has conventionally been interpreted as a competition between bubble coalescence

(Radovcick and Moissis, 1962) and bubble breakup due to turbulence (Taitel et al., 1980). However, when the bubbles are free to move relative to each other, coalescence may be rather rare. A more likely explanation is that regions of high bubble concentration are formed ("void waves") where the bubbles become closely packed, and coalescence is able to proceed. Studies on the void wave mechanism are reported by Beisheuvel and Gorissen (1989) and Bouré (1997).

(2) *Slug-churn transition.* The nature of the breakdown of slug flow leading ultimately to annular flow has been a subject of considerable controversy in the literature. The three principal interpretations of the transition seem to have been as follows:

(a) Churn flow as an entrance region phenomenon. In this view of churn flow, the regime is seen as part of the process of the formation of stable slug flow further downstream in the pipe (Dukler and Taitel; 1986; Mao and Dukler, 1993; Taitel et al., 1980).

(b) Slug flow breakdown into churn flow is due to critical void fraction conditions in which the liquid slugs are no longer sustainable. This class of models includes that of Mishima and Ishii (1984), who assumed that the transition occurred when the average void fraction in the pipe is just greater than the mean void fraction over the Taylor bubble region, and Brauner and Barnea (1986), who assumed that the transition occurred when the void fraction in the liquid slugs reached a given value, namely 0.52.

(c) Onset of flooding in the Taylor bubble. This mechanism was first proposed by Nicklin and Davidson (1962) and further developed by McQuillan and Whalley (1985), Govan et al. (1991), and Jayanti and Hewitt (1992). Within the Taylor bubble, a liquid film falls downwards around the bubble, and in the flooding mechanism, breakdown of slug flow occurs when the gas velocity in the bubble is sufficient to give rise to *flooding* (namely, a situation in which waves are formed on the liquid film, which are transported upwards by the gas phase, leading to the collapse of the slugs between the large bubbles).

Slug flows with short bubbles tend to be rather unstable, with the large bubbles coalescing until an equilibrium state is reached. In these circumstances (and also as the churn flow boundary is approached), the slug flow is clearly demonstrating an instability. It is important to recognize the distinction between *unstable slug flow* and *churn flow*, and this distinction has been explored in more detail by Hewitt and Jayanti (1993) and Costigan and Whalley (1997). The critical void fraction models may apply at very high liquid mass fluxes, but it seems probable that the flooding mechanism is the governing one for most conditions. A more detailed discussion of the transition to churn flow and of the churn flow regime itself if given by Jayanti and Brauner (1994). The large waves associated with flooding appear to persist into the churn flow region,

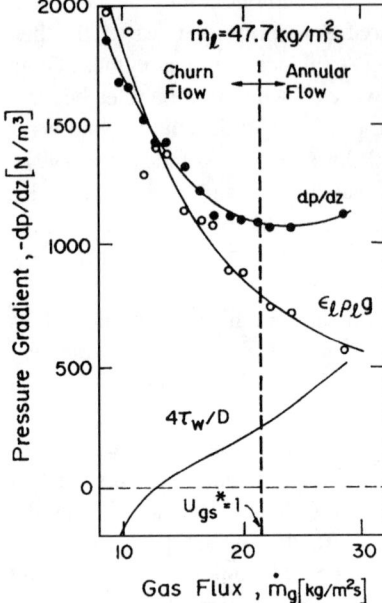

**Figure 4** Data for pressure gradient in churn flow (Govan et al., 1991, with permission).

these waves being levitated by the gas phase with regions of falling film flowing between them (Hewitt et al., 1985). Thus, churn flow is similar to annular flow in that there is a wavy liquid film on the wall and a gas core in the center. However, as the gas flow increases, the flooding waves are gradually damped out, leading to a reduction in pressure gradient with increasing gas velocity, as illustrated in Figure 4. Due to this peculiar behavior, it is argued (Hewitt and Jayanti, 1993) that churn flow should be regarded as a specific regime rather than considering it as a subset of annular flow.

(3) *Churn annular transition.* In the light of the above discussion on the slug-churn transition, it seems rational to regard the transition from churn flow to annular flow as one in which the pressure gradient begins to increase with increasing gas mass flux, signaling the disappearance of the flooding-type waves. The transition can be approximately represented by the condition that:

$$U_G^* = U_G \rho_G^{1/2} [gD(\rho_L - \rho_G)]^{-1/2} = 1 \quad (9.1\text{-}1)$$

where $g$ is the acceleration due to gravity and $D$ the tube diameter.

**9.1.2.2 Flow patterns in downflow in vertical tube.** Though downward flows are important (particularly in condensation applications), they have been the subject of much less investigation than have vertical upflows. Studies of flow patterns

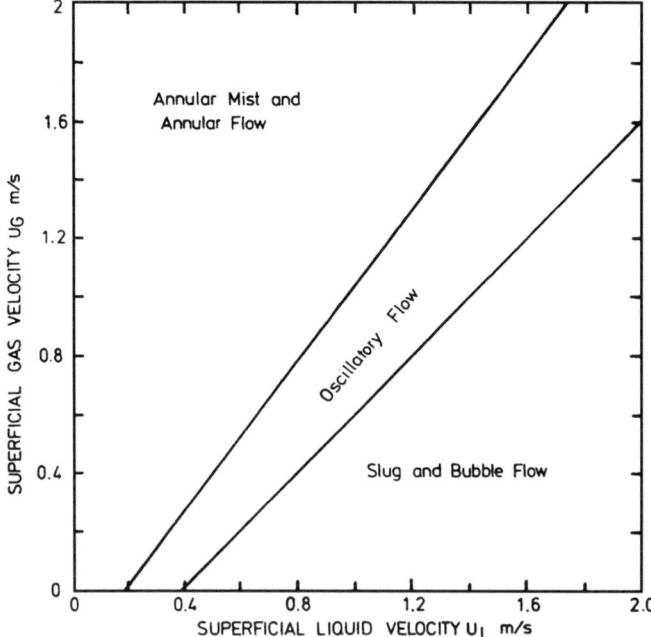

**Figure 5** Flow patterns in vertical downflow (from Golan and Stenning, 1969, with permission).

in co-current downward flow are reported by Golan and Stenning (1969), Barnea et al. (1982), and Crawford et al. (1986). The most important feature of such flows is the greater propensity to annular flow compared to upward flow systems. The flow pattern map given by Golan and Stenning is shown in Figure 5. Barnea et al. describe the annular to slug transition in terms of a critical liquid film thickness (obtained from an annular flow model) and describe the transition from slug flow to dispersed bubbly flow in terms of breakup and coalescence of bubbles in the turbulent flow field. Crawford et al. discuss both steady-state and transient flow patterns for this type of flow.

**9.1.2.3 Flow patterns in horizontal tubes.** The flow patterns commonly defined for horizontal flows are illustrated in Figure 6. The regimes tend to be more complex than those in vertical flows due to the asymmetry induced by the gravitational force acting normal to the direction of flow. The regimes shown in Figure 6 are defined as follows:

(1) Stratified flow. Here, the gravitational separation is complete with the liquid flowing at the bottom of the tube and the gas along the top part of the tube.

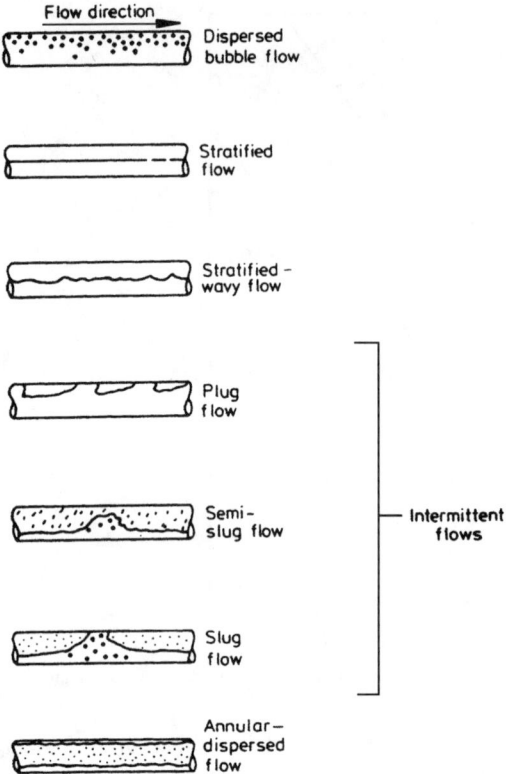

**Figure 6** Flow patterns in horizontal flows (from Hewitt, 1982, with permission).

(2) Stratified-wavy flow. At higher gas velocities, waves are formed on the gas-liquid interface, giving the stratified-wavy or wavy flow regime.

(3) Dispersed bubble flow. Here, the bubbles are dispersed in the liquid phase; in horizontal flow, these bubbles tend to congregate near the top of the tube, as illustrated.

(4) Annular-dispersed flow. This flow regime is similar to that observed in vertical flow, except that the film thickness is non-uniform. The film is generally much thicker at the bottom of the tube than at the top due to the effect of gravity.

(5) Intermittent flows. Though it is often appropriate to treat all intermittent flows as being of a single generic type, the class of intermittent flows is often conveniently divided into three subdivisions as follows:

 (a) Plug flow. Here, the characteristic bullet-shaped bubbles are observed, but they tend to move along in a position closer to the top of the tube, as shown in Figure 6.

 (b) Slug flow. Here, frothy "slugs" pass along the pipe containing entrained gas bubbles.

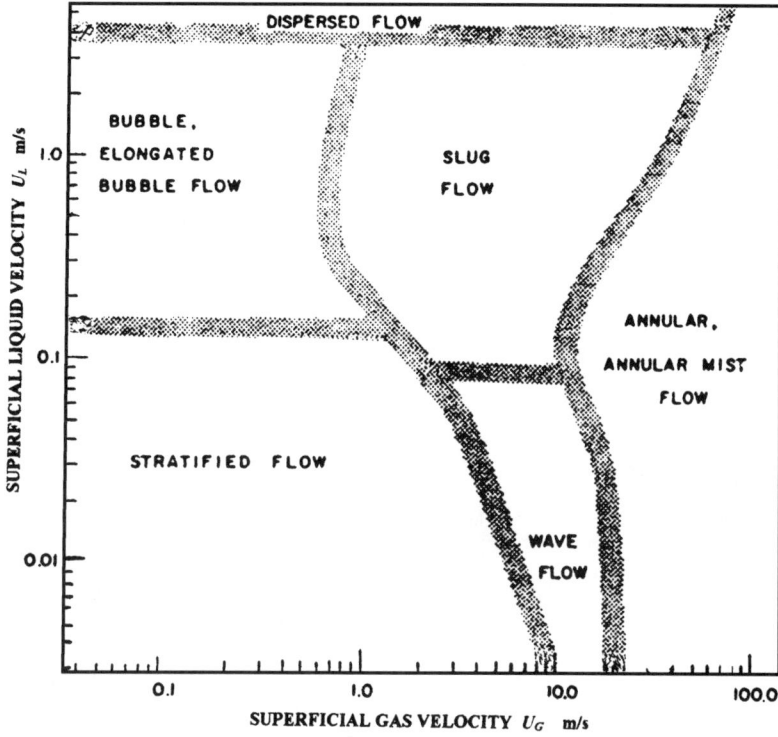

**Figure 7** Flow patterns in horizontal flow (from Mandhane et al., 1974, with permission).

(c) Semi-slug flow. Here, the frothy slug takes the form of a wave on the surface of the stratified layer at the bottom of the tube and does not actually touch the top of the tube.

There has been a great deal of interest in flow pattern maps for horizontal flows, particularly on the onset of intermittent flows. An example of a specific-type map is that of Mandhane et al. (1974), as illustrated in Figure 7, which is for the case of air-water flow at ambient conditions. This map was optimised for over 4000 data points collected from the literature and from the author's own work. There have been a number of generalized maps for horizontal flows. One simple approach is to modify the ordinates to take account of physical properties; the well-known early flow pattern map of Baker (1954) used this approach, which was also adopted by Mandhane et al. (1974) and others. Mandhane et al. noted that the effect of physical properties was relatively small and that the air-water flow pattern map (Figure 7) gave a reasonable first indication of the transition for other fluids and conditions. Empirically-based generalized maps have been presented, for instance, by Weisman et al. (1979) and Spedding and Spence (1993).

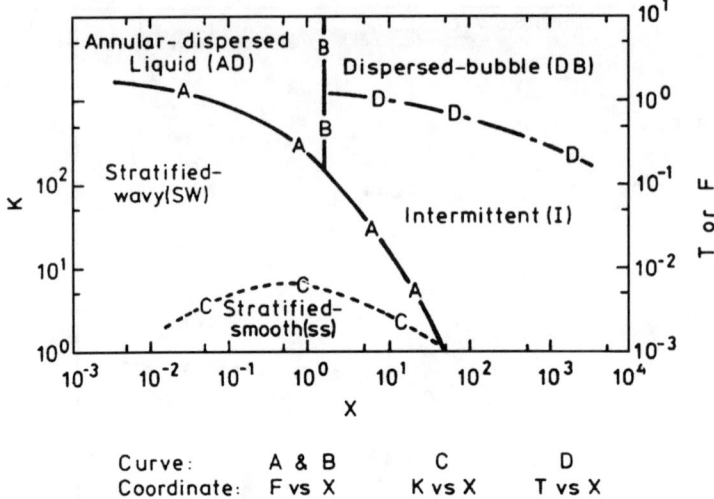

**Figure 8** Flow pattern map for horizontal flow (from Taitel and Dukler, 1976, with permission).

However, the most widely used flow pattern map for horizontal flows, that of Taitel and Dukler (1976), was based on semi-theoretical considerations, which means that the map should, in principle, be more readily applied to conditions outside those for which experimental data exists. The Taitel and Dukler flow pattern map is illustrated in Figure 8. The map is plotted in terms of dimensionless groups, and an important feature of it is that different ordinates are used, depending on the transition being addressed. All the transitions are plotted in terms of the Martinelli parameter $X$, which is defined as:

$$X = \left[ \frac{(dp_F/dz)_L}{(dp_F/dz)_G} \right]^{1/2} \quad (9.1\text{-}2)$$

where $(dp_F/dz)_L$ and $(dp_F/dz)_G$ are the frictional pressure gradients for the gas and liquid phases flowing alone in the pipe. The other dimensionless groups are defined as follows:

$$F = \left( \frac{\rho_G}{\rho_L - \rho_G} \right)^{1/2} \frac{U_G}{(Dg \cos \alpha)^2} \quad (9.1\text{-}3)$$

$$K^2 = \frac{\rho_G U_G^2}{(\rho_L - \rho_G) Dg \cos \alpha} \frac{DU_L}{\nu_L} \quad (9.1\text{-}4)$$

$$T = \left[ \frac{(dp_F/dz)_L}{(\rho_L - \rho_G)g \cos \alpha} \right]^{1/2} \quad (9.1\text{-}5)$$

where $\alpha$ is the angle of inclination of the channel to the horizontal and $v_L$ is the kinematic viscosity of the liquid.

Though the Taitel and Dukler map represented a major step forward in interpretation and understanding of flow regimes in horizontal flows, its generality has been increasingly questioned. For instance, it fails to predict the correct trend in the stratified-to-slug transition with pressure (Manolis, 1995), and it also fails to represent data for large tube diameter (Jepson and Taylor, 1988).

Much attention has been focused on specific flow regime transitions in horizontal flow, the most important being the transitions to slug and annular flow, respectively. The stratified-slug transition is commonly associated with the Kelvin-Helmholtz instability. In their generalized flow pattern map, Taitel and Dukler (1976) used inviscid Kelvin-Helmholtz instability as a basis, applying an arbitrary correction function to bring the results in line with experiments. A more satisfactory (though much more complicated) approach is to use viscous Kelvin-Helmholtz instability theory (Lin and Hanratty, 1986); this theory gives results that are similar to those obtained by Taitel and Dukler for air-water systems, though there is, of course, a significant effect of viscosity on the solution. The transition from stratified (or slug) flow to annular flow is one where there is a great deal of uncertainty. This is well illustrated by the results obtained by Reimann et al. (1981) and shown in Figure 9. As discussed by Spedding and Spence (1993), the effect of tube diameter is particularly important in considering this transition. The nature of the transition is intimately linked with the question of the mechanism of horizontal annular flow (see, for instance, Jayanti et al., 1990, for a discussion of this mechanism).

**9.1.2.4 Flow patterns in inclined tubes.** Even small deviations of the channel from the horizontal can have a dramatic effect on the transition to slug flow. When the flow is slightly upwards, there is a much greater propensity to the formation of slugs, and the reverse is true when the flow is slightly downwards. Studies of these effects are reported by Barnea et al. (1980), who showed that the effect of inclination on the slug flow transition was well predicted by the model of Taitel and Dukler (1976). The starting point of this model is the prediction of liquid level in an equivalent stratified flow, which is strongly influenced by angle of inclination, thus giving different relationships between the dimensionless variables for inclined flows. Thus, Equations 2–5 and Figure 8 should not be used directly in assessing flow patterns for slightly inclined tubes, though the general methodology proposed by Taitel and Dukler appears to work well. Other studies of flow in inclined tubes include those of Weisman and Kang (1981) and Mukherjee and Brill (1985).

**9.1.2.5 Flow patterns in evaporation and condensation.** There is a strong interaction between boiling (evaporation) and condensation mechanisms in tubes and

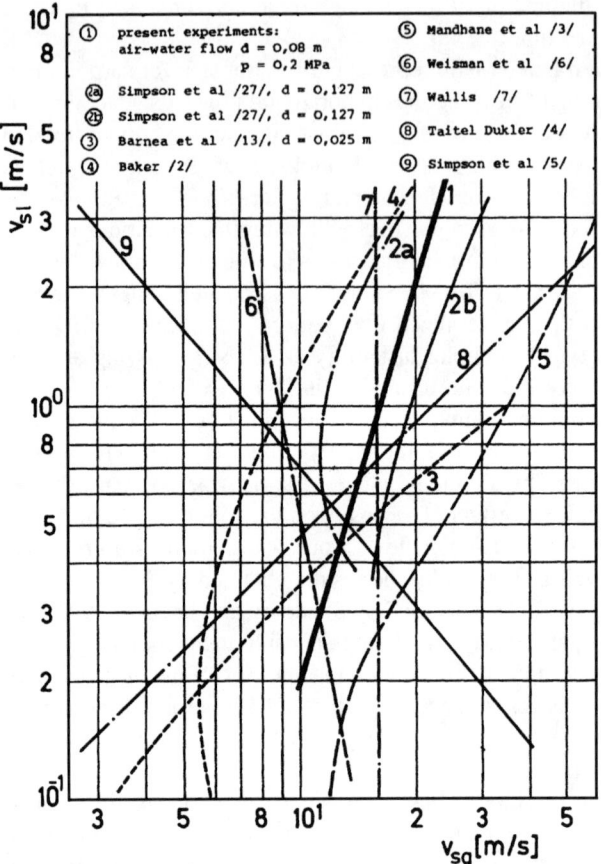

**Figure 9** Alternative models and correlation for the transition to annular flow (from Reimann et al., 1981, with permission).

the local two phase flow pattern. This can be illustrated by considering two cases, namely, evaporation in a vertical tube and condensation in a horizontal tube. The first case is illustrated in Figure 10, which shows the successive patterns of flow and heat transfer as the heat input is increased in equal steps. The heat input at step A is just sufficient to bring the liquid entering the tube at the bottom to the saturation temperature. Case B has twice this heat flux; case C has three times this heat flux, etc.

The following main features are observed in the diagram:

(1) Lines of constant quality $x$ are shown in the diagram, and of particular interest is the line for $x = 0$. The onset of nucleate boiling ($XX$) occurs above the

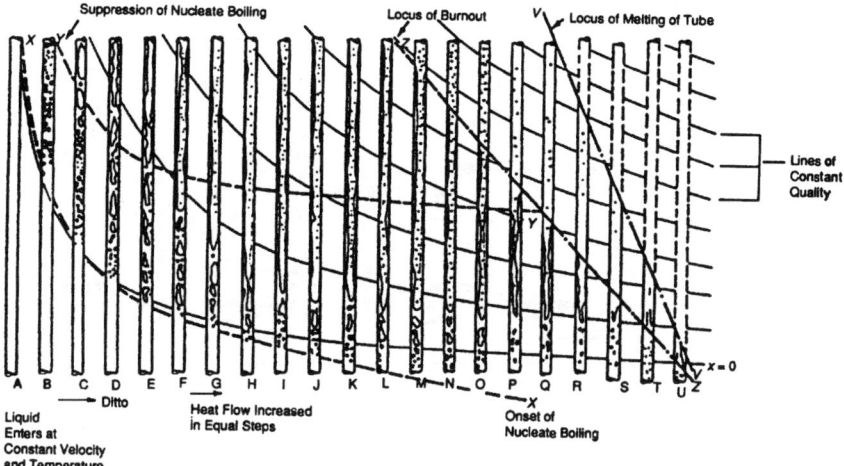

**Figure 10** Stages in the evaporation of liquid in a tube (from Hewitt et al., 1994, with permission).

$x = 0$ line at low heat flux (i.e., there is a net bulk superheat of the liquid), but occurs at qualities less than 0 for high heat fluxes, corresponding to the region of subcooled nucleate boiling.
(2) The various regimes of two phase flow as defined above and also illustrated in Figure 1 develop progressively with length and with heat input.
(3) At higher qualities, the heat transfer rate by direct forced convection through the liquid film in annular flow is so great that it is impossible to maintain a wall temperature that is sufficiently high to sustain nucleate boiling. The line $YY$ represents the onset of suppression of nucleate boiling, which, therefore, only exists between $XX$ and $YY$ on Figure 10.
(4) $ZZ$ is the locus of the onset of the critical heat flux (CHF) or burnout phenomenon. In annular flow, this corresponds to the dryout of the liquid film on the wall, but at lower qualities, it may correspond more closely to a film boiling type of transition.
(5) In the post-CHF region, the wall temperatures are high and may be sufficient to cause melting of the tube. The temperature rise is particularly severe when CHF occurs at low quality. The line $BV$ in Figure 10 shows a typical locus of melting of the tube or "physical burnout."

Typical regimes occurring in condensation are illustrated in Figure 11 for condensation inside a horizontal tube. The sequence of regimes depends on the initial flowrate of the vapor. At low vapor flowrates, the condensate may drain under gravity from the end of the tube, whereas at high flowrates, the condensate flows as subcooled liquid from the tube exit.

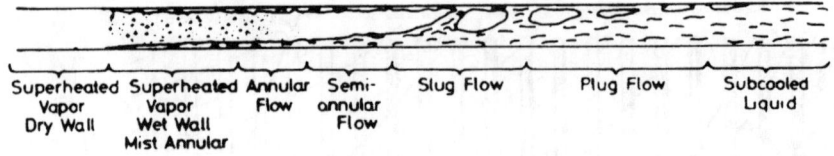

(a) **High initial vapor velocity**

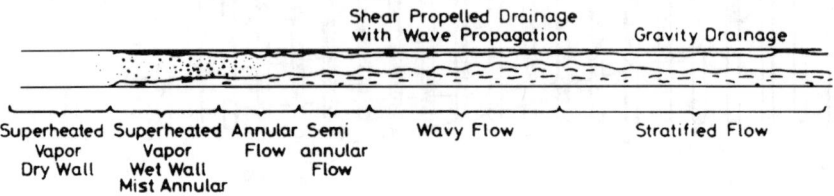

(b) **Low initial vapor velocity**

**Figure 11** Flow patterns in condensation in horizontal tubes (from Palen et al., 1979, with permission).

### 9.1.3 Basic Equations

The derivation and application of conservation equations is of fundamental basic importance in modeling two-phase flow systems. The relevant conservation equations are those for *mass (continuity), momentum,* and *energy,* respectively. Such equations can be written for the mixture as a whole or for the individual phases. It is beyond the scope of the present chapter to go into detail about the derivation of the equations, but the reader who wishes to have more information should consult standard texts (see, for instance, Delhaye, 1981; Hewitt, 1982; Roberts, 1997). Here, the basic equations will be stated in their various forms without derivation. The equations for the homogeneous model, separated flow model, and two-fluid model will be given, and brief discussion of phenomenological models will be presented. First, however, some basic quantities are defined.

The *mass rates of flow* of the two phases are $\dot{M}_G$ and $\dot{M}_L$ (kg/s), and the *mass fluxes* of the phases are $\dot{m}_G$ and $\dot{m}_L$ (kg/m²s). Thus, $\dot{m}_G = \dot{M}_G/A$ and $\dot{m}_L = \dot{M}_L/A$ where $A$ is the cross sectional area of the pipe. The *total mass flux* $\dot{m}$ is given as $\dot{m} = \dot{m}_G + \dot{m}_L$. The *volumetric flow rates* of the two phases are $\dot{V}_G$ and $\dot{V}_L$ (m³/s) and the *superficial velocities* of the two phases are defined as $U_G = \dot{V}_G/A$ and $U_L = \dot{V}_L/A$. The *quality* $x$ is defined as the fraction of the total mass flow that is in the form of gas. From these definitions, it follows that:

$$x = \frac{\dot{M}_G}{\dot{M}_G + \dot{M}_L} = \frac{\dot{m}_G}{\dot{m}_G + \dot{m}_L} = \frac{\dot{m}_G}{\dot{m}} = \frac{\rho_G U_G}{\rho_G U_G + \rho_L U_L} \qquad (9.1\text{-}6)$$

The *void fraction* $\varepsilon_L$ is the fraction of pipe cross sectional volume that is occupied by the gas phase, and the *liquid holdup* $\varepsilon_L$ is the fraction of the pipe volume that is occupied by the liquid phase. Clearly, $\varepsilon_G + \varepsilon_L = 1$. We may define *phase velocities* $u_L$ and $u_G$, which are the phase superficial velocities divided by the fraction of the cross sectional area occupied by the phase. The following relationships follow from the above definitions:

$$u_G = \frac{U_G}{\varepsilon_G} = \frac{\dot{V}_G}{\varepsilon_G A} = \frac{\dot{m}x}{\rho_G \varepsilon_G} \tag{9.1-7}$$

$$u_L = \frac{U_L}{\varepsilon_L} = \frac{U_L}{(1-\varepsilon_G)} = \frac{\dot{V}_L}{(1-\varepsilon_G)A} = \frac{\dot{m}(1-x)}{\rho_L(1-\varepsilon_G)} \tag{9.1-8}$$

The ratio $u_G/u_L$ is defined as the *slip ratio* $S$, and a *two-phase density* $\rho_{TP}$ is defined as the mass of fluid per unit volume of channel, given by:

$$\rho_{TP} = (1-\varepsilon_G)\rho_G + \varepsilon_G \rho_G \tag{9.1-9}$$

The following relationship also follows from the above definitions:

$$\varepsilon_G = \frac{x}{x + S(1-x)\rho_G/\rho_L} \tag{9.1-10}$$

In systems with phase change, the local quality often is not known directly and has to be calculated from a heat balance. We may define a *two-phase enthalpy* $h_{TP}$ as the sum of the inlet fluid ($h_{IN}$) plus the heat added per unit mass of fluid up to the point considered. Thus:

$$h_{TP} = h_{IN} + \frac{\dot{Q}}{\dot{m}A} \tag{9.1-11}$$

where $\dot{Q}$ is the total heat added up to the point considered. For a circular tube of diameter $D$ uniformly heated with a heat flux $\dot{q}$ through its walls, Eq. (9.1-11) may be written in the form:

$$h_{TP} = h_{IN} + \frac{4\dot{q}z}{\dot{m}D} \tag{9.1-12}$$

where $z$ is the distance along tube length. For thermodynamic equilibrium conditions, we may also write:

$$h_{TP} = xh_G + (1-x)h_L \tag{9.1-13}$$

where $h_G$ and $h_L$ are the saturation enthalpies of the vapor and liquid. It thus follows that the *thermodynamic quality* is given from the known enthalpy by the expression:

$$x = \frac{h_{TP} - h_L}{h_G - h_L} = \frac{h_{TP} - h_L}{h_{LG}} \tag{9.1-14}$$

where $h_{LG}$ is the latent heat of vaporization ($= h_G - h_L$).

### 9.1.3.1 Homogeneous model.

The simplest approach to modeling two-phase flows is to represent them as a single phase flow with averaged properties. In the homogeneous model, it is assumed that:

$$u_G = u_L = u_H \qquad (9.1\text{-}15)$$

$$S = \frac{u_G}{u_L} = 1 \qquad (9.1\text{-}16)$$

From which it follows that:

$$\varepsilon_G = \frac{x}{x + (1-x)\rho_G/\rho_L} \qquad (9.1\text{-}17)$$

$$\rho_{TP} = \rho_H = \frac{\rho_G \rho_L}{x\rho_L + (1-x)\rho_G} \qquad (9.1\text{-}18)$$

For the homogeneous model, the equations for the conservation of mass (the continuity equation), momentum, and energy are given as follows (Hewitt, 1982):

$$\frac{\partial}{\partial z}(\dot{m}A) + A\frac{\partial \rho_H}{\partial t} = 0 \qquad (9.1\text{-}19)$$

$$\frac{\partial \dot{m}}{\partial t} + \frac{1}{A}\frac{\partial(\dot{m}^2 A/\rho_H)}{\partial z} = -\frac{\partial p}{\partial z} - g\rho_H \sin\alpha - \frac{\tau_o P}{A} \qquad (9.1\text{-}20)$$

$$\rho_H\left(\frac{\partial e}{\partial t} + U\frac{\partial e}{\partial z}\right) = \frac{\dot{q}P}{A} + \dot{q}_v + \frac{\partial p}{\partial t} \qquad (9.1\text{-}21)$$

where $g$ is the acceleration due to gravity, $\tau_o$ the wall shear stress, $P$ the tube periphery, $\dot{q}_v$ the internal rate of heat generation within the fluid per unit volume, $U$ the total superficial velocity ($= U_G = U_L$), and $e$ the energy convected per unit mass of the fluid, given by:

$$e = h_{TP} + \frac{U^2}{2} + gz\sin\alpha \qquad (9.1\text{-}22)$$

where $h_{TP}$ is the (mixed) fluid enthalpy, defined as:

$$h_{TP} = \mu_{TP} + \frac{p}{\rho_H} \qquad (9.1\text{-}23)$$

where $\mu_{TP}$ is the specific internal energy per unit mass of the (mixed) fluid, given as:

$$\mu_{TP} = x\mu_G + (1-x)\mu_L \qquad (9.1\text{-}24)$$

where $\mu_G$ and $\mu_L$ are the specific internal energies for the saturated vapor and liquid, respectively.

For steady state flow in a circular tube of constant cross section, the momentum equation (Eq. 9.1-20) reduces to the widely used form:

$$-\frac{dp}{dz} = \frac{4\tau_o}{D} + \frac{d(\dot{m}^2/\rho_H)}{dz} + g\rho_H \sin\alpha \qquad (9.1\text{-}25)$$

It will be seen from Eq. (9.1-25) that the pressure gradient is the sum of three terms (frictional, accelerational, and gravitational), and the corresponding terms are:

$$-\frac{dp}{dz} = -\frac{dp_F}{dz} - \frac{dp_a}{dz} - \frac{dp_g}{dz} \quad (9.1\text{-}26)$$

For the homogeneous model, the second and third terms (accelerational and gravitational pressure gradients) are determined from the independent variables, and no correlation is required for them. However, a correlation is required for the first (frictional) term.

In general, the homogeneous model gives a poor representation of data for pressure gradient and void fraction in two-phase flows. As might have been expected, the closest fit to homogeneous model is obtained when the densities of the two phases begin to approach each other at high pressures.

### 9.1.3.2 Separated flow model. 
The separated flow model is the most widely used model for analyzing flows in phase change systems. Here, conservation equations are written for the whole channel, but allowance is made for the fact that the velocities of the two phases are not equal (i.e., $u_G \neq u_G$ and $S \neq 1$). The continuity, momentum, and energy equations for this case may be written as (Hewitt, 1982):

$$\frac{\partial}{\partial t}(\rho_{TP}A) + \frac{\partial}{\partial z}(\dot{m}A) = 0 \quad (9.1\text{-}27)$$

$$-\frac{\partial p}{\partial z} - g\rho_{TP}\sin\alpha - \frac{\tau_o P}{A} = \frac{\partial \dot{m}}{\partial t} + \frac{1}{A}\frac{\partial}{\partial z}\left\{\dot{m}^2 A\left[\frac{(1-x)^2}{\rho_L(1-\varepsilon_G)} + \frac{x^2}{\rho_G \varepsilon_G}\right]\right\} \quad (9.1\text{-}28)$$

$$A\frac{\partial}{\partial t}[\rho_L h_L(1-\varepsilon_G) + \rho_G h_G \varepsilon_G] + \frac{\partial}{\partial z}[\dot{m}A(h_L + xh_{LG})]$$

$$= \dot{q}P + \dot{q}_v A - \frac{\partial}{\partial z}\left\{\frac{\dot{m}^3 A}{2}\left[\frac{(1-x)^3}{\rho_L^2(1-\varepsilon_G)^2} + \frac{x^2}{\rho_G^2 \varepsilon_G^2}\right]\right\}$$

$$- g\dot{m}A\sin\alpha - \frac{\partial}{\partial t}\left\{\dot{m}^2\left[\frac{(1-x)^2}{\rho_L(1-\varepsilon_G)} + \frac{x^2}{\rho_G \varepsilon_G}\right]\right\} + A\frac{\partial p}{\partial t} \quad (9.1\text{-}29)$$

For steady-state flow in a constant cross section circular tube, the momentum equation reduces to:

$$-\frac{dp}{dz} = \frac{4\tau_o}{D} + \dot{m}^2\frac{d}{dz}\left[\frac{(1-x)^2}{\rho_L(1-\varepsilon_G)} + \frac{x^2}{\rho_G \varepsilon_G}\right] + g\rho_{TP}\sin\alpha \quad (9.1\text{-}30)$$

The three terms on the right hand side of Eq. (9.1-30) again correspond to the frictional, accelerational and gravitational components of the pressure gradient. Equation (9.1-30) is the most widely used equation for calculating pressure drops in two-phase flows. For the separated flow model, correlations are required both for the frictional pressure gradient (wall shear stress) and for the void fraction, which influences both the accelerational and gravitational terms. The separated flow model gives a somewhat better basis for correlation than does the homogeneous model.

### 9.1.3.3 Two-fluid model.
In the two-fluid model, separate continuity, momentum, and energy equations are written for each of the phases, making six equations in all (hence the name *two-fluid model* or *six-equation model* for this approach). For example, momentum equations can be written for the gas and liquid as follows:

$$-\varepsilon_G \frac{\partial p}{\partial z} - g\rho_G \varepsilon_G \sin\alpha - \frac{\tau_G P_G}{A} - \frac{\tau_i P_i}{A}$$
$$= \frac{\partial}{\partial t}(\rho_G \varepsilon_G u_G) + \frac{1}{A}\frac{\partial}{\partial z}\left(\rho_G A \varepsilon_G u_G^2\right) \quad (9.1\text{-}31)$$

$$-(1-\varepsilon_G)\frac{\partial p}{\partial z} - g\rho_L(1-\varepsilon_G) - \frac{\tau_L P_L}{A} + \frac{\tau_i P_i}{A}$$
$$= \frac{\partial}{\partial t}[\rho_L u_L(1-\varepsilon_G)] + \frac{1}{A}\frac{\partial}{\partial z}\left[\rho_L A u_L^2(1-\varepsilon_G)\right] \quad (9.1\text{-}32)$$

where $\tau_G$ and $\tau_L$ are the wall shear stresses in those regions of the channel where the wall is in contact with the gas and liquid, respectively, $P_G$ and $P_L$ are the peripheries in contact with the two phases respectively, $\tau_i$ is the interfacial shear stress, and $P_i$ the interfacial periphery. Making the assumption that

$$\tau_G P_G + \tau_L P_L = \tau_o P \quad (9.1\text{-}33)$$

(i.e., regarding $\tau_o$ as a mean shear stress around the periphery), Eqs. (9.1-31) and (9.1-32) may be added together and the summed equation manipulated to obtain Eq. (9.1-28). Thus, interfacial shear stress is eliminated in this process. The phasic equations (Eqs. 9.1-31 and 9.1-32) may be solved for both pressure gradient and void fraction, provided that relationships can be written for the shear stresses and peripheries. Specification of the peripheries is sometimes possible if the geometry of the flow is assumed; thus, the liquid periphery is equal to the total periphery and the gas periphery is equal to zero in annular flow, and the peripheries of the respective phases can be readily calculated if stratified flow is assumed. The wall shear stresses are often calculated from relationships based on single phase flow, but a major difficulty occurs in calculating the interfacial shear stress. Nevertheless, the two-fluid model represents a step forward over the separated flow models and is now widely used in, for instance, computer codes employed for calculating transients in nuclear systems, petroleum pipelines, etc. Further details are given by Delhaye (1981), Lahey and Moody (1977), and Roberts (1997).

### 9.1.3.4 Phenomenological models.
In a *phenomenological model*, observed features of the flow are taken into account in preparing the modeling scheme. Though

detailed presentation of such models is beyond the scope of the present chapter, the following examples illustrate the general methodology:

(1) *Horizontal stratified flow*. Here, simplified models have been developed by Agrawal et al. (1973) and Taitel and Dukler (1976a). These models start with Eqs. (9.1-31) and (9.1-32) but ignore changes with time and distance (i.e., eliminate the right hand sides of these equations). The shear stresses are then calculated by assuming that the wall shear stresses are governed by laws similar to those applying in single phase flows. Taitel and Dukler assume that the interfacial shear stress is equal to the gas-wall shear stress, but Agrawal et al. take into account the increase of interfacial shear stress resulting from the waviness of the interface. In fact, a whole variety of relationships have subsequently been used for interfacial shear stress; these are reviewed by Khor et al. (1997). Though there is still considerable uncertainty in the prediction of the pressure gradient and holdup in stratified flow, it can be certainly claimed that the phenomenological models give better results than do purely empirical ones.

(2) *Annular flow*. In annular flow, account has to be taken of the fact that a significant amount of the liquid phase is entrained in the gas core. There is a continuous exchange between the core and the film as droplets are deposited from the core and then drained from the film. The film itself has a wavy interface, which increases the interfacial shear stress. It is necessary to take all of these processes into account in deriving a model for annular flow. Earlier models for annular flow are discussed by Hewitt and Hall-Taylor (1970) and Hewitt (1982). Improved entrainment/deposition correlations have led to greatly improved predictions; some of this more recent work is described by Hewitt and Govan (1990).

(3) *Slug flow*. In the phenomenological modeling of slug flow, relationships are required for the velocity and liquid holdup in the slugs, the frequency of the slugs, and the behavior of the film or bubble region between the slugs. An early model for slug flow combining all relevant variables was that of Dukler and Hubbard (1975), and more recent studies have included those of Barnea and Taitel (1993), Bendiksen et al. (1996), and King (1998).

(4) *Churn flow*. With periodic flow reversals, churn flow is highly complex, and phenomenological models present special difficulties. However, modeling of the wave transport and of the flow reversal in the liquid film is reported by Hewitt et al. (1985), and a more recent review of modelling of churn flows is given by Jayanti and Brauner (1994).

## 9.1.4 PRESSURE DROP

The prediction of pressure drop is an important part of the design of multiphase flow systems. However, the accuracy of prediction of pressure drop is generally not very good, standard deviations of the order of 30% being typical even in the most advanced correlations. This uncertainty must be taken into account in design. In what follows here, we shall present some typical correlations based on the homogeneous and the separated flow model, respectively; further information is given, for instance, by Hewitt (1982). Presentation of results from phenomenological models is beyond the scope of the present chapter, and the reader is referred to the references cited in Section 9.1.3.4 for further information. Generally, phenomenological models perform better than the empirical correlations, though at the expense of additional complexity.

As was discussed earlier, the pressure gradient can be regarded as being composed of three terms, namely frictional, accelerational, and gravitational. For the separated flow model, the prediction of the latter two terms depends on the knowledge of the void fraction, and prediction of the void fraction is discussed in Section 9.1.5 below. In this section, attention is focussed only on the *frictional* pressure gradient term. This is defined for circular tubes as:

$$-\frac{dp_F}{dz} = \frac{4\tau_o}{D} \tag{9.1-34}$$

A commonly used procedure is to relate the pressure gradient for two-phase flow to that for a single phase flow of either the individual phases or of the total mass flux flowing with the properties of the liquid or the gas. These single phase pressure gradients may be calculated from standard equations as follows:

$$-\left(\frac{dp_F}{dz}\right)_G = \frac{2f_G \dot{m}^2 x^2}{D\rho_G} \tag{9.1-35}$$

$$-\left(\frac{dp_F}{dz}\right)_L = \frac{2f_L \dot{m}^2 (1-x)^2}{D\rho_L} \tag{9.1-36}$$

$$-\left(\frac{dp_F}{dz}\right)_{LO} = \frac{2f_{LO} \dot{m}^2}{D\rho_L} \tag{9.1-37}$$

$$-\left(\frac{dp_F}{dz}\right)_{GO} = \frac{2f_{GO} \dot{m}^2}{D\rho_G} \tag{9.1-38}$$

The friction factors $f_G$, $f_L$, $f_{LO}$, and $f_{GO}$ are related (through standard equations and charts for single-phase flow) to the respective Reynolds numbers defined as follows:

$$\text{Re}_G = \frac{\dot{m} x D}{\eta_G} \tag{9.1-39}$$

$$\text{Re}_L = \frac{\dot{m}(1-x)D}{\eta_G} \tag{9.1-40}$$

$$\text{Re}_{LO} = \frac{\dot{m}D}{\eta_L} \quad (9.1\text{-}41)$$

$$\text{Re}_{GO} = \frac{\dot{m}D}{\eta_G} \quad (9.1\text{-}42)$$

where $\eta_G$ and $\eta_L$ are the viscosities of the gas and liquid, respectively. For laminar flow (Re < 2000, $f = 16/\text{Re}$) and for turbulent flow (Re > 2000), the Blasius Equation,

$$f = 0.079 \left(\frac{\dot{m}D}{\eta}\right)^{-1/4} \quad (9.1\text{-}43)$$

is often used.

**9.1.4.1 Correlations based on the homogeneous model.** In the homogeneous model, the pressure gradient is calculated on the basis of a pseudo single-phase flow as follows:

$$-\frac{dp_F}{dz} = \frac{4\tau_o}{D} = \frac{2f_{TP}\dot{m}^2}{D\rho_H} \quad (9.1\text{-}44)$$

where $f_{TP}$ is a two-phase friction factor. One approach is to calculate the friction factor from standard single-phase flow charts and correlations, as a function of a two-phase Reynolds number $\text{Re}_{TP}$, defined as follows:

$$\text{Re}_{TP} = \frac{\dot{m}D}{\eta_{TP}} \quad (9.1\text{-}45)$$

where $\eta_{TP}$ is a two-phase viscosity. A variety of methods have been proposed to calculate this viscosity, a commonly used one being that due to McAdams et al. (1942), which is given as follows:

$$\frac{1}{\eta_{TP}} = \frac{1}{\eta_L} + \frac{1}{\eta_G} \quad (9.1\text{-}46)$$

where $\eta_L$ and $\eta_G$ are the liquid and gas viscosities. In general, homogeneous models using average viscosities do not fit the data very well. Beggs and Brill (1973) developed an empirical correlation for $f_{TP}$ based on experimental data. This correlation is linked to a parallel one for void fraction, with void fraction being one of the variables influencing $f_{TP}$. The Beggs and Brill correlation performs much better than the mean-viscosity correlations, but as the amount of data available has increased, the correlation has been found to generally overpredict the pressure drop (typically by 30–40%). Nevertheless, the Beggs and Brill correlation is a useful one to obtain a relatively conservative value of the pressure drop.

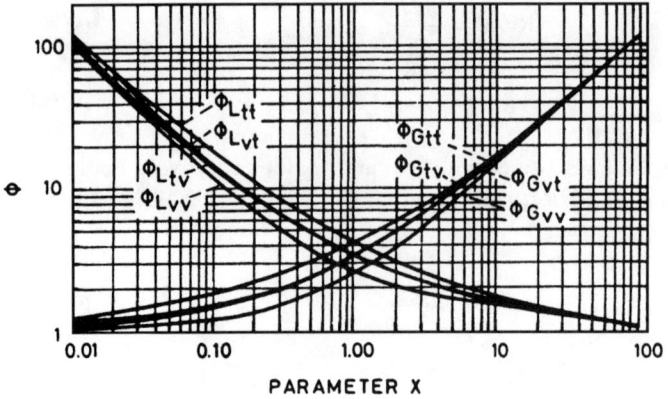

**Figure 12** Lockhart-Martinelli correlation for pressure drop (from Hewitt, 1982, with permission).

**9.1.4.2 Correlations based on the separated flow model.** The best known (and still widely used) correlation for frictional pressure drop is that due to Lockhart and Martinelli (1949). The correlation related the *pressure drop multipliers*:

$$\phi_L^2 = \frac{(dp_F/dz)}{(dp_F/dz)_L} \tag{9.1-47}$$

$$\phi_G^2 = \frac{(dp_F/dz)}{(dp_F/dz)_G} \tag{9.1-48}$$

to the parameter $X^2$ defined as:

$$X^2 = \frac{(dp_F/dz)_L}{(dp_F/dz)_G} \tag{9.1-49}$$

The correlation was presented in graphical form as illustrated in Figure 12.

Different curves were suggested depending on whether the phase-alone flows were laminar ("viscous") or turbulent, and the multipliers are subscripted accordingly. For example, the multiplier $\phi_{Lvt}$ applies to the case in which the liquid phase flowing alone in the channel would be a laminar flow, and the gas phase flowing alone would be turbulent. The Lockhart and Martinelli curves have been fitted by Chisholm (1967) by the relationships:

$$\phi_L^2 = 1 + \frac{C}{X} + \frac{1}{X^2} \tag{9.1-50}$$

$$\phi_G^2 = 1 + CX + X^2 \tag{9.1-51}$$

where $C$ is a dimensionless parameter whose value depends on the nature (i.e., viscous or turbulent) of the phase-alone flows. The values suggested by Chisholm for $C$ are shown in Table 1.

## Table 1 Values of C to fit empirical curves of Lockhart and Martinelli (Chisholm, 1967)

| Liquid | Gas | Subscript | C |
|---|---|---|---|
| Turbulent | Turbulent | tt | 20 |
| Viscous | Turbulent | vt | 12 |
| Turbulent | Viscous | tv | 10 |
| Viscous | Viscous | vv | 5 |

The Lockhart-Martinelli correlation generally gives much higher pressure gradients than does the homogeneous model and agrees best with data for low mass fluxes. As the mass flux is increased, the pressure gradient approaches that predicted by the homogeneous model. Later correlations have attempted to capture these mass flow effects. Baroczy (1965) produced a highly complex graphical correlation, and Chisholm (1973) took account of mass flux in a correlation that had the following form:

$$\phi_{LO}^2 = \frac{(dp_F/dz)}{(dp_F/dz)_{LO}}$$
$$= 1 + (Y^2 - 1)\left[Bx^{(2-n)/2}(1-x)^{(2-n)/2} + x^{1-n}\right] \quad (9.1\text{-}52)$$

where

$$Y^2 = \frac{(dp_F/dz)_{GO}}{(dp_F/dz)_{LO}} \quad (9.1\text{-}53)$$

and where $n$ is the exponent in the friction factor-Reynolds number relationship (0.25 for the Blasius Equation). The parameter $B$ is given by:

$$B = \frac{55}{\dot{m}^{1/2}} \quad for\ 0 < Y < 9.5 \quad (9.1\text{-}54)$$

$$B = \frac{520}{Y\dot{m}^{1/2}} \quad for\ 9.5 < Y < 28 \quad (9.1\text{-}55)$$

$$B = \frac{15000}{Y^2\dot{m}^{1/2}} \quad for\ 28 < Y \quad (9.1\text{-}56)$$

Another widely used correlation (based on a large data bank) is that of Friedel (1979), which is stated as follows:

$$\phi_{LO}^2 = E + \frac{3.24FH}{Fr^{0.045}We^{0.035}} \quad (9.1\text{-}57)$$

$$E = (1-x)^2 + x^2 \frac{\rho_L f_{GO}}{\rho_G f_{LO}} \quad (9.1\text{-}58)$$

$$F = x^{0.78}(1-x)^{0.24} \quad (9.1\text{-}59)$$

$$H = \left(\frac{\rho_L}{\rho_G}\right)^{0.91} \left(\frac{\eta_G}{\eta_L}\right)^{0.19} \left(1 - \frac{\eta_G}{\eta_L}\right)^{0.7} \quad (9.1\text{-}60)$$

$$Fr = \frac{\dot{m}^2}{gD\rho_H^2} \quad (9.1\text{-}61)$$

$$We = \frac{\dot{m}^2 D}{\rho_H \sigma} \quad (9.1\text{-}62)$$

None of the correlations is particularly accurate, especially when used over a wide range. The following approximate recommendations may be made regarding the correlations cited above (Whalley, 1980):

(1) For $\eta_L/\eta_G < 1000$, the Friedel (1979) correlation should be used.
(2) For $\eta_L/\eta_G > 1000$ and $\dot{m} > 100$, the Chisholm (1973) correlation should be used.
(3) For $\eta_L/\eta_G > 1000$ and for $\dot{m} < 100$, the Lockhart-Martinelli (1949) correlation should be used.

## 9.1.5 VOID FRACTION

As was explained in Section 9.1.3 above, the void fraction is an important parameter in calculating total pressure drops using the separated flow model, since it appears in the terms for both accelerational and gravitational pressure drop. The last term is zero for horizontal pipes, but even for horizontal pipes, knowledge of void fraction is needed to calculate the accelerational pressure drop term (though this is often quite small, compared to the frictional pressure gradient). However, void fraction is also important in accessing the inventory of valuable and/or toxic material within pipe systems. This inventory is significant both in fiscal terms and also from a safety point of view. Again, a wide range of relationships have been proposed for void fraction, and it would be beyond the scope of the present chapter to deal with these in detail. Nevertheless, some relationships will be given that may be used over reasonably wide ranges. Again, no details are given regarding the phenomenological models (which generally predict void fraction in addition to pressure gradient); the reader wishing to pursue this (potentially more accurate) methodology should refer to the references cited in Section 9.1.3.4 above.

### 9.1.5.1 Homogeneous void fraction.
For the homogeneous model, the void fraction is equal to the flow volume fraction of the gas and is given by:

$$\varepsilon_G = \frac{\dot{V}_G}{\dot{V}_L + \dot{V}_G} = \frac{\rho_L x}{\rho_G(1-x) + \rho_L x} \quad (9.1\text{-}63)$$

The void fraction approaches that calculated from the homogeneous model at high pressure and high mass flux, but in normal circumstances, there is a large overprediction of the void fraction, since the gas phase is traveling more rapidly than the liquid phase.

**9.1.5.2 Drift flux model.** The drift flux model is based on the idea that effective relative motion occurs between the two phases for two reasons:

(1) The gas phase at any one point in the cross section is traveling at a higher velocity than the liquid phase. Averaged over the cross section, the relative velocity is $u_{GU}$.
(2) Even if there is no local difference in velocity between the two phases, the weighting introduced by there being differences in the profiles of void fraction and velocity across the cross section results in an average effective slip between the phases. This can be accounted for through a *distribution parameter* $C_o$.

More detailed discussions of the drift flux model are given by Hewitt (1982) and Wallis (1969). The slip ratio and void fraction are given in terms of the parameters $C_o$ and $u_{GU}$ by the following equations:

$$S = \frac{u_G}{u_L} = \frac{(1-\varepsilon_G)}{1/(C_o + u_{GU}/U) - \varepsilon_G} \tag{9.1-64}$$

$$\varepsilon_G = \frac{x\rho_L}{C_o[x\rho_L + (1-x)\rho_G] + \rho_L\rho_G u_{GU}/\dot{m}} \tag{9.1-65}$$

It should be noted that for the limiting case where $C_o = 1.0$ and $u_{GU} = 0$, the above expressions reduce to those for the homogeneous flow model. The value of $C_o$ varies with the flow regime. For instance, in fully developed bubble and/or slug flow, $C_o = 1.1-1.2$ and $C_o$ approaches 1.0 for qualities approaching unity. For void fractions greater than 0.1, Rouhani (1969) suggests the following expressions for the drift flux parameters:

$$C_o = 1 + 0.2(1-x)\left(\frac{gD\rho_L^2}{\dot{m}^2}\right)^{0.25} \tag{9.1-66}$$

$$u_{GU} = 1.18\left[g\sigma(\rho_L - \rho_G)/\rho_L^2\right]^{0.25}(1-x) \tag{9.1-67}$$

A more recent correlation based on the drift flux model is that of Chexal and Lellouch (1986).

**9.1.5.3 Correlations associated with the separated flow model.** Lockhart and Martinelli (1949) presented a graphical relationship between void fraction and the Martinelli parameter $X$ (defined by Eq. 9.1-49), as illustrated in Figure 13. This

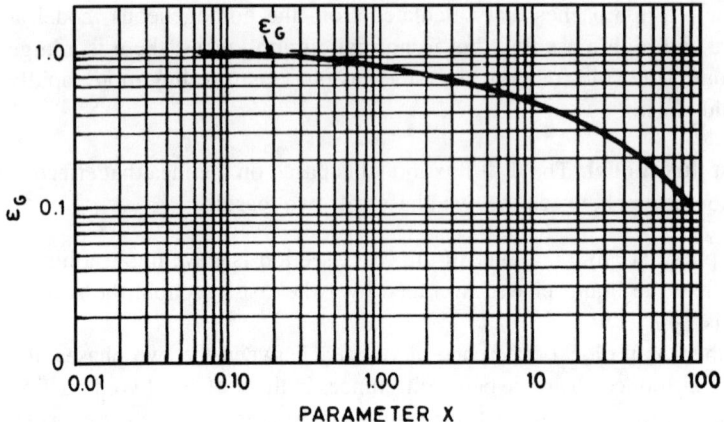

**Figure 13** Lockhart-Martinelli (1949) correlation for void fraction (from Hewitt, 1982, with permission).

relationship is fitted by the equation:

$$\varepsilon_G = \frac{\phi_L - 1}{\phi_L} \tag{9.1-68}$$

where $\phi_L$ may be obtained from Figure 12 or calculated from Eq. (9.1-50) using the values of $C$ given in Table 1.

The Lockhart-Martinelli correlation for void fraction tends to overpredict the void fraction at high mass fluxes, and a number of correlations have been proposed to offset this problem. The correlation of Premoli et al. (1971) covers a reasonably wide range of data and takes into account the mass flux effects. The correlation is in terms of slip ratio $S$; void fraction may be calculated from $S$ using Eq. (9.1-10). The Premoli et al. correlation has the form:

$$S = 1 + E_1 \left( \frac{y}{1 + yE_2} - yE_2 \right)^{1/2} \tag{9.1-69}$$

where

$$y = \frac{\beta}{1 - \beta} \tag{9.1-70}$$

where $\beta$ is the volume fraction of the vapor in the flow ($\beta = \dot{V}_G/(\dot{V}_G + \dot{V}_L)$). The parameters $E_1$ and $E_2$ are given by the equations:

$$E_1 = 1.578 \mathrm{Re}^{-0.19} \left( \frac{\rho_L}{\rho_G} \right)^{0.22} \tag{9.1-71}$$

$$E_2 = 0.0273 We \, \mathrm{Re}^{-0.51} \left( \frac{\rho_L}{\rho_G} \right)^{-0.08} \tag{9.1-72}$$

where the Reynolds and Weber numbers are defined as follows:

$$\text{Re} = \frac{\dot{m}D}{\eta_L} \tag{9.1-73}$$

$$\text{We} = \frac{\dot{m}^2 D}{\sigma \rho_L} \tag{9.1-74}$$

**9.1.5.4 Void fraction in subcooled boiling.** The correlations given above assume a knowledge of the gas and liquid flow rates. Usually, it is assumed that these may be calculated from a knowledge of the fluid enthalpy (see Eqs. 9.1-11–9.1-13), allowing the calculation of a *thermodynamic equilibrium* quality from Eq. (9.1-14), which we will define here as $x_e$. As was discussed earlier, void formation can occur due to subcooled boiling in the region where $x_e < 0$ (i.e., at *negative* thermodynamic qualities). The variation of void fraction with position along a uniformly heated tube is illustrated schematically in Figure 14.

The onset of nucleate boiling occurs at a distance of $x_n$ where the quality is $x(z_n)$, but significant void formation does not occur until the bubbles begin to depart from the surface at a distance $z_d$ with a corresponding quality of $x(z_d)$. Eventually, the point is reached where $x_e = 0$ at $z = z_{bulk}$. However, at this point,

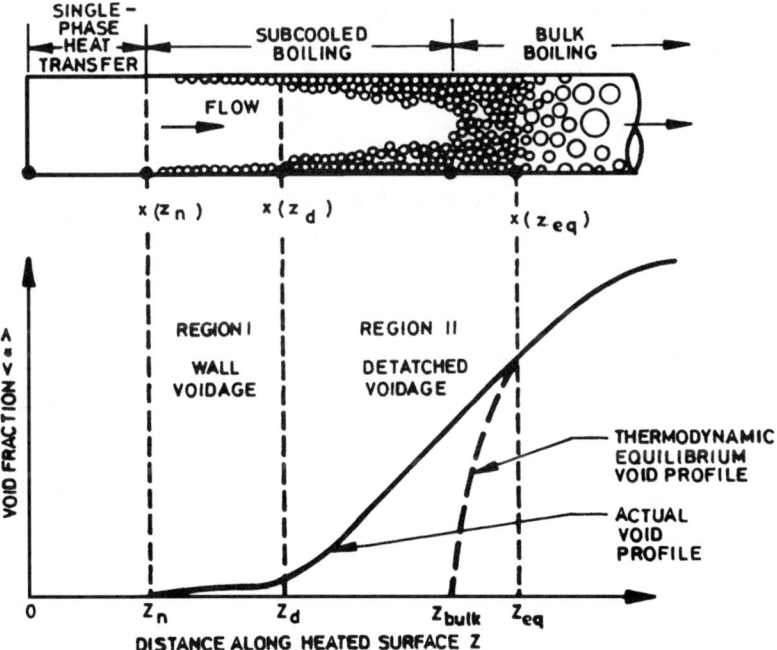

**Figure 14** Void formation in subcooled boiling (from Hewitt, 1982, with permission).

vapor and subcooled liquid coexist, and it is not until distance $z_{eq}$ is reached that the flow approximates to an equilibrium one.

Probably the most widely used methodology for predicting void fraction in subcooled boiling is that of Saha and Zuber (1974). The steps in the methodology are as follows:

(1) Estimate the point of bubble departure (point of significant void generation). Saha and Zuber give the following expressions for the local thermaldynamic equilibrium quality at the point of bubble departure as follows:

$$x_e(z_d) = -0.002 \frac{\dot{q} D c_{pL}}{h_{LG} \lambda_L} \quad \text{for Pe} < 70000 \quad (9.1\text{-}75)$$

$$x_e(z_d) = -154 \frac{\dot{q}}{\dot{m} h_{LG}} \quad \text{for Pe} < 70000 \quad (9.1\text{-}76)$$

where $c_{pL}$ is the specific heat capacity of the liquid and $\lambda_L$ its thermal conductivity. The Peclet number is defined as:

$$\text{Pe} = \frac{\dot{m} D c_{pL}}{\lambda_L} \quad (9.1\text{-}77)$$

(2) Calculate the *actual quality* $x(z)$. Any model for the calculation of flow quality must satisfy the conditions that $x(z) = 0$ at $x = z_d$ and that $x(z)$ should approach $x_e(z)$ in the quality region, as illustrated in Figure 14. A relationship developed by Levy (1966) that has been found to give good results when applied to the prediction of subcooled void fraction is as follows:

$$x(z) = x_e(z) - x_e(z_d) \exp\left[\frac{x_e(z)}{x_e(z_d)} - 1\right] \quad (9.1\text{-}78)$$

(3) Calculate the void fraction at position $z$ from the value of $x(z)$ estimated from Eq. (9.1-78). Here, any standard void fraction correlation may in principle be used, but the most popular approach is to use the drift flux model, since the constants in the model can be chosen to reflect the somewhat peculiar distribution of voids that occurs in subcooled boiling. Thus, from Eq. (9.1-65), it follows that:

$$\varepsilon_G = \frac{x(z)\rho_L}{C_o\{x(z)\rho_L + [1-x(z)]\rho_G\} + \rho_L \rho_G u_{GU}/\dot{m}} \quad (9.1\text{-}79)$$

Appropriate values of $C_o$ and $u_{GU}$ are given by Dix (1971) and Lahey and Moody (1977) as follows:

$$C_o = \beta\left[1 + \left(\frac{1}{\beta} - 1\right)^b\right] \quad (9.1\text{-}80)$$

$$u_{GU} = 2.9 \left[\frac{(\rho_L - \rho_G)\sigma g}{\rho_L^2}\right]^{0.25} \quad (9.1\text{-}81)$$

where $\beta$ is the volumetric flow fraction of the vapor phase, which is related to the local actual flow quality $x(z)$ by the expression:

$$\beta = \frac{x(z)}{x(z) + [1 - x(z)]\rho_G/\rho_L} \qquad (9.1\text{-}82)$$

and where the exponent $b$ is given by:

$$b = \left(\frac{\rho_G}{\rho_L}\right)^{0.1} \qquad (9.1\text{-}83)$$

The generalized drift flux model of Chexal and Lellouche (1986) can also be applied to the prediction of subcooled void fraction.

## 9.2 FLOW IN OTHER GEOMETRIES

### 9.2.1 Introduction

Two-phase flow in non-circular channels occurs in many industrial equipment/processes, such as tube bundles of shell-and-tube heat exchangers, fuel rod bundles of nuclear reactors, compact heat exchangers with narrow finned channels, and various types of chemical reactors and mass transfer equipment. This section describes the two-phase flow-regime, void fraction, and frictional pressure drop in various non-circular flow channels, including single channels with rectangular, triangular, and annular cross-sections, a flat channel between parallel plates, and interconnected channels found in rod bundles. The characteristics of the two-phase cross flow in tube bundles will be discussed separately in Chapter 12.

A comprehensive list of the literature available to date and covered in this chapter is shown in Table 2. Many similarities exist in the two-phase flow characteristics between circular pipes and non-circular channels with a hydraulic diameter, $D_h$, greater than about 10 mm, as summarized by Sadatomi et al. (1982) and Sato and Sadatomi (1986). However, significant differences appear in non-circular channels when the hydraulic diameter falls below 10 mm, as reviewed by Kawaji and Ali (1996). Thus, in this section, the two-phase flow characteristics in non-circular channels will be discussed for relatively large channels with $D_h > 10$ mm and narrow channels with $D_h < 10$ mm.

Narrow channels with internal fins are also used in various types of compact heat exchanger, and their two-phase flow characteristics have been reviewed by Westwater (1983), Carey (1993), and Kawaji and Ali (1996). The popular fin geometries include cross-ribbed fins, offset strip fins, and round dimple fins. The effects of fins on the two-phase flow characteristics in narrow flat channels will also be summarized, based on the available data listed in Table 3.

**Table 2** List of previous studies on two-phase flow in non-circular channels

| Investigators | Channel cross-section, (mm) | Hydr. dia., $D_h$ (mm) | Aspect ratio[1] | Flow orient[2] | Fluid mixture | Flow regime | Press. drop | Void fraction | Notes |
|---|---|---|---|---|---|---|---|---|---|
| Sadatomi et al. (1982) | Rectangular | | | V.-U. | Air/Water | Yes | Yes | Yes | Void fraction measured with a pair of quick shutoff valves. Flow regimes identified from slug frequency. |
| | 17 × 50 | 25.4 | 2.9 | | | | | | |
| | 10 × 50 | 16.7 | 5.0 | | | | | | |
| | 7 × 50 | 12.3 | 7.1 | | | | | | |
| | 7 × 20.6 | 10.4 | 2.9 | | | | | | |
| | Triangular | | | | | | | | |
| | Apex-angle = 20°, height = 55 | 16.3 | N/A | | | | | | |
| | Annulus, $D_i$ = 15, $D_o$ = 30 | 15.0 | N/A | | | | | | |
| Venkateswararao et al. (1982) | 4 × 4 rod bundle, Rod-diam. = 12.7 Pitch = 17.5 Square in-line | 18.0 | N/A | V.-U. | Air/Water | Yes | Yes | No | Flow regimes identified visually. Bubble velocity measured by high-speed photography. |
| Hasan & Kabir (1992) | Annulus O.D. = 127, I.D. = 48, 57, 87 | 79, 70, 40 | N/A | V-U, V-I. | Air/Water | No | No | Yes | Bubble rise velocity measured in stagnant liquid column. |
| Kelessidis & Dukler (1989) | Concentric and Eccentric Annulus O.D. = 76.2, I.D. = 50.8 | | | V.-U. | Air/Water | Yes | No | No | Flow regime identification: PDF of conductance probe signals |
| Caetano et al. (1992a, 1992b) | Annulus O.D. = 76 I.D. = 42 | 34 | N/A | V.-U. | Air/Water Air/Kerosene | Yes | Yes | Yes | Void fraction measured by quick closing valves. Flow regime identification: Visual observation |

| Author | Dimensions | | | Orientation | Fluid | | | | Notes |
|---|---|---|---|---|---|---|---|---|---|
| Ali et al. (1993) | 0.778 × 80<br>1.465 × 80 | 1.54<br>2.88 | 102.8<br>54.6 | V-U, V-D, H-H, H-V, I-U, I-D | Air/Water | Yes | Yes | Yes | Flow regime detection: PDF of void fluctuations; Void fraction measurement: electrical conductance probe. |
| Fujita et al. (1994) | 0.5 × 10<br>0.7 × 1.2<br>1.2 × 10 | 0.95<br>1.31<br>2.14 | 20<br>14<br>8 | H-H. | $N_2$ gas/Water-Ethanol Solution | Yes | Yes | Yes | Flow regime detection: Video camera; Void fraction measurement: Capacitance probe. Studied the effects of liquid viscosity and surface tension. |
| Iida & Takahashi (1976) | 0.7 × 40<br>1.6 × 80<br>3.8 × 80 | 1.38<br>3.14<br>7.26 | 57.1<br>50<br>21.1 | V-U, H-H.<br>H-H.<br>H-H. | Air/Water | Yes | Yes | Yes | Reported 'New' flow pattern called Fissure Flow. |
| Jones & Zuber (1975) | 63.5 × 4.98 | 9.27 | 12.7 | V-U. | Air/Water | Yes | No | Yes | Flow regime detection: PDF[3] of void fluctuations. X-ray void fraction measurement. |
| Lowry & Kawaji (1988) | 0.5 × 80<br>1.0 × 80<br>2.0 × 80 | 0.994<br>1.975<br>3.90 | 160<br>80<br>40 | V-U. | Air/Water | Yes | Yes | Yes | Flow regime detection: Photographic. Void fraction measurement: electrical conductance probe. |
| Mishima et al. (1991) | 1.0 × 50<br>2.4 × 50<br>5.0 × 50 | 1.96<br>4.58<br>9.09 | 50<br>20.8<br>10 | V-U. | Air/Water | Yes | Yes | Yes | Flow regime: High speed video. Void fraction: Neutron Radiography (NRG) & Image processing |

(Continued)

Table 2 (Continued)

| Investigators | Channel cross-section (mm) | Hydr. dia., $D_h$(mm) | Aspect ratio[1] | Flow orient[2] | Fluid mixture | Parameters investigated | | | Notes |
|---|---|---|---|---|---|---|---|---|---|
| | | | | | | Flow regime | Press. drop | Void fraction | |
| Moriyama & Inoue (1991) | 0.098 × 30 | 0.195 | 306 | H-H. | $N_2$ gas/R-113 | Yes | Yes | Yes | Local void fraction measurement: Laser beam reflection |
| | 0.052 × 30 | 0.104 | 577 | | | | | | |
| | 0.025 × 30 | 0.050 | 1200 | | | | | | |
| | 0.007 × 30 | 0.014 | 4286 | | | | | | |
| Wambsganss et al. (1991, 1992a, 1992b) | 1.59 × 9.52 | 2.72 | 6 | H-V. | Air/Water | Yes | Yes | No | Flow regime detection: Visual/ Photographic Void fraction: Quick closing valves |
| | 3.18 × 19.05 | 5.45 | 6 | H-H, H-V. | | | | | |
| Wilmarth & Ishii (1994) | 1 × 20 | 1.9 | 20 | V-U. | Air/Water | Yes | No | No | Flow regime detection: Optical (CCD video camera) |
| | 2 × 15 | 3.53 | 7.5 | V-U, H-V. | | | | | |

[a] Channels with $D_h$ > 10 mm.
[b] Narrow Rectangular Channels with $D_h$ < 10 mm.
[1] Aspect Ratio = long side/short side.
[2] Flow Orientation: V-U: Vertical Upward, V-D: Vertical Downward, H-H: Horizontal flow between Horizontal plates, H-V: Horizontal flow between Vertical Plates, I-U: Inclined Upward flow, I-D: Inclined Downward flow.
[3] PDF = Probability Density Function.

**Table 3  List of previous studies on two-phase flow in compact heat exchanger channels**

| Investigator(s) | Channel cross-section, (mm × mm) | Hydraulic diameter, $D_h$ (mm) | Fin type | Aspect ratio | Orientation | Fluid mixture | Test conditions | Flow regime | Pressure drop | Void fraction | Notes |
|---|---|---|---|---|---|---|---|---|---|---|---|
| Carey & Mandrusiak (1986) | 3.8 × 19.1 | 5.15 | Offset Strip Fins | 5 | V-U | Water Methanol N-Butanol | Mass Flux: 3–100 kg/m².s Mass Quality: 0.05–0.7 | Yes | No | No | Flow regime detection: Visual & Photography Heat transfer measurements |
| Carey & Schuh (1985) | 5.1 × 64  7.9 × 64  3.9 × 64 | — | Offset Strip Fins | 12.5  8.1  16.4 | H-H | Nitrogen gas Water/ R-11 | Mass Flux: 56–215 kg/m².s Mass Quality: 0–0.004 | No | Yes | No | Pressure Drop measurement: differential pressure transducer |
| Xu & Carey (1987) | 6.4 × 19.1 | 5.2 | Cross-rib | 3 | V-U, H-H | Methanol N-Butanol | Mass Flux: 5–90 kg/m².s Mass Quality 0.05–0.8 | Yes | No | No | Flow regime detection: Visual & Photography |
| Rong, Kawaji & Burgers (1993) | 2.6 × 80  2.6 × 80  2.3 × 76.2  2.3 × 15.0  2.3 × 74.0 | 5.0  5.0  4.4  3.9  4.4 | Round dimple  Cross-rib | 30.8  30.8  33.1  6.5  32.2 | V-U, V-D, H-H, H-V | Water/Air | $j_g$(m/s) $j_L$(m/s) 0.05–15 0.05–4 | Yes | Yes | Yes | Flow regime detection: High speed video camera Void Fraction: Conductivity probe |

### 9.2.2 Two-Phase Flow Regimes

Flow regimes commonly encountered in circular pipes as defined and described in Section 9.1, such as bubbly, slug, churn-turbulent, stratified, wavy, and annular flows, also occur in non-circular channels. Some differences are found in gas-liquid interface configurations between the flows in circular pipes and, for example, narrow flat channels.

**Flow regime maps.** Flow regimes at different combinations of gas and liquid flow rates are typically represented graphically in "flow regime maps," using, for example, the superficial gas and liquid velocities ($j_G$ vs. $j_L$) for the map coordinates. Some flow regime maps are presented using dimensionless coordinates that include the physical properties of the gas and liquid phases, such as the Lockhart-Martinelli parameter and the Reynolds numbers of gas and liquid, as well as the channel dimensions.

Various methods of flow regime identification ranging from visual observation to statistical analyses of void fraction and pressure fluctuations can be used for non-circular channels. Most investigators have relied on visual observation by still photography or a video camera. For tube bundles and non-transparent channels, flow visualization methods by x-ray tomography and neutron radiography are more useful.

***Channels with $D_h > 10$ mm.*** Sadatomi et al. (1982) have obtained and compared the flow regime data for upward flow in rectangular, triangular, and annular channels, as shown in Figure 15. The flow regime transition criteria used were the gas slug intervals greater than $100D_h$ for bubbly-slug flow transition, and $1,000D_h$ for

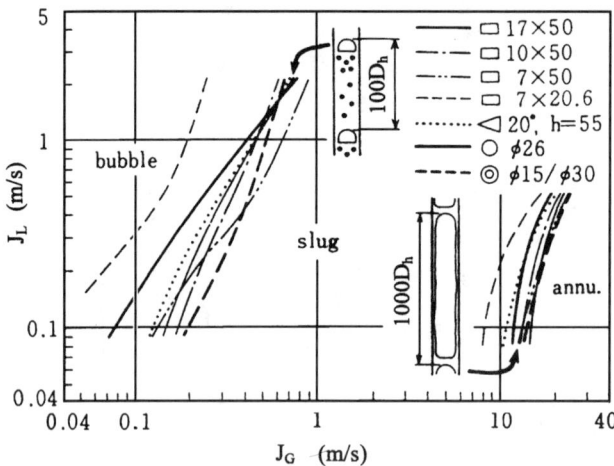

**Figure 15** Flow regime map for vertical upward flow in non-circular channels with $D_h > 10$ mm (from Sadatomi et al., 1982, with permission).

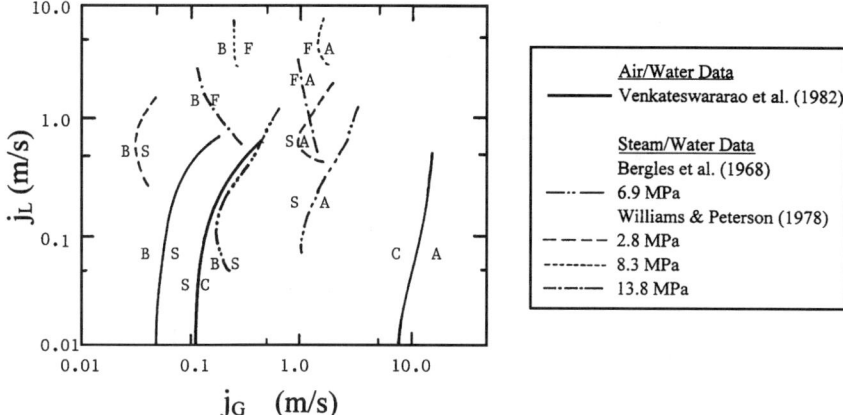

**Figure 16** Flow regime maps for vertical flow in rod bundles (B-bubbly, S-slug, C-churn, F-froth, A-annular).

slug-annular flow transition. Caetano et al. (1989a, 1989b) presented flow regime maps for a vertical annulus obtained for air/water and air/kerosene. Kelessidis and Dukler (1989) have presented flow regime data for concentric and eccentric annuli. For a rod or tube bundle geometry, a flow regime map for air/water flow in a vertical, 24-rod bundle with a subchannel hydraulic diameter, $D_h = 18.0$ mm, was reported by Venkateswararao et al. (1982), as shown in Figure 16. All of the above data have been obtained at near atmospheric pressures.

Compared to the flow regime maps available for circular tubes, non-circular channel data show little difference if $D_h > 10$ mm. Typically, at low gas and high liquid flow rates, bubbly flow occurs, and at high gas flow rates and low liquid flow rates, an annular flow regime is observed. At intermediate gas and liquid flow rates, intermittent flow regimes, such as slug and churn-turbulent flows, occur.

At high pressures, flow regime maps have been obtained for four-rod bundle geometries by Bergles et al. (1968) and Williams and Peterson (1978) by boiling water at pressures up to 13.8 MPa, as shown in Figure 16. In all of the high pressure data, transition from intermittent to annular flow occurs at much lower superficial gas velocities of about 1 m/s, in comparison with 10 m/s at 1 bar.

*Channels with $D_h < 10$ mm.* Flow regime maps for narrow channels, such as rectangular and flat channels, are generally similar, but the flow regime transition boundaries show some differences due possibly to the gradual nature of transition, differences in flow regime identification methods used, channel orientation, $D_h$, and aspect ratio. The flow regime maps obtained by Ali et al. (1993) are shown in Figure 17 for narrow channels between two flat plates with gaps of 0.778 mm and 1.465 mm for different channel orientations, excluding horizontal flow between vertical plates (H-V). In the data, annular flow is observed at high gas velocities

**240** HANDBOOK OF PHASE CHANGE: BOILING AND CONDENSATION

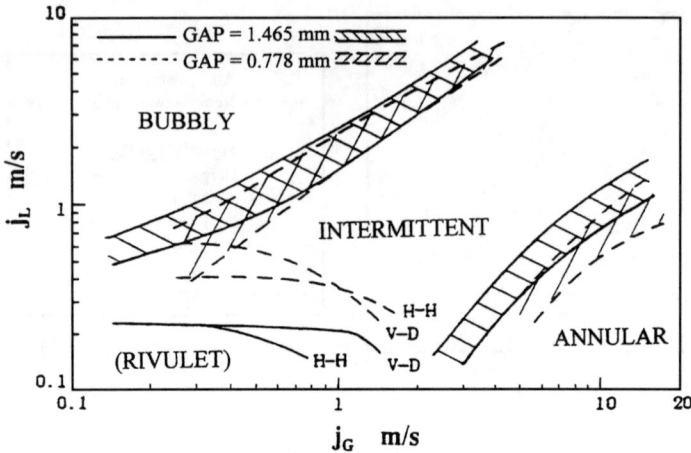

**Figure 17** Flow regimes in narrow flat channels for all orientations excluding H-V (from Ali et al., 1993, with permission).

($j_G > 4$ m/s) and low to intermediate liquid velocities ($j_L < 1$ m/s). Bubbly flow occurs at high liquid ($j_L > 1$ m/s) and low gas velocities. Between the annular and bubbly flow regimes, intermittent flow exists over a wide range of gas and liquid flow rates.

There are some differences among the flow regime maps reported for narrow flat and rectangular channels that may be attributed to the differences in channel orientation and geometry, such as gap thickness and the channel width or aspect ratio. Overall, however, the flow regime maps reported to date for narrow channels show generally compatible results. The flow regime boundaries are also similar between small rectangular channels and small circular tubes in horizontal and possibly vertical orientations, based on a comparison of data by Wambsganss et al. (1991) with the 1–5 mm diameter circular tube data of Damianides (1987) and Fukano et al. (1989).

A major difference that can be readily identified in the flow regime maps between the flat narrow channels and non-circular channels with larger hydraulic diameters ($D_h > 10$ mm) is in the transition from intermittent to annular flow regimes. In the larger channels, this transition occurs at a superficial gas velocity, $j_G$, greater than 10 m/s, for all liquid flow rates. In flat narrow channels, this transition can be observed at $j_G$ values between 3 and 10 m/s for low to moderate liquid flow rates ($j_L < 1$ m/s) for all channel orientations, excluding the horizontal flow between vertical plates (H-V) (Lowry and Kawaji, 1987; Mishima et al., 1991; Wambsganss et al., 1991; Wilmarth & Ishii, 1994).

**Effects of channel orientation and fluid properties.** For circular and non-circular channels, the flow regime transition boundaries are sensitive to the channel

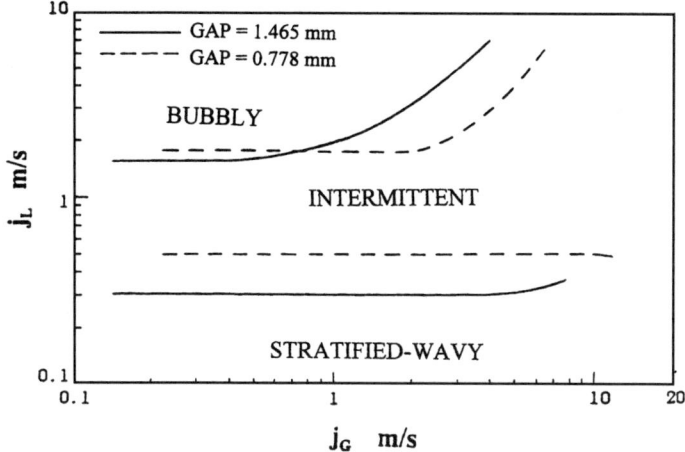

**Figure 18** Flow regime maps for horizontal flow between vertical plates (H-V) (from Ali et al., 1993, with permission).

orientation. In a horizontal channel, gravity can separate gas and liquid phases, and stratified or wavy flow appears at low liquid flow rates in addition to bubbly, plug, slug and annular flow regimes. Even for narrow channels, horizontal flow between vertical plates (H-V) presents completely different flow regime maps, as shown in Figure 18. As in larger pipes and channels, stratified flow occurs at $j_L$ below about 0.3 m/s for the 1.465 mm gap and 0.5 m/s for the 0.778 mm gap over the whole range of $j_G$ values up to 16 m/s. Annular flow was not observed even at the highest $j_G$ tested (16 m/s), due possibly to the negligible interfacial area and shear. If the vertical wall of the channel is not too high (<20 mm), however, an annular flow regime can occur at $j_G > 10$ m/s, as evident in the horizontal flow data of Wambsganss et al. (1991) and Wilmarth and Ishii (1994) for small rectangular channels.

For narrow channels, the effects of the fluid properties have been reported to be relatively small. The effect of liquid viscosity on two-phase flow regimes has been found to be insignificant for narrow rectangular channels in vertical and horizontal orientations (Troniewski and Ulbrich, 1984). As surface tension is decreased, the intermittent-annular transition boundary shifts to the lower $j_G$ values (Fujita et al., 1994). This means that in low surface tension systems in narrow channels, annular flow regime would occur over a wider range of gas flow rates, compared to the air/water system at atmospheric pressure.

**Effect of fins.** For various finned narrow channels found in compact heat exchangers, two-phase flow regime maps have been obtained for cross-ribbed fins, offset strip fins, and round dimple fins, as listed in Table 3. The flow regime maps by Rong et al. (1993) for different channel orientations shown in Figure 19 are qualitatively

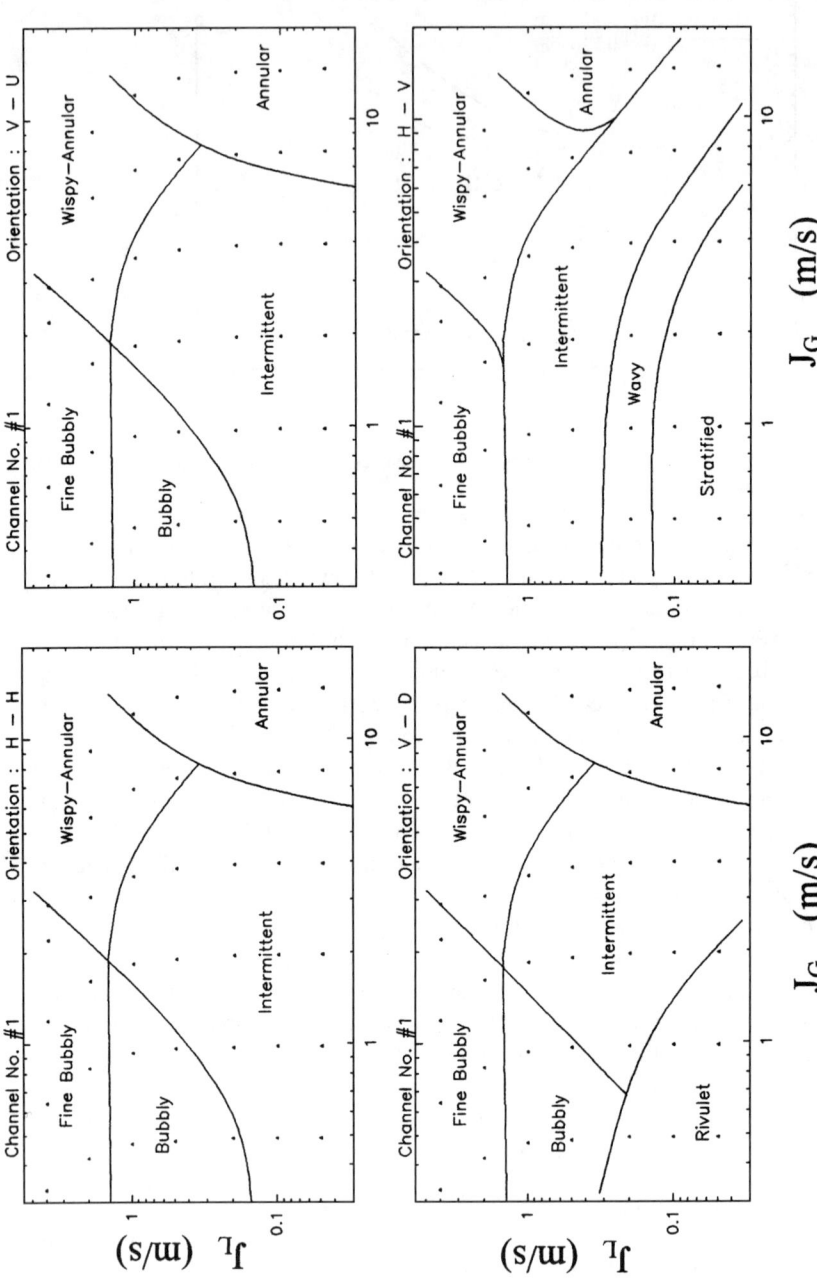

**Figure 19** Flow regime maps for a finned channel with round dimple fins in different channel orientations (H-H: Horizontal flow between horizontal plates, V-U: Vertical upward flow, H-V: Horizontal flow between vertical plates) (from Rong et al., 1993, with permission).

similar to those obtained for narrow smooth channels; however, several significant differences are found due to the enhanced turbulence levels in the two-phase mixture. For example, a fine-bubbly flow regime occurred for all channel orientations when the superficial liquid velocity ($j_L$) exceeded 1.3 m/s or so, rivulet flow was not found in horizontal flow, and annular flow occurred at higher gas velocities for all four orientations. The above differences can be attributed to the fact that the liquid is slowed down by the fins, and some liquid films are broken up into large droplets. Also, some gas bubbles are trapped in the wake of the fins due to the surface tension force and may not move even in the presence of a moderately strong liquid flow (Carey, 1993).

**Flow regime transition correlations.** In order to predict the flow regime transitions, various theories have been proposed for circular pipes with diameters greater than 10 mm. Widely used theories have been proposed by Taitel and Dukler (1976) for horizontal flow, Taitel et al. (1980) and Mishima and Ishii (1984) for vertical flow, and Barnea (1987) for inclined pipes, among others. These models and other correlations developed for circular pipes can also be used for non-circular channels if the hydraulic diameter is greater than about 10 mm.

For flat narrow channels, the applicability of the existing correlations is less certain, and correlations specific to small channels have been developed, as summarized in Table 4. For slug-annular transition in a narrow rectangular channel in vertical upward flow, the correlation by Jones and Zubers (1979) can predict well their own data obtained in a 5 mm × 63.5 mm rectangular channel and that of Mishima et al. (1991) obtained in 1 mm and 2.4 mm gap channels. For bubbly-slug flow transition in a narrow, vertical rectangular channel, the models of Taitel et al. (1980) and Mishima and Ishii (1984) are recommended. For the latter's correlation, a drift flux model (described later in this section) is used to determine the values of $j_L$ and $j_G$ that would give $\epsilon = 0.3$. For intermittent-annular flow transition in a horizontal rectangular channel in H-V orientation, Wilmarth and Ishii (1994) found that the modified model of Barnea et al. (1983) is applicable, where the height of the gas phase, $h_G$, must be predicted using a void fraction correlation.

**Table 4  Flow regime transition correlations for narrow channels**

| Flow regime transition | Channel orientation and flow direction | Recommended correlation | Reference |
|---|---|---|---|
| Slug-Annular | Vertical Upward | $j_L = 0.25 j_G - V_{gj}$ where $V_{gj} = (0.23 + 0.13\delta/W)\sqrt{(\Delta\rho g W/\rho_L)}$ | Jones & Zuber (1979) |
| Bubbly-Slug | Vertical Upward | $j_L = 3.0 j_G - 1.15(g\Delta\rho\sigma/\rho_L^2)^{0.75}$ $\varepsilon = 0.3$ | Taitel et al. (1980) Mishima & Ishii (1984) |
| Slug-Annular | Horizontal (H-V) | $h_G < (\pi/4)\sqrt{[\sigma/\rho_L g(1 - \pi/4)]}$ | Barnea et al. (1983) |

### 9.2.3 Void Fraction

The void fraction or liquid holdup in the flow channel is another important parameter in two-phase flow, as it affects the flow regime, pressure drop, and heat transfer characteristics. In this section, the experimental data available and methods of prediction will be discussed first, followed by the effects of channel geometry, orientation, size, and fluid properties.

**Mean void fraction.** The channel average void fraction data for non-circular channels have been successfully correlated in terms of the Lockhart-Martinelli parameter, described in the previous section or in the form of a drift flux model (Zuber and Findlay, 1965). For example, the void fraction data for flat channels obtained by Ali et al. (1993) are shown in Figures 20 and 21 for horizontal flow. They are fairly well correlated in terms of the Lockhart-Martinelli parameter, $X^2$, which for both phases turbulent is given by

$$X = [(1-x)/x]^{0.9}[\rho_G/\rho_L]^{0.5}[\eta_L/\eta_G]^{0.1} \quad (9.2\text{-}1)$$

where x is the mass quality (Lockhart and Martinelli, 1949).

A widely used correlation proposed by Chisholm and Laird (1958) to predict the mean void fraction in pipes and channels with $D_h > 10$ mm is given by

$$\epsilon = 1 - (1 + C/X + 1/X^2)^{-0.5} \quad (9.2\text{-}2)$$

The value of C ranges from 5 to 21, depending on whether each phase is laminar or turbulent. This correlation is indicated by solid curves for several values of C in

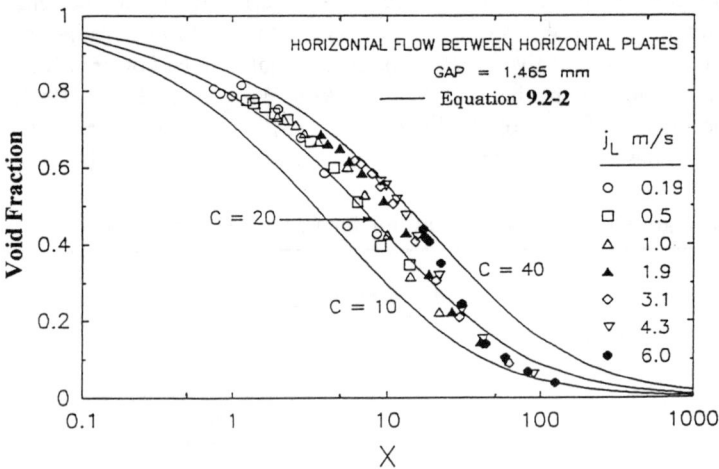

**Figure 20** Void fraction data for horizontal flow between plates (H-H) for 1.465 mm gap channel (from Ali et al., 1993, with permission).

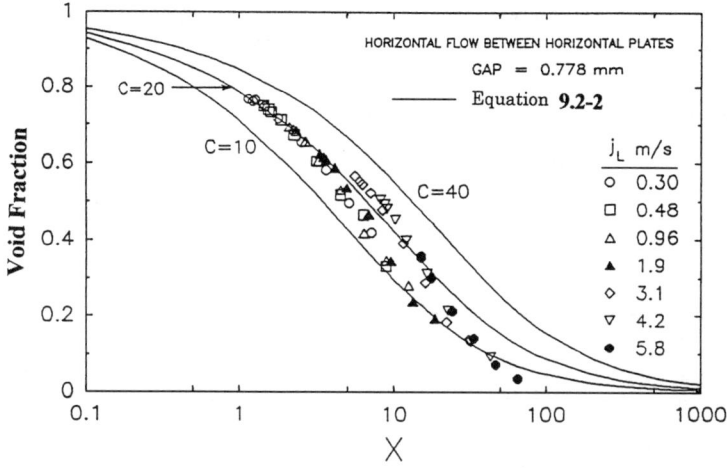

**Figure 21** Void fraction data for horizontal flow between horizontal plates (H-H) for a 0.778 mm gap channel (from Ali et al., 1993, with permission).

Figures 20 and 21. The mean void fraction data in Figure 21 obtained by Ali et al. (1993) can be predicted reasonably well with $C \approx 20$ for $\epsilon > 0.3$ and $C \approx 10$ for $\epsilon < 0.3$.

Another widely used approach is the drift flux model (Wallis, 1969; Zuber and Findlay, 1965), given by

$$U_G = j_G/\epsilon = C_o \langle j \rangle + V_{gj} \qquad (9.2\text{-}3)$$

where $U_G$ is the weighted mean gas velocity, $\langle j \rangle$ is the mixture mean velocity ($= j_G + j_L$), $C_o$ is the distribution parameter, and $V_{gj}$ is the mean drift velocity, which represents the difference between the gas velocity and the mixture mean velocity and is usually considered to be a function of the terminal rise velocity of a bubble in a stagnant liquid.

The void fraction data for vertical upward flow in triangular and rectangular channels (Sadatomi et al., 1982), narrow rectangular channels (Mishima et al., 1988, 1991), and a 4 × 4 rod bundle (Morooka et al., 1987) are shown in Figures 22–24. The distribution parameter, $C_o$, which accounts for the differences in velocity and void fraction profiles in the channel cross section, varies with the channel geometry, ranging from 1.068 for a rod bundle to 1.34 for a triangular channel. For non-circular channels with $D_h > 10$ mm, Sadatomi et al. (1982) recommended the values given in Table 5. For narrow rectangular channels, Mishima et al. found the correlation by Ishii (1977) to be adequate for rectangular channels,

$$C_o = 1.35 - 0.35\sqrt{(\rho_G/\rho_L)} \qquad (9.2\text{-}4)$$

Ali et al. (1993) found $C_o = 1.25$ for a narrow flat channel. In extremely narrow channels with gap thicknesses less than 0.1 mm, Moriyama and Inoue (1991)

**Table 5 Distribution parameter values for non-circular channels with $D_h > 10$ mm (from Sadatomi et al., 1982)**

| Shape | Dimension (mm) | $C_o$ |
|---|---|---|
| Rectangular, □ | 17 × 50 | 1.20 |
|  | 10 × 50 | 1.24 |
|  | 7 × 50 | 1.16 |
|  | 7 × 20.6 | 1.21 |
| Triangular, △ | 20°, h = 55 | 1.34 |
| Annulus, ◎ | $\phi15/\phi30$ | 1.30 |
| Circular, ○ | $\phi26$ | 1.25 |

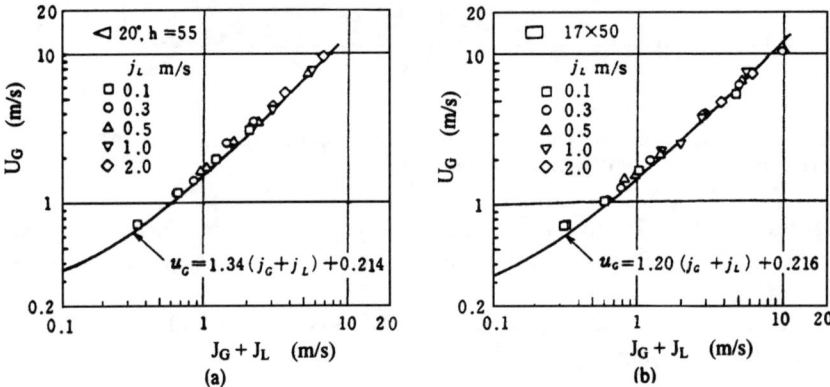

**Figure 22** Correlation of void fraction data by drift flux model (from Sadatomi et al., 1982, with permission).

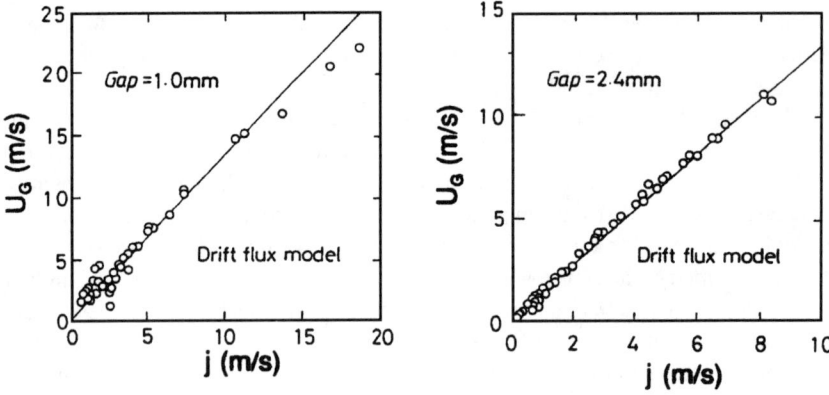

**Figure 23** Correlation of void fraction data by drift flux model (from Mishima et al., 1991, with permission).

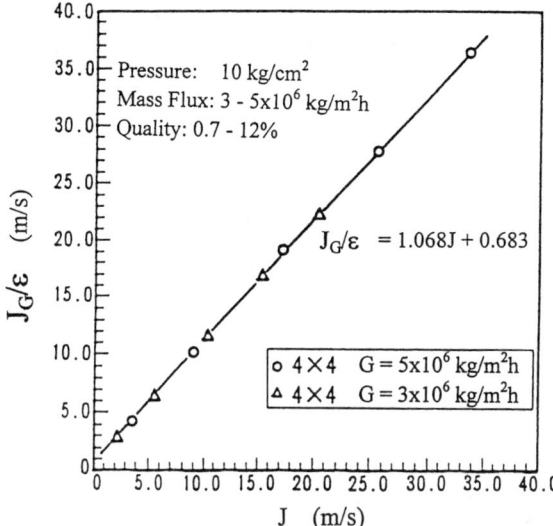

**Figure 24** Correlation of rod-bundle void fraction data by drift flux model (from Morooka et al., 1987, with permission).

reported that the distribution parameter takes on significantly larger values: 1.35 for 96 $\mu$m, 1.40 for 52 $\mu$m, and 1.80 for 25 $\mu$m gap.

For larger non-circular channels, Sadatomi et al. (1982) and Sato and Sadatomi (1986) have shown that the mean drift velocity, $V_{gj}$, can be given in terms of an equi-periphery diameter, $D_e$, which is defined to be the total wetted perimeter divided by $\pi$.

$$V_{gj} = (0.31 \sim 0.35)\sqrt{(gD_e)} \tag{9.2-5}$$

For an annular channel, $D_e = D_i + D_o$, where $D_i$ and $D_o$ are the inner and outer diameters, respectively. Hasan and Kabir (1992) have recommended the following equation for $V_{gj}$ for a vertical annulus.

$$V_{gj} = [0.345 + 0.1(D_i/D_o)][gD_o(\rho_L - \rho_G)/\rho_L]^{1/2} \tag{9.2-6}$$

On the other hand, for narrow non-circular channels such as rectangular and flat channels, the mean drift velocity is negligibly small and, in many cases, equal to zero (i.e., $V_{gj} = 0$). The small $V_{gj}$ values for the flat narrow channels and rectangular channels are attributed to the inability of the gas bubbles to rise through a stagnant liquid due to the surface tension force. When $V_{gj} = 0$, the drift flux model reduces to a simple equation, $\epsilon = \beta/C_o$, where $\beta$ is the homogeneous void fraction, given by the ratio of volumetric flow rates or superficial velocities, i.e., $\beta = j_G/(j_G + j_L)$. Thus, with the values of $C_o$ reported for narrow channels with gaps of 1.0 mm–5.0 mm, the available void fraction data for all channel orientations except for the horizontal flow between vertical plates (H-V) can be predicted by

$$\epsilon = (0.75 \sim 0.8)\beta \tag{9.2-7}$$

**Effects of channel geometry, orientation, and fluid properties.** For an annulus, Hasan and Kabir (1992) reported that the angle, $\theta$, of channel inclination from horizontal has a negligible effect on void fraction for bubbly flow ($\epsilon < 0.25$). However, for slug flow, a significant effect exists, and the mean drift velocity for use in Eq. (9.2-3) can be given by

$$V_{gj} = [0.345 + 0.1(D_i/D_o)]\sqrt{\sin\theta(1+\cos\theta)^{1.2}[gD_o(\rho_L - \rho_G)/\rho_L]^{1/2}} \tag{9.2-8}$$

On the other hand, the effect of channel orientation is not significant for narrow channels for all void fractions except for horizontal flow between vertical plates (H-V). If the channel aspect ratio is large and the long side of the channel cross section is oriented vertically, then the flow can stratify at low liquid flow rates due to gravity affecting both the void fraction and friction pressure drop.

For narrow flat channels, the effect of hydraulic diameter (or the gap thickness) on mean void fraction is small. At given superficial gas and liquid velocities, the void fraction decreases slightly as $D_h$ is reduced. Fujita et al. (1994) reported that the gap thickness effect disappears in low surface tension systems. They also found that the void fraction in narrow flat channels increases with decreasing viscosity and surface tension. For $j_G > 2.0$ m/s, the void fraction data could be correlated by using a modified superficial gas velocity, $j_G^* = j_G(\sigma_w/\sigma)(\eta_w/\eta)^2$, where the subscript, w, indicates pure water.

**Effect of fins.** Channel average void fractions for the finned channels have been reported by several researchers as listed in Table 3. For narrow flat channels with round dimple fins, Rong et al. (1993) found that the shapes and sizes of the fins do not have a large effect on the mean void fraction. Chisholm and Laird's correlation, Eq. (9.2-2), with a C-value of 50 can predict the mean void fraction for the range of $1/X$ less than about 0.2 (or $X > 5$), for all three orientations excluding H-V. For $\epsilon > 0.6$ (or $X < 10$), there is little difference between the void fractions in smooth and finned channels, but for $\epsilon < 0.6$ (or $X > 10$), the presence of the fins leads to an increase in void fraction by a factor of up to four, as shown in Figure 25. This is because the fins break up large bubbles into smaller ones, which tend to move more slowly in a liquid than the larger bubbles. Also, some bubbles can be trapped in the wake behind the protruding fins and increase the void fraction at low liquid flow rates. The channel orientation has only a small effect, except for the horizontal flow between vertical plates (H-V) at low liquid flow rates.

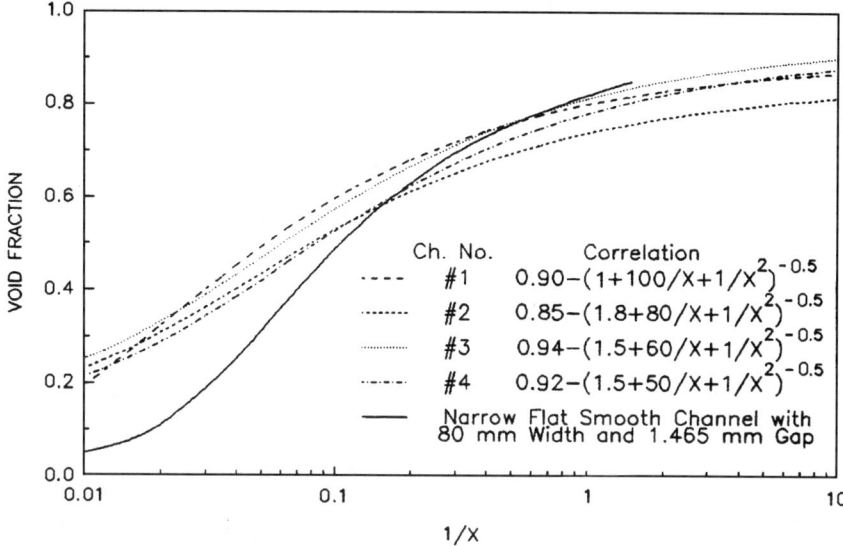

**Figure 25** Comparison of void fraction data between finned and smooth narrow channels (from Rong et al., 1993, with permission).

### 9.2.4 Two-Phase Pressure Drop

The total pressure drop in two-phase flow can be divided into gravitational, accelerational and frictional components. For adiabatic flows in channels of constant cross sectional area, the acceleration pressure drop can be neglected if the flow is well developed and void fraction does not change in the flow direction. The gravitational pressure drop is important for vertical and inclined channels and can be calculated as follows if the channel average void fraction, $\epsilon$, is known.

$$\Delta P_{gr}/\Delta z = [\rho_L(1 - \epsilon) + \rho_G \epsilon] g \sin\theta \qquad (9.2\text{-}9)$$

Here, $\theta$ is the angle of channel inclination from horizontal. The two-phase friction pressure drop, $\Delta P_{TP}^F$, is then given by the difference between the total pressure drop and the sum of gravitational and accelerational components and can be calculated using the Lockhart-Martinelli correlation.

$$\Delta P_{TP}^F = \phi_L^2 \Delta P_L^F = \phi_G^2 \Delta P_G^F \qquad (9.2\text{-}10)$$

Here, $\Delta P_L^F$ and $\Delta P_G^F$ are the single-phase friction pressure drop for liquid and gas, respectively, when each phase is assumed to flow alone in the channel, and $\phi_L^2$ and $\phi_G^2$ are the two-phase friction multipliers.

**Single-phase friction pressure drop.** The friction pressure drop for single-phase flow can be calculated using a Darcy's formula, involving a friction factor, f, hydraulic diameter, $D_h$, and the mean fluid velocity, U, as follows:

$$\Delta P_k^F / \Delta z = (f/2D_h)\rho U^2 \qquad (9.2\text{-}11)$$

For both laminar and turbulent flows, the friction factor is given by

$$f = \begin{cases} C_L/\text{Re} & \text{for Re} < 2300 \\ C_t/\text{Re}^{0.25} & \text{for Re} > 3500 \end{cases} \qquad (9.2\text{-}12)$$

where $\text{Re} = \rho U D_h/\eta$ and the hydraulic diameter is calculated as $D_h = 4A/P_w$.

The parameter, $C_L$, in Eq. (9.2-12) is called the geometry factor and is dependent on the geometry of the channel cross section as tabulated in Shah and London (1978) and plotted by Sadatomi et al. (1982) in Figure 26. For rectangular channels, as the aspect ratio decreases from $\infty$ for parallel flat plates to unity for a square channel, the value of $C_L$ decreases from 96 to 57. For turbulent flow, the friction factor can be estimated using the Blasius-type equation given above, and the value of $C_t$ can be calculated from the following formula suggested by Sadatomi et al. (1982):

$$C_t/C_{to} = (0.0154 C_L/C_{Lo} - 0.012)^{1/3} + 0.85 \qquad (9.2\text{-}13)$$

where $C_{to} = 0.316$ and $C_{Lo} = 64$ are for a circular pipe.

The single-phase friction factor increases significantly if fins are introduced into the channel and the shape and size of the fins also affect the single-phase friction factor so that measurements would be necessary. The data obtained by

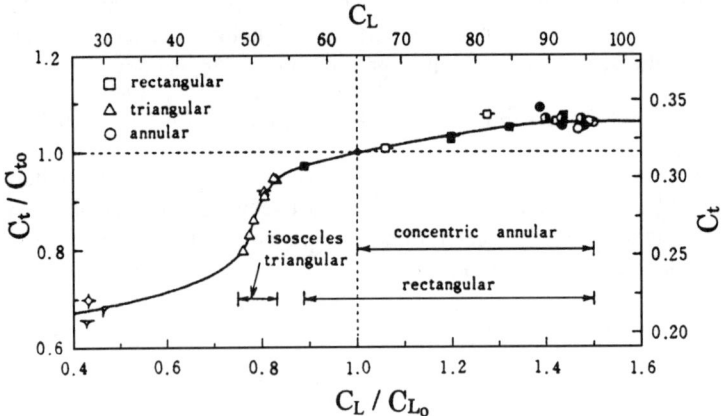

**Figure 26** Geometry factor for laminar friction factor (from Sadatomi et al., 1982, with permission).

Rong et al. (1993) for round dimple and cross-ribbed fins are approximately 5 to 13 times greater than those for the smooth channels. The fins also induce greater turbulence at significantly lower Reynolds numbers, and the finned channel friction factor data are well represented by the Blasius type equation for Re > 400.

**Two-phase friction multiplier.** The two-phase friction pressure drop data available for non-circular channels can be correlated in terms of a Lockhart-Martinelli parameter using Chisholm and Laird's correlation.

$$\phi_L^2 = 1 + (C/X) + (1/X^2) \qquad (9.2\text{-}14)$$

This equation with $C = 21$ represents the data well for relatively large ($D_h > 10$ mm) non-circular channels (Sadatomi et al., 1982) and high mass flux data ($G > 400$ kg/m²s) for narrow channels. The two-phase friction multiplier data shown in Figure 27 for narrow flat channels indicate that for a given value of the Lockhart-Martinelli parameter, the friction multiplier is greater at higher mass velocities or liquid flow rates, though this effect is diminished at high mass velocities. The low mass velocity data are correlated by a smaller C value.

**Effects of channel orientation, size, and fluid properties.** For narrow flat channels, only a small effect of channel orientation has been observed, except for the horizontal flow between vertical plates (H-V), for which stratification of the gas and liquid phases can occur at low mass fluxes ($G < 100$ kg/m²s) and the friction multiplier tends to decrease in value.

The effects of the channel size or gap thickness of narrow channels can be summarized by a plot of the C-value of Chisholm & Laird's correlation (Eq. 9.2-14) that best fit the data obtained in horizontal (H-H) or vertical (U-V) channels as shown in Figure 28. The C-value tends to generally decrease with the gap thickness, from a value of ~21 for the large gap thicknesses ($\delta > 5$ mm or $D_h > \sim 10$ mm) to about 10 for $\delta \sim 1$ mm and to zero for extremely narrow channels with gap thicknesses of less than 0.1 mm.

The effects of fluid properties (surface tension and liquid viscosity) were investigated by Fujita et al. (1994) in horizontal, 10 mm wide channels with gap thicknesses of 0.5 mm, 0.7 mm, and 1.2 mm. At moderately high liquid flow rates ($j_L > 0.4$ m/s or $G > 400$ kg/m²s) for all gap thicknesses, the effects of surface tension and liquid viscosity are quite negligible, being overwhelmed by the inertial effects. At lower mass velocities, the two-phase friction pressure drop, $\Delta P_{TP}^F/\Delta z$, increases with increasing liquid viscosity and surface tension but is more strongly controlled by the liquid viscosity at moderate liquid flow rates, ($j_L > 0.2$ m/s), and by surface tension at low liquid flow rates ($j_L < 0.2$ m/s).

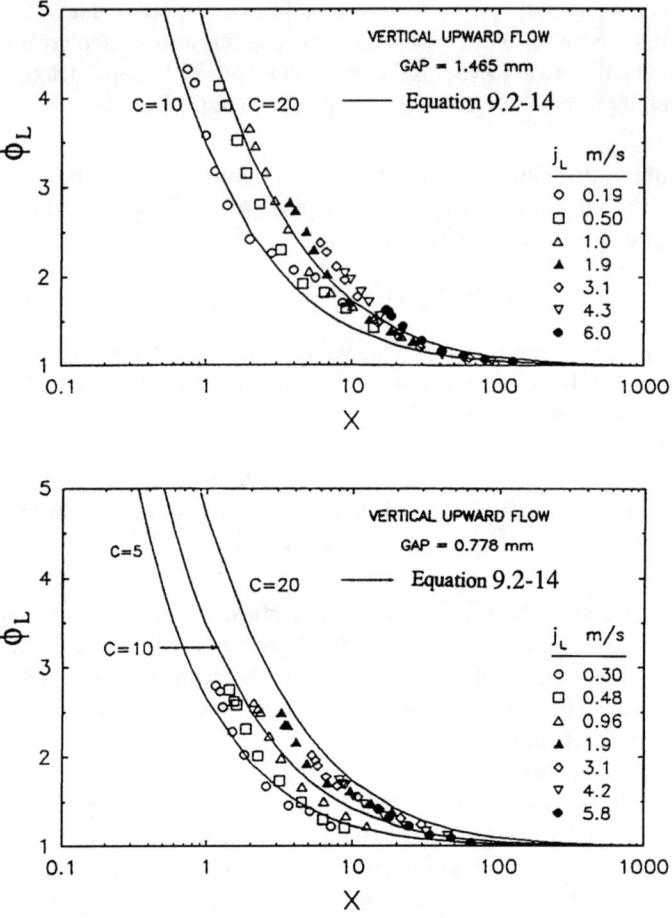

**Figure 27** Two-phase friction multiplier data for non-circular with $D_h < 10$ mm (from Ali et al., 1993, with permission).

**Prediction of friction pressure drop.** When there is a large effect of mass velocity on two-phase friction multiplier as in H-V flow, $\phi_L^2$ or $\phi_G^2$ can not be predicted by a correlation based on liquid and gas flow rate ratios, such as the Lockhart-Martinelli parameter. If the void fraction is known or can be predicted reasonably accurately, the friction pressure drop can be predicted using the mean void fraction as follows (Ali et al., 1993):

$$\Delta P_{F,TP}/\Delta z = f_{TP}\rho_L U_L^2/2D_h \qquad (9.2\text{-}15)$$

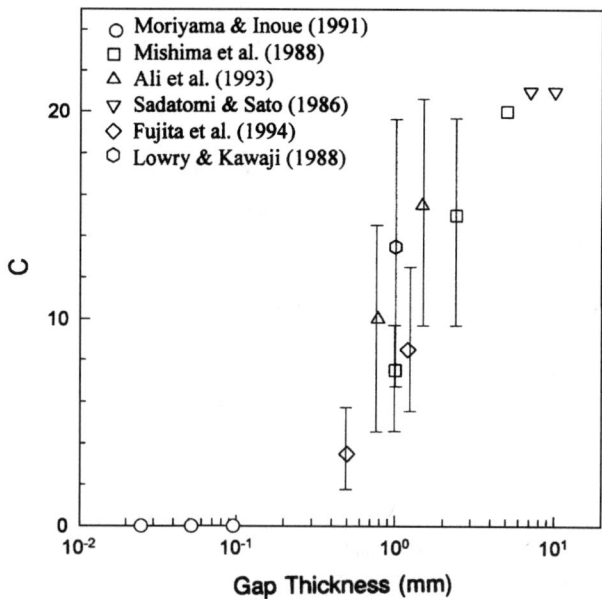

**Figure 28** Variation of C-value in the Chisholm and Laird (1958) correlation with gap thickness for Narrow Channels (from Kawaji and Ali, 1996, with permission).

where the liquid velocity, $U_L$, is dependent on the mean void fraction [i.e., $U_L = j_L/(1 - \epsilon)$], and two-phase friction factor, $f_{TP}$, is evaluated using the Blasius equation.

$$f_{TP} = C/\text{Re}_L^m \tag{9.2-16}$$

where

$$\text{Re}_L = \rho_L U_L D_h / \eta_L \tag{9.2-17}$$

The correlation by Beattie and Whalley (1982) given below is also recommended for predicting friction multiplier for all flow channel orientations.

$$\phi_{LO}^2 = [1 + x(\rho_L/\rho_G - 1)][(1 - \beta)(1 + 2.5\beta) + (\eta_G/\eta_L)\beta]^{0.25} \tag{9.2-18}$$

This friction multiplier is to be used with the single-phase friction pressure drop, $\Delta P_{LO}^F$, which assumes the entire two-phase mixture to flow as a liquid.

**Effect of fins.** The friction multiplier data available for various finned channels are similar to those of a smooth channel, and little effect of the fin shape and size has been observed. Although they show less satisfactory agreement with Chisholm and Laird's correlation, especially at low liquid flow rates, the friction multiplier values are bounded by Eq. (9.2-14) with C = 5 and C = 50, except for the H-V flow. For $X > 10$, the data are close to the C = 20 curve, and for $X < 10$, the data points lie between the curves with C-values of about 15 and 5. The channel orientation has a small effect at low liquid flow rates, ($j_L < 0.2$ m/s), and the friction multiplier, $\phi_L$, increased slightly in vertical upward (V-U) flow and decreased in horizontal flow between vertical plates (H-V).

# REFERENCES

Agrawal, S. S., Gregory, G. A., and Govier, G. W. 1973. An Analysis of Horizontal Stratified Two-Phase Flow in Pipes. *Canadian J. Chem. Eng.* 51:280–286.

Ali, M. I., Kawaji, M., and Sadatomi, M. 1993. Adiabatic Two-Phase Flow in Narrow Channels Between Two Flat Plates. *Can. J. Chem. Eng.* 71:657–666.

Baker, O. 1954. Simultaneous Flow of Oil and Gas. *Oil Gas J.* 53:185.

Banerjee, S., Rhodes, E., and Scott, D. S. 1969. Studies on Co-Current Gas-Liquid Flow in Helically Coiled Tubes, Part I: Flow Patterns Pressure Drop and Holdup. *Can. J. Chem. Eng.* 47:445–453.

Barnea, D. 1987. A Unified Model for Predicting Flow-Pattern Transitions for the Whole Range of Pipe Inclinations. *Int. J. Multiphase Flow* 13(1):1–12.

Barnea, D. and Taitel, Y. 1993. A Model for Slug Length Distribution in Gas-Liquid Slug Flow. *Int. J. Multiphase Flow*. 19:829–838.

Barnea, D., Luninsky, Y., and Taitel, Y. 1983. Flow Pattern in Horizontal and Vertical Two Phase Flow in Small Diameter Pipes. *Can. J. Chem. Eng.* 61:617–620.

Barnea, D., Shoham, O., and Taitel, Y. 1982. Flow Pattern Transition for Vertical Downward Two-Phase Flow. *Chem. Eng. Sci.* 37:741–744.

Barnea, D., Shoham, O., Taitel, Y., and Dukler, A. E. 1980. Flow Pattern Transition for Horizontal and Inclined Pipes: Experimental and Comparison with Theory. *Int. J. Multiphase Flow* 6:217–225.

Baroczy, C. J. 1965. A Systematic Correlation for Two-Phase Pressure Drop. *Chem. Eng. Prog. Symp. Ser.* 62:232–249.

Beattie, D. R. H. and Whalley, P. B. 1982. A Simple Two-Phase Frictional Pressure Drop Calculation Method. *Int. J. Multiphase Flow* 8:83–87.

Beggs, H. D. and Brill, J. P. 1973. A Study of Two-Phase Flow in Inclined Pipes. *J. Petroleum Technology Transactions* 255:607.

Beisheuvel, A. and Gorissen, W. C. M. 1989. Void Fraction Disturbances in a Uniform Bubbly Fluid. *Int. J. Multiphase Flow* 16:211–232.

Bendiksen, K. H., Malnes, D., and Nydal, O. J. 1996. On the Modeling of Slug Flow. *Chem. Eng. Comm.* 141–142:71–102.

Bennett, A. W., Hewitt, G. F., and Kearsey, H. A. 1965. Flow Visualization Studies of Boiling at High Pressure. *Proc. Inst. Mech. Eng.* 180(3C):1–11.

Bergles, A. E., Roos, J. P., and Bourne, J. G. 1968. Investigation of Boiling Flow Regimes and Critical Heat Flux. NYO-3304-13, Dynatech Corporation, Cambridge, Massachusetts.

Bouré, J. A. 1997. Wave Phenomena and One-Dimensional Two-Phase Flow Models. *Multiphase Science and Technology* 9:1–107.

Brauner, N. and Barnea, D. 1986. The Slug/Churn Transition in Upward Gas-Liquid Flow. *Chem. Eng. Sci.* 41:159–163.

Caetano, E. F., Shoham, O., and Brill, J. P. 1989a. Upward Vertical Two-Phase Flow Through an Annulus, Part I: Single Phase Friction Factor, Taylor Bubble Rise Velocity, and Flow Pattern Prediction. In: *Multiphase Flow—Proc. 4th Int. Conf.*, pp. 301–330. Cranfield, England: BHRA.

Caetano, E. F., Shoham, O., and Brill, J. P. 1989b. Upward Vertical Two-Phase Flow Through an Annulus, Part II: Modeling Bubble, Slug, and Annular Flow. In: *Multiphase Flow—Proc. 4th Int. Conf.*, pp. 331–362. Cranfield, England: BHRA.

Carey, V. P. 1993. Two-Phase Flow in Small-Scale Ribbed and Finned Passages for Compact Heat Evaporators and Condensers. *Nuclear Engineering and Design* 141:249–268.

Carey, V. P. and Mandrusiak, G. D. 1986. Annular Film-Flow Boiling of Liquids in a Partially Heated, Vertical Channel with Offset Strip Fins. *Int. J. Heat and Mass Transfer* 29(6):927–939.

Carey, V. P. and Schuh, W. E. 1985. Pressure Drop Characteristics of Horizontal Two-Phase Flow in Offset Strip Fin Geometries at Low Quality. ASME HTD-Vol. 44:25–33.

Chexal, B. and Lellouche, G. 1986. A Full-Range Drift Flux Correlation for Vertical Flows (Revision 1). *EPRI Report* NP-3989-SR.

Chisholm, D. 1967. A Theoretical Basis for the Lockhart-Martinelli Correlation for Two-Phase Flow. *Int. J. Heat Mass Transfer* 10:1767–1778.

Chisholm, D. 1973. Pressure Gradients Due to Friction During the Flow of Evaporating Two-Phase Mixtures in Smooth Tubes and Channels. *Int. J. Heat Mass Transfer* 16:347–348.

Chisholm, D. 1983. *Two-Phase Flow in Pipelines and Heat Exchanges*. Bath, UK: Pitman Press Limited.

Chisholm, D. and Laird, A. D. K. 1958. Two-Phase Flow in Rough Tubes. *Trans. ASME* 80(2):276–286.

Costigan, G. and Whalley, P. B. 1997. Slug Flow Regime Identification from Dynamic Void Fraction Measurements in Vertical Air-Water Flows. *Int. J. Multiphase Flow* 23:263–282.

Crawford, T. J., Weinberger, C. B., and Weismann, J. 1986. Two-Phase Flow Patterns and Void Fractions in Downward Flows. Part II: Void Fractions and Transient Flow Pattern. *Int. J. Multiphase Flow* 12:219–236.

Damianides, C. A. 1987. Horizontal Two-Phase Flow of Air-Water Mixtures in Small Diameter Tubes and Compact Heat Exchangers. Ph.D. Dissertation, Univ. of Illinois at Urbana-Champaign.

Delhaye, J.-M. 1981. Basic Equations for Two-Phase Flow Modelling. *Two-Phase Flow and Heat Transfer in the Power and Process Industries*, Chapter 2. Eds. A. E. Bergles, J. G. Collier, J.-M. Delhaye, G. F. Hewitt, and F. Mayinger. Washington, DC: Hemisphere Publishing Corporation.

Dix, G. E. 1971. Vapor Void Fractions for Forced Convection with Subcooled Boiling at Low Flow Rate. *General Electric Company Report* NEDO-10491.

Dukler, A. E. and Hubbard, M. G. 1975. A Model for Gas-Liquid Slug Flow in Horizontal and Near Horizontal Tubes. *Ind. Eng. Chem. Fundam.* 14:337–347.

Dukler, A. E. and Taitel, Y. 1986. Flow Pattern Transitions in Gas-liquid Systems: Measurement and Modeling. *Multiphase Science and Technology*, Volume 2. Ed. G. F. Hewitt, J. M. Delhaye, and N. Zuber, pp. 1–94. Washington, DC: Hemisphere Publishing Corporation.

Friedel, L. 1979. Improved Friction Pressure Drop Correlations for Horizontal and Vertical Two-Phase Pipe Flow. European Two-Phase Flow Group Meeting, Paper E2, Ispra, Italy.

Fujita, H., Ohara, T., Hirota, M., and Furuta, H. 1994. Two-Phase Flow in Narrow Flat Channels (Influences of Liquid Properties). *Proc. 31st National Heat Transfer Symposium of Japan* 1:142–144.

Fukano, T., Kariyasaki, A., and Kagawa, M. 1989. Flow Patterns and Pressure Drop in Isothermal Gas-Liquid Concurrent Flow in a Horizontal Capillary Tube. *ANS Proc. National Heat Trans. Conf.* 4:153–161.

Golan, L. P. and Stenning, A. H. 1969. Two-Phase Vertical Flow Maps. *Proc. Inst. Mech. Eng.* 184(3C):110–116.

Govan, A. H., Hewitt, G. F., Richter, H. J., and Scott, A. 1991. Flooding and Churn Flow in Vertical Pipes. *Int. J. Multiphase Flow* 17:27–44.

Hasan, A. R. and Kabir, C. S. 1992. Two-Phase Flow in Vertical and Inclined Annuli. *Int. J. Multiphase Flow* 18(2):279–293.

Hewitt, G. F. 1982. Flow Regimes. Pressure Drop. Void Fraction. *Handbook of Multiphase Systems* Sections 2.1–2.3. Ed. G. Hetsroni. New York: McGraw-Hill Book Company.

Hewitt, G. F. 1984. Two-Phase Flow Through Orifices, Valves, Bends, and Other Singularities. *Selected Topics in Two-Phase Flow*, Lecture Series No. 8, University of Trondheim, Norway, pp. 163–198.

Hewitt, G. F. 1997. Wisps in the Pipe: Annular Flow at High Mass Fluxes. *Proc. Fourth World Conference on Experimental Heat Transfer, Fluid Mechanics and Thermodynamics*, Brussels, June, 1997, Volume 1, pp. 3–14. Pisa: Edizioni ETS.

Hewitt, G. F. and Govan, A. H. 1990. Phenomena and Prediction in Annular Two-Phase Flow. *Advances in Gas-Liquid Flows*, 1990. Ed. J. H. Kim, U. S. Rohatgi, and A. Hashemi. ASME FED-Vol. 99, HTD-Vol. 155, pp. 41–56.

Hewitt, G. F. and Hall-Taylor, N. S. 1970. *Annular Two-Phase Flow*. Oxford: Pergamon Press.

Hewitt, G. F. and Jayanti, S. 1992. Prediction of Film Inversion in Two-Phase Flow in Coiled Tubes. *J. Fluid Mech.* 236:497–511.

Hewitt, G. F. and Jayanti, S. 1993. To Churn or Not to Churn. *Int. J. Multiphase Flow* 19:527–529.

Hewitt, G. F. and Roberts, D. N. 1969. Studies of Two-Phase Flow Patterns by Simultaneous X-Ray and Flash Photography. UK AEA Report AERE-M2159.

Hewitt, G. F., Martin, C. J., and Wilkes, N. S. 1985. Experimental and Modeling Studies of Annular Flow in the Region Between Flow Reversal and the Pressure Drop Minimum. *Physico-Chemical Hydrodynamics* 6:69–86.

Hewitt, G. F., Shires, G. L., and Bott T. R. 1994. *Process Heat Transfer*. Boca Raton, FL: CRC Press.

Iida, Y. and Takahashi, K. 1976. Gas-Liquid Two-Phase Flow Through Channels with Narrow Spaces. *Kagaku Kogaku Ronbunshu* 2:228–234.

Ishii, M. 1977. One-Dimensional Drift-Flux Model and Constitutive Equations for Relative Motion Between Phases in Various Two-Phase Flow Regimes. *ANL Report ANL-77-47*.

Jayanti, S. and Brauner, N. 1994. Churn Flow. *Multiphase Science and Technology*, Volume 8. Eds. G. F. Hewitt, J. H. Kim, R. T. Lahey, J.-M. Delhaye, and N. Zuber, pp. 471–522.

Jayanti, S. and Hewitt, G. F. 1992. Prediction of the Slug-to-Churn Flow Transition in Vertical Two-Phase Flow. *Int. J. Multiphase Flow* 18:847–860.

Jayanti, S., Wilkes, N. S., Clarke, T. S., and Hewitt, G. F. 1990. The Prediction of Turbulent Flows over Roughened Surfaces and Its Application to Interpretation of Mechanisms of Horizontal Annular Flow. *Proc. Roy. Soc.* A431:71–88.

Jepson, W. P. and Taylor, R. E. 1988. Slug Flow and Its Transitions in Large Diameter Horizontal Pipes. UKAEA Report AERE-R12992.

Jones, O. C. and Zuber, N. 1975. The Interrelation Between Void Fraction Fluctuations and Flow Patterns in Two-Phase Flow. *Int. J. Multiphase Flow* 2:273–306.

Jones, O. C. and Zuber, N. 1979. Slug-Annular Transition with Particular Reference to Narrow Rectangular Ducts. *Two-Phase Momentum, Heat and Mass Transfer in Chemical, Process and Energy Engineering Systems*, pp. 345–355. Washington, DC: Hemisphere Publishing Co.

Kawaji, M. and Ali, M. I. 1996. Adiabatic Two-Phase Flow in Narrow Channels Between Flat Plates. In: *Mixed-Flow Hydrodynamics, Advances in Engineering Fluid Mechanics*. Houston: Gulf Publishing Co., 1006.

Kelessidis, V. C. and Dukler, A. E. 1989. Modeling Flow Pattern Transition for Upward Gas-Liquid Flow in Vertical Concentric and Eccentric Annuli. *Int. J. Multiphase Flow* 15:173–191.

Khor, S. H., Mendes-Tatsis, M. A., and Hewitt, G. F. 1997. One-Dimensional Modeling of Phase Hold-Ups in Three-Phase Stratified Flow. *Int. J. Multiphase Flow* 23:885–897.

King, M. J. S. 1998. Experimental and Modeling Studies of Transient Slug Flow. Ph.D. Thesis, University of London, March 1998.

Lahey, R. T. and Moody, F. J. 1977. *The Thermal Hydraulics of a Boiling Water Nuclear Reactor*. American Nuclear Society.

Levy, S. 1966. Forced Convection Subcooled Boiling—Prediction of Vapor Volumetric Fraction. *General Electric Company Report* GEAP-5157.

Lin, P. Y. and Hanratty, T. J. 1986. Prediction of the Initiation of Slugs with Linear Stability Theory. *Int. J. Multiphase Flow* 12:79–98.

Lockhart, R. W. and Martinelli, R. C. 1949. Proposed Correlation of Data for Isothermal Two-Phase, Two-Component Flow in Pipes. *Chem. Eng. Prog.* 45:39–48.

Lowry, B. and Kawaji, M. 1988. Adiabatic Vertical Two-Phase Flow in Narrow Passages. *AIChE Symp. Series*, No. 263, Vol. 84:133–139.

Mandhane, J. M., Gregory, G. A., and Aziz, K. 1974. A Flow Pattern Map for Gas-Liquid Flow in Horizontal Pipes. *Int. J. Multiphase Flow* 1:537–533.

Manolis, I. G. 1995. High Pressure Gas-Liquid Slug Flow. Ph.D. Thesis, University of London, October 1995.

Mao, Z. S. and Dukler, A. E. 1993. The Myth of Churn Flow? *Int. J. Multiphase Flow* 19:377–383.

McAdams, W. H., Woods, W. K., and Heroman, L. C. 1942. Vaporization Inside Horizontal Tubes—II. Benzene-Oil Mixtures. *Trans. ASME.* 64:193.

McQuillan, K. W. and Whalley, P. B. 1985. Flow Patterns in Vertical Two-Phase Flow. *Int. J. Multiphase Flow* 11:161–175.

Mishima, K. and Ishii, M. 1984. Flow Regime Transition Criteria for Upward Two-Phase Flow in Vertical Tubes. *Int. J. Heat Mass Transfer* 27:723–737.

Mishima, K., Fujine, S., Yoneda, K., Yonebayashi, K., Kanda, K., and Nishihara, H. 1988. A Study of Air-Water Flow in a Narrow Rectangular Duct Using Image Processing Technique. *Proc. Japan-U.S. Seminar on Two-Phase Flow Dynamics*, pp. C.3-1–C.3-12.

Mishima, K., Hibiki, T., and Nishihara, H. 1991. Some Characteristics of Gas-Liquid Flow in Narrow Rectangular Ducts. *Proc. of Int. Conf. on Multiphase Flows*, Sept. 24–27, 1991, Tsukuba, Japan, Vol. 2, pp. 485–488.

Moriyama, K. and Inoue, A. 1991. Study on Two-Phase Flow in Very Narrow Channels. *Proc. 28th National Heat Transfer Symposium of Japan* 3:763–765.

Morooka, S., Iizuka, M., Mitsutake, T., Ishizuka, T., Kagawa, T., and Yoshimura, K. 1987. Experimental Study on Void Fraction in a 4 × 4 Rod Bundle. *Proc. 24th National Heat Transfer Symposium of Japan*, Matsuyama, May 27–29, 1987, pp. 458–460.

Mukherjee, H. and Brill, J. P. 1985. Empirical Equations to Predict Flow Patterns in Two-Phase Inclined Flow. *Int. J. Multiphase Flow* 11:299–315.

Nicklin, D. J. and Davidson, J. F. 1962. The Onset of Instability in Two-Phase Slug Flow. *Proc. Symp. Two-Phase Flow, Inst. Mech. Eng.*, UK, February 7, 1962, Paper No. 4.

Ohnuki, A., Akimoto, H., and Sudo, Y. 1995. Flow Pattern and Its Transition in Gas-Liquid Two-Phase Flow Along a Large Vertical Pipe. *Proc. 2nd International Conference on Multiphase Flow*, Kyoto, Japan, April 3–7 1995, pp. FT1/17–FT1/23.

Palen, J. W., Breber, G., and Taborek, J. 1979. Prediction of Flow Regimes in Horizontal Tube Side Condensation. *Heat Transfer Eng.* 1:47–57.

Premoli, A., Francesco, D., and Prina, A. 1971. A Dimensionless Correlation for Determining the Density of Two-Phase Mixtures. *Termotecnica* 25:17–26.

Radovcick, N. A. and Moissis, R. 1962. The Transition from Two-Phase Bubble Flow to Slug Flow. MIT Report 7-7673-22.

Reimann, J., John, H., and Seeger, W. 1981. Transition from Slug to Annular Flow in Horizontal Air-Water and Steam-Water Flow. *Kernforschungszentrum Karlsruhe Report* KfK3189, November 1981.

Roberts, D. N. 1997. Conservation Equations, Two-Phase. *International Encyclopedia of Heat & Mass Transfer*. Ed. G. F. Hewitt, G. L. Shires, and Y. V. Polehaev, pp. 223–230. Boca Raton, FL: CRC Press.

Rong, X. Y., Kawaji, M., and Burgers, J. G. 1993. Two-Phase Flow Characterization in Narrow Flow Channels with Round and Cross-Ribbed Fins. *AIChE Symp. Series*, No. 295, Vol. 89:236–243.

Rouhani, S. Z. 1969. Subcooled Void Fraction. *AB Atomenergi (Sweden) Report* AE-RTV841.

Sadatomi, M., Sato, Y. and Saruwatari, S. 1982. Two-Phase Flow in Vertical Noncircular Channels. *Int. J. Multiphase Flow* 8(6):641–655.

Saha, P. and Zuber, N. 1974. Point of Net Vapor Generation and Vapor Void Fraction in Subcooled Boiling. *Proc. 5th Int. Heat Transfer Conf., Tokyo* 4:175–179.

Sato, Y. and Sadatomi M. 1986. Two-Phase Flow in Vertical Noncircular Channels. *Encyclopedia of Fluid Mechanics*, Volume 3. Ed. Cheremisinoff, N. P., pp. 651–664. Houston: Gulf Publishing Co.

Shah, R. K. and London, A. L. 1978. *Laminar Flow Forced Convection in Ducts: A Sourcebook for Compact Heat Exchanger Analytical Data*. New York: Academic Press.

Spedding, P. L. and Spence, D. R. 1993. Flow Regimes in Two-Phase Gas-Liquid Flow. *Int. J. Multiphase Flow* 19:245–280.

Taitel, Y. and Dukler, A. E. 1976a. A Model for Predicting Flow Regime Transitions in Horizontal and Near Horizontal Gas-Liquid Flow. *AIChE J.* 22:47–55.

Taitel, Y. and Dukler, A. E. 1976b. A Theoretical Approach to the Lockhart-Martinelli Correlation for Stratified Flow. *Int. J. Multiphase Flow* 2:591–595.

Taitel, Y., Barnea, D., and Dukler, A. E. 1980. Modeling Flow Pattern Transitions for Steady Upward Gas-Liquid Flow in Vertical Tubes. *AIChE J.* 26(3):345–354.

Troniewski, L. and Ulbrich, R. 1984. Two-Phase Gas-Liquid Flow in Rectangular Channels. *Chem. Eng. Sci.* 39(4):751–765.

Venkateswararao, P., Semiat, R., and Dukler, A. E. 1982. Flow Pattern Transition for Gas-Liquid Flow in a Vertical Rod Bundle. *Int. J. Multiphase Flow* 8(5):509–524.

Wallis, G. B. 1969. *One-Dimensional Two-Phase Flow*. New York: McGraw-Hill.

Wambsganss, M. W., Jendrzejczyk, J. A., and France, D. M. 1991. Two-Phase Flow Patterns and Transitions in a Small, Horizontal, Rectangular Channel. *Int. J. Multiphase Flow* 17(3):327–342.

Wambsganss, M. W., Jendrzejczyk, J. A., and France, D. M. 1992a. Determination and Characteristics of the Transition to Two-Phase Slug Flow in Small Horizontal Channels. *Two-Phase Flow in Energy Exchange Systems*. Eds. M. S. Sohal and T.J. Rabas, pp. 63–71. ASME HTD-Vol. 220.

Wambsganss, M. W., Jendrzejczyk, J. A., and France, D. M. 1992b. Two-Phase Flow and Pressure Drop in Flow Passages of Compact Heat Exchangers. SAE Technical Paper Series, 920550.

Weisman, J. and Kang, S. Y. 1981. Flow Pattern Transitions in Vertical and Upwardly Inclined Lines. *Int. J. Multiphase Flow* 7:271–291.

Weisman, J., Duncan, D., Gibson, J., and Crawford, T. 1979. Effects of Liquid Properties and Pipe Diameter on Two-Phase Flow Patterns in Horizontal Lines. *Int. J. Multiphase Flow* 5:437–462.

Westwater, J. W. 1983. Boiling Heat Transfer in Compact and Finned Heat Exchangers. *Advances in Two-Phase Flow and Heat Transfer*, Volume 2. Eds. Kakaç, S. and Ishii, M., pp. 827–857. The Hague: Martinus Nijhoff.

Whalley, P. B. 1980. Private Communication.
Williams, C. L. and Peterson, Jr., A. C. 1978. Two Phase Flow Patterns with High Pressure Water in a Heated Four-Rod Bundle. *Nuclear Science and Engineering* 68:155–169.
Wilmarth, T. and Ishii, M. 1994. Two-Phase Flow Regimes in Narrow Rectangular Vertical and Horizontal Channels. *Int. J. Heat Mass Transfer* 37(12):1749–1758.
Xu, X. and Carey, V. P. 1987. Heat Transfer and Two-Phase Flow During Convective Boiling in a Partially-Heated Cross-Ribbed Channel. *Int. Heat Mass Transfer* 30:2385–2397.
Zuber, N. and Findlay, J. A. 1965. Average Volumetric Concentration in Two-Phase Flow Systems. *J. Heat Transfer* 87:453–468.

CHAPTER
# TEN

## TWO-PHASE FLOW INSTABILITIES

**Mamoru Ozawa**

*Kansai University, 3-3-35 Yamate-cho, Suita, Osaka 564-8680, Japan*

## 10.1 INTRODUCTION

In the design of boiling and/or condensing two-phase flow systems, the theoretical and/or empirical formulas related to thermal hydraulics are described in other chapters of this handbook. However, such formulas are mainly derived for static conditions. This chapter is devoted mainly to unanticipated dynamic behavior, i.e., flow instability problems, encountered even in systems that are well-designed on the basis of the steady state characteristics. Flow instabilities mean large-scale fluctuations of flow in the two-phase systems, which cause large-scale pressure fluctuations, departure from steady state and safe operation in the heat transfer process, and also the mechanical vibration of tubes. In this sense, the flow instabilities discussed in this chapter are in principle one-dimensional macroscopic phenomena, but are not localized in a rather narrow area of two-phase flow channel.

## 10.2 PROBLEM DESCRIPTION AND CLASSIFICATION

Consider a forced-flow boiling channel system having a volute-type water feed-pump and an evaporator tube. The steady-state characteristics of the pressure drop across the boiling channel are represented in Figure 1. Then the operation condition is given at a cross point, such as points $a$–$d$, of the two curves representing the external (pump), such as curves 1 and 2, and the internal (boiling channel),

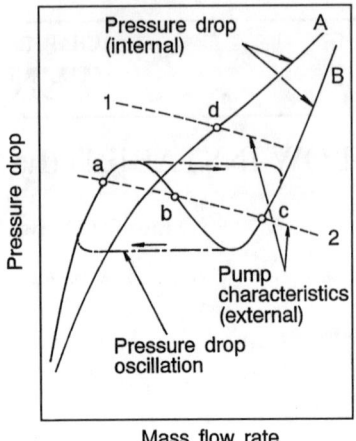

**Figure 1** Pressure drop and pump characteristics.

such as curves A and B, flow characteristics. When the initial condition is at point b, on the negative slope of the pressure drop vs. flow rate curve shown in Figure 1, the operation condition of point b seems to be a saddle point, which is easily transmitted to the other steady states, i.e., points a or c. The former may induce an unanticipated critical heat flux condition, and the latter may lead to a non-boiling single-phase liquid flow at the channel exit.

Such problems also occur in systems with negative slope of the pressure drop vs. flow rate curve and with an accumulation or compressible capacity, e.g., an accumulator or a surge tank, upstream of the boiling channel. Figure 2 demonstrates the flow oscillation with extremely large amplitude observed at point b, i.e., the

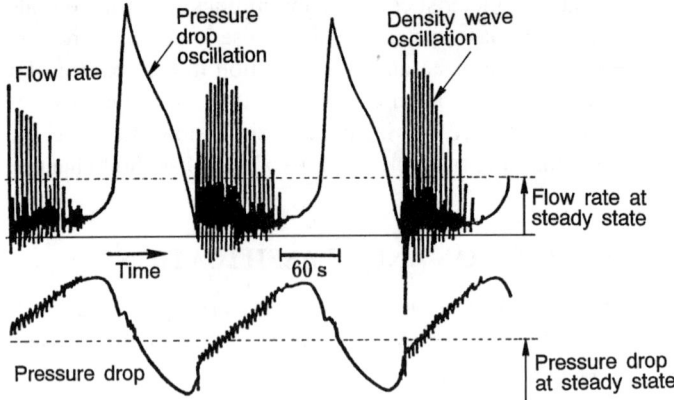

**Figure 2** Oscillation trace of flow instability.

time-averaged operation condition is located at point $b$. The transient state during this oscillation forms a limit cycle, shown by a dot-dash line in Figure 1. This oscillation is typically characterized by a relaxation process between the two quasi-steady states. Moreover, in the example shown in Figure 2, higher-mode oscillation appears temporally during the quasi-steady state of the positive slope of the pressure drop vs. flow rate curve, which seems to be a quite different instability mechanism superimposed on the basic mode oscillation. Such a large amplitude oscillation induces substantial reduction of the CHF to 40 to 50% of the steady state value. Summarizing these examples, the flow instability is defined as an unstable flow condition induced by the dynamic interaction between the internal and external systems and has various types or modes with different mechanisms.

The flow instabilities were first classified by Bouré et al. (1971). The classification is further revised and simplified as shown in Table 1. The first example described in this section is the Ledinegg instability in the first column in Table 1, and the second one is the pressure drop oscillation. The temporal higher-mode oscillation during the pressure drop oscillation (shown in Figure 2) is density wave oscillation, which is discussed later.

**Table 1  Classification of flow instabilities in boiling channel system**

| Category | Pattern | Mechanism | Feature |
| --- | --- | --- | --- |
| Negative resistance instability | Flow excursion or Ledinegg instability | Negative damping in 1st-order system | Transitional, significant flow maldistribution appears in parallel–channel system |
|  | Pressure drop oscillation | Dynamic interaction between flow excursion and accumulation mechanism of mass and momentum | Relaxation oscillation with large amplitude and long period |
| Time-delayed feedback instability | Density wave oscillation | Propagation delay of void wave (kinematic wave) and feedback effect provide negative damping | Oscillation, perod comparable with residence time, appears in positive resistance region of pressure drop vs. flow rate |
| Thermal non-equilibrium instability | Geysering Chugging | Insufficient nucleation sites bring about large superheat followed by violent boiling or condensation | Relaxation oscillation if liquid refilling mechanism exists |

The first class of instability is given by the negative resistance (slope) of the pressure drop vs. flow rate relationship. With reference to a mechanical vibration system, the first two types (the Ledinegg instability and the flow maldistribution in this class) are in principle expressed by a first-order differential equation, and the third type (pressure drop oscillation) by a second-order differential equation. The dynamic behavior in the whole channel system in this class can be expressed as a lumped-parameter system without taking into account the propagation delay of disturbance through the channel, which includes dynamic interaction between the internal and external systems, i.e., feedback effect. The negative resistance of the pressure drop vs. flow rate relationship in the internal system (boiling channel) directly brings about the negative damping factor in a second-order vibration system. Thus, the positive resistance may lead the system to a dynamically and statically stable condition.

On the other hand, when a certain amount of propagation delay exists in the density disturbance (i.e., void fraction disturbance, referred to as *void wave*, owing to the distributed-parameter effect), this propagation delay plays an important role in the stability of the system in relation to the feedback effect imposed by the pressure drop boundary condition. The system equation in this case, if expressed simply by the second-order vibration equation, has negative damping owing to such a feedback effect with time lag, even in case of the positive resistance. Thus, the second class is given by the time-delayed feedback between the pressure drop and the flow rate. This includes the density wave oscillation, which is often encountered in various boiling channel systems with pump, headers, or compressible capacity.

The last category is provided by heat transfer process, i.e., a violent boiling or condensation owing to the lack of sufficient nucleation sites and/or thermal nonequilibrium effect, which includes geysering and chugging.

The following sections discuss two typical flow instabilities, the pressure drop oscillation and the density wave oscillation, with relevance to boiler and/or steam power engineering.

## 10.3 BASIC MATHEMATICAL MODELING

### 10.3.1 Pressure Drop Oscillation

The simplified flow model is shown in Figure 3. The system has a single boiling channel with negative resistance and a large compressible capacity. The external characteristics, i.e., the compressible volume, provide an accumulation mechanism of mass as well as momentum or pressure. Neglecting the flow resistance or the fluid friction in the channel to the volume, the mass conservation equation and the momentum equation in integral form are expressed for the channel and

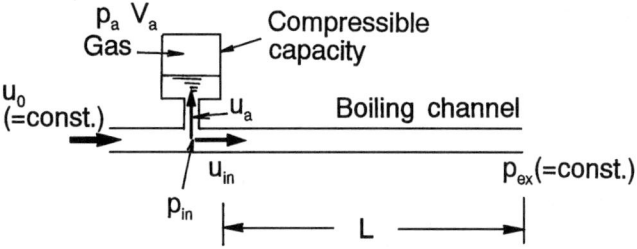

**Figure 3** Simplified model of boiling-channel system.

compressible capacity as follows:

$$u_0 \rho_l A_c = u_a A_c \rho_l + u_{in} A_c \rho_l \ (= \text{constant}) \quad (10.3\text{-}1)$$

$$p_{in} - p_{ex} = d/dt \int_0^L \rho u \, dz + \Delta p(u_{in}) \quad (10.3\text{-}2)$$

$$p_{in} - p_a = d/dt \int_0^{L_a} \rho_l u_a \, dz \quad (10.3\text{-}3)$$

The gas of the volume $V_a$ is assumed to undergo an isothermal state change, and then the inflow velocity $u_a$ into the volume is related to the pressure $p_a$ in the volume as

$$u_a = (V_a/A_c p_a) \, dp_a/dt = C_a dp_a/dt \quad (10.3\text{-}4)$$

Provided that the dynamic behavior, including that of pressure drop, is expressed as a lumped-parameter of inlet velocities $u_{in}$ and that the inertial mass in the channel leading to the compressible volume and in the boiling channel ($M_a$ and $M$, respectively) and the parameter $C_a$ are constant throughout the transients, the above equation system results in the following second-order differential equation:

$$(M + M_a) \, d^2(\delta u_{in})/dt^2 + [d(\Delta p)/du_{in}] \, d(\delta u_{in})/dt + (1/C_a)\delta u_{in} = 0 \quad (10.3\text{-}5)$$

where $\delta u_{in} = u_{in} - u_0$ and is the deviation from the steady-state value. When all the coefficients are positive constants—in reality, the first and third terms are always positive—then the system is statically and dynamically stable. On the other hand, when the second term is negative, which corresponds to the operation condition of $u_0$ located in the negative resistance region, then the system represents sustained oscillation with developing amplitude. Equation (10.3-5) is further developed to express non-linear behavior by assuming the relationship between the pressure drop and the inlet velocity to be a third-order polynomial (Ozawa et al., 1979) expressed by

$$d(\Delta p)/du_{in} = \xi (u_{in} - u_{max})(u_{in} - u_{min}) \quad (10.3\text{-}6)$$

Substituting Eq. (10.3-6) into Eq. (10.3-5) gives the normalized equation with dimensionless variables:

$$d^2y/d\tau^2 - \varsigma(1 - 2\beta y - y^2)\,dy/d\tau + y = 0 \qquad (10.3\text{-}7)$$

where

$$y = (u_{in} - u_0)/[(u_0 - u_{max})(u_{min} - u_0)]^{0.5}, \quad \tau = t/[C_a(M + M_a)]^{0.5},$$
$$\varsigma = [C_a/(M + M_a)]^{0.5}\xi(u_0 - u_{max})(u_{min} - u_0), \text{ and}$$
$$\beta = [u_0 - (u_{max} + u_{min})/2]/[(u_0 - u_{max})(u_{min} - u_0)]^{0.5}$$

The parameter $\xi$ is a positive constant, and $u_{max}$ and $u_{min}$ represent the velocities corresponding to maximum and minimum pressure drops, respectively, of the internal characteristics, e.g., curve B in Figure 1. Equation (10.3-7) is the well-known "van der Pol" equation, which represents limit cycle non-linear oscillation. The dimensionless oscillation period $\tau$ is approximately proportional to $\varsigma$, which leads to the relationship

$$T \propto [-d(\Delta p)/du_0]V_a/(A_c p_a) \qquad (10.3\text{-}8)$$

that is, the oscillation period $T$ is proportional to the compressible volume $V_a$, which has been well confirmed by experiments. Thus, the fundamental mechanism of the pressure drop oscillation is well interpreted by means of the van der Pol equation.

## 10.3.2 Density Wave Oscillation

The flow model of a boiling channel in a large number of parallel-channel system is illustrated in Figure 4a. The dynamic behavior of this boiling channel system is first simplified to that shown in Figure 4b, so as to deduce a simplified mathematical model in which the boiling channel is expressed as several lumped-parameter elements. Pressure drop $\Delta p_1$ in the subcooled region is expressed by the inlet restriction $K_{in}$. The restriction $K_{ex}$ at the channel exit provides the pressure drop $\Delta p_2$ in the boiling region, and an evaporator produces a two-phase mixture. The length $z_2$ in the boiling region is considered to be a riser of the length $z_{20}$. It provides the residence time, i.e., propagation delay of void wave, on the basis of experimental evidence that the oscillation period of density wave oscillation is twice the residence time or the same order.

The pressure drop in the subcooled region is expressed using the lumped-parameter model by

$$\Delta p_1 = M_1\,du_{in}/dt + K_{in}\,\rho_l\,u_{in}^2 \qquad (10.3\text{-}9)$$

where $M_1$ represents the inertial mass of the single-phase region and $u_{in}$ represents the inlet velocity. The pressure drop in the boiling region is expressed by

$$\Delta p_2 = K_{ex}\,\rho_{ex}\,u_{ex}^2 \qquad (10.3\text{-}10)$$

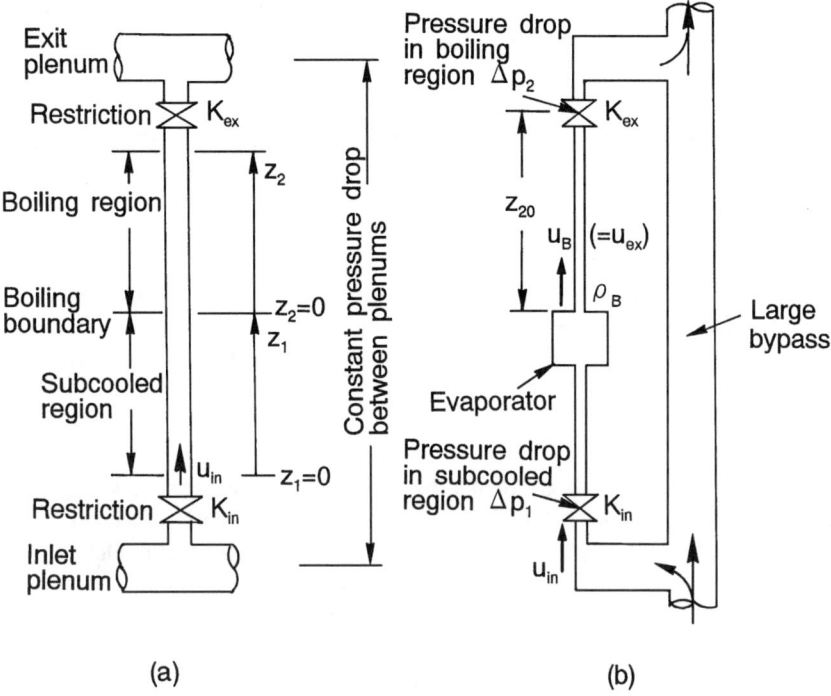

(a)　　　　　　　　　　　　(b)

**Figure 4** Flow model of density wave oscillation. (a) Distributed parameter model (b) Simplified lumped-parameter model.

where the inertial term in the boiling region is assumed to be negligible compared with the resistance term. The density $\rho_B$ of the outflow from the evaporator is expressed in terms of the outflow enthalpy $h_B$ on the basis of the homogeneous flow assumption,

$$1/\rho_B = 1/\rho_l + (h_B - h_l)/h_{lg}(1/\rho_g - 1/\rho_l) \qquad (10.3\text{-}11)$$

The mass continuity relationship, $\rho_l u_{in} = \rho_B u_B$, in the evaporator gives the outflow velocity $u_B$ of the two-phase mixture expressed by

$$u_B = u_{in}\{1 + (\rho_{lg}/h_{lg}\,\rho_g)(Q_B/A_c\,\rho_l\,u_{in} - \Delta h_{sub})\} \qquad (10.3\text{-}12)$$

where $Q_B$ is the heat input in the evaporator, and $\Delta h_{sub}$ is the subcooled enthalpy at the inlet. A small perturbation is introduced in variables to linearize the equation system. The density perturbation $\delta\rho_B$ from the evaporator propagates to the exit restriction through the riser section after the residence time $t_2$ ($=z_{20}/u_{B0}$); thus, $\delta\rho_{ex}$ is expressed using the delayed step function $U(t - t_2)$, i.e., $\delta\rho_{ex} = \delta\rho_B U(t - t_2)$. The velocity of the two-phase mixture is considered to be uniform in the riser, i.e., $\delta u_B = \delta u_{ex}$, and the constant pressure drop condition is imposed across the boiling channel by means of a large bypass,

$$\delta(\Delta p_1) + \delta(\Delta p_2) = 0 \qquad (10.3\text{-}13)$$

Then the dynamic behavior is expressed in the Laplace transformed form using the parameter $S$,

$$M_1 u_{in}^* S + 2\rho_l u_{in0}[K_{in} - K_{ex}(N_{sub} - 1)]u_{in}^* + \rho_l K_{ex} u_0 N_{pch} u_{in}^* \exp(-t_2 S) = 0 \qquad (10.3\text{-}14)$$

where the superscript $*$ represents the Laplace transformed variable, the subscript 0 represents the steady state value, and dimensionless parameters, the phase change number $N_{pch}$, and the subcooling number $N_{sub}$ are defined respectively as follows:

$$N_{pch} = \rho_{lg} Q_B / (A_c h_{lg} \rho_g \rho_l u_0), \quad N_{sub} = \rho_{lg} \Delta h_{sub} / (h_{lg} \rho_g)$$

The exponential term is approximated by applying the first-order Padé approximation: $\exp(-t_2 S) \approx 1/(1 + t_2 S)$. Then, finally, we have the next second-order equation to express the dynamic behavior of the present simplified model.

$$M_1 S^2 + \{M_1/t_2 + 2\rho_l u_0 [K_{in} - K_{ex}(N_{sub} - 1)]\}S + \{2[K_{in} - K_{ex}(N_{sub} - 1)] + K_{ex} N_{pch}\}\rho_l u_0 / t_2 = 0 \qquad (10.3\text{-}15)$$

This equation is equivalent to that of a mechanical system with a coiled spring and a damper. When the parameter of the second term is negative (negative damping), the perturbation develops with time and results in oscillatory instability. In the region $N_{sub} > 1$, an increase in $K_{ex}$ may lead to a negative value of the second term even in the case of a positive value of the third term, and an increase in $K_{in}$ may lead to a positive one. The restriction $K_{in}$ is a stabilizing factor, i.e., by increasing the inlet restriction, we can stabilize the flow, and $K_{ex}$ is a destabilizing factor. Moreover, it is easy to understand that the system expressed in Eq. (10.3-14) reduces to a first order system without oscillation in the case of the zero residence time. This emphasizes the critical importance of the propagation delay of void wave. In the following, a detailed analysis is presented on the basis of a distributed-parameter model of the boiling channel.

## 10.4 DENSITY WAVE OSCILLATION

### 10.4.1 Pressure Boundary Condition and Feedback System

The flow models in Figure 5 represent examples where density wave oscillation occurs. The first one ($a_1$) is a parallel-channel system with a large number of boiling channels; the second ($a_2$) has a large bypass slightly heated or unheated. These

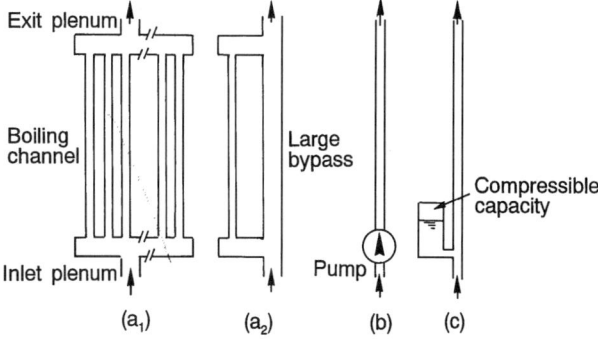

**Figure 5** Boiling channel system with various pressure drop boundary condition.

two systems are typical examples where the pressure drop across the channel is maintained constant even during the transient states. The natural circulation system gives the same situation as ($a_2$), and the downcomer makes the constant pressure drop condition. In case (b), the pressure drop fluctuation is fed back as flow rate fluctuation through the pump characteristics. The last model (c) has the compressible volume upstream of the boiling channel, as in the case of pressure drop oscillation.

In classical but fundamental analysis of density wave oscillation, transfer functions of the pressure drop against a flow perturbation at the inlet of the boiling channel are formulated so as to construct a feedback system, taking into account the pressure boundary conditions. When the transfer functions, defined in a frequency domain, of the pressure drop vs. inlet flow rate are expressed by $R_1(S)(=\Delta p_1^*/u_{in}^*)$ in the single phase subcooled region and $R_2(S)(=\Delta p_2^*/u_{in}^*)$ in the boiling region, the typical feedback systems are represented as shown in Figure 6, corresponding to each flow model in Figure 5, where $p_{dis}^*$ represents a small perturbation imposed on the system, $\Delta p_t^*$ the total pressure drop across the boiling channel, $C_p$ the pump characteristics, $\Delta p_t^* = C_p u_{in}^*$, and $C_a$ the constant in Eq. (10.4-1) corresponding to a capacitance.

## 10.4.2 Linear Stability Analysis of Density Wave Oscillation on the Basis of Distributed-Parameter Model

The analytical model is shown in Figure 4a. The flow is one-dimensional and uniformly heated in space and time. The heat capacity of the tube wall has, in fact, a certain influence on the stability boundary, but is ignored in the present discussion. The boiling channel is then divided into two parts, the subcooled liquid region and the boiling region. Both regions are dynamically connected through jump conditions.

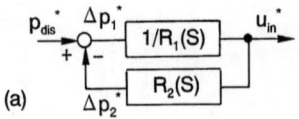

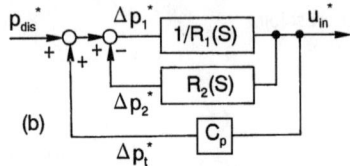

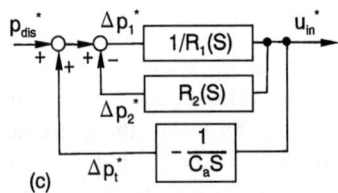

**Figure 6** Block diagram of boiling-channel system.

Mass and energy conservation equations are expressed, respectively, for the subcooled region by

$$\partial(\rho_l u_1)/\partial z = 0 \tag{10.4-1}$$

$$\partial(\rho_l h)/\partial t + \partial(\rho_l u_1 h)/\partial z = q_v \tag{10.4-2}$$

where $q_v$ is the volume heat flux and the subscript 1 represents the subcooled region. In the first term of Eq. (10.4-2), the internal energy has been replaced by the enthalpy because the mechanical work is negligible compared with the internal energy. Then these conservation equations, linearized by introducing small perturbations and then Laplace transformed, give the perturbations of the velocity and enthalpy at the subcooled region exit,

$$u_1^* = u_{in}^*, \quad h_1^* = -\{[1 - \exp(-t_1 S)]/S\} (q_v/\rho_l u_{10})u_{in}^* \tag{10.4-3}$$

where $t_1$ ($= z_{10}/u_{10}$) represents the residence time in the subcooled region.

The drift-flux model is applied to express two-phase flow in the boiling region, which includes the homogeneous flow model as a limiting case. Mass and energy conservation equations are listed as follows.

$$\partial/\partial t[\rho_l(1-\varepsilon) + \rho_g \varepsilon] + \partial/\partial z[\rho_l(1-\varepsilon)u_l + \rho_g u_g] = 0 \tag{10.4-4}$$

$$\partial/\partial t[\rho_l(1-\varepsilon)h_l + \rho_g \varepsilon h_g] + \partial/\partial z[\rho_l(1-\varepsilon)u_l h_l + \rho_g \varepsilon u_g h_g] = q_v \tag{10.4-5}$$

where $\varepsilon$ represents the void fraction, $u_l$ and $u_g$ are velocities of liquid and vapor phases, and internal energies have been approximated by enthalpies $h_l$ and $h_g$, as in the subcooled region. The volumetric flux and the vapor phase velocity are expressed by

$$J = (1-\varepsilon)u_l + \varepsilon u_g, \quad u_g = C_0 J + V_{gJ} \tag{10.4-6}$$

where $C_0$ is referred to as the distribution parameter, and $V_{gJ}$ represents the drift velocity. These conservation equations give the void propagation equations,

$$\partial \varepsilon/\partial t + \partial/\partial z(\varepsilon u_g) = q_0 \rho_l/\rho_{lg} \tag{10.4-7}$$

$$\partial/\partial t(1-\varepsilon) + \partial/\partial z[(1-\varepsilon)u_l] = -q_0 \rho_g/\rho_{lg} \tag{10.4-8}$$

where $q_0 = \rho_{lg} q_v/(\rho_l \rho_g h_{lg})$. The right hand term represents a source term due to the phase change. Eliminating this source term and integrating with respect to the coordinate $z$, we have the volumetric flux distribution,

$$J = J_{in} + q_0 z_2 \tag{10.4-9}$$

Small perturbations of the volumetric fluxes, phase velocities and void fraction are then introduced into Eqs. (10.4-6), (10.4-7), and (10.4-9), and Laplace transformed. Then we have

$$J^* = J_{in}^*, \quad u_g^* = C_0 J^*, \quad u_l^* = [J^*(1-C_0\varepsilon_0) + \varepsilon^*(u_{l0} - u_{g0})]/(1-\varepsilon_0) \tag{10.4-10}$$

$$(u_{g0}\varepsilon^*)S + d/dt_2[u_{g0}\varepsilon^*] = -C_0 J^*(d\varepsilon_0/dt_2) \tag{10.4-11}$$

where steady state distribution $u_{g0}$ and $\varepsilon_0$ and the residence time $t_2$ in the boiling region are expressed, respectively, by

$$u_{g0} = C_0 J_{in0} + V_{gJ} + C_0 q_0 z_2 = u_{gin0} + C_0 q_0 z_2,$$

$$\varepsilon_0 = [\rho_l/(C_0 \rho_{lg})][1 - \exp(-C_0 q_0 t_2)], \quad t_2 = [1/(C_0 q_0)]\log(u_{g0}/u_{gin0}) \tag{10.4-12}$$

Equation (10.4-11) is easily integrated to give the dynamics of the void fraction

$$u_{g0}\varepsilon^* = u_{gin0}\exp(-St_2)\varepsilon_{in}^* - (\rho_l C_0 q_0/\rho_{lg})[\exp(-C_0 q_0 t_2) - \exp(-St_2)]J_{in}^*/(S - C_0 q_0) \tag{10.4-13}$$

Similar manipulation is adopted to give the dynamics of the mass flux and quality,

$$m_t^* = [S\exp(-C_0 q_0 t_2) - C_0 q_0 \exp(-St_2)]\rho_l J_{in}^*/(S - C_0 q_0) - \exp(-St_2)u_{gin0}\rho_{lg}\varepsilon_{in}^* \tag{10.4-14}$$

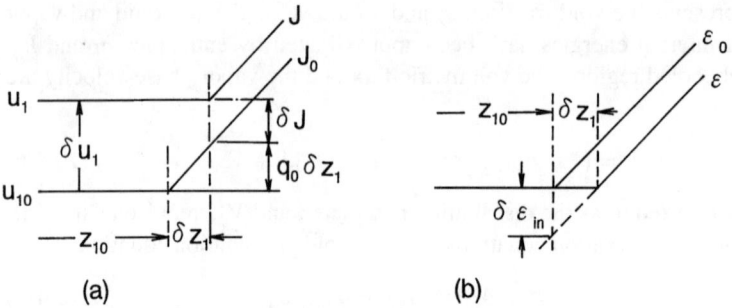

**Figure 7** Jump condition at boiling boundary.

$$x^* = (\rho_g \rho_l / \rho_{lg})[1 - \exp(-C_0 q_0 t_2)]J_{in}^* + \rho_g \{u_{g\,in0} \exp(-St_2)\varepsilon_{in}^*$$
$$- (\rho_l C_0 q_0 / \rho_{lg})[\exp(-C_0 q_0 t_2) - \exp(-St_2)]J_{in}^* / (S - C_0 q_0)\}$$
$$- [\rho_l \rho_g u_{g\,in0} / (\dot{m}_{t0} C_0 \rho_{lg})]\{\rho_l S[1 - \exp(-C_0 q_0 t_2)]J_{in}^* / (S - C_0 q_0)$$
$$- [\rho_{lg} u_{g\,in0} \varepsilon_{in}^* + \rho_l C_0 q_0 J_{in}^* / (S - C_0 q_0)][\exp(C_0 q_0 t_2 - St_2) - \exp(-St_2)]\}$$
$$(10.4\text{-}15)$$

The jump condition to relate the two reference regions at the boiling boundary is illustrated in Figure 7. The boiling boundary movement is expressed as a function of the enthalpy perturbation at the subcooled region exit, and those of velocity and void fraction are then deduced:

$$z_1^* = -(\rho_l u_{10}/q_v)h_1^*, \quad J_{in}^* = u_1^* - q_0 z_1^*, \quad \varepsilon_{in}^* = -\rho_l q_0/(\rho_{lg} u_{g\,in0}) z_1^* \quad (10.4\text{-}16)$$

Next, the momentum equation represents the pressure balance throughout the boiling channel system. The pressure drop in the boiling channel is then expressed by the sum of the gravitation, acceleration, and friction terms, including the flow restriction, e.g., for the subcooled region:

$$\Delta p_{gr1}^* = \rho_l g z_1^* \tag{10.4-17}$$

$$\Delta p_{a1}^* = St_1 \rho_l u_{10} u_{in}^* \tag{10.4-18}$$

$$\Delta p_{f1}^* = (\lambda/d)\rho_l u_{10} z_{10} u_{in}^* + (\lambda/2d)\rho_l (u_{10})^2 z_1^* \tag{10.4-19}$$

$$\Delta p_{Kin}^* = 2K_{in} \rho_l u_{10} u_{in}^* \tag{10.4-20}$$

In the boiling region, each pressure drop term is expressed by

$$\Delta p_{gr2}^* = -g\rho_{lg} \int_0^{t_2} \varepsilon^* u_{g0} dt_2 - g\rho_l z_1^* \tag{10.4-21}$$

$$\Delta p_{a2}^* = [\dot{m}_{l0} u_l^* + \dot{m}_l^* u_{l0} + \dot{m}_{g0} u_g^* + \dot{m}_g^* u_{g0}]_0^{z_2}$$
$$- z_1^* [d/dz(\dot{m}_{l0} u_{l0} + \dot{m}_{g0} u_{g0})]_{z=0} + S \int_0^{t_2} \dot{m}_t^* u_{g0} dt_2 \tag{10.4-22}$$

$$\Delta p_{f2}^* = -\lambda/(2d)\left(\Phi_0^2\right)(\dot{m}_{t0})^2 z_1^*/\rho_l + \lambda/(2d\rho_l)\int_0^{t_2}\left[(\dot{m}_{t0})^2(\Phi^2)^*\right.$$
$$\left. + 2\dot{m}_{t0}\left(\Phi_0^2\right)\dot{m}_t^*\right]u_{g0}dt_2 \tag{10.4-23}$$

$$\Delta p_{Kex}^* = K_{ex}(\dot{m}_{t0})^2\left(\Phi_{ex}^2\right)^*/\rho_l + 2K_{ex}\left(\Phi_{ex0}^2\right)\dot{m}_{t0}\dot{m}_t^*/\rho_l \tag{10.4-24}$$

where $\Phi^2$ represents the friction multiplier. When this multiplier is approximated by the quadratic equation of quality, the perturbation term is expressed by $(\Phi^2)^* = (a + 2bx_0)x^*$. Various transfer functions derived above give the transfer functions $R_1$ and $R_2$ of the pressure drops in respective two regions, and then the total pressure drop is expressed by

$$\Delta p_t^* = R_1 u_{in}^* + R_2 u_{in}^*$$
$$= (R_{gr1} + R_{a1} + R_{f1} + R_{Kin})u_{in}^* + (R_{gr2} + R_{a2} + R_{f2} + R_{Kex})u_{in}^* \tag{10.4-25}$$

In constructing such a block diagram, the transfer function $R_1$ in the subcooled region is generally set as the feed-forward element, and $R_2$ in the boiling region is set as the feedback element. The system stability is examined by drawing the trajectory of the open loop transfer function $R_2/R_1$ on the complex plane, which is well known as the "Nyquist method." An example of the stability map, i.e., the threshold condition of density wave oscillation, is shown on the inlet subcooling $\Delta T_{sub}$ vs. heat input plane in Figure 8. The experimentally-determined threshold conditions are indicated by the shaded region, and the predicted threshold conditions are represented by the dashed lines for various parameters of the drift-flux model.

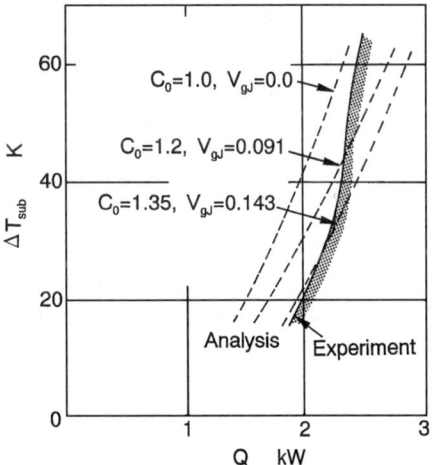

**Figure 8** Comparison between analytical and experimental results of threshold condition.

The curve for $C_0 = 1$, $V_{gJ} = 0$ corresponds to the homogeneous flow model, which under-predicts the threshold heat input.

### 10.4.3 Simplified Stability Criterion

Provided that only the frictional component dominates the dynamics of the boiling channel, a simplified stability criterion has been formulated on the basis of a distributed-parameter analysis and is listed in Table 2. The stability boundary by Ishii & Zuber (1970) is expressed by an equi-quality line on $N_{pch} - N_{sub}$ plane but substantially underpredicts in the low subcooling region. Saha (1974) pointed out this disagreement, which needs to be modified by taking into account the subcooled boiling. The model by Nakanishi et al. (1978) included a superheated vapor region additionally, but it has not been verified by experiments so far. The determination of the friction number has a significant influence on the validity of these models.

### 10.4.4 Representative Code and Analysis for Flow Stability

Some representative computer codes are listed in Table 3. The principal feature in linearized codes is the same as in the present analysis. The most fundamental analysis is given by LOOP code, while a practical application to steam generators is provided by DYNAM code. NUFREQ code was developed for the stability analysis of BWR, taking into account the nuclear feedback. The non-linear codes can simulate or trace limit cycle oscillations, where it is difficult to understand the mechanisms and/or scaling law of flow instabilities.

## 10.5 NON-LINEAR DYNAMICS AND CHAOS

The lumped-parameter model by Lahey et al. (1989,1992) gives qualitative understanding (to some extent) of density wave oscillation, when a small number of nodes is used. This method of analysis can provide numerical simulation of a variety of dynamic behaviors, including flow instability and CHF, by modifying the boundary or initial conditions suitable for respective problems. In this modeling, linear distributions are assumed for velocity, specific volume, and enthalpy along the designated subsections of the boiling channel. Then the conservation equations in the time-space domain can be integrated analytically in the corresponding regions, which results in a non-linear ordinary differential equation system. The most impressive feature deduced from this modeling and its numerical simulation is bifurcation diagrams and strange attractors (e.g., Lahey et al., 1989, 1992; Takenaka et al., 1991). It is however questionable whether the complex modeling gives sufficient understanding of non-linear dynamics of the density wave oscillation.

**Table 2** Simplified stability criterion for density wave oscillation

| Authors | Criterion | Validity System | Validity Condition | Remarks |
|---|---|---|---|---|
| Ishii & Zuber (1970) | $N_{pch} - N_{sub} = x_{eq}(\rho_{lg}/\rho_g)$ $\leq (2K_{in} + 2\Lambda_m + 2K_{ex})/ (1+\Lambda_m/2+K_{ex})$ | frictional pressure drop dominant, constant pressure drop between plenums | uniform heat flux, subcooled & boiling region | $\Lambda_m = 2\lambda_l$ is recommended. not valid for small $N_{sub}$, verified by experiments and extended by Saha(1974) to include subcooled boiling |
| Nakanishi et al. (1986) | $\rho_g N_{pch}/\rho_{lg} < (0.75 + 1.4 N_{sub}\rho_g/\rho_{lg})/ (1-1/\Lambda)$ | frictional pressure drop dominant, constant pressure drop between plenums | uniform heat flux, subcooled, boiling, & superheated vapor regions | $\Lambda$ is defined in subcooled region, applicable for $\Delta h_{sub}/h_{lg} > 0.2$ and $\rho_l/\rho_g > 30$, not verified by experiments |

subcooling number: $N_{sub} = \rho_{lg}\Delta h_{sub}/(h_{lg}\rho_g)$, phase change number: $N_{pch} = q_v L \rho_{lg}/(u_{in} h_{lg} \rho_g \rho_l)$, friction number: $\Lambda = \lambda L/(2d)$, $q_v$: volume heat flux, $\Delta h_{sub}$: subcooled enthalpy, $\lambda$: friction factor, $L$: heated length, and $d$: tube diameter.

**Table 3  Codes and analysis for flow stability**

| Code or Authors | Heat flux | Heater dynamics | Subcooled boiling | Two-phase model | Superheated region | Nuclear feedback |
|---|---|---|---|---|---|---|
| *Linearized and frequency domain* | | | | | | |
| LOOP code[1] (Davis & Potter, 1967) | uniform | not included | not considered | homogeneous model | included | not considered |
| NUFREQ code (Lahey & Yadigaloglu, 1974) | arbitrary in S.R., uniform in B.R. | considered in S.R. but not in B.R. | not considered | homogeneous model | not included | included |
| Saha (1974) | uniform | constant heat input | considered | drift-flux model | not included | not considered |
| Nakanishi et al.[2] (1978) | uniform | considered in S.R. but not in B.R. | not considered | drift-flux model, homogeneous if superheated region exist | included | not considered |
| STABLE (Jones, 1961) | arbitrary | considered | considered | slip flow model | not included | not considered |
| DYNAM code[3] (Efferding, 1968) | arbitrary | considered | considered | slip flow model | included | not considered |
| *Non-linear and time domain* | | | | | | |
| HYDNA code (Currin et al. 1961) | arbitrary | considered | considered | slip flow model | included | not considered |
| DEW code (Takitani & Sakano, 1979) | uniform or heat exchanger mode | considered | not considered | slip flow model | included | not considered |
| Lahey et al.[4] (1989, 1991[5], 1992) | constant in space but changable in time | considered or not considered | not considered | homogeneous model | not included | not considered or considered in BWR model |

1: Typical linearized stability analysis.
2: Detailed discussion is found in this handbook.
3: Applicable to SG in FBR, various extended versions exit.
4: Lumped-parameter analysis with several nodes, dynamics is expressed by ordinary differential equations, applied to discussion on non-linear dynamics, including chaos.
5: See Takenaka et al. (1991), which is based on Numerical Study on Non-Linear Two-Phase Flow Dynamics with Neutron Feedback and Fuel Heat Transfer in a Natural Circulation Loop and Parallel Channels, Internal Report of Dept. Nuclear Eng. & Eng. Physics, Rensselaer Polytechnic Institute, 1990.

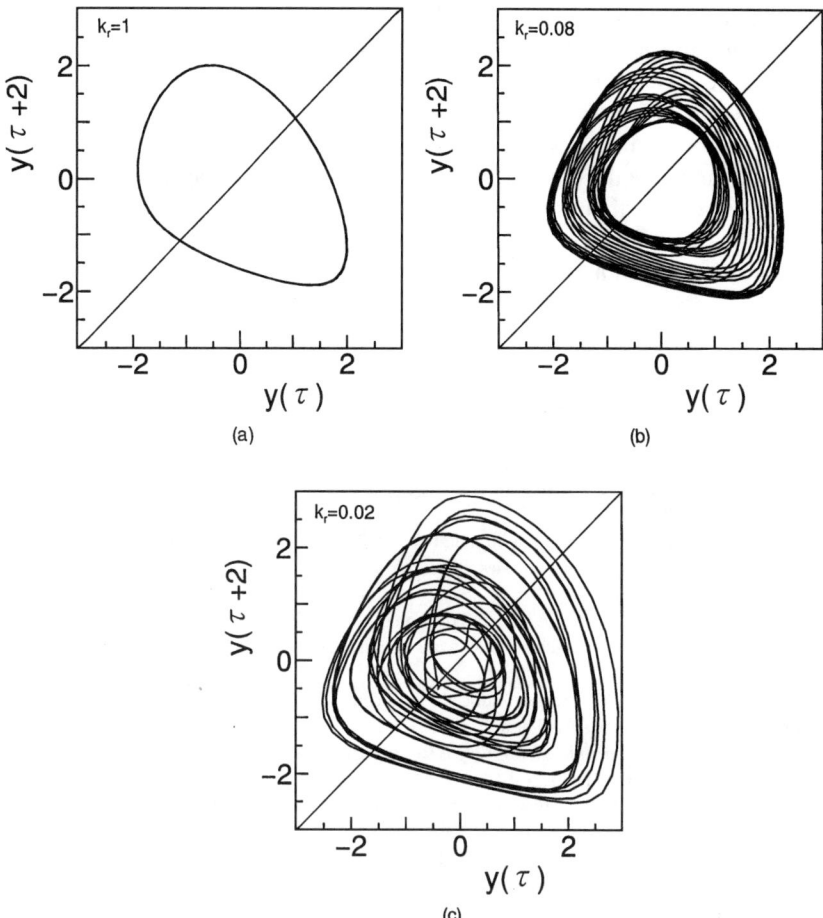

**Figure 9** Pseudo-phase plane trajectories of pressure drop oscillation (a) Steady limit cycle of pressure drop oscillation. (b) Torus. (c) Chaos.

Non-linear dynamics can be well understood, but only if the boiling channel or two-phase flow system is modeled as a limited-number of freedom system. For relevance to the readers, one of the examples is shown in Figure 9. This figure shows pseudo-phase plane trajectories obtained by the numerical simulation of the adiabatic two-phase flow system with two compressible volumes upstream of the channel of negative resistance (Ozawa & Umekawa, 1996). The parameters $y$ and $\tau$ represent the dimensionless velocity and time, respectively, similar to Eq. (10-7), while the equation system is slightly different from the equation, owing to the additional compressible volume. The dimensionless parameter $k_r$ represents the restriction to control the interaction between two compressible volumes and the two-phase channel. The large value of $k_r$ gives a simple limit cycle oscillation (a), i.e., the pressure drop oscillation, but the small value of $k_r$ realizes the torus (b) and then chaotic behavior (c). The qualitative tendency has been well verified by experiment, while the critical review on such a non-linear approach may give rise to a serious question as to what kind of physical model is reconstructed by means of the strange attractor and/or various dimensions of chaos. Further research is strongly encouraged in this new field of flow instability.

## REFERENCES

Bouré, J. A., Bergles, A. E., and Tong, L. S. 1971. Review of Two-Phase Flow Instability. ASME paper, 71-HT-42.

Currin, H. B., Hunin, C. M., Rivlin, L., and Tong, L. S. 1961. HYDNA-Digital Computer Program for Hydrodynamic Transients in a Pressure Tube Reactor or a Closed Channel Core. CVNA-77, Westinghouse Electric Co.

Davis, A. L. and Potter, R. 1967. Hydraulic Stability: An Analysis of the Causes of Unstable Flow in Parallel Channels. *Proc. Symp. on Two Phase Flow Dynamics*, Volume 2, Session 9, pp. 1225–1266. Eindhoven: Euratom.

Efferding, L. E. 1968. DYNAM, A Digital Computer Program for Study of the Dynamic Stability of Once-Through Boiling Flow with Steam Superheat. GAMD-8656, Gulf General Atomic.

Ishii, M. and Zuber, N. 1970. Thermally Induced Flow Instabilities in Two-Phase Mixtures. *Proc. 4th Int. Heat Transfer Conference*, Paris, Paper No. B5.11.

Jones, A. B. 1961. Hydrodynamic Stability of a Boiling Channel. KAPL-2170, KAPL-2208(1961), KAPL-2290(1963), KAPL-3070(1964).

Lahey, Jr., R. T., ed. 1992. Boiling Heat Transfer. Amsterdam: Elsevier Sci. Pub. B.v.

Lahey, Jr., R. T. and Yadigaroglu, G. 1973. NUFREQ, A Computer Program to Investigate Thermo-Hydrodynamic Stability. NEDO-13344, G.E.

Lahey, Jr., R. T., Clause, A., and DiMarco, P. 1989. Chaos and Non-Linear Dynamics of Density-Wave Instabilities in a Boiling Channel. *AIChE Symp. Ser.* 85-269:256–261.

Nakanishi, S., Ishigai, S., Ozaw, M., and Mizuta, Y. 1978. Analytical Investigation of Density Wave Oscillation. Osaka University Technology Report, 28-1421:243–251.

Nakanishi, S., Kaji, M., and Yamauchi, S. 1986. An Approximation Method for Construction of Stability Map of Density-Wave Oscillation. *Nuclear Eng. and Design* 95:55–64.

Ozawa, M. and Umekawa, H. 1996. Non-Linear Flow Oscillation in Two-Phase Flow System. *Proc. Japan-U.S. Seminar on Two-Phase Flow Dynamics*, Fukuoka, pp. 273–278.

Ozawa, M., Nakanishi, S., Ishigai, S., Mizuta, Y., and Tarui, H. 1979. Flow Instabilities in Boiling Channels, Part 1. Pressure Drop Oscillation. *Bulletin of the JSME*, 22-170:1113–1118.

Saha, P. 1974. Thermally Induced Two-Phase Flow Instabilities, Including the Effect of Thermal Non-Equilibrium Between the Phases. Ph.D. Thesis, Georgia Inst. Tech., Atlanta, GA.

Takenaka, N., Lahey, Jr., R. T., and Podowski, M. Z. 1991. The Analysis of Chaotic Density-Wave Oscillations. *Trans. ANS* 63:197–198.

Takitani, K. and Sakano, K. 1979. Density Wave Instability in Once-Through Boiling Flow System (III)-Distributed Parameter Model. *J. Nucl. Sci. & Tech.* 16:16–29.

CHAPTER
# ELEVEN

## CRITICAL TWO PHASE FLOW

### Hideki Nariai

*University of Tsukuba, Tsukuba, Ibaragi, Japan*

## 11.1 INTRODUCTION

When a vapor-liquid two phase mixture flows through a nozzle or a uniform cross section tube with the increase of the pressure difference between upstream and downstream of the nozzle, the flow rate is determined only by the upstream pressure, and it is not affected by the downstream pressure of the nozzle or the tube. The flow is named as the critical two phase flow, and the flow rate becomes maximum at the condition. Historically, the critical two phase flow has been an important factor in determining the discharge flow rate from the boiler vent valves. For the past thirty years, it has drawn considerable interest in the evaluation of the postulated Loss of Coolant Accident (LOCA) of water cooled nuclear reactors.

The critical flow condition is determined by the mass, momentum, and energy conservation equations of vapor-liquid two phase flow. The conservation equations and the constitutive equations have to be formulated as strictly as possible. However, since the two phase flow is, in general, of very complicated structure, simplified modeling is indispensable. For steady state two phase flow, the conservation law in differential equation form is written as n basic equations with n variables: $y_1, y_2, \ldots y_n$. etc.

$$\left.\begin{array}{l} a_{11}dy_1 + a_{12}dy_2 + \cdots\cdots + a_{1n}dy_n = b_1 \\ a_{21}dy_2 + a_{22}dy_2 + \cdots\cdots + a_{2n}dy_n = b_2 \\ \vdots \\ a_{n1}dy_n + a_{n2}dy_2 + \cdots\cdots + a_{nn}dy_n = b_n \end{array}\right\} \quad (11.1\text{-}1)$$

Here $a_{ij}$ (i, j = 1, 2, ... n) and $b_i$ (i = 1, 2, ... n) are the coefficients in each equation. In the system written in equation (11.1-1), the critical flow condition is determined as following two equations:

$$\begin{vmatrix} a_{11}, a_{12}, \cdots\cdots a_{1n} \\ a_{21}, a_{22}, \cdots\cdots a_{2n} \\ \vdots \\ a_{n1}, a_{n2}, \cdots\cdots a_{nn} \end{vmatrix} = 0 \quad (11.1\text{-}2)$$

and

$$\begin{vmatrix} b_1, a_{12}, \cdots\cdots a_{1n} \\ b_2, a_{22}, \cdots\cdots a_{2n} \\ \vdots \\ b_n, a_{n2}, \cdots\cdots a_{nn} \end{vmatrix} = 0 \quad (11.1\text{-}3)$$

Equation (11.1-2) gives the critical flow rate, and equation (11.1-3) gives the location of the critical flow occurrence in the flow passage. When the critical flow occurs at the exit of the flow passage, the critical flow condition is determined only by equation (11.1-2). This critical flow principle is applicable to the single phase flow, too. The principle was developed and applied to the vapor-liquid two phase flow by Ogasawara (1965), Katto (1968), Sudo and Katto (1975), and Boure (1977).

In two phase flow, when the slip between the liquid and the vapor, the thermal non-equilibrium state are well modeled, and basic equations are written in the form of Eq. (11.1-1), then the critical flow rate is derived by Eqs. (11.1-2) and (11.1-3). It is, however, very difficult to write the complicated flow in an accurate form of Eq. (11.1-1)—to overcome this difficulty, several simplified models have been proposed. We typically have two kinds of models: the *equilibrium critical flow model* for two phase equilibrium flow through the nozzle or the tube, and the *non-equilibrium critical flow model* for subcooled condition at the entrance of the tube or the nozzle followed by flashing in the tube or the nozzle. The equilibrium critical flow model assumes the thermal equilibrium state for both liquid and vapor phases; that means both phases have the same saturation temperature. On the other hand, the non-equilibrium critical flow model assumes the non-equilibrium state, such as the superheated liquid, at least for one phase.

Though the principle of two-phase critical flow has been made clear, the simplified methods have widely been used for the real applications. Typical of them will be presented in the following sections.

## 11.2 EQUILIBRIUM CRITICAL FLOW

### 11.2.1 Homogeneous Equilibrium Model

The vapor and the liquid are assumed to a be homogeneous mixture with equal velocities and temperatures. The mass velocity for the homogeneous mixture through the flow passage is given by the following equation.

$$\dot{m} = \frac{\{2[h_0 - (1-x)h_l - xh_g]\}^{1/2}}{\dfrac{1-x}{\rho_l} + \dfrac{x}{\rho_g}} \tag{11.2-1}$$

The quality $x$ is given by assuming isentropic flow from upstream reference location to the location of critical flow condition, which is at the smallest cross section of the nozzle or the tube exit of uniform cross section tube. The mass velocity at critical flow condition is derived by changing the downstream pressure until the mass velocity in equation (11.2-1) reaches a maximum value.

### 11.2.2 Slip Flow Model

The slip flow model assumes the different velocities for the liquid and the vapor, and the slip ratio $S$ is defined as the ratio of the vapor velocity to the liquid velocity. The mass velocity for slip flow is given as follows:

$$\dot{m} = \frac{\sqrt{2(h_0 - (1-x)h_l - xh_g)}}{\left[\dfrac{S(1-x)}{\rho_l} + \dfrac{x}{\rho_g}\right]^2 \left(x + \dfrac{1-x}{S^2}\right)} \tag{11.2-2}$$

Fauske (1962) gave the slip ratio at critical flow condition as Eq. (11.2-3), assuming the maximum pressure gradient at tube exit:

$$S = \left(\frac{\rho_l}{\rho_g}\right)^{1/2} \tag{11.2-3}$$

Moody (1965) gave the slip ratio at the critical flow condition, assuming the maximum kinetic energy as follows:

$$S = \left(\frac{\rho_l}{\rho_g}\right)^{1/3} \tag{11.2-4}$$

The quality x in Eq. (11.2-2) is determined by assuming isentropic flow. The maximum mass velocity is derived from Eq. (11.2-2) by decreasing the downstream pressure.

## 11.3 NON-EQUILIBRIUM CRITICAL FLOW

When the subcooled liquid enters into a nozzle or the uniform cross section tube, the liquid flows as superheated liquid at the entrance, and the flashing occurs during the flow in the nozzle or the tube. In this case, we have to consider the non-equilibrium effect in the model.

### 11.3.1 Zaloudek Model

When the subcooled liquid enters into a nozzle or a short tube, the flow is a single phase liquid flow at the entrance. The liquid flashes in the nozzle, and the two phase critical flow condition occurs at the nozzle exit. In this case, Zaloudek (1961) observed both upstream choke at the entrance and downstream choke at the exit. The mass velocity at upstream choking is given by the following equation, based on the superheated liquid flow at the entrance.

$$\dot{m} = C\sqrt{2\rho_l(P_o - P_{sat})} \qquad (11.3\text{-}1)$$

where C is an experimentally determined constant and has a value of about 0.6 for a sharp edged entrance.

### 11.3.2 Henry-Fauske Model

Henry and Fauske (1971) developed a critical flow model, taking into account the non-equilibrium effect in the flow in nozzles and short tubes. They assumed the retard of vaporization at small quality region and gave the relation between the true quality at non-equilibrium condition $x_a$ and the thermal equilibrium quality x as follows:

$$\frac{dx_a}{dP} = N\frac{dx}{dP} \qquad (11.3\text{-}2)$$

where N is the experimental parameter, given as follows:

$$N = \frac{x}{0.14} \quad \text{for } x \leq 0.14$$
$$N = 1.0 \quad \text{for } x > 0.14 \qquad (11.3\text{-}3)$$

Their assumption is that the change of actual quality with the decrease of pressure is very small at the small equilibrium quality region. When the quality x is larger than 0.14, the non-equilibrium effect disappears, and thermal equilibrium holds between liquid and vapor phases.

## 11.4 SUMMARY AND RECOMMENDATION

Moody (1975) showed that for the saturated liquid blowdown from a vessel, homogeneous equilibrium model was rather applicable at the entrance of the flow passage. The flow is accelerated to develop the vapor-liquid slip in the flow passage. At the tube exit, the slip model is applicable. For nozzles and short tubes, the Henry-Fauske non-equilibrium model generally holds.

For subcooled liquid discharge, the phenomena Zaloudek (1961) showed has to be taken into account. The upstream choking by superheated liquid flow and the downstream choking at tube exit has to be considered.

## REFERENCES

Boure, J. A. 1977. The Critical Flow Phenomenon with Reference to Two-Phase Flow and Nuclear Reactor Systems. *Thermal Hydraulic Aspects of Nuclear Reactor Safety*, Volume 1: Light Water Reactors. New York: ASME, pp.195–216.

Fauske, H. K. 1962. Contribution to the Theory of Two-Phase, One-Component Critical Flow. ANL-6633, ANL.

Henry, R. E. and Fauske, H. K. 1971. The Two-Phase Critical Flow of One-Component Mixtures in Nozzles, Orifices, and Short Tubes. Trans. ASME, Series C, *J. Heat Transfer* 93:179–187.

Katto, Y. 1968. Dynamics of Compressible Saturated Two-Phase Flow. *Trans. JSME* 34(260):731–742 (in Japanese).

Moody, F. J. 1965. Maximum Flow Rate of a Single-Component, Two-Phase Mixture. Trans ASME Series C. *J. Heat Transfer* 87(1):134–142.

Moody, F. J. 1975. Maximum Discharge Rate of Liquid-Vapor Mixtures from Vessels. *Non-Equilibrium Two-Phase Flows*. Eds. Lahey, R. T., Jr. and Wallis, G. B., pp.27–36. New York: ASME.

Ogasawaara, H. 1965. Theory of Two-Phase Critical Flow. *Trans. JSME* 31(225):751–768 (in Japanese).

Sudo, Y. and Katto, Y. 1975. Study on Compressible Two-Phase Critical Flow. *Trans. JSME* 41(342):624–655 (in Japanese).

Zaloudek, F. R. 1961. The Low Pressure Critical Discharge of Steam-Water Mixtures from Pipes. HW-68934 Rev.

CHAPTER
# TWELVE

## TWO-PHASE FLOW AND BOILING HEAT TRANSFER IN TUBE BUNDLES

**Ramin Dowlati**

*Owens-Corning Science and Technology Center, Granville, OH 43023-1200, USA*

**Masahiro Kawaji**

*University of Toronto, Toronto, Ontario M5S 3E5, Canada*

## 12.1 INTRODUCTION

A significant portion of all heat exchangers employed in the process and power industries are used to boil pure or liquid mixtures. Many of these heat exchangers involve boiling heat transfer, and hence two-phase (vapor-liquid) cross-flow on the shell-side of horizontal tube bundles. In the chemical and petroleum industries, such equipment is commonly referred to as 'reboilers,' or by the more general term, 'process vaporizers.' Ultimately, these reboilers add energy to distillation columns, remove energy in refrigeration cycles, or prepare charge for vapor-phase reactions. Kettle-type reboilers (Figure 1), for example, are commonly found at the base of distillation towers. Baffled heat exchangers, such as inverted U-tube steam generators commonly employed in nuclear power reactors, also experience two-phase cross-flow in the top U-bend region.

This chapter presents a summary of vertical upward two-phase cross-flow and boiling heat transfer data obtained to date on the shell-side of horizontal tube bundles. The focus will be on important physical parameters, such as void fraction (also known as vapor or liquid hold-up), two-phase frictional pressure drop, and boiling heat transfer coefficient. The first section will also review the status of two-phase flow regime maps for horizontal tube bundles. In the present chapter, the term "reboiler" will be used to refer to horizontal tube bundles subjected to two-phase cross-flow and shell-side boiling.

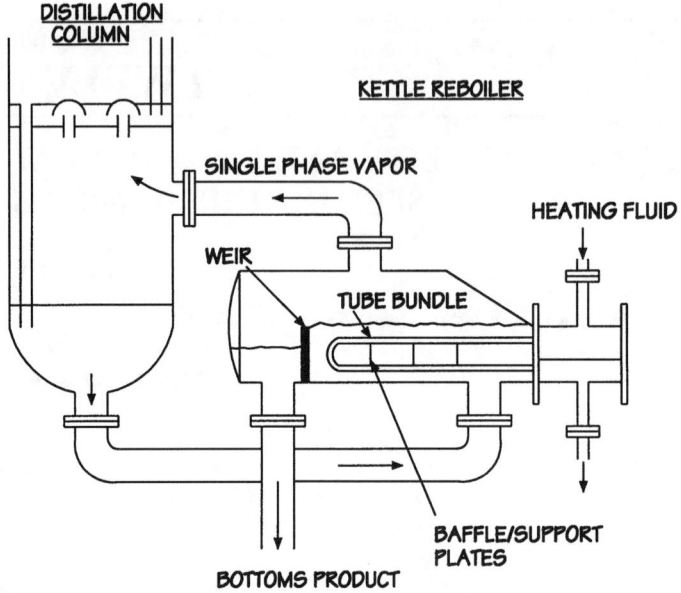

**Figure 1** Illustration of a kettle reboiler.

While the single-phase heat transfer correlations available for predicting thermal performance in tubular heat exchangers are typically accurate to within ±30%, the accuracy becomes worse for reboilers, as two-phase heat transfer is often very difficult to estimate, especially with mixtures of several components. Although the overall performance of reboilers has been extensively analyzed in the past, relatively few studies have been conducted to determine the local two-phase flow and boiling heat transfer conditions on the shell-side of a tube bundle. This is mainly due to the complex phenomena occurring in the reboiler under two-phase flow and the associated difficulty in gathering experimental data, even with sophisticated instrumentation.

As an example, the circulation pattern in a kettle reboiler is illustrated in Figure 2. At the bottom of the tube bundle, the subcooled liquid comes into contact with the hot outer surface of each tube, and as it flows past each row of tubes, more sensible heat is absorbed until the boiling point is reached and vaporization begins to occur. The two-phase (vapor-liquid) mixture continues to remove energy from the tube bundle in the form of latent heat, causing the flow or mass quality ($x$, defined as the ratio of the vapor mass flow rate to the total flow rate) to increase. Local conditions, such as liquid and vapor velocities and void fraction, are expected to vary throughout the bundle. As the two-phase mixture reaches the top of the tube bundle, the vapor phase is separated, and any remaining liquid phase is driven away from the tube bundle towards the shell wall. The difference between the

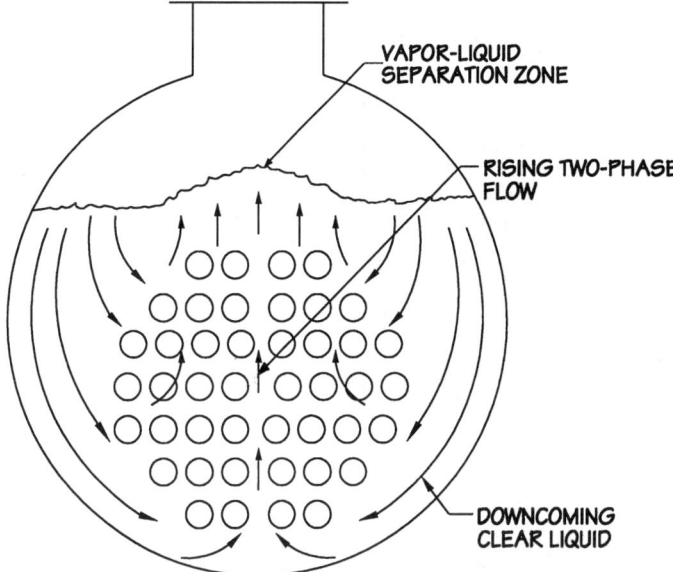

**Figure 2** Circulation patterns in a kettle reboiler.

two-phase mixture density in the core of the tube bundle and that of the liquid phase outside of the tube bundle creates the static head, which is the main driving force for recirculating the liquid phase.

According to a visual study by Cornwell et al. (1980) of a thin slice of a reboiler, the core of the bundle experiences nearly a vertical two-phase flow, and the void fraction is the highest near the top of the bundle (Figure 3). In the outer region of the bundle, a significant transverse flow from the sides of the bundle exists. With the presence of other physical effects, such as boundary layer separation and two-phase wake interactions, it is quite clear that such complex thermal-hydraulic behavior does not lend itself easily to instrumentation for the purpose of gathering experimental data and hence developing sound mechanistic models. Also, the bundle geometry is expected to have a significant effect on the flow characteristics.

Present design methods for reboilers are known to be very conservative (by as much as 300 percent), hence leading to over-design and additional capital costs (Bell, 1983; Grant et al., 1983; Niels, 1979; Schuller, 1982; Smith, 1985; Westwater, 1969). Nearly all studies on vertical cross-flow boiling in horizontal tube bundles to date have focused on the measurement and prediction of the heat transfer coefficient, and very few have directly addressed the two-phase hydrodynamics, which has an important effect on the overall heat transfer rate. From these studies, it is quite clear that the analysis of tube bundle performance must involve consideration of a strong interaction between heat transfer and the two-phase flow

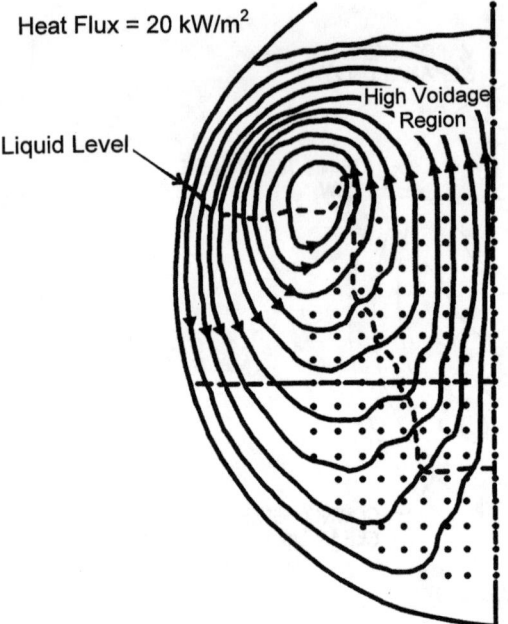

**Figure 3** Streamlines in kettle reboiler (from Leong and Cornwell, 1979, with permission).

parameters, such as void fraction, liquid and vapor velocities, two-phase pressure drop, as well as the flow regime. Many of the correlations developed to date to predict the heat transfer coefficient also require some knowledge of the two-phase flow parameters. Furthermore, knowledge of these parameters and two-phase flow regimes is an important factor in the prediction of critical heat flux (CHF) in a tube bundle in order to avoid dryout conditions that can severely degrade heat transfer.

The observation by Cornwell et al. (1980) of a nearly vertical crossflow (Figure 3) in the central region of a bundle suggested that the results from experiments in which a horizontal tube bundle, simulating the core of a reboiler, is subjected to forced vertical two-phase flow under controlled mass velocity and quality, could be used to develop heat transfer and pressure drop correlations for design purposes. Hence, many of the recent advances in the study of reboilers have been made based on experiments conducted in horizontal, rectangular tube bundles, simulating the core of a reboiler under controlled flow conditions.

Before proceeding further, it would be useful to explain some of the terminology associated with tube bundle geometry. Tube rows in a bundle are generally categorized as being *in-line* (aligned) or *staggered* in the direction of oncoming flow (Figure 4). The bundle geometry is further characterized by the outer tube diameter, $D$, and by the pitch-to-diameter (P/D) ratios defined with either the

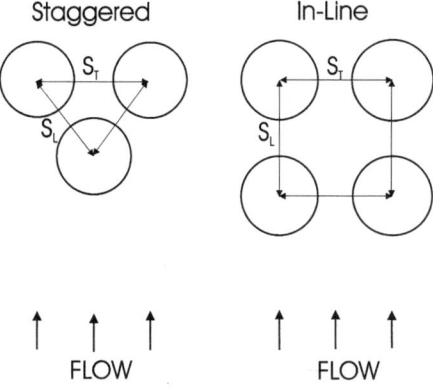

**Figure 4** Tube layout in bundles.

transverse pitch, $S_T$, or longitudinal pitch, $S_L$, measured between the tube centers. Typical P/D ratios used in industry vary between 1.25 and 2.5 (Rubin, 1984).

## 12.2 FLOW REGIMES

Several two-phase flow regime maps have been reported for upward air/water flow across horizontal tube bundles. Grant and Chisholm (1979) visually observed bubbly, intermittent, and spray (or annular-dispersed) flow regimes in a segmentally baffled model heat exchanger. The bundle had an equilateral triangular layout of 19 mm O.D. tubes with a P/D ratio of 1.25. Ulbrich and Mewes (1994) also visually detected the flow regimes in an in-line bundle consisting of 10 rows of 5 tubes with 20 mm O.D. and a P/D ratio of 1.5. They detected all the three flow regimes as reported by Grant and Chisholm for $j_L < 0.4$ m/s, but only bubbly and annular-dispersed flow regimes at $j_L > 0.4$ m/s.

Flow regimes have been studied in tube bundles using non-visual techniques as well. Hahne et al. (1990) used a fiber optics probe to measure local void fraction distributions in in-line and staggered tube bundles containing 18 finned tubes with P/D ratios of 1.3 and 1.15. The working fluid, R-11, was boiled in the heated tube bundle to create natural circulation driven two-phase cross flow. Probability density histograms of local void fractions and their higher moments were used to identify the flow regimes inside the bundles. Only bubbly flow regime was detected, and no slug or annular flow regimes were observed within the tube bundle. Although the flow conditions could not be determined under the pool boiling conditions, the detection of only the bubbly flow regime may have been due to the limitation in flow conditions or small gaps between the finned tubes, which could prevent formation of large vapor slugs. Ueno et al. (1995) employed double-sensor probes to measure the local void fraction and bubble velocities for vertical upward flow of

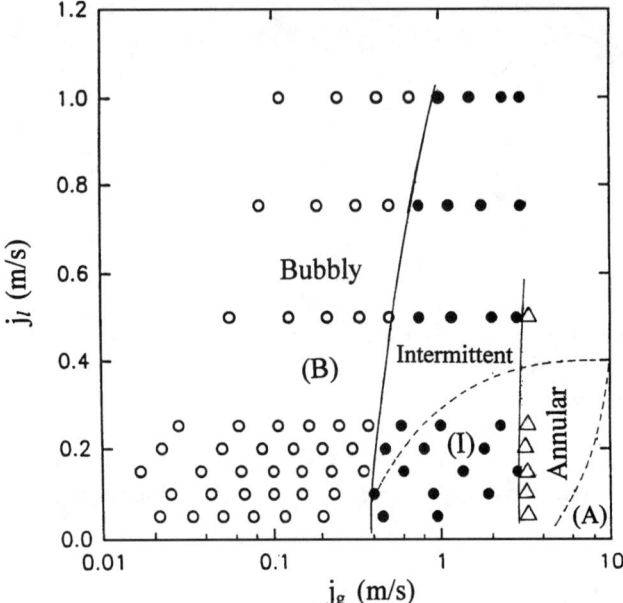

**Figure 5** Two-phase flow regime maps for in-line tube bundles (—Noghrehkar et al. (1995, 1999), P/D = 1.47; ---- Ulbrich and Mewes (1994), P/D = 1.5, (B) = bubbly flow, (I) = Intermittent flow, (A) = Annular-dispersed flow).

an air-water mixture across an in-line tube bundle containing 20 rows of two half rods with a P/D ratio of 1.42. Slug flow was identified by large bubbles, which had crowds of small bubbles in their tail, flowing mainly in the gap region. They also noted that gas slugs do not have a bullet shape, which is often observed in circular pipes.

Recently, Noghrehkar (1996) and Noghrehkar et al. (1995, 1999) have reported flow regime maps for both in-line and staggered bundles consisting of 24 and 26 rows, respectively, of five 12 mm O.D. rods per row arranged with a P/D ratio of 1.47. They analyzed the probability density function of void fraction fluctuations, which were measured with an electrical resistivity probe inserted deep into the bundle.

The flow regime maps of Noghrehkar et al. (1995, 1999) and Ulbrich & Mewes (1994) are shown in Figures 5 and 6 for in-line and staggered bundles, respectively. For the in-line bundle, the flow regime transition boundaries reported are consistent between the two maps at low liquid flow rates ($j_L < 0.2$ m/s). However, Noghrehkar et al. (1999) detected intermittent flow at higher liquid flow rates ($j_L > 0.4$ m/s), unlike the results of Ulbrich and Mewes (1994). The difference between the

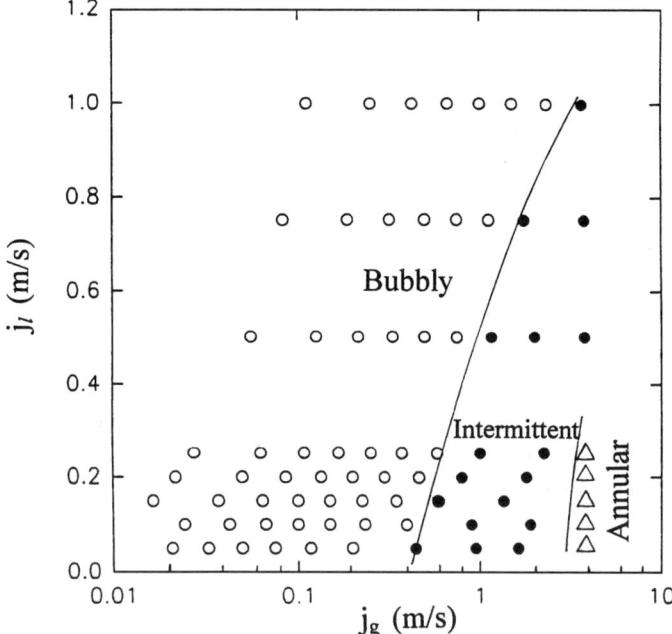

**Figure 6** Two-phase flow regime map of Noghrehkar et al. (1995, 1999) for a staggered tube bundle with P/D = 1.47.

two results is probably a result of the difference in the detection methods used. Noghrehkar et al. (1999) compared the void fluctuations near the vertical wall and well inside the bundle. They found that even though large fluctuations in void fraction (indicative of intermittent flow) were detected inside the bundle, the void fluctuation was suppressed near the vertical wall, indicating the existence of bubbly flow near the shell wall.

The flow regime boundaries for the staggered bundle tended to shift to higher gas velocities compared to those for the in-line bundle. For a given liquid flow rate, an intermittent flow regime did not occur until higher gas flow rates were reached than that in the in-line bundle. This is reasonable since the staggered rods can break up large gas bubbles more effectively and prevent formation of gas slugs until higher void fractions are reached.

## 12.3 VOID FRACTION

Accurate prediction of the void fraction or the volume fraction of gas, $\varepsilon$, is essential in understanding the two-phase flow phenomena. For example, $\varepsilon$ is needed to calculate the mixture density and hence the static head, which is the main driving force for liquid to recirculate in a reboiler shell. The void fraction term has also found use in several two-phase flow heat transfer correlations as well as two-phase flow-induced tube vibration models for reboilers.

In contrast with tube side flow, a rather scarce amount of information is available on void fraction for shell-side two-phase flow. Thus, in-tube void fraction correlations and models have been commonly used in tube bundle calculations. Nearly all in-tube void fraction models and correlations can be shown to take the following form (Butterworth, 1975):

$$\frac{1-\varepsilon}{\varepsilon} = A\left(\frac{1-x}{x}\right)^b \left(\frac{\rho_g}{\rho_l}\right)^c \left(\frac{\mu_l}{\mu_g}\right)^d \qquad (12.3\text{-}1)$$

where $A$, $b$, $c$, and $d$ are constants and take on different values in various correlations. One of the main limitations in the application of such a correlation in predicting the void fraction and liquid recirculation rate in a reboiler is the absence of the mass velocity effect on $\varepsilon$.

The void fraction can also be expressed in terms of another related parameter of interest, the slip velocity ratio, $K$. This ratio can be readily derived by linearly combining the continuity equations for both phases,

$$K = \frac{u_g}{u_l} = \left(\frac{1-\varepsilon}{\varepsilon}\right)\left(\frac{x}{1-x}\right)\left(\frac{\rho_l}{\rho_g}\right) \qquad (12.3\text{-}2)$$

The simplest case is the homogeneous flow model where $K = 1$, $A$, $b$, and $c$ are all equal to unity, and $d$ equals zero in Eq. (12.3-1). The main limitation of the homogeneous flow model is its assumption of equal vapor and liquid velocities.

Both the in-tube and homogeneous flow models have been widely employed in the prediction of shell-side circulation, frictional pressure drop, and heat transfer rates in reboiler and steam generator models (Brisbane et al., 1980; Carlucci et al., 1984; Fair and Klip, 1983; Payvar, 1985; Whalley and Butterworth, 1983). Other proprietary bundle void fraction correlations (Palen and Taborek, 1962; Palen and Yang, 1983) are believed to be modified in-tube correlations with empirically fitted constants. However, neither the in-tube nor homogeneous $\varepsilon$ models have been shown to predict reboiler data from independent studies.

Kondo and Nakajima (1980) made one of the first measurements of $\varepsilon$ in air-water cross-flow in staggered tube bundles with various P/D ratios and very low mass velocities (m < 5 kg/m²s) using quick-closing plate valves. They reported some dependence of $\varepsilon$ on superficial gas velocity but not on liquid velocity, due to the very small range of mass velocity tested. Their data also revealed that after about 11 rows of tubes, entrance effects on the $\varepsilon$ data disappeared.

**Table 1 Bundle geometry and test conditions used by Dowlati et al., (1990, 1992b, 1996)**

| Tube bundle layout | P/D ratio | Bundle size (column × row) | Fluids | Mass flux (kg/m²s) | Quality |
|---|---|---|---|---|---|
| In-line* | 1.3 | 5 × 20 | Air-Water | 27–818 | 0–0.33 |
| In-line* | 1.75 | 5 × 20 | Air-Water | 90–542 | 0–0.08 |
| Staggered** | 1.3 | 5 × 20 | Air-Water | 92–795 | 0–0.15 |
| Staggered** | 1.75 | 5 × 20 | Air-Water | 56–538 | 0–0.13 |
| In-line | $S_T = 1.75$ $S_L = 1.33$ | 5 × 20 | Air-Water | 58–542 | 0–0.2 |
| In-line | $S_T = 1.75$ $S_L = 2.17$ | 5 × 20 | Air-Water | 70–542 | 0–0.15 |
| In-line* | 1.3 | 5 × 20 | R-113 | 50–790 | 0–0.50 |

\* Square bundle ($S_T = S_L$).
\*\* Equilateral Triangle ($S_T = S_L$).

Schrage et al. (1987, 1988) also performed air-water measurements in an in-line 4 × 27 tube bundle (P/D = 1.3) using quick-closing plate valves. Their results indicated a strong over-prediction of the void fraction data by the homogeneous flow model as well as a strong mass velocity effect on void fraction. For $\varepsilon/\varepsilon_H \geq 0.1$, Schrage et al. proposed a correlation in terms of a Froude number,

$$\frac{\varepsilon}{\varepsilon_H} = 1 + 0.123 Fr^{-0.191} \ln x \qquad (12.3\text{-}3)$$

Dowlati (1992) and Dowlati et al. (1990, 1992b, 1996) reported void fraction data obtained in various tube bundles under air-water two-phase cross-flow and actual flow boiling conditions using R-113. In both air-water (adiabatic) and R-113 (diabatic) experiments, measurements were performed using gamma-densitometry, where the varying attenuation of a gamma ray beam across the two-phase mixture was used to determine the average void fraction in the bundle. Table 1 lists the bundle geometry and test conditions used by Dowlati et al. Typical void fraction data from their air-water experiments are shown in Figure 7. Strong over-prediction of the data by the homogenous flow model is clearly evident, as well as a strong mass velocity effect. Similar results were obtained for all tube bundles tested, including the R-113 boiling tests. The strong mass velocity effect was also evident when the $\varepsilon$ data were plotted against the Lockhart-Martinelli parameter, commonly used to correlate in-tube void fraction data and defined as the friction pressure drop ratio between single-phase liquid and gas, when each phase is assumed to flow alone in the channel. Hence, neither the in-tube nor homogeneous flow model can be recommended for predicting void fraction in a tube bundle.

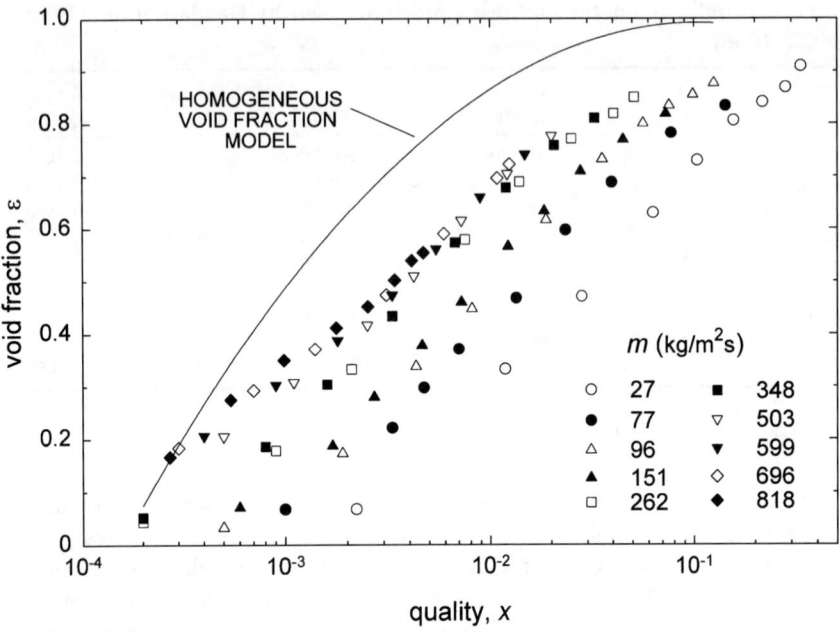

**Figure 7** Tube bundle void fraction data for air-water and R-113 (Dowlati et al., 1990, 1992b, 1996, with permission).

Dowlati et al. (1990, 1992b) recommended a new void fraction correlation,

$$\varepsilon = 1 - \frac{1}{\sqrt{1 + C_1 j_g^* + C_2 j_g^{*2}}} \quad (12.3\text{-}4)$$

in terms of the dimensionless gas velocity, $j_g^*$ (Wallis, 1969),

$$j_g^* = \frac{\rho_g^{1/2} j_g}{\sqrt{gD(\rho_l - \rho_g)}} \quad (12.3\text{-}5)$$

where the superficial gas velocity, $j_g$, is defined in terms of the minimum flow area and the rod diameter, D. Void fraction data from all six adiabatic tube bundle tests are plotted in Figure 8 in terms of $j_g^*$. The mass velocity effect is nearly eliminated, and all data are predicted with an absolute average deviation of 10.3 percent with Eq. (12.3-4) and constants $C_1$ and $C_2$ set equal to 35 and 50, respectively. There was little effect of P/D ratio on void fraction for the in-line tube bundles; however, the higher P/D ratio in staggered tube bundles resulted in about a 10 percent increase in void fraction. Also, the staggered tube layout resulted in about a 10–15 percent increases in void fraction, compared to the in-line geometry with similar P/D

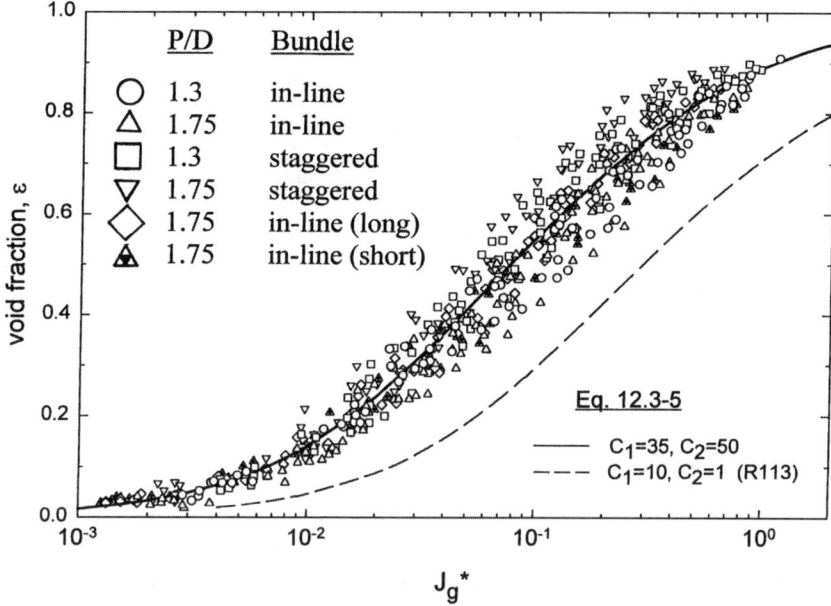

**Figure 8** Correlation of tube bundle void fraction data using equation 12.3-4 (Dowlati et al., 1990, 1992b, 1996, with permission).

ratios. The staggered tube layout is believed to enhance the mixing of the two phases and hence lead to higher void fraction.

Similarly, Eq. (12.3-4) was found to be successful in accounting for mass velocity effects in the void fraction data from R-113 boiling experiments. The constants $C_1$ and $C_2$ in Eq. (12.3-4), however, were set equal to 10 and 1, respectively, for an absolute average deviation of 15 percent, as shown by the dashed line in Figure 8. This curve clearly falls below that found to best fit the air-water data. Although the nature of the constants in Eq. (12.3-4) is not yet clear, the difference observed between the air-water and R-113 curves suggests that the constants may be property-dependent. Aside from differences in surface tension and average bubble size, the main difference between the two fluid systems was in the phase density ratio, $\rho_g/\rho_l$. In the experiments by Dowlati et al. (1996), the R-113 system had a phase density ratio nearly four times that of air-water. In other words, for a given value of $j_g^*$, higher phase density ratio results in lower void fraction, which has also been observed in high pressure steam-water flows in pipes by Martinelli and Nelson (1948). The two curves in Figure 8 cover a wide range of mass velocities, quality, and phase density ratio. It is believed that these two cases can be used to interpolate the void fraction for other vapor-liquid systems with intermediate phase density ratios.

Local void fraction measurements have also been made in tube bundles. Hahne et al. (1990) used a fiber optics probe to measure local void fraction in an in-line and staggered tube bundle. They found strong variations in the void fraction profile, with local maxima observed between the tubes and minima behind the tubes. Similar void fraction variations were found by Lian et al. (1992) and Ueno et al. (1995) in air-water upward flow across in-line tube bundles.

### 12.3.1 Drift Flux Model

Another void fraction model of both practical and analytical importance is the drift flux model. Although this model was derived for general two-phase flow and has been successfully used to predict void fraction in tube flow, it has only recently been applied to tube bundles.

The general expression for the weighted mean vapor velocity based on the drift flux model (Zuber and Findlay, 1965) is given by

$$\bar{u}_g = C_o \langle j \rangle + \bar{V}_{gj} \tag{12.3-6}$$

where the mixture mean velocity, $\langle j \rangle$, is based on the total volumetric flow rate and the minimum flow area. This expression takes into account the effect of non-uniform velocity and void profiles by use of the distribution parameter, $C_o$, and the effect of local relative velocity between the phases due to slip by the drift velocity, $\bar{V}_{gj}$. The weighted mean vapor velocity is related to the void fraction using the area-averaged superficial vapor velocity,

$$\bar{u}_g = \frac{\bar{j}_g}{\varepsilon} \tag{12.3-7}$$

Dowlati et al. (1992a) applied the drift flux model to their air-water and R-113 tube bundle void fraction data. For air-water data from six different tube bundle geometries, the following best fit curve was obtained:

$$\bar{u}_g = 1.104 \langle j \rangle + 0.33 \tag{12.3-8}$$

with an average deviation of 11.1%; for R-113 data,

$$\bar{u}_g = 1.076 \langle j \rangle + 0.85 \tag{12.3-9}$$

with an average deviation of 12%. Here, both the average gas velocity and mixture mean velocity are specified in m/s. The values determined for $C_o$ are close to unity and indicate a fairly uniform void fraction profile across the tube bundle. Higher drift velocity for R-113 indicates significantly greater slip in that system compared to air-water.

Equations have been recommended for predicting $C_o$ and $\bar{V}_{gj}$ in tube flows (Ishii, 1977; Zuber and Findlay, 1965), but they have not been successful in predicting the best-fit values given in Eqs. (12.3-8) and (12.3-9). The drift flux model certainly holds promise in predicting void fraction in tube bundles; however, at the present time, the two parameters discussed here need to be empirically determined.

## 12.4 TWO-PHASE FRICTIONAL PRESSURE DROP

One of the most important variables in the successful design of reboilers and condensers is the shell-side two-phase flow pressure drop. Reliable prediction of the pressure drop is needed in determining pumping requirements, fluid temperature and pressure profiles, allowable pressure drop for a given design, and other design and operating factors.

As in other two-phase flow systems, the overall pressure drop is given by a sum of the gravitational, frictional, and acceleration pressure drop components,

$$\Delta P_{2\phi,total} = \Delta P_{2\phi,grav} + \Delta P_{2\phi,fric} + \Delta P_{2\phi,acc} \qquad (12.4\text{-}1)$$

For steady state shell-side flows, the friction pressure drop, $\Delta P_{2\phi,fric}$, is considered to be the dominant component in the overall pressure drop for most flow regimes. Due to considerable difficulties in theoretical analyses of two-phase flow across tube bundles, prediction methods for $\Delta P_{2\phi,fric}$ have been necessarily empirical. However, these correlations, developed for different flow orientations across tube banks, have been shown by Ishihara et al. (1979) to have very limited application beyond the original data from which they were developed.

The friction pressure drop, $\Delta P_{2\phi,fric}$, must be obtained by subtracting from the total measured pressure drop both the gravitational and acceleration components, which requires accurate knowledge of the void fraction. The lack of reliable void fraction models has indirectly resulted in very scarce reliable frictional pressure drop data. The separated flow model, initially developed in the late 1940s by Lockhart and Martinelli (1949) and Martinelli and Nelson (1948) for two-phase flow in tubes, still represents the most reliable model for tube bundle applications. The assumptions of the separated flow model are discussed in Chapter 9.

Martinelli and co-workers defined the two-phase friction multiplier, $\phi_l^2$, as the ratio of two-phase friction pressure drop, $\Delta P_{2\phi,fric}$, to single-phase friction pressure drop that would be obtained if the liquid phase were flowing alone,

$$\phi_l^2 = \frac{\Delta P_{2\phi,fric}}{\Delta P_{l,fric}} \qquad (12.4\text{-}2)$$

The friction multiplier can be alternatively expressed as $\phi_g^2$ if the vapor phase pressure drop is used assuming the vapor phase to be flowing alone.

Martinelli found that $\phi_l^2$ could be correlated in terms of the Lockhart-Martinelli parameter, which is given by the following expression for turbulent flow regimes in both liquid and vapor phases:

$$X_{tt}^2 = \left(\frac{1-x}{x}\right)^{2-m} \left(\frac{\rho_g}{\rho_l}\right) \left(\frac{\mu_l}{\mu_g}\right)^m \quad (12.4\text{-}3)$$

where $m$ is the Reynolds number exponent in the Blasius-type single-phase friction factor correlation and subscripts indicate turbulent flow in both phases. This parameter represents the ratio of kinetic energies of liquid and vapor, and the effects of mass velocity, hydraulic diameter, relative roughness, etc., are included in the single-phase pressure drop term.

A simple curve fit to the $\phi_l^2 - X_{tt}$ relation for two-phase flow in tubes was first suggested by Chisholm and Laird (1958):

$$\phi_l^2 = 1 + \frac{C}{X_{tt}} + \frac{1}{X_{tt}^2} \quad (12.4\text{-}4)$$

Ishihara et al. (1979) tested the above correlation against a large set of tube bundle two-phase frictional pressure drop data, including downward and horizontal flow orientations. They found good agreement between the data and Eq. (12.4-4) for small values of $X_{tt} < 0.2$ (corresponding to high $\varepsilon$) with the parameter C (referred to as the C-factor) equal to 8. The scatter in the data was found to increase for $X_{tt} > 0.2$ (corresponding to low $\varepsilon$), where Ishihara et al. (1979) suggested that the empirical C-factor may be flow regime-dependent. Schrage et al. (1987) also correlated their tube bundle air-water data using Eq. (12.4-4), and suggested possible flow regime-dependence of the C-factor. They introduced an additional parameter in the numerator of the third term to account for flow regime and mass velocity dependence.

Dowlati et al. (1990, 1992b, 1996) showed that Eq. (12.4-4) can correlate the frictional pressure drop data obtained in air-water experiments using six different tube bundles as well as data from R-113 flow boiling experiments in a tube bundle. Table 2 summarizes the results of their findings, and some variations in the C-factor with bundle geometry were reported. For an in-line tube bundle and given value of $X_{tt}$, the two-phase friction multiplier (or the C-factor) was found to increase with P/D. Also, for a given P/D ratio and $X_{tt}$, the two-phase friction multiplier was higher in a staggered tube layout in comparison to in-line. Dowlati et al. speculated that various factors, such as the development of the two-phase wake behind a given tube and the effect of the upstream tube, influenced the C-factor. They also reported some mass velocity effects with air-water data for $G < 200$ kg/m²s, indicating possible flow regime and mass velocity dependence.

It is useful to note that for both air-water and R-113 boiling experiments using a similar tube bundle geometry (in-line, P/D = 1.3), the same C-factor ($C = 8$) was found to best fit the data (Figure 9). As mentioned previously, this value was

**Table 2** Variation of C-factor in Eq. 12.4-4 with bundle geometry (Dowlati et al., 1990, 1992b, 1996)

| Tube bundle layout | P/D ratio | Fluids | C-value (Eq. 12.4–4) |
|---|---|---|---|
| In-line | 1.3 | Air-Water | 8 |
| In-line | 1.75 | Air-Water | 50 |
| Staggered | 1.3 | Air-Water | 20 |
| Staggered | 1.75 | Air-Water | 20 |
| In-line | $S_T = 1.75$ $S_L = 1.33$ | Air-Water | 50 |
| In-line | $S_T = 1.75$ $S_L = 2.17$ | Air-Water | 30 |
| In-line | 1.3 | R-113 | 8 |

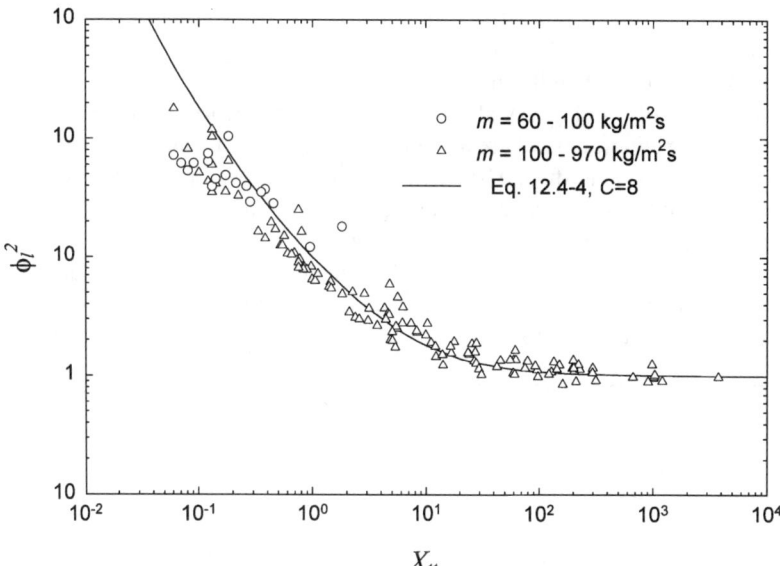

**Figure 9** Correlation of two-phase friction multiplier data for R-113 (Dowlati et al., 1996, with permission).

also chosen by Ishihara et al. (1979) to best fit their bundle data set, even for different flow orientations.

More studies are certainly needed on local two-phase flow in order to better understand the effects of flow regime and tube bundle geometry on two-phase frictional pressure drop. Nonetheless, Eq. (12.4-4) with reference to Table 2 is currently the correlation recommended for predicting the two-phase friction multiplier. This correlation also has the advantage of attaining the correct theoretical limits as the void fraction approaches 1 or 0 (or as $X_{tt}$ approaches 0 or $\infty$). Using Eqs. (12.4-2) and (12.4-4), the two-phase friction pressure drop can be obtained. If single-phase friction pressure drop information is not directly available for a given tube bundle of interest, the reader is referred to Zukauskas (1972) and ESDU (1979) to predict this value. Once the two-phase friction pressure drop is estimated, an appropriate void fraction correlation can be used to estimate the gravitational and acceleration pressure drops (as given by Eq. [9.2-9] and Section 9.1 to calculate the total pressure drop from Eq. [12.4-1]).

## 12.5 TWO-PHASE HEAT TRANSFER COEFFICIENT

While prediction accuracy of less than ±30% can be readily achieved for single-phase heat transfer coefficients, it may be more challenging to predict two-phase heat transfer coefficients for shell-side flow boiling with a similar degree of accuracy. Although there have been many studies performed to obtain heat transfer coefficient data for a tube bundle under boiling conditions, very few have been performed systematically, and nearly all of them have been performed under natural convective boiling conditions, where the effects of mass velocity and vapor quality could not be precisely quantified. Also, many correlations developed for two-phase heat transfer in a tube bundle have been based on results from single-tube boiling experiments, which have been extensively performed in the past.

The shape of the boiling curve for a tube bundle is very similar to that of a single-tube, as shown in Figure 10, with some distinct differences (Palen et al., 1972). Both have regions where two-phase convection and nucleate boiling show

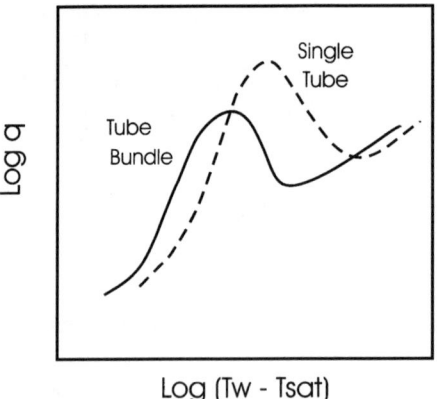

**Figure 10** Boiling curves for a tube bundle and a single tube in cross-flow (Collier, 1972, with permission).

their dominance in the overall heat transfer rate. Tube bundle studies by Leong and Cornwell (1979), Fujita et al. (1986), and Chan and Shoukri (1987), among others, have shown that at low boiling heat fluxes, heat transfer is strongly influenced by the inherent mixing of two-phase flow inside the bundle. This results in higher heat transfer coefficients at the upper parts of the bundle, as compared with the single-tube case. The increased turbulence caused by the rising two-phase mixture and the break-up of vapor blankets are also believed to enhance the Critical Heat Flux (CHF) in the upper tubes.

At high heat fluxes, where nucleate boiling is the dominant heat transfer mode, bundle effects become less significant in the upper tubes, and the heat transfer characteristics approach those of a single tube. The increased resistance to vapor escape in turn causes a slight reduction in the heat transfer coefficient at the bottom of the bundle. This resistance will cause a vapor blanketing effect, which is believed to be responsible for the decrease in CHF in comparison to a single-tube case. There is discrepancy as to how much the heat transfer coefficient can vary between the bottom and the top of the tube bundle. Leong and Cornwell (1979) obtained a variation up to a factor of eight, while Jensen and Hsu (1987) reported a factor of two to three.

To explain the heat transfer enhancement effect in bundles, Fujita et al. (1986) presented a sketch of cross-flow boiling in a small rod-bundle, as shown in Figure 11. They made observations under natural-circulation driven flow of R-113 at pressures between 0.1 and 1.0 MPa and at heat fluxes up to 100 kW/m$^2$. The convection effect at low or high heat flux and/or pressure was explained in terms of the tube surface areas influenced by the bubbles nucleating and growing on the tube surface and those flowing past the tube from below. The surface area not covered by the growing bubbles would be influenced by enhanced convection due to rising bubbles. Thus, if the bubble nucleation density is low at low heat flux or pressure, then the fraction of the surface area influenced by the rising bubbles would be greater, and the convection effects become important. On the other hand, if the nucleation site density is high at high heat fluxes or at high pressures, the bundle enhancement effect would be reduced.

To predict the flow boiling heat transfer coefficient in tube bundles, the classic approach by Rohsenow (1952) of superimposing the single-phase convection and nucleate boiling components of heat transfer has been the basis for several correlations, including that by Chen (1966). For saturated flow boiling heat transfer in tubes, Chen (1966) introduced correction factors into the convection and nucleate boiling terms as follows:

$$\alpha_{2\phi} = S\alpha_{nb} + F\alpha_{conv} \qquad (12.5\text{-}1)$$

The bubble-growth suppression factor, $S$, is a weighting function accounting for

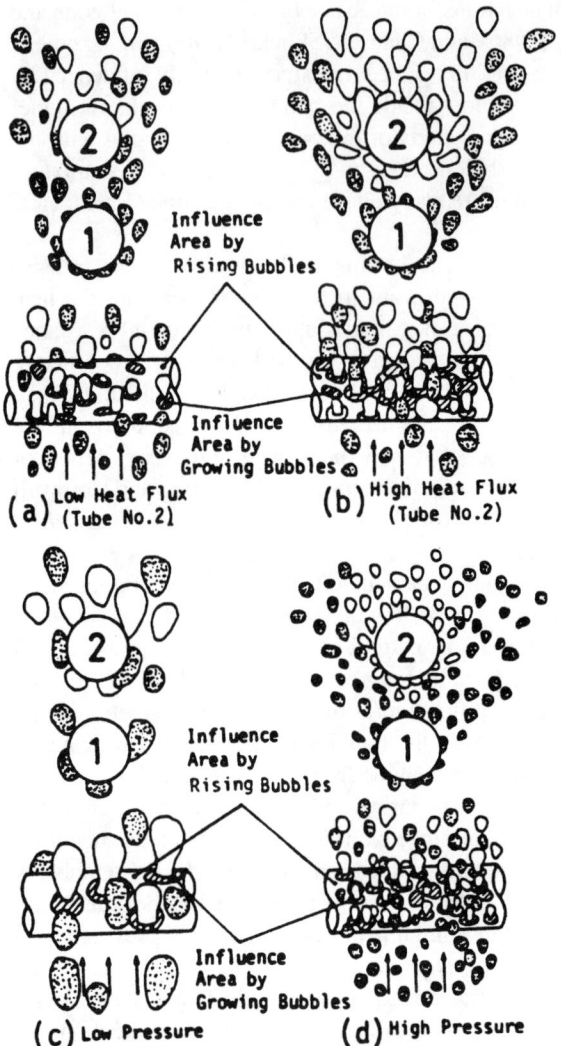

**Figure 11** Heat transfer enhancement effect in tube bundles (Fujita et al., 1986, with permission).

the suppression of nucleate boiling, resulting from a reduction in effective superheat when convection is present. Bennet et al. (1980) derived a semi-empirical expression for $S$ from a study of forced convective boiling of thin liquid films on the shell-side,

$$S = \frac{k_l}{\alpha_{conv} X_o} \left[ 1 - e^{-\left(\frac{\alpha_{conv} X_o}{k_l}\right)} \right] \quad (12.5\text{-}2)$$

where the bubble growth region, $X_o$, is given as,

$$X_o = 0.041 \left[\frac{g_c \sigma}{g(\rho_l - \rho_g)}\right]^{1/2} \quad (12.5\text{-}3)$$

The effect of the bundle geometry on $S$ is taken into account through the use of $\alpha_{conv}$.

The $F$-factor in Eq. (12.5-1) is defined as an effective two-phase Reynolds number. Using a momentum analogy, Jensen and Hsu (1987) derived an expression for $F$ in terms of the two-phase friction multiplier, $\phi_l^2$, for the case of liquid flowing alone in a tube bundle,

$$F = \left(\phi_l^2\right)^{n/(2-m)} \quad (12.5\text{-}4)$$

where $n$ and $m$ are the Reynolds number exponents in the single-phase convective heat transfer and Blasius-type friction factor correlations, respectively.

The single-phase heat transfer coefficient, $\alpha_{conv}$, can be obtained from well known references such as Zukauskas (1972) and ESDU (1973). For $Re$ in the range of $10^3$–$2 \times 10^5$, the correlations recommended by Zukauskas (1972) to predict the mean heat transfer coefficient in in-line and staggered tube bundles are given in Table 3.

Nucleate boiling heat transfer coefficient, $\alpha_{nb}$, is typically expressed using a simple power law relationship,

$$\alpha = A q^b \quad (12.5\text{-}5)$$

where $A$ and $b$ are empirically determined constants. There are many such correlations developed from saturated pool boiling studies on single horizontal wires and tubes. A number of researchers have successfully applied some of these correlations to predict nucleate pool boiling in tube bundles. However, as Figure 12 indicates, two of the more common single-tube correlations (Mostinski, 1963; Stephan and Abdelsalam, 1980) under-predicted the upper bundle data obtained by Dowlati et al. (1996) from forced convective boiling of R-113 in an in-line tube bundle with P/D = 1.3. Also shown in this figure are two correlations from

**Table 3  Single-phase convection heat transfer correlations for tube bundles (Zukauskas, 1972)**

| Correlation | Tube Bundle Geometry |
|---|---|
| $Nu = 0.27 \, Re^{0.63} \, Pr^{0.36} \, (Pr/Pr_W)^{0.25}$ | In-line bundle with $S_T/S_T > 0.7$ |
| $Nu = 0.35 \, (S_T/S_L)^{0.2} \, Re^{0.6} \, Pr^{0.36} \, (Pr/Pr_W)^{0.25}$ | Staggered bundle with $S_T/S_L < 2$ |
| $Nu = 0.40 \, Re^{0.6} \, Pr^{0.36} \, (Pr/Pr_W)^{0.25}$ | Staggered bundle with $S_T/S_L > 2$ |

*Note:* All properties used in dimensionless parameters are evaluated at the fluid bulk temperature except for $Pr_W$, which is evaluated at the wall temperature. Tube diameter and velocity at the minimum flow area are used to calculate $Re$.

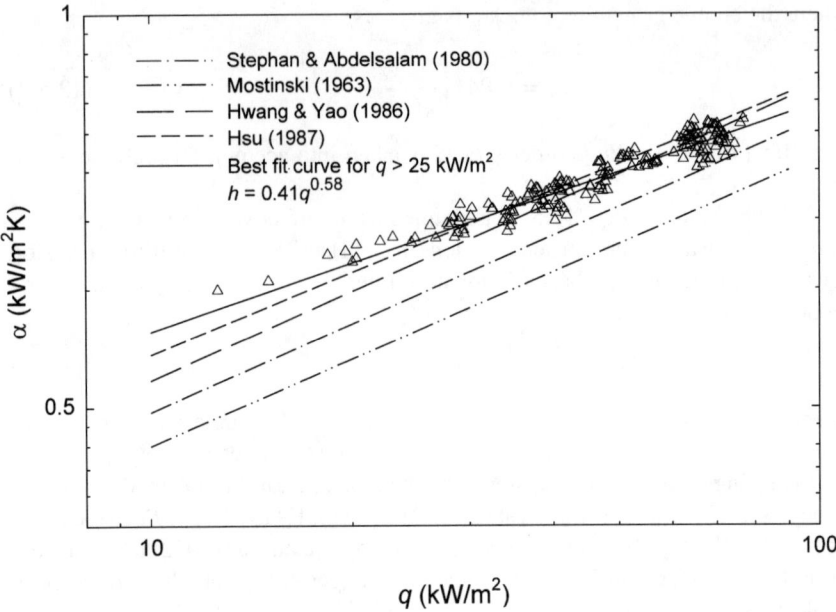

**Figure 12** Correlation of flow boiling heat transfer coefficient data for R-113 (Dowlati et al., 1996, with permission).

Hwang and Yao (1986) and Hsu (1987), which have also been obtained from forced convective boiling of R-113 in similar in-line tube bundles.

Hence, when semi-empirical correlations are available for specific tube bundle geometry and working fluids, such as the best fit curves shown in Figure 12, predictions of $\alpha_{nb}$ with accuracy of ±30 percent can be obtained. However, if no geometry and fluid specific correlations are available, the correlation by Stephan and Abdelsalam (1980) is recommended, as it appears to be the most comprehensive single-tube nucleate boiling heat transfer correlation derived from a regression analysis of nearly 5000 experimental data points, covering a wide range of fluids and pressures. Using Eq. (12.5-5), Stephan and Abdelsalam recommended that $b = 0.673$ for water, 0.67 for hydrocarbons, and 0.745 for refrigerants. The value of $A$ is given as functions of fluid and pressure in Figure 13 for water and hydrocarbons, and in Figure 14 for refrigerants. Their paper also provided data for cryogenic fluids. The application of the Stephan and Abdelsalam correlation for a tube bundle, however, will likely give a conservative estimate of the heat transfer coefficient, as observed in Figure 12.

The Chen-type correlation in Eq. (12.5-1) has found limited success in predicting two-phase heat transfer in tube bundles, yet for lack of more reliable

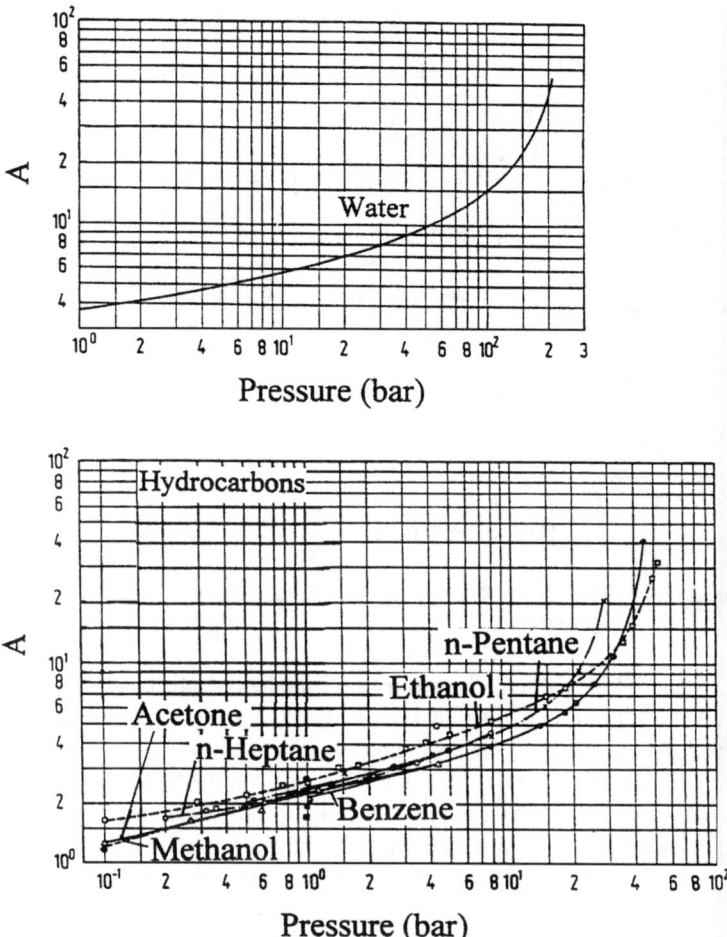

**Figure 13** Values of a constant, A, for water and hydrocarbons in the correlation by Stephan and Abdelsalam's (1980) (Eq. 12.5-5), with permission.

correlations, it appears to be the method of choice for most engineers in this area. However, further improvements in the $S$ and $F$ factors are certainly needed.

Another interesting feature to note in Figure 12 is that data by Dowlati et al. (1996) revealed no mass velocity effects for $q'' > 30$ kW/m². In this region, the heat transfer coefficient was seen to increase only as a function of heat flux. Similar results were reported by Hwang and Yao (1986) for $q'' > 30$ kW/m² in their tube bundle study. Hence, for sufficiently high values of heat flux, nucleate

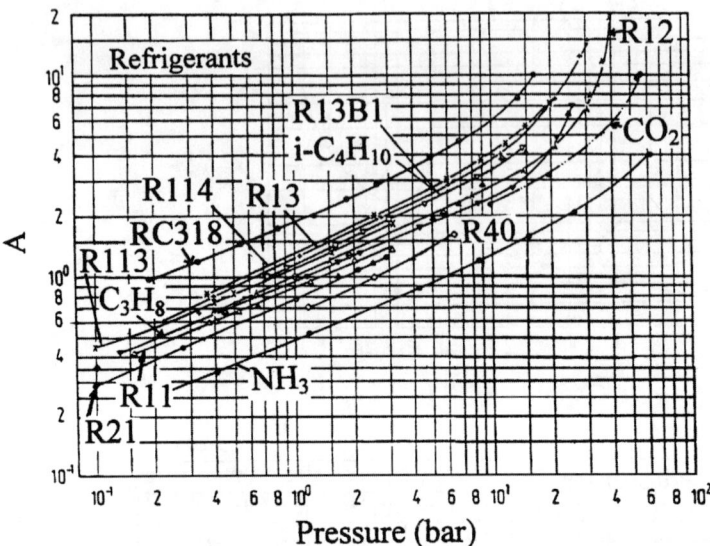

**Figure 14** Values of a constant, A, for various refrigerants in Stephan and Abdelsalam's (1980) correlation (Eq. 12.5-5), with permission.

boiling is expected to be the dominant heat transfer mode in a tube bundle, where a simple power law relationship given by Eq. (12.5-5) is capable of predicting the overall heat transfer coefficient with reasonable accuracy.

Bergles and Rohsenow (1964) also reported regions on the boiling curve for single horizontal tubes where either nucleate boiling or forced-convective boiling will dominate, and hence there would be no need to form an additive correlation such as Eq. (12.5-1). This mechanism appears to hold true for boiling in tube bundles as well as single tubes.

More recently, Cornwell (1990a, 1990b) and Houston and Cornwell (1996) have introduced an additional heat transfer mechanism based on the effect of sliding bubbles over a tube surface. The mechanism involves the process of bubbles sliding on the tube surface and enhancing heat transfer either by disruption of the liquid boundary layer or by direct evaporation. They concluded that for low quality flow regimes, the boiling heat transfer coefficient in the upper region of a tube bundle can be determined by the effect of sliding bubbles and that nucleation is important only at the lowest tubes where quality approaches zero. This new approach holds some promise; however, there are currently no viable correlations based on this mechanism that can be recommended.

The effect of tube bundle geometry on two-phase heat transfer is not yet fully clear. Cornwell et al. (1986) and Palen et al. (1972) reported that tube arrangement had little or no effect on the boiling heat transfer characteristics in horizontal tube bundles. On the other hand, as the P/D ratio was increased from 1.3 to 1.7, Hsu and Jensen (1988) reported an increase in heat transfer coefficient of nearly 20 percent for an in-line tube bundle at low heat fluxes ($q'' < 10$ kW/m$^2$). Reinke and Jensen (1987) also reported higher heat transfer coefficients in a staggered tube bundle when compared to an in-line bundle with the same P/D ratio at low to moderate heat fluxes. Intuitively, one would expect higher heat transfer coefficients in staggered tube bundles due to the additional turbulence and mixing created by the staggered tube arrangement. Also, a staggered layout can provide more surface area for a given shell diameter.

Finally, there are some tube bundle heat transfer data reported with finned tubes. Hahne and Muller (1983), Windisch et al. (1985), and Fujita et al. (1986) presented heat transfer data and correlations for finned tube bundles under natural circulation-driven two-phase cross-flow of R-11 and R-113. Compared to single finned tubes, finned tube bundles also provided higher heat transfer coefficient.

## REFERENCES

Bell, K. J. 1983. Heat Exchangers with Phase Change. *Heat Exchangers—Theory and Practice*. Eds. Taborek, J., Hewitt, G. F., and Afghan, N. Washington DC: Hemisphere Publishing Co.

Bennet, D. L., Davis, M. W., and Hertzler, B. L. 1980. Boiling by Forced Convective Flow. *AIChE Symp. Ser.* 76(199):91–103.

Bergles, A. E. and Rohsenow, W. M. 1964. The Determination of Forced-Convection Surface-Boiling Heat Transfer. *J. Heat Transfer* 86:365–372.

Brisbane, T. W. C., Grant, I. D. R., and Whalley, P. B. 1980. A Prediction Method for Kettle Reboiler Performance. ASME Paper No. 80-HT-42.

Butterworth, D. 1975. A Comparison of Some Void-Fraction Relationships for Co-Current Gas-Liquid Flow. *Int. J. Multiphase Flow* 1:845–850.

Carlucci, L. N., Gapin, P. F., and Brown, J. D. 1984. Numerical Predictions of Shellside Heat Exchanger Flows. *A Reappraisal of Shellside Flow in Heat Exchangers*. Eds. W. J. Marner and J. M. Chenoweth, HTD-Vol. 36, pp. 19–26. New York: ASME.

Chan, A. M. C. and Shoukri, M. 1987. Boiling Characteristics of Small Multitube Bundles. *J. Heat Trans.* 109:753–760.

Chen, J. C. 1966. A Correlation for Boiling Heat Transfer to Saturated Fluids in Convective Flow. *Industrial and Eng. Chemistry Process Design and Development* 5(3):322–329.

Chisholm, D. and Laird, A. D. K. 1958. Two-Phase Flow in Rough Tubes. *ASME Trans.* 80:276–286.

Collier, J. G. 1972. *Convective Boiling and Condensation*, New York: McGraw-Hill.

Cornwell, K. 1990a. The Influence of Bubbly Flow on Boiling from a Tube in a Bundle. *Int. J. Heat Mass Transfer* 33(12):2579–2584.

Cornwell, K. 1990b. The Role of Sliding Bubbles in Boiling on Tube Bundles. *Intl. Heat Transfer Conf.*, Jerusalem, Paper 9-TPF-11.

Cornwell, K., Duffin, H. W., and Schuller, R. B. 1980. An Experimental Study of the Effects of Fluid Flow on Boiling Within a Kettle Reboiler Tube Bundle. ASME Paper No. 80-HT-45.

Cornwell, K., Einarsson, J. G., and Andrews, P. R. 1986. Studies on Boiling Tube Bundles. *8th Intl. Heat Transfer Conf.*, San Francisco, Paper FB-03.

Dowlati, R. 1992. Hydrodynamics of Two-Phase Cross-Flow and Boiling Heat Transfer in Horizontal Tube Bundles. Ph.D. Thesis, University of Toronto.
Dowlati, R., Chan, A. M. C., and Kawaji, M. 1992b. Hydrodynamics of Two-Phase Flow Across Horizontal In-Line and Staggered Rod Bundle. ASME *J. Fluids Eng.* 114(3):450–456.
Dowlati, R., Kawaji, M., and Chan, A. M. C. 1990. Pitch-to-Diameter Effect on Two-Phase Flow Across an In-Line Tube Bundle. *AIChE J.* 36(5):765–772.
Dowlati, R., Kawaji, M., and Chan, A. M. C. 1996. Two-Phase Crossflow and Boiling Heat Transfer in Horizontal Tube Bundles. *J. Heat Transfer* 118(1):124–131.
Dowlati, R., Kawaji, M., Chisholm, D., and Chan, A. M. C. 1992a. Void Fraction Prediction in Two-Phase Flow Across a Tube Bundle. *A.I.Ch.E. J.* 38(4):619–622.
ESDU. 1973. Convective Heat Transfer During Crossflow of Fluids Over Plain Tube Banks. Engineering Sciences Data Unit, No. 73031, London.
ESDU. 1979. Crossflow Pressure Loss over Banks of Plain Tubes in Square and Triangular Arrays Including Effects of Flow Direction. Engineering Sciences Data Unit, No. 79034, London.
Fair, J. R., and Klip, A. 1983. Thermal Design of Horizontal Reboilers. *Chem. Eng. Progress* 79(8):86–96.
Fujita, Y., Ohta, H., Hidaka, S., and Nishikawa, K. 1986. Nucleat Boiling Heat Transfer on Horizontal Tubes in Bundles. *Proc. Int. Heat Transfer Conf.*, Volume 5, pp. 2131–2136, San Francisco.
Grant, I. D. R. and Chisholm, D.1979. Two-Phase Flow on the Shell Side of a Segmentally Baffled Shell-and-Tube Heat Exchanger. *J. Heat Transfer* 101:38–42.
Grant, I. D. R., Cotchin, C. D., and Henry, J. A. R. 1983. Tests on a Small Kettle Reboiler. *Heat Exchangers for Two-Phase Applications*. Eds. J. B. Kitto and J. M. Robertson, HTD-Vol. 27, pp. 41–45. New York: ASME.
Hahne, E. and Muller, J. 1983. Boiling on a Finned Tube and a Finned Tube Bundle. *Int. J. Heat Mass Transfer* 26(6):849–859.
Hahne, E., Spindler, K., Chen, Q., and Windisch, R. 1990. Local Void Fraction Measurements in Finned Tube Bundles. *Proc. Ninth Int. Conf. on Heat Transfer*, Volume 6. Jerusalem, Israel, pp. 41–45.
Houston, S. D. and Cornwell, K. 1996, Heat Transfer to Sliding Bubbles on a Tube Under Evaporating and Non-Evaporating Conditions. *Int. J. Heat Mass Transfer* 39(1):211–214.
Hsu, J. T. 1987. A Parametric Study of Boiling Heat Transfer in Horizontal Tube Bundles. Ph.D. Thesis, Univ. of Wisconsin, Milwaukee.
Hsu, J. T. and Jensen, M. K. 1988. Effect of Pitch-to-Diameter Ratio on Crossflow Boiling Heat Transfer in an Inline Tube Bundle. HTD-Vol. 104, pp. 239–245. New York: ASME.
Hwang, T. H. and Yao, S. C. 1986. Forced Convective Boiling in Horizontal Tube Bundles. *Int. J. Heat Mass Transfer* 29(5):785–795.
Ishihara, K., Palen, J. W., and Taborek, J. J. 1979. Critical Review of Correlations for Predicting Two-Phase Pressure Drop Across Tube Banks. *Heat Trans. Eng.* 1(3):1–8.
Ishii, M. 1977. One-Dimensional Drift-Flux Model and Constitutive Equations for Relative Motion Between Phases in Various Two-Phase Flow Regimes. Argonne Nat. Lab. Report, ANL-77-47, October 1977.
Jensen, M. K. and Hsu, J. T. 1987. A Parametric Study of Boiling Heat Transfer in a Tube Bundle. *2nd ASME/JSME Thermal Engineering Joint Conf.* 3:132–140.
Kondo, M. and Nakajima, K. 1980. Experimental Investigation of Air-Water Two-Phase Upflow Across Horizontal Tube Bundles, Part I: Flow Pattern and Void Fraction. *Bulletin JSME* 23(177):385–393.
Leong, L. S. and Cornwell, K. 1979. Heat Transfer Coefficients in a Reboiler Tube Bundle. *The Chemical Engineer* 343 (April 1979):219–221.

Lian, H. Y., Chan, A. M. C., and Kawaji, M. 1992. Effects of Void Fraction on Vibration of Tubes in Tube Bundles Under Two-Phase Cross Flow. *Proc. 3rd International Symposium on Flow-Induced Vibration and Noise*, Volume 1, pp. 109–118. New York: ASME.

Lockhart, R. W. and Martinelli, R. C. 1949. Proposed Correlation of Data for Isothermal Two-Phase Two-Component Flow in Pipes. *Chem. Eng. Prog.* 45(1):39–48.

Martinelli, R. C. and Nelson, D. B. 1948. Prediction of Pressure Drop During Forced-Circulation Boiling of Water. *Trans. ASME* 65:695–702.

Mostinski, J. L. 1963. Application of the Rule of Corresponding States for the Calculation of Heat Transfer and Critical Heat Flux. *Teploenergetika* 4:66.

Niels, G. H. 1979. Some Boiling Aspects in Kettle Reboilers. *Boiling Phenomena: Physicochemical and Engineering Fundamentals and Applications*, Volume 2, Chapter 29. New York: Hemisphere Publishing Corp.

Noghrehkar, R. 1996. Investigation of Local Two-Phase Flow Parameters in Cross Flow-Induced Vibration of Tubes in Tube Bundles. Ph.D. Thesis, University of Toronto.

Noghrehkar, R., Kawaji, M., and Chan, A. M. C. 1995. An Experimental Study of Local Two-Phase Parameters in Cross Flow Induced Vibration in Tube Bundles. *Proc. Sixth Int. Conf. On Flow Induced Vibrations.* Ed. Bearman, P. W., pp. 373–382. Rotterdam: Balkema.

Noghrehkar, R., Kawaji, M., and Chan, A. M. C. 1999. An Experimental Study of Two-Phase Flow Regimes In-Line and Staggered Tube Bundles Under Cross-Flow Conditions. *Int. J. Multiphase Flow*, submitted.

Palen, J. W. and Taborek, J. J. 1962. Refinery Kettle Reboilers-Proposed Method for Design and Optimization. *Chem. Eng. Progress* 58(7):37–46.

Palen, J. W. and Yang, C. C. 1983. Circulation Boiling Model for Analysis of Kettle and Internal Reboiler Performance. *Heat Exchangers for Two-Phase Applications*. Eds. J. B. Kitto and J. M. Robertson, HTD-Vol. 27, pp. 55–61. New York: ASME.

Palen, J. W., Yarden, A., and Taborek, J. J. 1972. Characteristics of Boiling Outside Large-Scale Horizontal Multitube Bundles. *AIChE Symp. Ser.* 68(118):50–61.

Payvar, P. 1985. Analysis of Performance of Full Bundle Submerged Boilers. *Two-Phase Heat Exchanger Symposium*, HTD-Vol. 44, pp. 11–18. New York: ASME.

Reinke, M. J. and Jensen, M. K. 1987. Comparison of Boiling Heat Transfer and Two-Phase Pressure Drop Between an In-Line and Staggered Tube Bundle. HTD-Vol. 85, pp. 41–50. New York: ASME.

Rohsenow, W. M. 1952. A Method of Correlating Heat-Transfer Data for Surface Boiling of Liquids. *Trans. ASME* 74:969–976.

Rubin, F. L. 1984. Heat Transfer Equipment. *Perry's Chemical Engineers' Handbook*, 6th edition, Section 11. Eds. R. H. Perry, D. W. Green, and J. O. Maloney. New York: McGraw-Hill.

Schrage, D. S., Hsu, J. T., and Jensen, M. K. 1987. Void Fraction and Two-Phase Friction Multipliers in a Horizontal Tube Bundle. *A.I.Ch.E. Symp. Ser.* 83(257):1–8.

Schrage, D. S., Hsu, J. T., and Jensen, M. K. 1988. Two-Phase Pressure Drop in Vertical Crossflow Across a Horizontal Tube Bundle. *A.I.Ch.E. J.* 34(1):107–115.

Schuller, R. B. 1982. Boiling on Horizontal Tube Bundles. Ph.D. Thesis, Heriot-Watt University, Edinburgh, U.K.

Smith, B. 1985. Update on Shellside Two-Phase Heat Transfer. *The Chemical Engineer* 414 (May 1985):16–19.

Stephan, K. and Abdelsalam, M. 1980. Heat-Transfer Correlations for Natural Convection Boiling. *Int. J. Heat Mass Transfer* 23:73–87.

Ueno, T., Leung, W. H., and Ishii, M. 1995. Local Measurement in Two-Phase Flow Across a Horizontal Tube Bundle. *Proc. 2nd Int. Conf. on Multiphase Flow*, Kyoto, Japan, April 3–7, 1995, pp. 89–95.

Ulbrich, R. and Mewes, D. 1994. Vertical, Upward Gas-Liquid Two-Phase Flow Across a Tube Bundle. *Int. J. Multiphase Flow* 20(2):249–272.

Wallis, G. B. 1969. *One-Dimensional Two-Phase Flow*. New York: McGraw-Hill.

Westwater, J. W. 1969. Nucleate Pool Boiling. *Advanced Heat Transfer*. Ed. B. T. Chao, pp. 217-232. Urbana, IL: Univ. of Illinois Press.

Whalley, P. B. and Butterworth, D. 1983. A Simple Method for Calculating the Recirculating Flow in Vertical Thermosyphon and Kettle Reboilers. *Heat Exchangers for Two-Phase Applications*, HTD-Vol. 27, pp. 47–53. New York: ASME.

Windisch, R., Hahne, E., and Kiss, V. 1985. Heat Transfer for Boiling on Finned Tube Bundles. *Int. Commun. Heat Mass Transfer* 12(4):355–368.

Zuber, N. and Findlay, J. A. 1965. Average Volumetric Concentration in Two-Phase Flow Systems. *J. Heat Transfer* 87:453–468.

Zukauskas, A. 1972. Heat Transfer from Tubes in Crossflow. *Advances in Heat Transfer* 8:93–160.

CHAPTER
# THIRTEEN

## EXTERNAL FLOW FILM BOILING

**Larry C. Witte**

*University of Houston, Houston, TX 77204-4792, USA*

## 13.1 INTRODUCTION

The theory of flow film boiling across bluff bodies that induce flow separation and wake formation is still not complete, especially for subcooled systems, even though it has been studied for many years. More than 40 years ago, Bromley et al. (1953) conducted the first systematic theoretical and experimental studies for heated cylinders experiencing flow film boiling and subcooled flow film boiling (Motte and Bromley, 1957) as extensions of his seminal work on pool film boiling. In the intervening years, research has been directed at refining the basic models proposed by Bromley and his co-workers, especially in the areas of finding the influence of liquid velocity and subcooling on the behavior of the vapor film that surrounds the body. This section will be directed toward summarizing the advances made in recent years to understand the basic nature of flow film boiling from bodies like cylinders and spheres, that is, bodies over which flow separation will occur.

## 13.2 PHYSICAL/MATHEMATICAL MODELS FOR FLOW FILM BOILING

Figure 1 shows the vapor envelope that surrounds a bluff body during flow film boiling. The picture shows an upward flow of liquid, though the orientation is

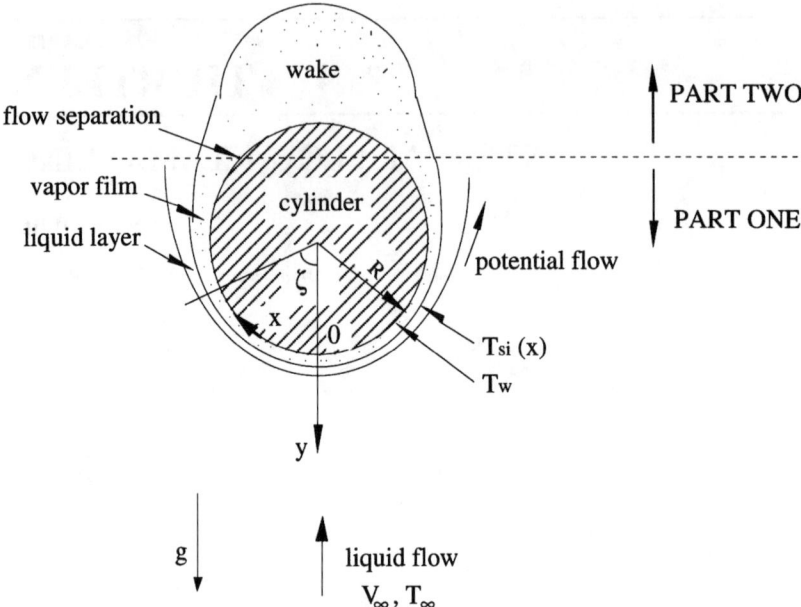

**Figure 1** Physical model of flow film boiling across a cylinder (Chou and Witte, 1995).

insignificant as long as the flows are strong enough so that buoyancy effects are not important. A thin, smooth vapor layer over the forward part of the body feeds into a wake region beyond the flow separation point. This is the basic model that was proposed by Bromley et al., though they did not attempt to analyze the processes that occur in the wake region. Indeed, only recently have efforts been undertaken at predicting the heat transfer in the wake region. In Figure 1, Part One refers to the region where a local similarity (boundary-layer-like) analysis can be justified, while Part Two refers to the wake region for which only crude models for heat transfer have been explored.

The key to predicting heat transfer is being able to predict how the vapor layer develops around the body. Doing this requires knowledge of the vapor velocity and temperature profiles. Once the vapor thickness is known, it is a straightforward matter to integrate for the total heat transfer from the body.

Analyses usually fall within two categories, depending on the boundary condition that is imposed at the heater surface. The most common boundary condition is a uniform temperature, though some studies have been done using a uniform heat flux condition at the surface.

Other conditions that are commonly assumed are:

- the liquid-vapor interface is smooth and is at the local saturation temperature

- the liquid free stream velocity and temperature are uniform.
- the vapor layer and the adjacent liquid boundary layer are thin and laminar.
- viscous dissipation and liquid compression work are negligible. Usually, radiation heat transfer is considered negligible as well, even though surface temperature might be relatively high. If needed, a correction to include radiation can be performed following the method proposed by Bromley et al.
- a potential flow exists in the far-field of the liquid.

Steady state conditions are usually assumed, and if thermophysical properties are variable, they depend only on temperature.

Several researchers have performed analyses that generally follow the assumptions stated above. Brief summaries of some of them follow.

Witte (1968) studied saturated film boiling from a sphere, assuming that the vapor velocity is a simple linear function, going from zero at the wall to the potential flow velocity at the liquid-vapor interface. However, the assumption of linear velocity in the vapor cannot be physically justified. Indeed, as recognized by Kobayashi (1965), Epstein and Hauser (1980), and Witte and Orozco (1984), the imposition of the liquid pressure gradient caused by the flow around the body causes a non-linear velocity profile.

Epstein and Hauser (1980) modeled only the processes near the stagnation region of the body. They then drew inferences about the nature of the film boiling process, assuming basically a vapor film of uniform thickness around the body. Wilson (1979) used an integral technique to describe the behavior of the vapor boundary layer. A result similar to that of Epstein and Hauser was found.

Witte and Orozco (1984) ignored inertial effects in the vapor film while retaining the assumption of potential flow in the liquid overiding the vapor film. They found that if a non-dimensional velocity is formed using the velocity at the edge of the vapor layer as the reference, one can write

$$\frac{u_v}{u_\delta} = \frac{y}{\delta} + \frac{3}{4}\frac{\rho_l V_\infty}{\mu_v R}\cos\zeta(y\delta - y^2) \quad (13.2\text{-}1)$$

Figure 2 shows Eq. (13.2-1) plotted for one particular case of subcooled film boiling over a sphere. The velocity profiles appear to be "squeezed" into the vapor thickness over the forward portion of the body, going to a linear distribution at the 90-degree point, and actually demonstrating flow reversal (separation) at some point past the 90-degree point. The shape of the profile is a response to the liquid pressure profile, which is represented by the last term on the right side of Eq. (13.2-1).

If Eq. (13.2-1) is differentiated and set to zero at $y = 0$, a relationship for the separation angle in terms of $\delta_r$ at $\zeta_{sp}$ can be obtained as

$$\cos\zeta_{sp} = -\frac{4\mu_v R}{3\rho_l V_\infty \delta_r^2} \quad (13.2\text{-}2)$$

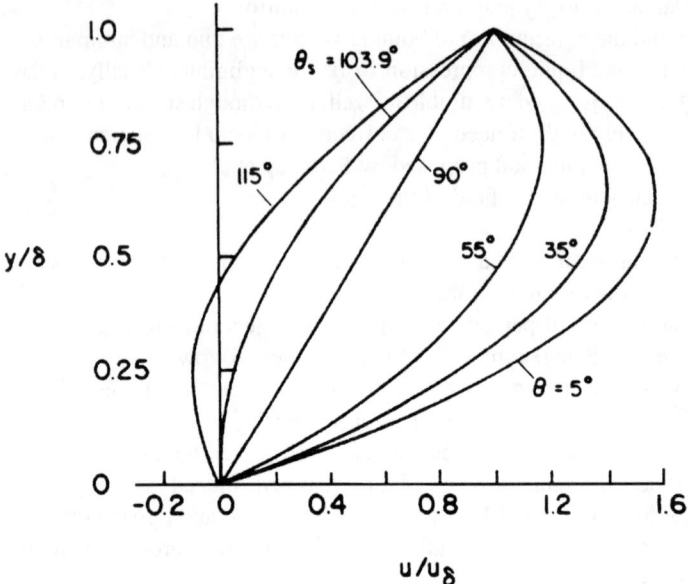

**Figure 2** Vapor velocity profiles for subcooled water flowing over a 6.35-mm sphere at 4.26 m/s: $T_w = 400°C$, $\Delta T_{sub} = 40°C$ (Witte and Orozco, 1984).

Equation (13.2-2) does not predict $\zeta_{sp}$; rather, it gives the relationship between $\zeta_{sp}$ and $\delta_r$ at separation for a given boiling case.

Recently, Liu and Theofanous (1995a) analyzed flow film boiling from spheres using essentially the same laminar model as Witte and Orozco (1984) up to the separation point. They found that for saturated liquids, the heat transfer in the wake could be adequately accounted for by assuming a constant thickness of the vapor film in the wake equal to the vapor film thickness at the separation point. For subcooled systems, however, they found this to be inadequate. Consequently, they invoked a heat transfer version of a turbulent eddy model developed by Theofanous et al. (1976) for mass transfer at a free gas-liquid interface.

Additional theoretical work related to flow film boiling around spheres was done by Fodemski and Hall (1982) and Fodemski (1992). Chappidi et al. (1991) and Walsh and Wilson (1979) performed boundary-layer like analyses for film boiling on wedges.

Chou and Witte (1995) performed a much more rigorous analysis of film boiling around a cylinder, relaxing the potentially-restrictive assumptions of Witte and Orozco. While the analysis is lengthy and complicated, some of the details are given below to illustrate the nature of recent analytical research.

### 13.2.1 Governing Equations

The governing equations, including mass, momentum, and energy conservation, in the vapor layer (j = v) and the liquid layer (j = L) are

$$\frac{\partial}{\partial x}(\rho u)_j + \frac{\partial}{\partial y}(\rho v)_j = 0 \tag{13.2-3}$$

$$\rho_j \left( u_j \frac{\partial u_j}{\partial x} + v_j \frac{\partial u_j}{\partial y} \right) = \frac{2\rho_{L\infty} V_\infty^2}{R} \sin\left(\frac{2x}{R}\right) + g(\rho_{L\infty} - \rho_j) \sin\left(\frac{x}{R}\right)$$

$$+ \frac{\partial}{\partial y}\left( \mu_j \frac{\partial u_j}{\partial y} \right) \tag{13.2-4}$$

$$(\rho c_p)\left( u_j \frac{\partial T_j}{\partial x} + v_j \frac{\partial T_j}{\partial y} \right) = \left[ -\frac{2\rho_{L\infty} V_\infty^2}{R} \sin\left(\frac{2x}{R}\right) u \right]_j + \frac{\partial}{\partial y}\left( \lambda_j \frac{\partial T_j}{\partial y} \right) \tag{13.2-5}$$

where the index j denotes whether the vapor or the liquid region is being described.

The boundary conditions and the vapor (without subscript)–liquid (with subscript L) interface conditions are

$$y = 0; \quad u = 0, \quad v = 0, \quad T = T_w, \tag{13.2-6}$$

$$y = \delta; \quad u = u_L, \quad \mu \frac{\partial u}{\partial y} = \mu_L \frac{\partial u_L}{\partial y}, \quad T = T_L = T_{si}(x),$$

$$\rho\left( v - u \frac{d\delta}{dx} \right) = \rho_L \left( v_L - u_L \frac{d\delta}{dx} \right) \tag{13.2-7}$$

$$-\lambda \frac{\partial T}{\partial y} + q_r = -\lambda_L \frac{\partial T_L}{\partial y} - \rho\left( v - u \frac{d\delta}{dx} \right) h_{fg} \tag{13.2-8}$$

$$y = \delta + \delta_L; \quad u_L = 2V_\infty \sin\left(\frac{x}{R}\right), \quad T_L = T_\infty \tag{13.2-9}$$

#### 13.2.1.1 Local-similarity transformations.
To simplify Eqs. (13.2-3) to (13.2-9), Chou and Witte (1995) developed a local-similarity transformation—a well-known technique for computing the heat transfer in the non-separated region on bluff bodies. The detailed steps of the transformation are given by Chou and Witte (1995); only a summary is presented here. Stream functions for the vapor and liquid are defined, and it is assumed that they can be separated by two single-variable functions $\Phi(\zeta)$ and $f(\eta)$ so that

$$[f(\eta)]_j = \left[ \frac{\psi}{M\Phi(\zeta)} \right]_j, \tag{13.2-10}$$

where $\zeta$ and h are new independent variables, defined as

$$\zeta = \frac{x}{R}, \qquad \eta_j = N_j \frac{\gamma_j(\zeta)}{R} \int_{\substack{0(j=v) \\ \text{or} \\ \delta(j=L)}}^{y} \left(\frac{\rho}{\rho_s}\right)_j dy \qquad (13.2\text{-}11)$$

where

$$M_j(\nu_s)_j \left[g(\rho_{L\infty} - \rho_s)R^3/\left(\nu_s^2 \rho_s\right)\right]_j^{1/4}, \qquad N_j = (M/\nu_s)_j \qquad (13.2\text{-}12)$$

The following variables for the vapor and the liquid layers are introduced:

$$\theta = \frac{T - T_s}{\Delta T_{sat}}, \qquad \theta_L = \frac{T_L - T_\infty}{\Delta T_{sub}}, \qquad (13.2\text{-}13)$$

$$q_{rp} = \frac{\sigma_s}{1/\varepsilon_w + 1/\alpha - 1}\left[T_w^4 - T_{si}^4(\zeta)\right],$$

where $q_{rp}$ is the radiation heat flux between two parallel plates.

The transformed equations become a set of ordinary differential equations locally for any given location $\zeta$ that yields a local-similarity solution. By assigning a succession of $\zeta$ values, the streamwise dependence of velocity and temperature fields can be determined.

**13.2.1.2 Selected results of the model.** The equations were solved using a finite-difference method. Once f is obtained, $\psi$ can be found, which in turn gives both the u- and v-components of velocity everywhere. Energy is balanced at the vapor-liquid interface to determine $\delta$.

The temperature profiles in the vapor are virtually linear, suggesting that conduction dominates heat transfer in the vapor film. In the liquid, however, the T-distributions are in general non-linear, indicating that convection plays a role in the total heat transfer in the liquid.

The effects of bulk liquid velocity, superheat, cylinder diameter, and system pressure were also studied (see Chou and Witte, 1995). Results showed that the velocities of the vapor and liquid layers are increased with bulk liquid velocity, as expected. $\delta$ is reduced with increased bulk liquid velocity. For a given angle $\zeta$, $\delta$ increases with the superheat $\Delta T_{sat}$ and the cylinder diameter, D. The effect of $\Delta T_{sat}$ on $\delta$ is nearly linear. For a given angle $\zeta$, increasing the system pressure p has only a small effect on $\delta$ in the p-range explored by Chou.

## 13.2.2 Uniform Heat Flux Models

Shoji and Montasser (1993) used an extension of Witte and Orozco's model to study the influence of a uniform $q_w$ condition on flow film boiling from cylinders.

In this analysis, $\delta$ and $T_w$ must take on values necessary to accommodate the imposed q. They showed that local Nu's for the uniform-q condition were about 25% higher than those for the uniform-$T_w$ model at any given location.

### 13.2.3 The Wake Region

Until recenly, most analyses simply omitted the heat transfer in the wake region. Chou and Witte (1995), however, attempted to include the wake region in their heat transfer analysis from a uniform $T_w$ cylinder. The wake begins at the separation points predicted by the analysis described in the previous sections. The vapor was assumed to form a continuous, smooth, and steady film layer (vapor bubble) in the wake. The $\delta$ of the wake region must match the $\delta$ at the same point on the front part of the body. Based on these assumptions, Chou performed energy and mass balances as follows.

**13.2.3.1 Energy balance.** Considering the right half of a symmetric vapor bubble, as shown in Figure 3, for steady-state, the heat flow-in from the front part at the separation point, $Q_{sp}$, and the heat conducted-in from the hot cylinder wall, $Q_w$, should balance the net heat flow-out across the vapor-liquid interface, $Q_\delta$, i.e.,

$$Q_{sp} + Q_w = Q_\delta \qquad (13.2\text{-}14)$$

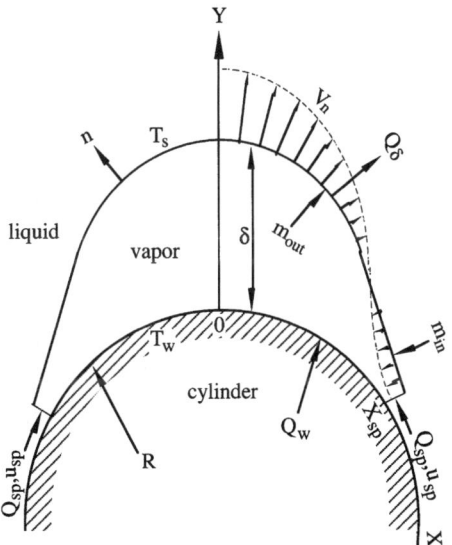

**Figure 3** Two-dimensional wake model (Chou and Witte, 1995).

where

$$Q_{sp} = \int_0^{\delta_{sp}} \left(\lambda \frac{\partial T}{\partial X}\right)_{sp} dY + \int_0^{\delta_{sp}} (\rho u h)_{sp} dY$$

$$Q_w = \int_0^{X_{sp}} \left(-\lambda \frac{\partial T}{\partial Y}\right)_w dX$$

$$Q_\delta = \int_0^{X_{sp}} \left(-\lambda \frac{\partial T}{\partial n}\right) \sqrt{1+\delta'^2}\, dX + \int_0^{X_{sp}} (\rho_s V_n h_s) \sqrt{1+\delta'^2}\, dX$$

**13.2.3.2 Mass balance.** For a steady-state vapor bubble, the mass flow-in from the front part at the separation point, $m_{sp}$, and across the lower part of the bubble interface, $m_{in}$, should balance the mass flow-out across the upper part of the bubble interface, $m_{out}$, i.e.,

$$m_{sp} + m_{in} = m_{out}$$

where

$$m_{sp} = \int_0^{\delta_{sp}} (\rho u)_{sp}\, dY$$

and

$$m_{out} - m_{in} = \int_0^{X_{sp}} \rho_s V_n \sqrt{1+\delta'^2}\, dX$$

is the net mass flux across the interface.
Therefore, we have

$$\int_0^{X_{sp}} \rho_s V_n \sqrt{1+\delta'^2}\, dX = \int_0^{\delta_{sp}} (\rho u)_{sp}\, dY \qquad (13.2\text{-}15)$$

Combining energy and mass balance equations (13.2-14) and (13.2-15) gives

$$\int_0^{X_{sp}} \left(\lambda_w \frac{\partial T}{\partial Y}\right)_w dX - \int_0^{X_{sp}} \left(\lambda_s \frac{\partial T}{\partial n}\right) \sqrt{1+\delta'^2}\, dX = Q'_{sp} \qquad (13.2\text{-}16)$$

where

$$Q'_{sp} = \int_0^{\delta_{sp}} \left[\lambda \frac{\partial T}{\partial X} + \rho u (h - h_s)\right]_{sp} dY$$

$Q'_{sp}$ is evaluated at the separation section ($X = X_{sp}$) and thus can be obtained using the numerical results on the front of the cylinder at the separation point.

By applying $\theta = (T - T_s)/(T_w - T_s)$, $\tau = X/X_{sp}$ and $\omega = Y/\delta$, a regular flat interface results, and Eq. (13.2-16) can be transformed into

$$\Delta T_{sat} X_{sp} \int_0^1 \left\{ \frac{\lambda_w}{\delta}\left(\frac{\partial \theta}{\partial \omega}\right)_{\omega=0} + \lambda_s \left[\frac{1}{X_{sp}^2}\frac{d\delta}{d\tau}\left(\frac{\partial \theta}{\partial \tau} - \frac{1}{\delta}\frac{d\delta}{d\tau}\frac{\partial \theta}{\partial \omega}\right) - \frac{1}{\delta}\frac{\partial \theta}{\partial \omega}\right]_{\omega=1} \right\} d\tau$$
$$= Q'_{sp} \tag{13.2-17}$$

To solve Eq. (13.2-17), the following additional assumptions were made:

- $\theta = 1 - \omega$ (linear temperature distribution across the vapor film) (13.2-18)
- $\delta(\tau) = A[1 + \cos(\pi \tau)] + \delta_{sp}$, where $A = [\delta(0) - \delta_{sp}]/2$; cosine function for the interface shape) (13.2-19)

The cosine shape gives a closed curve that satisfies the boundary conditions: $\delta = \delta_{sp}$ at $X = X_{sp}$; $\delta' = 0$ at $X = 0$; and $\delta = \delta_{max}$ at $X = 0$. By applying the assumed temperature and interface profiles and integrating Eq. (13.2-17), we get

$$\frac{\pi^2 \lambda_s \Delta T_{sat}}{X_{sp}}\left[A + \delta_{sp} - \sqrt{\delta_{sp}(2A + \delta_{sp})}\right] - \frac{(\lambda_w - \lambda_s)\Delta T_{sat} X_{sp}}{\sqrt{\delta_{sp}(2A + \delta_{sp})}} = Q'_{sp}. \tag{13.2-20}$$

Equation (13.2-20) yields a unique solution for the variable 'A' that determines a cosine shape given in Eq. (13.2-19).

The average $\bar{\alpha}$ is determined by integrating the local $\alpha$ over the entire surface. The integration includes the front and the wake of the cylinder. In other words, the $\bar{\alpha}$ of a cylinder can be calculated by using the following equation:

$$\bar{\alpha} = \frac{Q}{2\pi R(T_w - T_s)}, \tag{13.2-21}$$

where Q is the total heat transfer over the entire cylinder surface given by

$$Q = \int_0^\pi \alpha(\zeta) \Delta T_{sat} R \, d\zeta \tag{13.2-22}$$

The average Nu for a cylinder can then be calculated as:

$$Nu = \frac{\bar{\alpha} D}{\lambda}, \tag{13.2-23}$$

where $\lambda$ is evaluated at $(T_w + T_s)/2$. The numerical solutions for Nu as a function of liquid subcooling at one set of system variables are shown in Figure 4. It is clear that Nu is a strong function of liquid subcooling.

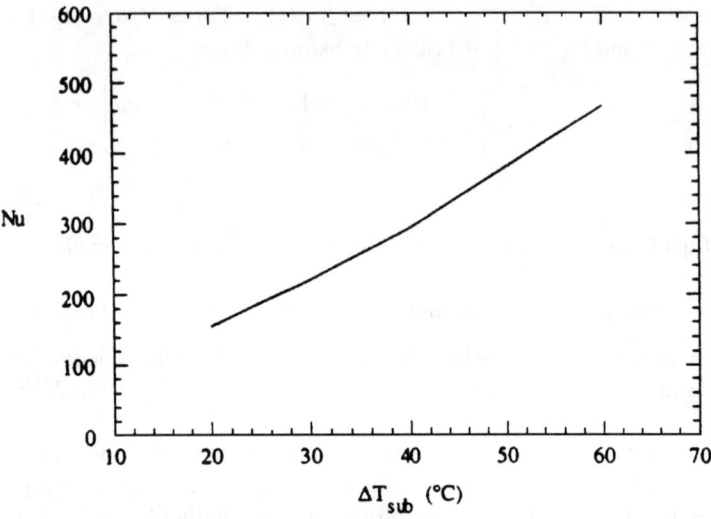

**Figure 4**  The effect of liquid subcooling on average Nusselt number for a 3.2-mm cylinder for water at 2.95 m/s: $\varepsilon_w = 0.12$, $\Delta T_{sub} = 515°C$, p = 0.313 MPa, $Pr_v = 0.85$, $Re_L = 77,400$, $Ja_L = 0.03$ to 0.1 (Chou and Witte, 1995).

The relative magnitude ($Q_{wake}/Q_{front}$) of wake and front heat transfer is increased with increased subcooling, as shown in Figure 5. The magnitude is up to about 20% at high subcooling and therefore should not be neglected, especially at high subcooling. This result helps explain why previous flow-film-boiling models that neglected the wake underestimated experimental data by a significant amount.

## 13.3 DATA CORRELATION AND COMPARISON TO THEORY

### 13.3.1 Cylinders

Bromley et al. (1953) found that the results of their analysis of flow film boiling did not correlate data very well. Consequently, they turned to dimensional reasoning to develop a correlation. For saturated boiling, Bromley found separate correlations that fit different velocities according to the value of the parameter $V/(gD)^{1/2}$.

$$\bar{\alpha} = 0.62 \left[ \frac{\lambda_v^3 g \rho_v (\rho_l - \rho_v) h_{fg}}{\mu_v D \Delta T_{sat}} \right]^{1/4} \quad \text{where} \quad \frac{V_\infty}{\sqrt{gD}} < 1 \quad (13.3\text{-}1)$$

This is the same expression that Bromley developed for pool film boiling, so it is apparent that this fits data when the influence of forced convection is low. He also

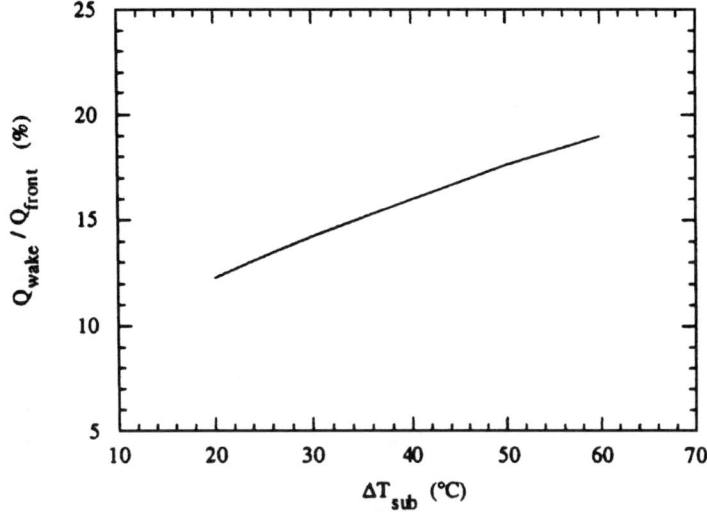

**Figure 5** Relative magnitudes of wake and front heat transfer at different subcoolings for a 3.2-mm cylinder for water at 2.95 m/s. $\varepsilon_w = 0.12$, $\Delta T_{sub} = 515°C$, $p = 0.313$ MPa, $Pr_v = 0.85$, $Re_L = 77,400$, $Ja_L = 0.01$ to $0.1$ (Chou and Witte, 1995).

proposed that

$$\bar{\alpha} = 2.7 \left[ \frac{\rho_v V_\infty \lambda_v h_{fg}}{D \Delta T_{sat}} \right]^{1/2} \quad \text{when} \quad \frac{V_\infty}{\sqrt{gD}} > 2 \quad (13.3\text{-}2)$$

Epstein and Hauser (1980) developed a semi-theoretical correlation for horizontal cylinders, based on their analysis for heat transfer in the near-stagnation region of the cylinder. Their correlation is

$$\frac{\beta Nu_v}{\sqrt{Re_l}} = 2.5 Z^{1/2} \quad \text{for } V_\infty > \sqrt{gD} \quad (13.3\text{-}3)$$

The factor Z is defined as

$$Z = \frac{1}{27 A_1} + \left( \frac{4}{3\pi} \right)^2 \left( \frac{B_1}{A_1} \right)^4 \quad (13.3\text{-}4)$$

and

$$\beta = \left[ \sqrt{\frac{\rho_v}{\rho_l}} \frac{v_v}{v_l} \right]^2, \quad A_1 = c_{pv} \Delta T_{sat} / (Pr_v h_{fg}),$$

$$B_1 = \beta \left( \frac{\lambda_l}{\lambda_v} \right) \left[ \frac{c_{pv} \Delta T_{sat}}{Pr_v h_{fg}} \right] Pr_l^{1/2}$$

Liu et al. (1992) found that Epstein and Hauser's correlation agreed reasonably well with their experimental data for larger cylinders but not for smaller ones; thus, Liu concluded that a more general correlation was needed.

Yilmaz and Westwater (1980) found that they could correlate their data for flow film boiling of R-113 in a manner similar to Bromley et al. (1953):

$$\bar{\alpha} = 3.68 \left[ \frac{\rho_v V_\infty \lambda_v h_{fg}}{D \Delta T_{sat}} \right]^{1/2}$$

the only exception being the lead constant, 3.68, compared to 2.7 for Bromley's correlation.

Chou et al. (1995) compared her solution (described in previous sections) that includes the $Q_{wake}$ to the data of Motte and Bromley (1953), Yilmaz and Westwater (1980), Chang and Witte (1990), Sankaran and Witte (1990), and Liu et al. (1992). Figure 6 shows a comparison between available experimental data, the correlation,

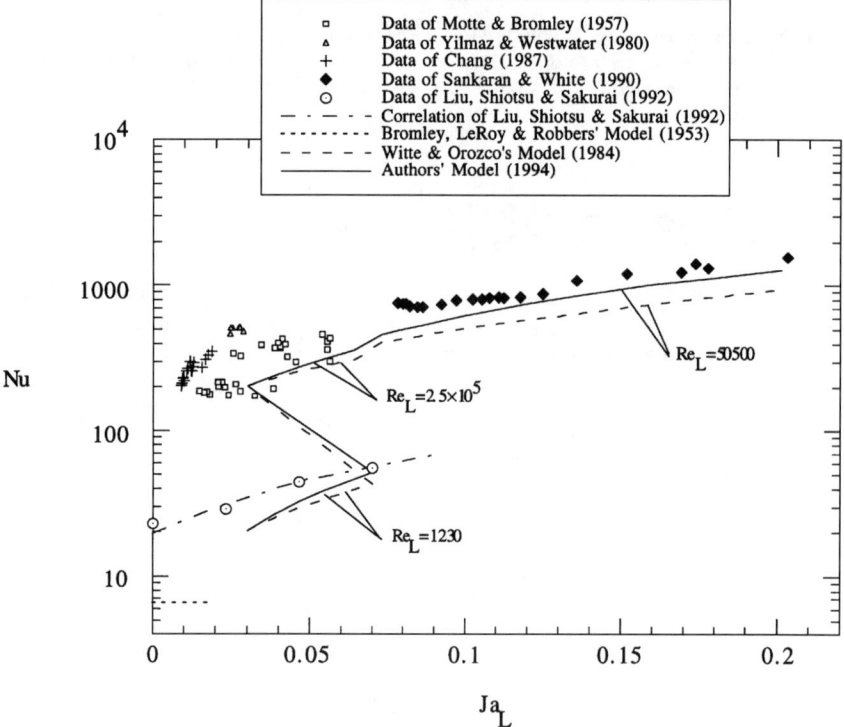

**Figure 6**  Comparison of various models to experimental data and correlations (Chou et al., 1995).

and the models of Chou and Witte, Witte and Orozco, and Bromley, Leroy, and Robbers. The data are plotted as average vapor Nu vs. liquid Ja, which represents the liquid subcooling. Three different Re's are used that represent as close a match as possible to experimental conditions. The model by Bromley et al. (1953) did not consider the liquid subcooling effect; therefore, it can be used only for very small subcooling cases.

As shown in Figure 6, Motte and Bromley's data are scattered in their subcooling range. Both the Chou/Witte and the Witte/Orozco models predict lower heat transfer than the data. It should be pointed out that Motte and Bromley's data overlap the $Ja_L$ range where the Chou/Witte model begins to lose its applicability. The applicable range of the Chou/Witte model is for $Ja_l > 0.04$, and non-zero liquid velocity. The data of Chang and Yilmaz and Westwater fall at $Ja_L$ values less than the applicable range of the Chou/Witte model. Hence, comparative calculations were not performed for those data.

Figure 6 shows that the Chou/Witte model is in better agreement with the subcooled-flow-film boiling data than the previous models. The merit of the Chou/Witte model is much more obvious at high Ja than at low Ja. The model of Bromley et al. is significantly lower than the data, especially with increasing Ja. The Witte/Orozco model is better than Bromley's model; however, it diverges from the data when subcooling is increased. The Chou/Witte model yields higher q results than the previous models. The difference between the Chou/Witte model and the Witte/Orozco model is greater at higher Ja, and the two models are closer at lower subcooling, since $Q_{wake}$ is less important at lower Ja. The Chou/Witte model gives closer predictions to experimental data than previous models, especially at high subcooling.

Figure 6 also shows selected data from Liu et al. (1992), along with the correlation developed by Liu. Their correlation indeed fits their data better in the low $Ja_L$ range than does the Chou/Witte model. However, at the higher $Ja_L$ end of Liu's data, the Chou/Witte model results appear to coincide well with the experimental data. Because Liu's correlation was based on data limited to relatively low $Ja_L$ and $Re_L$ ranges, it was deemed inappropriate to extend it into the range where it could be compared to Sankaran's data.

Montasser (1994) compared his data for cylinders to those of Motte and Bromley (1957), Yilmaz and Westwater (1980), Sankaran and Witte (1990), and Chang and Witte (1990). The result is shown in Figure 7. The data are plotted in terms of modified Nu and Ja (as shown below). Also shown on the figure is the correlation

$$Nu^{**} = 0.41 \left(Ja_l^{**}\right)^{1.38} \tag{13.3-5}$$

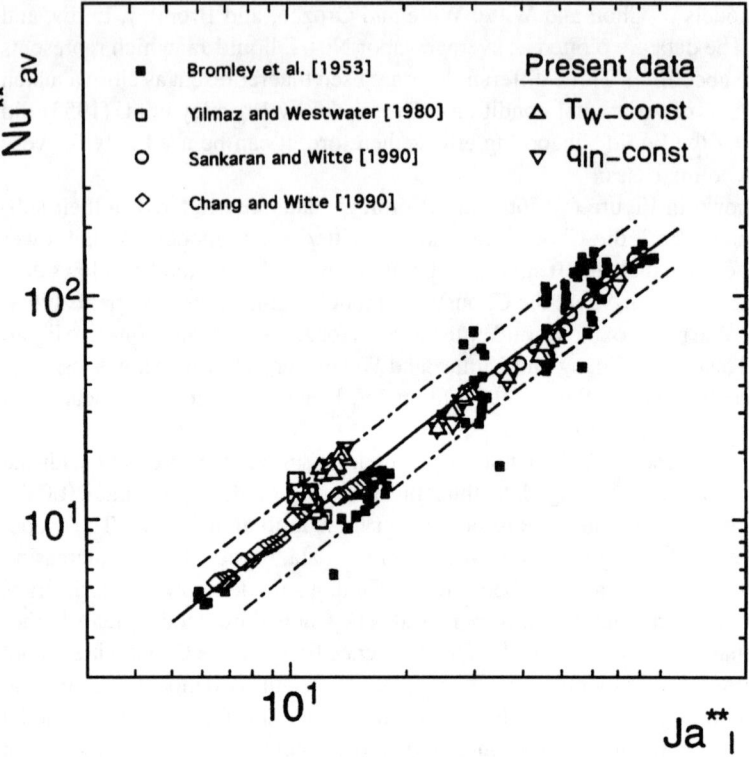

**Figure 7** Comparison of data for flow film boiling from cylindrical heaters (Montasser, 1994).

where

$$Nu^{**} = Nu^* \left(Ja_v^{**}\right)^{n_{sub}}, \quad Nu^* = \frac{Nu}{\sqrt{Re_v \dfrac{\rho_l}{\rho_v}}},$$

$$Ja_l^{**} = \frac{Ja_l \dfrac{\rho_l}{\rho_v}}{\sqrt{Pr_l \dfrac{\mu_v}{\mu_l}}}, \quad Ja_v^{**} = \frac{Ja_v \dfrac{\rho_l}{\rho_v}}{Pr_v}$$

and

$$n_{sub} = 0.356 \left( \frac{Ja_l \dfrac{\rho_l}{\rho_v}}{\sqrt{Pr_l \dfrac{\mu_v}{\mu_l}}} \right)^{0.24}$$

The figure shows that Montasser's data are in good agreement with those of Sankaran and Witte. Motte and Bromley's data are widely scattered within the range of $Ja_l^{**}$. The data are correlated to within ±40% by Eq. (13.3-5).

Liu et al. (1992) obtained an extensive set of data for different fluids over a fairly wide range of velocities, pressures, diameters, and subcoolings. They developed correlations for saturated liquids as well as for subcooled liquids. For saturated conditions, their correlation took the form of

$$\frac{Nu_v}{\left(1 + \frac{2}{Nu_v}\right)} = H(Fr, D')K(D')M^{1/4} \qquad (13.3\text{-}6)$$

where Fr is a Froude number, $V^2/gD$. The Nu is defined as $Nu_v = \alpha_{co}D/\lambda$, where $\alpha_{co}$ is the convective part of the heat transfer only. Other parameters are defined as follows

$$D' = D\left[g\frac{(\rho_l - \rho_v)}{\sigma}\right]^{1/2},$$

and

$$H(Fr, D') = (1 + 0.68Fr^{0.625})^{0.4} + 0.45\tanh[0.4(D' - 1.3)Fr]$$

The parameter K(D') depends upon the value of D' as

$$K(D') = 0.44(D')^{-1/4} \quad \text{for } D' < 0.14$$

$$K(D') = \frac{0.75}{(1 + 0.28D')} \quad 0.14 \leq D' \leq 1.25$$

$$K(D') = \frac{21D'}{(1 + 3.0D')} \quad 1.25 \leq D' \leq 6.6$$

$$K(D') = 0.415(D')^{1/4} \quad D' \geq 6.6$$

The factor M is one that Liu et al. developed for pool film boiling and is defined as

$$M = \frac{Gr}{Sp}\left[\frac{E^3}{1 + \frac{E}{SpPr_l}}\right](RPr_lSp)^{-2}$$

where $Sp$ is the nondimensional superheat

$$Sp = \frac{C_p\Delta T_{sat}}{h'_{fg}Pr_v}$$

and

$$E = (A + C\sqrt{B})^{1/3} + (A - C\sqrt{B})^{1/3} + \frac{1}{3}Sc^*$$

$$A = \frac{1}{27}Sc^{*3} + \frac{1}{3}R^2 Sp Pr_l + \frac{1}{4}R^2 Sp^2 Pr_l^2$$

$$B = \frac{-4}{27}Sc^{*2} + \frac{2}{3}Sp Pr_l Sc^* - \frac{32}{27}Sp R^2 Pr_l + \frac{1}{4}Sp^2 Pr_l^2 + \frac{2}{27}Sc^{*3}/R^2$$

$$C = \frac{1}{2}R^2 Sp Pr_l, \quad Sc = \frac{C_{pl} \Delta T_{sub}}{h'_{fg}}, \quad Sc^* = 0.93 Pr_L^{0.22} Sc$$

Sc is a nondimensional subcooling while $Sc^*$ is a modified subcooling parameter. The Grashof number also appears in M and is defined below, along with the modified latent heat and R.

$$Gr = \frac{g(\rho_l - \rho_v)D^3}{\rho_v \nu_v^2}, \quad h'_{fg} = h + 0.5 c_{pv} \Delta T_{sat}, \quad R = \sqrt{\frac{\rho_v \mu_v}{\rho_l \mu_l}}$$

Liu found that he could use the same basic form of Eq. (13.3-6) to correlate subcooled data if a modification of Sc is performed. He redefined Sc as $Sc^* = K_{sc} Sc$, where $K_{sc}$ must take on appropriate values to fit experimental data. Liu found he could fit an equation for the modified $K_{sc}$, shown below

$$K_{sc} = 0.92 Pr_l^{0.22} + 0.18 (Fr Pr_l)^{0.22}$$

For purposes of data correlation, Liu recast Eq. (13.3-6) into the form

$$N = Nu_v/(1 + 2/Nu_v)/K(D')/H(Fr, D') = M^{1/4} \quad (13.3\text{-}7)$$

Figure 8 shows Liu's data for water at various pressures compared to Eq. (13.3-7). The agreement is excellent. Comparisons to other data for water and R-113 (1992) show equally good agreement between the correlating equation and the data.

Liu also compared his correlation to the data of Shigechi (1983). Liu's correlation, accounting for radiation, predicts Shigechi's data to within $-15\%$ to $+20\%$, which is a reasonably good fit for boiling data.

### 13.3.2 Spheres

Liu and Theofanous (1995b) found that they could correlate their data for spheres in single phase flow with separate expressions for saturated and subcooled conditions. For saturated water, they found

$$Nu_s = 0.5 Re_l^{1/2} \frac{\mu_l}{\mu_v} \left( \frac{K R^4}{Sp} \right)^{1/4} \quad (13.3\text{-}8)$$

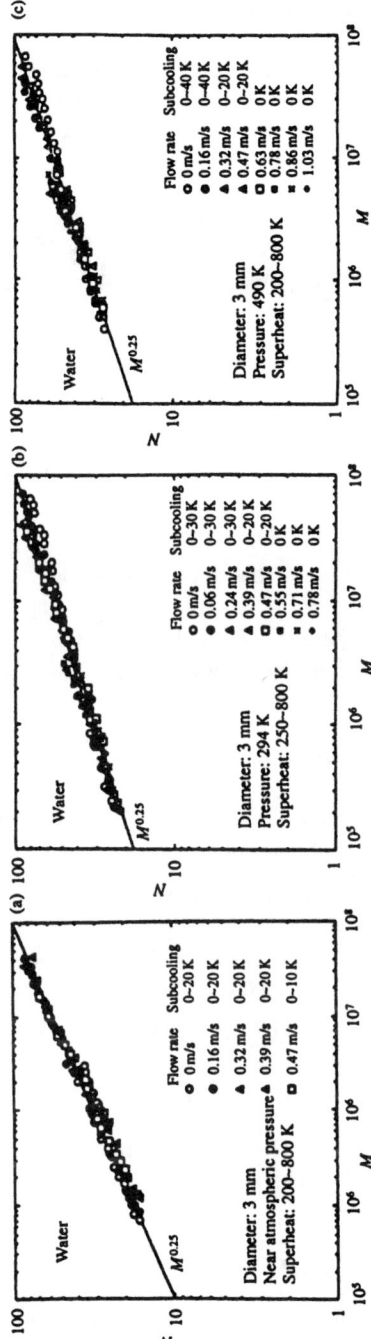

**Figure 8 (a), (b), (c)** Comparison of flow film boiling correlation with experimental data on 3-mm dia. cylinders in subcooled water at various pressures (Liu et al., 1992).

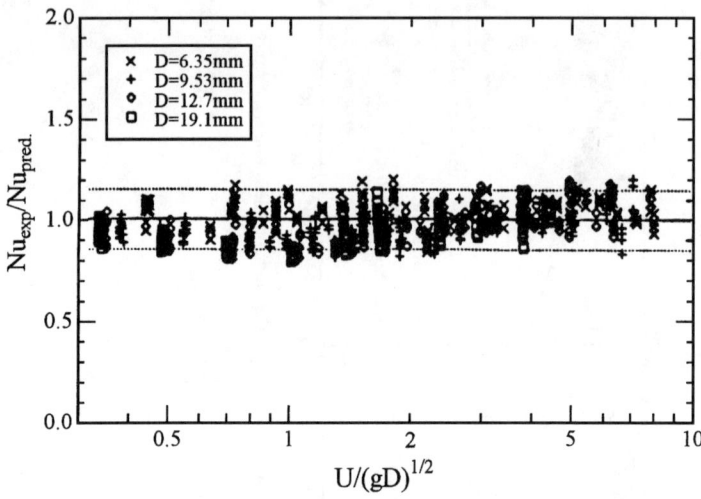

**Figure 9** Comparison of the data of Liu and Theofanous (1995b) to their correlation, (13.3-10).

correlated their data well, where $K$, $R$, and $Sp$ are the same as used by Liu et al. (1992) for film boiling from cylinders. For subcooled flow, they found the correlation

$$Nu_{sc} = Nu_s + 0.07 Re_l^{0.77} Pr_l^{0.5} \frac{\mu_l}{\mu_v} \frac{Sc}{Sp} \qquad (13.3\text{-}9)$$

worked well, where $Sc$ is the subcooling parameter defined by Liu et al. They found a general correlation by combining Eqs. (13.3-8) and (13.3-9), which is

$$Nu = \left[Nu_p^5 + (F(Fr)Nu_{sc}))^5\right]^{1/5} \qquad (13.3\text{-}10)$$

where

$$Nu_p = 0.64(Ar/Sp)^{1/4} \qquad (13.3\text{-}11)$$

Ar is the Archimedes number, and F(Fr) is an empirical function

$$Ar = \frac{g(\rho_l - \rho_v)D^3}{\rho_v \nu_v^2}, \qquad F(Fr) = 1 - \frac{0.2}{1 + |Fr^{0.5} - 1|}$$

Figure 9 shows the data of Liu and Theofanous plotted in terms of the Fr. It shows that the data can be correlated in a band within ± 15%.

## 13.4 CONCLUDING REMARKS

In this article, a review of the status of present-day understanding of external flow film boiling has been undertaken. The concentration was on flow film boiling over bodies that have wakes behind them—primarily cylinders and spheres. A brief review of a typical analytical method of treating the phenomenon was presented. Analyses can be characterized as being laminar boundary-layer-like on the forward portions of the bodies, with few attempts at modelling the heat transfer in the wake until just recently. Emphasis was placed on the correlations that have been developed to predict film boiling heat transfer.

It is clear that our understanding of flow film boiling is incomplete, especially as it relates to treating the behavior of film boiling wakes properly.

# REFERENCES

Bromley, L. A., LeRoy, N. R., and Robbers, J. A. 1953. Heat Transfer in Forced Convection Film Boiling. *Ind. and Eng. Chem.* 45(12):2639–2646.

Chang, K. H. and Witte, L. C. 1990. Liquid-Solid Contact During Flor Film Boiling of Subcooled Freon-11. *J. Ht. Trans.* 112:465–471.

Chappidi, P. R., Gunnerson, F. S., and Pasamehmetoglu, K. O. 1991. Subcooled Forced Convection Film Boiling Drag and Heat Transfer of a Wedge. *J. Therm. and Ht. Trans.* 5(3):355–365.

Chou, X. S. and Witte, L. C. 1995. Subcooled Flow Film Boiling Across a Horizontal Cylinder, Part I: Analytical Model. *J. Ht Trans.* 117(1):167–174.

Chou, X. S., Witte, L. C., and Sankaran, S. 1995. Subcooled Flow Film Boiling Across a Horizontal Cylinder, Part II: Comparison to Experimental Data. *J. Ht Trans.* 117(1):175–178.

Epstein, M. and Hauser, G. 1980. Subcooled Forced Convection Film Boiling in the Forward Stagnation Region of a Sphere or Cylinder. *Int. J. Ht. Mass Trans.* 23:179–189.

Fodemski, T. R. 1992. Forced Convection Film Boiling in the Stagnation Region of a Molten Drop and Its Application to Vapor Explosions. *Int. J. Ht. Mass Trans.* 35(8):2005–2016.

Fodemski, T. R. and Hall, W. B. 1982. Forced Convection Boiling on a Sphere in a Subcooled or Superheated Liquid. *Proc. 7th Int. Ht. Trans. Conf.* Volume 4, pp. 375–379, Munich.

Huang, L., and L. C. Witte, 1996. An Experimental Investigation of the Effects of Subcooling and Velocity on Boiling of Freon-113, *J. Ht. Trans*, 118(2):436–441.

Kobayashi, K. 1965. Film Boiling Heat Transfer Around a Sphere in Forced Convection. *J. Nucl. Sci. and Tech.* 2(2):62–67.

Liu, C, and Theofanous, T. G. 1995a. Film Boiling on Spheres in Single- and Two-Phase, Part II: A Theoretical Study. *Proc. of 1995 National Heat Transfer Conference (ANS)*, pp. 48–61.

Liu, C. and Theofanous, T. G. 1995b. Film Boiling on Spheres in Single- and Two-Phase, Part I: Experimental Studies. *Proc. of 1995 National Heat Transfer Conference (ANS)*, pp. 34–47.

Liu, Q. S., Shiotsu, M., and Sakurai, A. 1992. A Correlation for Forced Convection Film Boiling Heat Transfer from a Horizontal Cylinder Under Subcooled Conditions. *Fundamentals of Subcooled Flow Boiling, ASME 1992*, HTD-Vol. 217:21–32.

Montasser, O. 1994. Effect of Wall Heat Flux Conditions on Cross Flow Film Boiling Heat Transfer. Ph.D. Dissertation, University of Tokyo.

Motte, E. A. and Bromley, L. A. 1957. Film Boiling of Flowing Subcooled Liquids. *Ind. and Eng. Chem.* 49(11):1921–1928.

Sankaran, S. and Witte, L. C. 1990. Highly Subcooled Flow Boiling of Freon-113 over Cylinders. Presented at the AIAA/ASME Heat Transfer and Thermophysics Conference, Seattle; ASME HTD Vol. 136:29–34.

Shigechi, T. 1983. Studies on External Forced Convection Film Boiling Heat Transfer. Doctoral Thesis, Kyushu University, Japan (in Japanese).

Shoji, M. and Montasser, O. 1993. Theoretical Analysis of Uniform Wall Heat Flux and Uniform Wall Temperature Forced Convection Film Boiling Heat Transfer. *J. Faculty Engineering, The University of Tokyo (B)* XLII, (1):41–56.

Theofanous, T. G., Houze, R. N., and Brumfield, L. K. 1976. Turbulent Mass Transfer at Free, Gas-Liquid Interface, with Applications to Open-Channel, Bubble, and Jet Flows. *Int. J. Ht. Mass Trans.* 19:613–624.

Walsh, S. and Wilson, S. D. R. 1979. Boundary-Layer Flow in Forced Convection Film Boiling on a Wedge. *Int. J. Ht. Mass Trans.* 22:596–574.

Wilson, S. D. R. 1979. Steady and Transient Film Boiling on a Sphere in Forced Convection. *Int. J. Ht. Mass Trans.* 22:207–218.

Witte, L. C. 1968. Film Boiling From a Sphere. *I. E. C.-Fundamentals* 7(3):517.

Witte, L. C. and Orozco, J. 1984. The Effect of Vapor Velocity Profile Shape on Flow Film Boiling from Submerged Bodies. *J. Ht. Trans.* 106:191–197.

Yilmaz, S. and Westwater, J. W. 1980. Effect of Velocity on Heat Transfer to Boiling Freon-113. *J. Ht. Trans.* 102:26–31.

CHAPTER
# FOURTEEN

## AUGMENTATION TECHNIQUES AND EXTERNAL FLOW BOILING

**14.1 Masanori Monde**

*Saga University, 1 Honjo Saga, 840 Japan*

**14.2 Tatsuhiro Ueda**

*University of Tokyo, Tokyo, 113 Japan*

**14.2 Yasuo Koizumi**

*Kogakuin University, Hachioji, Tokyo, 192 Japan*

**14.3 Masanori Monde and Vijay K. Dhir**

*University of California, Los Angeles, CA 90024, USA*

In this chapter, jet impingement technique is discussed extensively under external flow boiling systems. Flow structure under impinging jet is first presented, and then characteristics in boiling heat transfer as well as critical heat flux are discussed. Correlations are presented for predicting critical heat flux in several configurations. Another external flow boiling system investigated here is the falling film evaporation and boiling. Finally, techniques to improve heat transfer and CHF in external flow boiling systems are reviewed.

## 14.1 IMPINGING JETS AND OTHER GEOMETRIES

Boiling provides an efficient heat transfer mechanism for applications such as the cooling of electric components (Incropera, 1988), metal processing (Viskanta and Incropera, 1992), and fusion components (Boyd, 1983), where heat transfer coefficients commonly exceed 10,000 W/(m$^2$K) at relatively high heat fluxes. The critical heat flux (CHF), which defines the upper limit of the efficient range of boiling heat transfer, limits the maximum heat flux that may be dissipated from the components. For enhancement of the CHF, it is important to utilize the boiling

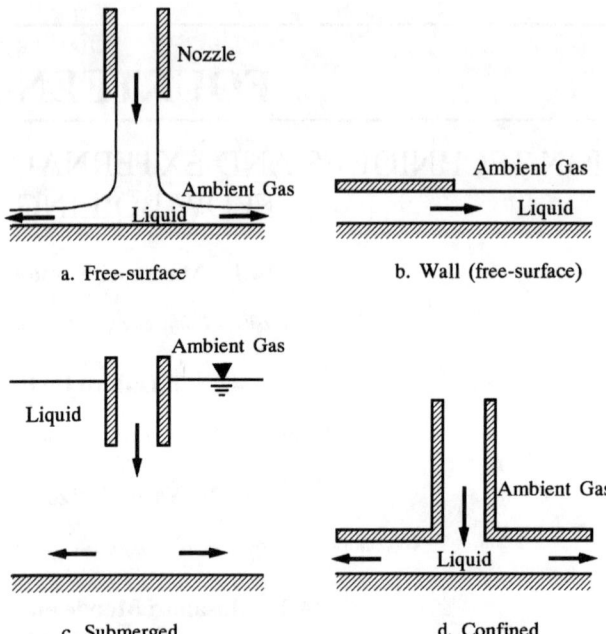

**Figure 1** Schematic of various jet configurations.

heat transfer properly and to satisfy the demands of efficient cooling processes. Jet impingement systems offer a very attractive means to enhance the CHF.

### 14.1.1 Configurations of Jet Impingement Systems

The jet system may be categorized into four different configurations: free-surface jets, submerged jets, confined jets, and wall jets, as schematically shown in Figure 1. From a viewpoint of enhancing heat transfer as well as CHF, one has to first focus on the free-surface jets, especially the circular one, because it provides a simple and basic geometry that can be extended to other configurations.

Circular free-surface impinging jets have been extensively studied (Azuma and Hoshino, 1984; Liu et al., 1991; Stevens and Webb, 1993; Watson, 1964). Figure 2 shows representative flow conditions of velocity profile, pressure change, and the liquid layer thickness. The flow structure in the radial layer is demarcated into impinging zone, laminar region, and turbulent region. Within the impinging zone ($r/(d/2) < 1.57$, r is radius and d is jet diameter; Liu et al., 1991), the liquid is continuously accelerated with decreasing static pressure due to the dynamic

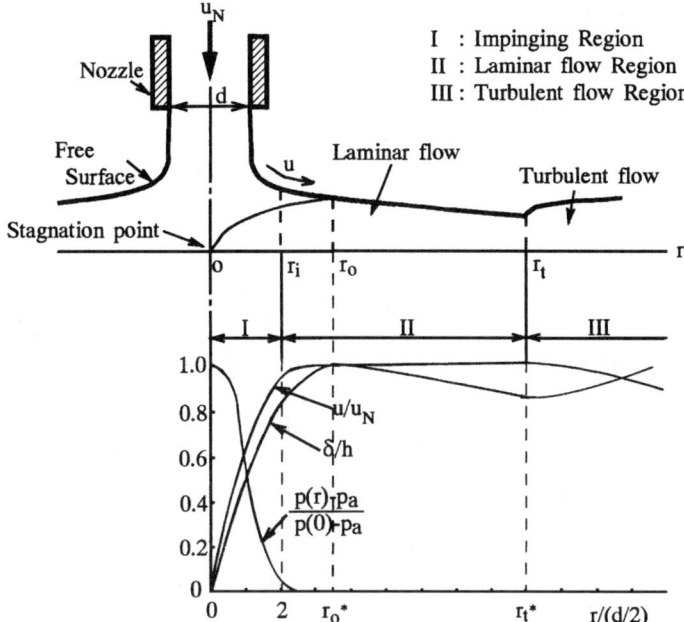

**Figure 2** Distribution of pressure, velocity, and boundary layer thickness for a circular, free surface impinging jet along with the r-direction.

pressure of jet impingement, and then it approaches the jet velocity at the nozzle exit. For the laminar region ($1.57 < r/(d/2) < r_t^*$ ($=600(u_N d/\nu)^{-0.422}$, $u_N$ is jet velocity; Liu et al., 1991), the liquid spreads radially in laminar flow, and the streamwise velocity is essentially that of the jet. The hydrodynamic effects of impingement completely disappear within the flow in this region. The laminar boundary layer is developed along the r-direction and then reaches the free surface at $r_o^*$ ($=0.282(u_N d/\nu)^{-1/3}$ (see Azuma and Hoshino, 1984). Beyond this point, the thickness of the boundary layer starts decreasing, while the streamwise velocity in the layer is almost the same as the jet velocity. For the turbulent region ($r_t^* < r/(d/2)$), the liquid flow becomes turbulent where the streamwise velocity starts decreasing while the liquid film thickness increases.

For the planar free surface jet, the flow characteristics are similar to that of a circular jet, except for a change in the liquid film thickness. For the wall free-surface jet (Figure 1b), the flow conditions are similar to that of a planar jet, except for the existence of an impingement zone.

For submerged and confined arrangements (Figures 1c and d), the flow conditions may be largely influenced by geometrical conditions, such as the distance between nozzle exit and wall and the confined space between nozzle plate and wall. Consequently, these flow conditions become more complicated.

For this reason, much interest has been paid to the free surface jets. In addition, most studies have focused on heat transfer problems in the laminar and turbulent flow regions of the free-surface jets, shown in Figure 1. Heat transfer problems related to the free-surface jet will be mainly discussed in the following sections.

## 14.1.2 Heat Transfer Characteristics

Occurrence of nucleate boiling is generally suppressed or delayed due to the forced convection effects. Therefore, the wall superheat ($\Delta T_{sat} = T_W - T_{sat}$) needed for nucleate boiling to commence is increased, depending on the liquid velocity and subcooling of the jet.

Nucleation is delayed in the film due to improved heat transfer from forced convective effects. After commencement of nucleate boiling, a further increase in heat flux activates more sites, eventually leading into fully developed nucleate boiling.

**Incipience of nucleate boiling.** Few experiments have been conducted on the incipient point of nucleate boiling with impinging jets, so a parametric understanding about it is rather limited. From an application point of view, however, the incipient point is of less interest than understanding the CHF phenomenon and extending the fully developed boiling region further.

**Fully developed nucleate boiling for free-surface jets.** Free-surface jets have been extensively investigated in literature (Copeland, 1970; Furuya et al., 1995; Katto and Ishii, 1978; Katto and Kunihiro, 1973; Katto and Monde, 1974; Monde and Katto, 1978; Monde et al., 1980; Nonn et al., 1988; Ruch and Holman, 1975; Vader et al., 1992). For fully developed nucleate boiling, the heat flux was almost independent of impinging jet velocity, diameter, heater dimension, and surface orientation, and depended only on the wall superheat.

Katto and Monde (1974) pointed out that even for a jet velocity range as large as 5.3–60 m/s with saturated water, the fully developed nucleate boiling curve roughly lay on an monotonic extension of the data for pool boiling to larger heat fluxes and wall superheats. In addition, Monde et al. (1980) reported that even for multiple impinging jets, flow conditions are more complicated compared with a single impinging jet, the number or placement of jets has little effect on the boiling curve except for the degree of scatter in the data, and these data eventually merged into the extension of pool boiling curve (see Figure 3). For a planar free-surface jet of saturated water, the characteristics of boiling heat transfer were reported to be consistent with this result (Furuya et al., 1995; Katto and Ishii, 1978).

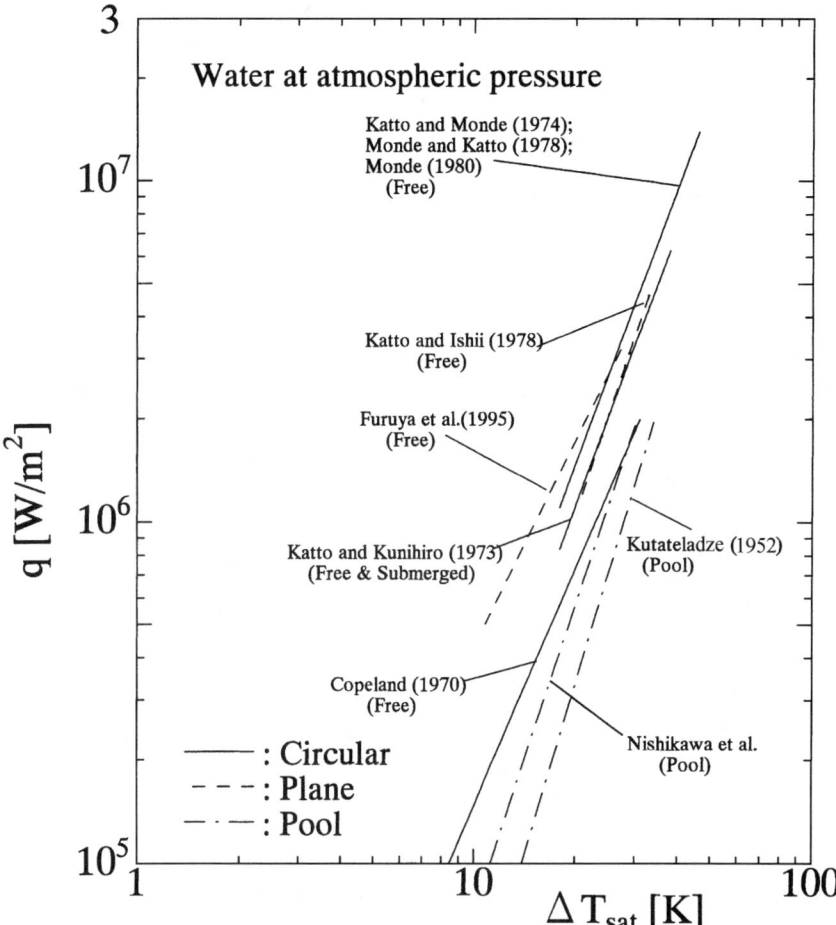

**Figure 3** Comparison of nucleate boiling correlations for free-surface and submerged jets of water with circular, plane, and wall jet configurations. (The lines presented here are chosen to pass through the mean of their respective data. The data scatter around the corresponding line).

Figure 3 depicts a comparison of nucleate boiling curves for free-surface jets for saturated and subcooled water at atmospheric pressure. Despite significant differences between jet configurations, there is generally good agreement between their respective curves and the pool boiling curve (Kutateladze, 1952; Nishikawa and Yamagata, 1960). It should be mentioned that the agreement for Rl13 is rather poor as compared to that for water (Monde and Katto, 1978; Monde et al., 1980; Ruch and Holman, 1975).

Roughly speaking, the heat transfer characteristics for the fully developed nucleate boiling are not significantly different in the jet impingement and pool boiling configurations (Katto and Kunihiro, 1973; Monde and Katto, 1978). The difference between the two is mainly attributed to the different surface conditions, such as roughness and wettability.

The correlations for pool boiling are recommended to predict the heat transfer coefficient for the fully developed nucleate boiling with free-surface jets.

### 14.1.3 Critical Heat Flux

Impinging jet system is capable of cooling at extremely high heat fluxes, more than 10 MW/m$^2$. Effects of system parameters on CHF for some jet configurations are studied extensively, and specific correlations for CHF are available for a number of these configurations with high accuracy. Theoretical understanding of the CHF, however, still is not clear, in spite of some efforts (Kandula, 1990; Lienhard and Eichhorn, 1979; Monde, 1985; Mudawar and Wadsworth, 1991) to model the CHF mechanism for each jet configuration.

**Circular impinging jet.** A number of studies are available for the circular impinging geometry over a wide range of experimental conditions.

*Single jet impingement.* Several authors (Katto and Kunihiro, 1973; Katto and Monde, 1974; Katto and Shimizu, 1979; Monde, 1987; Monde and Katto, 1978; Monde and Okuma, 1985) obtained experimental data for this configuration and categorized the CHF characteristics into four regimes, referred to as the L-, V-, I-, and HP-regimes. The CHF dependence on parameters such as jet velocity and heated diameter markedly changes in each regime (Katto and Shimizu, 1979; Monde, 1987; Monde and Okuma, 1985). As for the general feature of each region, region L appears for low velocity and large disk, either region V or I appears at moderate pressure (whether the CHF depends on the jet velocity or not), and region HP appears at high pressure. Generalized correlations for the CHF in the respective regimes are proposed to predict them with a good accuracy, while the boundaries between them remain ambiguous; the boundary between I- and HP-regimes especially is not yet specified. This is attributed mainly to a shortage of the CHF data in HP-regime. The vast majority of the CHF data belongs to the V-regime, and their reproducibility is also very good.

The following correlations and boundaries are proposed by Monde (1985, 1987), and Monde and Okuma (1985):

For the L-regime

$$\frac{q_{co}}{\rho_g h_{lg} u_N} = k(\rho_l/\rho_g)(d/D)^2 \qquad (14.1\text{-}1)$$

**Table 1 Exponent and constant in Eq. (14.1-2) for each regime**

|  | m | n | k | C |  |
|---|---|---|---|---|---|
| V-regime | 0.645 | 0.343 | −0.364 | 0.221 | Eq. (14.1-2a) |
| I-regime | 0.466 | 0.421 | −0.303 | 0.691 | Eq. (14.1-2b) |
| HP-regime | 1.27 | 0.28 | −0.101 | 0.172 | Eq. (14.1-2c) |

where $\frac{1}{k} = 0.0389(\rho_l/\rho_g)^{0.674}(d/\sqrt{\sigma/g(\rho_l - \rho_g)})^{1.24}$

For the V-I-and HP-regimes,

$$\frac{\dot{q}_{co}}{\rho_g h_{lg} u_N} = C(\rho_l/\rho_g)^m \left(\frac{2\sigma}{\rho_l u_N^2 (D - d)}\right)^2 (1 + D/d)^k \qquad (14.1\text{-}2)$$

where each component, m, n, and k, and the constant, C, are listed for the respective regimes in Table 1. The correlation for the HP-regime should be considered tentative because it is derived from only 24 CHF data points.

For the boundaries between L- and V-regimes, the CHF only in the L-regime appears for

$$D/d \geq 18.4(\rho_l/\rho_g)^{-0.194}(d/\sqrt{\sigma/g(\rho_l - \rho_g)})^{-0.76}(2\sigma/\rho_l u_N^2(D - d))^{-0.209} \qquad (14.1\text{-}3)$$

otherwise, the CHF only in the V-regime appears under the following condition for the boundaries between V- and I-regimes:

$$\begin{aligned}&\rho_l/\rho_g > 67.1 \text{ or} \\ &\rho_l/\rho_g < 67.1\end{aligned} \qquad (14.1\text{-}4a)$$

$$2\sigma/\rho_l u_N^2(D - d) \geq 4.5 \times 10^{-7}(\rho_l/\rho_g)^{2.29}(1 + D/d)^{-0.78} \qquad (14.1\text{-}4b)$$

The boundary between I- and -HP-regimes remains indistinguishable.

Most of the CHF data for each regime can be correlated well within an accuracy of ±20% by corresponding equations.

Aihara et al. (1993) mentioned that the CHF data for liquid nitrogen jet impingement are 20–50% higher than the values evaluated by Eq. (14.1-2) for V-regime. They attribute this to a returning flow produced in an extremely small and confined space.

Other types of correlations have been proposed by Katto and Yokoya (1988) and Sharan and Lienhard (1985). Both correlations have merit in avoiding some uncertainty associated with the demarcation between the regimes and in providing all CHF data without L-regime with an accuracy similar to that for V- and I-regimes.

*Multiple impinging jets for saturated liquid.* The heater size, which can be cooled by a single jet impingement, is limited due to the hydrodynamic character of the

**Table 2 Experimental range for multiple impinging jets**

|  | Water | R113 |
|---|---|---|
| N | 2, 3, 4 | 2, 3, 4 |
| L[mm] | 9.1–24.6 | 9.1–24.6 |
| D[mm] | 2 | 2 |
| $u_N$ | 2.51–15.1 | 3.37–16.5 |
| P[Mpa] | 0.1 | 0.1 |

jets and also to the fact that the CHF continuously decreases with any increase in heater diameter. Therefore, cooling with multiple jets is very attractive for large heaters. Monde et al. (1980) measured the CHF by employing circular, free-surface jets of saturated water and Rl13 within an experimental range listed in Table 2.

Figure 4 shows the various arrangements and the domain controlled by each jet. The distance L denotes the maximum flow length from the position of the jet to the boundary of the domain. Monde and Inoue (1991) concluded that (i) the characteristics of the CHF for single and multiple jets are totally similar in the domain controlled by a jet, in spite of the difference in the appearance of the thin liquid film on the heater, and (ii) Eq. (14.1-2) for a single jet can be simply extended to the CHF for multiple jets by replacing the heater diameter, D, by 2L. The multiple jet data could be correlated with an accuracy of ±20 percent. The reason why multiple jet data can be correlated with single jet correlation may be explained on the basis of the observations (Monde and Katto, 1978; Monde et al., 1980) of flow near the CHF location: (i) most of the liquid is splashed out, while the residual liquid flowing over the heater is still enough to maintain the fully developed nucleate boiling, and (ii) in the domain controlled by a single jet, the flow situation in the domain becomes similar, and the CHF occurs at the same position that is farthest from the position of the impinging jet, independent of any geometrical configuration of the domain.

*Effect of subcooling on CHF.* Visual observations (Monde and Mitsutake, 1996; Monde et al., 1994) show that the flow situation can be divided into subcooled and saturated regions. With increasing heat flux, the saturation region gradually extends from the outer edge of the heated surface toward the center, and conversely, the subcooled region shrinks back. Near the CHF, similar to that in a saturated liquid jet, most of the liquid flowing over the heated surface is splashed out as droplets, but a residual liquid still remains as a very thin liquid film totally covering the heated surface. Consequently, in the saturated region, the flow situation for the subcooled liquid is very similar to that for the saturated liquid.

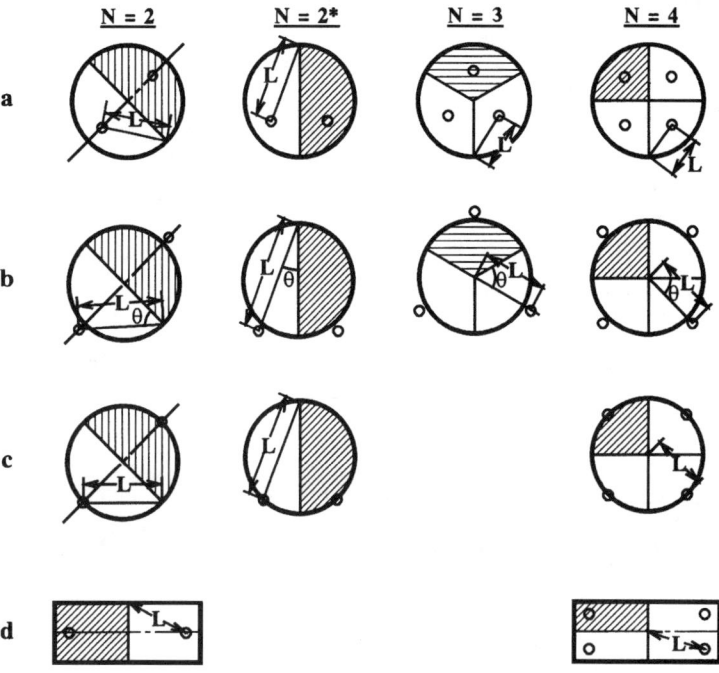

**N** : Number of jets
**○** : Posotion of impinging jet
**▨** : Domain controlled by an impinging jet

**Row a** : Jets impinging inside disk
**Row b** : Jets impinging right outside disk
**Row c** : Jets impinging on the edge
**Row d** : Jets impinging inside rectangle

**Figure 4** Relative location of the jets on the disk heater (Note: * means that the two jets are not located on a diameter).

The CHF for subcooled jets approaches that for the corresponding saturated conditions with decreasing subcooling. Consequently, the effect of the subcooling on the CHF is described by introducing a function similar to $(1 + \varepsilon_{sub})$ such that as $\Delta T_{sub} \to 0$, $\varepsilon_{sub} \to 0$ or $f(\Delta T_{sub}) \to 1$.

Monde et al. (1994) and Monde and Mitsutake (1996) obtained the CHF in the V-regime for single and multiple impinging jets for the range of conditions given in Table 3. They proposed the following generalized correlation to evaluate

**Table 3 Experimental range for subcooled impinging jets**

|  | Water |  | R113 | R22 |
|---|---|---|---|---|
| N | 1 | 2, 4 | 1 | 1 |
| L[mm] | 20, 30 | 22.5, 23.3 | 20, 30 | 20, 30 |
| D[mm] | 2 | 2 | 2 | 2 |
| $u_N$ | 5–16 | 5–25 | 4.2–18.2 | 6.6–33.9 |
| $\Delta T_{sub}$[K] | 0–115 | 0–80 | 0–80 | 0–30 |
| P[Mpa] | 0.1, 0.3 | 0.1, 0.3 | 0.1–0.5 | 1.6–2.5 |
| $\rho_l/\rho_g$ | 658–1605 | 658–1605 | 8.1–202 | 8.8–16.1 |
| Ja | 0–210 | 0–170 | 0–3.1 | 0–3.1 |

the subcooling effect on the CHF based on Eq. (14.1-2) for saturated liquids:

$$\frac{\dot{q}_c}{\dot{q}_{co}} = \frac{1+\sqrt{1+4CJa}}{2} \qquad (14.1\text{-}5)$$

where $q_c$ is the CHF for the subcooled liquid, Ja is Jakob number, and

$$C = \frac{0.95(d/D)^2(1+D/d)^{-0.364}}{(\rho_l/\rho_g)^{0.43}\left(2\sigma/\rho_l u_N^2(D-d)\right)^{0.343}} \qquad (14.1\text{-}6)$$

For the case of 4CJa < 1, $q_c/q_{co}$ can be approximated to $(1 + CJa)$, and then the subcooled CHF increases linearly with the subcooling.

For a single jet (Monde et al., 1994) and multiple jets (Monde and Mitsutake, 1996), most of the CHF data can be predicted well with an accuracy of ±20% by Eq. (14.1-5).

For the subcooled jet impingement, the CHF of I- and HP-regimes does not appear for any condition within the experimental range, while for the saturated case, the CHF of I- or HP-regimes falls in $\rho_l/\rho_g < 60$. The reason for this is not known yet.

Finally, Nonn et al. (1988) measured the CHF for configurations of one, four, and nine free-surface, circular jets of FC-72 impinging on a heated surface. For the multiple jet configurations, the jets are equally distributed over a heated surface. Their CHF data can be correlated well for all combinations of jets by slightly revising Eq. (14.1-5).

**Free-surface wall jet.** Katto and Ishii (1978) measured CHF for single free-surface wall jets of saturated water, R113, and trichlorethane, and proposed a correlation over a range of velocity from 1.5 to 13 m/s and a heater length from L = 10 to 20 mm with good agreement.

Wang and Monde (1997) have recently measured the CHF for water ($\rho_l/\rho_g = 1603$) and R22 ($\rho_l/\rho_g = 25$–6.2) for $\Delta T_{sub} = 0$ to 80 K and $u_N = 3$ to 15 m/s. The

CHF data for saturated water can be correlated with the same accuracy as the Katto and Ishii data by their equation. On the other hand, their equation was found to consistently underpredict 3–4 times the CHF for saturated R22. Wang and Monde (1997) revised their equation on the basis of Haramura and Katto (1983) criterion to predict the CHF data of R22 in both saturated and subcooled conditions:

$$\frac{q_c}{\rho_g h_{lg} u_N} = 0.193 \left(\frac{\rho_l}{\rho_g}\right)^{0.533} \left(\frac{\sigma}{\rho_l u_N^2 L}\right)^{1/3} (1 + 0.35(\rho_g/\rho_l)^{0.46} Ja) \quad (14.1\text{-}7)$$

Equation (14.1-6) overpredicts the CHF data of saturated R113 by about 40–80 percent for very high velocities up to 61 m/s (Katto and Haramura, 1981), while for saturated water, the CHF values are 10 percent lower than those predicted by Eq. (14.1-7).

Mudawar et al. (1987) measured the CHF for FC-72 flowing along vertical heater ($L = 63.5$ and $127.0$ mm) for $\Delta T_{sub} = 1.0$ to 6 K, $u_N = 0.5$ to 2.0 m/s, and four different jet widths of 0.5, 1.0, 1.5, and 2.0 mm. The CHF values predicted for saturated water by their correlation ($q_{co} \propto u_N^{0.16}$) are 2 to 2.5 times larger than those predicted by Eq. (14.1-6), and the dependence of CHF on the velocity is also quite different. This difference may be attributed to the effect of gravity on the film flow.

On the other hand, Furuya et al. (1995) measured the CHF for water at atmospheric pressure for a plane jet vertically impinging on heater (flow length: $L < 27.5$ mm) over $\Delta T_{sub} = 2.2$ to 60 K and $u_N = 1.3$ to 3.2 m/s. Their CHF data including subcooled condition are predicted with fairly good agreement by Eq. (14.1-6) (Wang and Monde, 1997).

Finally, the CHF is almost uninfluenced by the thickness of the jet as confirmed by several investigators (Furuya et al., 1995; Katto and Ishii, 1978; Wang and Monde, 1997).

### Submerged and confined jets

***Submerged impinging jet.*** Ma and Bergles (1983) obtained a limited amount of CHF data ($u_N = 1.08$–$2.72$ m/s) for R113. The CHF data revealed a dependence of cube root of velocity; however, no correlation was proposed. From an engineering point of view, this system does not result in a significant increase in CHF due to the vapor blockage and significant reduction in the jet velocity due to the bulk liquid.

***Submerged wall jet.*** Katto and Kurata (1980) measured the CHF of saturated water and R113 flowing parallel and upward along a vertical heater ($L = 10$–$20$ mm and $u_N = 1.3$–$9.1$ m/s). The CHF data were correlated well by changing each constant in Eq. (14.1-6) from 0.193, 0.533, and 0.333 into 0.196, 0.441, and 0.264, respectively.

*Confined jet.* Mudawar and Wadsworth (1991) examined the effects of velocity ($u_N$ = 1 to 13 m/s) and subcooling ($\Delta T_{sub}$ = 4.8–41.4 K) on CHF for a plane jet of FC-72. The characteristic of CHF was divided into two regimes depending on the velocity: in the medium-velocity regime, the CHF increased with increasing velocity, while in the high-velocity regime, the CHF was approximately independent of velocity. The velocity at which this transition took place is not specified. Although a correlation proposed for the medium-velocity data predicts their CHF data with a mean absolute deviation of 7.4%, its application should be limited to the range of conditions of their experiments.

## 14.2 FALLING FILM EVAPORATION AND BOILING

First, basic features of the falling film without heat transfer will be introduced in this section, and convective heat transfer to the falling film without a phase change will be discussed. Then, evaporation and boiling of the falling film, including critical heat flux, will be presented. When a liquid film falls down on a heated wall and the film flow rate decreases due to the resulting phase change, breakup of the film may occur. The film breakup causes a sharp and large increase in the wall temperature.

### 14.2.1 Falling Liquid Film Flow

A liquid film falling downwards on a wall is generally covered with waves of various sizes. Therefore, the film may be divided into two layers: a continuous base-film layer that flows down clinging to the wall, and a discontinuous wavy layer that flows over the base film.

Figure 5 shows a liquid film of mean thickness $y_m$ flowing down on the inner surface of a vertical pipe. D is the inside diameter of the pipe and $u_{gm}$ is the gas velocity flowing down on the liquid film. Experimental results of $y_m$ and

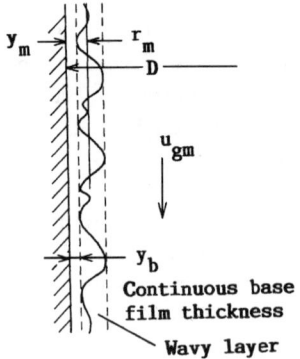

**Figure 5** Flow state of a falling liquid film with co-current gas flow.

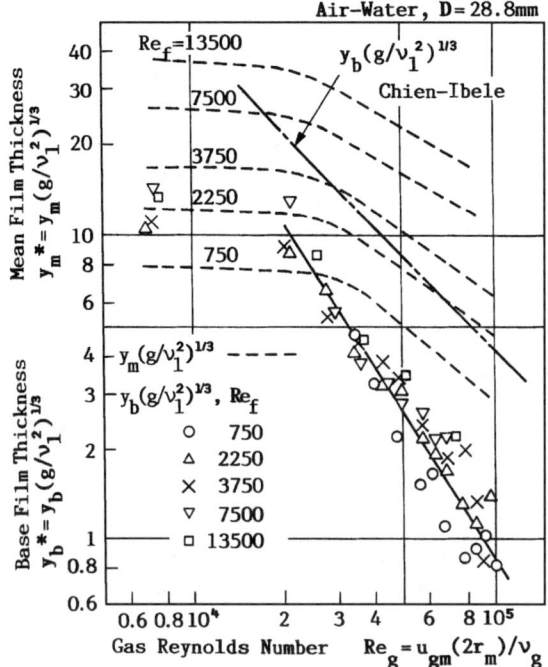

**Figure 6** Mean film thickness and base film thickness of falling films with co-current gas flow.

the continuous base film thickness $y_b$ obtained with an air-water system are presented in Figure 6 (Ueda and Tanaka, 1974). Non-dimensional mean film thickness $y_m^* = y_m(g/v_l^2)^{1/3}$ and base film thickness $y_b^* = y_b(g/v_l^2)^{1/3}$ are shown against the gas Reynolds number $Re_g$. The parameter $Re_f = 4\Gamma/\eta_l$ is the film Reynolds number, and $\Gamma$ denotes the film flow rate per unit width of the wall.

The mean film thickness $y_m$ is relatively insensitive to the gas velocity for low $Re_g$ and decreases with increasing gas velocity for a higher $Re_g$ region due to the high shear stress acting on the film surface. The base film thickness $y_b$ is little affected by the film flow rate and decreases with an increase in the gas flow rate. The significant difference between $y_m$ and $y_b$ suggests that the film is accompanied by a thick wavy layer, i.e., high waves on the base film. Chien and Ibele (1964) proposed the following correlation for the non-dimensional base film thickness $y_b^*$.

$$y_b^* = 4.873 \times 10^5 Re_f^{-1.011} \qquad (14.2\text{-}1)$$

which is presented by a chain line in Figure 6.

In the low gas flow rate region, the base film thickness and the mean film thickness both are insensitive to the gas velocity. The liquid film flowing downwards by gravity in this region, where the shear stress at the film surface is negligible, is usually called a falling film.

The base film of the falling film is not so much thinner than the mean film thickness in a range of low $Re_f$. However, the wavy layer thickness increases sharply as $Re_f$ is increased. The waves become large as the film falls down, and after traveling a certain distance, they cease growing (Ishigaya et al., 1971; Takahama et al., 1978). It has been known that the wave amplitude is also affected by the surface tension of liquid in a complex manner.

Our knowledge of the waves flowing on the base film is still limited. However, the mean film thickness of the falling film is fairly well investigated. Analytical results are presented by Nusselt (1916):

$$y_m^* = (3/4)^{1/3} Re_f^{1/3} \qquad (14.2\text{-}2)$$

which was derived from a force balance for the laminar falling film, and by Kapitza (Fulford, 1964)

$$y_m^* = (2.4/4)^{1/3} Re_f^{1/3} \qquad (14.2\text{-}3)$$

which was derived for the laminar falling film with waves on the surface.

Knowing the velocity profile u(y) in the film, the relation between $\Gamma$ and the mean film thickness $y_m$ can be obtained using a non-dimensional velocity $u^+ = u/\sqrt{\tau_w/\rho_l}$ and non-dimensional distance $y^+ = (y/v_l)\sqrt{\tau_w/\rho_l}$ from the wall,

$$\Gamma = \rho_l \int_0^{y_m} u\, dy = \eta_l \int_0^{y_m^+} u^+ dy^+ \text{ and} \qquad (14.2\text{-}4)$$

$$Re_f = 4 \int_0^{y_m^+} u^+ dy^+ \qquad (14.2\text{-}5)$$

Due to the shear stress at the wall, the film flow structure may be assumed to be similar to that of the boundary layer of the single-phase flow in a pipe. Thus, the law of the wall, $u^+ = f(y^+)$, may be applied to the film flow. Substituting the universal velocity profile by von Karman (1939) into Eq. (14.2-5) and integrating the following relation between $Re_f$ and $y_m^+$ is obtained.

$$Re_f = 2(y_m^+)^2 \quad \text{for } y_m^+ \leq 5 \qquad (14.2\text{-}6)$$

$$Re_f = 50 - 30.2 y_m^+ + 20 y_m^+ \ln(y_m^+) \quad \text{for } 5 < y_m^+ \leq 30 \qquad (14.2\text{-}7)$$

$$Re_f = -256 + 12 y_m^+ + 10 y_m^+ \ln(y_m^+) \quad \text{for } 30 < y_m^+ \qquad (14.2\text{-}8)$$

In the case of falling films, the shear stress at the wall is $\tau_w = \rho_l g y_m$, then $y_m^+$ is related to $y_m^*$ by the following equation.

$$(y_m^+)^2 = (y_m^*)^3 \qquad (14.2\text{-}9)$$

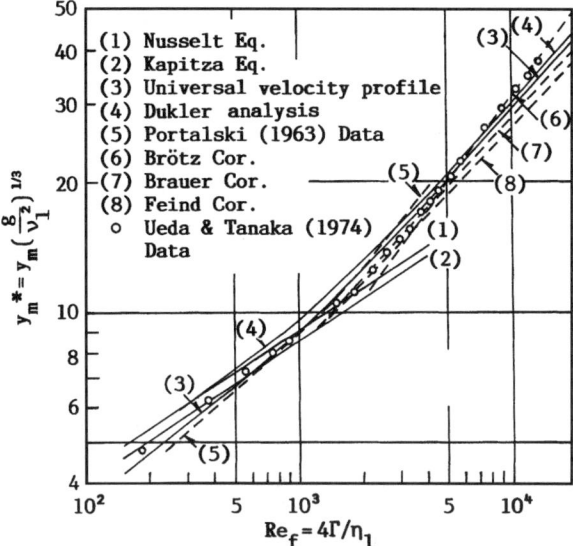

**Figure 7** Mean film thickness of a falling film ($\tau_i = 0$).

Similar efforts to use the eddy diffusivity of the single-phase flow have been made by Dukler (1960), Davis (1965), and Kunz and Yerazunis (1969).

There have also been experimental studies to obtain correlations for $y_m$,

$$y_m^* = 0.0682 \mathrm{Re}_f^{2/3} \quad \text{by Brötz (1954)} \tag{14.2-10}$$

$$y_m^* = 0.208 \mathrm{Re}_f^{8/15} \quad \text{by Brauer (1956)} \tag{14.2-11}$$

$$y_m^* = 0.266 \mathrm{Re}_f^{1/2} \quad \text{by Feind (1960)} \tag{14.2-12}$$

Equations (14.2-10)–(14.2-12) are valid for turbulent falling films.

These analytical and experimental results for the mean film thickness $y_m$ are compared with the measured values by Ueda and Tanaka (1974) and Portalski (1963) in Figure 7. The Kapitza correlation and the universal velocity profile results work well for $\mathrm{Re}_f < 1000$. For $\mathrm{Re}_f > 4000$, application of the universal velocity profile, the Dukler correlation, and the Brötz correlation produces good results.

### 14.2.2 Convective Heat Transfer to Falling Films

When a film falls down on a heated surface at a constant flow rate with a fully developed velocity profile, fluid temperature increases, and a certain temperature profile will be established in the film (see Figure 8).

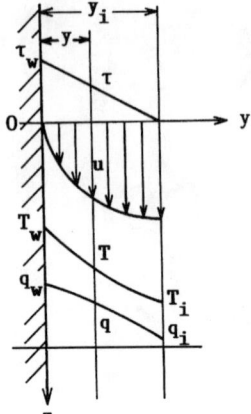

**Figure 8**  Heat transfer to a falling film.

The shear stress $\tau$ is related to the velocity gradient in the film:

$$\frac{\tau}{\tau_w} = \left(1 + \frac{\varepsilon_l}{\nu_l}\right)\frac{du^+}{dy^+} \qquad (14.2\text{-}13)$$

where $\nu_l$ is the kinematic viscosity of liquid and $\varepsilon_l$ is the eddy diffusivity. Denoting the heat flux at the wall by $q_w$, the heat flux can be described in terms of the temperature gradient in the film

$$\frac{q}{q_w} = \left(\frac{1}{\Pr_l} + \frac{\varepsilon_l}{\nu_l}\right)\frac{dT^+}{dy^+} \qquad (14.2\text{-}14)$$

where $T^+$ is the non-dimensional temperature difference, defined by

$$T^+ = \frac{\rho_l c_{pl}(T_w - T)}{q_w}\sqrt{\frac{\tau_w}{\rho_l}} \qquad (14.2\text{-}15)$$

In the film flow,

$$\frac{dq}{dy} = -\rho_l c_{pl} u \frac{\partial T}{\partial z} \qquad (14.2\text{-}16)$$

and $(\partial T/\partial z)$ is kept constant at any point on the y-axis for the developed film of $q_w(z) = $ constant.

Therefore,

$$q = q_w - \rho_l c_{pl} \frac{\partial T}{\partial z} \int_0^y u\, dy \qquad (14.2\text{-}17)$$

and in the case that all the heat from the wall is absorbed by the film, i.e., the heat flux at the film surface $q_i = 0$,

$$\frac{q}{q_w} = 1 - \frac{\int_0^{y^+} u^+ dy^+}{\int_0^{y_i^+} u^+ dy^+} = 1 - \frac{4}{\mathrm{Re}_f} \int_0^{y^+} u^+ dy^+ \qquad (14.2\text{-}18)$$

A heat transfer coefficient can be derived by applying the above equations to Eq. (14.2-15). The heat transfer coefficient, defined by

$$\alpha = q_w/(T_w - T_b) \qquad (14.2\text{-}19)$$

is generally used for this situation, where $T_b$ represents the bulk mean temperature of the film.

For a developed laminar film ($\varepsilon_1 = 0$) with a smooth surface,

$$\tau = \tau_w - \rho_l g y \quad \text{and} \quad \tau_w = \rho_l g y_i \qquad (14.2\text{-}20)$$

Then, Eq. (14.2.-13) is reduced to

$$\frac{du^+}{dy^+} = 1 - \frac{y^+}{y_i^+} \qquad (14.2\text{-}21)$$

Integrating Eq. (14.2-21) results in the following equations:

$$u^+ = y^+ - \frac{(y^+)^2}{2y_i^+} \qquad (14.2\text{-}22)$$

$$\mathrm{Re}_f = \frac{4\Gamma}{\eta_l} = 4\int_0^{y_i^+} u^+ dy^+ = \frac{4}{3} y_i^3 \frac{g}{v_l^2} = \frac{4}{3}(y_i^*)^3 \qquad (14.2\text{-}23)$$

where $y_i^* = y_i(g/v_l^2)^{1/3}$ and is related by $(y_i^*)^3 = (y_i^+)^2$.

Equating Eqs. (14.2-14) and (14.2-18) leads to the following non-dimensional temperature difference:

$$T^+ = \mathrm{Pr}_l y^+ - \frac{\mathrm{Pr}_l}{\mathrm{Re}_f} \left\{ \frac{2}{3}(y^+)^3 - \frac{1}{6y_i^+}(y^+)^4 \right\} \qquad (14.2\text{-}24)$$

The bulk mean temperature of the film is defined by

$$T_b^+ = \frac{\rho_l c_{pl}(T_w - T_b)}{q_w} \sqrt{\frac{\tau_w}{\rho_l}} = \frac{\int_0^{y_i^+} T^+ u^+ dy^+}{\mathrm{Re}_f/4} \qquad (14.2\text{-}25)$$

Therefore, an expression of the heat transfer coefficient for the fully developed-laminar falling film of $q_w(z) = $ constant and $q_i = 0$ is derived by substituting Eqs. (14.2-22) and (14.2-24) into Eq. (14.2-25):

$$\frac{\alpha}{\lambda_l} \left( \frac{v_l^2}{g} \right)^{1/3} = 2.27/\mathrm{Re}_f^{1/3} \qquad (14.2\text{-}26)$$

When evaporation occurs at the surface of the film and the heat flux across the film is constant ($q = q_w$), the above analysis leads to the following equation:

$$\frac{\alpha}{\lambda_l}\left(\frac{\nu_l^2}{g}\right)^{1/3} = 1.76/\text{Re}_f^{1/3} \qquad (14.2\text{-}27)$$

For $T_w$ = constant and $q_i = 0$, Nusselt (1923) derived the average heat transfer coefficient over the length of the wall

$$\bar{\alpha} = \frac{\Gamma c_{pl}}{z}\ln\left[\frac{1}{1-\varphi(S)}\right] \qquad (14.2\text{-}28)$$

where $\varphi$ is a function of a non-dimensional parameter $S = \lambda_1\nu_1 z/(c_{pl}\rho_l g y_i^4)$, which includes length $z$ of the wall. Substituting Eq. (14.2-23) into Eq. (14.2-28) and using the approximate form of $\varphi$,

$$\bar{\alpha} = 0.0236\frac{\rho_l \nu_l c_{pl}}{z}\text{Re}_f + 2.07\lambda_l\left(\frac{g}{\nu_l^2}\right)^{1/3}\bigg/\text{Re}_f^{1/3} \qquad (14.2\text{-}29)$$

When the wall length $z$ is large, the first term in the right hand side of Eq. (14.2-29) is small, and Eq. (14.2-29) reduces to:

$$\frac{\alpha}{\lambda_l}\left(\frac{\nu_l^2}{g}\right)^{1/3} = 2.07/\text{Re}_f^{1/3} \qquad (14.2\text{-}30)$$

It should be noted that the film is usually attended with waves, and the uniformity of the film flow is easily lost. Therefore, the actual heat transfer coefficient tends to be lower than that calculated from the above equations.

Wilke (1962) conducted experiments with the film falling down on an outer surface of a 42 mm diameter pipe heated by hot water and proposed the following correlations for heat transfer coefficients:

$$\frac{\alpha}{\lambda_l}\left(\frac{\nu_l^2}{g}\right)^{1/3} = (1.76 \sim 2.07)/\text{Re}_f^{1/3} \quad \text{for } \text{Re}_f < 2460\text{Pr}_l^{-0.646} \qquad (14.2\text{-}31)$$

$$\frac{\alpha}{\lambda_l}\left(\frac{\nu_l^2}{g}\right)^{1/3} = 0.0323\text{Pr}_l^{0.344}\text{Re}_f^{1/5} \quad \text{for } 2460\text{Pr}_l^{-0.646} < \text{Re}_f < 1600 \qquad (14.2\text{-}32)$$

$$\frac{\alpha}{\lambda_l}\left(\frac{\nu_l^2}{g}\right)^{1/3} = 0.00102\text{Pr}_l^{0.344}\text{Re}_f^{2/3} \quad \text{for } 1600 < \text{Re}_f < 3200 \qquad (14.2\text{-}33)$$

$$\frac{\alpha}{\lambda_l}\left(\frac{\nu_l^2}{g}\right)^{1/3} = 0.00870\text{Pr}_l^{0.344}\text{Re}_f^{2/5} \quad \text{for } 3200 < \text{Re}_f \qquad (14.2\text{-}34)$$

Figure 9 shows the heat transfer coefficients predicted by Eqs. (14.2-26), (14.2-27), and (14.2-31)–(14.2-34) together with the experimental data.

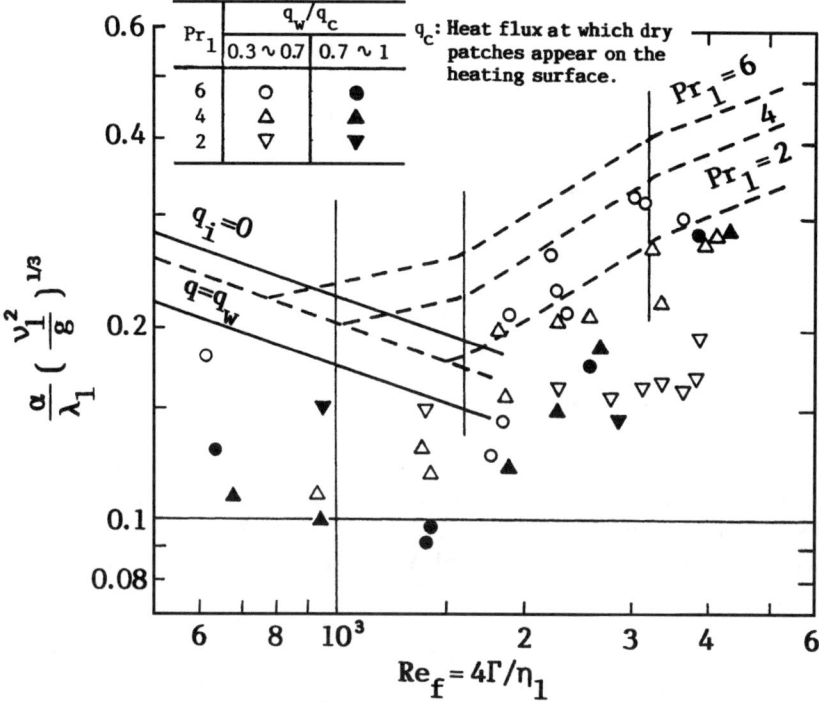

**Figure 9** Heat transfer coefficients of falling films.

Heat transfer data for high heat flux heating (Fujita and Ueda, 1978a) are also included in Figure 9. It should be noted that the experimental data give lower values than the above correlations and tend to decrease with increasing $q_w$. This trend is caused by film distortion, which takes place in the case of subcooled film heating.

When a subcooled falling film is heated, non-uniformity in temperature occurs on the wavy surface. Since the fluid temperature at the thick portion of the film is lower than that at the thin film portion, the surface tension at the thick film portion is higher. Then, liquid at the thin film portion is attracted toward the thick film portion, and the film thickness at the thin film portion becomes thinner. Eventually, the film breaks down to form permanent dry patches. The flow rate at which the permanent dry patches are formed is called as the *minimum wetting rate* (MWR) $\Gamma_c$ for the distorted film heating.

The values of $\Gamma_c$ measured (Hallet, 1966) with a water film flowing down on a long pipe of L = 1500 mm and D = 25.4 mm are compared in Figure 10 with values obtained from the following correlation:

$$\frac{3\Gamma_c \eta_l}{\rho_l^2 g} = 1.2 \times 10^6 - 1.76 \times 10^{-8} \sigma_b \Delta\sigma \qquad (14.2\text{-}35)$$

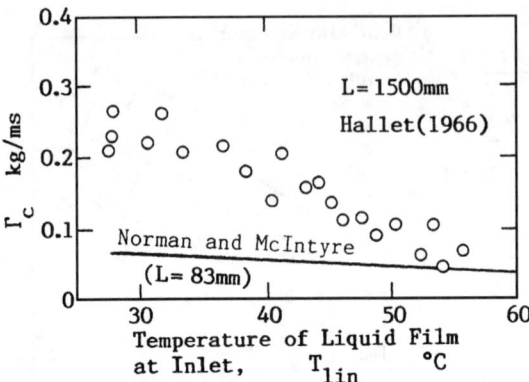

**Figure 10** Minimum wetting rates for subcooled falling film heating.

which was derived by Norman and Binns (1960) and Norman and McIntyre (1960) from experiments for a laminar film on a short pipe of L = 83 mm. In this equation, units are CGS, $\Gamma_c$ is the MWR g/(cm s), $\sigma_b$ denotes the surface tension in dyne/cm at the bulk temperature of the film, and $\Delta\sigma = \sigma_w - \sigma_b$, where $\sigma_w$ is the surface tension dyne/cm at the wall temperature.

The data of Norman and McIntyre (1960) indicate that the flow rate of the film flowing on a short pipe can be reduced to a lower value without dry patch formation. This trend suggests that the film distortion grows as the film flows down and needs a certain length to reach the developed state.

Fujita and Ueda (1978a) examined the distortion of subcooled-heated films. They found that when the parameter $K = \Delta\sigma/(1/2) \int_0^{y_i} \rho_l u^2 dy$, which is a ratio of the surface tension difference on the film surface to a dynamic pressure of the film, reaches a certain value, the film breaks down to form a permanent dry patch on the heated wall. They correlated the relation between a heat flux $q_c$ at the film breakdown and $\text{Re}_f$ for a laminar film:

$$q_c = 5.6 \times 10^{-4} \frac{\lambda_l \rho_l g \left(v_l^2/g\right)^{1/3}}{(-\partial\sigma/\partial T)} \text{Re}_f^{4/3} \qquad (14.2\text{-}36)$$

and for a turbulent film:

$$q_c = 5.7 \times 10^{-7} \frac{\lambda_l \rho_l g \left(v_l^2/g\right)^{1/3} \text{Pr}_l^{0.344}}{(-\partial\sigma/\partial T)} \text{Re}_f^{2.12} \qquad (14.2\text{-}37)$$

### 14.2.3 Falling Film Evaporation

When a saturated film falls down on a heated wall, the film surface temperature $T_i$ is equal to the saturation temperature $T_s$ and $q_i = q_w$ (see Figure 8). The heat transfer coefficient is defined using the film surface temperature $T_i$,

$$\alpha_i = q_w/(T_w - T_i) \qquad (14.2\text{-}38)$$

The correlation for a laminar film with a smooth surface, given by Eq. (14.2-27), becomes

$$\frac{\alpha_i}{\lambda_l}\left(\frac{\nu_l^2}{g}\right)^{1/3} = 0.693\left(\frac{\text{Re}_f}{4}\right)^{-1/3} \qquad (14.2\text{-}39)$$

Chun and Seban (1971) proposed the following correlations from their experimental work for a laminar film:

$$\frac{\alpha_i}{\lambda_l}\left(\frac{\nu_l^2}{g}\right)^{1/3} = 0.606\left(\frac{\text{Re}_f}{4}\right)^{-0.22} \qquad (14.2\text{-}40)$$

and a turbulent film:

$$\frac{\alpha_i}{\lambda_l}\left(\frac{\nu_l^2}{g}\right)^{1/3} = 3.8 \times 10^{-2}\text{Re}_f^{0.4}\text{Pr}_l^{0.65} \qquad (14.2\text{-}41)$$

These results are compared in Figure 11. The analytical results of Dukler (1960), in which the eddy diffusivity was applied in Eqs. (14.2-13) and (14.2-14), are also included. Measured heat transfer coefficients are higher than the values predicted by Eq. (14.2-39), since the effective film thickness becomes thinner, due to the wavy motion of the surface. Dukler's analytical results show a slightly different trend from the measured ones for the turbulent films.

Since the film surface temperature is almost uniform in the falling film evaporation, the film flow distortion that gives rise to the film breakdown does not occur.

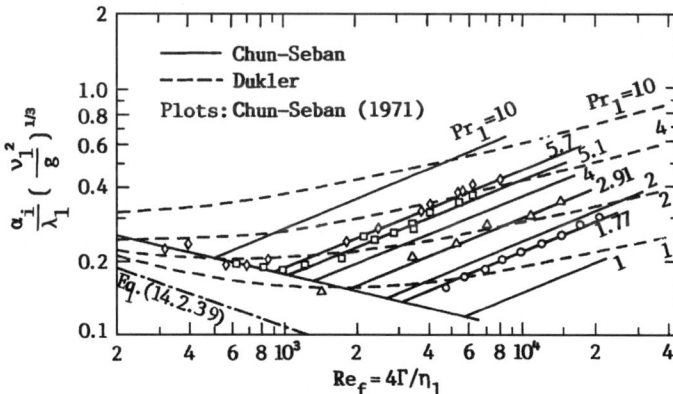

**Figure 11** Heat transfer coefficients of falling films ($\tau_i = 0$).

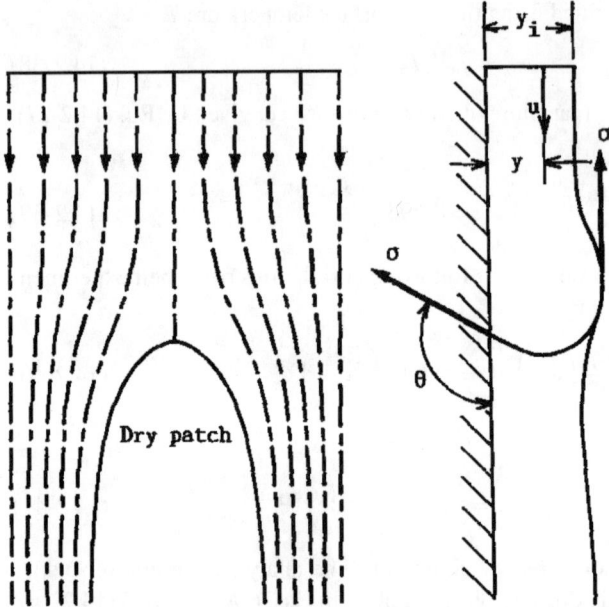

**Figure 12** Force balance at the top edge boundary of a dry patch.

However, when the film thickness becomes very thin as the film falls down, a dry patch is formed or the film disrupts into rivulets. The minimum flow rate at which the film can flow as a continuous film is called the *minimum wetting rate* (MWR). At the front edge of the permanent dry patch, the dynamic pressure of the film flow is balanced by the upward component of the surface tension (see Figure 12; Hartley and Murgatroyd, 1964). If the film is laminar with a smooth surface and uniform thickness $y_i$,

$$\frac{1}{2}\int_0^{y_i} \rho_l u^2 dy = \sigma(1 - \cos\theta) \qquad (14.2\text{-}42)$$

From Eqs. (14.2-22) and (14.2-23),

$$\Delta P_f = \frac{1}{2}\int_0^{y_i} \rho_l u^2 dy = \frac{1}{15}\frac{\rho_l^3 g^2}{\eta_l^2} y_i^5 \quad \text{and} \qquad (14.2\text{-}43)$$

$$\Gamma = \int_0^{y_i} \rho_l u\, dy = \frac{1}{3}\frac{\rho_l^2 g}{\eta_l} y_i^3 \qquad (14.2\text{-}44)$$

respectively. Then, MWR $\Gamma_c$ is expressed from these as

$$\Gamma_c = 1.69[\sigma(1 - \cos\theta)]^{3/5}\left(\frac{\eta_l \rho_l}{g}\right)^{1/5} \qquad (14.2\text{-}45)$$

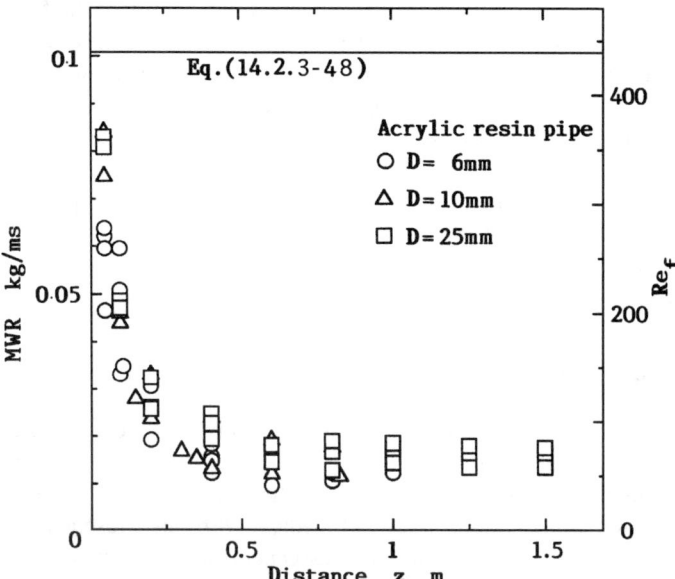

**Figure 13** Minimum wetting rates of isothermal falling films.

However, it has been known that Eq. (14.2-45) gives too high values compared with the measured MWRs (Norman and McIntyre, 1960). Similar results have been obtained by Hewitt and Lacey (1965) for a climbing film.

Koizumi et al. (1996) obtained MWRs by blowing an air jet to a water film to artificially form a dry patch and measuring the lowest film flow rate at which the dry patch was rewetted by the film flow (Figure 13). The MWRs measured the decrease with distance z from the top of the film, which corresponds to the growth of height of waves on the film. Since the film is associated with many waves and the dynamic pressure fluctuates largely, the appropriate value to apply to the left hand term of Eq. (14.2-42) seems to be the maximum of the fluctuating dynamic pressure. It has been observed that the contact angle $\theta$ increased with increasing the film flow rate, and the dry patch was rewetted when $\theta$ reached the advancing contact angle $\theta_A$ ($\theta_A = 120$ degree for water). Therefore, the force balance at the MWR condition should be

$$\left[\frac{1}{2}\int_{film} \rho_l u^2 dy\right]_{max} = \sigma(1 - \cos\theta_A) \tag{14.2-46}$$

Koizumi et al. suggested that the above equation is approximately reduced to

$$\Delta P_f \left(\frac{y_{max}}{y_i}\right)^5 = \sigma(1 - \cos\theta_A) \tag{14.2-47}$$

where $y_{max}$ is the maximum film thickness, including the wave height.

The other analytical approach to the MWR is to look into energy of the film flow (Bankoff, 1971; Hartley and Murgatroyd, 1964). Considering that the critical thickness of the film below which the film disrupts is given by the condition that the sum of the kinetic and the surface energy becomes minimum, Hartley and Murgatroyd derived the following equation

$$\Gamma_c = 0.803\sigma^{3/5}\left(\frac{\eta_l\rho_l}{g}\right)^{1/5} \qquad (14.2\text{-}48)$$

This correlation overpredicts MWRs like Eq. (14.2-45), since the wavy motion of the film is not reflected.

### 14.2.4 Falling Film Boiling

When a falling film on a heated surface is at saturated condition, temperature over the film surface is almost uniform and close to the saturation temperature. Relations between the heat flux $q_w$ and the wall superheat $\Delta T_s = T_w - T_s$ measured for boiling-falling water films (Fujita and Ueda, 1978b) are presented in Figure 14. Since the film thickness is thin, bubbles generated form hemispherical domes on the film and the domes grow to burst while flowing down with the film.

In a range of $q_w < 0.80 \times 10^5$ W/m², the number of nucleation sites is small and $q_w \propto \Delta T_s$. The heat transfer coefficient

$$\alpha = q_w/(T_w - T_s) \qquad (14.2\text{-}49)$$

is dependent on the film flow rate, and the convective heat transfer is dominant. The heat transfer coefficients show values about 10% higher than those of Chun and Seban (1971) correlations for the falling film evaporation, Eqs. (14.2-40) and (14.2-41).

In the range of $q_w > 1.2 \times 10^5$ W/m², the number of the nucleation sites increases greatly. The relation between $q_w$ and $\Delta T_s$ shows no dependency on the film flow rate and is expressed by a unique line of saturated pool nucleate boiling. In this nucleate-boiling-dominant condition, the amount of the droplet entrainment due to the bubble burst cannot be neglected.

Although the droplet entrainment by the bubble burst has not been well understood, the surface tension or the kind of liquid has a large effect on the droplet entrainment rate. Petrovichev et al. (1971) measured droplet entrainment rates $m_{EB}$ from a boiling water film flowing down on the outer surface of 50 mm in heated length and proposed the following correlation:

$$m_{EB} = 2.09 \times 10^3 y_i \left(\frac{q_w}{10^6} - \frac{q_{ei}}{10^6}\right)^{2.7} \text{ [kg/m}^2\text{s]} \qquad (14.2\text{-}50)$$

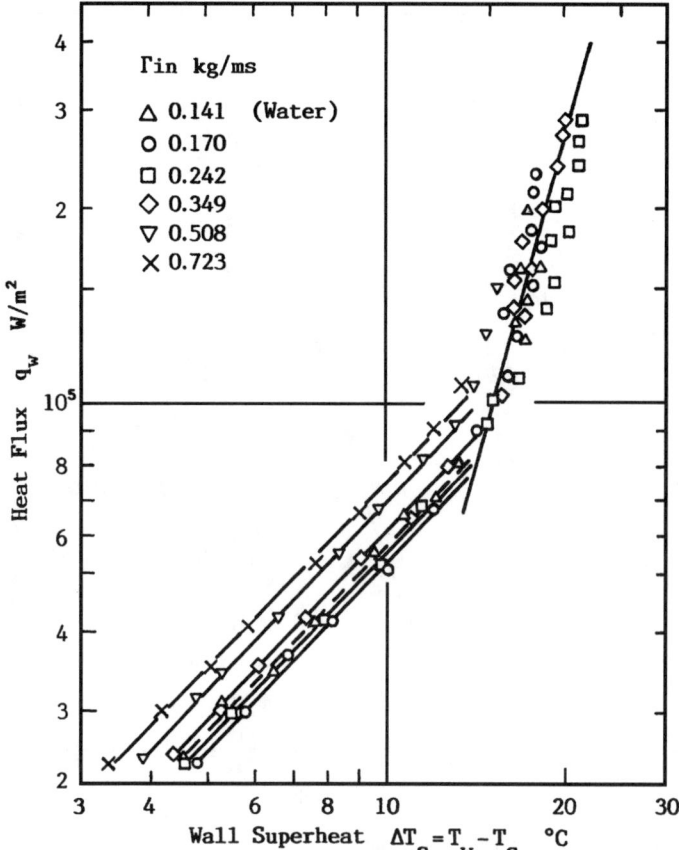

**Figure 14** Boiling curves of falling films.

where $y_i$ is the film thickness in $m$ and $q_{ei} = 0.15 \times 10^6$ W/m² is the heat flux at which the entrainment is initiated. Ueda et al. (1981) correlated $m_{EB}$ measured for falling film boiling of R-113, R-11, and water at the atmospheric pressure (see Figure 15),

$$\frac{m_{EB}}{q_w/h_{lg}} = C\left[\frac{(q_w/h_{lg})^2 y_i}{\sigma \rho_g}\right]^{0.75} \quad (14.2\text{-}51)$$

The constant $C$ depends on the kind of liquid, and $C = 4.77 \times 10^2, 6.63 \times 10^2$, and $1.33 \times 10^2$ for water, R-113, and R-11, respectively.

As the film flows down, the film flow rate decreases due to evaporation and droplet entrainment. Fujita and Ueda (1978b) measured the film flow rate $\Gamma_{ex}$ at

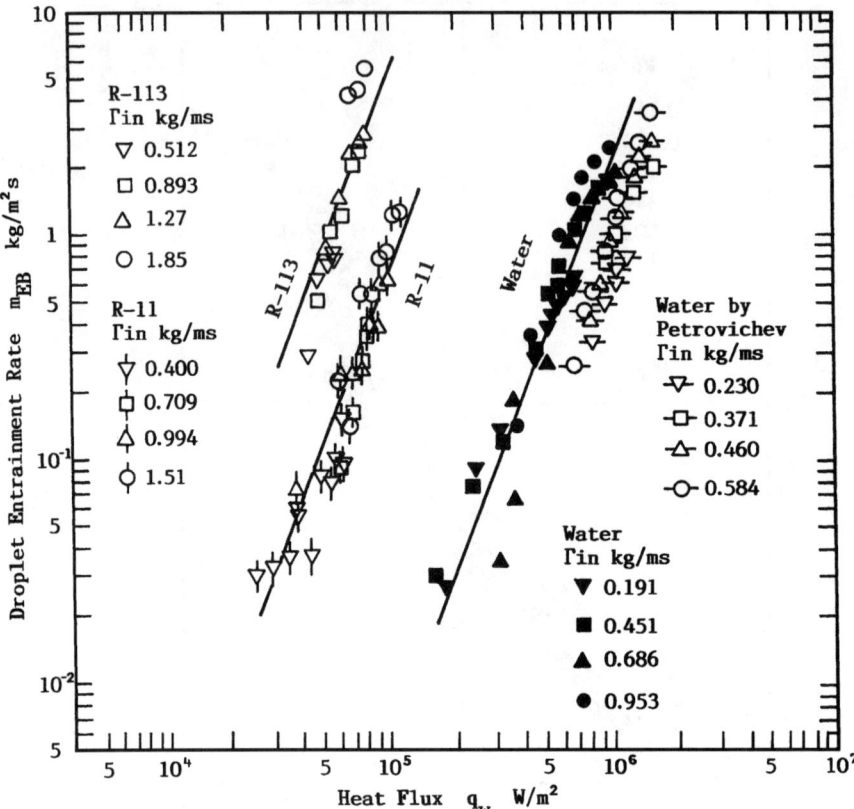

**Figure 15** Droplet entrainment rates of falling film boiling.

the bottom end of the vertical-heated pipe on which the saturated water film fell down (see Figure 16). Dashed lines in the figure represent $\Gamma_{ex}$ calculated from heat balance, i.e., only the evaporation is taken into account. The chain lines show the case that both the evaporation and the droplet entrainment (Eq. [14.2-51]) are considered. As is expected, when $q_w$ is low, $\Gamma_{ex}$ is close to the only evaporation case; however, when $q_w$ is increased, the entrainment becomes significant.

As $\Gamma_{ex}$ becomes low, unstable dry patches appear and disappear repeatedly near the bottom end of the heated pipe. Solid circle symbols in Figure 16 indicate this state. Further decrease in $\Gamma_{ex}$ results in forming stable dry patches (square symbols in Figure 16) to bring about a sharp rise in the heated surface temperature; that is the critical state by the dry-out. This dry-out occurs when $\Gamma_{ex}$ decreases to the MWR of an evaporating or isothermal film flow.

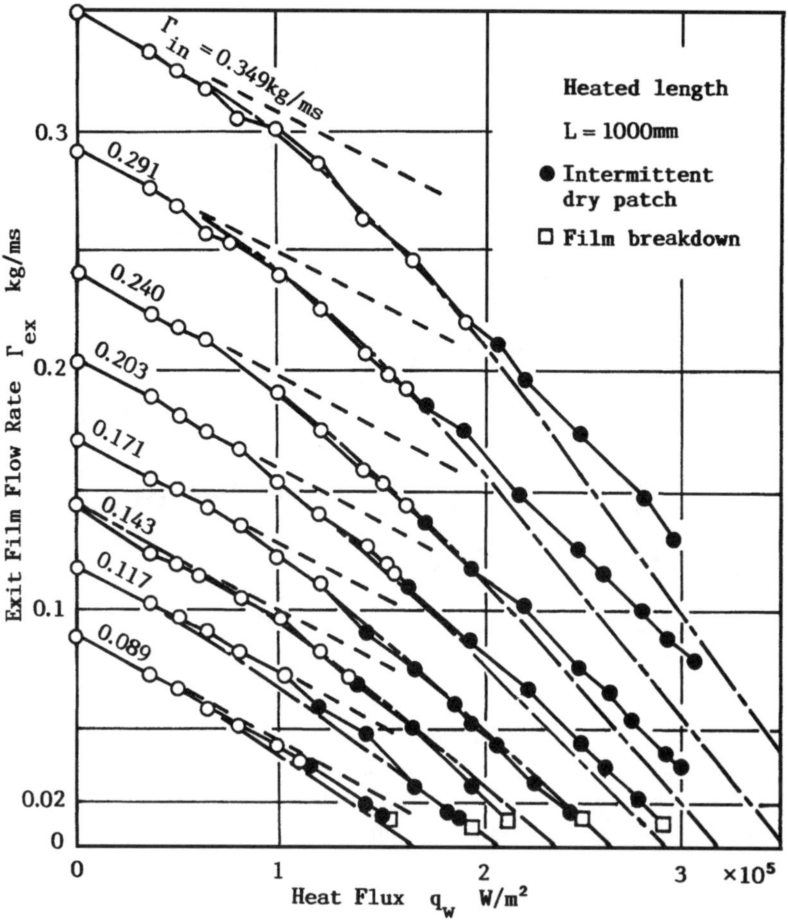

**Figure 16** Variation of exit film flow rate and film breakdown.

The above critical heat flux increases with increasing the inlet film flow rate $\Gamma_{in}$. However, when $q_w$ becomes high enough to cause vigorous nucleate boiling, the critical condition can be reached even if $\Gamma_{ex}$ is larger than the MWR. This type of the critical condition seems to be associated with the local dry-out of the surface under the liquid film caused by vapor generation. The critical heat flux $q_c$ of this type increases as well, with an increase in $\Gamma_{ex}$.

In this dryout-type critical condition, the relation among the vapor generation rate, the momentum flux of the film flow, and the surface tension to hold the dry patch is considered to be closely connected. Ueda et al. (1981) and Koizumi

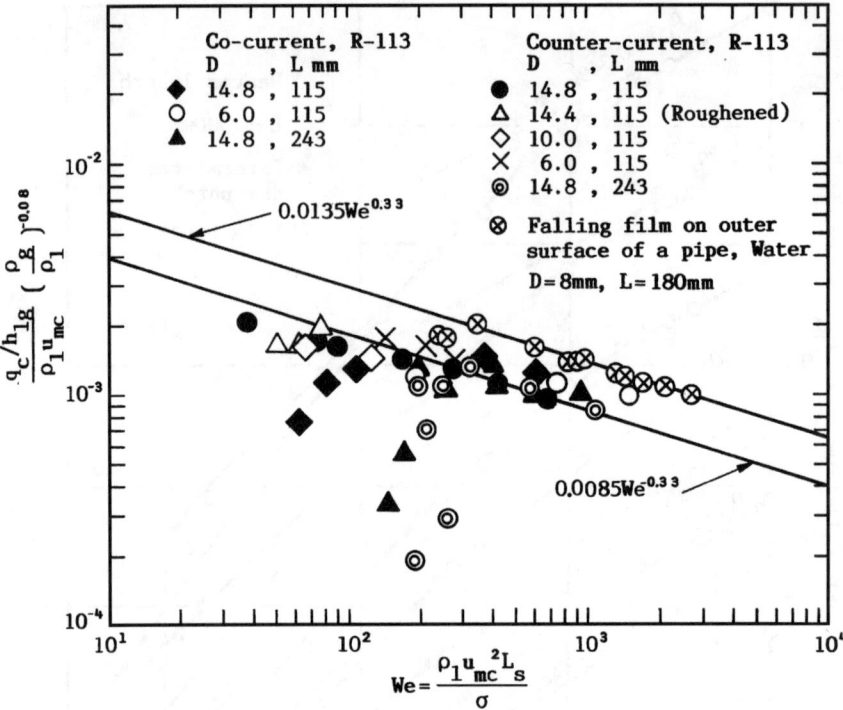

**Figure 17** Critical heat fluxes of falling film boiling.

et al. (1998) correlated the critical heat flux $q_c$ for water films falling on the outer surface of a heated pipe and R-113 films falling on the inner surface of heated pipes (see Figure 17) and proposed

$$\frac{q_c/h_{lg}}{\rho_l u_{mc}}\left(\frac{\rho_g}{\rho_l}\right)^{-0.08} = (0.85 \sim 1.35) \times 10^{-2} \left(\frac{\rho_l u_{mc}^2 L_s}{\sigma}\right)^{-0.33} \quad (14.2\text{-}52)$$

where $u_{mc}$ is the average velocity of the film of $\Gamma_{exc}$ at the critical condition and $L_s$ is the saturated boiling length. The value of $u_{mc}$ was calculated by assuming that all of the liquid phase estimated from heat balance is in the film and applying the universal velocity profile (von Karman, 1939) to the film.

It is considered that the dynamic pressure fluctuation due to the wavy motion of the falling film has a significant effect on the occurrence of local dry patches, as discussed earlier following Eq. (14.2-46). Therefore, the coefficient on the right hand side of Eq. (14.2-52) seems to vary depending on the degree of the fluctuation of the film. Interestingly enough, the critical heat fluxes of the climbing film of upflow boiling are correlated with the same form as Eq. (14.2-52), except for the larger coefficient of $2.8 \times 10^{-2}$ on the right hand side, since the film flow is pulsative and fluctuates considerably (Koizumi et al., 1998).

Plots that do not fall on the relation given by Eq. (14.2-52) are observed in Figure 17. These data were obtained for longer pipes, and $q_c$s were low. These dryout heat fluxes do not depend on the film flow rate at the point of the critical condition. This critical condition corresponds to that of the MWR-type. The boundary between the above dryout-type and the MWR-type is expressed by Ueda et al. (1981):

$$\frac{\rho_l u_{mc}^2 y_{ic}}{\sigma} = 0.06 \qquad (14.2\text{-}53)$$

where $y_{ic}$ denotes the film thickness calculated by $\Gamma_{exc}/(\rho_l u_{mc})$.

It should be noted that when vapor generated flows upward countercurrently and the flow space of the vapor is narrow, special attention should be paid, since flooding easily occurs to decrease the critical heat flux considerably.

## 14.3 AUGMENTATION TECHNIQUES IN EXTERNAL FLOW BOILING

### 14.3.1 Heat Transfer

Only a few studies dealing with the enhancement of already high nucleate boiling heat fluxes on surfaces cooled by liquid jets impinging normal to them have been reported in the literature. Since heat transfer in an external flow boiling with jet configurations is hardly influenced in fully developed nucleate boiling region on a smooth heater by flow condition, the only way is to use structured surfaces, such as microfin and microstud, that can prevent temperature overshoot and augment heat transfer.

Grimley et al. (1988) examined the augmentation of heat transfer in flowing liquid film of FC-72 using microfin and microstud. The heat transfer for structured surface is increased by superheat of 3–4 K, compared with that of smooth surface in a developing nucleate boiling region where a forced convection still contributes to heat transfer, and the temperature overshoot can be prevented with either a microfin or a microstud. In fully developed nucleate boiling region, however, respective boiling curves for different velocity, height of fin, and subcooling merge into the single curve for the same configuration; that is, boiling heat transfer for the same shape becomes dependent only on the superheat like smooth surface.

Lay and Dhir (1995) experimentally investigated the enhancement of nucleate boiling heat fluxes and critical heat fluxes by modifying the boiling surface. They employed both macro and micro modifications that consisted of circumferential ridges and radial grooves, by which the splashing of liquid droplets during nucleate boiling can be reduced and therefore better liquid distribution can be provided on the heated surface. The micro modifications were obtained by sintering the copper plate or a macro-structured surface with copper powder. The thickness of the sintered layer was 0.4 mm, and the particle size was 60 $\mu$m. Two different surfaces with porosities of 0.3 and 0.4 were tested. The sintering of the surface mostly provided increases in active nucleation sites at low wall superheats and in the evaporation area.

They reported that for the surface with radial and rectangular grooves (see Figure 18), a 50% increase in heat transfer rate at low heat flux and a 2 to 3 fold improvement at high heat flux could be achieved.

The available data for augmentation of heat transfer is quite limited because much research is focused on CHF enhancement.

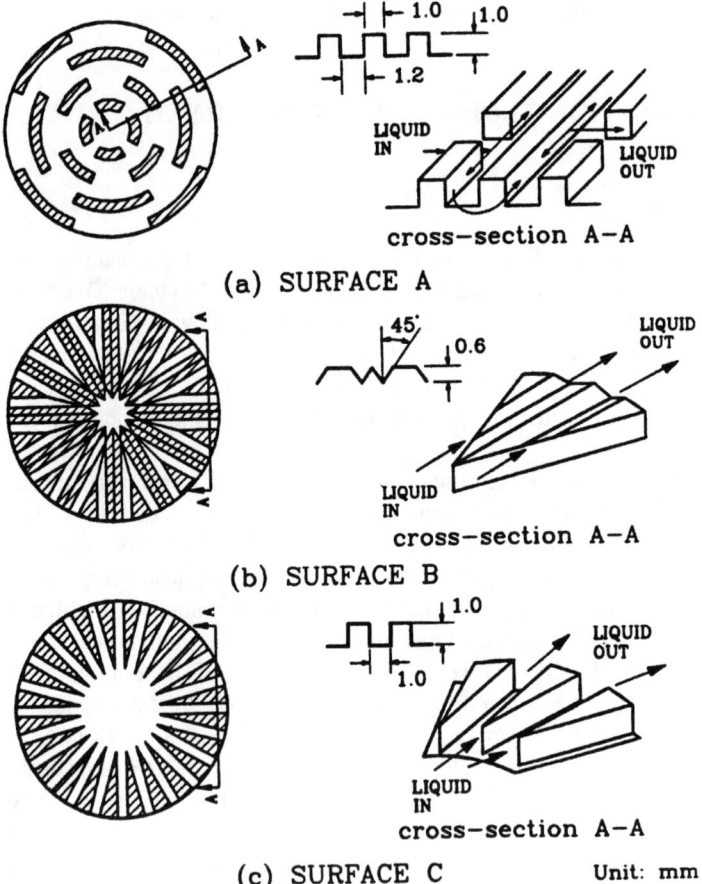

**Figure 18** Macro- and micro-structured surfaces.

## 14.3.2 Augmentation of CHF

There are some methods to increase CHF, depending on the flow conditions. For a free-surface jet configuration, most of liquid is splashed out near the CHF point, due to strong ejection of vapor generated on heaters. The CHF can be significantly increased by returning some of the splashed droplets with flow deflectors. Grimley et al. (1988) reported that significant CHF enhancement is achieved by installing a louvered deflector over the falling film. On the other hand, the structured surfaces that enhance nucleate boiling heat transfer are not expected to significantly enhance the CHF because the enhancement is basically governed by how fast liquid is fed while the generated vapor is taken away.

Lay and Dhir (1995) succeeded in designing the modified surface (see Figure 18c) by which the critical heat flux is raised 60% over than that on a plane surface. For the other micro-structured surface, the improvement of critical heat flux is not expected, though heat transfer prior to CHF is greatly improved.

Kugler (1997) studied multiple jet cooling of macro/micro-structured surfaces using a three-cell configuration (see Figure 19) as an extension of the macro/micro-modified surfaces studied by Lay and Dhir. Kugler found that boiling curves obtained under multiple jet cooling were almost the same as those obtained for a single jet, as long as the surface supported by one jet remained about the same; then, the extension of single jet results to surfaces cooled by multiple jets was

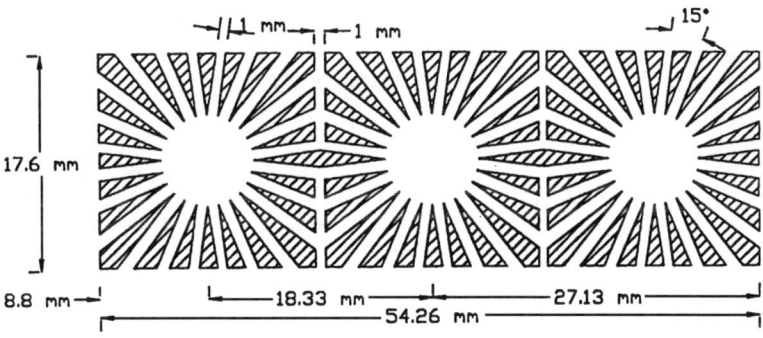

**Figure 19** Configurations of macro/micro-structured surface cooled by three jets.

possible. The same result for a flat plate was obtained by Monde and Inoue (1991). Consequently, basic characteristics between single jet and multiple jets are the same when focusing on the region governed by a single jet. Kugler proposed his correlation to predict critical heat flux for subcooled water and R113 up to a subcooling of 70°C on macro/micro-structured surfaces as

$$\frac{\dot{q}_c}{\dot{q}_{co}} = 1 + 4.8 \frac{c_{pl}(T_{sat} - T_l)}{h_{lg}} \qquad (14.3\text{-}1)$$

Incidentally, when comparing Eqs. (14.3-1) and (14.1-5), one notices that the effects of subcooling, velocity, and density ratio on CHF are significantly different. In comparing Eqs. (14.3-1) and (14.1-5), however, it is observed that Eq. (14.3-1) is in good agreement with Eq. (14.1-7) for water within a wide range of jet velocity and geometrical conditions, while for R113, the values calculated from Eq. (14.3-1) are always significantly higher than that from Eq. (14.1-5). It is not yet known whether this depends on the difference in the surface configurations and working liquid or not.

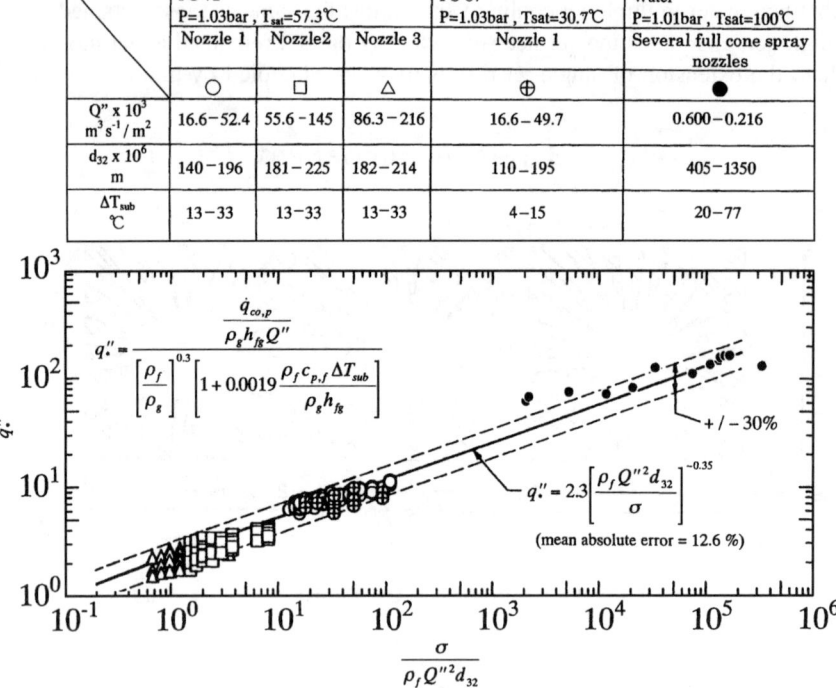

**Figure 20** CHF Correlation (Q" : volumetric flux, $d_{32}$: Sauter mean diameter).

Another potential method may be mist or spray cooling (Estes and Mudawar, 1995; Holman et al., 1972; Monde, 1979; Mudawar and Valentine, 1989; Toda, 1972). In these configurations, generated vapor can easily escape without blockage of liquid from the heater. Sufficient liquid to maintain fully developed nucleate boiling can be directly supplied to the heater. Estes and Mudawar (1995) examined CHF for spray cooling and proposed the CHF correlation together with CHF data as shown in Figure 20, though the CHF dependence on the velocity is slightly different depending on the test liquid. In Figure 20, $\dot{q}_{co,p}$ means CHF with spray cooling and $q''$ is a non-dimensional value of CHF as defined in Figure 20. A relationship between $q''$ and Weber number is also given in Figure 20.

CHF is increased with any increase in subcooling because it greatly helps vapor to escape from the heater due to condensation of vapor, resulting in CHF enhancement. The effect of subcooling on CHF is widely investigated for different configurations, as described in Sections 14.1 and 14.2.

## 14.4 CONCLUSIONS

Characteristics in boiling heat transfer and critical heat flux for external flow, including jet impinging system and falling liquid film, were discussed in detail. Boiling heat transfer in impinging jet system can be augmented prior to reaching the fully-developed region by using special structured surfaces. In the fully-developed region, the augmentation of heat transfer gradually disappears on any surface. Comprehensive correlations are summarized, predicting critical heat flux in jet impingement and falling film systems, including the effect of subcooling.

## REFERENCES

Aihara, T., Kim, J-K., Suzuki, K., and Lasahara, K. 1993. Boiling Heat Transfer of a Micro-Impinging Jet of Liquid Nitrogen in a Very Slender Cryoprobe. *Int. J. Heat Mass Transfer* 36:169–175.

Azuma, T. and Hoshino, T. 1984. The Radial Flow of a Thin Liquid Film (Liquid Film Thickness). *Trans. of JSME, B* 50:982–989, 1126–1135 (in Japanese).

Bankoff, S. G. 1971. Minimum Thickness of a Draining Liquid Film *Int. J. Heat Mass Transfer* 14:2143–2146.

Boyd, R. D. 1983. Review of Subcooled Boiling Critical Heat Flux (CHF) and Its Application to Fusion Systems. *Fundamentals of Heat Transfer in Fusion Energy Systems, Parts I and II*. Eds. Kazimi, M. S. and Jones, O. C. 21st National Heat Transfer Conf., Seatle, Washington, 1983, HTD-Vol. 24:19–42.

Brauer, H. 1956. Strömung und Wärmeubergang bei Rieselfilmen. *VDI Forschungsheft* 457:B22.

Brötz, W. 1954. Uber die Vorausberechnung der Absorptionsgeschwindigkeit von Gasen in Strömenden Flüssigkeitsschichten. *Chemie. Ing. Techn.* 26:470–478.

Chien, S. F. and Ibele, W. 1964. Pressure Drop and Liquid Film Thickness of Two-Phase Annular and Annular-Mist Flow. *Trans. of ASME, Ser. C, J. of Heat Transfer* 86:89–96.

Chun, K. R. and Seban, R. A. 1971. Heat Transfer to Evaporating Liquid Films. *Trans. of ASME, Ser. C, J. of Heat Transfer* 93:391–396.
Copeland, R. J. 1970. Boiling Heat Transfer to a Water Jet Impinging on a Fiat Surface(-lg). Ph. D. Thesis, Southern Methodist University, Dallas, TX.
Davis, E. J. 1965. An Analysis of Liquid Film Flow. *Chem. Eng. Sci.* 20:265–272.
Dukler, A. E. 1960. Fluid Mechanics and Heat Transfer in Vertical Falling-Film Systems. *Chem. Eng. Prog. Symp. Ser.* 30–56:1–10.
Estes, K. A. and Mudawar, I. 1995. Correlation of Sauter Mean Diameter and Critical Heat Flux for Spray Cooling of Small Surfaces. *Int. J. Heat Mass Transfer* 38:2985–2996.
Feind, K. 1960. Strömungsuntersuchungen bei Gegenstrom von Riselfilm und Gas in lotrechten Rohren. *VDI Forschungsheft* 481:B26.
Fujita, T. and Ueda, T. 1978a. Heat Transfer to Falling Liquid Films and Film Breakdown—I: Subcooled Liquid Films. *Int. J. Heat Mass Transfer* 21:97–108.
Fujita, T. and Ueda, T. 1978b. Heat Transfer to Falling Liquid Films and Film Breakdown—II: Saturated Liquid Films with Nucleate Boiling. *Int. J. Heat Mass Transfer* 21:109–118.
Fulford, G. D. 1964. The Flow of Liquid in Thin Films. *Advances in Chem. Engng.*, Volume 5:151–236. New York: Academic Press.
Furuya, M., Inoue, A., and Tanno, R. 1995. Critical Heat Flux and Convective Heat Transfer with a Two-Dimensional Liquid Jet Impinging on Flat and Concave Surfaces. *Trans. of JSME, B* 61:4094–4100 (in Japanese).
Grimley, T. A., Mudawwar, I., and Incropera, F. P. 1988. CHF Enhancement in Flowing Fluorocarbon Liquid Films Using Structured Surfaces and Flow Deflectors. *Int. J. Heat Mass Transfer* 31:55–65.
Hallet, V. A. 1966. Surface Phenomena Causing Breakdown of Falling Liquid Films During Heat Transfer. *Int. J. Heat Mass Transfer* 9:283–294.
Haramura, Y. and Katto, Y. 1983. A New Hydrodynamic Model of Critical Heat Flux, Applicable Widely to Both Pool and Forced Convection Boiling on Submerged Bodies in Saturated Liquids. *Int. J. Heat Mass Transfer* 26:389–399.
Hartley, D. E. and Murgatroyd, W. 1964. Criteria for the Break-up of Thin Liquid Layers Flowing Isothermally over Solid Surfaces. *Int. J. Heat Mass Transfer* 7:1003–1015.
Hewitt, G. F. and Lacey, P. M. C. 1965. The Breakdown of the Liquid Film in Annular Two-Phase Flow, *Int. J. Heat Mass Transfer* 8:781–791.
Holman, J. P., Jenkins, P. E., and Sullivan, F. G. 1972. Experiments on Individual Droplet Heat Transfer Rates. *Int. J. Heat Mass Transfer* 15:1489–1495.
Incropera, F. P. 1988. Convection Heat Transfer in Electronic Equipment Cooling. *J. Heat Transfer* 110:1097–1111.
Ishigaya, S., Nakanishi, S., Koizumi, T., and Oyabu, J. 1971. Hydrodynamics and Heat Transfer of Vertical Liquid Films, Part 1: Classification of Flow Regimes. *Trans. of JSME* 37:1708–1715 (in Japanese).
Kandula, M. 1990. Mechanisms and Predictions of Burnout in Flow Boiling over Heated Surfaces with an Impinging Jet. *Int. J. Heat Mass Transfer* 33:1795–1803.
Katto, Y. and Haramura, Y. 1981. Effect of Velocity (Weber Number) on CHF for Boiling on Heated Plates Cooled by a Plane Jet. *Proc. 18th National Heat Transfer Symposium of Japan*, pp. 382–384 (in Japanese).
Katto, Y. and Ishii, K. 1978. Burnout in a High Heat Flux Boiling System with a Forced Supply of Liquid Through a Plane Jet. *Proc. 6th Int. Heat Transfer Conf.*, Volume 1, FB-28:435–448.
Katto, Y. and Kunihiro, M. 1973. Study of the Mechanism of Burn-Out in Boiling System of High Burn-Out Heat Flux. *Bull of JSME* 16:1357–1366.

Katto, Y. and Kurata, C. 1980. Critical Heat Flux of Saturated Convective Boiling on Uniformly Heated Plates in a Parallel Flow. *Int. J. Multiphase Flow* 6:575–582.

Katto, Y. and Monde, M. 1974. Study of Mechanism of Burn-Out in a High Heat -Flux Boiling System with an Impinging Jet. *Proc. 5th Int. Heat Transfer Conf.*, B6.2:245–249.

Katto, Y. and Shimizu, M. 1979. Upper Limit of CHF in the Saturated Forded Convection Boiling on a Heated Disk with an Impinging Jet. *J. Heat Transfer* 101:265–269.

Katto, Y. and Yokoya, S. 1988. Critical Heat Flux on a Disk Heater Cooled by a Circular Jet of Saturated Liquid Impinging at the Center. *Int. J. Heat Mass Transfer* 31:219–227.

Koizumi, Y., Kodama, Y., Ohtake, H., and Miyashita, T. 1996. Study on Minimum Wetting Rate of a Falling Film on Outer Surfaces of Vertical Pipes. *Proc. 33rd National Heat Transfer Symposium of Japan*, Volume 3, pp. 801–802 (in Japanese).

Koizumi, Y., Matsuo, T., Miyota, Y., and Ueda, T. 1998. Dry-Out Heat Fluxes of Falling Film and Low-Mass Flux Upward-Flow in Heated Tubes. *Trans. of JSME, B* 64:2578–2585 (in Japanese).

Kugler, S. 1997. Enhancement of Nucleate Boiling Heat Flux on Macro/Micro Structured Surfaces Cooled by Multiple Impinging Jets. M.S. Thesis, University of California, Los Angeles, CA.

Kunz, H. R. and Yerazunis, S. 1969. An Analysis of Film Condensation, Film Evaporation, and Single-Phase Heat Transfer for Liquid Prandtl Number from $10^{-3}$ to $10^4$. *Trans. of ASME, Ser. C, J. of Heat Transfer* 91:413–420.

Kutateladze, S. S. 1952. Heat Transfer in Condensation and Boiling. U.S. AEC Report AEC-tr-3370.

Lay, J. H. and Dhir, V. K. 1995. Nucleate Boiling Heat Flux Enhancement on Macro/Micro Structured Surfaces Cooled by an Impinging Jet. *J. Enhancement Heat Transfer* 3:177–188.

Lienhard, J. H. and Eichhorn, R. 1979. On Predicting Boiling Burnout for Heaters Cooled by Liquid Jets. *Int. J. Heat Mass Transfer* 22:774–776.

Liu, X., Lienhard, V. J. H., and Lombara, J. S. 1991. Convective Heat Transfer by Impingement of Circular Liquid Jets. *J. Heat Transfer* 113:571–582.

Ma, C. F. and Bergles, A. E. 1983. Boiling Jet Impingement Cooling of Simulated Microelectronic Chips. In: *Heat Transfer in Electronic Equipment—1983*. Eds. S. Oktay and A. Bar-Cohen, HTD-Vol. 28:5–12. New York: ASME.

Monde, M. 1979. Critical Heat Flux in the Saturated Forced Convective Boiling on a Heated Disk with Impinging Droplets. *Heat Transfer—Japanese Research* 8:54–64.

Monde, M. 1985. Critical Heat Flux in Saturated Forced Convective Boiling on a Heated Disk with an Impinging Jet: A New Generalized Correlation. *Wärme und Stoffübertragung* 19:205–209.

Monde, M. 1987. Critical Heat Flux in Saturated Forced Convection Boiling on a Heated Disk with an Impinging Jet. *J. Heat Transfer* 109:991–996.

Monde, M. and Inoue, T. 1991. Critical Heat Flux in Saturated Forced Convective Boiling on a Heated Disk with Multiple Impinging Jets. *J. Heat Transfer* 113:722–727.

Monde, M. and Katto, Y. 1978. Burnout in a High Heat-Flux Boiling System with an Impinging Jet. *Int. J. Heat Mass Transfer* 21:295–305.

Monde, M. and Mitsutake, Y. 1996. Critical Heat Flux in Forced Convective Subcooled Boiling with Multiple Impinging Jets. *J. Heat Transfer* 117:241–243.

Monde, M. and Okuma, Y. 1985. Critical Heat Flux in Saturated Forced Convective Boiling on a Heated Disk with an Impinging Jet—CHF in L-Regime. *Int. J. Heat Mass Transfer* 28:547–552.

Monde, M., Kitajima, K., Inoue, T., and Mitsutake, Y. 1994. Critical Heat Flux in Forced Convective Subcooled Boiling with an Impinging Jet. *Heat Transfer 1994* 7:515–520.

Monde, M., Kusuda, H., and Uehara, H. 1980. Burnout Heat Flux in Saturated Forced Convection Boiling with Two or More Impinging Jets. *Heat Transfer—Japanese Research* 9:18–31.

Mudawar, I. and Valentine, W. S. 1989. Determination of the Local Quench Curve for Spray-Cooled Metallic Surface. *J. Heat Treat* 7:107–121.

Mudawar, I. and Wadsworth, D. C. 1991. Critical Heat Flux from a Simulated Chip to a Confined Rectangular Impinging Jet of Dielectric Liquid. *Int. J. Heat Mass Transfer* 34:1465–1479.

Mudawar, I., Incropera, T. A., and Incropera, F. P. 1987. Boiling Heat Flux and Critical Heat Flux in Liquid Films Falling on Vertically-Mounted Heat Sources. *Int. J. Heat Mass Transfer* 30:2083–2095.

Nishikawa, K. and Yamagata, Y. 1960. On the Correlation of Nucleate Boiling Heat Transfer. *Int. J. Heat Mass Transfer* 1:219–235.

Norman, W. S. and Binns, D. T. 1960. The Effect of Surface Tension Changes on the Minimum Wetting Rates in a Wetted-Rod Distillation Column. *Trans. Inst. Chem. Engrs.* 38:294–300.

Norman, W. S. and McIntyre, V. 1960. Heat Transfer to a Liquid Film on a Vertical Surface. *Trans. Instn. Chem. Engrs.* 38:301–307.

Nonn, T., Dagan, Z., and Jiji, L. M. 1988. Boiling Jet Impingement Cooling of Simulated Microelectronic Heat Sources. ASME Paper 88-WA/EEP-3.

Nusselt, W. 1916. Die Oberflüchenkondensation des Wasserdampfes. *Z. VDI* 60:541–546, 569–575.

Nusselt, W. 1923. Der Wärmeaustausch und Berieselungskühler. *Z. VDI* 67:206–210.

Petrovichev, V. I., Kokorev, L. S., Didenko, A. Ya., and Dubvrovskiy, G. P. 1971. Droplet Entrainment in Boiling of Thin Liquid Films. *Heat Transfer—Soviet Research* 3:19–22.

Portalski, S. 1963. Studies of Falling Liquid Film Flow. *Chem. Eng. Sci.* 18:787–804.

Ruch, M. A. and Holman, J. P. 1975. Boiling Heat Transfer to a Freon-113 Jet Impinging Upward onto a Flat Heated Surface. *Int. J. Heat Mass Transfer* 18:51–60.

Sharan, A. and Lienhard, J. H. 1985. On Predicting Burnout in the Jet-Disk Configuration. *J. of Heat Transfer* 107:398–481.

Stevens, J. and Webb, B. W. 1993. Measurements of Flow Structure in the Radial Layer of Impinging Free-Surface Liquid Jets. *Int. J. Heat and Mass Transfer* 36:3751–3758.

Takahama, H., Kato, S., and Kiuchi, T. 1978. Longitudinal Flow-Characteristics in Vertical Falling Liquid Film Without Concurrent Gas Flow. *Trans. of JSME* 44:3514–3525 (in Japanese).

Toda, S. 1972. A Study in Mist Cooling. *Trans. of JSME* 38:581–588 (in Japanese).

Ueda, T. and Tanaka, T. 1974. Studies of Liquid Film Flow in Two-Phase Annular and Annular-Mist Flow Regions, Part 1: Down Flow in a Vertical Tube. *Bull. of JSME* 17:603–613.

Ueda, T., Inoue, M., and Nagatome, S. 1981. Critical Heat Flux and Droplet Entrainment Rate in Boiling of Falling Liquid Films. *Int. J. Heat Mass Transfer* 24:1257–1266.

Vader, D. T., Incropera, F. P., and Viskanta, R. 1992. Convective Nucleate Boiling on a Heated Surface Cooled by an Impinging, Planer Jet of Water. *J. of Heat Transfer* 114:152–160.

Viskanta, R. and Incropera, F. P. 1992. Quenching with Liquid Jet Impingement. In: *Heat and Mass Transfer in Materials Processing.* Eds. I. Tanasawa and N. Lior, pp. 455–476. New York: Hemisphere.

von Karman, T. 1939. Analogy Between Fluid Friction and Heat Transfer. *Trans. of ASME* 61:705–710.

Wang, X. and Monde, M. 1997. Critical Heat Flux in Forced Convective Subcooled Boiling with a Plane Jet (Effect of Subcooling on CHF). *Heat and Mass Transfer* 33:167–175.

Watson, E. J. 1964. The Radial Spread of a Liquid Jet over a Horizontal Plane. *J. Fluid Mech.* 20:481–499.

Wilke, W. 1962. Wärmeübertragung an Rieselfilme. *VDI Forschungsheft* 490:B-28.

CHAPTER
# FIFTEEN

## FLOW BOILING IN CIRCULAR TUBES

**15.1–15.3 Satish G. Kandlikar**

*Rochester Institute of Technology, Rochester, NY, USA*

**15.2.5, 15.2.6, 15.3.8 Hideki Nariai**

*University of Tsukuba, Tsukuba, Ibaragi, 305, Japan*

## 15.1 INTRODUCTION

The process of flow boiling of a liquid in heated confined passages is commonly encountered in many applications. Steam generators in power plants and evaporators in refrigeration and air conditioning equipment are some commonly encountered examples. In this chapter, the flow boiling inside smooth circular tubes will be covered. Although augmented tubes are becoming common, especially in the refrigeration and air conditioning industry, smooth tubes are still widely used in power, petrochemical, and process industries.

Heat transfer to a liquid flowing inside a tube is by single phase mode as long as the liquid and wall are both below the saturation temperature of the liquid at the local pressure. As the wall temperature exceeds the local saturation temperature, boiling can occur, depending on the tube surface characteristics and the operating conditions. The bulk liquid may still be in the subcooled region. Boiling under these conditions is called *subcooled flow boiling*. Saturated flow boiling covers the region when the wall temperature exceeds the local saturation temperature, and the thermodynamic quality (mass fraction of vapor) is between 0 and 1. Section 15.2 covers the subcooled flow boiling, and saturated flow boiling is covered in section 15.3.

## 15.2 SUBCOOLED FLOW BOILING

### 15.2.1 Subregions of Subcooled Flow Boiling

Consider a subcooled liquid flowing in a heated channel. As long as the channel wall is below the local saturation temperature of the liquid, heat transfer is by single-phase mode. As the wall temperature exceeds the saturation temperature, boiling may be initiated, depending on the wall, heater surface, and flow conditions.

The boiling process in the subcooled flow improves the heat transfer rate considerably over the single-phase value. Subcooled flow boiling has therefore received considerable attention where high heat flux cooling is required, such as in emergency core cooling of nuclear reactors, first-wall cooling of fusion reactors, neutron generators for cancer therapy and material testing, high power electronic applications, cooling of rocket nozzles, and pressurized water reactors (Bergles, 1984; Boyd, 1988).

Figure 1 shows a schematic illustrating important locations and regions of subcooled flow boiling. Although the discussion presented here refers to a circular

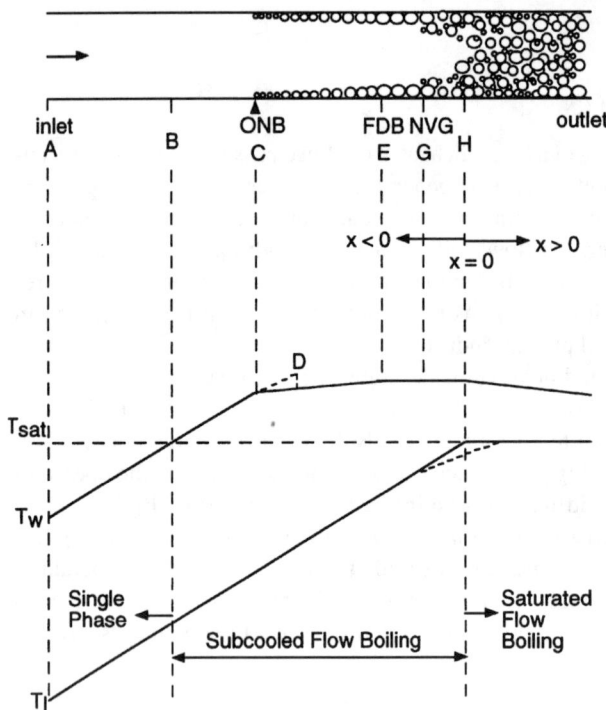

**Figure 1** Schematic representation of flow regimes in subcooled flow boiling.

tube, the analysis can be easily extended to other simple geometries using the concept of hydraulic diameter. Liquid enters the tube at **A** under subcooled conditions, and the tube wall is below the local saturation temperature. The bulk liquid temperature and the wall temperature vary along the length of the tube. Under a constant heat flux surface boundary condition for a circular tube of diameter $D$, the bulk fluid temperature variation in the flow direction in the non-boiling region can be obtained from an energy balance over the tube length $L$. In the single-phase region, the heat transfer coefficient $\alpha_l$ is almost constant (neglecting property variation with temperature), and the wall temperature rises linearly and parallel to the bulk liquid temperature. At location **B**, the wall temperature reaches the saturation temperature of the liquid. However, nucleation does not occur immediately, as a certain amount of wall superheat is needed to nucleate cavities existing on the surface of the tube wall.

The first bubbles appear on the wall at location **C**, which is identified as the *onset of nucleate boiling*, or *ONB*. The wall temperature begins to level off as more nucleation sites are activated beyond *ONB*. Further downstream, as more sites are activated, the contribution to heat transfer from nucleate boiling continues to rise, while the single-phase convective contribution diminishes. This region is called *partial boiling* region. At **E**, the convective contribution becomes insignificant and the *fully developed boiling*, or *FDB*, is established. Subsequently, the wall temperature remains almost constant in the *FDB* region until some point where the convective effects become important again due to the two-phase flow in the newly defined *significant void flow* region.

The bubbles generated at the wall immediately following *ONB* cannot grow due to condensation occurring at the bubble surface exposed to the subcooled liquid flow. A thin layer of bubbles is formed on the wall. As the bulk liquid temperature increases in the flow direction, the layer becomes populated with more bubbles, whose size also increases with decreasing subcooling. At some location **G**, the bubbles eventually detach from the wall and flow toward the liquid core. Some bubbles condense along the way. Point **G** is identified as the point of *net vapor generation*, or NVG (also called *OSV, Onset of Significant Void*), prior to which the vapor volumetric flow fraction is insignificant. Heat transfer subsequent to *NVG* can be considered to be in the two-phase region.

The vapor present in the subcooled flow following *NVG* is at the saturation temperature. This gives rise to a thermodynamic non-equilibrium condition, with the liquid temperature being below the equilibrium subcooled liquid temperature dictated by the local enthalpy. As heat addition continues downstream, a saturation condition under thermodynamic equilibrium is reached at **H**. Due to the non-equilibrium conditions, the true liquid temperature is below the saturation temperature, as indicated by a dashed line. Flow beyond **H** is covered under saturated flow boiling in Section 15.3.

The state of a subcooled liquid can be defined in terms of an equilibrium "quality," based on the liquid enthalpy relative to its saturation state at the same pressure.

$$x = (h_l - h_{l,sat})/h_{lg} = -c_p \Delta T_{sub}/h_{lg} \quad (15.2\text{-}1)$$

Equation (15.2-1) results in a negative quality in the subcooled region. In the single-phase region, before any boiling is initiated, the single-phase liquid heat transfer coefficient is based on the wall to liquid temperature difference.

$$\dot{q} = \alpha_l(T_w - T_l) = \alpha_l(\Delta T_{sat} + \Delta T_{sub}) \quad (15.2\text{-}2)$$

Further discussion on the heat transfer rates in different regions is presented in the following sections.

## 15.2.2 Onset of Nucleation in Subcooled Flow

As long as the wall temperature is below the local saturation temperature, nucleate boiling cannot be initiated under steady flow conditions (Sometimes dissolved gases are released from the surface. These are called *rogue sites*). The bubbles are nucleated on cavities present on the heater surface and require a certain amount of wall superheat, depending on the cavity size and flow conditions. Presence of trapped gases or vapor in the cavities initiates the nucleus formation. Generally at the start-up, cavities are flooded and require a higher degree of wall superheat. Once boiling is initiated, the superheat required to sustain bubble activity is lower due to the presence of vapor inside the cavities. This behavior is known as the *hysteresis effect*, and it is significant in highly wetting liquids such as refrigerants.

In the absence of hysteresis effect, the nucleation criterion suggested by Hsu and Graham (1961) has shown to be valid by many later investigators. Bergles and Rohsenow (1964) described the nucleation criterion graphically in terms of the tangency condition and presented an empirical correlation for the *ONB* condition. Hsu (1962) and Sato and Matsumura (1964) presented equations for $\Delta T_{sat,ONB}$ and $\dot{q}_{ONB}$.

$$\Delta T_{sat,ONB} = \frac{4\sigma T_{sat} v_{lg} \alpha_l}{\lambda_l h_{lg}} \left[ 1 + \sqrt{1 + \frac{\lambda_l h_{lg} \Delta T_{sub}}{2\sigma T_{sat} v_{lg} \alpha_l}} \right] \quad (15.2\text{-}3)$$

and

$$\dot{q}_{ONB} = [\lambda_l h_{lg}/(8\sigma v_{lG} T_{sat})][\Delta T_{sat,ONB}]^2 \quad (15.2\text{-}4)$$

The range of active cavity radii were also presented by Hsu and Sato and Matsumura. A non-dimensionalized-form of these equations was presented by

Kandlikar and Spiesman (1997) using the following parameters:

$$r_c^* = r_c/\delta_t \tag{15.2-5}$$

$$\Delta T_{sat}^* = \Delta T_{sat} h_{lv} \delta_t / (8\sigma T_{sat} v_{lv}) \tag{15.2-6}$$

$$\Delta T_{sub}^* = \Delta T_{sub} h_{lv} \delta_t / (8\sigma T_{sat} v_{lv}) \tag{15.2-7}$$

The range of the active cavity radii in non-dimensional form is then given by the following equation:

$$r_{max}^*, r_{min}^* = \frac{1}{2}\left[\frac{\Delta T_{sat}^*}{\Delta T_{sat}^* + \Delta T_{sub}^*} \pm \sqrt{\left(\frac{\Delta T_{sat}^*}{\Delta T_{sat}^* + \Delta T_{sub}^*}\right)^2 - \frac{1}{\left(\Delta T_{sat}^* + \Delta T_{sub}^*\right)}}\right] \tag{15.2-8}$$

The properties in Eqs. (15.2-3)–(15.2-8) are evaluated at the saturation temperature, and $\alpha_l$ is determined from an appropriate single-phase correlation incorporating a wall temperature correction factor if necessary. Additional factors such as dissolved gases and cavity geometry further affect the nucleation characteristics.

Figure 2 shows the plot of the nucleation criteria given by Eq. (15.2-8) for three values of non-dimensional subcooling. For a given wall superheat, the range of active cavity radii fall within the intersection of a vertical line with the specific curve for a given subcooling. An illustrative plot showing the range of active cavity radii for saturated water (zero subcooling) at 1 atmosphere is shown in Figure 3. Three plots corresponding to the three values of $\alpha_l$ are shown. The cavity size that is activated first with increasing wall temperature is called the *critical cavity size*. Thus, it can be seen that corresponding to $\alpha_l = 25{,}000$ W/m$^2$K, nucleation is

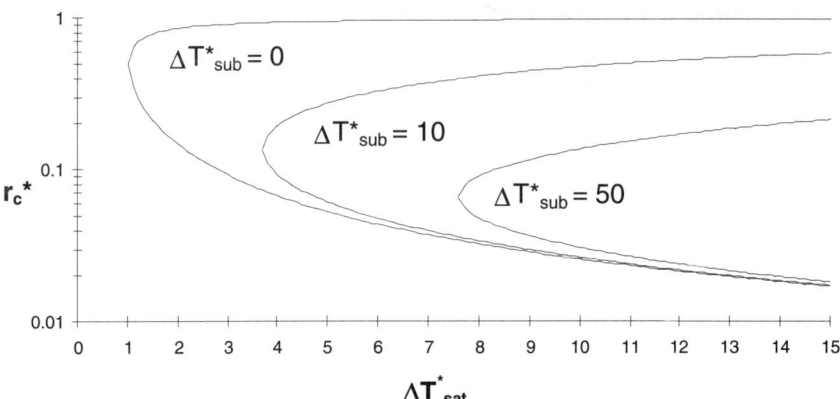

**Figure 2** Non-dimensional form of nucleation criterion (presented by Kandlikar and Spiesman, 1997).

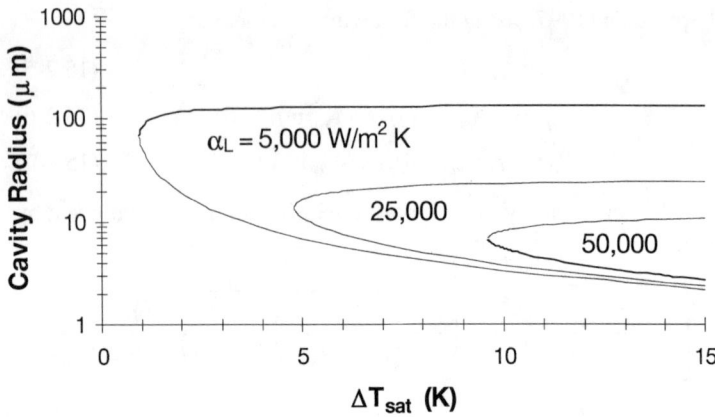

**Figure 3** Range of active cavity radii for saturated water at 1 atmosphere pressure, Kandlikar and Spiesman (1997).

initiated at about 4.8 K superheat, and the critical cavity radius is about 13.6 $\mu$m. At a superheat of 10 K, the range of active cavity radii is 3.8 to 23.4 $\mu$m.

Kandlikar et al. (1997) studied the nucleation behavior of water in subcooled flow and noted that the above criteria given by Eq. (15.2-8) represents the experimental data well. A slight improvement was obtained by locating the stagnation streamline around the bubble and using the liquid temperature at this location as the temperature at the top of a nucleating bubble. However, further experimental validation with other fluids is needed before recommending this procedure.

### 15.2.3 Bubble Dynamics in Subcooled Flow Boiling

Bubble dynamics in subcooled flow boiling can be studied as an extension of pool boiling with additional effects due to the flow. The flow field changes the temperature distribution in the liquid near the wall, and the nucleation criterion is modified, as seen in Section 15.2.2. Once the bubbles grow beyond the critical radius, their growth is governed by the surrounding temperature field. The condensation occurring at the top of a bubble in highly subcooled flow may cause a total collapse of the bubble. The bubble growth rate is thus strongly influenced by the bulk liquid subcooling.

Gunther (1951) conducted experiments on subcooled flow boiling of water in a transparent channel and photographed the bubble growth on the heater surface. He observed that bubbles grow and collapse while remaining attached to the heater surface. Bubbles were also seen to slide along the heater surface. Tsung-Chang and Bankoff (1990) postulated that the sliding motion of bubbles helped in augmenting the heat transfer. They presented an analysis for heat transfer with a moving bubble at constant wall temperature. Thorncroft and Klausner (1997) studied the effect of sliding bubbles and noted the differences in the vertical up-flow and down-flow cases. The problem is further complicated by the heater wall dynamics, which needs to be considered in the bubble growth modeling. Such an attempt has been done by Chen et al. (1995) for pool boiling, but it needs to be extended to flow boiling.

Kandlikar (1992), Kandlikar and Stumm (1995), Kandlikar and Mizo (1995), Kandlikar and Cartwright (1995), and Kandlikar et al. (1997) studied the bubble growth in subcooled flow of water in a 3 mm × 40 mm horizontal flow channel with a 10 mm diameter heater, centrally placed in the 40-mm bottom wall. The bubble nucleation and growth were observed under a microscope and a high-speed camera (1000 fps). Kandlikar (1992) observed that the bubbles are distorted due to the flow field, and the front and rear contact angles are different. Figure 4 shows the effect of flow on these contact angles. A force balance on the bubble (Kandlikar and Stumm, 1995) indicated that the bubble removal could be initiated by one of the four mechanisms: i) shear removal at the front edge, ii) lift removal at the front edge, iii) shear removal at the rear edge, and iv) lift removal at the rear edge. When bubbles are removed by lift forces, they tend to take off from their sites, whereas when they are removed by shear forces, they tend to slide along the wall.

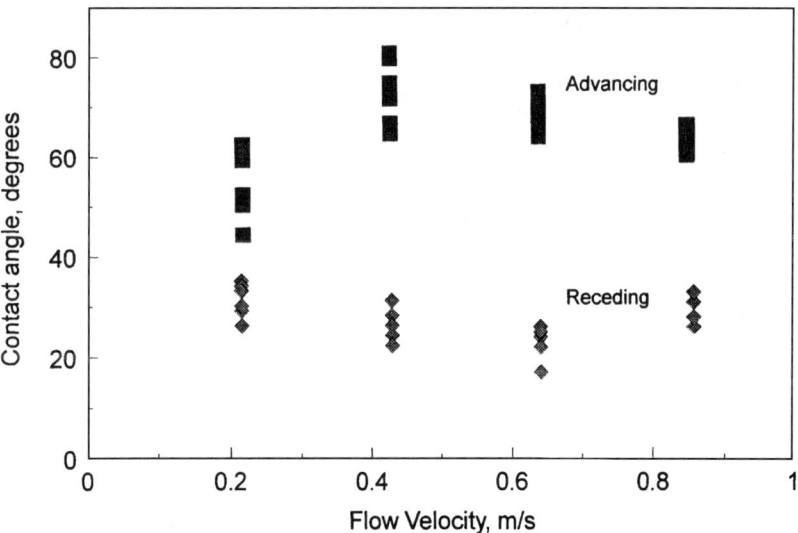

**Figure 4** Variation of front (advancing) and rear (receding) contact angles with flow velocity, subcooled water in a 3 × 40 mm horizontal channel at atmospheric pressure, Kandlikar and Stumm (1995).

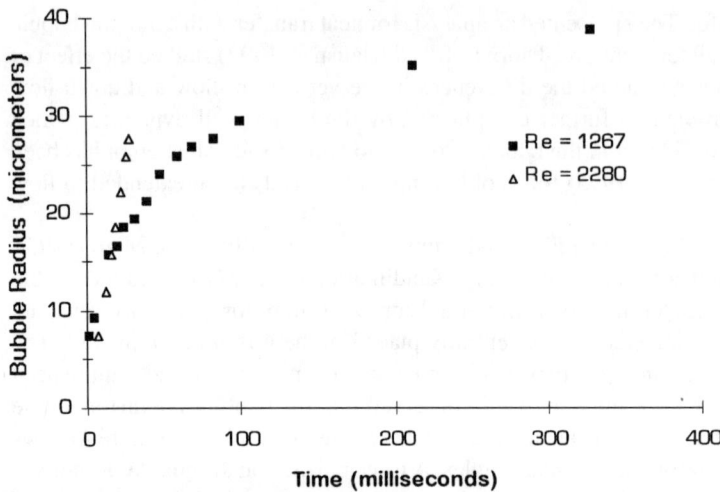

**Figure 5** Effect of flow on bubble growth, subcooled flow of water at 1 atmospheric pressure in 3 × 40 mm rectangular channel, $T_{wall} = 108°C$, $T_{bulk} = 80°C$, cavity radius 3.2 $\mu$m; Kandlikar et al. (1997).

It is quite common to see bubbles sliding along the wall. Klausner et al. (1993) made similar observations in saturated flow experiments with FC-87; however, they noted the bubble growth and departure to be stochastic processes due to the presence of two-phase bulk flow in their experiments. The growth and departure of bubbles were expressed in terms of probability density functions.

Figure 5 shows the results obtained by Kandlikar et al. (1997) on the bubble growth rates as a function of flow velocity with subcooled flow of water. A higher flow velocity causes the bubbles to depart or collapse sooner in their growth cycle. The growth rates were increased dramatically with a reduction in the subcooling and an increase in the wall temperature. Figure 6 shows the effect of increasing the wall temperature. Closer to saturation condition, the bubble activity could not be captured even with a 6000 fps camera speed. Further research in this area is warranted. In the study of bubble growth, the heating surface also participates in the dynamic behavior, and its characteristics need to be included in future modeling efforts.

### 15.2.4 Heat Transfer in Subcooled Flow Boiling

**Fully developed boiling region.** In the region prior to *ONB*, the heat transfer is by single-phase mode. After *ONB*, heat transfer is by combination of convective

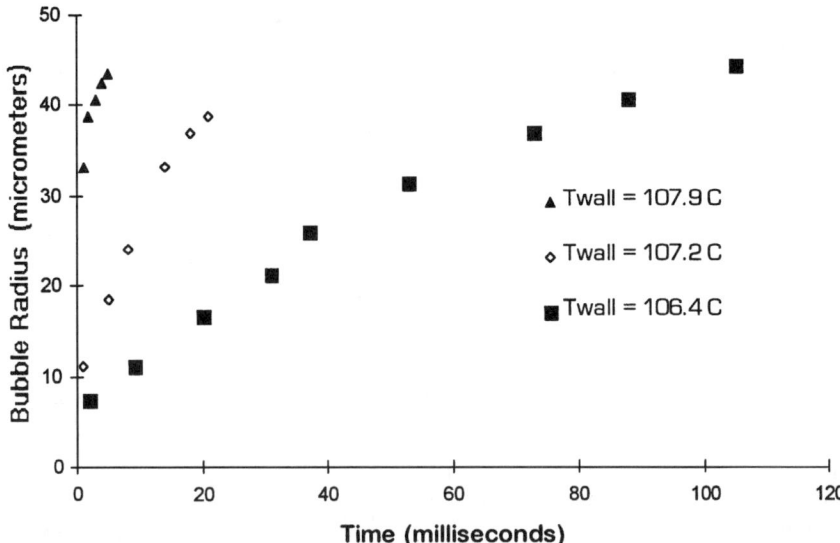

**Figure 6** Effect of wall temperature on bubble growth, subcooled flow of water at 1 atmospheric pressure in 3 × 40 mm rectangular channel, $T_{bulk} = 80°C$, Re = 1664, cavity radius 3.2 μm; Kandlikar et al. (1997).

and nucleate boiling modes. With a decrease in subcooling along the flow length due to heat addition, nucleation activity continues to increase. At some point, heat transfer is essentially by nucleate boiling mode with little contribution from the convective mode. The region beyond this point is called *fully developed boiling* and has been studied extensively for water by earlier investigators in nuclear reactor applications. Table 1 provides a summary of some of the important work reported in literature. The Jens and Lottes (1951) correlation was one of the first ones reported with water data. Thom et al. (1965) later found that this correlation underpredicted their data and proposed a correlation, which is recommended by Collier (1981) and Rohsenow (1985) for water. The correlation by Thom et al. agrees well with the low heat flux data of Brown (1967), as reported by Rohsenow (1985).

Shah (1977) compiled the available experimental data on twelve fluids from fifteen different sources. The *FDB* and the *partial boiling* regions are not clearly identified in his correlation; instead, he employs the level of subcooling relative to the wall superheat as a criterion and recommends separate correlations for the two regions. The demarcation between the two regions is made with a hand-drawn line through the data sets on a plot of $\Delta T_{sub}/\Delta T_{sat}$ vs. $Bo$.

**Table 1  Some Important Correlations for Fully Developed Heat Transfer in Subcooled Flow Boiling**

| Investigator year | Fluid | Correlation | Comments |
|---|---|---|---|
| McAdams et al. (1949) | water | $\dot{q} = C(\Delta T_{sat})^{3.86}$ | Perhaps the first reported correlation for FDB. The constant C depends on the dissolved air content. |
| Jens and Lottes (1951) | water | $\Delta T_{sat} = 25 \dot{q}^{0.25} \exp(p/62)$ × p-bar, $\dot{q}$-MW/m², T-K | One of the earlier correlations, modified by later investigators |
| Thom et al. (1965) | water | $\Delta T_{sat} = 22.65 \dot{q}^{0.25} \exp(p/87)$ × p-bar, $\dot{q}$-MW/m², T-K | $\dot{q} \propto \Delta T_{sat}^2$ from the correlation, data indicates an exponent of 3, tested for low heat flux water data. |
| Mikic and Rohsenow (1969) | water | $\dot{q} = 1.89 \times 10^{-4} g^{1/2} h_{lg}^{1/2}$ $\times \rho_l^{17/8} c_{p,l}^{19/8} \rho_g^{1/8} (\Delta T_{sat})^3 /$ $\left[ \sigma^{9/8} (\rho_r \rho_g)^{5/8} T_{sat}^{1/8} \right]$ | Developed for pool boiling, includes surface effects, recommended by Rohsenow (1985) for FDB |
| Shah (1977) | R-11, R-12 R-113, water, other fluids, | $\dot{q} = [230(\dot{m} \, h_{lg})^{-0.5} \alpha_{lo} \Delta T_{sat}]^2$ $\alpha_{lo}$ from Dittus-Boelter correlation | $\dot{q} \propto \Delta T_{sat}^2$, not supported by data: no clear distinction between *partial* and *fully developed boiling*; hand-drawn line through data to include the effect of subcooling. |
| Kandlikar (1997, 1998) | water, refrigerants | $\dot{q} = [1058(\dot{m} \, h_{lg})^{-0.7}$ $\times F_{Fl} \alpha_{lo} \Delta T_{sat}]^{1/0.3}$ $\alpha_{lo}$ from Gnielinski, and Petukhov and Popov correlations; $F_{Fl}$-fluid-surface parameter, given by Kandlikar (1991a). | Represents correct dependence of $\dot{q}$ on $\Delta T_{sat}$; compares well with Bergles and Rohsenow (1964), McAdams et al. (1949), and Del Valle and Kenning (1985) water data, and other refrigerant data. |

Kandlikar (1997, 1998) proposed that the nucleate boiling term in the saturated flow boiling correlation by Kandlikar (1990a) should be able to represent the fully developed boiling in a subcooled flow, since the convective contribution is negligible. One of the features of this correlation as reported by Kandlikar (1990b) is its ability to predict the trends in $\alpha$ vs. $x$ in the low quality region, explaining the reasons for increasing or decreasing $\alpha$ for different cases. The heat transfer coefficient $\alpha^*$ in the *fully developed boiling* region is thus given by the following equation, derived from the nucleate boiling dominant region of the Kandlikar correlation:

$$\alpha^* = 1058.0 \, Bo^{0.7} F_{fl} \alpha_{lo} \quad (15.2\text{-}9)$$

Note that $\alpha^*$ is based on the wall superheat with $\dot{q} = \alpha^* \Delta T_{sat}$, $Bo = \dot{q}/(\dot{m}h_{lg})$, and $\dot{m}$ is the total mass flux, kg/m²s. $F_{fl}$ is the fluid-surface parameter, and $\alpha_{lo}$ is the single-phase heat transfer coefficient for all liquid flow (same as $\alpha_l$ in the subcooled region) obtained from Gnielinski (1976) and Petukhov-Popov (1963) correlations, along with the following property correction factor recommended by Petukhov (1970).

$$Nu_{lo} = Nu_{lo,\,cp} (\eta_b/\eta_w)^{0.11} \quad (15.2\text{-}10)$$

where $Nu_{lo,cp}$ is the Nusselt number with constant properties obtained from the following equations, and the subscripts b and w refer to the properties at bulk and wall temperatures, respectively.

Petukhov-Popov (1963), for $0.5 \leq Pr \leq 2000$ and $10^4 \leq Re_{lo} \leq 5 \times 10^6$,

$$Nu_{lo,cp} = \frac{Re_{lo} \, Pr_l(f/2)}{[1.07 + 12.7(Pr^{2/3} - 1)(f/2)^{0.5}]} \quad (15.2\text{-}11)$$

Gnielinski (1976), for $0.5 \leq Pr \leq 2000$ and $2300 \leq Re_{lo} < 10^4$,

$$Nu_{lo,cp} = \frac{(Re_{lo} - 1000)(f/2)Pr_l}{[1 + 12.7(Pr^{2/3} - 1)(f/2)^{0.5}]} \quad (15.2\text{-}12)$$

where $f$ is the friction factor given by the following equation.

$$f = [1.58 \ln(Re_{lo}) - 3.28]^{-2} \quad (15.2\text{-}13)$$

The heat transfer coefficient in the *FDB* region of the subcooled flow is expressed in terms of the temperature difference between the wall and the fluid, or $\dot{q} = \alpha^* \Delta T_{sat} = \alpha_{FDB}(\Delta T_{sub} + \Delta T_{sat})$. Combining the definition of $\alpha^*$ and $Bo$ with Eq. (15.2-9) results in the following expression for $\dot{q}$ in the *FDB* region.

$$\dot{q} = [1058(\dot{m} \, h_{lg})^{-0.7} F_{fl} \alpha_{lo} \Delta T_{sat}]^{1/0.3} \quad (15.2\text{-}14)$$

Figure 7 shows a comparison of Eq. (15.2-14) and some of the correlations listed in Table 1 with the experimental data of Bergles and Rohsenow (1964) for water flowing in an annulus over a heated stainless steel tube. The Thom et al. (1965) correlation considerably underpredicts the results. The pool boiling curve represented by the Mikic and Rohsenow (1969) correlation is below the *FDB* curve but has the same slope as the experimental *FDB* data. The Shah (1977) correlation underpredicts the results and exhibits a flatter slope. The dependence

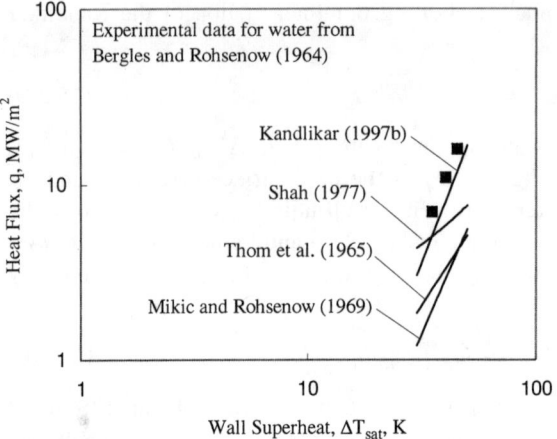

**Figure 7** Comparison of *fully* developed *boiling* correlations with experimental data from Bergles and Rohsenow (1964); subcooled water, 4.5 m/s flow velocity, 109-72°C subcooling, 2.2 bar pressure.

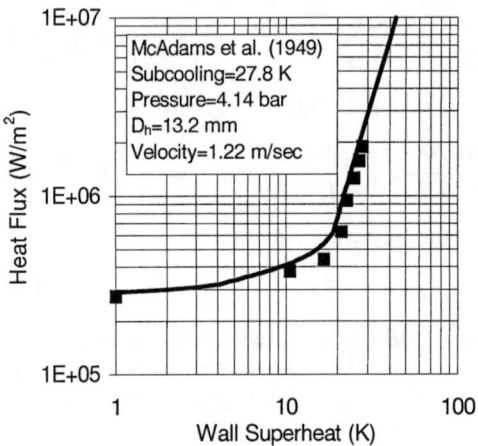

**Figure 8** Comparison of the present model with McAdams et al. (1949) data in the *partial boiling* and the *FDB* regions, water velocity 1.22 m/s.

of $\dot{q}$ on $\Delta T_{sat}$ is expressed through an exponent of 3.86 by McAdams et al. (1949), whereas it is 2.0 in the equations by Shah and Thom et al. and 3.33 in Eq. (15.2-14). This equation, given by Kandlikar (1997, 1998), agrees closely with the data and displays the same trend as seen from Figure 7.

Equation (15.2-14) was also able to represent the refrigerant R-11 by Riedle and Purcupile (1973) for plain tubes and McAdams et al. (1949) data for water in annuli within an absolute mean error of less than 14.5 percent. Figure 8 shows the

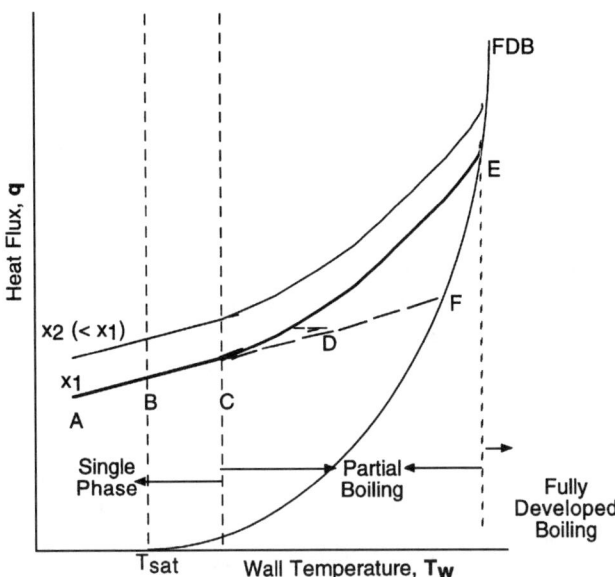

**Figure 9** Heat transfer in partial boiling region.

comparison with McAdams et al. (1949) data for water at 27.8 K subcooling and 4.14 bar flowing at a velocity of 1.22 m/s in an annulus with a hydraulic diameter of 13.2 mm. The steep vertical line represents Eq. (15.2-14) in the *FDB* region. Also shown in the figure is the partial boiling region, which is discussed later in this section.

**Location of FDB.** Figure 9 shows a plot of $\dot{q}$ vs. $T_w$ at constant subcooling. **A-B** lies in the single-phase region, with *ONB* starting at **C** and the *fully developed boiling* beginning at **E**. The location of **E** where *FDB* begins has been investigated by many investigators, and the model by Bowring (1962) is widely recommended. The intersection of the extension of the single-phase line **A-B-F** given by Eqs. (15.2-2) and (15.2-10)–(15.2-13) and the fully developed boiling curve E-F-G given by Eq. (15.2-14) identifies **F**, and $\dot{q}_F$ is obtained by solving the two equation sets.

$$1058 F_{fl}(\dot{m} h_{lg})^{-0.7} \dot{q}_F - \dot{q}_F^{0.3}$$
$$-1058 \alpha_{lo} F_{fl}(\dot{m} h_{lg})^{-0.7} \Delta T_{sub} = 0 \qquad (15.2\text{-}15)$$

An iterative scheme is needed to solve Equation (15.2-15) for $\dot{q}_F$ at given values of $\dot{m}$ and $\Delta T_{sub}$. After locating **F**, $\dot{q}_E$ is obtained from the Bowring (1962) model given by the following equation.

$$\dot{q}_E = 1.4\, \dot{q}_F \qquad (15.2\text{-}16)$$

The wall superheat at **E** can be calculated from the *FDB* equation, Eq. (15.2-14). Note that the above calculations for $\dot{q}_E$ need to be reworked for each section along the flow length as the degree of subcooling decreases and the single-phase line in Figure 9 shifts lower.

**Partial boiling region.** The *partial boiling* region is identified as the region between **C**, where *ONB* begins, and **E**, where *FDB* begins, as shown in Figure 9. Heat transfer in this region is calculated by a procedure outlined by Kandlikar (1997, 1998) as follows.

The heat flux $\dot{q}_E$ at **E** is obtained from Eq. (15.2-14), and $\dot{q}_C$ at **C** is obtained from Eqs. (15.2-3) and (15.2-4) at *ONB*. In the *partial boiling* region **B-E**, the following equation is employed:

$$\dot{q} = a + b(T_w - T_{sat})^m \qquad (15.2\text{-}17)$$

The constants $a$ and $b$, are obtained from the known heat fluxes at **C** and **E**.

$$b = \frac{\dot{q}_E - \dot{q}_C}{(\Delta T_{sat,E})^m - (\Delta T_{sat,C})^m} \qquad (15.2\text{-}18)$$

and

$$a = \dot{q}_C - b(\Delta T_{sat,C})^m \qquad (15.2\text{-}19)$$

The exponent $m$ is allowed to vary linearly with heat flux as follows:

$$m = n + p\dot{q} \qquad (15.2\text{-}20)$$

where the constants n and p are obtained by matching the slopes of $m = 1$ at **C** to $m = 1/0.3$ at **D**.

$$p = (1/0.3 - 1)/(\dot{q}_E - \dot{q}_C) \qquad (15.2\text{-}21)$$

and

$$n = 1 - p\dot{q}_C \qquad (15.2\text{-}22)$$

The above procedure assures smooth transitions from the single-phase region to the *partial boiling* region and then to the *FDB* region. The gradual change in the slope also reflects the fact that an increasing number of nucleation cavities are activated as wall superheat increases.

Figure 10 shows a comparison of the current model and Shah's (1977) correlation with Riedle and Purcupile's data for R-11 in the *partial boiling* region.

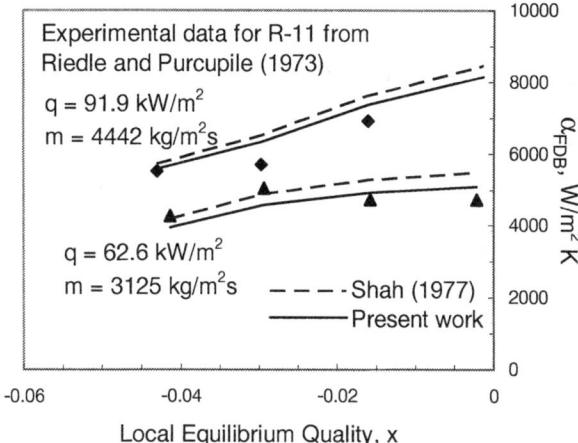

**Figure 10** Comparison of Eqs. (15.2-15)–(15.2-15 22), and Shah (1977) correlation with Riedle and Purcupile (1973) data for R-11 in the *Partial Boiling* region.

In their experiments, the liquid temperature increases as it is heated along the length of the tube. The results are therefore plotted on $\alpha$ vs. $x$ coordinates, where $\alpha = \dot{q}/(\Delta T_{sub} + \Delta T_{sat})$. This data set was used in the correlation development by Shah. As can be seen from Figure 10, the current model results in a slightly better agreement than the Shah correlation. For the entire data set, the absolute mean error with the Shah correlation is 11 percent, while it is 7.9 percent with the current method. Similar results were obtained with the data of Yin and Abdelmessih (1974) for R-11 and that of Hino and Ueda (1984) data for R-113.

Comparison of McAdams et al. (1949) data in the *partial boiling* region is shown in Figure 8. The agreement is excellent. It can be seen that the Bowring's model for the transition to *FDB* is also well represented.

**Significant void flow region.** The point of net vapor generation identifies the location in the subcooled flow where the net vapor flow fraction begins to be significant. It is postulated by Kandlikar (1997, 1998) that the two-phase flow effects would become important, and the saturated flow boiling correlations should hold well. Although the thermodynamic quality is negative in this region, the non-equilibrium quality based on the void fraction would be positive. An apparent quality, $x_a$, is therefore used to account for the non-equilibrium effects. In literature, $x_a$ is also referred to as the *true mass fraction*.

Saha and Zuber (1974) correlations are employed to locate the thermodynamic quality $x_{NVG}$ at location **G**, shown in Figure 1.

For $Re_{lo} Pr_l < 70{,}000$:

$$x_{NVG} = -0.0022 \frac{\dot{q} D}{\rho_l h_{lg} \kappa_l} = -0.0022 \, Bo \, Re_{lo} \, Pr_l \qquad (15.2\text{-}23)$$

and for $Re_{lo} Pr_l > 70{,}000$:

$$x_{NVG} = -154 \, Bo \qquad (15.2\text{-}24)$$

The apparent quality in the *significant void flow* region beyond $x_{NVG}$ is obtained from a correlation also recommended by Saha and Zuber (1974).

$$x_a = \frac{x - x_{NVG} \exp(x/x_{NVG} - 1)}{1 - x_{NVG} \exp(x/x_{NVG} - 1)} \qquad (15.2\text{-}25)$$

where x is the actual thermodynamic quality (negative value in the subcooled region).

Figure 11 shows the results of comparison with the subcooled flow boiling data obtained by Del Valle and Kenning (1985) for a heater thickness of 0.2 mm and three different velocities. The experimental data are obtained for the flow of water in a rectangular channel. Del Valle and Kenning compared their data with the available models for the fully developed boiling and found large errors (predicted heat fluxes were lower by a factor of over two). The data reported by Del Valle and Kenning correspond to the thermocouple location toward the exit of the test section located 130 mm from the inlet. Kandlikar (1998) obtained the local temperature and the equilibrium quality from the reported data by applying the heat balance equation over the heated length between the inlet section and the thermocouple location. It can be seen from Figure 11 that the agreement is excellent for all

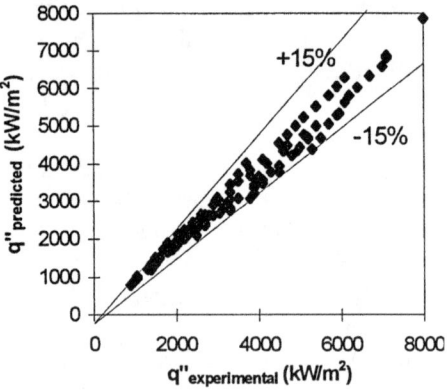

**Figure 11** Comparison of the Kandlikar (1998) model with subcooled water data by Del Velle and Kenning (1985) for 0.2 mm heater thickness.

three velocities. The effect of heater thickness is seen in Del Valle and Kenning's data. As stated earlier in Section 15.2-3, the heater thermal characteristics play an important role in the nucleate boiling heat transfer and should be included in future works. As the heater thickness becomes large, this effect reduces. This effect may therefore be critical in microelectronic cooling applications where the heating surface thickness is very small.

**Word of caution in analyzing subcooled flow boiling data.** In applying the equations and models in subcooled flow boiling, it is essential to determine the local subcooling at the section where wall temperature is measured. In many data sets reported in the literature, including Del Valle and Kenning (1985), the subcooling at the inlet to the test section is reported. As the liquid flows through the test section, it gets heated, and the local subcooling decreases in the flow direction. This effect is quite significant in long test sections under high heat flux conditions.

### 15.2.5 Void Fraction

In Figure 1, the void fraction at the region between C, where *ONB* begins, and G, where the net vapor flow fraction begins to be important, is negligible in the sense that the two-phase flow effects would become important. The main part of the region is the partial boiling region, where the void fraction is quite small and is negligible. In this section, the void fraction downstream of the NVG is considered.

In subcooled flow boiling, bubbles exist mainly along the heated surface and in a very small amount in the core region, showing the highly thermal non-equilibrium state. Then, the local void fractions differ radially across the cross-section of a channel. In defining the average void fraction in the channel, the true mass fraction $x_a$ has to be known, since the thermal equilibrium quality is negative.

Saha and Zuber (1974) used the true mass fraction $x_a$ in Eq. (15.2-25) and adopted the following equation to relate the average void fraction $\varepsilon$ and true mass fraction $x_a$.

$$\varepsilon = \frac{x_a}{C_o \left[ \dfrac{x_a \Delta \rho}{\rho_l} + \dfrac{\rho_g}{\rho_l} \right] + \dfrac{\rho_g V_{gj}}{\dot{m}}} \tag{15.2-26}$$

where $C_o$ is the distribution parameter and $V_{gj}$ drift velocity. They recommended $C_o = 1.13$ for circular tube and $V_{gj}$ in the following relation:

$$V_{gj} = 1.41 \left[ \frac{\sigma g \Delta \rho}{\rho_l^2} \right]^{1/4} \tag{15.2-27}$$

Levy (1967) is almost the same as Saha and Zuber and adopted Eq. (15.2-26), though the true mass fraction $x_a$ is approximated in the following equation.

$$x_a = x - x_{NVG} \exp(x/x_{NVG} - 1) \tag{15.2-28}$$

Equation (15.2-28) is derived from Eq. (15.2-26) by assuming

$$x_{NVG} \exp(x/x_{NVG} - 1) \ll 1$$

Levy used $C_o = 1.13$ and Zuber and Findlay for $V_{gj}$.

$$V_{gj} = 1.18 \left[ \frac{\sigma g \Delta \rho}{\rho_l^2} \right]^{1/4} \tag{15.2-29}$$

Ahmad (1970) calculated the average void fraction in the following equation by using the slip ratio S:

$$\varepsilon = \frac{x_a}{x_a + \left(\dfrac{\rho_g}{\rho_l}\right) S(1 - x_a)} \tag{15.2-30}$$

The true mass fraction $x_a$ is calculated by Eq. (15.2-25). He adopted slip ratio S in the following relation:

$$S = \left(\frac{\rho_l}{\rho_g}\right)^{0.205} \left(\frac{\dot{m} D}{\mu}\right)^{-0.016} \tag{15.2-31}$$

The void fractions predicted by three models are of good agreement with experimental data.

### 15.2.6 Friction Pressure Drop

Friction pressure drop in flow boiling system is usually evaluated using a two-phase friction multiplier, $\phi_{lo}^2$.

$$\phi_{lo}^2 = \frac{\Delta p_l}{\Delta p_{lo}} \tag{15.2-32}$$

where $\Delta P_l$ is the two-phase friction pressure drop and $\Delta P_{lo}$ is the single-phase friction pressure drop. In subcooled flow boiling, friction pressure drop before net vapor generation point or at partial boiling region is very small and almost equivalent to single phase friction pressure drop. However, the friction pressure drop increases rapidly downstream at the NVG or at the bubble detached region (Nariai and Inasaka, 1992). Several empirical correlations for an average two-phase friction multiplier along a heated tube have been proposed based on experimental results.

Owens and Schrock (1960) gave the following correlation for water above ambient pressure with tubes of 3, 4, and 6 mm inside diameter and 38 and 41 cm tube length.

$$\phi_{lo}^2 = 0.97 + 0.046(\exp(6.13Y) - 1)/Y \tag{15.2-33}$$

$$Y = 1 - \Delta T_{sub,exp}/\Delta T_{sub,DB} \tag{15.2-34}$$

Tarasova (1966) derived the multiplier for water at 1 to 20 MPa with 2.9 to 8.3 mm inside diameter.

$$\phi_{lo}^2 = 1 + \left(\frac{q\rho_l}{h_{lg}\dot{m}\rho_g}\right)^{0.7} \left(\frac{\rho_l}{\rho_g}\right)^{0.08} \left(\frac{26.3}{Y}\ln\left(\frac{1.315}{1.315 - Y}\right) - 20\right) \tag{15.2-35}$$

Ueda (1981) made a correlation based on the Martinelli-Nelson correlation for steam water systems as follows:

$$\phi_l^2 = 1 + 1.2x^{0.75(1+0.01\sqrt{\rho_l/\rho_g})}\left(\left(\frac{\rho_l}{\rho_g}\right)^{0.8} - 1\right) \tag{15.2-36}$$

In saturated flow boiling, the two-phase friction multiplier is correlated to the local or outlet quality through Lockhart-Maltinelli parameter X (Lockhart and Martinelli, 1945).

$$X = \left(\frac{1-x}{x}\right)^{\frac{2-n}{2}} \left(\frac{\rho_g}{\rho_l}\right)^{0.5} \left(\frac{\eta_l}{\eta_g}\right)^{\frac{n}{2}} \tag{15.2-37}$$

The parameter n is taken as 0.2 for turbulent flow. When we discuss the two-phase friction multiplier in subcooled flow boiling, similar with that in saturated flow boiling, the true mass fraction $x_a$ has to be used in estimating the local or outlet quality and/or the Lockhart-Martinelli parameter $X$.

The subcooled flow friction pressure drop was measured by Nariai and Inasaka (1992) using a 3 mm inside diameter tube with high velocity water flow. In evaluating the two-phase friction multiplier with the Lockhart-Martinelli parameter, the true mass fraction by Ahmad was used. Figure 12 shows a comparison of the empirical correlations with experimental data. The relation between $\phi_{f0}$ and X by Lockhart and Martinell for adiabatic flow condition is also investigated. As shown in the figure, the Lockhart and Martinelli and Tarasova correlations give higher values, and the Owens and Schrock correlation agrees well with the experimental data. Ueda's correlation comes between the two groups. An empirical correlation between the multiplier and the Lockhart-Martinelli parameter in Eq. (15.2-38) is also shown in the figure.

$$\phi_{lo}^2 = 1 + \frac{2.42}{X} + \frac{2.80}{X^2} \tag{15.2-38}$$

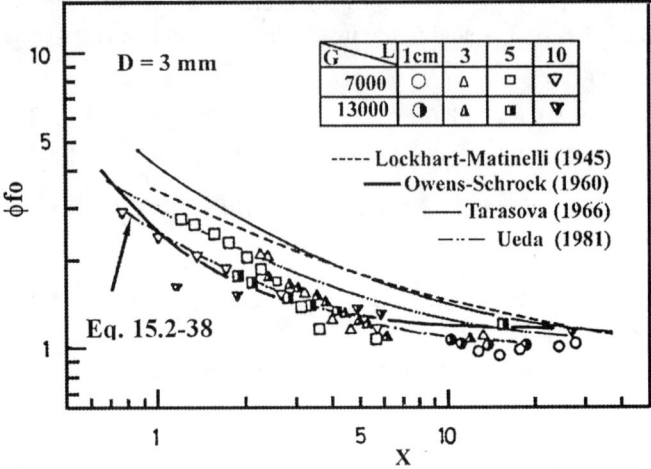

**Figure 12** Comparison of experimental two-phase pressure drop data with correlations.

In summary, the two-phase friction multiplier in subcooled flow boiling is close to that in saturated flow boiling and can be estimated reasonably if the true mass fraction is adequately evaluated.

## 15.3 SATURATED FLOW BOILING

### 15.3.1 Overview

The process of converting liquid into vapor is basic to many thermodynamic cycles. It is encountered in applications ranging from steam generation in oil or coal-fired boilers, nuclear reactors, refrigeration, and air-conditioning applications, to processes in chemical and petrochemical industries. Saturated flow boiling refers to the condition when both the liquid and vapor phases are at the saturation condition and heat supplied at the wall provides the latent heat for the evaporation process. The focus here is on the boiling inside smooth circular tube. The concepts developed here are later extended to augmented tubes, compact heat exchangers, and external flow boiling.

Consider the flow of a liquid through a circular tube. Saturated boiling begins from the point where the thermodynamic quality reaches zero. Heat transfer prior to this location is covered earlier under subcooled boiling in Section 15.2. In the saturated region, the liquid and vapor are close to saturation conditions, and the non-equilibrium effects become less pronounced. These conditions become important in the region close to $x = 0$ and after dryout condition is reached at higher qualities.

### 15.3.2 Flow Patterns in Flow Boiling

The saturated flow boiling starts when the thermal equilibrium quality or vapor mass fraction x becomes positive. The flow pattern changes with the increase of the quality. In the low quality region, just at the start of the saturated flow boiling, the "bubbly flow" appears as the continuation from the subcooled flow boiling. As the quality increases, the bubbles coalesce and form large slugs. The flow pattern is named the "slug flow" when the shape of the slug is not disturbed so much or "churn flow" when it is disturbed by the fluid motion. Details of each flow pattern are described in Chapter 9. As the quality increases, the slugs in churn flow coalesce in the flow direction and form continuous vapor flow in the core region and the liquid film flow on the heated wall. The flow pattern is named the "annular flow." With the increase of the vapor and liquid mass velocities, liquid droplets generated from the wavy liquid film on the wall are dispersed in the vapor in the core region. The flow pattern is named the "annular flow with entrainment." With further increase in quality, the liquid film on the heated wall becomes thin and finally disappears or dryout occurs. Beyond this point, the heated wall temperature increases sharply above the saturation temperature, and the liquid and vapor are in a non-equilibrium state. The flow pattern is named as the "mist flow," which continues beyond $x = 1$ due to non-equilibrium effects. Actual single phase vapor flow starts at the point where all of the mist evaporates and disappears.

### 15.3.3 Heat Transfer in Saturated Flow Boiling—Wetted Wall Region

Heat transfer in the saturated flow boiling is a combination of the convective heat transfer from the wall to the liquid (and subsequent film evaporation at the liquid-vapor interface) and nucleate boiling at the wall. The modeling of the convective heat transfer is complicated by the two-phase flow in the bulk. The effect of the two-phase flow on the nucleation, growth, and departure characteristics of bubbles is also very complex and does not easily lend itself to exact analytical treatment.

The presence of nucleation in the flow has been a controversial issue in the research conducted in the past decade. The bubble activity tends to be very rapid under saturated boiling conditions, and the presence of the two phases further complicates visual examination of the heater surface. Some studies are reported in which glass tubes are heated with thin transparent gold coatings. It seems reasonable to assume that bubble nucleation will occur in the flow so long that the nucleation criterion shown in Figure 2 is satisfied and that cavities of the required sizes are available on the heater surface. In the absence of the detailed local description of the temperature field, the actual two-phase heat transfer coefficient could be employed in this criterion in place of the single-phase heat transfer coefficient. Estimation of the resulting nucleate boiling heat transfer under such conditions is an area where further research is warranted.

There are two approaches possible for estimating heat transfer in two-phase flow. In the flow pattern based approach, the existing flow pattern is first predicted and the specific model for that flow pattern is employed. In the second approach, the heat transfer is directly predicted from the flow parameters and properties; since the parameters governing the flow pattern are also responsible for heat transfer, the uncertainty associated with flow pattern prediction is not carried forward. Many researchers are conducting numerical study of the two-phase flow and heat transfer phenomena, and some specialized codes have been developed for specific applications.

**Overview of available correlations.** There are a large number of correlations presented in literature on flow boiling of saturated liquids. A number of good surveys reviewing these correlations are available, e.g., Melin (1996), Wattelet (1994), and Darabi et al. (1995). Table 2 lists three of the more commonly used correlations.

The Chen (1966) correlation has been employed most commonly for water. It is based on the additive model for the nucleate boiling and convective boiling contributions. The convective contribution is enhanced due to the two-phase effects, while the nucleate boiling is suppressed due to the flow effects. Chen used 600 experimental data points for water, cyclohexane, and pentane in vertical flow in arriving at his correlation. The Chen correlation works well with low-pressure water data, but large deviations are observed with refrigerants.

Schrock and Grossman (1962) also proposed an additive form of correlation using Bo and $X_{tt}$ as parameters. They also proposed a chart, which was later refined by Shah (1972) by removing the viscosity ratio term from $X_{tt}$. Shah (1982) proposed equations to fit the chart, but it lacked accuracy, and the trends in heat transfer coefficients were not accurately represented.

The Gungor and Winterton (1987) correlation combines the Chen model and the Shah (1982) model. Other recent correlations, such as Liu and Winterton (1991) and Steiner and Taborek (1992), employ an asymptotic model in which $\alpha_{TP}^n = \alpha_{con}^n + \alpha_{nuc}^n$ with n = 2 and 3, respectively. The $\alpha_{con}$ and $\alpha_{nuc}$ are obtained from a combination of earlier models. These models work well in some cases; however, they do not correctly represent the trends of $\alpha$ vs. x. Also, it becomes difficult to identify the role of different parameters in studying the parametric effects.

Kandlikar's (1990a) correlation is developed using over 10,000 data points for refrigerants, water, and cryogens. The data covered wide ranges of density ratio between the two phases, heat flux and mass flux. The effect of density ratio and

## Table 2 Summary of some important correlations in saturated flow boiling

Investigator/Details/ Correlation/Comments

Chen (1966), Bennett and Chen (1980): Vertical flow, water, cyclohexane, pentane; 600 data points

$$\alpha_{TP} = \alpha_{mac} + \alpha_{mic}; \alpha_{mac} = \alpha_l E; \alpha_{mic} = \alpha_{pb} S; E = (1 + X_{tt}^{-0.5})^{1.78} \left[\frac{Pr_l + 1}{2}\right]^{0.444}$$

$$S = 0.9622 - \tan^{-1}(Re_l E^{1.25}/6.18 \cdot 10^4); \alpha_l = 0.023 Re_l^{0.8} Pr_l^{0.4} \lambda_l/d$$

$$\alpha_{pb} = \frac{0.00122 \lambda_l^{0.79} c_{p,l}^{0.45} \rho_l^{0.49}}{\sigma^{0.5} \eta_l^{0.29} h_{lg}^{0.24} \rho_g^{0.24}} \Delta T_{sat}^{0.24} \Delta p_{sat}^{0.75}$$

Works well with water at relatively low pressure, but large deviations observed with refrigerants; above equations are modified form of the original correlation proposed by later investigators using curve fits.

Gungor and Winterton (1987): water, R-11, R-12, R-22, R-113, R-114, ethylene glycol, 3,600 data points

$$\alpha_{TP}/\alpha_l = [1 + 3000 Bo^{0.86}]E_2 + 1.12[x/(1-x)]^{0.75}[\rho_l/\rho_g]^{0.41} S_2$$

For horizontal tubes with $Fr_{lo} < 0.05$, $E_2 = Fr_{lo}^{(0.1-2Fr_{lo})}$ and $S_2 = Fr_{lo}^{0.5}$; otherwise, $E_2 = 1$ and $S_2 = 1$. The agreement with experimental data is good; however, the trends in heat transfer coefficient with quality are not correctly represented.

Kandlikar (1990a, 1991a): refrigerants, water, cryogens, over 10,000 data points

$$\alpha_{TP}/\alpha_{lo} = higher\ of\ the\ NBD\ and\ CBD\ correlations\ given\ below$$

$$\alpha_{TP}/\alpha_{lo}|_{NBD} = 0.6683(\rho_l/\rho_g)^{0.1} x^{0.16}(1-x)^{0.64} f_2(Fr_{lo}) + 1058 Bo^{0.7}(1-x)^{0.8} F_{fl}$$

$$\alpha_{TP}/\alpha_{lo}|_{CBD} = 1.136(\rho_l/\rho_g)^{0.45} x^{0.72}(1-x)^{0.08} f_2(Fr_{lo}) + 667.2 Bo^{0.7}(1-x)^{0.8} F_{fl}$$

$$\alpha_{lo} = \frac{Re_{lo} Pr_l(f/2)(\lambda_l/d)}{1.07 + 12.7(Pr_l^{2/3} - 1)(f/2)^{0.5}}, \text{ for } 0.5 \leq Pr_l \leq 2000 \text{ and } 10^4 \leq Re_{lo} \leq 5.10^6$$

$$\alpha_{lo} = \frac{(Re_{lo} - 1000)Pr_l(f/2)(\lambda_l/d)}{1 + 12.7(Pr_l^{2/3} - 1)(f/2)^{0.5}}, \text{ for } 0.5 \leq Pr_l \leq 2000 \text{ and } 2300 \leq Re_{lo} < 10^4$$

$$f_2(Fr_{lo}) = (25 Fr_{lo})^{0.3} \text{ for } Fr_{lo} < 0.04 \text{ in horizontal tubes, otherwise } f_2(Fr_{lo}) = 1$$

$F_{fl}$ is fluid-surface parameters listed here. It depends on the surface finish of the tube affecting its nucleate boiling behavior. The correlation is able to predict the data well, and also the parametric trends, especially the variation of heat transfer coefficient versus x. Applicable in the quality range $0 < x \leq 0.8$ prior to dryout.

---

the boiling number was seen to be critical. A simple model was presented following the additive concept for convective and nucleate boiling contributions. An additional parameter $F_{Fl}$ was introduced to account for the fluid-surface effects.

The Kandlikar (1990a), (1991a) correlation:

$$\alpha_{TP} = \text{larger of} \begin{cases} \alpha_{TP}|_{NBD} \\ \alpha_{TP}|_{CBD} \end{cases} \quad (15.3\text{-}1)$$

where NBD and CBD refer to the nucleate boiling dominant and convective boiling dominant regions, and the respective $\alpha_{TP}$ are given by the following equations.

$$\alpha_{TP,NBD} = 0.6683\, Co^{-0.2}(1-x)^{0.8} f_2(Fr_{lo})\alpha_{lo} + 1058.0\, Bo^{0.7}(1-x)^{0.8} F_{Fl}\alpha_{lo} \tag{15.3-2}$$

$$\alpha_{TP}|_{CBD} = 1.136\, Co^{-0.9}(1-x)^{0.8} f_2(Fr_{lo})\alpha_{lo} + 667.2\, Bo^{0.7}(1-x)^{0.8} F_{Fl}\alpha_{lo} \tag{15.3-3}$$

where Co is the convection number, $= (\rho_g/\rho_l)^{0.5}((1-x)/x)^{0.8}$, Bo is the boiling number, $= \dot{q}/(\dot{m}h_{lg})$, and $Fr_{lo}$ is the Froude number with all flow as liquid, $= \dot{m}^2/(\rho_l g\, D)$. The Froude number multiplier $f_2(Fr_{lo})$ is 1 for vertical tubes, and for horizontal tubes with $Fr_{lo} > 0.4$. For $Fr_{lo} \leq 0.4$, $f_2(Fr_{lo})$ is given by the following equation.

$$f_2(Fr_{lo}) = \begin{cases} (25Fr_{lo})^{0.3}, & \text{for } Fr_{lo} < 0.04 \text{ in horizontal tubes} \\ 1, & \text{for vertical tubes and for } Fr_{lo} \geq 0.04 \text{ in horizontal tubes} \end{cases} \tag{15.3-4}$$

The single phase all liquid heat transfer coefficient $\alpha_{lo}$ is obtained from the Gnielinski (1976) correlation in the range $0.5 \leq Pr_l \leq 2000$ and $2300 \leq Re_{lo} < 10^4$.

$$\alpha_{lo} = \frac{(Re_{lo} - 1000)Pr_L(f/2)(\lambda_l/d)}{1 + 12.7(Pr_l^{2/3} - 1)(f/2)^{0.5}} \tag{15.3-5}$$

The Petukhov and Popov (1963) correlation is employed for $0.5 \leq Pr_l \leq 2000$ and $10^4 \leq Re_{lo} \leq 5 \times 10^6$.

$$\alpha_{lo} = \frac{Re_{lo}\, Pr_l(f/2)(\lambda_l/d)}{1.07 + 12.7(Pr_l^{2/3} - 1)(f/2)^{0.5}} \tag{15.3-6}$$

The friction factor f is given by the following equation.

$$f = [1.58 \ln(Re_{lo}) - 3.28]^{-2} \tag{15.3-7}$$

$F_{Fl}$ is a fluid-surface parameter that depends on the fluid and the heater surface characteristics. Table 3 lists the $F_{Fl}$ values for several fluids in copper tubes. These values should be considered as representative for commercial tubing. For stainless steel tubes, $F_{Fl}$ should be taken as 1.0. The value for the azeotropic mixture R-32/R-125 is reported by Wattelet (1994). His experimental data for refrigerants R-12, R-134a, R-22, and R-32/R-125 could be predicted by an earlier version of the above correlation (with the Dittus–Boelter correlation for $\alpha_{LO}$) to within 12.6–14.8 percent mean deviation. Introduction of the improved single-phase correlation is expected to improve the agreement further.

Introduction of $F_{Fl}$ in the nucleate boiling term is an important aspect of the Kandlikar correlation. It has been recognized that nucleation characteristics and associated heat transfer depend on contact angle, surface tension, available cavity

### Table 3  $F_{Fl}$ recommended by Kandlikar (1990a, 1991a)

| Fluid | $F_{Fl}$ |
|---|---|
| Water | 1.00 |
| R-11 | 1.30 |
| R-12 | 1.50 |
| R-13B1 | 1.31 |
| R-22 | 2.20 |
| R-113 | 1.30 |
| R-114 | 1.24 |
| R-134a | 1.63 |
| R-152a | 1.10 |
| R-32/R-132 60%–40% wt. | 3.30 |
| Kerosene | 0.488 |

For stainless steel tubes, use $F_{Fl} = 1.0$ for all fluids.

$F_{Fl}$ Kerosene from Chen and Cheng (1998).
$F_{Fl}$ depends on the surface-fluid combination.
The values listed are for commercial tubing.

sizes, and their distribution on the heater surface. It is therefore reasonable to expect a surface-fluid effect on the nucleate boiling contribution. Kandlikar and Spiesman (1997) studied the effect of surface structure on the heat transfer in flow boiling with water in a rectangular test section. The same aluminum heater surface was tested with different surface roughness in the range of 0.3 to 14 micrometer. Although the surface roughness varied considerably, a microscopic study of the surface revealed that the cavity size distribution was essentially similar. The differences between the surfaces were mainly seen in the larger cavity sizes that are not activated. The heat transfer performance for all surfaces was within 10 percent of each other. Further work is warranted to include the effect of cavity size distribution on flow boiling heat transfer.

Melin (1996) conducted experiments with a fluid heated copper test section for a number of fluids. From his data, the values of $F_{Fl}$ were obtained for many refrigerants. For the tubes tested by Melin, in general, the $F_{Fl}$ values are higher than the values obtained by Kandlikar (1990a) using extensive data sets reported in literature for R-12, R-22, and R-134a. The $F_{Fl}$ values recommended by Melin for additional fluids are: 1.88 for R-32, 2.27 for R-125, 1.74 for R-142b, 2.39 for R-143a, 2.15 for propane, and 1.50 for butane. An independent check is advised for specific tubes before using these values.

The parametric dependence of the heat transfer coefficient on quality is an important consideration in studying the relative contributions of the two mechanisms in flow boiling. The nucleate boiling contribution is expected to decrease with increasing quality, while the convective contribution is expected to increase.

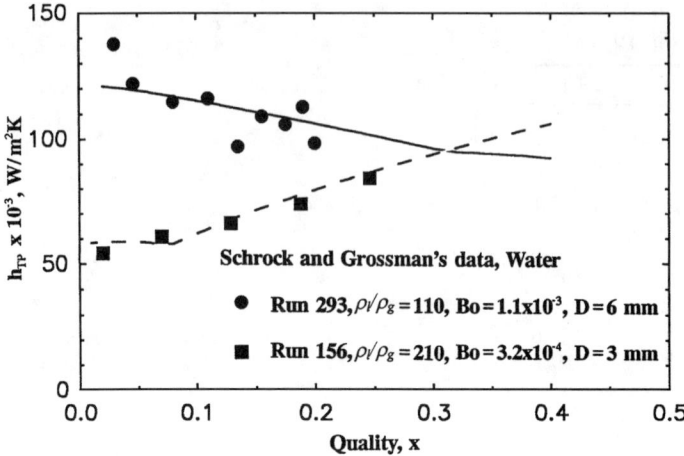

**Figure 13** Dependence of $\alpha$ on $x$; comparison of Schrock and Grossman (1959) data with Kandlikar (1990a) correction.

The overall trend is then dependent on the relative contributions from these two mechanisms.

Figure 13 by Kandlikar (1990b) compares the flow boiling data from the Schrock and Grossman (1959) and Kandlikar (1990a) correlations. It is seen that $\alpha$ increases with x for one set, while it decreases with x in other. The density ratio and boiling number are identified as the main parameters responsible for this trend. Low-pressure water with a high value of density ratio coupled with a low Bo yields an increasing trend, while the high-pressure data yields a decreasing trend. Similar results are obtained with the R-114 data by Jallouk (1974), the R-113 data by Khanpara (1986), and the R-113 data by Jensen and Bensler (1986). The experimental data of Kenning and Cooper (1988) near atmospheric pressure shows an increasing trend in $\alpha$ vs $x$ and is very well represented by the Kandlikar correlation. Further discussion on the parametric trends is presented in Section 15.3.4.

Considering the accuracy of predicting the heat transfer coefficient and the parametric trends, the Kandlikar correlation is recommended in the wetted wall region below a quality of about 0.8. At higher qualities, local dryout may occur with significant reduction in the heat transfer coefficient.

### 15.3.4 Flow Boiling Map—Subcooled and Saturated Regions

The parametric relationship among heat transfer coefficient, heat flux, mass flux, and quality are often displayed on a map. The basis of an earlier map presented by Collier (1981) was that the heat transfer at low qualities was essentially by nucleate boiling without any effect of mass flux or quality, and that in the high quality region, heat flux had a negligible effect.

Kandlikar (1988) reported that there are many data sets in literature for which heat transfer coefficient in fact decreases with quality, and the Collier (1981) map does not represent this trend. It was postulated that the nucleate boiling and convective mechanisms are both present, but their contribution depends on the flow rate and heat flux conditions. Two regions are identified as nucleate boiling dominant and convective boiling dominant, indicating the relative strength of the respective mechanisms. In the nucleate boiling dominant region, increasing quality causes a reduction in the nucleate boiling component, and since it is the dominant contributor, the overall heat transfer coefficient also decreases. On the other hand, in the convective boiling dominant region, the contribution due to nucleate boiling is small, and the increase in the convective contribution with increasing quality is reflected in the overall heat transfer coefficient. The Kandlikar (1990a) correlation captures this trend, and it is used as the basis in developing a flow boiling map shown in Figure 14 by Kandlikar (1991a).

The thermodynamic equilibrium quality is plotted on the x-axis, and the non-dimensionalized heat transfer coefficient, $\alpha_{TP}/\alpha_{lo}$, is plotted on the y-axis. Negative values of quality indicate the subcooled region. The combined effect of heat flux and mass flow rate is represented by a modified boiling number, $Bo^* = Bo \cdot F_{Fl}^{(1/0.7)}$, and the density ratio of the two-phases, $\rho_l/\rho_g$, represents the two-phase effects. In the subcooled region prior to the onset of nucleation, heat transfer is by single-phase mode, $\alpha_{TP}/\alpha_{lo} = 1$. The heat transfer coefficient then gradually increases at a given heat flux as the quality increases (subcooling decreases in this region). The curves in this region can be obtained from the equations presented for the partial boiling, fully developed boiling, and significant void flow regions in Section 15.2. As the heat flux increases, the onset occurs earlier at lower qualities (higher values of subcooling). The thermodynamic non-equilibrium effects are not shown on the map but are important in the significant void flow region.

In the saturated region, the heat transfer is divided into nucleate boiling dominant (NBD) and convective boiling dominant (CBD) regions. In the NBD region, for high values of $Bo^*$ and low values of density ratio (high pressure data with high heat flux), the nucleate boiling component is significantly higher than the convective boiling component. The convective component in this case does not increase as rapidly (due to small difference in the phase densities), resulting in a decrease in $\alpha_{TP}/\alpha_{lo}$ with increasing quality. In the CBD region, at low Bo and high values of density ratio (low pressure data with low heat flux), the nucleate boiling contribution is small, and an increase in quality results in a significant increase in the flow velocity, resulting in an increasing $\alpha_{TP}/\alpha_{lo}$ trend with quality. For intermediate values of $Bo^*$ and $\rho_l/\rho_g$, the plots would lie between the two

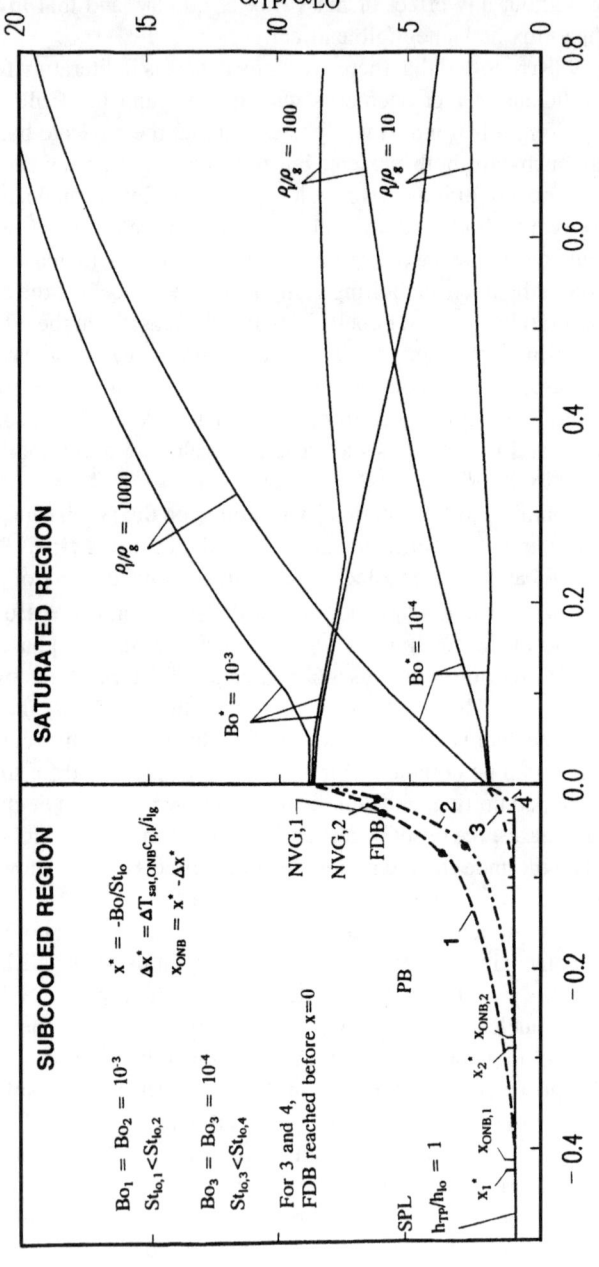

Figure 14  Flow boiling map for the subcooled and saturated flow boiling in smooth tubes (Kandlikar, 1991a).

extremes. Kandlikar (1991a) derived these plots from his (1990a) correlation and verified them with the experimental data for water, refrigerants, and other chemical compounds. The map can also be used directly to estimate the heat transfer coefficient.

### 15.3.5 Effect of Flow Geometry

**Flow boiling in rectangular geometry.** The effect of channel dimension on flow boiling heat transfer has been studied by a number of investigators. Tran et al. (1996) provide a good summary of these studies. Their experimental results for R-12 in a circular brass tube 2.46 mm diameter and a rectangular channel (4.06 × 1.70 mm) with a hydraulic diameter of 2.4 mm were similar, indicating that the hydraulic diameter concept could be employed for these cases. They also found that the nucleate boiling contribution was significant in the rectangular channels. Other investigators, e.g., Mandrusiak and Carey (1989), found very little nucleation in compact heat exchanger passages. Another aspect noted by Tran et al. (1996) was that the heat transfer was higher than that predicted from the flow boiling correlations. These correlations employ turbulent flow correlations for single-phase flow, while the flow in narrow passages is generally laminar. To eliminate some of the uncertainties, it is suggested that all single phase liquid flow experiments should be carried out to obtain the single phase coefficients. Also, to account for the surface effects, the fluid-surface parameter $F_{fl}$ for each geometry should be established before employing the flow boiling correlation. The pressure drop in the small diameter channels also changes considerably along the flow length, and its effect needs to be included in determining the local conditions and properties.

### 15.3.6 Heat Transfer Mechanism in Flow Boiling

Heat transfer in flow boiling has long been recognized due to the nucleate boiling and convective mechanisms. Dengler and Addoms (1956) presented a systematic study measuring temperature difference profile along the length of a steam evaporator tube. They observed that the nucleate boiling was present at low qualities and low mass flow rates. At higher qualities, the heat transfer coefficient was insensitive to temperature difference. Complete suppression of nucleation was assumed at this location. The heat transfer in the entire region was correlated with Martinelli parameter, $X_{tt}$, with a nucleate boiling correction term based on the ratio of actual temperature difference to the temperature difference at the location where nucleation was assumed to be totally suppressed. Mesler (1977) observed nucleate boiling in thin film flows and argued that nucleation is still present in the flow past the point of suppression as identified by Dengler and Addoms. Schrock and Grossman (1962) conducted a dimensional analysis and proposed an additive mechanism for heat transfer using the boiling number, Bo, and $X_{tt}$ as parameters. Shah (1982) extended the original charts proposed by Schrock and Grossman, and simplified the convective component by removing the weak viscosity ratio term. The Kandlikar correlation (1990a) employs the same basic form as the Schrock and Grossman correlation, with the nucleate boiling being represented by Bo and density ratio identified as an important parameter. The presence of nucleation in flow has been a major issue in arriving at the current understanding of flow boiling.

The nucleation was assumed to be suppressed by many investigators who employed high speed photography to detect the presence of bubbles. Since the heat transfer coefficients are generally very high, the nucleation criterion presented in Section 15.2 indicates that cavities as small as 1–10 micron will be activated. Kandlikar and Stumm (1995) emphasized the need to combine high speed photography with high resolution microscopes to detect the nucleating bubbles. They observed the bubbles in the flow, which seemed to disappear as the heat flux was increased. However, the bubbles were visible again as the camera speed was increased. The bubbles will be generated on the heater surface so long as the nucleation criterion for the given flow conditions is satisfied and there are cavities in the active range present on the heater surface.

Some of the areas where further research is still needed are heat transfer under two-phase conditions, effect of flow on nucleation, bubble growth, and related heat transfer at the microscopic level, and the cavity size distribution on flow boiling heat transfer.

### 15.3.7 Heat Transfer in Post-Dryout Region

This topic is covered in Section 17.3.2.

### 15.3.8 Pressure Drop and Void Fraction

The relation between void fraction $\varepsilon$ and actual quality $x$ is expressed in Eq. (15.3-8) using the drift flux model.

$$\varepsilon = \frac{x}{C_0 \left[ \frac{x \Delta \rho}{\rho_l} + \frac{\rho_g}{\rho_l} \right] + \frac{\rho_g V_{gj}}{\dot{m}}} \quad (15.3\text{-}8)$$

where $C_0$ is the distribution parameter and $V_{gj}$ is the vapor phase drift velocity. $C_0$ is usually taken between 1.13 and 1.2. $V_{gj}$ depends on the existing flow pattern.

Zuber and Findlay (1965) present the following expressions for $V_{gj}$:

$$\text{Bubble flow: } V_{gj} = 1.53 \left[ \frac{\sigma g \Delta \rho}{\rho_l^2} \right]^{1/4} \quad (15.3\text{-}9)$$

$$\text{Slug flow: } V_{gj} = 0.35 \left[ \frac{g \Delta \rho D}{\rho_l} \right]^{1/2} \quad (15.3\text{-}10)$$

The relation between the void fraction and the actual quality is expressed by using slip ratio $S$.

$$\varepsilon = \frac{x}{x + \frac{\rho_g}{\rho_l} S(1-x)} \quad (15.3\text{-}11)$$

where the slip ratio $S$ by Thom is expressed as follows:

$$S = 0.93 \left( \frac{\rho_l}{\rho_g} \right)^{0.11} + 0.07 \left( \frac{\rho_l}{\rho_g} \right)^{0.561} \quad (15.3\text{-}12)$$

Two-phase friction pressure drop is evaluated by using the two-phase friction multiplier $\phi_{lo}^2$.

$$\phi_{lo}^2 = \frac{\Delta p_l}{\Delta p_{lo}} \quad (15.3\text{-}13)$$

Several models have been proposed for the multiplier.

**Homogeneous flow model.** Two-phase flow is assumed as a homogeneous mixture flow of vapor and liquid. In estimating the friction coefficient for the flow, modeling of the viscosity in the Reynolds number is the key issue. The following relation is obtained by assuming the same viscosity as the liquid phase:

$$\phi_{lo}^2 = 1 + \left( \frac{\rho_l}{\rho_g} - 1 \right) x \quad (15.3\text{-}14)$$

**Lockhart-Martinelli model.** As already explained, Lockhart and Martinelli (1945) proposed the relation between two-phase friction multiplier $\phi_{lo}^2$ and Lockhart-Martinelli parameter $X$. They derived the relation assuming two-phase separate flow under adiabatic condition. Vapor and liquid flows are either in laminar or turbulent conditions. Then they obtained the relation for four combinations of flow conditions. Figure 15 shows the relation between $\phi_{lo}$ and $X$. In usual two-phase

**398** HANDBOOK OF PHASE CHANGE: BOILING AND CONDENSATION

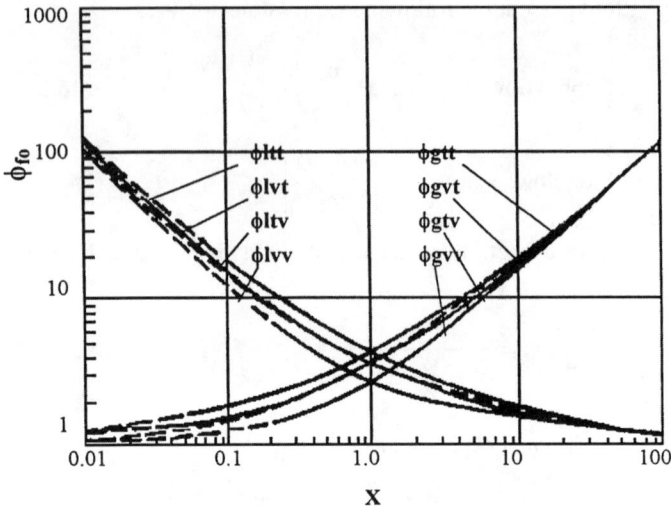

**Figure 15** $\phi$ versus $X_{tt}$.

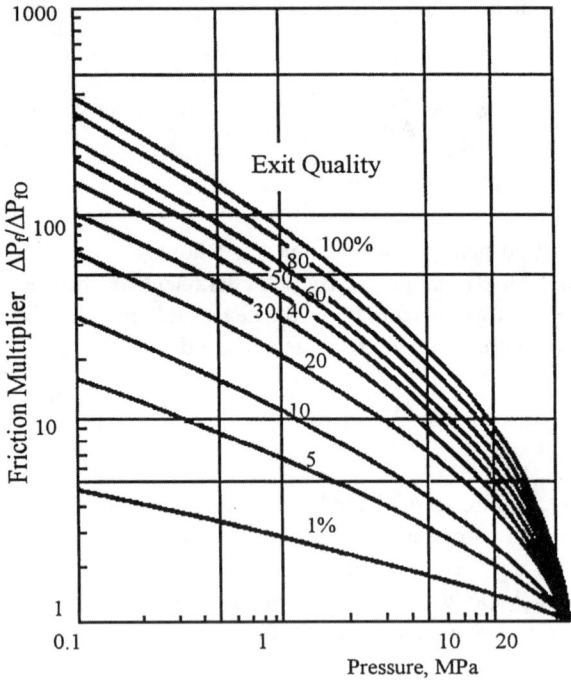

**Figure 16** Pressure drop versus pressure for steam at different exit qualities (inlet quality is zero).

flow, both vapor and liquid flows are under turbulent condition. For the turbulent-turbulent flow, the Lockhart-Martinelli parameter X is expressed as follows:

$$X_{tt} = \left(\frac{1-x}{x}\right)^{0.9} \left(\frac{\rho_g}{\rho_l}\right)^{0.5} \left(\frac{\mu_l}{\mu_g}\right)^{0.1} \quad (15.3\text{-}15)$$

The multiplier $\phi_{lo}$ is presented as a function of the local quality x. However, we usually need to estimate the friction pressure drop in a boiling system in which the quality changes from x = 0 to the exit quality at tube outlet. Martinelli and Nelson (1948) extended the Lockhart-Martinelli relation to the evaporating channel in order to derive the multiplier from exit quality for steam-water system. Figure 16 shows the multiplier against the pressure for various exit qualities.

As the figure is a little bit complicated, Chisholm (1973) correlated the multiplier $\phi_{lo}^2$ as a function of Lockhart-Martinelli parameter X as follows:

$$\phi_{lo}^2 = 1 + \frac{C}{X} + \frac{1}{X^2} \quad (15.3\text{-}16)$$

For Lockhart-Martinelli correlation, C in Eq. (15.3-9) is 20 for turbulent-turbulent flow.

## REFERENCES

Ahmad, S. Y. 1970. Axial Distribution of Bulk Temperature and Void Fraction in a Heated Channel with Inlet Subcooling. *Journal of Heat Transfer, Trans. ASME* 92(4):595–609.

Al-Hayes, R. A. M. and Winterton, R. H. S. 1981. Bubble Diameter on Detachment in Flowing Liquids. *International Journal of Heat and Mass Transfer* 24:223–230.

Bennett, D. L. and Chen, J. C. 1980. Forced Convective Boiling in Vertical Tubes for Saturated Pure Components and Binary Mixtures. *AIChE Journal* 26(3):454–461.

Bergles, A. E. 1964. Heat Transfer Mechanisms in Nuclear Reactor Thermal-Hydraulics. *Latin American Journal of Heat and Mass Transfer* 8:107–129.

Bergles, A. E. and Rohsenow, W. M. 1964. The Determination of Forced-Convection Surface-Boiling Heat Transfer. *Journal of Heat Transfer, Trans. ASME, Series C* 86(3):365–372.

Bowring, W. R. 1962. Physical Model of Bubble Detachment and Void Volume in Subcooled Boiling. OECD Halden Reactor Project Report HPR-10.

Boyd, R. D. 1988. Subcooled Water Flow Boiling Experiments Under Uniform High Heat Flux Conditions. *Fusion Technology* 13:131–142.

Brown, W. 1967. Study of Flow Surface Boiling. Sc.D. Thesis, Massachusetts Institute of Technology, Cambridge, MA.

Chen, J. C. 1966. A Correlation for Boiling Heat Transfer to Saturated Fluids in Convective Flow. *Industrial and Engineering Chemistry, Process Design and Development* 5(3):322–329.

Chen, T. and Cheng, L. 1998. Evaluation of Several Typical Correlations for Flow Boiling Heat Transfer of Kerosene in Smooth Tubes. Paper presented at the 1998 ASME International Mechanical Engineering Congress and Exposition, Nov. 15–20, Anaheim, CA.

Chen, W. C., Klausner, J. F., and Mei, R. 1995. A Simplified Model for Predicting Vapor Bubble Growth Rates in Heterogeneous Boiling. *Journal of Heat Transfer* 117:976–980.

Collier, J. G. 1981. *Convective Boiling and Condensation*. New York: McGraw Hill Publishers.
Darabi, J., Salehi, M., Saeedi, M. H., and Ohadi, M. M. 1995. Review of Available Correlations for Prediction of Flow Boiling Heat Transfer in Smooth and Augmented Tubes. *ASHRAE Transactions* 101(1):965–975.
Del Valle, V. H. and Kenning, D. B. R. 1985. Subcooled Boiling at High Heat Flux. *Int. J. Heat Mass Trans.* 28(10):1907–1920.
Dengler, C. E. and Addoms, J. N. 1956. Heat Transfer Mechanism for Vaporization of Water in a Vertical Tube. *Chemical Engineering Symposium Series* 52:95–103.
Gnielinski, V. 1976. New Equations for Heat and Mass Transfer in Turbulent Pipe and Channel Flow. *International Chemical Engineer* 16:359–368.
Gungor, K. E. and Winterton, R. H. S. 1987. Simplified General Correlation for Saturated Flow Boiling and Comparisons of Correlations with Data. *The Canadian Journal of Chemical Engineering* 65(1):148–156.
Gunther, F. C. 1951. Photographic Study of Surface-Boiling Heat Transfer to Water with Forced Convection. *Transactions of ASME* 73:115–124.
Hsu, Y. Y. 1962. On the Size Range of Active Nucleation Cavities on a Heating Surface. *Journal of Heat Transfer, Trans. of the ASME* 84: 207–216.
Hsu, Y. Y. and Graham, R. W. 1961. An Analytical and Experimental Study of the Thermal Boundary Layer and Ebullition Cycle in Nucleate Boiling. NASA TN-D-594.
Jallouk, P. A. 1974. Two-Phase Flow Pressure Drop and Heat Transfer Characteristics of Refrigerants in Vertical Tubes. Ph.D. Dissertation, University of Tennessee.
Jens, W. H. and Lottes, P. A. 1951. An Analysis of Heat Transfer, Burnout, Pressure Drop, and Density Data for High Pressure Water. *Argonne National Lab Report*, ANL-4627-1951.
Jensen, M. K. and Bensler, H. P. 1986. Saturated Forced Convection Boiling Heat Transfer with Twisted Tape Inserts. *ASME J. Heat Transfer* 108:93–99.
Jung, D. S., McLinden, M., Radermacher, R., and Didion, D. 1989. A Study of Flow Boiling Heat Transfer with Refrigerant Mixtures. *International Journal of Heat and Mass Trasnfer* 32(9):1751–1764.
Kandlikar, S. G. 1988. A Parametric Study of Saturated Flow Boiling Heat Transfer Inside Horizontal and Vertical Tubes. In: *Experimental Fluid Mechanics, Heat Transfer, and Thermodynamics*. Eds. Shah, R. K., Ganic, E. N., and Yang, K. T. Washington, DC: Hemisphere Publishing Corp.
Kandlikar, S. G. 1990a. A General Correlation for Two-Phase Flow Boiling Heat Transfer Coefficient Inside Horizontal and Vertical Tubes. *Journal of Heat Transfer* 112:219–228.
Kandlikar, S. G. 1990b. A Mechanistic Model for Flow Boiling Heat Transfer. Paper presented at the 1990 ASME Winter Annual Meeting, Nov. 10, Dallas.
Kandlikar, S. G. 1991a. Development of a Flow Boiling Map for Subcooled and Saturated Flow Boiling of Different Fluids in Circular Tubes. In: *Heat Transfer with Phase Change*. Eds. Habib, I. S. et al. ASME HTD-Vol. 114:51–62, 1990. Also published in *Transactions of ASME, Journal of Heat Transfer* 113:190–200.
Kandlikar, S. G. 1991b. A Model for Predicting the Two-Phase Flow Boiling Heat Transfer Coefficient in Augmented Tube and Compact Heat Exchanger Geometries. *ASME Journal of Heat Transfer* 113:966–972.
Kandlikar, S. G. 1992. Bubble Behavior and Departure Bubble Diameter of Bubbles Generated over Nucleating Cavities in Flow Boiling. *Pool and External Flow Boiling*. Eds. V. K. Dhir and A. E. Bergles, Proceedings of the Engineering Foundation Conference, March 22–27, Santa Barbara, CA.
Kandlikar, S. G. 1997. Further Developments in Subcooled Flow Boiling Heat Transfer. Paper presented at the Engineering Foundation Conference on Convective and Pool Boiling, May 18–25, Irsee, Germany.

Kandlikar, S. G. 1998. Heat Transfer and Flow Characteristics in Partial Boiling, Fully Developed Boiling, and Significant Void Flow Regions of Subcooled Flow Boiling. *ASME Journal of Heat Transfer* 120:395–401.

Kandlikar, S. G. and Cartwright, M. D. 1995. A Photographic Study of Nucleating Bubble Characteristics in Flow Boiling. *Convective Flow Boiling*. Proceedings of Convective Flow Boiling, Banff, Alberta, Canada, April 30–May 5, Taylor and Francis, pp. 73–78.

Kandlikar, S. G. and Mizo, V. 1995. Bubble Growth and Departure in Flow Boiling. *Convective Flow Boiling*. Proceedings of Convective Flow Boiling. Banff, Alberta, Canada, April 30–May 5, Taylor and Francis, pp. 161–166.

Kandlikar, S. G. and Spiesman, P. H. 1997. Effect of Surface Characteristics on Flow Boiling Heat Transfer. Paper presented at the Engineering Foundation Conference on Convective and Pool Boiling. May 18–25, Irsee, Germany.

Kandlikar, S. G. and Stumm, B. 1995. A Control Volume Approach to Predict Departure Bubble Diameter in Flow Boiling. *Transactions of ASME, Journal of Heat Transfer* 117 (November): 990–997.

Kandlikar, S. G., Mizo, V. R., and Cartwright, M. D. 1997. Bubble Nucleation and Growth Characteristics in Subcooled Flow Boiling. *HTD-Vol. 342, ASME Proceedings of the 32nd National Heat Transfer Conference* 4:11–18.

Kenning, D. B. R. and Cooper, M. G. 1988. Saturated Flow Boiling of Water in Vertical Tubes. *International Journal of Heat and Mass Transfer* 31:445–458.

Khanpara, J. C. 1986. Augmentation of In-Tube Evaporation and Condensation with Micro-Fin Tubes. Ph.D. Dissertation, Iowa State University, Ames, IA.

Klausner, J. F., Mei, R., Bernhard, D. M., and Zeng, L. Z. 1993. Vapor Bubble Departure in Forced Convection Boilling. *International Journal of Heat and Mass Transfer* 36:651–662.

Levy, S. 1967. Forced Convection Subcooled Boiling—Prediction of Vapor Volumetric Fraction. *International Journal of Heat Mass Transfer* 10:951–965.

Liu, Z. and Winterton, R. H. S. 1991. A General Correlation for Saturated and Subcooled Flow Boiling in Tubes and Annuli Based on Nucleate Pool Boiling. *International Journal of Heat and Mass Transfer* 34:2759–2765.

Lockhart, R. W. and Martinelli, R. C. 1949. Proposed Correlation of Data for Isothermal Two-Phase Two-Component Flow in Pipes. *Chem. Eng. Prog.* 45:39.

Mandrusiak, G. D. and Carey, V. P. 1989. Convective Boiling in Vertical Channels with Different Offset Strip Fin Geometries. *ASME Journal of Heat Transfer* 111(1):156–165.

McAdams, W. H., Minden, C. S., Carl, R., Picornell, D. M., and Dew, J. E. 1949. Heat Transfer at High Rates to Water with Surface Boiling. *Ind. Eng. Chem.* 41(9):1945–63.

Melin, M. 1996. Measurements and Modeling of Convective Vaporization for Refrigerants in a Horizontal Tube. Ph.D. Thesis, Department of Heat and Power Technology, Chalmers University of Technology, Göteborg, Sweden.

Mesler, R. B. 1977. An Alternate to the Dengler and Addoms Convection Concept of Forced Convection Boiling Heat Transfer. *AIChE Journal* 23(4):448–453.

Mikic, B. B. and Rohsenow, W. M. 1969. New Correlation of Pool Boiling Data Including the Effect of Heating Surface Characteristics. *Journal of Heat Transfer* 91:241–250.

Nariai, H. and Inasaka, F. 1992. Critical Heat Flux and Flow Characteristics of Subcooled Flow Boiling with Water in Narrow Tubes. *Dynamics of Two-Phase Flow*. Eds. Jones, O. C. and Michiyoshi, I., pp. 689–708. CRC Press.

Owens, W. L. and Schrock, V. E. 1960. Local Pressure Gradients for Subcooled Boiling of Water in Vertical Tubes. ASME Paper 60-WA-249.

Petukhov, B. S. 1970. Heat Transfer and Friction in Turbulent Pipe Flow With Variable Physical Properties. In: *Advances in Heat Transfer*, Volume 6. Eds. T. F. Irvine, et al., 503–564.

Petukhov, B. S. and Popov, V. N. 1963. Theoretical Calculation of Heat Exchange in Turbulent Flow in Tubes of an Incompressible Fluid with Variable Physical Properties. *High Temp.* 1(1):69–83.

Riedle, K. and Purcupile, J. C. 1973. Experimental and Analytical Investigation—Boiling Heat Transfer in Evaporator Tubes—Horizontal Flow. *ASHRAE Trans.*, Part I:142–155.

Rohsenow, W. M. 1985. Boiling. *Handbook of Heat Transfer*, Chapter 12. Eds. Rohsenow, W. M., Hartnett, J. P., and Ganic, E. N. New York: McGraw Hill Publishers.

Saha, P. and Zuber, N. 1974. Point of Net Vapor Generation and Vapor Void Fraction in Subcooled Boiling. *Proceedings of the 5th International Heat Transfer Conference*, Tokyo, Paper B4.7, pp. 175–179.

Sato, T. and Matsumura, H. 1964. On the Conditions of Incipient Subcooled Boiling with Forced Convection. *Bulletin of JSME* 7(26):392–398.

Schrock, V. E. and Grossman, L. M. 1962. Forced Convection Boiling in Tubes. *Nuclear Science and Engineering* 12:474–481.

Shah, M. M. 1977. A General Correlation for Heat Transfer During Subcooled Boiling in Pipes and Annuli. *ASHRAE Trans.* 83(1):205–215.

Shah, M. M. 1982. Chart Correlation for Saturated Boiling Heat Transfer: Equations and Further Study. *Transactions of American Society of Heating, Refrigerating and Air Conditioning Engineers* 88(I):185–196.

Tarasova, N. Y., Leontiev, A. I., Hlopushin, V. I., and Orlov, V. M. 1966. Pressure Drop of Boiling Subcooled Water and Steam-Water Mixture Flowing In Heated Channels. *Proc. 3rd International Heat Transfer Conference*, Chicago, Volume 4, pp.178–183.

Thom, J. R. S., Walker, W. M., Fallon, T. A., and Reising, G. F. S. 1965. Boiling in Subcooled Water During Flow up Heated Tubes or Annuli. Paper presented at the Symposium on Boiling Heat Transfer in Steam Generating Units and Heat Exchangers, Manchester, Sept. 15–16, Institute of Mech. Eng., London.

Thorncroft, G. E. and Klausner, J. F. 1997. Visual Observations of Vapor Bubble Dynamics in Vertical Flow Boiling. Paper presented at the Convective Flow and Pool Boiling Conference, May 18–23, Irsee. New York: Engineering Foundation.

Tran, T. N., Wambsganss, M. W., and France, D. M. 1996. Small Diameter- and Rectangular-Channel Boiling with Two Refrigerants. *International Journal of Multiphase Flows*, 22(3):485–498.

Tsung-Chang, G. and Bankoff, S. G. 1990. On the Mechanics of Forced-Convection Subcooled Nucleate Boiling. *Journal of Heat Transfer* 112:213–218.

Ueda, T. 1981. *Kieki-Nisouryu*. Tokyo: Yokendo, 44, (in Japanese).

Wattelet, J. P. 1994. Heat Transfer Flow Regimes of Refrigerants in a Horizontal-Tube Evaporator. Ph.D. Thesis, University of Illinois, Urbana-Champaign, IL.

Yin, S. T. and Abdelmessih, A. H. 1974. Prediction of Incipient Flow Boiling from a Uniformly Heated Surface. *AIChE Symposium Series* 73(164):236–243.

CHAPTER
# SIXTEEN

## FLOW BOILING IN ADVANCED GEOMETRIES AND APPLICATIONS

**16.1  Wataru Nakayama**

*920-7 Higashi Koiso, Oh-Iso Machi, Kanagawa 255-0004, Japan*

**16.1  Akira Yabe**

*AIST, Min. Int. Tsukuba, Ibaraki, 305-8564, Japan*

**16.2  Peter Kew**

*Heriot-Watt University, Edinburgh EH14 4AS, United Kingdom*

**16.2  Keith Cornwell**

*Heriot-Watt University, Edinburgh EH14 4AS, United Kingdom*

**16.3  Satish G. Kandlikar**

*Rochester Institute of Technology, Rochester, NY 14623, USA*

**16.4  Vijay K. Dhir**

*University of California, Los Angeles, CA 90024, USA*

## 16.1 FLOW BOILING IN NARROW CHANNELS FOR THERMAL MANAGEMENT OF MICROELECTRONIC EQUIPMENT

### 16.1.1 Introduction

This section reviews the cooling technologies for microelectronic equipment from the viewpoint of their efficiency in space-constrained heat transfer, focusing on the flow boiling cooling. Also, some practical issues involved in the design of microchannel cooling systems are discussed.

In the early years of heat transfer research, some milestone studies on enhancement of heat transfer were motivated by the need to cope with rising heat dissipation from electrical equipment (Nakayama and Bergles, 1990). With the advent of microelectronics technology, enhancement of heat transfer has again become the subject of industrial importance in the face of rising heat dissipation from integrated-circuit chips. Pertinent information about recent studies and applications of heat transfer enhancement techniques to microelectronics cooling have been compiled by Incropera (1988) and Bar-Cohen (1993). The volume of literature on this subject is still growing, reflecting industrial efforts to achieve more effective thermal management of electronic equipment.

The need for microchannel cooling will become imminent at the highest and lowest ends of the computer spectrum—supercomputers and portable computers. Those classes of computers need enhancement techniques for heat transfer in tight spaces (Nakayama, 1998a). Section 16.1.2 reviews the current cooling technologies of direct phase change cooling. Section 16.1.3 compares the performance of various cooling methods, assuming their applications to cooling an electronic module of typical size. Finally, in Section 16.1.4, the unsolved problems in microchannel heat transfer are discussed.

### 16.1.2 Some Examples of Direct Phase Change Cooling

The flow boiling cooling system has large heat transfer capacity and advanced characteristics that can be used to realize very low thermal resistances.

Johns and Mudawar (1996) studied two-phase jet-impingement cooling in constrained space using FC72 as coolant. The channel height was 4.3 mm, and the total thickness (including the coolant supply channel and the nozzle plate) was 8.5 mm. With a subcooling of 25 K and a coolant velocity of 0.5 m/s, (6 m/s on a 12.7 mm × 12.7 mm chip), a critical heat flux of 40–125 W/cm$^2$ was obtained. The temperature difference between the chip and the jet reached 40 K.

Mizunuma et al. (1998) obtained boiling data with forced flow of FX3250 in narrow channels. The heat transfer surface (2 cm × 2 cm) was either flat or equipped with 0.5 mm-wide × 0.5 mm-high fins. The channel height was 1 mm at minimum; this height leaves free space of only 0.5 mm above the fin tips. The coolant velocity was in the range 0.125–4 m/s, and the coolant temperature at the channel inlet was held at 26°C, that is, 30 K below the boiling point.

Pool boiling heat transfer from chips to fluorinert coolant has been studied by many investigators since the early 1970s. Among various attempts to enhance nucleate boiling heat transfer, the performance of the 5–10 mm-long microporous studs reported by Nakayama et al. (1984) still stands as a measure to assess the state-of-the-art of enhancement technique. A level of 100 W/cm$^2$ (based on the chip area) is feasible with the wall superheat of 20 K.

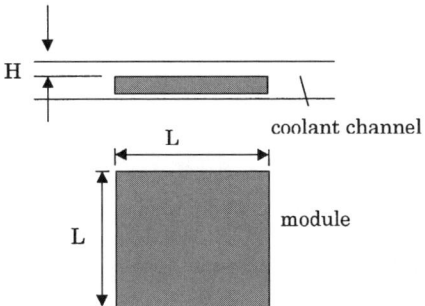

**Figure 1** Module in coolant channel.

### 16.1.3 Comparison of Available Cooling Methods for a 4 cm × 4 cm Module

In this section, various cooling methods are discussed. They are low-velocity air cooling, heat sinking with low speed air flow, heat sinking with high-speed impinging air flow, direct single-phase liquid cooling, heat pipe (indirect cooling), and direct phase-change cooling (Nakayama, 1998b). In order to contain the discussion within a manageable length, a simple situation is assumed and the emphasis is placed on forced boiling cooling.

Consider a module mounted on the board (the geometric parameters are shown in Figure 1). The module has a horizontal dimension 4 cm × 4 cm ($L = 0.04$ m), and the coolant channel has a height $H$ measured from the upper surface of the module. This module size is considered typical of those expected in future computers, that is, the size of chip carriers mounted on the substrate of supercomputers or portable computers. The thermal parameters are the heat dissipation from the module, $QM$, and the allowable temperature difference between the module and the incoming coolant, $\Delta T$. The module is assumed to be isothermal. The coolant parameters are the kind of coolant and the coolant velocity, $v$. In the following discussion, particular attention is directed to the relationship between the thermal resistance ($R = \Delta T / QM$) and the gap height $H$. The comparison is shown in Figure 2.

It was necessary to convert the data obtained with different heater sizes to the thermal resistance values for this particular module size. The conversion is straightforward where the correlations are available. For heat sinking with low-speed air flow, a correlation is developed from the data reported by Matsushima and Yanagida (1993) and Wong and Lee (1996) (Nakayama, 1998a). The following correlation was obtained.

$$\text{Nu} = 0.0132 \, \text{Re}^{0.892} \, \text{Pr}^{0.33} \qquad (16.1\text{-}1)$$

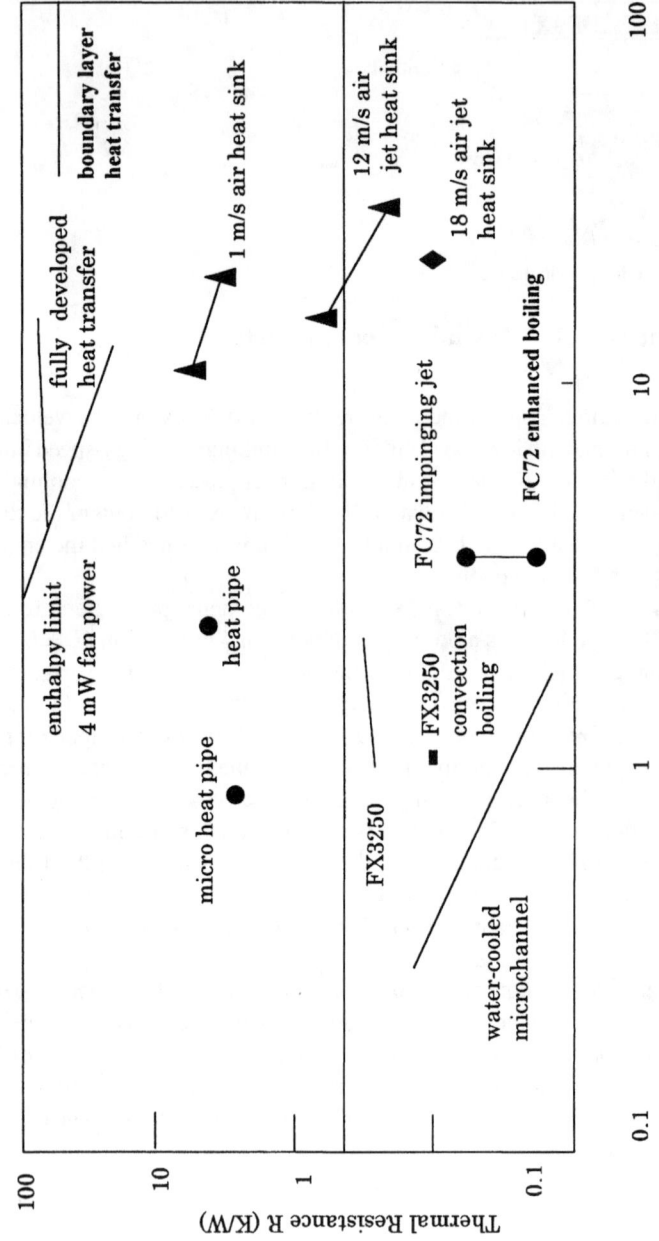

**Figure 2** Thermal resistance versus gap height for a 4 cm × 4 cm module.

where Nu is the average Nusselt number based on the length of the heated section, Re the Reynolds number based on the hydraulic diameter, and Pr the Prandtl number. This correlation is valid for Re = 2000–12000. It was found that for the coolant velocity in the range 0.25–2 m/s, the heat transfer coefficient becomes relatively insensitive to the change of channel height between 1 and 3 mm. For those data that lack any means of conversion, it was assumed that the specific thermal resistance—the thermal resistance per unit heater area—is insensitive to the overall heater area. Most of such data pertain to phase change cooling.

The upper bound of thermal resistance is represented by air-cooling with a 4 mW fan power. This fan power is assumed because it produces a 1 m/s velocity in channels wider than about 50 mm. The thermal resistance for a module without a heat sink is 32 K/W in wide channels. The flow is laminar, so that the fully-developed heat transfer coefficient increases with decreasing gap height; hence, the thermal resistance decreases with reducing gap height. The line labeled 'enthalpy-limit' is computed using the enthalpy balance equation. It reflects the temperature rise of air in the gap. The curve of 'fully-developed heat transfer' merges to the enthalpy limit line as the gap height decreases.

A densely finned heat sink is assumed in the estimation of thermal resistance to air flow of moderate velocity. The bar with triangles labeled "1 m/s air heat sink" shows the level of thermal resistance and the dependence of thermal resistance on the fin height.

Heat sinks with high-speed air flows reduce the thermal resistance from that of moderate-speed air-flow by an order of magnitude, as illustrated by the data marked as "12 m/s air jet heat sink" and "18m/s air jet heat sink" in Figure 2. The air flow was directed from an overhead plenum through a slot nozzle to the middle of a heat sink. The data were plotted including the thickness of the overhead plenum, which was assumed to be 10 mm.

Direct single-phase liquid cooling by FX3250 ("FX3250 single phase") produces thermal resistance of a comparable magnitude with those of high-speed air-cooling, but with gap heights reduced by an order of magnitude. The bar in Figure 2 shows a range of thermal resistance for $v = 0.5$ m/s and $H = 1$–2 mm.

The bar labeled "FC72 impinging jet boiling" is plotted referring to the data of Johns and Mudawar (1996). The highest thermal resistance corresponds to the jet velocity $v = 0.5$ m/s, and the lowest to $v = 6$ m/s. The impinging jet device composed of the liquid supply channel, the nozzle plate, and the exhaust channel occupies a 4.32 mm-thick space. The bar labeled "FC72 enhanced boiling" represents the data of enhanced nucleate boiling on the porous studs (Nakayama et al., 1984).

The data of Mizunuma et al. (1998) was used to draw the bar labeled "FX3250 convection boiling." The thermal resistance is as low as 0.1 K/W at the onset of boiling in a 1–3 mm-high channel.

The data point of 'heat pipe' shows that the overall thermal resistance, which is based on the difference between the evaporator temperature and the air temperature, is on the condenser side. Large thermal resistance on the air-cooled end is attributed to a high level of overall thermal resistance. The data point of "micro heat pipe" represents the level of thermal resistance based on the difference between the heater temperature and the condenser temperature. This new technology is effective in reducing the thickness of cooling devices.

A lower bound of thermal resistance is set by micro-channel cooling using water. In Figure 2, a reference point is plotted at $H = 1.7$ mm and $R = 0.02$ K/W for a 200 $\mu$m-wide micro-channel, and a line is drawn to pass the reference point assuming a fixed pumping power. The line almost matches the enthalpy-limit of laminar flow.

A line is drawn in Figure 2 at 0.5 K/W. Where a temperature difference of 50 K is permissible, this thermal resistance value allows a heat dissipation rate of 100 W. The 100 W chip has often been cited as a milestone target for the integrated circuit technology. Figure 2 illustrates that only high speed air cooling or liquid cooling could lower the thermal resistance below this line.

Figure 2 indicates possible directions of cooling technology in the context of computer's hardware development. Server computers, workstations, and traditional mainframe computers may continue to afford internal space of more than a few centimeter thick over the module. For those computers, the thrust for higher processing speed at the chip level is intense. The chip-level heat dissipation can be raised to 100 W by the combination of finned heat sink and air jet of more than 10 m/s velocity. The optimization of heat sink design is becoming an important issue to obtain the required thermal resistance while keeping the acoustic noise and the fan power as low as possible. Beyond air cooling, phase change cooling (jet boiling and enhanced nucleate boiling) would serve future chips having heat dissipation higher than 200 W. However, such scenarios would be materialized only when the cost of liquid cooling is made low enough not to hurt the commercial competitiveness of the product.

Heat transfer in the gap of less than a few millimeters height will become important for supercomputers and portable computers. In supercomputers, the liquid coolant exiting the CPU core can be led to an air-cooled heat exchanger, which affords wide space outside of the computing system. At this point, it is worth commenting on the potential of phase-change cooling. The enthalpy-limit for the phase-change cooling can be estimated by assuming total evaporation of coolant within the coolant path length. For example, for H = 0.5 mm and v = 0.25 m/s, the FC72 flow can absorb 700 W when the whole mass is completely evaporated at the channel exit. The corresponding thermal resistance falls close to that of water-cooled micro-channels.

For portable computers, the overall thermal resistance between the module and the environment air has to be considered. Hence, the power dissipation from the chip is constrained by the thermal resistance on the air-cooled side. The total heat dissipation from the passively cooled notebook computer is constrained in the range 8–10 W (Nakayama, 1998b). Hence, the chip's power consumption cannot be raised beyond the limit set by natural convection and radiation heat transfer on the system's exterior surface. Then, heat spreading inside the system enclosure is the key in thermal management rather than removing high heat dissipation from the chip's surface. The internal space available for heat spreading is becoming very thin, making it harder to use metallic heat spreaders. This is where the use of liquid coolant is a viable option.

The heat pipe, already incorporated in many portable computers, is a forerunner of technological development in this direction. It should be noted that the heat flux on the heat source could be low, so that the focus needs to be set on the driving mechanism for coolant circulation in long narrow passages. Capillary action in microgrooves may not be sufficient to overcome flow resistance in such passages. Other mechanisms such as a piezo-electric device will have to be employed to assist coolant circulation. This is where the MEMS (micro electromechanical systems) concept will find its applications.

### 16.1.4 Unsolved Problems and Future Directions

Riehl et al. (1998) made a comprehensive review of the recent literature on microchannel cooling. They compared the correlations for single-phase and phase-change heat transfer proposed by various investigators and found considerable divergence among the predicted heat transfer coefficients. A different physical mechanism working in the micro-channels may cause the divergence of heat transfer data, according to some investigators. For example, the transition to fully turbulent flow may occur at lower Reynolds numbers than in large diameter channels (Peng and Wang, 1993), and the constraint on bubble growth in narrow channels may cause the dependence of nucleate boiling data on the channel size (Peng et al., 1998). Riehl et al. (1998) emphasized the need to take into account the changes in thermophysical properties of liquid phase in narrow channels.

There are, however, other sources that are likely to cause divergence in heat transfer and pressure drop data from various sources. They are geometric precision of the experimental channel, rectification of flow at the channel inlet, and extraneous heat conduction from the heat transfer surface to the surroundings.

As the channel is miniaturized, it becomes harder to maintain the geometric precision of the channel's cross section and the smooth transition from the running length section to the heat transfer section. Uncertainty of a similar nature arises from the micro-roughness of the heat transfer surface and the presence of dust particles in the flow.

Heat conduction from the test heater to the unheated part of the channel wall and the thermal insulation surrounding the test section increases as the test section

## Table 1 Simulated cases of heat transfer in channels having geometric inaccuracy. [C and x are the coefficient and exponent, respectively, of Eq. (16.1-3)]

| Case | Inlet side dimensions (mm) | Outlet side dimensions (mm) | C | |
|------|---------------------------|----------------------------|--------|-------|
| A    | 1, 1                      | 1, 1                       | 0.0132 | 0.892 |
| B    | 1.5, 0.5                  | 1.5, 0.5                   | 0.0243 | 0.869 |
| C    | 1.5, 0.5                  | 1.5, 0.5                   | 0.0233 | 0.883 |
| D    | 1.1, 0.9                  | 1.1, 0.9                   | 0.0350 | 0.862 |
| E    | 1.1, 1.1                  | 0.9, 0.9                   | 0.0155 | 0.963 |
| F    | 0.9, 0.9                  | 1.1, 1.1                   | 0.0340 | 0.831 |

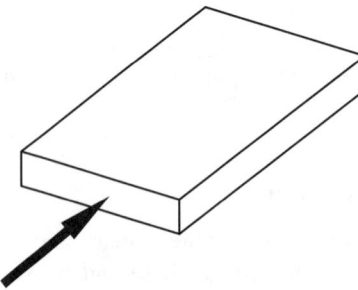

**Figure 3** Rectangular coolant channel with slanted ceiling.

is miniaturized. Also, the coolant may lose the heat received from the heater surface to the opposite channel wall as it flows in the narrow channel if the opposite wall is not thermally insulated or not yet brought to steady state temperature.

Those issues described above have not been fully addressed in the previous research literature. They will also become important in actual designs of micro-channel cooling systems. Expecting emerging needs to reduce the uncertainty involved in micro-channel cooling design, Nakayama and Behnia (1998) proposed a synthetic approach based on the experiment and the CFD simulation.

Figure 3 shows a sample problem, where a rectangular channel has the slanted ceiling. The ceiling slope is represented by the heights of four corners. Table 1 shows a list of cases studied. CFD simulations of flow and heat transfer were conducted assuming FX3250 as coolant and the heat transfer area (base of the channel) of 2 cm × 2 cm. Figure 4 shows the results for the cases of Table 1 and the experimental data obtained by Mizunuma et al. (1997) with a 1 mm-high channel (solid circles). The Nusselt and Reynolds numbers are based on the nominal hydraulic diameter of the channel. The simulation confirmed that the channel was fabricated with a reasonable geometric precision. The results,

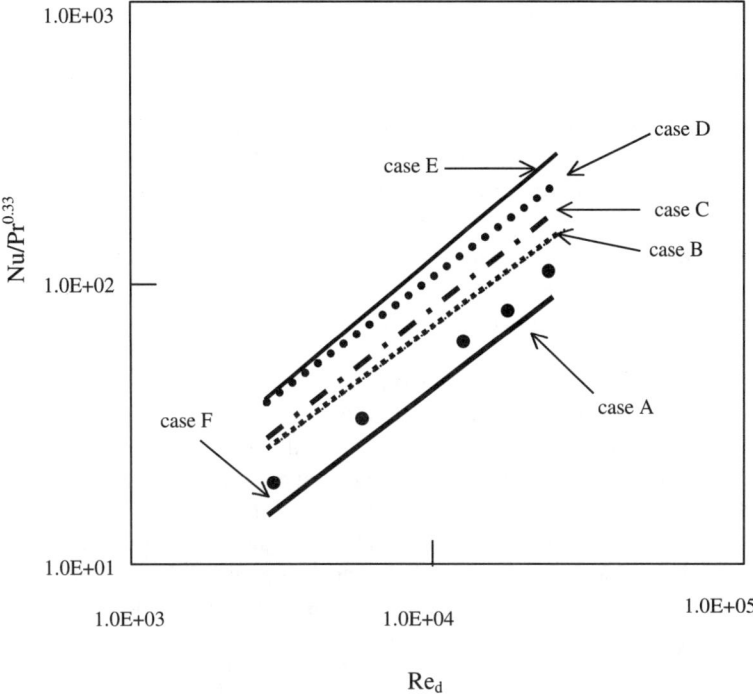

**Figure 4** Nusselt number versus Reynolds number for cases listed in Table 1.

however, imply that for smaller channels, the possibility of data divergence may increase. The non-dimensional results allow scaling down the size of the channel in question. For example, consider a channel having a 0.1 mm nominal height. The curve for case A gives the Nusselt number for the channel fabricated with exact dimensions. That of case E gives the Nusselt number in a channel that has an 0.11 mm-high inlet and an 0.09 mm-high outlet. The Nusselt number of case E is roughly twice that of case A at the same Reynolds number due mostly to acceleration of flow in the channel. Table 1 also contains the coefficient C and the exponent $\chi$ of the Reynolds number correlation.

$$\mathrm{Nu}/\mathrm{Pr}^{0.33} = C\,\mathrm{Re}_d^{\chi} \qquad (16.1\text{-}2)$$

As the above example illustrates, CFD simulations are useful to evaluate the effects of various sources of uncertainty involved in the research and design of microchannel cooling.

## 16.2 FLOW BOILING IN COMPACT HEAT EXCHANGERS

### 16.2.1 Introduction

The majority of boilers and evaporators produced today are still based upon the shell-and-tube design, with boiling occurring either on the inside of the tubes, as in most chemical process applications, water-tube boilers, and direct expansion evaporators, or on the outside, as in fire-tube boilers, some reboilers, and flooded evaporators. However, compact arrangements are becoming more popular. Plate heat exchangers are widely employed in the food industry, and welded and brazed units are used increasingly in refrigeration applications. Plate-fin heat exchangers were initially developed for use in cryogenic applications, characterized by the need for high effectiveness and close approach temperatures, but are now being employed more extensively. The refrigeration industry has been the most adventuresome in the use of compact systems, possibly due to the necessarily clean working fluids, but increasing interest is being shown by the process industries, particularly where space and weight are at a premium. Some of the more common compact heat exchanger geometries are illustrated in Figure 5. The use of compact evaporators is increasing due to the evolution of new types of unit (for example, the Printed Circuit Heat Exchanger [PCHE]) and through advances in the knowledge and understanding of compact heat exchangers.

Intensification of process evaporators and boilers by the use of more compact designs has several advantages. These may include a reduction of capital, installation, and housing costs, reduction in working fluid inventory, and close fluid approach temperatures. Compact evaporators may have area densities of $1000 \text{ m}^2/\text{m}^3$, some 10 times those found in many tubular arrangements, and typical passage diameters in the range of 1–6 mm. The two-phase flow regimes that occur in these passages differ from those in larger systems. This is particularly the case in the bubbly and slug regimes that can persist to relatively high voidages, where the physical size of the vapor bubbles is of similar magnitude to the channel dimensions. Both lead to interference with the heat transfer mechanisms and to flow instabilities, as will be discussed later. However, it is worth noting here that the unsteady nature of two-phase flow in narrow channels is such that great care must be taken in applying data from single channel experiments to the multiple channel arrangements often found in compact systems. In fact, available data suggest that for multiple channel and serrated or perforated fin arrangements, the use of correlations derived for larger systems may provide more satisfactory results.

The interference of the vapor bubbles with the flow channel sides provides a key to defining the size at which a flow passage becomes narrow or *confined*. One of the earliest studies of boiling in confined spaces, Bondurant and Westwater (1971) showed that when boiling occurred between closely-spaced fins, there is no

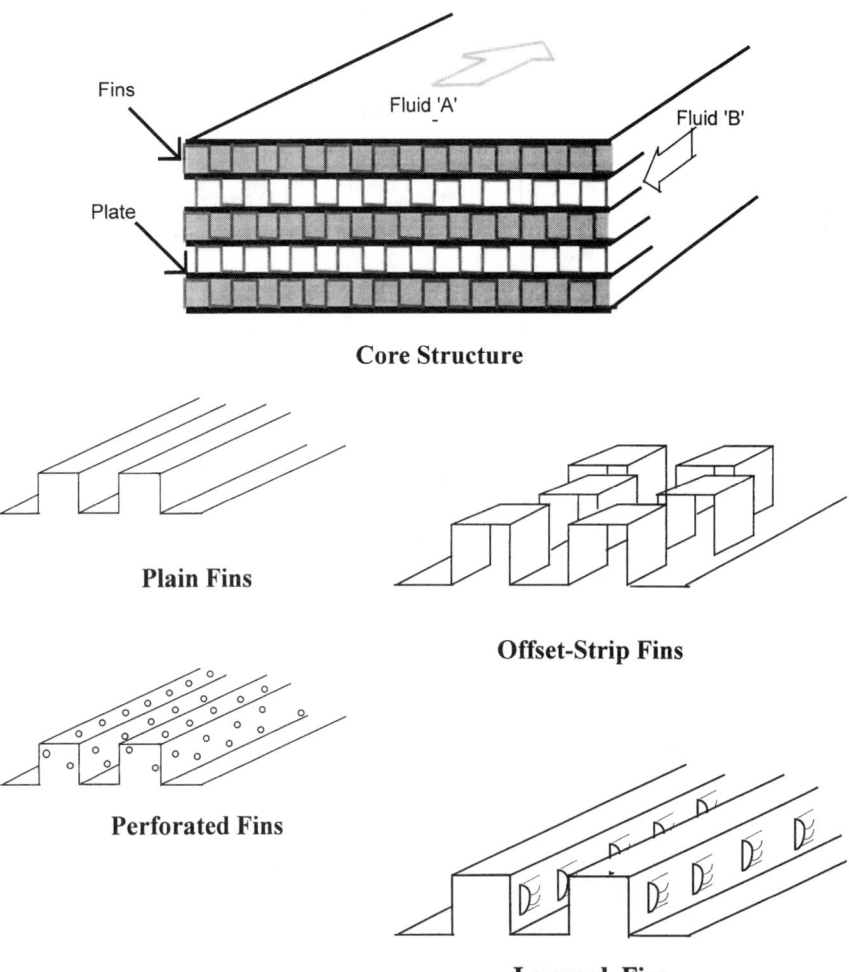

**Figure 5** Core structure and typical fins for plate-fin heat exchangers.

influence of fin spacing when the fins are further apart than the bubble departure diameter, $d_b$. Acceptance of the simple expression for the departure diameter of a single bubble quoted by Kutateladze (1981) yields

$$d_b = 0.02\theta \left[ \frac{\sigma}{g(\rho_l - \rho_g)} \right]^{0.5} \tag{16.2-1}$$

where $\theta$ is the liquid contact angle in degrees.

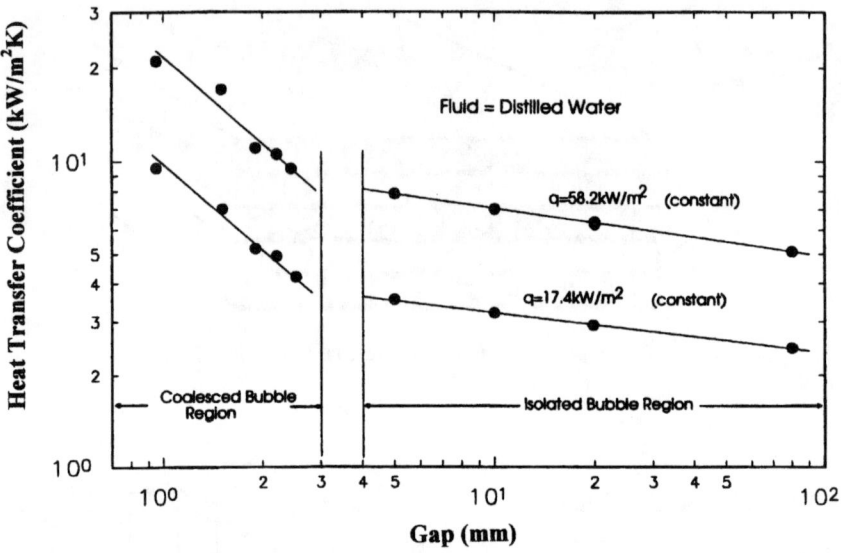

**Figure 6** Variation of heat transfer coefficient with gap size (data of Nishikawa and Fujita, 1990).

It is useful (Cornwell and Kew, 1993) to define a Confinement Number, $Co$,[1] to represent the ratio of the characteristic bubble departure size and the hydraulic diameter, $d_h$, of the flow channel.

$$Co = \frac{\left[\frac{\sigma}{g(\rho_l - \rho_g)}\right]^{0.5}}{d_h} \quad (16.2\text{-}2)$$

Bearing in mind that for a rectangular channel, $d_h$ is between one and two times the fin spacing, then for a typical contact angle of 90°, the critical value for the Confinement Number is about 0.5. For larger values of $Co$ the effects of confinement on two-phase flow and heat transfer are likely to be significant. Consideration of the mechanism of flooding during counter-current gas liquid flow (Wallis and Makkenchery, 1974) and of rising bubbles in vertical round tubes (Wallis, 1969) leads to a similar conclusion. The experimental results of, for example, Yao and Chang (1983) and Nishikawa and Fujita (1990, reproduced here as Figure 6) show a distinct inflection in the heat transfer characteristic for water boiling at one atmosphere as the gap size is reduced below approximately 4 mm, corresponding to $Co \approx 0.6$.

---

[1] Note that in this section, $Co$ refers to the confinement number defined by Equation 16.2.2, rather than the widely used Convention Number.

While it has been recognized for some time that boiling in confined spaces such that as found in some electronic systems (see Section 16.1) and small-bore tubes differs from that in larger systems, there has been only limited work recorded in the literature of relevance to compact heat exchangers. Early work tended to be application specific, and it was not until the 1970s that general correlations for boiling between fins were attempted. Westwater (1983) developed a model based on knowledge of the local heat transfer conditions, while Robertson (1982) and Carey (1985) concentrated on analysis of the conduction through a liquid layer on the fins. While empirical and semi-empirical correlations are now available from these studies, the range of conditions and geometries for which they are valid remains uncertain. With this in mind, it is useful to outline some of the features of flow in confined geometries that influence the heat transfer.

## 16.2.2 Flow Regimes

Conventional boiling heat transfer correlations (for example, those of Chen [1963], Shah [1982], Liu and Winterton [1991], and Kandlikar [1990]) consider two mechanisms, nucleate boiling and forced convection, to contribute to heat transfer in flow boiling. The contribution of each of these mechanisms is calculated separately and then either combined additively or the larger is taken to be the dominant mechanism and the other is neglected. The rationale for assessing the relative combination of these two separate mechanisms has been the subject of much debate (Hewitt, 1995), and while several correlations give satisfactory results over their range of application, their success can be explained by the incorporation of empirical constants rather than seen as confirmation that they have a sound physical basis. It is therefore desirable to examine the flow regimes and heat transfer mechanisms that occur during evaporation in compact geometries before deriving or selecting an appropriate heat transfer correlation.

The familiar flow regimes of bubbly, slug, churn, wispy annular, and full-annular flow have been described for gas-liquid two-phase systems in conventionally sized channels (e.g., Collier, 1981). The regimes are somewhat different in narrow channels. It can be demonstrated, using the analysis of Wallis and Makkenchery (1974), that conventional slug flow cannot occur for values of Confinement Number in excess of 0.5. Furthermore, observations have shown that even when annular flow is predominant, there is a tendency for slugs of liquid to pass through the tube. Four flow regimes may be used to characterize the flow in narrow channels; these are summarized with respect to a boiling fluid as follows:

**Isolated bubble flow.** As boiling commences, bubbles detach from nucleation sites on the channel wall. Heat addition results in an increase in the number and size of the bubbles.

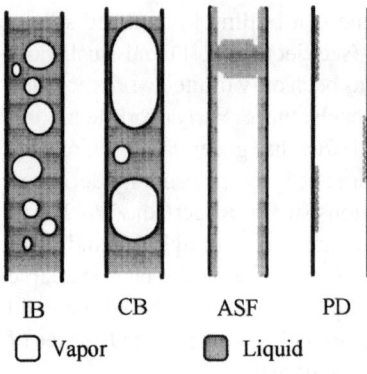

**Figure 7** Schematic representation of flow regimes. IB: Isolated bubble; CB: Confined bubble; ASF: Annular slug flow; PD: Partial dryout

**Confined bubble flow.** Growth or coalescence of isolated bubbles leads to the formation of bubbles that span almost the entire channel cross section. The bubbles are separated from the wall by a layer of liquid that evaporates and causes the bubble to grow exponentially.

**Annular-slug flow.** As the confined bubbles expand, the liquid in the slugs between them is deposited on the wall, and the flow becomes essentially annular with random, irregular slugs of liquid interspersed with the vapor.

**Partial dryout.** During evaporation in the annular-slug flow regime, the liquid film thickness varies with time, having a maximum value immediately after the passage of a slug and then reducing until the passage of the next slug. The film may intermittently evaporate, leaving local dry patches on the wall at relatively low qualities. Similarly, complete evaporation of areas of the film beneath a confined bubble can result in temporary dry-out of the wall.

The four regimes described above are shown schematically in Figure 7. These regimes have been observed by several investigators, but the resulting flow regime maps are generally appropriate only to air-water flow in a particular geometry. As yet no generalized set of criteria for determining flow regime is available. It is evident that caution should be applied when using maps derived from limited data. Adiabatic studies, such as that of Damianades and Westwater (1988), naturally exhibit no dryout regime, and the boundaries between regimes are somewhat subjective.

### 16.2.3 Heat Transfer Correlations

General correlations derived for single channels must be applied with care to multi-channel compact heat exchangers. However, for compact heat exchangers comprising plain channels, with no opportunity for lateral flow between channels, they can provide the best, if conservative, method of estimating heat transfer. Some general correlations derived from small channel data are presented in Table 2.

Early studies of boiling in compact heat exchangers are of extremely limited use, giving order of magnitude values for heat transfer coefficient for specific applications. The recommended coefficients of, say, Lenfestey (1961) and Clark and Thorogood (1971) were the best available design tools at the time, and a similar, application-specific approach is used by some manufacturers today in the selection of plate heat exchangers for refrigeration and food processing.

The work of Sydoriak and Roberts (1957) produced a correlation derived from work on channels typical of those used in the cooling of electro-magnets with boiling nitrogen coolant. This semi-theoretical analysis related the pressure drop and flow rate in the channels and hence determined the rate of heat removal corresponding to dry-out at exit of the channels for a given pressure drop. This correlation is thus equivalent to burn-out correlations of Bar-Cohen and Schweitzer (1985) and Fujita and Uchida (1990) and gives no indication of the heat transfer coefficients expected. In all of these studies, the two-phase pressure drop, heat flux, and fluid flow were related and, for a given pressure drop, the heat flux corresponding to dryout at exit from a channel was estimated.

Galezha et al. (1976) presented a correlation based on experiments over a range of pressures with R12 and R22 as working fluids. Five plate-fin geometries were tested in a natural circulation loop. The mass flow rate and mass flux were not measured but were always low (the mass flux was less than 16 kg/m$^2$s); it was observed that the mass flux had no effect on the heat transfer coefficient. The measured heat transfer coefficient was the mean over the length of the test section and was correlated by an equation of the form

$$\bar{\alpha} = C' f(p_{cr}, p, T_{cr}) q^{\frac{1}{3}} \qquad (16.2\text{-}3)$$

the factor $C'$ being a function of geometry. The correlation cannot be used in design since no theoretical or empirical method of determining $C'$ is available without recourse to experiment with a particular geometry. Equation 16.2-3 does, however, serve to indicate that the heat transfer coefficient at low mass flux in compact heat exchanger geometries is likely to be proportional to the heat flux to a low power (approximately 1/3) rather than the power of 0.5–0.7 typical of pool boiling correlations.

Robertson and co-workers have been largely concerned with cryogenic applications but have also published results of experiments using boiling hydrocarbons and refrigerants. Robertson (1982) has suggested that a film flow model based on conduction and convection through a film laid down on the fins is appropriate for use with serrated fin plate fin heat exchangers. Robertson calculated a liquid film thickness using a force balance on a fluid element and a measured pressure gradient.

Table 2  Correlations for the prediction of flow boiling coefficients in narrow channels

| Reference | Fluid | Geometry | Mass flux | Heat flux kW/m$^2$K | Quality | Press. bar | Correlation |
|---|---|---|---|---|---|---|---|
| Lazarek and Black (1982) | R113 | Tube 3.15 mm $\phi$ | 125–750 | 1.4–380 | | 1.3–4.1 | $Nu = 30\,Re^{0.857}\,Bo^{0.714}$ |
| Wambsnganns et al. (1993) | R113 | Tube 2.92 mm $\phi$ | 50–500 | 8.8–90.75 | 0–0.9 | | Found good agreement with Lazarek and Black |
| Tran et al. (1995) | R113 R12 R134a | Tube 2.92 mm $\phi$ Channel 1.7 × 4.06 mm Tube 2.46 mm $\phi$ | 500–832 | 8.8–129 | 0–0.9 | $p_r = 0.1$–$0.2$ | $\alpha = 840(Bo^2\,We_l)^{0.3} \times \left(\dfrac{\rho_l}{\rho_g}\right)^{-0.4}$ kW/m$^2$K |
| Tran et al. (1997) | R113 R12 R134a R12 | Tube 2.92 mm $\phi$ Channel 1.7 × 4.06 mm Tube 2.46 mm $\phi$ Tube 2.46 mm $\phi$ | 500–832 | 7.7–129 | 0.2–0.8 | $p_r = 0.1$–$0.2$ | $Nu = 770(Bo\,Re\,Co)^{0.62} \times \left(\dfrac{\rho_g}{\rho_l}\right)^{0.297}$ |

$Bo = \langle \dot{q}/h_{lg}\dot{m}\rangle$.

At low film Reynolds numbers, the film Nusselt number, defined by:

$$Nu_f = \frac{\alpha \delta_f}{k} \tag{16.2-4}$$

was found to be equal to unity, indicating that the heat transfer was purely by conduction through the liquid film. At film Reynolds numbers in excess of 300, the film Nusselt number was found to be proportional to the Reynolds number to a power of approximately 0.8, suggesting turbulent flow in the film.

Yung et al. (1980) have developed a similar model with data obtained with boiling ammonia. Carey (1985) further developed the film flow model to account for the apparently high values of heat transfer coefficient predicted at low vapor qualities. This was explained by the influence of bubbles held by surface tension in the smallest channel sections. High heat transfer coefficients at low quality in a perforated fin test section were partially accounted for by Wadekar (1992) using the slug flow model of Wadekar and Kenning (1990) and Wadekar (1991). Wadekar (1992) suggested that for correlations of the form

$$\alpha = F\alpha_l \tag{16.2-5}$$

the heat transfer coefficient, $\alpha_l$, for the liquid fraction occupying the channel should be estimated using a correlation appropriate for turbulent flow, even if the Reynolds number indicated laminar flow. This approach eliminated the discontinuity that was otherwise apparent in measured F values at the Reynolds number corresponding to transition from laminar to turbulent flow for a single-phase liquid.

A method for designing plate fin heat exchangers has been suggested by Westwater (1983) and tested by co-workers based on the "Local Assumption." This model implies that at any point on the heat exchanger surface, the heat transfer coefficient is a known function of the fluid velocity and the difference between the local surface temperature and the fluid saturation temperature.

$$\alpha = f(u, \Delta T) \tag{16.2-6}$$

The local surface temperature was calculated from a numerical analysis of the heat flow through the fin with the heat transfer coefficient varying along its length.

In principle, the "Local Assumption" is applicable to all serrated and perforated fin geometries and all working fluids, but in practice, the requirement for boiling curves for a range of velocities for the particular working fluid limits the application of this design method. However, Yilmaz and Westwater (1980) have published curves for R113 at velocities up to 6.8 m/s. Panitsidis et al. (1975) showed that the Local Assumption gave results that were in agreement with experiments. Their test conditions included a range of heat flux that would be expected to lead to both nucleate and film boiling in different areas of the heat exchanger.

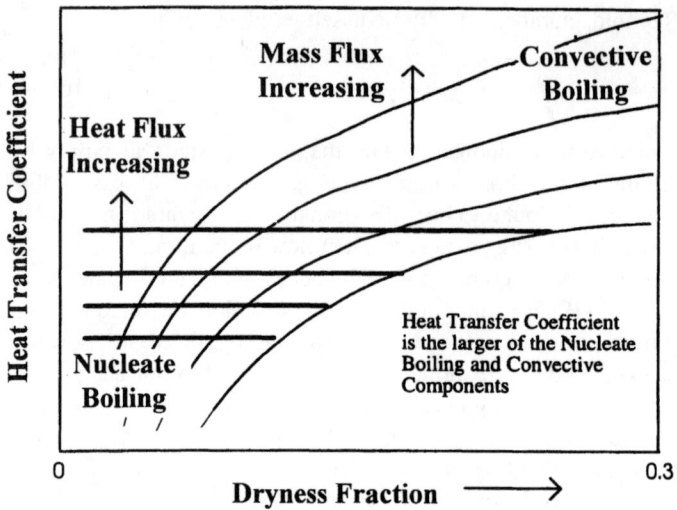

**Figure 8** Variation of heat transfer coefficient with dryness fraction.

Neither the film flow nor the nucleate boiling based models can be expected to span the complete range of heat and mass fluxes, qualities, and geometries that might be encountered. In general, the film flow models are appropriate at low heat flux (i.e., low wall superheat) and relatively high quality and velocity. The "Local Assumption," which is a nucleate boiling based model, is applicable at high heat fluxes or wall superheat but is limited in application by the availability of boiling curves for non-stationary fluids. The model was verified at relatively low mass flux but, if appropriate boiling curves were available, it could be used at higher values.

In general, the heat transfer coefficient quality profile for compact heat exchangers is similar to that shown in Figure 8, but the inflection point between predominantly boiling controlled evaporation (heat flux dependent) and convective controlled evaporation (mass flux dependent) may vary strongly with the type of exchanger.

Flow instability, as mentioned earlier, has the overall effect of increasing the heat transfer in a heat exchanger. This is illustrated in Figure 9 for flow of R113 at 1 atmosphere in a multi-channel heat exchanger (Cornwell and Kew, 1993). As the mass flux was reduced, the flow became highly unstable, leading to explosive ejection of liquid from the channels and high but random heat transfer coefficients. Similar instabilities have been recorded in the study by Mertz et al. (1996).

Kandlikar (1991) proposed an approach that, as with the Local Assumption, involved prediction of the local heat transfer coefficient for both the primary surface and the fins. The correlation proposed by Kandlikar requires calculation of heat

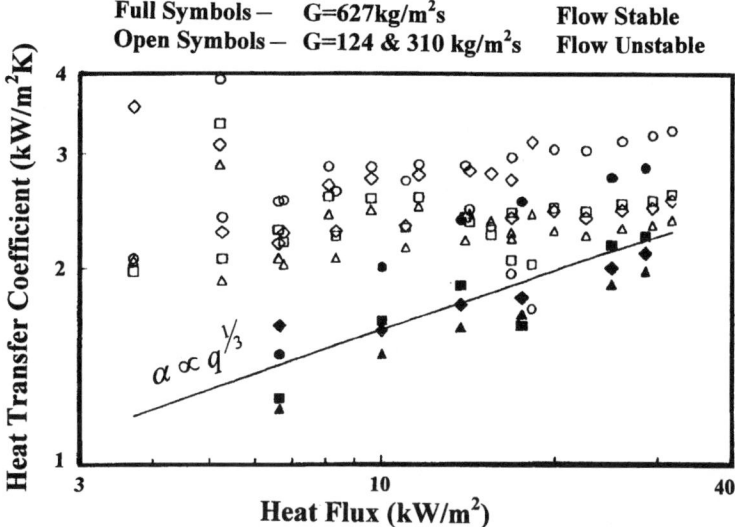

**Figure 9** Variation of heat transfer coefficient with heat flux for R113 boiling in rectangular (0.9 mm × 1.2 mm) channels (Cornwell and Kew, 1993).

transfer coefficients for both nucleate and convective boiling and use of the larger of the two coefficients. The local heat transfer coefficients were predicted by applying correction factors to the single-phase heat transfer coefficient, in this case all the flow being regarded as liquid. With appropriate, experimentally determined single-phase data, Kandlikar was able to represent experimental two-phase data to within 15% for a range of geometries. However, the method is limited to geometrical situations where single-phase data are available.

In view of these difficulties, the recent experimental work undertaken at GRETh (Groupement pour la Recherché sur les Echangeurs Thermiques, Grenoble, France) will be welcomed by the process designer who needs to assess the thermal suitability of compact heat exchangers for given conditions of temperature pressure, flow rate, and quality. Feldman et al. (1996) report on evaporation heat transfer in plate fin arrangements with off-set and perforated fins, as shown in Figure 10. Typical results for the perforated fins using R114 as the working fluid are shown in Figure 11, where the symbols represent sets of data at particular heat fluxes ranging from 1790 to 4300 W/m². The sharp transition from the confined nucleate boiling regime to the convective regime is clearly seen. In some exchangers, this transition may be at very low quality and hardly noticeable (as was found to be the case with the off-set fins) or it may occur at very high quality. It can be seen from Figure 8 that low mass flow rates will extend the range of the nucleate

**422** HANDBOOK OF PHASE CHANGE: BOILING AND CONDENSATION

|  | Offset Strip Fins | Perforated Fins |
|---|---|---|
|  | 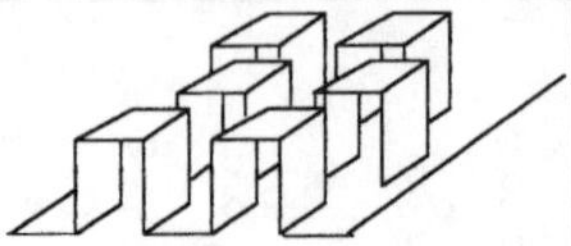  | 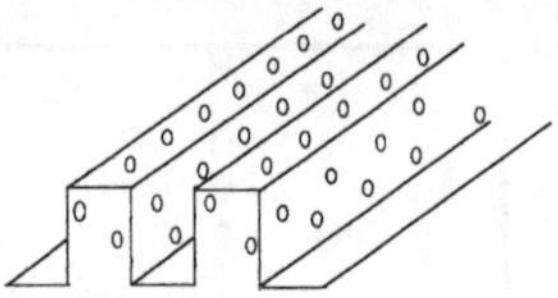  |
| **Designation** | OSF01 / OSF02 | Perf01 / Perf02 / Perf03 |
| Fin Height (mm) | 6.93 / 6.93 | 6.93 / 3.33 / 6.93 |
| Fin Length (mm) | 3.18 / 9.52 |  |
| Fin Thickness (mm) | 0.2 / 0.2 | 0.2 / 0.2 / 0.2 |
| Number of Fins Per Inch | 18 / 22 | 18 / 18 / 25 |
| Channel Width (mm) | 1.21 / 0.99 | 1.21 / 1.21 / 0.87 |
| Hydraulic Diameter (mm) | 2.06 / 1.98 | 2.06 / 1.78 / 1.67 |

**Figure 10**  Description of geometries tested at GRETh (Feldman et al., 1996).

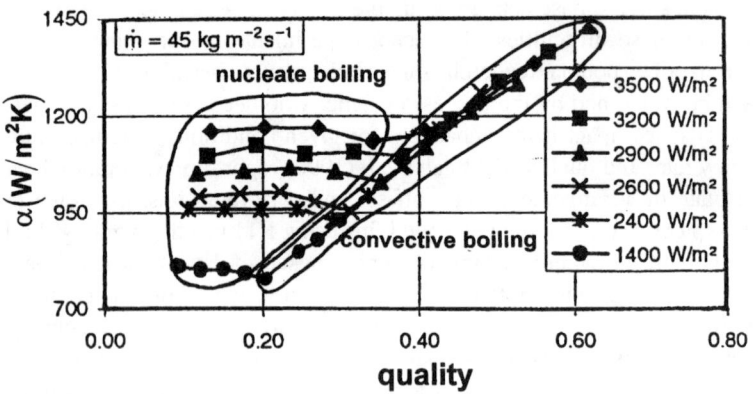

**Figure 11**  Typical heat transfer data for compact heat exchanger (Feldman et al., 1996).

boiling regime. The authors found that their heat transfer data was well correlated by a relationship of the simple form:

$$\alpha = F\alpha_\ell$$

or

$$\alpha = S\alpha_{npb} \qquad (16.2\text{-}7)$$

whichever is the greater. Here, the $F$-factor is given by

$$F = 1 + 1.8X_{tt}^{-0.79} \qquad (16.2\text{-}8)$$

and $S$, the Suppression factor, is unity. The nucleate boiling heat transfer coefficient was estimated from Cooper (1984):

$$\alpha_{npb} = 55 p_r^{0.12} (-\log_{10} p_r)^{-0.55} M^{-0.5} q^{0.67} \qquad (16.2\text{-}9)$$

where $q$ and $\alpha_{npb}$ are expressed in W/m² and W/m²K, respectively. $M$ is the fluid molecular mass, and $p_r$ is the reduced pressure.

The Wieting (1975) correlation (below) was used to determine values of the liquid only heat transfer coefficient, $\alpha_l$, which was applied to the offset strip fin geometry:

$$Re \leq 2000: \quad j = \frac{\alpha_{lo}}{c_p \dot{m}} Pr^{\frac{2}{3}} = 0.483 (l/d_e)^{-0.162} (w/h)^{-0.184} Re^{-0.536}$$

$$Re \geq 2000: \quad j = \frac{\alpha_{lo}}{c_p \dot{m}} Pr^{\frac{2}{3}} = 0.242 (l/d_e)^{-0.322} (t/d_e)^{0.089} Re^{-0.368}$$

$$(16.2\text{-}10)$$

The dimensions $t$, $l$, $w$, and $h$ represent the fin thickness, fin length (in the flow direction), the flow passage width, and the flow passage height, respectively.

It should be noted, however, that there is some evidence (Cornwell and Grant, 1995) that at high mass fluxes, the expected enhancement at high quality due to the $F$-factor does not occur. A cautious starting point at the current stage of development may be to assume the nucleate pool boiling value, unless higher values due to convective enhancement are assured by data on similar heat exchangers and with similar fluids. This approach is not as detrimental to the overall heat transfer coefficient as may at first appear, owing to the reduced effect of the enhancement when integrated over the complete quality range.

In summary, while the local processes are complex and an exact solution based on analysis of the detailed mechanisms is fairly intractable, the overall characteristics are similar to larger systems with either nucleate or convective boiling being predominant.

Partial dryout readily occurs in compact systems, and the correlations presented are only applicable prior to the onset of dryout. A method of predicting the onset of partial dryout has been proposed by Shollenberger et al. (1992). It was observed in automobile air conditioners that dryout frequently occurs in the latter stages of compact evaporators. A simple correlation for the onset of dryout was derived. The heat transfer coefficient in the convective boiling region (dominant in air conditioning evaporators, since the fluid entering is at a quality in excess of 20%) may be expressed in the form

$$\alpha = K_h x^{p'} \tag{16.2-11}$$

where $K_h$ is a constant depending on the heat exchanger geometry, working fluid, and the mass flux, and the exponent $p'$ is dependent upon the heat exchanger geometry and ranges from 0.5–0.8. The value of $x$ corresponding to the onset of dryout was found to be given by:

$$x_{do} = \frac{p'}{1+p'} + 800 \, \text{Re}_{core}^{-0.8} \tag{16.2-12}$$

The core Reynolds Number, $\text{Re}_{core}$ was determined using the total mass flux, passage hydraulic diameter, and a two-phase viscosity, calculated as

$$\mu_{core} = \left[\frac{x}{\mu_g} + \frac{(1-x)}{\mu_f}\right] \tag{16.2-13}$$

This procedure for estimating dryout can be used to determine the likelihood of the phenomenon being problematic in a particular situation.

### 16.2.4 Pressure Drop and Flow Instability

It is conventional to consider two-phase flow in a passage as having a pressure drop composed of three components:

$$\frac{dp}{dz} = \frac{dp_f}{dz} + \frac{dp_a}{dz} + \frac{dp_h}{dz} \tag{16.2-14}$$

where

$\frac{dp}{dz}$ = pressure gradient at position $z$ in the channel

$\frac{dp_f}{dz}$ = frictional pressure gradient at position $z$ in the channel

$\frac{dp_a}{dz}$ = pressure gradient due to the momentum change at position $z$ in the channel

$\dfrac{dp_h}{dz}$ = hydrostatic pressure gradient at position $z$ in the channel and $z$ is the co-ordinate in the flow direction along the channel

To calculate the pressure drop along a channel, it is necessary to integrate the expressions for the three components of pressure change over the length of the channel, taking into account the change in quality along the length. In practice, this may be carried out analytically or numerically by evaluating the three gradients for a number of sections along the channel, assuming a mean value of quality and physical properties in that section. Each component of the pressure gradient may be evaluated individually as follows:

The hydrostatic pressure gradient is given by

$$\frac{dp_h}{dz} = g \sin\theta [v\rho_g + (1-v)\rho_l] \qquad (16.2\text{-}15)$$

where $\theta$ is the angle of inclination of the channel, measured from the horizontal. Clearly, the hydrostatic pressure gradient is zero for a horizontal channel. The void fraction, $v$, may be evaluated using one of many available correlations. The CISE correlation (Premoli et al., 1970) and the Lockhart and Martinelli (1949) correlation, as adapted by Chisholm (1973) (see Equation 16.2.16), have been shown by Bao et al. (1994) and confirmed by Azzopardi and Holt (1995) to be the most appropriate for use in the estimation of void fraction in small channels.

$$v = 1 - \frac{1}{\Phi}$$

$$\Phi = 1 + \frac{20}{X} + \frac{1}{X^2} \qquad (16.2\text{-}16)$$

$X$ is the Martinelli Parameter, defined by Equation 16.2.19.

The change in the static pressure due to acceleration of the fluid is calculated from

$$\frac{dp_a}{dz} = -G^2 \frac{d}{dz}\left(\frac{x^2}{v\rho_g} + \frac{(1-x)^2}{(1-v)\rho_l}\right) \qquad (16.2\text{-}17)$$

which, when integrated, gives an expression for the pressure drop between 1 and 2 along the channel:

$$\Delta p_{a,1-2} = K_a G^2 \left[\frac{x_2^2}{v_2 \rho_{g,2}} + \frac{(1-x_2)^2}{(1-v_2)\rho_{l,2}} - \frac{(1-x_1)^2}{(1-v_1)\rho_{l,1}}\right] \qquad (16.2\text{-}18)$$

The empirically determined constant, $K_a$, approximately equal to 2, is introduced to take into account the velocity profiles within the flow. As with the gravitational component, the void fraction, $v$, may be evaluated using one of many available correlations, e.g., Premoli et al. (1970).

Estimation of the friction component is somewhat more complex, and various approaches have been taken. The Martinelli Parameter, defined by

$$X^2 = \frac{(dp_f/dz)_l}{(dp_f/dz)_g} \tag{16.2-19}$$

is frequently used in the correlation of pressure drop data.

The Martinelli Parameter may be related to the single phase liquid pressure drop by

$$\frac{(dp_f/dz)_{tp}}{(dp_f/dz)_l} = 1 + \frac{C}{X} + \frac{1}{X^2} \tag{16.2-20}$$

when the single phase pressure gradient is given by

$$\left(\frac{dp_f}{dz}\right)_l = f \frac{G^2}{2D\rho_1}(1-x)^2 \tag{16.2-21}$$

For turbulent flow of both liquid and gas, the Martinelli parameter is commonly calculated from

$$X = \left[\frac{1-x}{x}\right]^{0.9} \left[\frac{\rho_g}{\rho_l}\right]^{0.5} \left[\frac{\mu_l}{\mu_g}\right]^{0.1} \tag{16.2-22}$$

and the Blasius Equation is used to determine the friction factor

$$f = 0.079 \left[\frac{G(1-x)d_e}{\mu_l}\right]^{-0.25} \tag{16.2-23}$$

If single-phase data or a correlation for a specific geometry is available, the appropriate friction factor may be used. For example, Wieting (1975) proposes the correlation

$$f = 1.136(l/d_e)^{-0.781}(t/d_e)^{0.534} Re^{-0.198} \tag{16.2-24}$$

The value of the constant C in Equation 16.2-20 is selected from Table 3 as reported by Chisholm (1967).

**Table 3 Values of Constant C in Equation 16.2-20**

| $Re_l$ | $Re_g$ | C |
|---|---|---|
| ≥2000 | ≥2000 | 20.0 |
| <2000 | ≥2000 | 12.0 |
| ≥2000 | <2000 | 10.0 |
| <2000 | <2000 | 5.0 |

Alternatively, for small channels, Mishima and Hibiki (1996) has correlated C as a function of hydraulic diameter:

$$C = 21\left(1 - e^{-0.319d_e}\right) \qquad (16.2\text{-}25)$$

There are few reported studies of pressure drop and void fraction in narrow channels at the relatively low mass fluxes encountered in compact evaporators. This has been illustrated by Holt et al. (1993), who showed the number of data points in published works relating to channels of 6 mm diameter or smaller and mass flux below 1000 kg/m$^2$s was very small. Holt and co-workers have undertaken a systematic study to produce data relating to small circular, rectangular, and trapezoidal channels. Their study covered adiabatic flow of air-water, helium-water, and air-glycerol solutions. It was concluded (Azzopardi and Holt, 1995) that no single correlation was consistently good for predicting the data over the range of conditions. However, the best results overall were achieved using the Lockhart-Martinelli correlation for frictional pressure drop. The Friedel (1979) correlation, which is now widely used for conventionally sized tubes, was found to overpredict the frictional pressure drop. The Lockhart-Martinelli and CISE predictions were both found to be acceptable for predicting void fraction.

The pressure drop calculated using the method outlined above can at best be regarded as an average value. It has been shown (Kew and Cornwell, 1996) that significant pressure fluctuations occur during boiling in narrow tubes or channels. Aligoodarz et al. (1998) have shown that these pressure fluctuations, linked with local fluctuations in wall temperature, can have significant effects on the local heat transfer mechanisms within narrow channels. This phenomenon leads to unsteady flow through individual channels and can precipitate the onset of partial dryout. The instability leads to partial dryout at relatively low vapor qualities in single channels. In multiple channels, temporary flow reversal may occur with excess flow in other channels, which limits the potential for premature dryout.

In serrated and perforated fin heat exchangers, inter-channel flow is possible, owing to the growing bubbles and the inflow of liquid following their departure. Intermittent partial dryout is thus a common feature of flow in single channels, though it is much less likely in multi-channel systems, particularly in heat exchanger geometries with discontinuous fin arrangements where crossflow between the short passages is prevalent.

### 16.2.5 Conclusions

This is a new area, and considerably more data covering a much wider range of fluids and pressures are needed before conclusions can be drawn with much confidence. However, some general points and guidelines for the manufacturer or equipment specifier are given as follows:

- **Flow boiling regimes** in narrow channels (with Co > 0.5) may differ somewhat from those in larger systems. Slug flow will occur at lower quality owing to the confinement, and annular flow will not commence until higher quality is reached. Effectively bubbly and slug flow will occur over a wide quality range.
- **Pressure drop** correlations used in larger systems are applicable to the first approximation. However, some relationships should be used with caution at effective diameters less than 1 mm.
- **Instabilities** will occur at low quality in narrow spaces. These range from local perturbations to explosive fluctuations in parallel channel systems. These instabilities may not affect the overall pressure drop and will enhance rather than reduce the heat transfer.
- There is some evidence that there are **preferred sizes and aspect ratios** for maximum heat transfer, but this needs further investigation. The retention of liquid in the corners of channels at higher quality will be beneficial.
- There is some evidence that the designer can use Chen-type correlations, but this needs to be confirmed with more data. A more cautious approach would be to simply **use a nucleate pool boiling correlation** such as Cooper (1984) or Mostinski (1963) in the first instance.

In general, therefore, the heat transfer coefficients in compact evaporating systems are of a similar order to those in larger systems. Given similar saturation temperature differences, this means that the considerable increase in surface area per unit volume (10 to 100 times) is reflected in the increase of heat transfer per unit volume.

## 16.3 FLOW BOILING OF BINARY MIXTURES IN PLAIN TUBES

### 16.3.1 Introduction

Heat transfer in flow boiling of binary mixtures is an important process in chemical, petrochemical, and process industries. Recently, it has been receiving increasing attention in the refrigeration industry, as refrigerant mixtures are being evaluated to replace the conventional pure refrigerants. The advantages of using refrigerant mixtures over pure refrigerants include the improvement of coefficient of performance, better match with the product thermal load, and safer, environment-friendly refrigerants.

The nucleate boiling contribution in flow boiling is affected by the mass diffusion around a growing bubble. Any changes in the convective boiling component are seen through the changes in property.

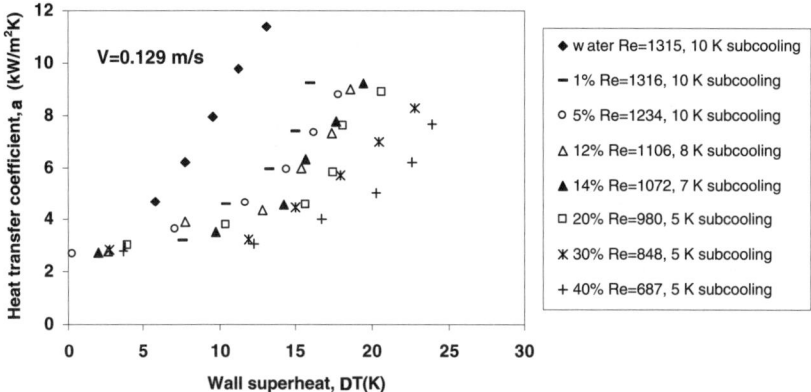

**Figure 12** Heat transfer characteristics of water/ethylene glycol solution under subcooled flow boiling, flow velocity = 0.4 m/s in 3 mm × 40 mm rectangular channel, Kandlikar and Bulut (1999).

There are relatively fewer studies available in the open literature on modeling the flow boiling heat transfer compared to those on pool boiling of binary mixtures. Table 4 provides a summary of some of the available correlations.

Kandlikar and Bulut (1999) conducted basic experiments to gain an insight into the effect of flow on boiling of mixtures. The experiments were conducted with subcooled flow of water/ethylene glycol solutions over a flat 9.5 mm circular heater placed flush on the lower wall of a 3 mm × 40 mm horizontal flow channel. Figure 12 shows the dependence of heat transfer coefficient on wall superheat for pure water and for different mass concentrations of water/ethylene glycol solution. The heat transfer coefficient with pure water is almost constant at lower values of wall superheat. Nucleation begins at ONB (onset of nucleate boiling), and $\alpha$ increases slowly with wall superheat. This region is similar to the CBD region in flow boiling. Beyond a certain value of wall superheat, $\alpha$ begins to rise rapidly due to increased nucleation activity, and this region corresponds to the NBD region. The results for the aqueous ethylene glycol solution, also shown in Figure 12, indicate the same trend of slowly increasing $\alpha$ in the CBD region, but the curve is shifted considerably to the higher superheat values. The convective mechanism is seen to be the dominant mechanism in flow boiling of binary mixtures.

### 16.3.2 Flow Boiling Model for Binary Mixtures

Kandlikar (1998) extended his pure component correlation (Kandlikar [1990], given by Eqs. [15.3-1]–[15.3-7]) by considering the mixture effects through a diffusion-induced suppression factor $F_D$, derived in Section 4.7 on pool boiling of binary mixtures. Three ranges are identified depending on the level of the mixture

**Table 4 Summary of available methods for predicting binary flow boiling heat transfer**

| Authors (Year) | Correlation | Comments |
|---|---|---|
| Calus et al. (1973) | $(\alpha_{TP}/\alpha_L) = 0.065(1/X_{tt})(T_{sat}/\Delta T_{sat})(\sigma_{water}/\sigma_L^*)^{0.9} F^{-0.6}$; $F = 1 - (y_1 - x_1)(c_{p,L}/h_{LV})(\kappa/D_{12})^{0.5}(dT/dx_1)$ | Considers only convective contribution; large errors are seen when nucleate boiling is present. |
| Bennett and Chen (1980) | $\alpha_{TP}/\alpha_{LO} = \{[(dP/dz)_{2\phi}/(dP/dz)_L](\mathrm{Pr}_L + 1)/2\}^{0.444} [\Delta T_m/\Delta T_s]$ $+ 0.00122(\lambda_L^{0.79} c_{p,L}^{0.45} \rho_L^{0.49} g_c^{0.25})/$ $(\sigma^{0.5} \mu_L^{0.29} h_{LV}^{0.24} \rho_V^{0.24})(\Delta T_{sat})^{0.24}(\Delta P_{sat})^{0.75} S_B \mathrm{Re}_{2\phi}$; $S_B = [1 - (c_{p,L}/h_{LV})(y_1 - x_1)(dT/dx_1)(\kappa/D_{12})^{0.5} S$; $[\Delta T_m/\Delta T_s] = 1 - (1 - y_1)(\dot{q}/\Delta T_s)(dT/dx_1)\vert_p$; $\alpha_m = 0.023(\mathrm{Re}_{2\phi})^{0.8}(Sc)^{0.4} \rho_L D_{12}/d$; $\mathrm{Re}_{2\phi} = \mathrm{Re}_L\{[(dP/dz)_{2\phi}/(dP/dz)_L](\mathrm{Pr}_L + 1)/2\}^{0.555}$; $S$ – Chen (1966) Suppression factor, function of $\mathrm{Re}_{2\phi}$ | Mass transfer analogy employed to predict the suppression in nucleate boiling. Convective component modified through a temperature difference correction term. |
| Jung (1988) | $\alpha_{TP} = (N/C_{UN})\alpha_{UN} + C_{me}F\alpha_L$ $N = 4048X_{tt}^{1.22}Bo^{1.13} \text{ for } X_{tt} < 1; N = 2 - 0.1X_{tt}^{-0.28}Bo^{-0.33} \text{ for } 1 \leq X_{tt} \leq 5$; $\alpha_{SA} = 207(\lambda_L/b_d)[q_d^b/(\lambda_L T_{sat})]^{0.674}(\rho_V - \rho_L)^{0.581}\mathrm{Pr}_L^{0.533}$; $b_d = 0.0146\beta[2\sigma/[g(\rho_V - \rho_L)]]^{0.5} \text{ with } \beta = 35°$; $F_p = 2.37(0.29 + 1/X_{tt})^{0.85}; C_{UN} = [1 + (b_2 + b_3)(1 + b_4)(1 + b_5)]$; $b_2 = (1 - \tilde{x}_1)\ln[(1.01 - \tilde{x}_1)/(1.01 - \tilde{y}_1)] + \tilde{x}_1 \ln(\tilde{x}_1/\tilde{y}_1) + \vert\tilde{x}_1 - \tilde{y}_1\vert^{1.5}$; $b_3 = 0 \text{ for } \tilde{x}_1 \geq 0.01; b_3 = (\tilde{x}_1/\tilde{y}_1)^{0.1} - 1 \text{ for } \tilde{x}_1 < 0.01; b_4 = 152(p/p_{cmvc})^{3.9}$ $b_5 = 0.92\vert\tilde{x}_1 - \tilde{y}_1\vert^{0.001}(p/p_{cmvc})^{0.66}, x_1/y_1 = 1 \text{ for } x_1 = y_1 = 0$; $\alpha_{UN} = \alpha_i/C_{UN}; \alpha_i = [\tilde{x}_1/\alpha_1 + x_2/\alpha_2]^{-1}; C_{me} = 1 - 0.35\vert\tilde{x}_1 - \tilde{y}_1\vert^{1.56}$ | The ideal mixture $\alpha$ concept for pool boiling is extended for flow boiling. It causes the averaging of the convection contribution as well as the pure component flow boiling $\alpha$ values. A large number of empirically determined constants are introduced. |
| Kandlikar (1991) | $\alpha_{TP,B} = \alpha_{Conv} + \dfrac{\alpha_{Nucl}}{[1 + \vert y_1 - x_1\vert(\kappa/D_{12})^{1/2}]^{0.7}}$ $\alpha_{Conv}$ and $\alpha_{Nucl}$ obtained from Kandlikar (1990) correlation for flowboiling | The nucleate boiling term was modified to account for the mixture effects. |
| Kandlikar (1998) | see Equations (16.3.1-10) | The theoretical model for pool boiling extended to flow boiling without addition of empirical constants. |

effects as obtained from a volatility parameter $V_1$, given by the following equation:

$$V_1 = \left(\frac{c_{p,L}}{\Delta h_{LG}}\right)\left(\frac{\kappa}{D_{12}}\right)^{0.5}\frac{dT}{dx_1}(x_1 - y_1) \qquad (16.3\text{-}1)$$

**Region I.** Near-Azeotropic Region; $V_1 < 0.03$. In this region, the mixture effects are negligible, and the pure component correlation holds well.

$$\alpha_{TP,B} = larger\ of \begin{cases} \alpha_{TP,B}|_{NBD} \\ \alpha_{TP,B}|_{CBD} \end{cases} \qquad (16.3\text{-}2)$$

and

$$\frac{\alpha_{TP,B}|_{NBD}}{\alpha_{LO}} = 0.6683\left(\frac{\rho_L}{\rho_G}\right)^{0.1} x^{0.16}(1-x)^{0.64} f_2(Fr_{LO})$$

$$+ 1058\left(\frac{\dot{q}}{\dot{m}\Delta h_{LG}}\right)^{0.7}(1-x)^{0.8} F_{Fl,m} \qquad (16.3\text{-}3)$$

$$\frac{\alpha_{TP,B}|_{CBD}}{\alpha_{LO}} = 1.136\left(\frac{\rho_L}{\rho_G}\right)^{0.45} x^{0.72}(1-x)^{0.08} f_2(Fr_{LO})$$

$$+ 667.2\left(\frac{\dot{q}}{\dot{m}\Delta h_{LG}}\right)^{0.7}(1-x)^{0.8} F_{Fl,m} \qquad (16.3\text{-}4)$$

The liquid and vapor properties in Eqs. (16.3-3) and (16.3-4) are calculated at the equilibrium phase concentrations. $\alpha_{LO}$ is the single phase all liquid heat transfer coefficient, determined from Eq. (15.3-5) and (15.3-6), and $f_2(Fr_{LO})$ is calculated using Eq. (15.3-4). $F_{Fl,m}$ is calculated as the mass-fraction averaged value of pure component values.

$$F_{Fl,m} = x_1 F_{Fl,1} + x_2 F_{Fl,2} \qquad (16.3\text{-}5)$$

$F_{Fl}$ for a number of refrigerants are listed in Table 5. Figure 13 shows the comparison of the equations in the near-azeotropic region with the data of Jung (1988) for azeotrope R-500, which is an azeotrope of R-12 and R-152a. $V_1$ is in the range of 0.0006–0.002. The equations correlate the data quite well, and the trend of $\alpha$ with x is also well represented.

**Region II.** Moderate Diffusion-Induced Suppression Region, $0.03 < V_1 < 0.2$ and $Bo > 1E\text{-}4$. In this region, the convective dominant region is primarily responsible for the heat transfer, as discussed in Figure 14.

$$\frac{\alpha_{TP,B}}{\alpha_{LO}} = 1.136\left(\frac{\rho_L}{\rho_G}\right)^{0.45} x^{0.72}(1-x)^{0.08} f_2(Fr_{LO})$$

$$+ 667.2\left(\frac{\dot{q}}{\dot{m}\Delta h_{LG}}\right)^{0.7}(1-x)^{0.8} F_{Fl,m} \qquad (16.3\text{-}6)$$

**Table 5  Details of the experimental data available for flow boiling of binary mixtures**

| Source (Year) | Binary system | Press. (bar) | Tube/ orient. | Mass fraction | Quality | Heat flux kW/m² | Mass flux, kg/m²s |
|---|---|---|---|---|---|---|---|
| Jung et al. (1988) | R-12R-152a R-22/R-114 R-500 | 3.1–4.8 | 9 mm, SS, Hor. | 0–1 | 0–0.9 | 10–45 | 250–720 |
| Hihara et al. (1989) | R-12/R-22 R-22/R-114 | 0.23–0.83 | 8 mm, SS, Hor. | 0–1 | 0–1 | 5.8–28.5 | 100–350 |
| Takamatsu et al. (1993) | R-22/R-114 | 4–8.1 | 7.9 mm, Copper, | 0–1 Only 0.5 lused | 0–0.9 | 1.8–72.8 | 214–393 |
| Celata et al. (1993) | R-12/R-114 | 10–30 | 7.57 mm, SS, Hor. | 0–1 | 0–1 | 10–45 | 300–1800 |
| Murata and Hashizume (1993) | R-34a/R-123 | 2.2 and 2.4 | 10.3 mm, Copper, Hor. | 90/30 mole- fraction | 0.1–1 | 10–30 | 100–300 |

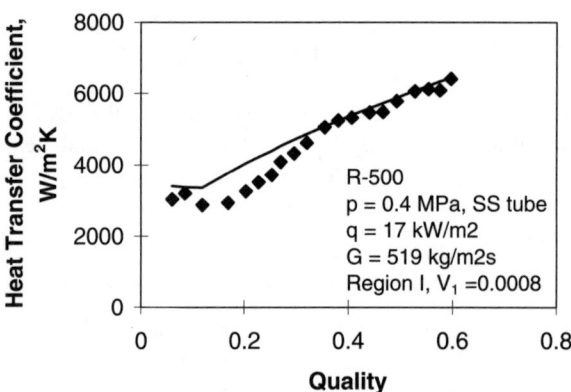

**Figure 13** Comparision of model predictions with the experimental data of Jung (1988) for R-500 azeotrope in region I, near the azeotropic region.

The properties and other terms are calculated similar to those for Eqs. (16.3-3) and (16.3-4), as discussed for Region I. Figure 14 shows a plot of the predicted values with the data of Celata et al. (1993) for R-22/R-114 mixtures obtained in an electrically heated stainless steel test section. $F_{Fl}$ with stainless steel tubes is 1.0 in the entire range of concentrations.

**Region III.** Severe Diffusion-Induced Suppression Region, (a) For $0.03 < V_1 < 0.2$ and $Bo < 1E-4$, and (b) $V_1 > 0.2$. In this region, the mixture effects are quite

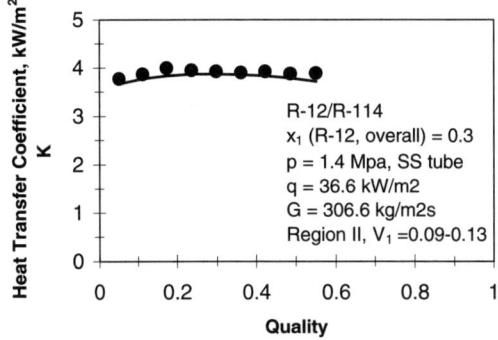

**Figure 14** Comparision of model prediction with the experimental data of Celata et al. (1993) for R-12/R-114 in region II, moderate diffusion-induced suppression region.

severe, and the nucleate boiling term in the convective boiling dominant correlation is further suppressed due to mixture effects. A mixture induced suppression factor $F_D$ is introduced in the nucleate boiling term.

$$\frac{\alpha_{TP,B}}{\alpha_{LO}} = 1.136 \left(\frac{\rho_L}{\rho_G}\right)^{0.45} x^{0.72}(1-x)^{0.08} f_2(Fr_{LO})$$

$$+ 667.2 \left(\frac{\dot{q}}{\dot{m}\Delta h_{LG}}\right)^{0.7} (1-x)^{0.8} F_{Fl,m} F_D \qquad (16.3\text{-}7)$$

The mixture-induced suppression factor $F_D$ is given by the following equation.

$$F_D = 0.678 \left[1 + \left(\frac{c_{p,L}}{\Delta h_{LG}}\right)\left(\frac{\kappa}{D_{12}}\right)^{0.5} \frac{dT}{dx_1}(x_1 - y_1)\right]^{-1} \qquad (16.3\text{-}8)$$

The slope $dT/dx_1$ corresponds to the bubble point curve. The equilibrium phase concentrations $x_1$ and $y_1$ are calculated at the total system pressure. The diffusivity $D_{12}$ is calculated from the following equation.

$$D_{12} = \left(D_{12}^0\right)^{\tilde{x}_2} \left(D_{21}^0\right)^{\tilde{x}_1} \qquad (16.3\text{-}9)$$

$D_{12}^0$ and $D_{21}^0$ are diffusion coefficients at low concentrations and are given by the Wilke-Chang correlation.

$$D_{12}^0 = 1.1782 \times 10^{-16} \frac{(\phi M_2)^{1/2} T}{\eta_{L,2} V_{m,1}} \qquad (16.3\text{-}10)$$

$\phi$ is the association factor for the solvent (2.26 for water, 1.9 for methanol, 1.5 for ethanol, 1.9 for ethylene glycol, and 1.0 for unassociated solvents, including benzene, methane, and refrigerants). $V_m$ is the molar volume, m³/kg-mol, and $T$ is temperature in degree K.

Figure 15 shows Murata and Hashizume (1993) data set for R-134a/R-22 system under the severe diffusion-induced suppression region. This data was obtained in a copper tube. The agreement between the correlation and the data is very good, with the mean absolute error of 12.1 percent.

Table 6 by Kandlikar (1998) shows a comparison of the correlation scheme with the additional data sets. The properties of the mixtures were calculated using NIST (1995) REFPROP computer program. The agreement is quite good in all

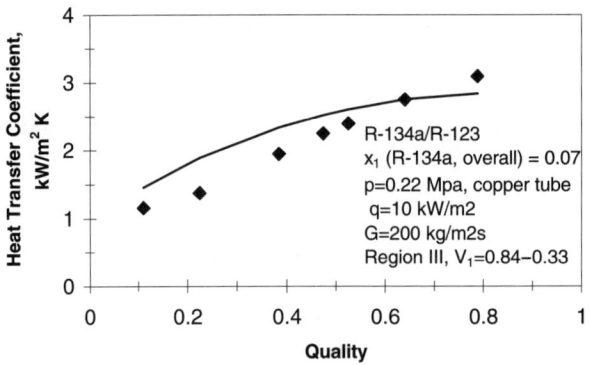

**Figure 15** Comparision of Kandilkar (1998) with R-13a/R-123 flow boiling data of Murata and Hashizume (1993) in the severe diffusion-induced suppression region.

**Table 6** Parameter ranges of data sources and comparison with correlation

| Data source | Binary system | Bo × 10e-5 | Co | V | Mean Abs. Deviation,% |
|---|---|---|---|---|---|
| Jung et al. | R-12/R-152a | 6.1–6.3 | 0.52–1.8 | 0.025–0.044 | 8.3% |
| (1988) | R-12/R-152a | 8.8–71 | 0.01–1.45 | 0.013–0.022 | 10.4% |
| | R-22/R-114 | 7.1–77 | 0.04–1.39 | 0.1–0.72 | 13.0% |
| | R-500 | 7.5–77 | 0.01–1.83 | 0.0006–0.002 | 11.4% |
| Hihara et al. | R-12/R-22 | 47–61 | 0.01–1.91 | 0.015–0.064 | 13.3% |
| (1989) | R-22/R-114 | 37–60 | 0.023–1.64 | 0.07–0.67 | 9.0% |
| Takamatsu et al. (1993) | R-22/R-114 | 19–76 | 0.018–3.2 | 0.28–0.54 | 9.2% |
| Celata et al. (1993) | R-12/R-114 | 9.4–88 | 0.52–1.83 | 0.06–0.15 | 8.9% |
| Murata and Hashizume (1993) | R-134a/R-123 | 20–185 | 0.004–0.05 | 0.28–0.34 | 12.1% |

three regions. In improving our understanding further, it is suggested that systematic experiments be conducted by varying the heat flux, mass flux, quality, and the volatility parameter. Simultaneously, interaction of bubble growth with flow in binary mixtures should be investigated. Further data is needed in other non-refrigerant systems. The work could then be extended to multi-component systems, which are of practical importance in chemical and petrochemical industries.

## 16.4 FLOW BOILING IN MICROGRAVITY

Experimental studies of flow boiling under low gravity conditions are far fewer and limited than those for pool boiling. The earliest study of flow boiling under reduced gravity conditions is that of Cochran (1970). The experiments were conducted in drop towers with flow velocities varying from 4.2 to 11.5 cm/s. These short-duration (2.2 second) low gravity tests were focused on the boiling process near inception. In comparison to normal gravity tests, it was found that in microgravity, bubbles tended to stay on the heating surface, became large enough to coalesce with neighboring bubbles, and acquired irregular shapes. The size of bubbles along the heating surface was found to correlate with the thickness of the thermal layer. Recently Saito et al. (1994) have studied flow boiling of water on a heater rod placed in a square channel. The experiments were conducted in Japanese low gravity experimental aircraft (MU-300) at about 1% of earth normal gravity for 20 seconds. In the experiments, subcooled nucleate boiling heat transfer data for water were taken at velocities varying from 3.7–22.9 cm/s and pressures in the range of 0.9 to 2.40 bars. Nucleate boiling heat transfer coefficients were found to slightly increase in the direction of flow, and the magnitudes of the heat transfer coefficients were about the same as at normal gravity. Figure 16 shows their photographs of nucleate boiling at a flow velocity of 6 cm/sec under both normal and low gravity conditions. Existence of relatively large bubbles on the heated surface is evident. The measurements by Saito et al. were limited to low nucleate boiling heat fluxes, and no data for critical heat flux were taken.

Several studies of flow boiling under variable gravity conditions have also been reported in the literature. In these studies (Brusstar and Merte, 1994; Papell et al. 1966), the effect of the magnitude of the gravitational acceleration component parallel to the heater surface was investigated by changing the direction of flow and orientation of the surface. The main conclusion drawn from these studies is that maximum heat flux for downward flow is lower than that for upward flow. The magnitude of the difference is dependent on the system pressure, liquid subcooling, and flow velocity. Lienhard (1988) has shown from data obtained with upflow and downflow across horizontal cylinders that maximum heat flux in saturated boiling

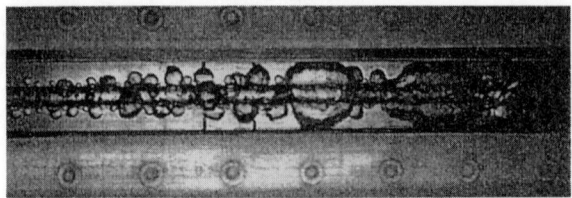

microgravity; V = 6 cm/s, $q_w$ = 18.2 W/cm$^2$

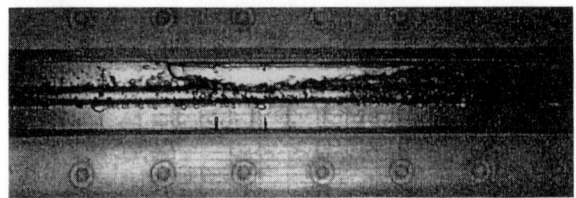

normal gravity; V = 6 cm/s, $q_w$ = 18.2 W/cm$^2$

**Figure 16** Comparison of normal and microgravity results: flow boiling (Saito et al., 1994).

is sensitive to the direction of flow if

$$r^{1.7}/Fr \geq 3000 \qquad (16.4\text{-}1)$$

where

$$r = p_l/p_v \qquad (16.4\text{-}2)$$

$$Fr = v/\sqrt{Dg} \qquad (16.4\text{-}3)$$

In Eq. (16.4.3), $v$ is the velocity of liquid normal to the cylinder and $D$ is the diameter of the cylinder. Although these latter studies have enhanced our understanding of the phenomena, data obtained in these studies are never free of the effect of gravity.

# REFERENCES

Aligoodarz, M. R., Yan, Y-Y., and Kenning, D. B. R. 1998. Wall Temperature and Pressure Variations During Flow Boiling in Narrow Channels. *11th International Heat Transfer Conference*, Korea, Paper FB1.

Azzopardi, B. J. and Holt, A. J. 1995. Two-Phase Pressure Drop and Void Fraction Relevant to Compact Two-Phase Heat Exchangers. *Proceedings 4th UK National Conference on Heat Transfer*, Manchester, UK., I.Mech.E: 437–442.

Bao, Z-Y., Bosnich, M. G., and Haynes, B. S. 1994. Estimation of Void Fraction and Pressure Drop for Two-Phase Flow in Fine Passages. *Transactions IChemE* 72 (A):625–632.

Bar-Cohen, A. 1993. Thermal Design of Electronic Systems—Methodology, Technology Trends, and Future Challenges. In: *Advances in Thermal Modeling of Electronic Components and Systems*, Chapter 1. Eds. Bar-Cohen, A. and Kraus, A. D. pp.1–60. New York: ASME Press, NY/IEEE Press.

Bar-Cohen, A. and Schweitzer, H. 1985. Thermosyphon Boiling in Vertical Channels. *Journal of Heat Transfer* 107:772–778.

Bennett, D. L. and Chen, J. C. 1980. Forced Convective Boiling in Vertical Tubes for Saturated Pure Components and Binary Mixtures. *AIChE J.* 26(3):454–461.

Bondurant, D. L. and Westwater J. W. 1971. Performance of Transverse Fins for Boiling Heat Transfer. *Chem. Eng Prog Symp Series* 67(113):30–37.

Brusstar, M. J. and Merte, H. 1994. Effect of Buoyancy on the Critical Heat Flux in Forced Convection. *J. Thermophysics and Heat Transfer* 8:322–328.

Calus, W. F. di Montegnacco, A., and Kenning, D. B. R. 1973. Heat Transfer in a Natural Circulation Single Tube Reboiler, Part II: Binary Liquid Mixtures. *The Chem. Eng. J.* 6:251–264.

Carey, V. P. 1985. Surface Tension Effects on Convective Boiling Heat Transfer in Compact Heat Exchangers with Offset Strip Fins. *Journal of Heat Transfer* 107:970–975.

Celata, G. P., Cumo, M., and Setaro, T. 1993. Forced Convective Boiling in Binary Mixtures. *Int. J. Heat Mass Transfer* 36(13):3299–3309.

Chen, J. C. 1963. A Correlation for Boiling Heat Transfer to Saturated Fluids in Convective Flow. ASME Paper 63-HT-34, *6th International Heat Transfer Conference*, Boston.

Chen, J. C. 1966. A Correlation for Boiling Heat Transfer to Saturated Fluids in Convective Flow. *Industrial and Engineering Chemistry, Process Design and Development* 5(3):322–329.

Chisholm, D. 1967. A Theoretical Basis for the Lockhart-Martinelli Correlation for Two-Phase Flow. *International Journal of Heat and Mass Transfer* 10:1767–1768.

Chisholm, D. 1973. Void Fraction in Two-Phase Flow. *Journal Mechanical Engineering Science* 15:235–236.

Clark, J. A. and Thorogood, R. M. 1971. *Selection and Design of Heat Exchangers, Cryogenic Fundamentals*. Ed. G. G. Haselden. Academic Press.

Cochran, T. H. 1970. Forced Convection Boiling Neat Inception in Zero Gravity. NASA TND-5612.

Collier, J. G. 1981. Convective Boiling and Condensation. 2nd Edition. New York: McGraw-Hill.

Cooper, M. G. 1984. Saturated Nucleate Pool Boiling—A Simple Correlation. *1st UK National Heat Transfer Conference, IChemE Symposium Series No. 86* 2:785–93.

Cornwell, K. and Grant, I. G. 1995. The Physical Dimension in Convective Boiling. *Convective Flow Boiling*, Engineering Foundation Conference, Banff, pp. 167–174.

Cornwell, K. and Kew, P. A. 1993. Boiling in Small Parallel Channels. *Proceedings of CEC Conf. on Energy Efficiency in Process Technology*, Athens, October 1992, Paper 22, Elsevier Applied Sciences, pp. 624–638.

Damianides, C. A. and Westwater, J. W. 1988. Two-Phase Flow Patterns in a Compact Heat Exchanger and in Small Tubes. *2nd National UK Heat Transfer Conference*, IMechE, Volume 2: 1257–1268.

Feldman, A., Marvillet, C. H., and Lebouche, M. 1996. An Experimental Study of Boiling in Plate-Fin Heat Exchangers. *Proceedings 14th UIT National Heat Transfer Conference*, Rome, 445–450.

Friedel, L. 1979. Improved Friction Drop Correlations for Horizontal and Vertical Flow. *European Two-Phase Flow Group Meeting*, Ispra, Italy.

Fujita, Y. and Uchida, S. 1990. Boiling Heat Transfer and Critical Heat Flux in a Confined Narrow

Space. Effects of Gap Size, Inclination Angle, and Peripheral Conditions at the Space Edge. *9th International Heat Transfer Conference* 2:153–158.
Galezha, V. B., Usyukin, I. P., and Kan, K. D. 1976. Boiling Heat Transfer with Freons in Finned Plate Heat Exchangers. *Heat Transfer—Soviet Research* 8(3):103–110.
Goodson, K. E., Kurabayashi, K., and Pease, R. F. W. 1997. Improved Heat Sinking for Laser-Diode Arrays Using Microchannels in CVD Diamond. *IEEE Trans. Components, Packaging, and Manufacturing Technology—Part B* 20(1):104–109.
Hewitt, G. F. 1995. Forced Convective Boiling. *Proceedings 4th UK National Conference on Heat Transfer*, Manchester UK., I.Mech.E, Invited Lecture, Sept. 26–27, 1993.
Hihara, E., Tanida, K., and Saito, T. 1989. Forced Convective Boiling Experiments of Binary Mixtures. *JSME Int. J., Ser. II* 32(1):98–106.
Holt, A. J., Azzopardi, B. J., and Biddulph, M. W. 1993. Pressure Drop and Void Fraction in Narrow Channels. *Eurotherm 26*, Edinburgh.
Incropera, F. P. 1988. Convection Heat Transfer in Electronic Equipment Cooling. *ASME Journal of Heat Transfer* 110:1079–1111.
Johns, M. E. and Mudawar, I. 1996. An Ultra-High Power Two-Phase Jet-Impingement Avionic Clamshell Module. *ASME Journal of Electronic Packaging* 118(4):264–270.
Jung, D. S. 1988. Horizontal Flow Boiling Heat Transfer Using Refrigerant Mixtures. Ph.D. Dissertation, University of Maryland.
Jung, D. S., McLinden, M., Radermacher, R., and Didion, D. 1988. Horizontal Flow Boiling Experiments with a Mixture of R-22/R-114. *Int. J. Heat Mass Transfer* 32(1):131–145.
Kandlikar, S. G. 1990. A General Correlation for Saturated Two-Phase Flow Boiling Heat Transfer Inside Horizontal and Vertical Tubes. *ASME Journal of Heat Transfer* 112:219–228.
Kandlikar, S. G. 1991. A Model for Predicting the Two-Phase Flow Boiling Heat Transfer Coefficient in Augmented Tube and Compact Heat Exchanger Geometries. *ASME J. Heat Transfer* 113 (Nov.): 966–972.
Kandlikar, S. G. 1998. Boiling Heat Transfer with Binary Mixtures, Part II: Flow Boiling. *ASME J. Heat Transfer* 120:388–394.
Kandlikar, S. G. and Bulut, M. 1999. An Experimental Investigation on Subcooled Flow Boiling of Ethylene-Glycol/Water Mixtures. Paper to be presented at the 1999 ASME National Heat Transfer Conference, Albuquerque, NM, August 15–17.
Kew, P. A. and Cornwell, K. 1996. On Pressure Fluctuations During Boiling in Narrow Channels. *Proceedings 14th UIT National Heat Transfer Conference*, Rome, pp.1323–1330.
Kondo, Y., Behnia, M., Nakayama, W., and Matsushima, H. 1998. Optimization of Finned Heat Sinks for Impinging Cooling of Electronic Packages. *ASME Journal of Electronic Packaging*, in press.
Kutateladze, S. S. 1981. Principle Equations of Thermohydrodynamics of Nucleate Boiling. *Heat Transfer—Soviet Research* 13(3):1–14.
Lazarek, G. M. and Black, S. H. 1982. Evaporative Heat Transfer, Pressure Drop, and Critical Heat Flux in a Small Vetical Tube with R113. *International Journal of Heat and Mass Transfer* 25(7):945–960.
Lenfestey, A. G. 1961. Low Temperature Heat Exchangers. *Progress in Cryogenics* 3:25–47.
Lienhard, J-H. 1988. Burnout on Cylinders. *J. Heat Transfer* 110:1271–1286.
Liu, Z. and Winterton, R H. S. 1991. A General Correlation for Saturated and Subcooled Flow Boiling in Tubes and Annuli Based on a Nucleate Pool Boiling Equation. *Int. J. Heat Mass Transfer* 34(11):2750–2766.
Lockhart, R. W. and Martinelli, R. C. 1949. Proposed Correlation of Data for Isothermal Two-Phase, Two-Component Flow in Pipes. *Chemical Engineering Progress* 45(1):39–48.
Matsushima, H. and Yanagida, T. 1993. Heat Transfer from VLSI Packages with Longitudinal Fins in a Free Air Stream. *ASME EEP-4-2*. Eds. Engel, P. A. and Chen, W. T., pp. 793–800.

Mertz, R., Wein, A., and Groll, M. 1996. Experimental Investigation of Flow Boiling Heat Transfer in Narrow Channels. *Proceedings 14th UIT National Heat Transfer Conference*, Rome, 219–226.

Mishima, K. and Hibiki, T. 1996. Some Characteristics of Air-Water Two-Phase Flows in Small Diameter Tubes. *International Journal of Multiphase Flow* 22(4):703–712.

Mizunuma, H., Behnia, M., and Nakayama, W. 1997. Heat Transfer from Micro-Finned Surfaces to Flow of Flurinert Coolant in Reduced-Size Channels. *IEEE Trans. Components, Packaging, and Manufacturing Technology, Part A* 20(2):138–145.

Mizunuma, H., Behnia, M., and Nakayama, W. 1998. Heat Transfer from Micro-Finned Surfaces to Flow of Flurinert Coolant: Boiling Heat Transfer. *Proc. 6th ITHERM*, Seattle, WA, May 27–30, pp. 386–391.

Mostinski, I. L. 1963. Application of the Rule of Corresponding States for the Calculation of Heat Transfer and Critical Heat Flux. *Teploenergetika* 4:66. (English Abstract in *British Chemical Eng.* 8:580, 1963.)

Murata, K. and Hashizume, K. 1993. Forced Convection Boiling of Nonazeotropic Refrigerant Mixtures Inside Tubes. *ASME J. Heat Transfer* 115:680–689.

Nakayama, W. 1998a. Enhanced Heat Transfer in Tight Space—A Frontier for Thermal Management of Microelectronic Equipment. *J. Enhanced Heat Transfer*, in press.

Nakayama, W. 1998b. Thermal Management of Portable Computers. *Future Circuits* 3:81–88.

Nakayama, W. 1996. Thermal Management of Electronic Equipment: Research Needs in the Mid-1990s and Beyond. *Applied Mechanics Reviews* 39(12):S167–S174.

Nakayama, W. and Behnia, M. 1998. Roles of CFD Simulation in Thermal Analysis of Microelectronic Equipment. *Modeling of Engineering Heat Transfer Phenomena*, Chapter 3. Eds. B. Sunden and M. Faghri. Southampton, U.K: Computational Mechanics Publications.

Nakayama, W. and Bergles, A. E. 1990. Cooling Electronic Equipment: Past, Present, and Future. *Heat Transfer in Electronic and Microelectronic Equipment*. Ed. Bergles, A. E., pp. 3–39. New York: Hemisphere Publishing Corp.

Nakayama, W., Nakajima, T., and Hirasawa, S. 1984. Heat Sink Studs Having Enhanced Boiling Surfaces for Cooling of Microelectronic Components. ASME Paper No.84-WA/HT-89.

Nguyen, T., Mochizuki, M., Mashiko, K., Saito, Y., Sauciuc, I., and Boggs, R. 1998. Advanced Cooling System Using Miniature Heat Pipes in Mobile PC. *Proc. 6th ITHERM*, Seattle, WA, May 27–30, pp. 507–511.

Nishikawa, K. and Fujita, Y. 1990. Nucleate Boiling Heat Transfer and Its Augmentation. *Advances in Heat Transfer* 20:1–82.

NIST. 1995. *REFPROP*. Washington, DC: National Institute for Science and Technology.

Panitsidis, R. D., Gresham, R. D., and Westwater, J. W. 1975. Boiling of Liquids in a Compact Plate-Fin Heat Exchanger. *International Journal of Heat and Mass Transfer* 18:37–42.

Papell, S. S., Simoneau, R-J., and Brown, D. D. 1966. Buoyancy Effects on Critical Heat Flux of Forced Convection Boiling in Vertical Flow. NASA TND-3672.

Peterson, G. P. 1996. Modeling, Fabrication, and Testing of Micro Heat Pipes: An Update. *Applied Mechanics Reviews*, 45(5):S175–S183.

Peng, X. F. and Wang, B. X. 1993. Forced Convection and Flow Boiling Heat Transfer for Liquid Flowing Through Microchannels. *Int. J. Heat Mass Transfer* 36(14):3421–3427.

Peng, X. F., Hu, H. Y., and Wang, B. X. 1998. Boiling Nucleation During Liquid Flow in Microchannels. *Int. J. Heat Mass Transfer* 41(1):101–106.

Phillips, R. J. 1988. Microchannel Heat Sinks. *Advances In Thermal Modeling Of Electronic Components and Systems*, Volume 2, Chapter 3. Eds. Bar-Cohen, A. and Kraus, A. D. New York: ASME Press.

Premoli, A., Francesco, D., and Prina, A. 1970. An Empirical Correlation for Evaluating Two-

Phase Mixture Density Under Adiabatic Conditions. *European Two-Phase Flow Group Meeting*, Milan.

Riehl, R. R., Seleghim, Jr., P., and Ochterbeck, J. M. 1998. Comparison of Heat Transfer Correlations for Single- and Two-Phase Microchannel Flows for Microelectronics Cooling. *Proc. 6th ITHERM*, Seattle, WA, May 27–30, pp. 409–416.

Robertson, J. M. 1982. The Correlation of Boiling Coefficients in Plate-Fin Heat Exchanger Passages with a Film-Flow Model. *7th International Heat Transfer Conference, Munich* 6:341–345.

Saito, M., Yamaoka, N., Miyazaki, K., Kinoshita, M., and Abe, Y. 1994. Boiling and Two Phase Flow Under Microgravity. *Nuclear Engineering and Design* 106:451–461.

Shah, M. M. 1982. Chart Correlation for Saturated Boiling Heat Transfer: Equations and Further Study. *Transactions of ASHRAE* 88:185–196.

Shollenberger, K., Carey, Y. P., and Tervo, P. 1992. Onset of Dryout and Post-Dryout Heat Transfer in Enhanced Passage Geometries for Compact Evaporators. *ASME Heat Transfer Digest* 197:83–91.

Sydoriak, S. G. and Roberts, T. R. 1957. Study of Boiling in Short Narrow Channels and Its Application to Design of Magnets Cooled by Liquid H2 and N2. *Journal of Applied Physics* 28(2):143–149.

Takamatsu, H., Momoki, S., and Fujii, T. 1993. A Correlation for Forced Convection Boiling Heat Transfer of Nonazeotropic Refrigerant Mixture of HCFC22/CFC114 in a Horizontal Smooth Tube. *Int. J. Heat Mass Transfer* 36(14):3555–3563.

Take, K., Furukawa, Y., and Ushioda, S. 1998. Fundamental Investigation of Roll Bond Heat Pipe as Heat Spreader Plate for Notebook Computers. *Proc. 6th ITHERM*, Seattle, WA, May 27–30, pp.501–506.

Tasaka, M., Hayashi, C., and Aihara, T. 1996. Heat Transfer Characteristics of Very Compact Heat Sinks with Plate Fins by Jets. *Proc. Japan National Heat Transfer Symposium*, Niigata, pp. 795–796.

Tran, T. N., Wambsganss, M. W., Chyu, M-C., and France, D. M. 1997. A Correlation for Nucleate Flow Boiling in Small Channels. *Compact Heat Exchangers for the Process Industries*, Engineering Foundation Conference, Snowbird, pp. 353–363.

Tran, T. N., Wambsganss, M. W., and France, D. M. 1995. Boiling Heat Transfer with Three Fluids in Small Circular and Rectangular Channels. *Argonne National Laboratory, Report ANL-95-9*, NTIS, Springfield, VA.

Tuckerman, D. B. and Pease, R. F. W. 1981. High-Performance Heat Sinking for VLSI. *IEEE Electron. Device Lett.*, Vol. EDL-2:126–129.

Wadekar, V. V. 1991. Vertical Slug Flow Heat Transfer with Nucleate Boiling. *ASME Heat Transfer Digest* 159:157–161.

Wadekar, V. V. 1992. Flow Boiling of Heptane in a Plat-Fin Heat Exchanger Passage. *ASME Heat Transfer Digest* 201:1–6.

Wadekar, V. V. and Kenning, D. B. R. 1990. Flow Boiling Heat Transfer in Vertical Slug and Churn Flow Regions. *9th International Heat Transfer Conference* 3:449–454.

Wallis, G. B. 1969. One-Dimensional Two-Phase Flow. New York: McGraw-Hill.

Wallis, G. B. and Makkenchery, S. 1974. The Hanging Film Phenomenon in Vertical Annular Two-Phase Flow. *Journal of Fluids Engineering* Sept: 297–298.

Wambsganss, M. W., France, D. M., and Jendrzejczyk, J. A. 1993. Boiling Heat Transfer in a Horizontal Small Diameter Tube. *Journal of Heat Transfer* 115:963–972.

Westwater, J. W. 1983. Boiling and Heat Transfer in Compact and Finned Heat Exchangers. *Advances in Two Phase Flow and Heat Transfer*, NATO ASI Series E 64:827–857.

Wieting, A. R. 1975. Empirical Correlations for Heat Transfer and Flow Friction Characteristics of Rectangular Offset Fin Plate Fin Heat Exchangers. *Journal of Heat Transfer* 97(3):488–490.

Wong, H. and Lee, T-Y. 1996. Thermal Evaluation of a PowerPC 620 Microprocessor in a Multiprocessor Computer. *IEEE Trans. Components, Packaging, and Manufacturing Technology, Part A* 19(4):469–477.

Yao, S-C. and Chang, Y. 1983. Pool Boiling Heat Transfer in a Confined Space. *International Journal of Heat and Mass Transfer* 26(6):841–848.

Yilmaz, S. and Westwater, J. W. 1980. Effect of Velocity on Heat Transfer to Boiling Freon113. *Journal of Heat Transfer* 102:26–31.

Yung, D., Lorenz, J. J., and Panchal, C. 1980. Convective Vaporization and Condensation in Serrated Fin Channels. *ASME Heat Transfer Digest—Heat Transfer in OTEC Systems* 12:29–37.

CHAPTER
# SEVENTEEN

## CHF AND POST-CHF (POST-DRYOUT) HEAT TRANSFER

**Gian Piero Celata**

*ENEA National Institute of Thermal-Fluid Dynamics, Rome, Italy*

**Andrea Mariani**

*ENEA National Institute of Thermal-Fluid Dynamics, Rome, Italy*

## INTRODUCTION

The term 'critical heat flux' (CHF) indicates an abrupt worsening of the heat transfer between a heating wall and a coolant fluid, generally with undesired consequences. This is typically due to the presence on the heated wall of a vapor layer, which strongly reduces the heat transfer rate from the heater to the coolant.

In systems where the heat transfer is temperature-controlled, (i.e., when a variation in the coolant thermal-hydraulic conditions implies only a variation in the heat flux and not in the wall temperature), the sudden decrease in the heat transfer coefficient leads to a reduction in the performance of the "heat exchanger," and may cause chemical consequences for the wall (fouling, etc.) or safety consequences for the plant. This is immediately clear once we consider Eq. (17.0.1):

$$\dot{q} = \alpha(T_W - T_1) \qquad (17.0\text{-}1)$$

As the wall-to-fluid temperature difference is imposed, a reduction in the heat transfer coefficient $\alpha$ will cause a decrease in the heat flux $\dot{q}$. A typical temperature controlled system is that where the wall is heated by a condensing fluid on one side and cooled on the other side. In systems with imposed heat flux (i.e., when a variation in the coolant thermal-hydraulic conditions implies only a variation in the wall temperature and not in the heat flux), the sudden decrease in the heat transfer coefficient leads to a sharp increase in the wall temperature, as given by Eq. (17.0-1). This increase may lead to the wall melting or deteriorating. Tubes exposed to the flame, like in a furnace, a nuclear reactor core, or an electrically heated rod or channel, are typical heat flux controlled systems.

The term CHF, which is the limiting phenomenon in the design and operating conditions of water-cooled nuclear reactors as well as many other thermal industrial equipment, will be used to represent the heat transfer deterioration described above, though different mechanisms of the thermal crisis might also suggest different names. Under subcooled or low-quality saturated flow boiling conditions, nucleate boiling being the main boiling mechanism, the onset of thermal crisis is following the departure from nucleate boiling (DNB), which is often the name used in this case. Under high-quality saturated flow boiling conditions typically characterized by the annular flow regime, the "dryout" of the liquid film adjacent to the heated wall is the leading mechanism to the thermal crisis (which is therefore named dryout).

In a heat flux-controlled situation (which will be the only one treated here), the rapid wall temperature rise may cause rupture or melting of the heating surface, which is termed as "physical burnout." The burnout heat flux is generally different from the DNB or the dryout heat flux. Only in the case of extremely high heat fluxes under subcooled flow boiling conditions (expected to occur in some components of the thermonuclear fusion reactor) is the CHF characterized by extremely high temperature differences. Failure of the heating wall is experienced very often, and therefore the heat flux causing the DNB is practically identical with the physical burnout heat flux (Celata, 1996). This is absolutely not the case in situations where higher heat transfer coefficients and lower critical heat fluxes give rise to only reduced temperature excursions at the DNB or dryout (Bergles et al., 1981; Collier and Thome, 1994; Hewitt, 1978; Hsu and Graham, 1986; Katto, 1994; Weisman, 1992). If the temperature rise does not cause failure of the heating surface, a post-CHF heat transfer is possible, though the heat transfer rate will be much lower than that before the CHF occurring.

In the following sections, the CHF in subcooled and saturated flow boiling will be discussed, together with the post-CHF heat transfer, with special reference to the most recent literature. Although many of the considerations reported in this chapter are generally valid, attention will be paid only to tubes.

## 17.1 CHF IN SUBCOOLED FLOW BOILING

Simply speaking, forced convective subcooled boiling involves a locally boiling liquid with a bulk temperature that is below the saturation value flowing over a surface exposed to a heat flux. Under such conditions, the critical heat flux is always of the DNB type, resulting in a significant increase in the wall temperature; the larger the temperature increase, the higher the heat flux.

CHF in subcooled flow boiling is relevant to the thermal-hydraulic design of Pressurized Water Reactor cores and has been studied extensively in the past (Bergles, 1977; Bergles et al., 1981; Collier and Thome, 1994; Gambill, 1968; Hewitt, 1978; Hsu and Graham, 1986; Katto, 1994; Weisman, 1992). It is receiving renewed attention recently due to the possible use of water in subcooled flow boiling for the cooling of some components of the thermonuclear fusion reactor believed to be subjected to operating conditions characterized by extremely high thermal loads (Boyd, 1985a; Celata, 1996). Hereafter, the parametric trends experimentally observed will be discussed, together with available correlations and theoretical models.

### 17.1.1 Parametric Trends

The magnitude and occurrence of the CHF are affected by many parameters, such as thermal-hydraulic, geometric, and external parameters. Among thermal-hydraulic parameters, we have subcooling, mass flux, pressure, and binary component fluids, while important geometry parameters are channel diameter, heated length, channel orientation, tube wall thickness and material. External parameters of interest are heat flux distribution and content of dissolved gas.

**17.1.1.1 Influence of subcooling.** As reported by Boyd (1985a), most of the early experimental studies reveal that the relationship between subcooling and CHF is almost linear. Bergles (1963) indicated that for very large subcooling at moderate to large liquid velocity (1 to 10 m/s), the relationship between CHF and subcooling is nearly linear, but it becomes highly nonlinear as the subcooling decreases, showing a minimum at small positive subcooling. Recent experiments under conditions of high liquid subcooling confirmed the almost linear relationship between CHF and subcooling (Celata et al., 1993a; Nariai et al., 1987; Vandervort et al., 1992). Figure 1 shows the CHF versus inlet subcooling for data carried out by Celata et al. (1993a) in 2.5 mm I.D. stainless steel tubes, 0.25 mm wall thickness, 10 cm long, uniformly heated by the Joule effect, with vertical upflow of water. The functional dependence of the CHF on the subcooling is practically linear, up to very high subcooling and very high liquid velocity. The CHF versus $\Delta T_{sub,in}$ curves, plotted at different liquid velocities, show results parallel to each other, and no inter-relation between u and $\Delta T_{sub,in}$ would seem to exist.

**17.1.1.2 Influence of mass flux.** The CHF is an increasing function of the mass flux (or fluid velocity) with less than a linear fashion. This was observed up to very

**446** HANDBOOK OF PHASE CHANGE: BOILING AND CONDENSATION

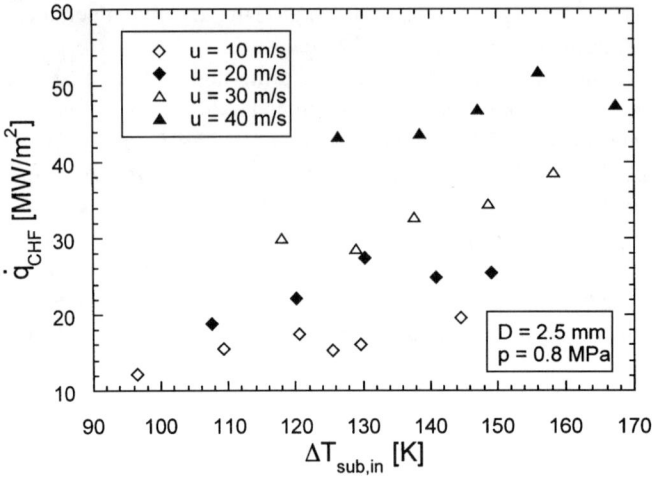

**Figure 1**  CHF versus inlet subcooling, Celata et al. (1993a).

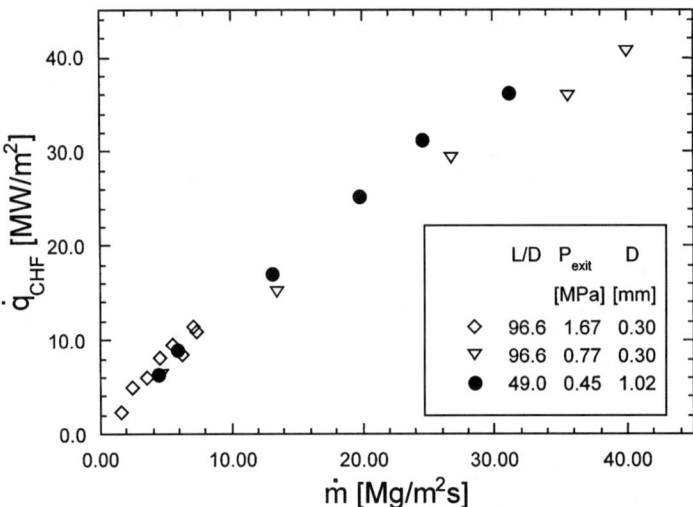

**Figure 2**  CHF versus mass flux, Boyd (1988, 1989, 1990).

high values of mass flux (90 Mg/m²s). Figure 2 shows the results of experiments carried out by Boyd (1988, 1989, 1990) using water as a fluid in horizontal test sections of amzirc (copper-zirconium alloy). Boyd (1988, 1989) employed a tube with an inner diameter of 3.0 mm, wall thickness around 0.5 mm, and a heated length of 0.29 m, while Boyd (1990) used 10.2 mm I.D., 0.125 mm wall thickness and 0.5 m long copper tubes. Tests were performed at a constant inlet temperature of 20°C. Similar results were obtained by Celata et al. (1993a).

**17.1.1.3 Influence of pressure.** Recent experiments (Celata et al., 1993a, 1993b; Nariai et al., 1992; Vandervort et al., 1992) showed that in the range 0.1–5.0 MPa, direct influence of the pressure on the CHF is weak, with other conditions being equal (i.e., for same subcooling and liquid velocity). This is demonstrated in Figure 3a, where the CHF is plotted versus exit pressure p for Vandervort et al. (1992) data, obtained with stainless steel tubes of 1.07 mm I.D., 26.75 mm long. Virtually no pressure effect was noted; in fact, there seemed to be a very slight decrease of the CHF with increasing pressure. Figure 3b shows the results of Celata et al. (1993b) obtained with stainless steel tubes of 8.0 mm I.D., 10 cm long, with uniform heating. The CHF versus subcooling data lie on a unique curve independent of the pressure, evidencing the negligible effect of this parameter.

Boyd (1985a) reported how other researchers found a maximum in the CHF versus pressure trend in the vicinity of a reduced pressure of 0.75, this value being somewhat variable with the mass velocity.

**17.1.1.4 Binary component fluids.** Tolubinsky and Matorin (1973) used ethanol-water, acetone-water, ethanol-benzene, ethylene-glycol-water with a 4 mm i.d., and 60 mm long tube; Andrews et al. (1968) tested acetone-toluene and benzene-toluene with an annulus 6.35 mm i.d., 20.9 mm o.d., and 76 mm long; Sterman et al. (1968) used mono-iso-propyldiphenyl-benzene with an annulus 10 mm i.d., 16 mm o.d., and 110 mm long; Naboichenko et al. (1965) tested the same fluids using an annulus 6 mm i.d., 16 mm o.d., and 80 mm long; Carne (1963) used acetone-toluene and benzene-toluene with an annulus 6.35 mm i.d., 19.05 mm o.d., and 76.2 mm long; and finally Bergles and Scarola (1966) tested water-1-pentanol using a 6.26 mm i.d., and 170 mm long tube. Typical trends of CHF are shown in Figure 4; the CHF tends to reach a maximum value, which increases with increasing values of the mole fraction, subcooling, and velocity. The maximum corresponds to the maximum difference between the vapor and liquid composition of the more volatile component (y-x).

As the difference between the more volatile component concentration in the vapor and the liquid phase increases (in absolute value), a reduction occurs in the vapor bubble departure diameter, the bubble rate of growth, and the number of active nucleation sites. This results in a reduction of the vapor content of the wall layer of the boiling fluid and therefore gives rise to an increase in the CHF (Tolubinsky and Matorin, 1973).

**17.1.1.5 Influence of channel diameter.** Works to identify the dependence of the CHF on the channel diameter have been conducted up to the recent past (Bergles, 1963; Celata et al., 1993c; Kramer, 1976; Nariai and Inasaka, 1992; Vandervort et al., 1992). It is well established that CHF is inversely related to the channel diameter. Figure 5 shows CHF versus the channel diameter D for Vandervort et al. (1992) data. As observed by previous researchers, for given values of exit

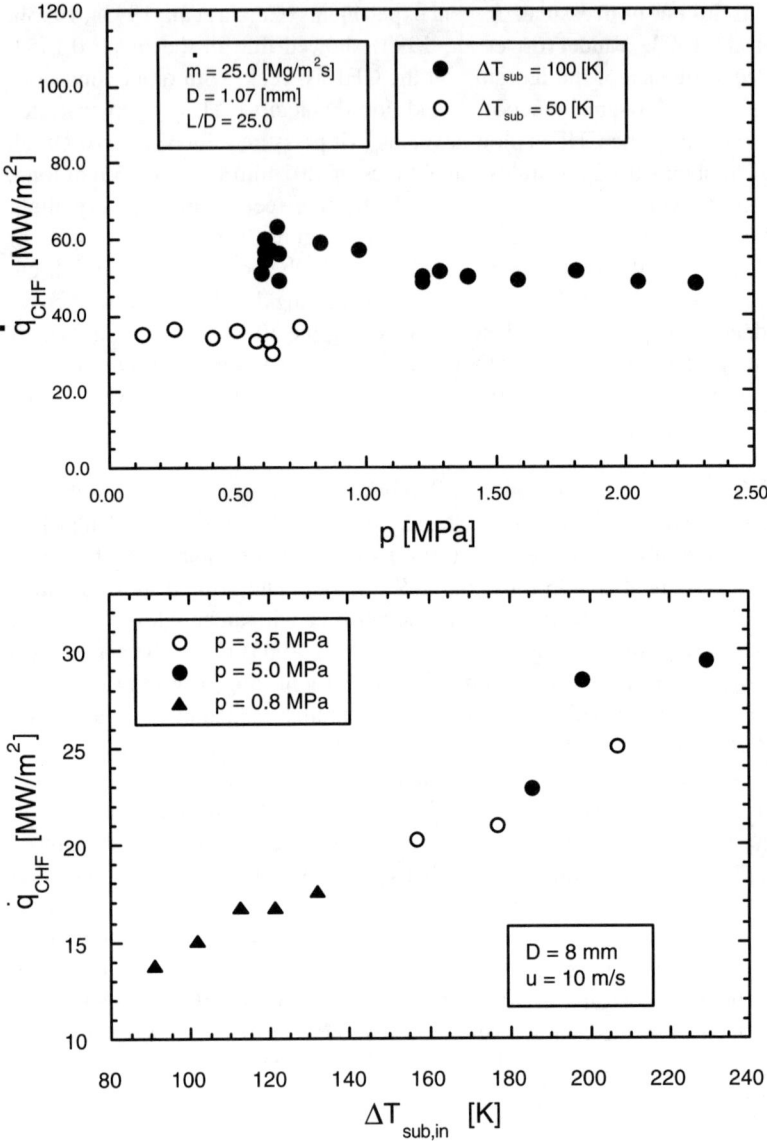

**Figure 3** CHF versus pressure, Vandervort et al. (1992) (top graph) versus inlet subcooling, Celata et al. (1993b) (bottom graph).

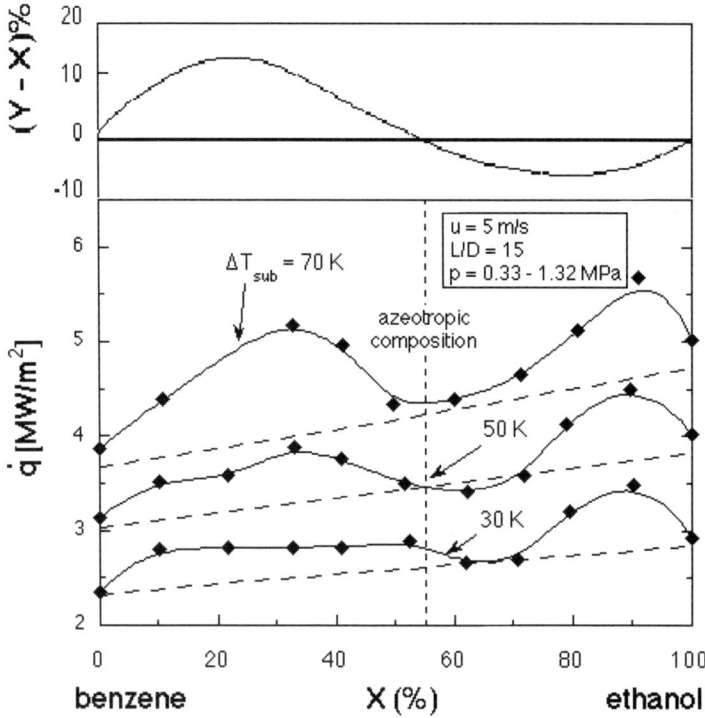

**Figure 4** CHF versus mixture composition for forced convection boiling of benzene/ethanol mixtures, Tolubinsky and Matorin (1973). In the top figure, Y-X represents the difference between the composition of the vapor phase, Y, and the liquid phase, X, for the more volatile component.

thermal hydraulic conditions, heated length, and liquid velocity, the CHF increases with the decrease in the tube inside diameter, but the effect was less significant for decreased mass flux. A threshold is observed beyond which the effect of the tube inside diameter may be considered negligible that is a function of the channel geometry and thermal hydraulic conditions. To explain the observed dependence of the CHF on the tube inside diameter, it is worth reporting here three different reasons proposed by Bergles (1963). For a tube with a smaller inside diameter, we have: (1) a small bubble diameter, (2) an increased velocity of the bubbles with respect to the liquid, and (3) the fluid subcooled bulk closer to the growing bubbles (collapsing in the bulk). From the analysis of experimental data of void fraction in narrow tubes, Nariai and Inasaka (1992) concluded that as the tube inside diameter decreases and mass velocity increases, (i) the diameter of generated bubbles and the thickness of the two-phase boundary layer become smaller due to the intense condensation effect caused by subcooled water in the core region, and

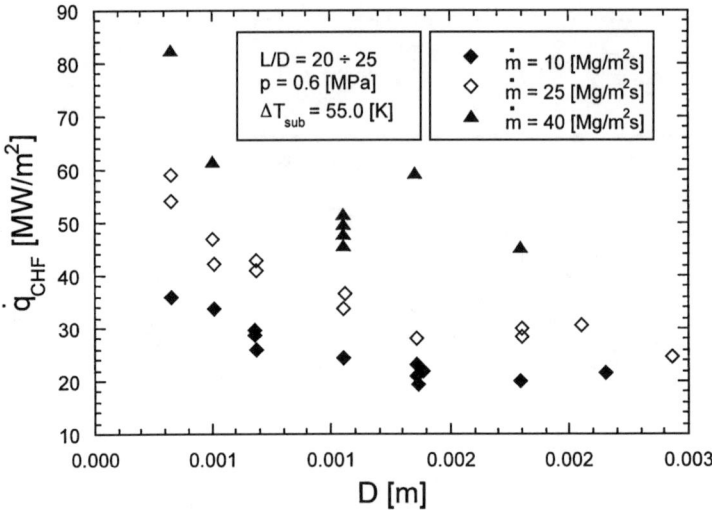

**Figure 5** CHF versus channel diameter, Vandervort et al. (1992).

(ii) the void fraction becomes smaller, making the CHF higher. The decrease in the diameter gives rise to an increase in the slope of the velocity profile in the two-phase boundary layer, making the detachment of growing bubbles and the consequent condensation in the core region easier. The higher the mass flux, the most consistent the effect.

**17.1.1.6 Influence of channel heated length.** The heated length of the channel seems to be inversely related to the CHF. Generally, investigators use the ratio of the heated length to the inside (or equivalent) diameter of the channel L/D as the characteristic non-dimensional length, but this still needs to be established. Recent experiments were carried by Nariai et al. (1987) and Vandervort et al. (1992). Figure 6 reports the results of Nariai et al. (1987) showing the CHF versus L/D. The CHF increases as L/D decreases, and the effect is more significant for smaller channel diameter. As the effect seems to be greatest for L/D < 20 (depending on the diameter), this would indicate that the CHF is related to the state of development of the bubble-boundary layer. Vandervort et al. (1992) verified that the functional dependence between CHF and L/D is independent of mass flux. As for the case of the channel diameter, experiments showed the presence of a threshold beyond which the CHF is practically independent of L/D, and this limit (between 20 and 40) is related to flow parameter, since L/D is related directly to the flow development.

**17.1.1.7 Influence of channel orientation.** The effect of flow orientation (e.g., horizontal versus vertical upflow) may be significant if the buoyant force is a non-negligible percentage of the axial inertial force in flow boiling. Quantitatively, this

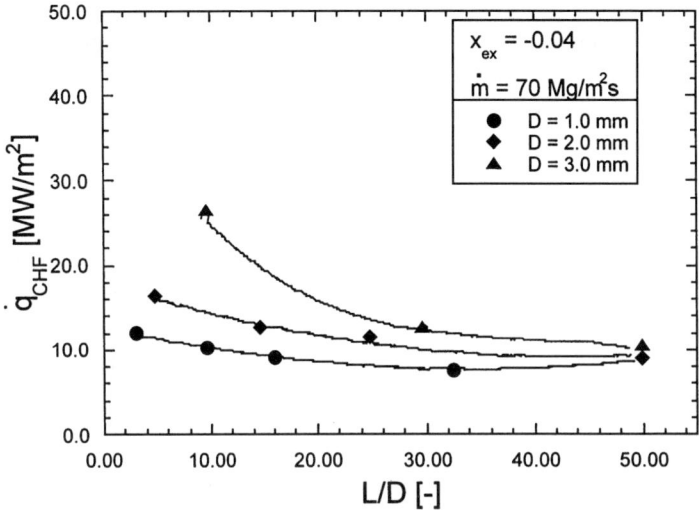

**Figure 6** CHF versus channel heated length, Nariai et al. (1987).

can be evaluated by considering the modified Froude number Fr, defined as:

$$\mathrm{Fr} = \frac{\dot{m} \cos \phi}{\rho_l \left[ gD \left( \frac{\rho_l - \rho_g}{\rho_l} \right) \right]^{1/2}} \quad (17.1\text{-}1)$$

where $\phi = 0$ represents the horizontal case. For a modified Froude number greater than 5–7, the effects of stratification and orientation may disappear. Wherever flow orientation plays a relevant role, the CHF for horizontal flow is always less than the value for vertical flow (Cumo et al., 1978; Merilo, 1977). Recent experiments carried out by Celata et al. (1993b) using water under conditions relevant to the NET/ITER divertor (p around 3.5 MPa) showed that for a liquid velocity greater than 5.0 m/s, horizontal and vertical data do not show any remarkable difference (at 5.0 m/s, the modified Froude number is greater than 20).

**17.1.1.8 Influence of tube wall thickness and material.** Celata et al. (1997) tested a number of SS 304 tubes having almost the same inner diameter but different wall thicknesses (from 0.25 to 1.75 mm) and found a slight effect of the tube wall thickness on the CHF: a slight decrease in the CHF as the wall thickness increased, but within 20% for the smallest to the largest thickness.

Vandervort et al. (1992) used five different materials in their experiments, i.e., SS 304, SS 316, nickel 200, brass 70/30, and inconel 600; under very similar geometric and thermal-hydraulic conditions, they did not observe any significant effect of the tube material on the CHF.

**17.1.1.9 Influence of heat flux distribution.** The optimum axial heat flux distribution for subcooled flow boiling is one where the peak heat flux occurs near the inlet (Boyd, 1985a). Groeneveld (1981) notes that a short pulse spike has a significant effect on subcooled flow boiling CHF, finding a CHF increase but a critical power decrease. Doroschuk et al. (1978) found that the CHF was lower for cosine distribution than for uniform ones.

Ad hoc experiments were recently performed by Nariai et al. (1992) and by Gaspari (1993) to investigate the effect of the circumferential heat flux distribution on the CHF. In particular, Gaspari made a comparison between peripherally full and half-heated tubes, straight flow, analyzing the CHF at both inlet and exit thermal hydraulic conditions. Using a 10 mm I.D. channel, 0.15 m long, Gaspari noted that under constant inlet liquid subcooling, higher CHF values were observed for half-heated tubes. Plotting the CHF versus exit liquid subcooling, such a difference tends to disappear (as reported in Figure 7), where the CHF is plotted versus inlet/exit subcooling.

**17.1.1.10 Influence of dissolved gas.** On the basis of previous literature, it is reasonable to conclude that dissolved gas has no effect on CHF. However, for experiments carried out with small diameter tubes, the bubble boundary layer may be smaller, and it is conceivable that even small amounts of dissolved air coming out of solution could affect the CHF. Specific tests were performed by Vandervort

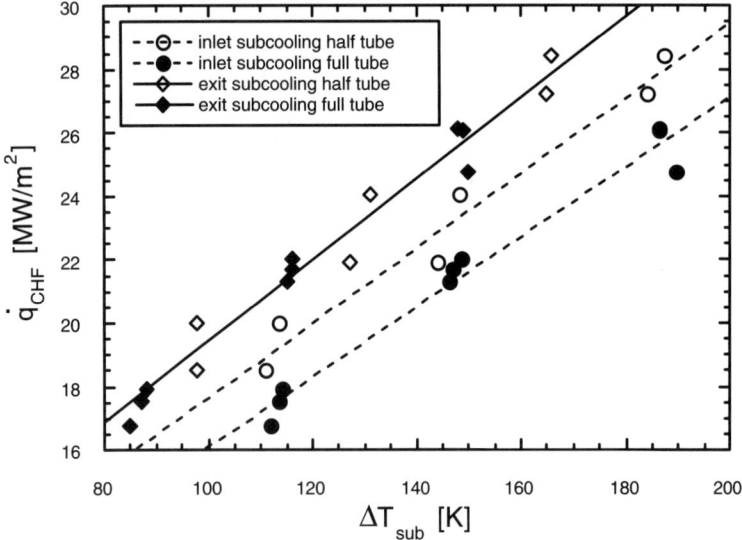

**Figure 7** Influence of circumferential heat flux distribution on CHF, Gaspari (1993).

et al. (1992) using 1.07 mm I.D. channels, at a mass flux of 25 Mg/m²s, an exit pressure of 0.6 Mpa, and an exit subcooling of 100 K. No significant change was observed in the CHF results over the range of dissolved gas concentration in water from near zero (2 ppm) up to the saturation level (~9.5 ppm).

## 17.1.2 Available Correlations for the Prediction of Subcooled Flow Boiling CHF

Many different types of correlational approaches have been proposed. These include empirical, dimensional analysis or similitude-based, analytical, tabular, and graphical, the first two categories being the most widely used. A thorough review of them has been given by Boyd (1985b), listing as many as 38 correlations. The correlations reported here are selected as being either the most widely used or on the basis of their possible extrapolation to conditions different from the originating ones (Celata et al., 1994a; Inasaka and Nariai, 1996), though this must be done with great care.

Gunther (1951):
$$\dot{q}_{CHF} = 71987 u^{0.5} \Delta T_{sub,ex} \tag{17.1-2}$$
(recommended ranges: $p = 0.1$–$1.1$ MPa; $u = 1.5$–$12.1$ m/s; CHF $= 0.4$–$11.4$ MW/m²; $\Delta T_{sub} = 11$–$39$ K)

Tong et al. (1968):
$$\dot{q}_{CHF} = (0.23 \cdot 10^6 + 0.094\dot{m})(3 + 0.018 \Delta T_{sub})[0.435 + 1.23 \exp(-0.0093 \, L/D)]^*$$

$$\left\{ 1.7 - 1.4 \exp\left[ -0.532 \left( \frac{h_l - h_{in}}{h_{lg}} \right)^{3/4} \left( \frac{\rho_g}{\rho_l} \right)^{-1/3} \right] \right\} \tag{17.1-3}$$

(recommended ranges: $p = 5.5$–$19.0$ MPa; $u = 0.3$–$12.1$ m/s; CHF $= 0.4$–$4$ MW/m²; $L/D = 21$–$365$; $\Delta T_{sub} = 0$–$126.7$ K)

Tong (1975):
$$\dot{q}_{CHF} = 0.23 f \dot{m} h_{lg} [1 + 0.0216(p_{out}/p_c)^{1.8} Re^{0.5} Ja] \tag{17.1-4}$$
where
$$f = 8(D/D_o)^{0.32} Re^{-0.6}, \quad \text{with } D_o = 1.27 \cdot 10^{-2} \text{ m}$$
$$Ja = \frac{c_p(T_b - T_{sub})}{h_{lg}} \frac{\rho_l}{\rho_g}$$
$$Re = \frac{\dot{m} D}{\eta_l (1 - \varepsilon)}$$

with $\varepsilon$ (void fraction) evaluated using Thom's correlation (Collier and Thome, 1994; Thom et al., 1965) (recommended ranges: p = 6.8–13.6 MPa; u = 0.68–5.9 m/s; void fraction at CHF < 0.35; D = 3–10 mm; L/D = 5–100).

Tong (1968):

$$\frac{\dot{q}_{CHF}}{h_{lg}} = C \frac{\dot{m}^{0.4}\eta_1^{0.6}}{D^{0.6}} \qquad (17.1\text{-}5)$$

with $C = 1.76 - 7.433 x_{out} + 12.222 x_{out}^2$
(recommended ranges: p > 7 MPa). The Tong-68 correlation can also be written as:

$$Bo = \frac{C}{Re^{0.6}}$$

where Bo and Re are Boiling number and Reynolds number, respectively.

A modification of the Tong-68 correlation, for pressures lower than 7.0 Mpa, has been proposed by Celata et al. (1994a):

$$Bo = \frac{C'}{Re^{0.5}} \qquad (17.1\text{-}6)$$

where

$C' = (0.216 + 4.74 \cdot 10^{-2} p)\psi$ (p in MPa)
$\psi = 1$ if $x_{out} < -0.1$
$\psi = 0.825 + 0.986 x_{out}$ if $0 > x_{out} \geq 0.1$

(recommended ranges: $p \leq 5.5$ MPa; u = 2.2–40 m/s; $\Delta T_{sub,out}$ = 15–190 K; D = 0.3–15 mm).

In using the above reported correlations, two methods are generally followed: the *heat balance method* (HBM), which requires an iterative procedure, and the *direct substitution method* (DSM) (Groeneveld et al., 1986; Inasaka and Nariai, 1986). The two methods lead to different results, and their use has been deeply debated in the recent past, with the possible conclusion that the HBM would give better results and should therefore be preferred (Theofanous, 1996).

For binary mixtures (Celata and Cumo, 1996; Collier and Thome, 1994), the CHF in subcooled flow boiling may be expressed as the sum of two terms: the first term, $\dot{q}_{CHF,i}$, is the ideal value evaluated from the CHF value of the two components at the same pressure, velocity, and subcooling (linear combination), while the second term, $\dot{q}_{CHF,E}$, is an additional CHF connected to the increase in the CHF due to mass transfer effects. Thus, the final expression is given by:

$$\dot{q}_{CHF} = \dot{q}_{CHF,i} + \dot{q}_{CHF,E} = \dot{q}_{CHF,i}(1 + C_{ll}) \qquad (17.1\text{-}7)$$

where

$$\dot{q}_{CHF,i} = [x\dot{q}_{CHF,1} + (1-x)\dot{q}_{CHF,2}]$$

1 and 2 refer to the more and the less volatile component, respectively, and $C_{11}$ the mole fraction of the more volatile component in the liquid phase.

Sterman et al. (1968) verified in their experiments that $C_{11}$ varies between 0 and 0.8 and proposed an expression for $C_{11}$, as:

$$C_{11} = A\frac{|C_{21} - x|^3}{Re_2} + B\frac{|C_{21} - x|^{1.5}}{Re_2^{0.4}} \left[\frac{T_{s,1}}{T_{s,m} - T_{s,1}}\right] \quad (17.1\text{-}8)$$

with

$$A = 3.2 \, 10^5; \quad B = 6.9$$

with $C_{21}$ being the mole fraction of the more volatile component in the vapor phase. This correlation was proved valid also for refrigerant mixture (Celata et al., 1994b).

Tolubinsky and Matorin (1973) gave the following expression of $C_{11}$, as:

$$C_{11} = 1.5|C_{21} - x|^{1.8} + 6.8|C_{21} - x| \left[\frac{T_{s,m} - T_{s,1}}{T_{s,1}}\right] \quad (17.1\text{-}9)$$

Equation (17.1-9) is applicable to ethanol-water, acetone-water, ethanol-benzene, and ethylene-glycol-water mixtures with ±20% error.

### 17.1.3 Available Models for the Prediction of Subcooled Flow Boiling CHF

As is known, correlations have the drawback of not being reliable outside the recommended ranges of application. In this respect, models may have the advantage to characterize not only the existing and developing data base, but also to predict CHF beyond the established data base. Recent reviews about CHF modeling were given by Katto (1994, 1995), Weisman (1992), and Celata (1997).

Major theoretical approaches to CHF can be categorized into five groups, according to the basic mechanism assumed by relative authors to be the main cause of the CHF occurrence:

(1) *Liquid layer superheat limit model*. The difficulty of heat transport through the bubbly layer causes a critical superheat in the liquid layer adjacent to the wall, giving rise to the occurrence of the CHF (Tong et al., 1965).
(2) *Boundary layer separation model*. This model is based on the assumption that an "injection" of vapor from the heated wall into the liquid stream causes a reduction in the velocity gradient close to the wall. Once the vapor effusion

increases beyond a critical value, the consequent flow stagnation is assumed to originate the CHF (Hancox and Nicoll, 1973; Kutateladze and Leontiev, 1966; Purcupile and Gouse, 1972; Thorgerson et al., 1974; Tong, 1966, 1975). The weak physical basis of the model has been demonstrated by the studies reported above (Fiori and Bergles, 1970; Hino and Ueda, 1985; Mattson et al., 1973; van der Molen and Galjee, 1978).

(3) *Liquid flow blockage model*. It is assumed that the CHF occurs when the liquid flow normal to the wall is blocked by the vapor flow. Bergel'son (1980) considers a critical velocity raised by the instability of the vapor-liquid interface, while Smogalev (1981) considers the effect of the kinetic energy of vapor flow overcoming that of the counter motion of liquid.

(4) *Vapor removal limit and near-wall bubble crowding model*. It is assumed that the turbulent interchange between the bubbly layer and the bulk of the liquid may be the limiting mechanism leading to the CHF occurrence. The CHF occurs when bubble crowding near the heated wall prevents the bulk cold liquid from reaching the wall (Hebel et al., 1981). According to Weisman and Pei (1983) and Weisman and Ying (1983), the CHF occurs when the void fraction in the bubbly layer, calculated under the assumption of homogeneous two-phase flow in the bubbly layer (Weisman and Pei, 1983) and using the slip model (Weisman and Ying, 1983), just exceeds the critical value of 0.82. The void fraction in the bubbly layer is determined through the balance between the outward flow of vapor bubbles and the inward liquid flow at the bubbly layer-bulk liquid flow interface. The Weisman and Ileslamlou model (1988) is an improvement of the Weisman and Pei model for subcooled exit conditions. A research work carried out by Styrikovich et al. (1970) showed that measured void fraction at the CHF ranges from as low as 0.3 to as high as 0.95, making the validity of the near-wall bubble crowding models questionable. In addition, the models are quite empirical in the determination of the turbulent exchange in the bubbly layer.

(5) *Liquid sublayer dryout model*. The model is based on the dryout of a thin liquid sublayer underneath a vapor blanket or elongated bubble, due to coalescent bubbles flowing over the wall. (Celata et al., 1994c; Katto, 1990a; Lee and Mudawar, 1988).

At present, the liquid sublayer dryout theory is receiving significant attention, is well developed, and is able to provide good predictions over a wide range of conditions. Lee and Mudawar (1988) are the first in developing and proposing a mechanistic model based on the liquid sublayer dryout theory, which was assessed for data at a pressure above 5.0 MPa.

Following the same principles as Lee and Mudawar, Katto (1990a, 1990b) developed a generalized CHF model applicable to not only water but also non-aqueous fluids (water, nitrogen, helium, R 11, R 12, and R 113). Then Katto extended his model so as to cover the CHF of water boiling at low pressure (Katto, 1992).

The Lee and Mudawar and Katto models make use of empirical constants determined through the experimental data. This somewhat limits the use of these models within the data base on which they are assessed. Further, the Katto model is applicable only to those cases where the local void fraction at the CHF in the near-wall bubbly layer is lower than 0.7. The most recent model developed in the frame of the liquid sublayer dryout theory was proposed by Celata et al. (1994c). It does not use any empirical constants yet is capable of predicting the CHF of water boiling in a wide range of conditions for the subcooled flow boiling (Celata et al., 1995).

To describe the Celata et al. model, let us briefly consider the situation at the tube exit (locus of the CHF for axial uniform heating) approaching the CHF, as shown in Figure 8 (Celata et al., 1995a). A thin vapor clot or blanket forms in the vicinity of the heated wall due to small bubbles coalescence, holding a liquid sublayer between the vapor clot and the wall surface. The occurrence of the CHF is determined by the evaporation of the liquid sublayer during the passage time of the blanket, which insulates the liquid sublayer between the heating surface and the bulk of the liquid:

$$\dot{q}_{CHF} = \frac{\delta \rho_l h_{lg}}{L_B} u_B \quad (17.1\text{-}10)$$

where $\delta$ is the initial liquid layer thickness, $\rho_l$ is the liquid layer density, and $L_B$ and $u_B$ are the blanket length and velocity, respectively. The vapor blanket length, $L_B$, is assumed to be given by the Helmholtz instability wavelength at the interface facing to the liquid sublayer. The vapor blanket velocity, $u_B$, is evaluated considering the velocity distribution of the main stream in the tube under the assumption of homogeneous flow. The Celata et al. model considers the temperature distribution of the main stream in the tube under the assumption of homogeneous flow and determines the thickness $s^*$ of the superheated layer (distance from the heated wall at which the liquid temperature is equal to the saturation value). Beyond the superheated layer, the vapor blanket cannot develop or exist due to subcooled conditions. The vapor blanket can develop and exist only in the near-wall region where the local liquid temperature is above the saturation value. As the temperature distribution is linked to the inside tube wall temperature, this is obtained by equating the local cross-section average fluid temperature, given by the coolant heat balance, with that provided by the temperature profile. Then, $\delta$ can be determined as the difference between the superheated layer $s^*$ (where the vapor clot can exist only, and as close as possible to the saturation line) and the vapor blanket thickness, $D_B$. The latter is calculated from the Staub (1968) model, under the assumption (common with the Lee and Mudawar model) that the circumferential growth of a vapor blanket is strongly limited by adjacent blankets and the steep velocity

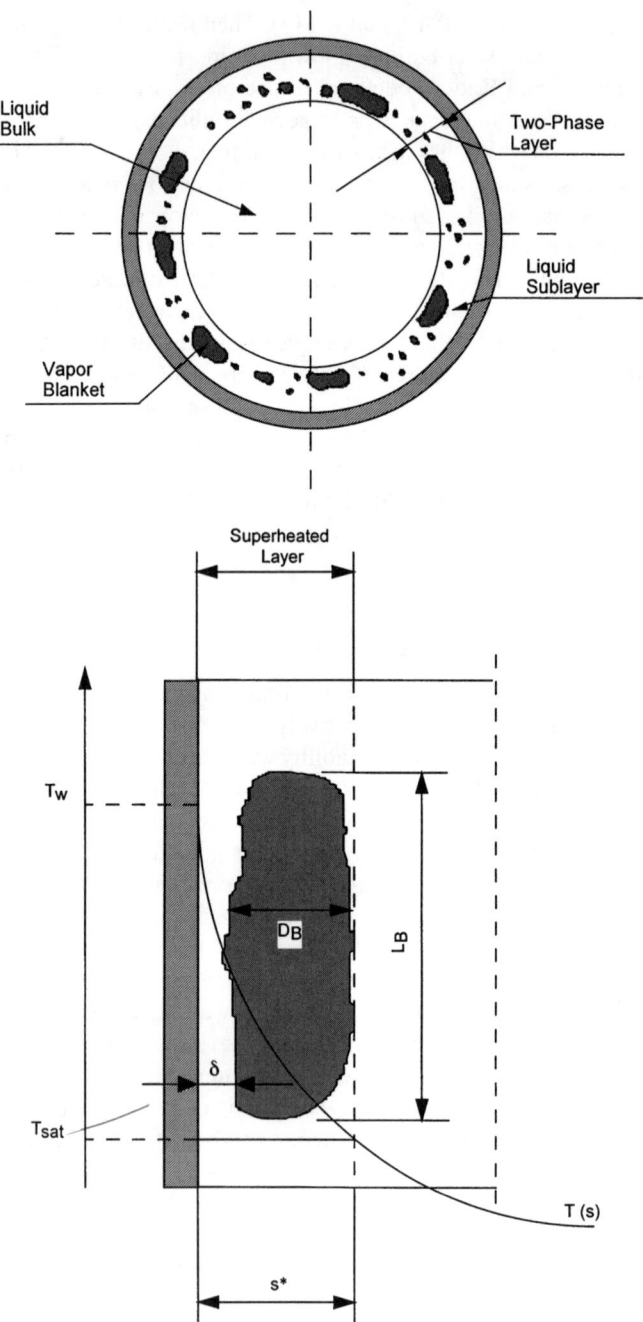

**Figure 8** Schematic of the liquid sublayer dryout theory, Celata et al. (1994c).

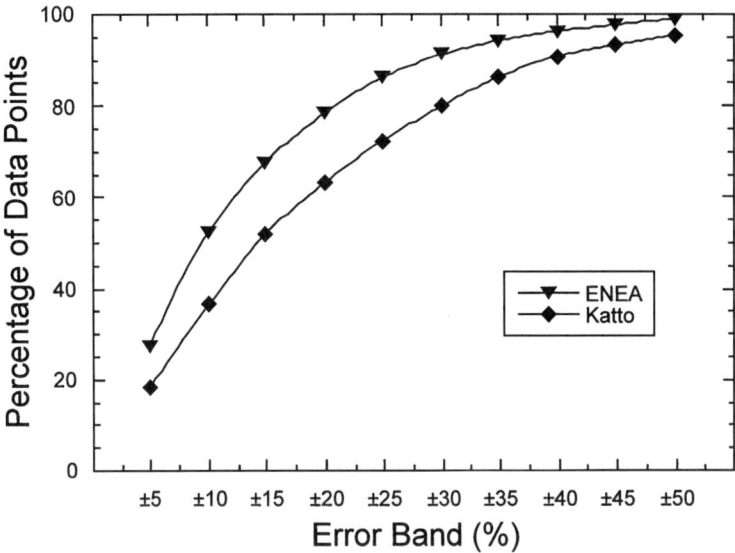

**Figure 9** Comparison between Katto (1990b) and Celata et al. (1994c) models for the prediction of water subcooled flow boiling CHF.

gradient in case of high liquid velocity. It is therefore assumed that the equivalent diameter of each blanket (i.e., its thickness) may be approximated by the diameter of a bubble at the departure from the wall. In other words, it is assumed that departing bubbles may coalesce into a distorted blanket that stretches along the fluid flow direction due to vapor generation by sublayer evaporation and keeps almost a constant equivalent diameter (thickness). Equations used in the mathematical description of the Celata et al. model are reported in the Appendix. A comparison between Katto and Celata et al. models is reported in Figure 9 for the data set published in Celata and Mariani (1993) (about 1900 data). The figure reports the percentage of data points calculated with a given error band (%).

The Celata et al. model, unlike the other liquid sublayer dryout models, can also be used for peripheral non-uniform heating simply by considering the total thermal power delivered to the fluid in the coolant heat balance for the calculation of the local average coolant temperature (Celata et al., 1995b).

## 17.2 CHF IN SATURATED FLOW BOILING

Forced convection saturated flow boiling involves a boiling liquid whose average bulk temperature is at the saturation temperature, flowing over a surface exposed to a heat flux. The critical heat flux always occurs with a positive quality at the CHF. Generally speaking, under saturated conditions, we may have two different types of CHF: i) the DNB type, typically occurring at low quality conditions, and ii) the dryout type, which is encountered in high quality flow. Although the two types of CHF are much different than each other from a phenomenological point of view, this kind of classification is somewhat schematic, the threshold being very difficult to establish. As the quality at the CHF increases, we gradually pass from DNB to dryout. An interesting simple method to identify a priori the CHF type has been given recently by Lombardi and Mazzola (1998).

Nonetheless, although DNB and dryout types of the CHF are associated with different mechanisms leading to the onset of thermal crisis, parametric trends of the CHF in saturated flow boiling may be more or less independent of the CHF mechanisms, and the general trends can be given for the CHF in saturated flow boiling.

### 17.2.1 Parametric Trends

The magnitude and the occurrence of the CHF are affected by many parameters, including thermal-hydraulic, geometric, and external. Among thermal-hydraulic parameters we have subcooling, mass flux, pressure, while important geometry parameters are channel diameter, heated length, channel orientation, and tube wall thickness. External parameters of interest are heat flux distribution and binary component fluids.

**17.2.1.1 Influence of subcooling.** For fixed mass flux $\dot{m}$, tube length L, and tube diameter D, the CHF increases almost linearly with inlet subcooling but decreases with decreasing mass flux (as reported in Figure 10, where data of

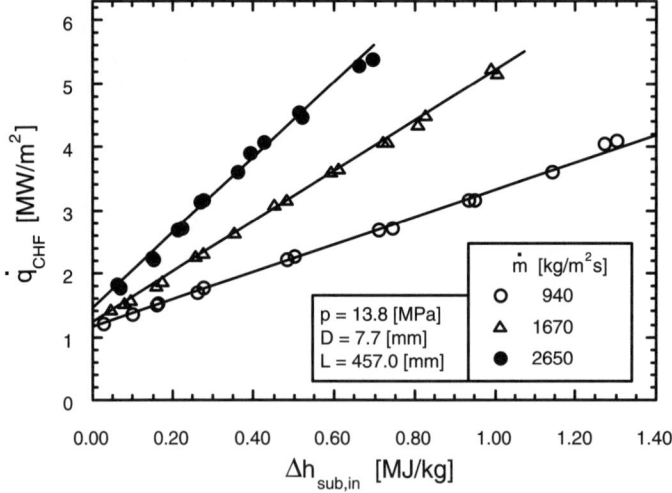

**Figure 10** Critical heat flux versus inlet subcooling for different mass fluxes.

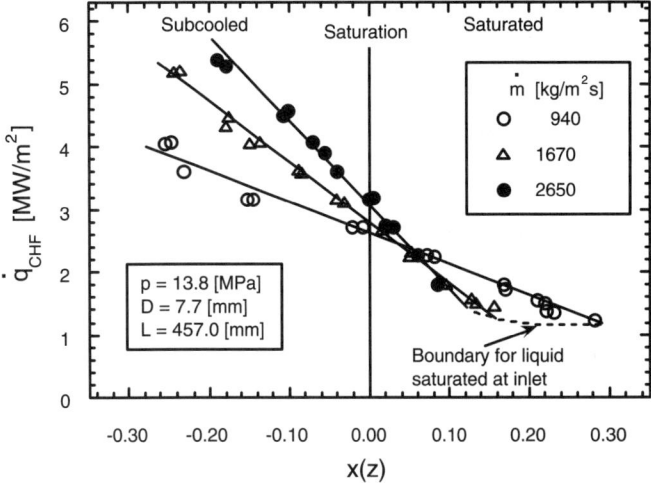

**Figure 11** Critical heat flux versus exit quality, for different mass fluxes.

Weatherhead [1963] are plotted). At a mass flux of 500 kg/m²s, Moon et al. (1996) observed that the inlet subcooling effect on the CHF is very small, suggesting that it can be negligible at much lower mass fluxes (Chang et al., 1991; Mishima, 1984). If we plot the same data of Figure 10 in terms of exit conditions (see Figure 11), we find an interesting feature that accounts for the inter-relation between exit quality and mass flux effects on the CHF. In the subcooled region (x < 0), the CHF increases as mass flux increases for a given exit quality x. In the saturated region (x > 0), we may find a cross-over, and the CHF decreases with increased mass flux for a given x. It is therefore important to establish which variables are kept constant when considering the influence of a specific variable on the CHF and to specify if we refer to inlet or exit condition.

**17.2.1.2 Influence of mass flux.** For fixed inlet conditions and geometry, the CHF increases with increasing mass flux. At low values of $\dot{m}$, the CHF rises approximately linearly with $\dot{m}$, but then rises much less rapidly for higher $\dot{m}$ values. The effect of mass flux on the CHF depends on the pressure, which is stronger at lower pressures. The influence of mass flux on the CHF for fixed exit conditions has been already outlined in the previous sections: the CHF increases with $\dot{m}$ for x < 0, while decreases with $\dot{m}$ for x > 0, x being the exit quality.

**17.2.1.3 Influence of pressure.** The influence of the pressure on the CHF is very complex, as indicated by Collier and Thome (1994) and reported in Figure 12, where data of Alekseev et al. (1965) are plotted. Overall, for fixed inlet conditions, the CHF increases with increasing pressure at low pressure, passes through a

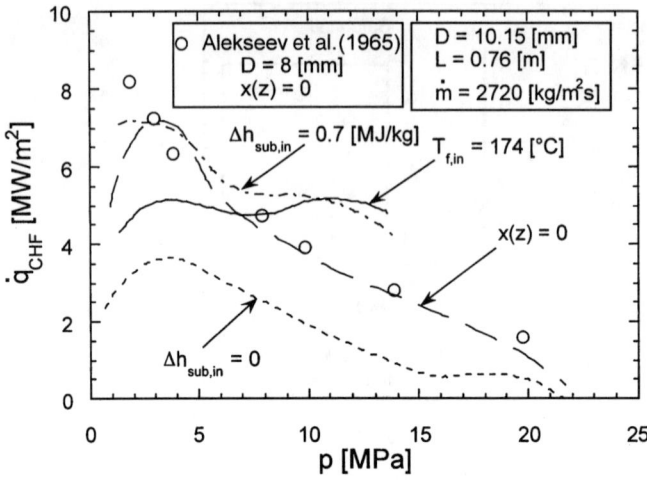

**Figure 12** Influence of the pressure on the critical heat flux.

maximum at around 3.0 MPa, and then decreases at higher pressures. Yin et al. (1988) experienced a secondary maximum at 19.0 MPa for $\dot{m}$ = 2040 kg/m²s and inlet subcooling of 33 and 55 K. For fixed exit conditions, Moon et al. (1996) report a clearer trend than that for fixed inlet conditions. As the pressure increases, the CHF sharply increases, passes a maximum, then gradually decreases. The pressure corresponding to the maximum CHF decreases as quality increases.

**17.2.1.4 Influence of diameter.** The effect of tube diameter on the CHF for fixed inlet and exit conditions is shown in Figures 13 and 14, respectively. For fixed inlet conditions, the CHF increases with increasing tube diameter, the effect increasing with the inlet subcooling. For fixed exit conditions, the CHF is a decreasing function of tube diameter. It appears that the diameter effect strongly depends on the flow regime due to the difference in CHF mechanisms. In terms of the critical power input, other conditions being equal, this is found to increase monotonously with the diameter, approximately proportionally to $D^2$ (for D < 1 cm); for larger diameters (D > 1.5 cm), the critical power input becomes progressively proportional (approximately) to D. An intermediate dependence is obtained for intermediate values of D (Bertoletti et al., 1965).

**17.2.1.5 Influence of heated length.** For fixed inlet conditions, there is a common evidence (Chang et al., 1991; Collier and Thome, 1994; Hewitt, 1980) that the CHF decreases with increasing heated length. For fixed exit conditions, from the interesting study of Moon et al. (1996) reported in Figure 15, we may say that for short tubes, the CHF decreases with the heated length, while for heated lengths above a

CHF AND POST-CHF (POST-DRYOUT) HEAT TRANSFER    463

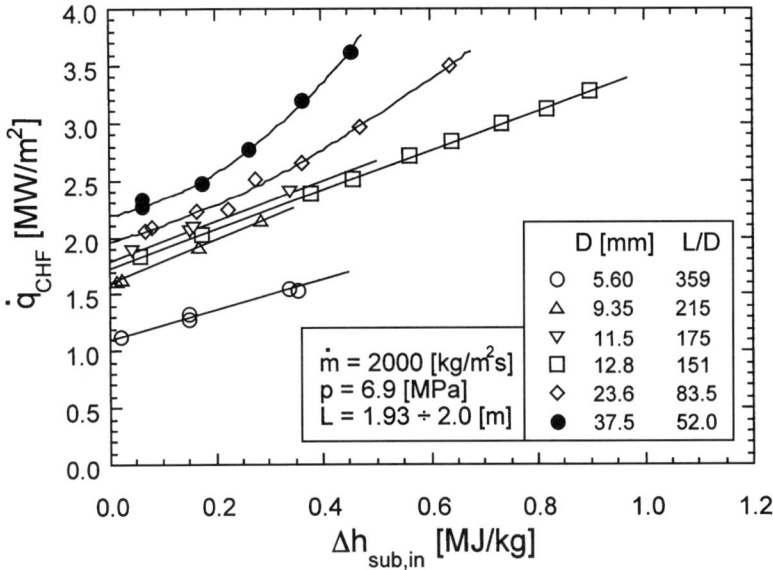

**Figure 13** Effect of tube diameter on the CHF for fixed inlet conditions.

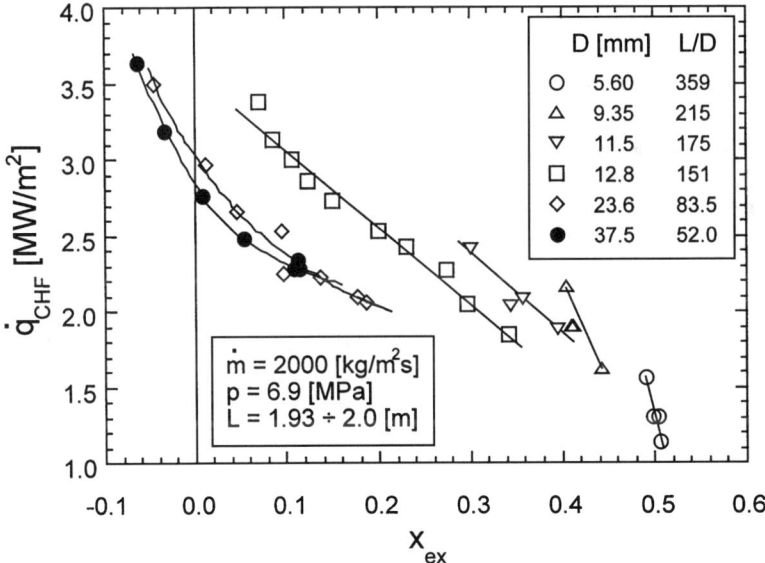

**Figure 14** Effect of tube diameter on the CHF for fixed exit conditions.

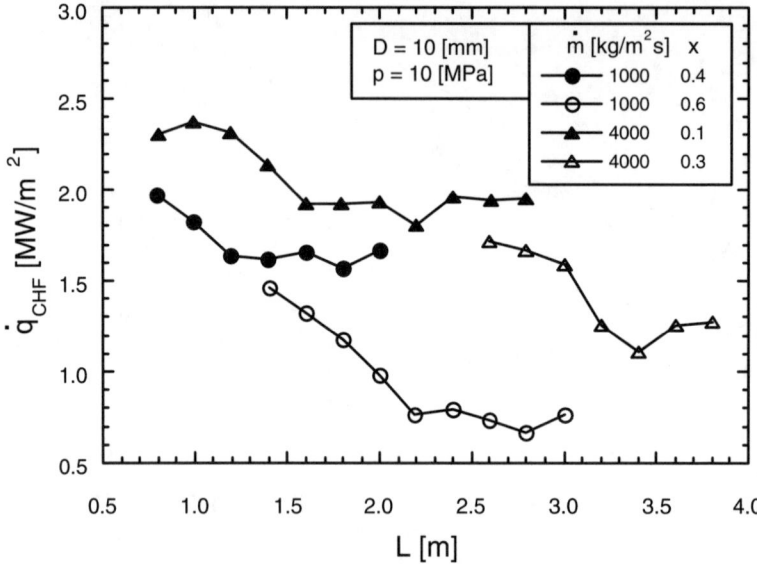

**Figure 15** Effect of tube length on the CHF for fixed exit conditions.

threshold the heated length effect would seem to disappear. The threshold length is a function of other system parameters. In terms of the critical power input, other conditions being equal, this is found to increase monotonously with length, and asymptotically saturates for large values of the heated length (Bertoletti et al., 1965).

**17.2.1.6 Effect of channel orientation.** Vertical downflow against upflow CHF studies have been performed by Papell et al. (1966) using liquid nitrogen, Kirby et al. (1967) using water, and Bertoni et al. (1976) using R-12. Generally speaking, downflow CHF was found to be 10–30% lower than upflow, with buoyancy effects playing the main role in the reduction. The buoyancy effect was found to be an inverse function of pressure and subcooling and was proved to be small if the liquid downflow velocity is significantly above the bubble rise velocity.

Among others, Becker (1971) found that the CHF for horizontal tubes is lower than that experienced for vertical upflow if the mass flux is lower than a critical value. This is because bubbles formed in the nucleate boiling regime move upwards due to gravity and concentrate in the upper region of the tube, thus causing a premature burnout with respect to vertical upflow as the void increases. Larger diameter tubes require larger critical mass fluxes to avoid the separation of the phases.

Cumo et al. (1978) carried out experiments using R-114 at different pipe inclinations between horizontal and vertical upflow, conditions included. The tube inclination has a significant influence on the CHF, which varies up to a factor of two passing from horizontal to upward vertical flow. The authors found that the buoyancy effect on the CHF may be neglected when the modified Froude number, as given by Eq. (17.1-1), is greater than 5–7.

**17.2.1.7 Influence of wall thickness.** Relatively little information is available on the effect of wall thickness. As reported by Collier and Thome (1994), some experiments on the wall thickness effect were performed by Aladyev et al. (1961), Barnett (1963), Lee (1965), and Tippets (1962). Results are quite contradictory, as Aladyev et al. (1961) did not find any effect in the range 0.4 to 2.0 mm, Lee (1965) observed a 5% reduction as the tube wall thickness is decreased from 2.1 to 0.86 mm, and Tippets (1962) found up to 20% decrease as a 0.254 mm ribbon heater was replaced by a 0.152 mm thick ribbon.

**17.2.1.8 Influence of heat flux distribution.** The effect of the axial heat flux distribution has been investigated, for example, by Keeys et al. (1972) and Cumo et al. (1980). The authors found a considerable difference in heat flux for burnout at a given quality for the uniform and non-uniform heating mode, noting that with the non-uniform heating, burnout can occur first up-stream of the end of the tube.

**17.2.1.9 Influence of mixture composition.** The effect of composition on the CHF in the case of binary mixtures has been studied by Auracher and Marroquin (1995), Celata et al. (1994), and Mori et al. (1990). The composition of the binary mixture has little or no effect on the CHF for long tubes, i.e., $L/D > 30$. For shorter tubes, as also reported by Collier and Thome (1994), the CHF increases with the mixture composition, passes through a maximum, and then decreases, all with respect to the ideal linear behavior between the values of the pure fluids for the same thermal hydraulic conditions.

## 17.2.2 Available Correlations for the Prediction of Saturated Flow Boiling CHF

For a given fluid, thermal-hydraulic and geometric conditions, and a given heat flux, axially uniform, experimental data are usually found to lie approximately on a single curve in a CHF versus burnout quality representation, the CHF being located at the end of the channel. This implies that the local quality conditions govern the magnitude of the CHF and are thus termed *local conditions hypothesis*.

We can plot the same data in terms of burnout quality and boiling length at burnout, the latter being the length between the location where the saturation condition is reached and the CHF location. The boiling length is easily obtained from a heat balance, knowing heat flux, quality, mass flux, and tube geometry. This type of plot can be regarded a indicating the possibility of some *integral* rather than *local* phenomenon.

Existing correlations are given in one of the two above reported forms and, for uniform heat flux, can be converted easily to the other, providing with equivalent results. When the heat flux is non-uniform, the two forms give quite different results, and this will be discussed later.

Referring the reader also to other sources collecting CHF correlations, such as Lee (1977), Katto (1986), Whalley (1987), and Collier and Thome (1994), some widely used correlations for uniform heat flux are reported here, for which great care is recommended in their application. As usual, such correlations are not based on a physical background and should be regarded as mathematical interpolation for the data range they cover. Their use outside this range can give high inaccuracy in the prediction.

Bertoletti et al. (1965) (called CISE):

$$\frac{\dot{q}_{CHF}}{\pi DLM h_{lg}} = \frac{a - x_{in}}{1 + \frac{b}{L}} \quad (17.2\text{-}1)$$

where $\dot{q}_{CHF}$ is the critical heat flux in kW/cm², D and L are the tube internal diameter and length, respectively, in cm, $\dot{M}$ is the mass flow rate in g/s, and

$$a = \left(1 - \frac{p}{p_c}\right)\left(\frac{\dot{m}}{\dot{m}_o}\right)^{-0.33} \quad \dot{m}_o = 100 \text{ g/cm}^2\text{s}$$

$$b = 0.315 \left(\frac{p_c}{p} - 1\right)^{0.4} D_e^{1.4} \dot{m}$$

with $p_c$ being the water critical pressure and $D_e$ the equivalent hydraulic diameter in cm (recommended ranges: $p = 45\text{--}150$ kg/cm²; $100(1 - p/p_c)^3 \leq \dot{m} \leq 400$ g/cm²s; $x_{in} \leq 0.2$; $D > 0.7$ cm; $L = 20.3\text{--}267$ cm).

Tong (1969) (called W-3):

$$\frac{\dot{q}_{CHF}}{10^6} = \{(2.022 - 0.0004302p) + (0.1722 - 0.0000984p)$$

$$\times \exp[(18.177 - 0.004129p)x]\}$$

$$[(0.1484 - 1.596x + 0.1729x|x|)\dot{m}/10^6 + 1.037](1.157 - 0.869x)$$

$$[0.2664 + 0.8357 \exp(-3.151 D_e)][0.8258 + 0.000784(h_l - h_{in})]$$

$$(17.2\text{-}2)$$

The heat flux $\dot{q}_{CHF}$ is in Btu/(hr)(ft²) (recommended range and units of the parameters are: $p = 1000\text{--}2300$ psia; $\dot{m} = 1.0\ 10^6\text{--}5.0\ 10^6$ lb/(hr)(ft²); $D_e = 0.2\text{--}0.7$ in; $x = -0.15$ to $+0.15$; $h_{in} \geq 400$ Btu/lb; $L = 110\text{--}144$ in; heated perimeter/wetted perimenter $= 0.88\text{--}1.0$).

Bowring (1972):

$$\dot{q}_{CHF} = \frac{A + 0.25 D\dot{m}(\Delta h_{sub})_{in}}{F + L} \qquad (17.2\text{-}3)$$

$$A = \frac{2.317\left[\dfrac{D\dot{m}h_{lg}}{4}\right]F_1}{1.0 + 0.0143 F_2 \dot{m} D^{1/2}}, \qquad F = \frac{0.077 F_3 D\dot{m}}{1.0 + 0.347 F_4 (\dot{m}/1356)^n},$$

$$n = 2.0 - 0.00725 p$$

where $\dot{q}_{CHF}$ is the critical heat flux in W/m², $(\Delta h_{sub})_{in}$ is the inlet subcooling expressed in J/kg, L is the tube length expressed in m, D is the internal tube diameter in m, $\dot{m}$ the mass flux in kg/m²s, $h_{lg}$ is the latent heat of vaporization in J/kg, and p is the system pressure in bar. Parameters $F_1$, $F_2$, $F_3$, and $F_4$ are given by:

$p' = p/69$

$p' < 1$

$$F_1 = \frac{\{p'^{18.942} \exp[20.8(1-p')]\} + 0.917}{1.917};$$

$$\frac{F_1}{F_2} = \frac{\{p'^{1.316} \exp[2.444(1-p')]\} + 0.309}{1.309}$$

$$F_3 = \frac{\{p'^{17.023} \exp[16.658(1-p')]\} + 0.667}{1.667}; \qquad \frac{F_4}{F_3} = p'^{1.649}$$

$p' > 1$

$$F_1 = p'^{-0.368} \exp[0.648(1-p')]; \qquad F_2 = p'^{-0.448} \exp[0.245(1-p')]$$

$$F_3 = p'^{0.219}; \qquad \frac{F_4}{F_3} = p'^{1.649}$$

(recommended ranges: p = 2–190 bar; D = 0.002–0.045 m; L = 0.15–3.7 m; $\dot{m}$ = 136–18600 kg/m²s).

Katto and Ohno (1984):
a) In the case of $\rho_g/\rho_l < 0.15$,

$$\frac{\dot{q}_{CHF}}{\dot{m} h_{lg}} = \frac{C}{(l_b/D)} \left(\frac{\sigma \rho_l}{\dot{m}^2 l_b}\right)^{0.043} \qquad (17.2\text{-}4)$$

$$\frac{\dot{q}_{CHF}}{\dot{m} h_{lg}} = 0.10(\rho_g/\rho_l)^{0.133} \left(\frac{\sigma \rho_l}{\dot{m}^2 l_b}\right)^{1/3} \frac{1}{(1 + 0.0031 l_b/D)} \qquad (17.2\text{-}5)$$

$$\frac{\dot{q}_{CHF}}{\dot{m} h_{lg}} = 0.098(\rho_g/\rho_l)^{0.133} \left(\frac{\sigma \rho_l}{\dot{m}^2 l_b}\right)^{0.433} (l_b/D)^{0.27} \frac{1}{(1 + 0.0031 l_b/D)} \qquad (17.2\text{-}6)$$

where C is given as $C = 0.25$ for $l_b/D < 50$, $C = 0.25 + 0.0009[(l_b/D) - 50]$ for $l_b/D = 50\text{--}150$, and $C = 0.34$ for $l_b/D > 150$, $l_b$ being the boiling length. Roughly speaking, Eqs. (17.2-4) and (17.2-5) correspond to the CHF in annular flow, and Eq. (17.2-6) to the CHF in froth or bubbly flow. With increasing $\dot{m}$ (i.e., with decreasing $\sigma\rho_l/\dot{m}^2 l_b$), the above equations are employed in the order of the first, second, and the third equation so as to connect the value of the CHF continuously.

b) In the case of $\rho_g/\rho_l > 0.15$,

$$\frac{\dot{q}_{CHF}}{\dot{m} h_{lg}} = C \left(\frac{\sigma\rho_l}{\dot{m}^2 l_b}\right)^{0.043} (l_b/D) \tag{17.2-7}$$

$$\frac{\dot{q}_{CHF}}{\dot{m} h_{lg}} = 0.234(\rho_g/\rho_l)^{0.513} \left(\frac{\sigma\rho_l}{\dot{m}^2 l_b}\right)^{0.433} (l_b/D)^{0.27} \frac{1}{(1 + 0.0031 l_b/D)} \tag{17.2-8}$$

$$\frac{\dot{q}_{CHF}}{\dot{m} h_{lg}} = 0.0384(\rho_g/\rho_l)^{0.6} \left(\frac{\sigma\rho_l}{\dot{m}^2 l_b}\right)^{0.173} \frac{1}{(1 + 0.28(\sigma\rho_l/\dot{m}^2 l_b)^{0.233} l_b/D)} \tag{17.2-9}$$

where C takes the same value as in Eq. (17.2-4) (recommended ranges: $L = 0.01\text{--}8.8$ m; $D = 0.001\text{--}0.038$ m; $L/D = 5\text{--}880$; $\rho_g/\rho_l = 0.00003\text{--}0.41$; $(\sigma\rho_l/\dot{m}^2 L) = 3 10^{-9}\text{--}2\, 10^{-2}$).

The Katto and Ohno (1984) correlation has been tested for water, ammonia, benzene, ethanol, helium, hydrogen, nitrogen, R12, R21, R22, R113, and potassium.

**Correlations for the CHF in binary mixtures.** The above reported correlations have been developed for pure fluids such as water only (CISE, W-3, and Bowring, 1972) or more fluids (Katto and Ohno, 1984). Much different is the case where we have to face with binary mixtures. An exhaustive description of the CHF in binary mixtures can be found in Collier and Thome (1994), while Celata et al. (1994), Auracher and Marroquin (1995), and Celata and Cumo (1996) dealt specifically with refrigerant binary mixtures. Upon results obtained with mixtures of refrigerants and on the basis of the parametric trends described in Section 17.2.1.9, it is possible to say here that for short tubes, i.e., $L/D < 30$, the CHF can be calculated using the Tolubinsky and Matorin (1973) correlation, given by Eqs. (17.1-7) and (17.1-9). For long tubes, i.e., $L/D > 30$, Celata et al. (1994) found that the CISE correlation, proposed by Bertoletti et al. (1965), provides quite good results. Also, the Katto and Ohno (1984) correlation may be directly applied to binary mixtures in long tubes, though the accuracy is less than the CISE correlation.

**Correction for axial non-uniform heat flux.** For non-uniform heat flux single channels, Tong et al. (1966) recommends using a shape factor $F_c$ so that

$$\dot{q}_{CHF,nu} = \dot{q}_{CHF,nu}/F_c \qquad (17.2\text{-}10)$$

where subscript nu indicates the non-uniform heating, subscript u indicates uniform heating supply, and $F_c$ is expressed as

$$F_c = \frac{C}{\dot{q}_{loc}[1 - \exp(-Cl_{CHF,u})]} \int_{l_{OB}}^{l_{CHF,nu}} \dot{q}(z) \exp[-C(l_{CHF,nu} - z)]\,dz \qquad (17.2\text{-}11)$$

with

$$C = 0.44 \frac{(1 - x_{CHF,nu})^{7.9}}{(\dot{m}/10^6)^{1.72}} \; (\text{in.}^{-1})$$

In Eq. (17.2-11), $\dot{q}_{loc}$ is calculated using one of the available correlations for uniform heat flux, and $l_{CHF,nu}$ is the axial location at which the CHF occurs for non-uniform heat flux, in., $l_{CHF,u}$ is the axial location at which the CHF occurs for uniform heat flux, in., $l_{OB}$ is the axial location at which nucleate boiling begins, in., $x_{CHF,nu}$ is the quality at the CHF location under non-uniform heat flux, and $\dot{m}$ is in lb/(hr)(ft$^2$). The term $F_c$ is a *memory effect parameter*, which accounts for the thermal history of the fluid along the tube. $F_c$ is small in the subcooled region, and local heat flux determines the boiling crisis. At high qualities, C is small, the memory effect is high, and the average heat flux, or enthalpy rise, primarily determines the boiling crisis.

### 17.2.3 The Artificial Neural Network as a CHF Predictor

An advanced information processing technique such as artificial neural networks (ANNs) might provide a valuable alternative to the current techniques for estimating the CHF, since there exists a large number of experimental data for the CHF. Yapo et al. (1992), Moon and Chang (1994), Moon et al. (1996), and Mazzola (1997) applied the ANNs to the CHF prediction, showing promising results. An artificial neural network is composed of elements that are analogous to the elementary functions of biological neurons. ANNs have the characteristic of tolerance against experimental noise owing to the massive internal structure of the network. Also, it is easy to update the performance of the ANN for new experimental data.

Although the ANNs do not require accurate information about physical phenomena, their main drawbacks are the loss of model transparency ('black-box' character) and the lack of any indicator for evaluating the accuracy and reliability of the ANN answer when 'never-seen' patterns are presented. From applications to CHF of Moon et al. (1996) and Mazzola (1997), it appears nonetheless that the ANNs are able to predict CHF data within ±20–25% for most of data points, providing a consistent alternative method to empirical correlations.

### 17.2.4 The Tabular Method for the Prediction of Saturated Flow Boiling CHF

Another interesting method for the prediction of the CHF in saturated flow boiling is that proposed by Doroshchuk et al. (1975), which consists of a series of standard tables of CHF values as a function of the local bulk mean water condition and for various pressures and mass fluxes for a fixed tube diameter of 8 mm. Correction factors for tube length and for tube diameters other than 8 mm must be used. The latest updating of these 'look-up tables', (Groeneveld et al., 1996) consists of 22,946 data points covering the range 0.1 to 20.0 MPa, up to 8.0 Mg/m²s, and −0.5 to 1.0 for discrete values of pressure, mass flux and CHF quality, respectively. For tube diameters other than 8 mm, the CHF is given by the approximate equation:

$$\dot{q}_{CHF} = \dot{q}_{CHF,8mm} \left( \frac{D}{0.008} \right)^k \quad (17.2\text{-}12)$$

with $k = -1/2$ being the best parameter found by Groeneveld et al. (1996) in the range of tube diameter from 3 to 25 mm. Other researchers propose $k = -1/3$, such as Smith (1986) and Groeneveld et al. (1986).

The CHF look-up table method has become a widely accepted prediction technique. It has the following advantages over correlations or semi-analytical CHF models: i) accurate prediction, ii) the widest range of applications, iii) ease of use (no fluid properties are needed), iv) ease of updating, and v) correct parametric and asymptotic trends. Main drawbacks are the complexity of their use in a computer code with respect to a correlation, providing more or less the same accuracy.

### 17.2.5 Available Models for the Prediction of Saturated Flow Boiling CHF

The main advantage of mechanistic methods is that because they are based on the physical mechanisms leading to the CHF, in principle their validity should not be confined to the range of the available experimental data. The models should be only linked to the range of validity of the mechanisms identified, which should result in much more general application. As a matter of fact, sometimes some models for the mathematical description of bubble dynamics rely on empirical constants or correlations that restrict their general validity.

As a model is strictly linked to the mechanisms that can be responsible of the CHF occurrence, it is necessary to group existing models in DNB and dryout models.

**17.2.5.1 DNB type critical heat flux.** Different CHF mechanisms have been postulated for the DNB type thermal crisis in order to develop reliable correlations or predicting methods for the CHF calculation or identify possible methods to avoid the CHF occurrence. Typically, for low quality flow, the flow regime consists in an agglomeration of vapor in the near-wall region and a prevailing presence of liquid in the center of the channel. The governing heat transfer mechanisms are the bubble growing and detachment at the wall and their migration in the liquid bulk. Among the many mechanisms proposed, see, for instance, detailed reviews by Tong and Hewitt (1972), Hewitt (1980), Weisman (1992), and Katto (1994); those that appear to be somehow established experimentally are the following:

1) Hot spot formation under a growing bubble. As observed by Kirby et al. (1967), a dry patch forms between the growing bubble and the nucleation cavity as the micro-layer of liquid under the bubble evaporates. The dry patch may be rewetted at the bubble departure and the process can go on. Before the rewetting of the dry patch, the wall temperature rises due to the heat transfer deterioration. However, if the dry temperature exceeds a critical temperature (often called Leidenfrost temperature), then rewetting does not happen readily, thus causing local overheating and hence burnout. A schematic of this mechanism is drawn in Figure 16.

2) Near-wall bubble crowding model. Tong et al. (1966) first started from the idea that a *bubble boundary layer* takes place on the surface, and vapor generated by boiling at the heated wall must leave the near-wall region through this two-phase boundary layer. Burnout occurring when vapor escapes through the layer is prevented due to a critical crowding of the boundary layer with bubbles. More recently, Hebel et al. (1981), Weisman and Pei (1983), and Weisman and Ying (1983) assumed that the turbulent interchange between the bubbly layer

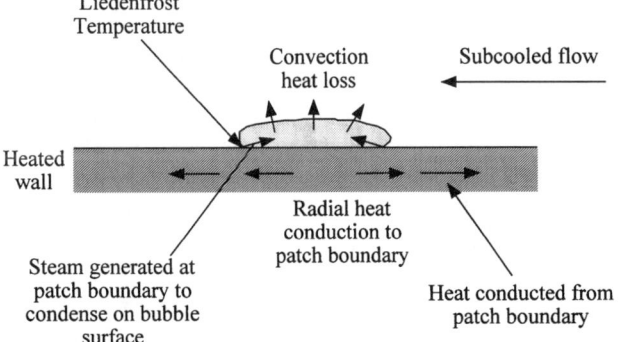

**Figure 16** Schematic of the hot spot formation under a growing bubble model, Kirby et al. (1967).

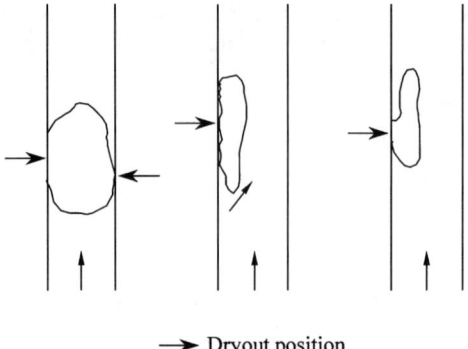

→ Dryout position

**Figure 17** Schematic of the dryout under a slug or vapor clot model, Fiori and Bergles (1968, 1970).

and the bulk of the liquid may be the limiting mechanism leading to the CHF occurrence. CHF occurs when bubble crowding near the heated wall prevents the bulk cold liquid from reaching the wall. This mechanism is discussed in more detail below.

3) Dryout under a slug or vapor clot. Fiori and Bergles (1968, 1970) observed that in plug flow, the thin liquid film around the large bubble may dry out, causing burnout. Alternatively, a stationary vapor clot can form on the heated wall, being a thin liquid film present between the clot and the wall. In this case, the local drying out of the film causes the wall to overheat and then burn out. A schematization of this mechanism is shown in Figure 17.

4) Liquid sublayer dryout theory. This mechanism has been already discussed for the understanding of the CHF in subcooled flow boiling in Section 17.1.3. The Lee and Mudawwar (1988) liquid sublayer dryout model was developed for subcooled flow boiling, on the basis of the Helmholtz instability at the microlayer/vapor interface as a trigger condition for microlayer dryout. Such a model has been extended to low-quality flow by Lin et al. (1989) under pressurized water reactor conditions. Basically, the main improvements of Lee and Mudawwar's model include the following: 1) the homogeneous two-phase flow model is assumed to be suitable for high-pressure, high-mass flux conditions. Fluid properties are calculated using the effective homogeneous flow rather than single-phase fluid properties; 2) the liquid enthalpy flowing into the microlayer is assumed to be independent of bulk subcooling and is approximated by the saturated liquid enthalpy for maintaining the local boiling.

Among the models listed above, it is interesting to give few details on the Weisman and Pei (1983) model (described in 2), which is currently the only

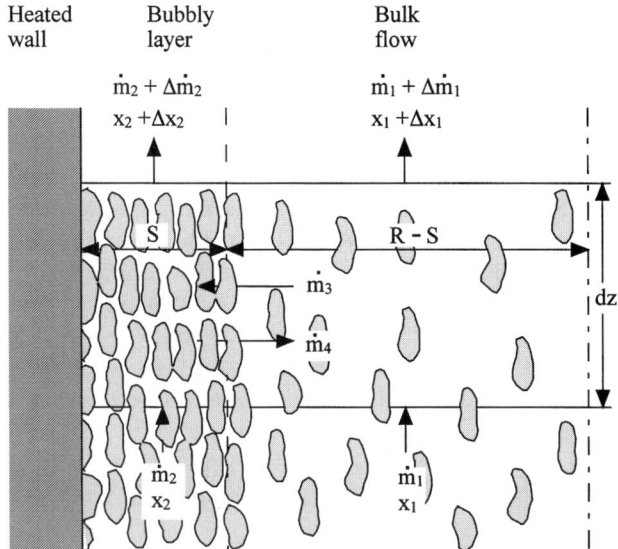

**Figure 18** Schematic of the near-wall bubble crowding model, Weisman and Pei (1983).

theoretically based CHF prediction procedure that has been shown to give good accuracy with fluids other than water, especially refrigerants.

The Weisman and Pei (1983) model, as shown in Figure 18, assumes that: 1) During low-quality boiling, the bubbly layer builds up along the channel until it fills the region near the wall, where the turbulent eddies are too small to transport bubbles radially. At the CHF site, the bubbly layer is assumed to be at this maximum thickness; 2) CHF occurs when the volume fraction of steam in the bubbly layer just exceeds the volume fraction (critical void fraction), at which an array of slightly flattened ellipsoidal bubbles can be maintained without significant contact between the bubbles; 3) the volume fraction of steam in the bubbly layer is determined by a balance between the outward flow of vapor and the inward flow of liquid at the bubbly layer-core interface. Considering a bubbly layer control volume, the total flow rate from core to bubbly layer was set equal to the total flow rate from bubbly layer to the core, plus the axial flow in and out of the bubbly layer control volume. From a simple mass balance over the bubbly layer, they obtain:

$$\frac{\dot{q}_{CHF}}{h_{lg}\dot{m}'} = \frac{x_2 - x_1}{F} \qquad (17.2\text{-}13)$$

where $\dot{m}'$ represents the mass flow rate into the bubbly layer. This mass flow rate is determined by the turbulent velocity fluctuations at the bubbly layer edge. The distance from the edge of the bubbly layer to the wall is taken as the distance at which the size of the turbulent eddies is k times the average bubble diameter. Only a fraction of the turbulent velocity fluctuations produced are assumed to be effective in reaching the wall. The effective velocity fluctuations are those in which the velocity exceeds the average vapor velocity away from the wall produced by the vapor being generated at the wall. The quantities $x_1$ and $x_2$ represent the vapor qualities in the core region and bubbly layer, respectively, at the CHF (these are actual values and not thermodynamic equilibrium qualities). The factor F represents the fraction of the heat flux producing vapor that enters the core region. It is given by the ratio of the difference of the enthalpy of saturated liquid and that at the bubble detachment point, and the difference between the enthalpy of liquid at a given axial location and that at the bubble detachment point. The occurrence of the CHF is for that quality in the bubbly layer that corresponds to the maximum void fraction that is possible in a bubbly layer of independent bubbles just prior to agglomeration. For slightly flattened elliptically shaped bubbles with a length-to-diameter ratio of 3/1, this void fraction is estimated as 0.82.

**17.2.5.2 Dryout type critical heat flux.** This type of CHF mechanism consists of the gradual depletion of the liquid film wetting the heating wall until the liquid film flow rate is zero and the consequent drying of the wall. It is evident that the dryout type is linked to the annular flow regime in convective flow boiling, as reported in the sketch of Figure 19. Observations of transparent test sections and flow pattern maps show that for most CHF cases where there is an exit quality greater than 10%, the flow pattern is annular. This is probably the most frequent situation in steam generation apparatuses.

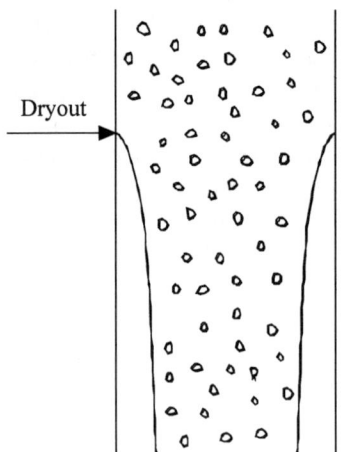

**Figure 19** Schematic of the dryout type critical heat flux.

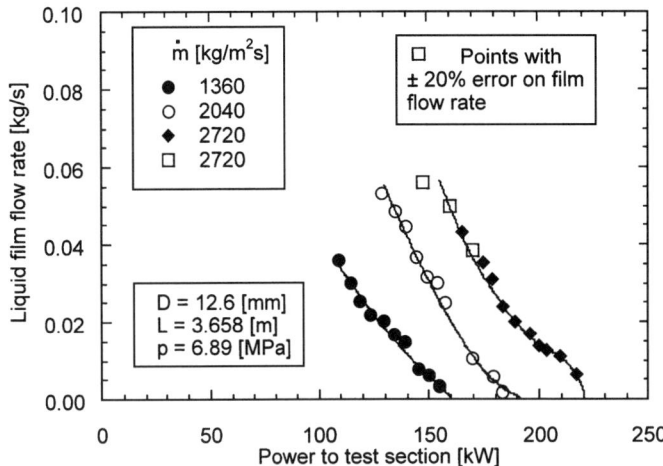

**Figure 20** Measurement of the film flow rate at the end of a heated channel as a function of power input to the channel, Hewitt et al. (1963, 1965).

Many studies have suggested that the CHF may occur when the liquid film flow rate goes to zero due to the combined effects of: i) liquid droplet entrainment from the liquid film, produced by the gas flow in the core (droplets are mainly entrained from liquid waves on liquid film surface), ii) liquid droplet deposition on the liquid film (some droplets initially entrained by the gas flow hit the liquid film and are "captured"), and iii) evaporation of the liquid film due to the heat flux delivered from the wall.

The first evidence showing that dryout occurs at the point where the film flow rate becomes zero was provided by Hewitt et al. (1963, 1965) and detailed in Hewitt and Hall-Taylor (1970). Hewitt et al. performed the measurements of the film flow rate at the end of a heated channel as a function of power input to the channel. The results are shown in Figure 20, where it is possible to observe that the critical heat flux point occurs at the power delivered to the fluid for which the film flow rate at the tube outlet is zero. More exactly, the occurrence of dryout should happen when the liquid film flow rate becomes smaller than the minimum value that is necessary to wet the whole heating wall and the liquid film breaks. Also, the so-called *cold patch* experiments by Bennet et al. (1967) represent a further evidence of this CHF mechanism.

The first attempt to use an annular flow model for the prediction of dryout is due to Whalley et al. (1974), while the model has been recently updated by Govan et al. (1988) and by Hewitt and Govan (1989). For the complexity of the model description, the reader is referred to the original sources, while a brief review will be given here. Figure 21 shows the postulated mechanisms in which dryout occurs

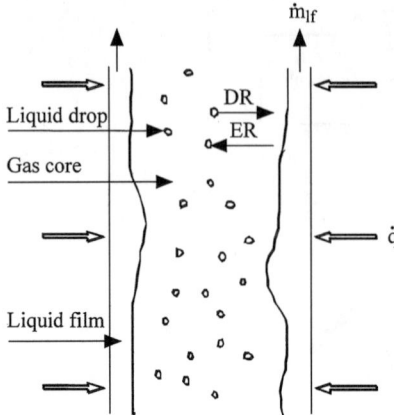

**Figure 21** Schematic of the annular flow model, Whalley et al. (1974).

when the liquid film flow rate falls smoothly to zero as a result of entrainment and evaporation. A mass balance, which also accounts for deposition, gives

$$\frac{d\dot{m}_{lf}}{dz} = \frac{4}{D}\left(DR - ER - \frac{\dot{q}}{h_{lg}}\right) \qquad (17.2\text{-}14)$$

where $\dot{m}_{lf}$ is the liquid film mass flux, DR the deposition rate, and ER the entrainment rate. In order to integrate this equation, the following are required:

1) a value for $\dot{m}_{lf}$ at the start of annular flow. Typically, it is assumed that at the start of annular flow $x_1 = 0.01$ and $\dot{m}_{lfl} = 0.99\dot{m}_l$. Govan (1984) found that the predicted CHF was sensitive to $\dot{m}_{lfl}$ but not to $x_1$. However, very little information exists on the transition to annular flow in a boiling channel.
2) a means to calculate the entrainment rate ER. Whalley et al. (1974) expressed this as a function of surface tension, interfacial shear, and liquid film thickness. Govan (1984) tried using various entrainment correlations but found that the CHF predictions were not greatly affected, mainly because the entrainment becomes small as dryout is approached.
3) a means to calculate the deposition rate DR. Whalley et al. (1974) assumed a simple proportionality between DR and the droplet concentration in the gas core, the constant of proportionality depending on surface tension. Govan (1984) found that the predicted CHF is sensitive to DR.

This mechanism of dryout is widely accepted, though there is some debate about the details. Anyway, recent updates by Govan et al. (1988) and Hewitt and Govan (1989) demonstrated that comparison with 5300 CHF data points shows a mean error of $-9.7\%$ with a standard deviation of 16% for a wide range of fluids, provided the CHF mechanism is dryout.

## 17.3 POST-CHF HEAT TRANSFER

Post-CHF heat transfer is of interest in all cases when the CHF condition can be reached or exceeded and the heating wall temperature is still low in comparison with the melting temperature or that value for which the wall material failure may happen. Heat transfer knowledge in these areas is required in many engineering applications, such as in the design of once-through steam generators (where complete evaporation of the feedwater occurs) or very high pressure recirculation boilers (where the CHF levels are low). The thermal-hydraulic design of pressurized water reactors has also called for an intensive investigation of heat transfer rates beyond the CHF point for transient and accident analyses.

Main heat transfer regimes in post-CHF heat transfer are film boiling and liquid deficient region. Film boiling typically occurs after the CHF in subcooled flow boiling, with low-quality CHF or in pool boiling. A schematic representation of such a heat transfer regime is given in Figure 22. The liquid deficient region or dispersed flow boiling, which occurs after the high-quality CHF, is schematically drawn in Figure 23.

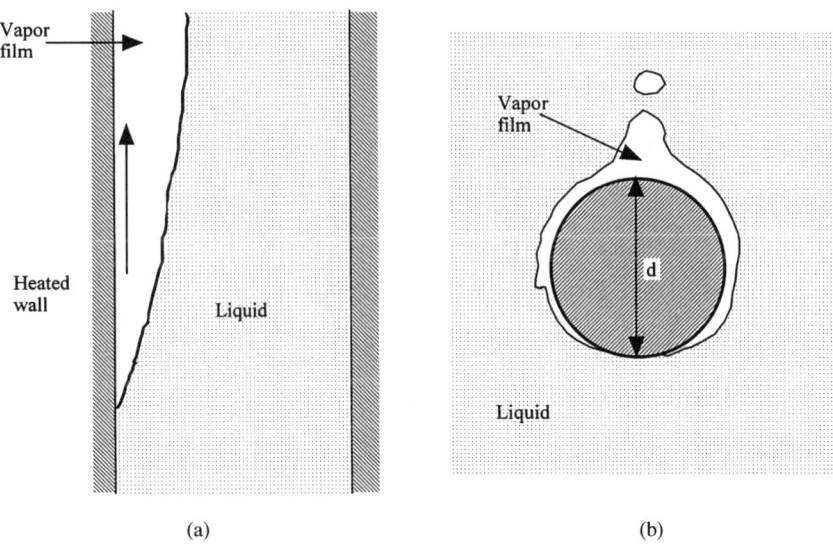

**Figure 22** Film boiling (a) on a vertical flat plate and (b) on a horizontal cylinder.

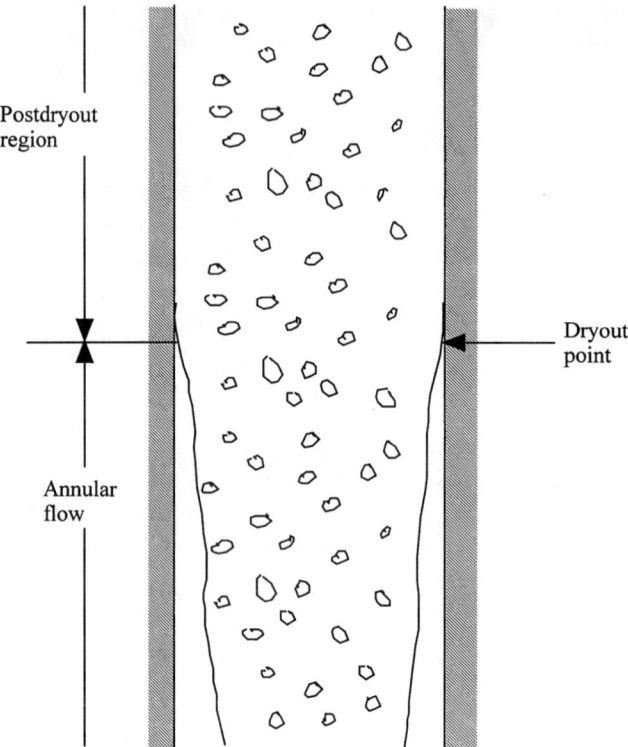

**Figure 23** High quality-post CHF flow.

### 17.3.1 Film Boiling

In pool boiling or after the subcooled flow boiling CHF, we may have the occurrence of the film boiling heat transfer regime once the CHF has been exceeded. The heat is transferred by conduction through the vapor film, and evaporation takes place at the liquid-vapor interface. Nucleation is absent and, in general, the problem may be simply treated as an analogy to filmwise condensation. Many theoretical solutions can be obtained for a horizontal and vertical flat surface, and also inside and outside tubes under both laminar and turbulent conditions with and without interfacial stress. The simplest solution may be obtained for laminar flow and linear temperature distribution. For a flat vertical surface, the local heat transfer coefficient is given by:

$$\alpha(z) = C \left[ \frac{\lambda_g^3 \rho_g (\rho_l - \rho_g) g h_{lg}}{z \Delta T \eta_g} \right]^{1/4} \quad (17.3\text{-}1)$$

where C is dependent on boundary conditions; for zero interfacial stress we have

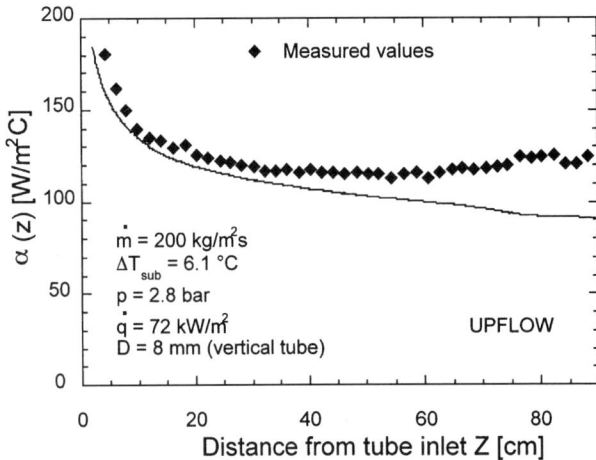

**Figure 24** Film boiling heat transfer for water, Costigan et al. (1984).

$C = 0.707$, while for zero interfacial velocity, we have $C = 0.5$. For film boiling outside a cylinder of diameter D, we have $C = 0.62$ and Eq. (17.3-1) calculated for $z = D$.

Wallis and Collier (from Collier and Thome, 1994) for turbulent flow in the vapor film found (vertical flat surface):

$$\frac{\alpha(z)}{\lambda_g} = 0.056 \mathrm{Re}_g^{0.2} [\mathrm{PrGr}^*]^{1/3} \qquad (17.3\text{-}2)$$

where

$$\mathrm{Gr}^* = \frac{z^3 g \rho_g (\rho_l - \rho_g)}{\eta_g^2}$$

Fung et al. (1979) developed a model which covers both the laminar and the turbulent flow. Although Eq. (17.3-1) gives good predictions in some cases (see Figure 24, where the Costigan et al. [1984] data for water in an 8 mm diameter vertical tube are compared with theoretical predictions), the vapor film is not smooth in reality (Dougall and Rohsenow, 1963), and more refined equations are necessary for a better physical description of the phenomenon (Bailey, 1971; Denham, 1984). Further experimental evidence (Bromley et al., 1953; Liu et al., 1992; Motte and Bromley, 1957; Newbold et al., 1976; Papell, 1970, 1971) can be summarized as follows: classical laminar film boiling may be a valid approximation up to 5 cm downstream of the CHF front; the heat transfer coefficient is an increasing function of the velocity and a decreasing function of the channel diameter (for film boiling inside and on tubes); the heat transfer coefficient in downflow is generally lower (up to 3–4 times) than in upflow. Information on hydrocarbons can be found in Glickstein and Whitesides (1967).

## 17.3.2 Heat Transfer in the Liquid Deficient Region

This heat transfer regime is sketched in Figure 23, and its knowledge is important in the design of high-pressure once-through steam generators and recirculation boilers. Experimental data for steam-water mixtures, up to 25 MPa, have been produced in the past (Bahr et al., 1969; Herkenrath et al., 1967; Schmidt, 1959; Swenson et al., 1961). The liquid deficient region heat transfer in circular bends has been recently experimented (Lautenschlager and Mayinger, 1986; Wang and Mayinger, 1995), together with the use of refrigerants (Lautenschlager and Mayinger, 1986; Nishikawa et al., 1986; Obot and Ishii, 1988; Wang and Mayinger, 1995; Yoo and France, 1996). Kefer et al. (1989) studied the post-CHF heat transfer in inclined evaporator tubes, while Burdunin et al. (1987) and Unal et al. (1988) investigated complex geometries.

Three types of predictive tools have been adopted for the calculation of the heat transfer coefficient (generally through wall temperature calculation), as reviewed by Groeneveld (1972) and Wang and Weisman (1983):

1) empirical correlations (no theoretical background, only functional equations between the heat transfer coefficient and independent variables)
2) correlations that take into account the thermodynamic non-equilibrium and calculate the true vapor quality and temperature
3) theoretical or semi-theoretical models

**17.3.2.1 Empirical correlations.** Many empirical correlations have been proposed for the calculation of the heat transfer coefficient, mostly based on modifications of the well-known Dittus-Boelter type equation for liquid single-phase flow. None of them takes into account non-equilibrium effects. One of the most accurate among available correlations is that proposed by Groeneveld (1973):

$$\mathrm{Nu}_g = a\left\{\mathrm{Re}_g\left[x + \frac{\rho_g}{\rho_l}(1-x)\right]\right\}^b \mathrm{Pr}_{gw}^c Y^d \qquad (17.3\text{-}3)$$

where:

$$Y = 1 - 0.1\left(\frac{\rho_l}{\rho_g} - 1\right)^{0.4}(1-x)^{0.4}$$

For tubes, $a = 1.09\,10^{-3}$; $b = 0.989$, $c = 1.41$, and $d = -1.15$, while for annuli, $a = 5.2\,10^{-2}$, $b = 0.688$, $c = 1.26$, and $d = -1.06$. For tubes and annuli, $a = 3.27\,10^{-3}$, $b = 0.901$, $c = 1.32$, and $d = -1.5$. The range of data on which correlations are based is reported in Table 1. Improvements of Eq. (17.3-3) have been given by Slaughterback et al. (1973a, 1973b).

**Table 1  Range of data for the Groeneveld correlation (1973)**

|  | Geometry | |
| --- | --- | --- |
|  | Tube | Annulus |
| Flow direction | Vertical and horizontal | Vertical |
| $D_e$, cm | 0.25 to 2.5 | 0.15 to 0.63 |
| p, MPa | 6.8 to 21.5 | 3.4 to 10.0 |
| m, kg/m²s | 700 to 5300 | 800 to 4100 |
| x, fraction by weight | 0.1 to 0.9 | 0.1 to 0.9 |
| q, kW/m² | 120 to 2100 | 450 to 2250 |
| $Nu_g$ | 95 to 1770 | 160 to 640 |
| $Re_g(x + (1-x)\rho_g/\rho_l)$ | $6.6\ 10^4$ to $1.3\ 10^6$ | $1.0\ 10^5$ to $3.9\ 10^5$ |
| $Pr_{g,w}$ | 0.88 to 2.21 | 0.91 to 1.22 |
| Y | 0.706 to 0.976 | 0.61 to 0.963 |

**17.3.2.2 Correlations accounting for thermodynamic non-equilibrium.** These correlations account for thermodynamic non-equilibrium. Theoretically, two extreme conditions would be possible, i.e.:

1) all the heat is transferred to liquid drops until their complete evaporation (complete equilibrium, hypothesis valid for very high pressure, nearly critical, and mass flux > 3000 kg/m²s);
2) all the heat is transferred to the vapor phase, causing its superheating (complete non-equilibrium, hypothesis acceptable for low pressure and low flow rate).

As generally real situations will be in between, we may think to split the heat flux in two components:

$$\dot{q}_{tot} = \dot{q}_g + \dot{q}_l \qquad (17.3\text{-}4)$$

where $\dot{q}_g$ is the component of the heat flux delivered to the vapor (which raises its temperature) and $\dot{q}_l$ is the heat flux absorbed by liquid drops (which causes their evaporation). Usually, correlations provide an evaluation of:

$$\varepsilon = \frac{\dot{q}_l}{\dot{q}_{tot}} \qquad (17.3\text{-}5)$$

through which it is possible to obtain the vapor and wall temperature with thermodynamic calculations. Such correlations have been proposed by a variety of investigators (Chen et al., 1977; Groeneveld and Delorme, 1976; Jones and Zuber, 1977; Plummer et al., 1977). That proposed by Plummer et al. (1977) is reported here:

$$\varepsilon = C_1 \ln\left[G\left(\frac{D_h}{\rho_g \sigma}\right)^{0.5} (1 - x_{CHF})^5\right] + C_2 \qquad (17.3\text{-}6)$$

**Table 2 Constant for Plummer et al. (1977) correlation**

| Fluid | C1 | C2 |
|---|---|---|
| Nitrogen | 0.082 | 0.290 |
| Water | 0.07 | 0.400 |
| R 12 | 0.078 | 0.255 |
| R 113[a] | 0.078[a] | 0.13[a] |

[a] values given by Yoo and France (1996).

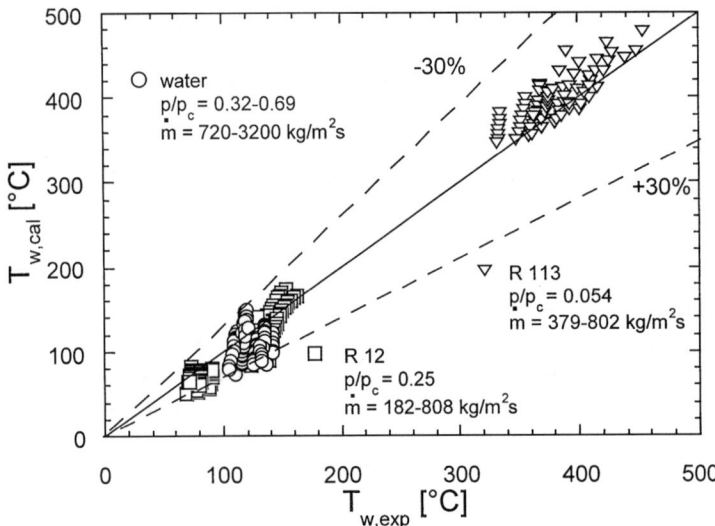

**Figure 25** Prediction of wall temperature in post-CHF heat transfer using Eq. (17.3-6), Yoo and France, 1996.

where $D_h$ is the hydraulic diameter, and the constants $C_1$ and $C_2$ have been given by authors for nitrogen, water, and R 12. More recently, Yoo and France (1996) have proposed $C_1$ and $C_2$ for R 113, showing that the parameter $C_2$ could be correlated using the molecular weight. $C_1$ and $C_2$ values are given in Table 2, while Figure 25 shows the prediction of experimental data obtained using Eq. (17.3-6).

Nishikawa et al. (1986) also proposed a method based on a non-dimensional parameter representing the ratio of the heat capacitance of the vapor flow to the thermal conductance from the vapor to the liquid droplets. Such a parameter was described as a function of non-dimensional thermodynamic parameters. Prediction of experimental data with the Nishikawa et al. correlation is shown in Figure 26.

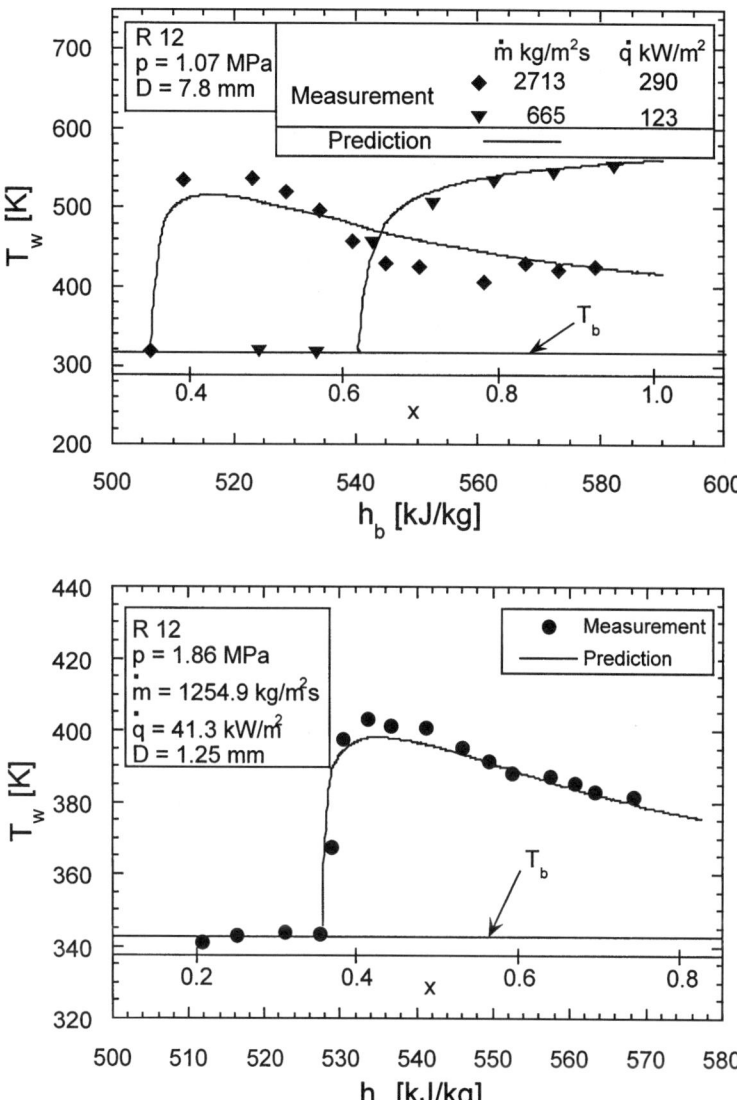

**Figure 26** Prediction of wall temperature in post-CHF heat transfer using Nishikawa et al. correlation (1986).

### 17.3.2.3 Theoretical models.
Many theoretical models have been proposed with different levels of complexity (Bennett et al., 1968; Chen et al., 1977; Ganic and Rohsenow, 1976; Groeneveld, 1972; Hein and Köhler, 1984; Iloeje et al., 1974; Kirillov et al., 1987; Moose and Ganic, 1982; Rohsenow, 1988; Whalley et al., 1982; Yagov et al., 1987). These models account in a more or less detailed way for the various heat transfer paths from the heating surface to the bulk vapor phase. Specifically, these models account for: a) the heat transferred to liquid droplets impacting on the wall, b) the heat transferred to liquid droplets entering the thermal boundary layer without 'wetting' the surface, c) the heat transferred from the heating surface to the vapor bulk by convection, d) the heat transferred from the vapor bulk to suspended droplets in the vapor core by convection, e) the heat transferred from the heating surface to liquid droplets by radiation, and f) the heat transferred from the surface to the vapor bulk by radiation. Nonetheless, following the starting assumption, not all of the above mechanisms are generally considered in a single model. Due to the complexity of the general mathematical description of existing models, the reader is referred to original papers reported in the bibliography.

## APPENDIX. CHF CALCULATION PROCEDURE IN THE CELATA ET AL. MODEL (1994C)

Input parameters $\dot{m}$, $p_{out}$, D, L, $T_{in}$. Assume a value of $\dot{q}_1$. Necessary physical properties are: $c_{pl}$, $\lambda_l$, $\eta_l$, $h_{lg}$, $\rho_l$, $\rho_g$, and $\sigma$. Where not specified, physical properties are calculated at the saturated state at $p_{out}$.

$$T_{in} + \frac{\dot{q}A}{\dot{M}c_{pl}} = \frac{5}{s^+(R)}T_{m1} + \frac{25}{s^+(R)}T_{m2} + \frac{s^+(R) - 30}{s^+(R)}T_{m3}$$

where $c_{pl}$ is calculated at $(T_m + T_{in})/2$ and $T_{m1}$, $T_{m2}$, and $T_{m3}$ are calculated from the temperature distributions:

$$T_w - T = QPrs^+ \qquad 5 > s^+ \geq 0$$

$$T_w - T = 5Q\left\{Pr + \ln\left[1 + Pr\left(\frac{s^+}{5} - 1\right)\right]\right\} \qquad 30 > s^+ \geq 5$$

$$T_w - T = 5Q\left[Pr + \ln(1 + 5Pr) + 0.5\ln\left(\frac{s^+}{30}\right)\right] \qquad s^+ \geq 30$$

$$Q = \dot{q}/\rho_l c_{pl} u_\tau$$

In the above temperature distribution equations, $c_{pl}$ is calculated at saturated conditions at $p_{out}$, $s^+$ is the non-dimensional distance from the wall, and $u_\tau$ is the friction velocity. From the above calculation, the wall temperature $T_w$ is obtained. Using the above temperature distribution equations, it is possible to calculate s*, that is, the value of the distance from the heated wall, s, at which the fluid temperature is equal to the saturation value at $p_{out}$. Calculation of $D_B$:

$$D_B = \frac{32}{f} \frac{\sigma f(\beta) \rho_l}{\dot{m}^2}$$

where $f(\beta) = 0.03$ and the friction factor f comes from

$$\frac{1}{\sqrt{f}} = 1.14 - 2.0 \log \left( \frac{0.72 \sigma \rho_l}{fD\dot{m}^2} + \frac{9.35}{Re\sqrt{f}} \right)$$

Calculation of $\delta$:

$$\delta = s^* - D_B$$

Calculation of $C_D$:

$$C_D = \frac{2}{3} \frac{D_B}{\left( \dfrac{\sigma}{g(\rho_l - \rho_g)} \right)^{0.5}}$$

Calculation of $u_B$ and $L_B$ (linked to each other) through an iterative procedure:

$$u_B = \left( \frac{2L_B g(\rho_l - \rho_g)}{\rho_l C_D} \right)^{0.5} + 0.125 \left( \delta + \frac{D_B}{2} \right) \frac{\dot{m}^2}{\rho_l \eta_1} \qquad s^+ < 5$$

$$u_B = \left( \frac{2L_B g(\rho_l - \rho_g)}{\rho_l C_D} \right)^{0.5} + 1.768\sqrt{f}\frac{\dot{m}}{\rho_l}$$
$$\times \left\{ \ln \left[ 0.354 \frac{\dot{m}}{\eta_1} \sqrt{f} \left( \delta + \frac{D_B}{2} \right) \right] - 0.61 \right\} \qquad 5 \leq s^+ < 30$$

$$u_B = \left( \frac{2L_B g(\rho_l - \rho_g)}{\rho_l C_D} \right)^{0.5} + 0.884\sqrt{f}\frac{\dot{m}}{\rho_l}$$
$$\times \left\{ \ln \left[ 0.354 \frac{\dot{m}}{\eta_1} \sqrt{f} \left( \delta + \frac{D_B}{2} \right) \right] + 2.2 \right\} \qquad s^+ \geq 30$$

where $L_B$ is given by

$$L_B = \frac{2\pi \sigma (\rho_B + \rho_l)}{\rho_B \rho_l u_B^2}$$

Calculation of $\dot{q}_2$:

$$\dot{q}_{CHF} = \frac{\rho_l \delta h_{lg}}{L_B} u_B$$

The condition of critical heat flux, $\dot{q}_{CHF}$, is reached when $\dot{q}_1 = \dot{q}_2$.

# REFERENCES

Aladyev, I. T., Miropolsky, Z. L., Doroshchuk, V. E., and Styrikovich M. A. 1961. Boiling Crisis in Tubes. *Int. Developments in Heat Transfer*, Vol. II. Paper 28, University of Colorado, Boulder.

Alekseev, G. V., Zenkevitch, B. A., Peskov, O. L., Sergeev, N. D., and Subbotin, V. I. 1965. Burnout Heat Fluxes Under Forced Water Flow. *Teploenergetika* 12(3):47–51.

Andrews, D. G., Hooper, F. C., and Butt, P. 1968. Velocity, Subcooling, and Surface Effects in the Departure from Nucleate Boiling of Organic Binaries. *Can. J. Chem. Engng.* 46:194–199.

Auracher, H. and Marroquin, A. 1995. Critical Heat Flux and Minimum Heat Flux of Film Boiling of Binary Mixtures Flowing Upwards in a Vertical Tube. *Engineering Foundation Conference on Convective Flow Boiling*, Paper V-3, Banff, May.

Bahr, A., Herkenrath, H., and Mork-Morkenstein, P. 1969. Anomale Druck-Abhängigkeit der Wärmeübertragung im Zweiphasengebeit bei Annäherung an der Kritischen Druck. *Brennstoff-Wärme-Kraft* 21(12):631–633.

Bailey, N. A. 1971. Film Boling on Submerged Vertical Cylinders. AEEW-M1051.

Barnett, P. G. 1963. An Investigation into the Validity of Certain Hypotheses Implied by Various Burnout Correlations. AEEW-R 214.

Becker K., 1971. Measurements of Burnout Conditions for Flow of Boiling Water in Horizontal Round Tubes. AERL-1262.

Bennet, A. W., Hewitt, G. F., and Keeys, R. K. F. 1968. Heat Transfer to Steam-Water Mixtures Flowing in Uniformly Heated Tubes in Which the Critical Heat Flux Has Been Exceeded. Paper 27, *Thermodynamics and Fluid Mechanics Convention*, IMechE, Bristol, March, 1968 (Also AERE-R 5573).

Bennet, A. W., Hewitt, G. F., Kearsey, H. A., Keeys, R. K. F., and Pulling, D. J. 1967. Studies of Burnout in Boiling Heat Transfer to Water in Round Tubes with Non-Uniform Heating. AERE-R 5076.

Bergel'son, B. R. 1980. Burnout Under Conditions of Subcooled Boiling and Forced Convection. *Thermal Engineering* 27(1):48–50.

Bergles, A. E. 1963. Subcooled Burnout in Tubes of Small Diameter. ASME Paper 63-WA-182.

Bergles, A. E. 1977. Burnout in Boiling Heat Transfer, Part II: Subcooled and Low-Quality Forced Convection Systems. *Nuclear Safety* 18(2):154.

Bergles, A. E. and Scarola, L. S. 1966. Effect of a Volatile Additive on the Critical Heat Flux for Surface Boiling of Water in Tubes. *Chem. Engng. Science* 21:721–723.

Bergles, A. E., Collier, J. G., Delhaye, J. M., Hewitt, G. F., and Mayinger, F. 1981. *Two-Phase Flow and Heat Transfer in the Power and Process Industries*. New York: Hemisphere Publishing Corporation.

Bertoletti, S., Gaspari, G. P., Lombardi, C., Peterlongo, G., Silvestri, M., and Tacconi, F. A. 1965. Heat Transfer Crisis with Steam-Water Mixtures. *Energia Nucleare* 12(3):121–172.

Bertoni, R., Cipriani, R., Cumo, M., and Palazzi, G. 1976. Upflow and Downflow Burnout. CNEN Report RT/ING(76)24.

Bowring, R. W. 1972. A Simple but Accurate Round Tube Uniform Heat Flux. Dryout Correlation over the Pressure Range 0.7–17 $MN/m^2$ (100–2500 psia). AAEW-R 789.

Boyd, R. D. 1985a. Subcooled Flow Boiling Critical Heat Flux (CHF) and Its Application to Fusion Energy Components. Part I: A Review of Fundamentals of CHF and Related Data Base. *Fusion Technology* 7:7–30.

Boyd, R. D. 1985b. Subcooled Flow Boiling Critical Heat Flux (CHF) and Its Application to Fusion Energy Components. Part II: A Review of Microconvective, Experimental, and Correlational Aspects. *Fusion Technology* 7:31–52.

Boyd, R. D. 1988. Subcooled Water Flow Boiling Experiments Under Uniform High Flux Conditions. *Fusion Technology* 13:131–142.

Boyd, R. D. 1989. Subcooled Water Flow Boiling at 1.66 MPa Under Uniform High Heat Flux Conditions. *ASME Winter Annual Meeting*, S. Francisco, December 10–15, HTD—Vol. 119: 9–15.

Boyd, R. D. 1990. Subcooled Water Flow Boiling Transition and the L/D Effect on CHF for a Horizontal Uniformly Heated Tube. *Fusion Technology* 18:317–324.

Bromley, L. A., LeRoy, N. R., and Robbers, J. A. 1953. Heat Transfer in Forced Convection Film Boiling. *Ind. and Engng. Chem.* 45(12):2639–2646.

Burdunin, M. N., Zvonarev, Y. A., Komendatov, A. S., and Kuzma-Kichta, Y. A. 1987. Investigation of Post-Dryout Heat Transfer in Channel of Complex Shape. *Heat Transfer—Soviet Research* 19(1):115–121.

Carne, M. 1963. Studies of the Critical Heat Flux for Some Binary Mixtures and Their Components. *Can. J. Chem. Engng.* Dec. 1963:235–240.

Celata, G. P. 1996. Critical Heat Flux in Water Subcooled Flow Boiling: Experimentation and Modeling. Keynote lecture. *Proc. 2nd European Thermal-Sciences Conference* I:27–40. Edizioni ETS, Pisa, May.

Celata, G. P. 1997. Modeling of Critical Heat Flux in Subcooled Flow Boiling. Keynote lecture. *Convective Flow and Pool Boiling Conference.* Irsee, 18–23 May, 1997.

Celata, G. P. and Cumo, M. 1996. Forced Convective Boiling of Refrigerant Binary Mixtures. Keynote lecture. *Proc. 4th International Symposium on Heat Transfer*, pp. 70–80, Beijing, September.

Celata, G. P. and Mariani, A. 1993. A Data Set of Critical Heat Flux in Water Subcooled Flow Boiling. *The 3rd Specialists' Workshop on the Thermal-Hydraulics of High Heat Flux Components in Fusion Reactors.* Ed. J. Schlosser, Cadarache, September.

Celata, G. P., Cumo, M., Inasaka, F., Mariani, A., and Nariai, H. 1993c. Influence of Channel Diameter on Subcooled Flow Boiling Burnout at High Heat Fluxes. *Int. J. Heat Mass Transfer* 36(13):3407–3410.

Celata, G. P., Cumo, M., and Mariani A. 1993a. Burnout in Highly Subcooled Water Flow Boiling in Small Diameter Tubes. *Int. J. Heat Mass Transfer* 36(5):1269–1285.

Celata, G. P., Cumo, M., and Mariani A. 1993b. Enhancement of CHF Water Subcooled Flow Boiling in Tubes Using Helically Coiled Wires. *Int. J. Heat Mass Transfer* 37(1):53–67.

Celata, G. P., Cumo, M., and Mariani, A. 1994a. Assessment of Correlations and Models for the Prediction of CHF in Subcooled Flow Boiling. *Int. J. Heat Mass Transfer* 37(2):237–255.

Celata, G. P., Cumo, M., and Mariani, A. 1997. Geometrical Effects on the Subcooled Flow Boiling Critical Heat Flux. *Proc. 4th World Conference on Experimental Heat Transfer, Fluid Mechanics, and Thermodynamics*, Vol. II:867–872. Bruxelles, 2–6 June 1997. Pisa: Edizioni, ETS.

Celata, G. P., Cumo, M., Mariani, A., Simoncini, M., and Zummo, G. 1994c. Rationalization of Existing Mechanistic Models for the Prediction of Water Subcooled Flow Boiling Critical Heat Flux. *Int. J. Heat Mass Transfer* 37(7 Suppl. 1):347–360.

Celata, G. P., Cumo, M., Mariani, A., and Zummo, G. 1995a. Preliminary Remarks on Visualization of High Heat Flux Burnout in Subcooled Water Flow Boiling. *Proc. International Symposium on Two-Phase Flow Modeling and Experimentation* 2:859–866. Rome, October.

Celata, G. P., Cumo, M., Mariani, A., and Zummo, G. 1995b. The Prediction of Critical Heat Flux in Water Subcooled Flow Boiling. *Int. J. Heat Mass Transfer* 38(6):1111–1119.

Celata, G. P., Cumo, M., and Setaro, T. 1994b. Critical Heat Flux in Upflow Convective Boiling of Refrigerant Binary Mixtures. *Int. J. Heat Mass Transfer* 37(7):1143–1153.

Chang, S. H., Baek, W. P., and Bae, T. M. 1991. A Study of Critical Heat Flux for Low Flow of Water in Vertical Round Tubes Under Low Pressure. *Nuclear Engineering and Design* 132:225–237.

Chen, J. C., Sundaram, R. K., and Ozkaynak, F. T. 1977. A Phenomenological Correlation for Post-CHF Heat Transfer. Lehigh University, NUREG-0237.

Collier, J. G. and Thome, J. R. 1994. *Convective Boiling and Condensation.* Oxford: Clarendon Press.

Costigan, G., Holmes, A. W., and Ralph, J. C. 1984. Steady-State Post-Dryout Heat Transfer in a Vertical Tube with Low Inlet Quality. *Proc. 1st UK National Heat Transfer Conference* 1:1–11 (IChemE Symp. Ser., 86).
Cumo, M., Fabrizi, F., and Palazzi, G. 1978. The Influence of Inclination on CHF in Steam Generator Channels. CNEN Report RT/ING (78)11.
Cumo, M., Palazzi, G., Urbani, G., and Frazzoli, F. V. 1980. Full Scale Tests on Axial Profile Heat Flux Influence on the Critical Quality in PWR Steam Generators. CNEN Report RT/ING (80)5.
Denham, M. K. 1984. Inverted Annular Flow Film Boiling and the Bromley Model. *Proc. 1st UK National Heat Transfer Conference* 1:13–23 (IChemE Symp. Ser. 86).
Doroshchuk, V. E., Levitan, L. L., and Lantzman, F. P. 1975. Investigation into Burnout in Uniformly Heated Tubes. ASME Publication 75-WA/HT-22.
Doroschuk, V. E., Levitan, L. L., Lantzman, E. P., Nigmatulin, R. I., and Borevsky, L. Ya. 1978. Investigation into Burnout Mechanism in Steam-Generating Tubes. *Proc. 6th International Heat Transfer Conference* 1:393–398. New York: Hemisphere.
Dougall, R. S. and Rohsenow, W. M. 1963. Film Boiling on the Inside of Vertical Tubes with Upward Flow of the Fluid at Low Qualities. *Mech. Engng. Dept. Engineering Project Laboratory*, MIT Report 9079–26.
Fiori, M. P. and Bergles, A. E. 1968. Model of Critical Heat Flux in Subcooled Flow Boiling. MIT Report-DSR 70281-56.
Fiori, M. P. and Bergles, A. E. 1970. Model of Critical Heat Flux in Subcooled Flow Boiling. *Proc. 4th International Heat Transfer Conference* VI, paper B6.3.
Fung, K. K., Gardiner, S. R. M., and Groeneveld, D. C. 1979. Subcooled and Low Quality Flow Boiling of Water at Atmospheric Pressure. *Nuclear Engineering and Design* 55:51–57.
Gambill, W. R. 1968. Burnout in Boiling Heat Transfer, Part II: Subcooled Forced-Convection Systems. *Nuclear Safety* 9(6):467.
Ganic, E. N. and Rohsenow, W. M. 1976. Dispersed Flow Heat Transfer. *Int. J. Heat Mass Transfer* 20:855–866.
Gaspari, G. P. 1993. Comparison Among Data of Electrically and E-Beam Heated Tubes. *Proc. 3rd International Workshop on High Heat Flux Components Thermal Hydraulics in Fusion Reactors*. Ed. J. Schlosser, Cadarache, September.
Glickstein, M. R. and Whitesides, R. H. 1967. Forced Convection Nucleate and Film Boiling of Several Aliphatic Hydrocarbons. ASME Paper 67-HT-7. *ASME-AIChE Heat Transfer*, Seattle.
Govan, A. H. 1984. Comparison of the Harwell Annular Flow Model with Critical Heat Flux Data. AERE-R 11298.
Govan, A. H., Hewitt, G. F., Owen, D. G., and Bott, T. R. 1988. An Improved CHF Modeling Code. *Proc. 2nd UK National Conference on Heat Transfer* 1:33–48. IMechE, 14–16 September.
Groeneveld, D. C. 1972. The Thermal Behavior of a Heated Surface at and Beyond Dryout. *Atomic Energy of Canada Report*, AECL-4309.
Groeneveld, D. C. 1973. Post-Dryout Heat Transfer at Reactor Operating Conditions. AECL-4513.
Groeneveld, D. C. 1981. Heat Transfer Phenomena Related to the Boiling Crisis. AECL-7239, Chalk River National Laboratory.
Groeneveld, D. C. and Delorme, G. G. J. 1976. Prediction of the Thermal Non-Equilibrium in the Post-Dryout Regime. *Nuclear Engineering and Design* 36:17–26.
Groeneveld, D. C., Cheng, S. C., and Doan, T. 1986. 1986 AECL-UO Critical Heat Flux Look-up Table. *Heat Transfer Engineering* 7:46–62.
Groeneveld, D. C., Leung, L. K. H., Kirillov, P. L., Bobkov, V. P., Smogalev, I. P., Vinogradov, V. N., Huang, X. C., and Royer, E. 1996. The 1995 Look-up Table for Critical Heat Flux in Tubes. *Nuclear Engineering and Design* 163:1–23.
Gunther, F. C. 1951. Photographic Study of Surface-Boiling Heat Transfer to Water with Forced Convection. *Trans. ASME* 73(2):115–123.

Hancox, W. T. and Nicoll, W. B. 1973. On the Dependence of the Flow-Boiling Heat Transfer Crisis on Local Near-Wall Conditions. ASME, 73-HT-38.
Hebel, W., Detavernier, A., and Decreton, M. 1981. A Contribution to the Hydrodynamics of Boiling Crisis in a Forced Flow of Water. *Nuclear Engineering and Design* 64:433–445.
Hein, D. and Köhler, W. 1984. A Simple-To-Use Post-Dryout Heat Transfer Model Accounting for Thermal Non-Equilibrium. Report USNRC-NUREG/CP-0060, 369–372.
Herkenrath, H., Mork-Morkenstein, P., Jung U., and Weckermann, F. J. 1967. Heat Transfer in Water with Forced Circulation in 140–150 Bar Pressure Range. EUR 3658d.
Hewitt, G. F. 1978. Critical Heat Flux in Flow Boiling. *Proc. 6th International Heat Transfer Conference*, Toronto. Volume 6:143–171.
Hewitt, G. F. 1980. Burnout. In: *Handbook of Multiphase Systems*. Ed. Hetsroni G., McGrawHill. pp. 6.66–6.141.
Hewitt, G. F. and Govan, A. G. 1989. Phenomenological Modeling of Non-Equilibrium Flows with Phase Change. *Proc. EUROTHERM Seminar 7, Thermal Non-Equilibrium in Two-Phase Flow* pp. 7–40, ENEA, 23–24 March.
Hewitt, G. F. and Hall-Taylor, N. S. 1970. *Annular Two-Phase Flow*. New York: Pergamon Press.
Hewitt, G. F., Kearsey, H. A., Lacey, P. M. C., and Pulling, D. J. 1963. Burnout and Nucleation in Climbing Film Flow. *Int. J. Heat Mass Transfer* 8:793.
Hewitt, G. F., Kearsey, H. A., Lacey, P. M. C., and Pulling, D. J. 1965. Burnout and Film Flow in the Evaporation of Water in Tubes. *Proc. Inst. Mech. Eng.* 80(3C):206.
Hino, R. and Ueda, T. 1985. Studies on Heat Transfer and Flow Characteristics in Subcooled Flow Boiling—Part 2: Flow Characteristics. *Int. J. Multiphase Flow* 11:283–298.
Hsu, Y. Y. and Graham, R. W. 1986. *Transport Processes in Boiling and Two-Phase Systems*. La Grange Park, IL: American Nuclear Society.
Iloeje, O. C., Plummer, D. N., Rohsenow, W. M., and Griffith, P. 1974. A Study of Wall Rewet and Heat Transfer in Dispersed Vertical Flow. *Mech. Engng. Dept. MIT*, Report 72718-92, September.
Inasaka, F. and Nariai, H. 1996. Evaluation of Subcooled Critical Heat Flux Correlations for Tubes with and Without Internal Twisted Tapes. *Nuclear Engineering and Design* 163:225–239.
Jones, O. C. and Zuber, N. 1977. Post-CHF Heat Transfer—A Non-Equilibrium Relaxation Model. ASME Paper 77-HT-79. *17th National Heat Transfer Conference*, Salt Lake City, August.
Katto, Y. 1986. Forced-Convection Boiling in Uniformly Heated Channels. In: *Handbook of Heat and Mass Transfer, Volume 1: Heat Transfer Operations*. Ed. Cheremisinoff, N.P., Chapter 9, pp. 303–325. Houston: Gulf Publishing Company.
Katto, Y. 1990a. A Physical Approach to Critical Heat Flux of Subcooled Flow Boiling in Round Tubes. *Int. J. Heat Mass Transfer* 33(4):611–620.
Katto, Y. 1990b. Prediction of Critical Heat Flux of Subcooled Flow Boiling in Round Tubes. *Int. J. Heat Mass Transfer* 33(9):1921–1928.
Katto, Y. 1992. A Prediction Model of Subcooled Water Flow Boiling CHF for Pressure in the Range 0.1–20 MPa. *Int. J. Heat Mass Transfer* 35(5):1115–1123.
Katto, Y. 1994. Critical Heat Flux. *Int. J. Multiphase Flow* 20(Suppl.):563–590.
Katto, Y. 1995. Critical Heat Flux Mechanisms. Keynote Lecture V. *Proc. Eng. Foundation Convective Flow Boiling Conference*, Banff, May.
Katto, Y. and Ohno, H. 1984. An Improved Version of the Generalized Correlation of Critical Heat Flux for the Forced Convective Boiling in Uniformly Heated Vertical Tubes. *Int. J. Heat Mass Transfer* 26(8):1641–1648.
Keeys, R. K. F., Ralph, J. C., and Roberts, D. N. 1972. Post Burnout Heat Transfer in High Pressure Steam-Water Mixtures in a Tube with Cosine Heat Flux Distribution. *Progress in Heat and Mass Transfer* 6:99–118.
Kefer, V., Köhler, W., and Kastner, W. 1989. Critical Heat Flux (CHF) and Post-CHF Heat Transfer in Horizontal and Inclined Evaporator Tubes. *Int. J. Multiphase Flow* 15(3):385–392.

Kirby, G. J., Staniforth, R., and Kinneir, J. H. 1967. A Visual Study of Forced Convective Boiling. Part II: Flow Patterns and Burnout for a Round Test Section. AEEW-R506.

Kirillov, P. L., Kahcheyev, V. M., Muranov, Y. V., and Yuriev, Y. S. 1987. A Two-Dimensional Mathematical Model of Annular-Dispersed and Dispersed Flows—Parts I and II. *Int. J. Heat Mass Transfer* 30(4):791–806.

Kramer, T. J. 1976. Fluid Flow and Convective Heat Transfer in Square Capillary Ducts Subjected to Nonuniform High Heat Flux. ASME Paper 76-WA-HT-29.

Kutateladze, S. S. and Leontiev, A. I. 1966. Some Applications of the Asymptotic Theory of the Turbulent Boundary Layer. *Proc. 3rd International Heat Transfer Conference* 3:1–6, Chicago, IL, August.

Lautenschlager, G. and Mayinger, F. 1986. Post-Dryout Heat Transfer to R 12 in a Circular 90-Deg-Tube-Bend. *Proc. 8th International Heat Transfer Conference* 6:2373–2378.

Lee, C. H. and Mudawar, I. 1988. A Mechanistic Critical Heat Flux Model for Subcooled Flow Boiling Based on Local Bulk Flow Conditions. *Int. J. Multiphase Flow* 14:711–728.

Lee, D. H. 1965. An Experimental Investigation of Forced Convection Burnout in High Pressure Water. Part 4. Large Diameter Tubes at About 1600 psia. AEEW-R 479.

Lee, D. H. 1977. Prediction of Burnout, in Two-Phase Flow and Heat Transfer. Eds. Butterworth, D. and Hewitt, G. F., pp. 295–322. Oxford: Oxford University Press.

Lee, D. H., and Obertelli, J. D. 1963. An Experimental Investigation of Forced Convection Boiling in High Pressure Water. Part I, AEEW-R 213.

Lin, W. S., Lee, C. H., and Pei, B. S. 1989. An Improved Theoretical Critical Heat Flux Model for Low-Quality Flow. *Nuclear Technology* 88:294–306.

Liu, Q. S., Shiotsu, M., and Sakurai, A. 1992. A Correlation for Forced Convection Film Boiling Heat Transfer from a Hot Cylinder Under Subcooled Conditions. *Fundamentals of Subcooled Flow Boiling*, HTD-Vol. 217:21–32.

Lombardi, C. and Mazzola, A. 1998. A Criterion Based on Independent Parameters for Distinguishing Departure from Nucleate Boiling and Dryout in Water Cooled Systems. *Revue Generale de Thermique* 37(1):31–38.

Mattson, R. J., Hammit, F. G., and Tong, L. S. 1973. A Photographic Study of the Subcooled Flow Boiling Crisis in Freon-113. ASME Paper 73-HT-39.

Mazzola, A. 1997. Integrating Artificial Neural Networks and Empirical Correlations for the Prediction of Water Subcooled Critical Heat Flux. *Revue Generale de Thermique* 36(11):799–806.

Merilo, M. 1977. Critical Heat Flux Experiments in a Vertical and Horizontal Tube with Both Freon-12 and Water as Coolant. *Nuclear Engineering and Design* 44(1):1–16.

Mishima, K. 1984. Boiling Burnout at Low Flow Rate and Low Pressure Conditions. Ph.D. Thesis, Kyoto University, Japan.

Moon, S. K. and Chang, S. H. 1994. Classification and Prediction of the Critical Heat Flux Using Fuzzy Clustering and Artificial Neural Networks. *Nuclear Engineering and Design* 150:151–161.

Moon, S. K., Baek, W. P., and Chang, S. H. 1996. Parametric Trends Analysis of the Critical Heat Flux Based on Artifical Neural Networks. *Nuclear Engineering and Design* 163:29–49.

Moose, R. A. and Ganic, E. N. 1982. On the Calculation of Wall Temperatures in the Post-Dryout Heat Transfer Region. *Int. J. Multiphase Flow* 8(5):525–542.

Mori, H., Yoshida, S., Ohno, M., Kusumoto, K., and Itoh, T. 1990. Critical Heat Flux for Non-Azeotropic Binary Mixtures at High Pressures. *Proceedings of JSME*, No. 908-2, Saga, pp. 210–214.

Motte, E. I. and Bromley, L. A. 1957. Film Boiling of Flowing Subcooled Liquids. *Ind. and Engng. Chem.* 49(11):1921–1928.

Naboichenko, K. V., Kiryutin, A. A., and Gribov, B. S. 1965. A Study of Critical Heat Flux with Forced Flow of Monoisopropyldeiphenyl-Benzene Mixture. *Teploenergetika* 12(11):81–86.

Nariai, H. and Inasaka, F. 1992. Critical Heat Flux and Flow Characteristics of Subcooled Flow Boiling with Water in Narrow Tubes. In: *Dynamics of Two-Phase Flows.* Eds. Jones, O. C. and Michiyoshi, I., pp. 689–708, CRC Press.

Nariai, H., Inasaka, F., and Shimura, T. 1987. Critical Heat Flux of Subcooled Flow Boiling in Narrow Tube. *ASME-JSME Thermal Engineering Joint Conference,* Honolulu, March.

Nariai, H., Inasaka, F., Ishikawa, A., and Fujisaki, W. 1992. Critical Heat Flux of Subcooled Flow Boiling in Tube with Internal Twisted Tape Under Non-Uniform Heating Conditions. *Proc. 2nd JSME-KSME Thermal Engineering Conference* 3:285–288.

Newbold, F. J., Ralph, J. C., and Ralph, J. A. 1976. Post-Dryout Heat Transfer Under Low Flow and Low Quality Conditions. AERE-R 8390.

Nishikawa, K., Yoshida, S., Mori, H., and Takamatsu, H. 1986. Post-Dryout Heat Transfer to Freon in a Vertical Tube at High Subcritical Pressures. *Int. J. Heat Mass Transfer* 29(8):1245–1251.

Obot, N. T. and Ishii, M. 1988. Two-Phase Flow Regime Transition Criteria in Post-Dryout Region Based on Flow Visualization Experiments. *Int. J. Heat Mass Transfer* 31(12):2559–2570.

Papell, S. S., 1970. Buoyancy Effects on Liquid Nitreogen Film Boiling in Vertical Flow. *Advances in Cryogenic Engng.* 16:435–444.

Papell, S. S. 1971. Film Boiling of Cryogenic Hydrogen During Upward and Downward Flow. Paper NASA-TMX-67855. *13th Int. Congress on Refrigeration,* Washington.

Papell, S. S., Simoneau, R. J., and Brown, D. D. 1966. Buoyancy Effects on Critical Heat Flux of Forced Convective Boiling in Vertical Flow. NASA-TND-3672.

Plummer, D. N., Griffith, P., and Rohsenow, W. M. 1977. Post-Critical Heat Transfer to Flowing Liquid in a Vertical Tube. *J. Heat Transfer* 4:151–158.

Purcupile, J. C. and Gouse, S. W. Jr. 1972. Reynolds Flux Model of Critical Heat Flux in Subcooled Forced Convection Boiling. ASME Paper 72-HT-4.

Rohsenow, W. M. 1988. Post-Dryout Heat Transfer Prediction Method. *Int. Comm. Heat Mass Transfer* 15:559–569.

Schmidt, K. R. 1959. Wärmetechnische Untersuchungen and Hoch Belasteten Kesselheizflächen. *Mitteinlungen der Vereinigung der Grosskessel-Bezitzer,* December, 391–401.

Slaughterback, D. C., Veseley, E. W., Ybarrondo, L. J., Condie, K. G., and Mattson, R. J. 1973a. Statistical Regression Analyses of Experimental Data for Flow Film Boiling Heat Transfer. *ASME-AIChE Heat Transfer Conference,* Atlanta, August.

Slaughterback, D. C., Ybarrondo, L. J., and Obenchain, C. F. 1973b. Flow Film Boiling Heat Transfer Correlations—Parametric Study with Data Comparison. *ASME-AIChE Heat Transfer Conference,* August, Atlanta, GA.

Smith, R. A. 1986. Boiling Inside Tubes: Critical Heat Flux for Upward Flow in Uniformly Heated Tubes. ESDU Data Item No. 86032. London: Engineering Science Data Unit Inter- national Ltd.

Smogalev, I. P. 1981. Calculation of Critical Heat Fluxes with Flow of Subcooled Water at Low Velocity. *Thermal Engineering* 28(4):208–211.

Staub, F. W. 1968. The Void Fraction in Subcooled Boiling—Prediction of Vapor Volumetric Fraction. *J. Heat Transfer* 90:151–157.

Sterman, L., Abramov, A., and Checheta, G. 1968. Investigation of Boiling Crisis at Forced Motion of High Temperature Organic Heat Carriers and Mixtures. *Int. Symposium on Research into Co-Current Gas-Liquid Flow,* Univ. of Waterloo, Ontario, Canada, Paper E2.

Styrikovich, M. A., Newstrueva, E. I., and Dvorina, G. M. 1970. The Effect of Two-Phase Flow Pattern on the Nature of Heat Transfer Crisis in Boiling. *Proc. 4th International Heat Transfer Conference* 9:360–362. New York: Hemisphere.

Swenson, H. S., Carver, J. R., and Szoeke, G. 1961. The Effects of Nucleate Boiling Versus Film Boiling on Heat Transfer in Power Boiler Tubes. ASME Paper 61-W-201, *ASME Winter Annual Meeting,* New York, 26 November–1 December.

Theofanous, T. G. 1996. Introduction to a Round Table Discussion on Reactor Power Margins. *Nuclear Engineering and Design* 163:213–282.

Thom, J. R. S., Walker, W. W., Fallon, T. A., and Reising, G. F. S. 1965. Boiling in Subcooled Water During Flow Up Heated Tubes or Annuli. *Symposium on Boiling Heat Transfer in Steam Generating Units and Heat Exchangers*, Paper 6, Manchester, IMechE, September.

Thorgerson, E. J., Knoebel, D. H., and Gibbons, J. G. 1974. A Model to Predict Convective Subcooled Critical Heat Flux. *J. Heat Transfer* 96:79–82.

Tippets, F. E. 1962. Critical Heat Fluxes and Flow Patterns in High Pressure Boiling Water Flows. Paper 62-WA-162, presented at the ASME Winter Annual Meeting, New York, 25–30 November.

Tolubinsky, V. I. and Matorin P. S. 1973. Forced Convective Boiling Heat Transfer Crisis with Binary Mixtures. *Heat Transfer—Soviet Research* 5(2):98–101.

Tong, L. S. 1966. Boundary Layer Analysis of the Flow Boiling Crisis. *Proc. 3rd International Heat Transfer Conference* III:1–6. New York: Hemisphere.

Tong, L. S. 1968. Boundary-Layer Analysis of the Flow Boiling Crisis. *Int. J. Heat Mass Transfer* 11:1208–1211.

Tong, L. S. 1969. Critical Heat Fluxes in Rod Bundles. *Proc. Symp. on Two-Phase Flow and Heat Transfer in Rod Bundles*. ASME Winter Annual Meeting, Los Angeles, CA, pp. 31–46.

Tong, L. S. 1975. A Phenomenological Study of Critical Heat Flux. ASME Paper 75-HT-68.

Tong, L. S. and Hewitt, G. F. 1972. Overall View Point of Film Boiling CHF Mechanisms. ASME Paper No. 72-HT-54.

Tong, L. S., Currin, H. B., Larsen, P. S., and Smith, O. G. 1965. Influence of Axially Non-Uniform Heat Flux on DNB. *AIChE Symposium Series* 64:35–40.

Tong, L. S., Currin, H. B., Larsen, P. S., and Smith, D. G. 1966. Influence of Axially Non-Uniform Heat Flux on DNB. *Chem. Eng. Prog. Symp. Ser.* 62(64):35.

Tong, L. S., Currin, H. B., and Thorp, A. G. 1968. An Evaluation of the Departure from Nucleate Boiling in Bundles of Reactor Fuel Rods. *Nuclear Science Engineering* 33:7–15.

Unal, C., Tuzla, K., Badr, O., Neti, S., and Chen, J. C. 1988. Parametric Trends for Post-CHF Heat Transfer in Rod Bundles. *J. Heat Transfer* 110:721–727.

van der Molen, S. B. and Galjee, F. W. B. M. 1978. The Boiling Mechanism During Burnout Phenomena in Subcooled Two-Phase Water Flow. *Proc. 6th International Heat Transfer Conference* 1:381–385, New York: Hemisphere.

Vandervort, C. L., Bergles, A. E., and Jensen, M. K. 1992. The Ultimate Limits of Forced Convective Subcooled Boiling Heat Transfer. RPI Interim Report HTL-9 DE-FG02-89ER14019.

Wang, M. J. and Mayinger F. 1995. Post-Dryout Dispersed Flow in Circular Bends. *Int. J. Multiphase Flow* 21(3):437–454.

Wang, S. W. and Weisman, J. 1983. Post-Critical Heat Flux Heat Transfer: A Survey of Current Correlations and Their Applicability. *Progress in Nuclear Energy* 12(2):149–168.

Weatherhead, R. J. 1963. Nucleate Boiling Characteristics and the Critical Heat Flux Occurrence in Subcooled Axial Flow Water Systems. ANL 6675.

Weisman, J. 1992. The Current Status of Theoretically Based Approaches to the Prediction of the Critical Heat Flux in Flow Boiling. *Nuclear Technology* 99:1–21.

Weisman, J. and Ileslamlou, S. 1988. A Phenomenological Model for Prediction of Critical Heat Flux Under Highly Subcooled Conditions. *Fusion Technology* 13:654–659 (Corrigendum in Fusion Technology 15:1463–1989).

Weisman, J. and Pei, B. S. 1983. Prediction of Critical Heat Flux in Flow Boiling at Low Qualities. *Int. J. Heat Mass Transfer* 26:1463–1477.

Weisman, J. and Ying, S. H. 1983. Theoretically Based CHF Prediction at Low Qualities and Intermediate Flows. *Transactions American Nuclear Society* 45:832–833.

Whalley, P. B. 1987. *Boiling, Condensation, and Gas-Liquid Flow*. Oxford: Clarendon Press, pp. 163–166.

Whalley, P. B., Azzopardi, B. J., Hewitt, G. F., and Owen, R. G. 1982. A Physical Model of Two-Phase Flow with Thermodynamic and Hydrodynamic Non-Equilibrium. *Proc. 7th International Heat Transfer Conference* 5:181–188, Munich, August.

Whalley, P. B., Hutchinson, P., and Hewitt, G. F. 1974. The Calculation of Critical Heat Flux in Forced Convection Boiling. *Proc. 5th Int. Heat Transfer Conference*, Tokyo, Paper B6.11.

Yagov, V. V., Puzin, V. A., and Kudryavtsev, A. A. 1987. Investigation of the Boiling Crisis and Heat Transfer in Dispersed-Film Boiling of Liquids in Channels. *Heat Transfer—Soviet Research* 19(1):1–8.

Yapo, T., Embrechts, M. J., Cathey, S. T., and Lahey, R. T. 1992. Prediction of Critical Heat Fluxes Using a Hybrid Kohonen-Backpropagation Neural Networks. In: *Topics in Intelligent Engineering Systems Through Artificial Neural Networks*, Volume 2. Eds. Dali C. H., et al., New York: ASME Press.

Yin, S. T., Liu, T. J., Huang, Y. D., and Tain, R. M. 1988. An Investigation of the Limiting Quality Phenomenon of Critical Heat Flux. In: *Particulate Phenomena and Multiphase Transport*, Volume 2. Eds. Veziroglu, T. S., pp. 157–173. Washington: Hemisphere Publishing Corporation.

Yoo, S. J. and France, D. M. 1996. Post-CHF Heat Transfer with Water and Refrigerants. *Nuclear Engineering and Design* 163:163–175.

CHAPTER
# EIGHTEEN

## FLOW BOILING AUGMENTATION

**18.1, 18.2   Satish G. Kandlikar**

*Rochester Institute of Technology, Rochester, NY 14623, USA*

**18.3   Gian Piero Celata**

*ENEA National Institute of Thermal-Fluid Dynamics, Rome, Italy*

**18.3   Andrea Mariani**

*ENEA National Institute of Thermal-Fluid Dynamics, Rome, Italy*


## 18.1 AUGMENTATION OF SUBCOOLED BOILING HEAT TRANSFER

The augmentation of subcooled flow boiling can be accomplished in two ways. In the partial boiling region, the single phase contribution to heat transfer can be increased by the use of fins, twisted tapes, and similar devices used in augmenting heat transfer in single phase flow. Another way is by increasing the nucleate boiling contribution, which is beneficial in partial as well as fully developed boiling regions. Some techniques focus on initiating the nucleate boiling sooner, either by decreasing the local pressure through vibrations or by modifying the nucleation characteristics of the surface.

Mechanical vibrations effectively cause localized pressure fluctuations in the liquid adjacent to a heat transfer surface. When the liquid is close to its saturation temperature, enhancement is possible from nucleation and collapse of bubbles on the heater surface. Bergles (1964) used this in cooling of high-field electromagnets. To enhance the heat transfer to water flowing in the cooling channels, the channel walls were subjected to vibrations. The localized instantaneous reduction in pressure during a cycle resulted in cavitation in the water at the channel walls. For wall temperatures of about 30 °C below the saturation temperature, the single-phase heat transfer coefficient remained unaffected. However, as the wall temperature approached the saturation temperature, the heat transfer coefficient gradually increased, yielding up to a 100 percent increase. The enhancement was reduced, as fully developed boiling conditions were established at higher wall temperatures. The effect of ultrasonic vibrations was tested further by Bergles and Newell (1965) with water flowing in annuli. They provided experimental results in a parametric form to show the effect of system pressure, annulus dimensions, vibration intensity, and wall superheat. The presence of vapor in the flow channel drastically reduced the enhancement, indicating the applicability of this technique only in the subcooled region.

Hysteresis effects delay the beginning of the nucleation, especially in highly wetting systems such as fluorinerts used in electronic cooling application. The effects of vibrations on causing early nucleation has been reported for pool boiling by a number of investigators. For example, Liaou and di Marzo (1995) showed that the application of selective frequencies between 180 and 200 Hz initiated fully developed pool boiling in Freon-113 systems with wall superheats of 35 to 40 K prior to nucleation. Similar studies are needed to determine the optimum frequency of vibration for specific systems.

The effect of porous coating on subcooled flow boiling was studied by Ammerman and You (1998). A porous coating was applied to the heated walls of the square horizontal channels with 0.5 and 2 mm heights. The heat transfer and pressure drop characteristics of these channels were investigated with flowing FC-87 by varying flow velocity and subcooling.

Figure 1 shows illustrative results from Ammerman and You (1998). The flow velocity is 1.25 m/s in a 2-mm square channel. The porous coating results in early nucleation at low wall superheats, as compared to the uncoated channels at all flow velocities and subcooling levels. At higher wall superheats, the boiling becomes dominated by convective effects, and the performance of the uncoated channels approaches that of the coated channels. At lower velocities (not shown here), the convective effects remain small, and the performance of the coated channels exceeds that of the uncoated channels in the entire range of testing, extending to about 35 K wall superheat.

Figure 2 shows an interesting feature of the subcooled boiling performance of coated surfaces. In this figure, the pressure drop is plotted against the heat flux. It is seen that at high levels of subcooling such as 15 K or 24 K, though the heat transfer is improved significantly as seen from Figure 1, there is virtually no pressure drop penalty. This is due to the collapse of the nucleating bubbles while they are still attached to the wall or immediately upon their release in the flow. This type of heat transfer enhancement in subcooled flow boiling is therefore highly desirable.

Electrohydrodynamic (EHD) phenomenon causes fluid motion and interfacial instabilities that can result in dramatically altering the bubble motion and departure. This phenomenon has been successfully applied in pool boiling and saturated flow boiling applications (see Chapter 5 and Section 18.2). It is expected that

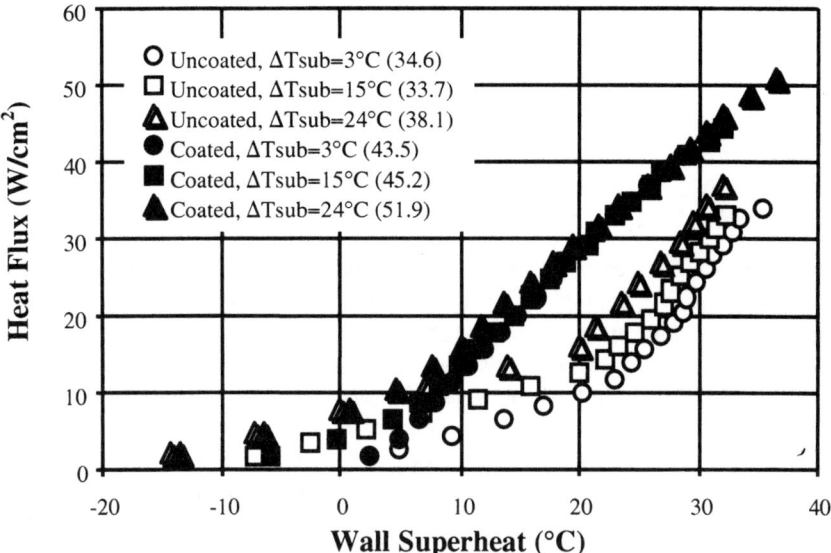

**Figure 1** Heat transfer characteristics for 2-mm square and 80-mm long channel with and without porous surface coating, FC-87 with exit pressure of 100 kPa, Ammerman and You (1998), reproduced with permission.

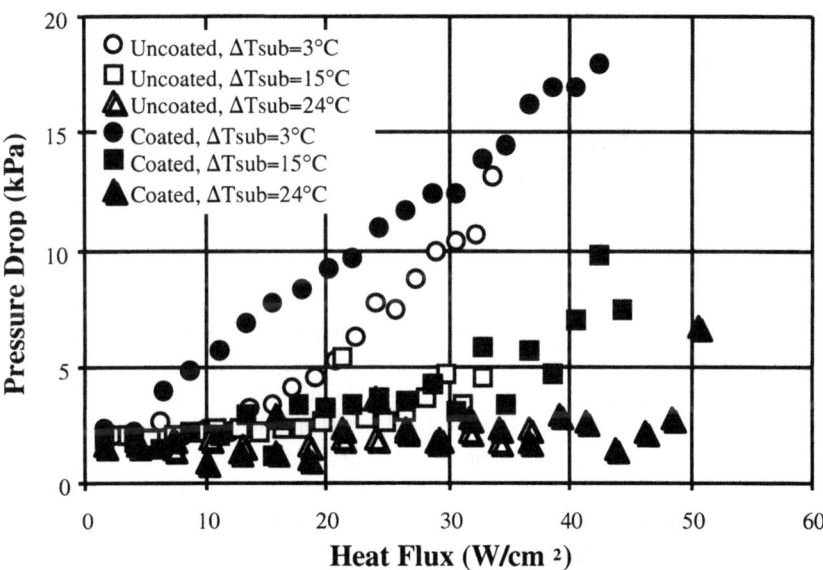

**Figure 2** Pressure drop characteristics for 2-mm square and 80-mm long channel with and without porous surface coating, FC-87 with exit pressure of 100 kPa, Ammerman and You (1998), reproduced with permission.

similar benefits can be derived for subcooled boiling application, as the bubble activity can be controlled to provide the intended bubble motion on the heater, resulting in significant heat transfer improvements. Further research in this area is warranted.

## 18.2 AUGMENTATION OF SATURATED FLOW BOILING HEAT TRANSFER

Augmentation devices used for flow inside tubes can be broadly categorized into two types, depending on whether the nucleate boiling mechanism or the convective mechanism is augmented. Specially designed structured and porous surfaces and the application of electohydrodynamic fields enhance the nucleate boiling component, while devices such as internal fins, twisted tapes, helical wire inserts, microfins, and corrugations are mainly employed to enhance the convective component. The nucleate boiling augmentation devices are suitable where nucleate boiling is dominant, such as at low qualities and at high heat fluxes, while the convective boiling augmentation devices are suitable in the high quality range.

Excellent surveys of the augmentation devices are provided by Bergles (1987), Thome (1990), and Webb (1994). Here, only a brief survey is presented, with special attention to the recent developments and future applications.

### 18.2.1 Microfin Tubes

Microfin or grooved tubes represent the fastest growing augmentation technique for in-tube evaporator application in refrigeration industry. Fujie et al. (1977) of Hitachi Cable Ltd. are attributed with the development of the first microfin tube. The basic geometry has multi-start spiral grooves of approximately 0.2 mm height and 19° spiral angle. The profile, depth of the grooves, and the spiral angle influence performance of the microfin tubes. There are, however, multitudes of configurations tested by manufacturers in an effort to optimize the performance for specific refrigerant and application. Due to the current research interest in microfin tubes, there are a large number of papers published every year. Webb (1994) presents a comprehensive compilation of microfin research until 1992. Table 1 lists some of the published work, as compiled by Kandlikar and Raykoff (1997).

The effect of microfin profile on heat transfer and pressure drop performance during evaporation and condensation of refrigerants was studied by Khanpara et al. (1987). Their experimental study identified the best performing tube and provided some guidelines for enhancing performance.

Yoshida et al. (1987) conducted experiments with microfin tubes having a minimum diameter of 11.4 mm and groove depths of 0.24 and 0.15 mm with

Table 1 Summary of the experimental data sets on flow boiling in microfin tubes, Kandlikar and Raykoff (1996)

| Researcher | Tube OD (mm) | Tube material | Refrigerant | Test setup[a] | Data[b] | Quality% | Mass flux Kg/m$^2$s | Heat flux kW/m$^2$ | Efmax% | Parameters varied |
|---|---|---|---|---|---|---|---|---|---|---|
| Ito and Kimura, 1979 | 12.7 | Cu/Al | R-22 | ER | loc | 25–90 | 14–230 | | 200 | p, b, f, G, q |
| Shinohara and Tobe,** 1985 | 9.52 | | R-22 | | avg | 60 | | | 250 | n, b, s, f, G |
| Khanpara et al., 1986 | 9.52 | Cu | R-113 | ER | loc | 15–85 | 200–600 | 11–55 | 200 | n, p, b, s, f, G |
| Khanpara et al., 1987a | 9.52 | Cu | R-113 | ER | avg/loc | 10–90 | 200–600 | 11–55 | 270 | n, p, b, s, f, G, q |
| Khanpara et al.,* 1987b | 9.52 | Cu | R-22/R-113 | ER | loc | 2.5–75 | 248–600 | 7.1–39.7 | 220 | G, q |
| Schlager et al., 1990 | 11.7/12.7 | Cu | R-22 | HE | avg | 15–85 | 75–400 | | 220 | D, G, f, b, n, q |
| Reid et al.,* 1991 | 9.53 | Cu | R-113 | ER | loc | 0–75 | 370–380 | 18–26 | 160 | q |
| Eckels et al., 1992 | 7.9/9.5 | Cu | R-22 | HE | avg | 8–88 | 135–400 | | 150 | D, G, s |
| Ha and Bergles,* 1993 | 9.5 | Cu | R-22/oil[d] | ER | loc | 20–100 | 25–100 | 5–10 | 150 | G, q |
| Chiang, 1993 | 7.5/10 | Cu | R-22/1% oil | HE | q-loc | 15–100+ | 135–400 | | | D, n, b, G |
| Thors and Bogart, 1994 | 9.5/15.9 | Cu | R-22 | HE | avg | 10–80 | 75–500 | 11–58 | | D, G, n, b, f |
| Chamra and Webb, 1995 | — | Cu | R-22 | HE | avg | 0.1–0.9 | 255–327 | 17.3–26.5 | 230 | g, q, T |
| Koyama et al.,* 1995 | 10 | Cu | R-22/R-134a/R-12 | HE | q-loc | 0–100 | 200–400 | 5–64 | 200 | G, q |
| Singh et al., 1996 | 12.7 | Cu | R-134a | ER | loc | 5–75 | 50–150 | 5–30 | | G, q |

[a] ER—Electrical resistance heating, HE—annular heat exchanger
[b] avg-average, loc-local, q-loc quasi-local (segmented test setup)
[c] Max reported factor over plain tube performance
[d] Pure refrigerant and refrigerant/oil mixtures * denotes data used by Kandlikar and Raykoff (1997)

n = number of fins    b = helix angle    f = fin height
p = pitch of fins    s = fin shape    G = mass flux
q = heat flux    D = diameter
** From Webb (1994)

R-22 and R-12, respectively. Their results indicated an enhancement factor ranging from 3 to 10 for these tubes over smooth tubes. They showed that enhancement in horizontal tubes in particular results from better distribution of liquid around the circumference. As the liquid flows through the grooves, it wets the top surface, thereby delaying the dryout to higher qualities. Liquid flows mainly in the grooves at the top, while the bulk flow prevails in the thick stratified layer at the bottom at low mass rates.

The heat transfer enhancement during flow boiling in microfin tubes is primarily through an increase in the convective contribution, though in some microfin geometries, the nucleate boiling contribution is also seen to increase. The swirl flow caused by the spirals improves the heat transfer performance. Presence of vapor phase in the flow makes it difficult to develop computerized fluid flow and heat transfer models.

Many investigators have presented specific correlations to cover their own experimental data set. A general predictive scheme was presented by Kandlikar (1991) for compact evaporators and microfin tubes. In this scheme, the original Kandlikar (1990) correlation for saturated flow boiling in plain tube is modified to incorporate two factors representing nucleate boiling and convective boiling enhancements. Kandlikar and Raykoff (1997) applied this scheme to different data sets from literature and found satisfactory agreements. According to their scheme, the heat transfer coefficient is given by

$$\alpha_{TP} = \text{larger of } \begin{cases} \alpha_{TP,NBD} \\ \alpha_{TP,CBD} \end{cases} \quad (18.2\text{-}1)$$

where

$$\alpha_{TP,NBD} = 0.6683\, Co^{-0.2}\, (25\, Fr_{LO})^{C5}\, \alpha_L E_{CB} + 1058.3\, Bo^{0.7}\, F_{Fl} E_{NB} \quad (18.2\text{-}2)$$

and

$$\alpha_{TP,CBD} = 1.1360\, Co^{-0.9}\, (25\, Fr_{LO})^{C5}\, \alpha_L E_{CB} + 667.2\, Bo^{0.7}\, F_{Fl} E_{NB} \quad (18.2\text{-}3)$$

The first terms in Eqs. (18.2-2) and (18.2-3) represent the convective contribution, while the second terms represent the nucleate boiling contribution. The Froude number effect is seen only in the low mass flow rate range; for a Froude number less than 0.04, the value of the constant $C5$ is 0.3, while it is 0 for Froude numbers greater than 0.04. $F_{fl}$ is a fluid dependent parameter that accounts for the effect of different refrigerants on the nucleate boiling contribution. Values of $F_{fl}$ used in the present work are given in Table 3 of Chapter 15. $E_{CB}$ and $E_{NB}$ are the enhancement factors for the convective and the nucleate boiling components, respectively.

The single-phase heat transfer coefficient with only liquid fraction flowing full in the tube, $\alpha_L$, may be expressed by a Dittus-Boelter type correlation for smooth tubes. Assuming a similar functional dependence, $\alpha_L$ for microfin tubes is given by:

$$\alpha_L = C \operatorname{Re}_L^n \operatorname{Pr}_L^{0.4} [\lambda/D] \qquad (18.2\text{-}4)$$

Combining Eqs. (18.2-2) and (18.2-3) with (18.2-4), and noting that $\operatorname{Re}_L = (1-x) \operatorname{Re}_{LO}$, we get

$$\alpha_{TP,NBD} = 0.6683 \, Co^{-0.2} (25 \, Fr_{LO})^{C5} (1-x)^n \operatorname{Re}_{LO}^n \operatorname{Pr}_L^{0.4} [\lambda/D] \, E'_{CB}$$
$$+ 1058.3 \, Bo^{0.7} F_{Fl} (1-x)^n \operatorname{Re}_{LO}^n \operatorname{Pr}_L^{0.4} [\lambda/D] \, E'_{NB} \qquad (18.2\text{-}5)$$

and

$$\alpha_{TP,NBD} = 1.1360 \, Co^{-0.9} (25 \, Fr_{LO})^{C5} (1-x)^n \operatorname{Re}_{LO}^n \operatorname{Pr}_L^{0.4} [\lambda/D] \, E'_{CB}$$
$$+ 667.2 \, Bo^{0.7} F_{Fl} (1-x)^n \operatorname{Re}_{LO}^n \operatorname{Pr}_L^{0.4} [\lambda/D] \, E'_{NB} \qquad (18.2\text{-}6)$$

The modified enhancement factors, $E'_{cb}$ and $E'_{nb}$, combine the enhancement factors $E_{cb}$ and $E_{nb}$ in Eqs. (18.2-2) and (18.2-3) and the constant $C$ in Eq. (18.2-4), since $C$ is not known for individual microfin tubes.

The factors $E'_{CB}$ and $E'_{NB}$ represent the enhancement in the convective boiling and the nucleate boiling terms, respectively. These enhancement factors are dependent on the microfin geometry alone. In the original augmented tube correlation, Kandlikar (1991) was able to correlate the microfin data of Khanpara et al. (1987) for refrigerants R-22 and R-113 within less than 9 percent, and the compact evaporator data of Robertson and Lovegrove (1983) for R-11 and Cohen and Carey (1990) for R-113 within less than 8 percent.

It should be noted that the enhancement factors $E'_{cb}$ and $E'_{nb}$ and the Reynolds number exponent n in the microfin correlation presented in Eqs. (18.2-1)–(18.2-6) are specific to a microfin geometry. For each microfin geometry, one needs to determine a new set of enhancement factors and the exponent $n$.

Another aspect to note is that the single-phase heat transfer coefficient in microfin tubes is not well represented by the Dittus-Boelter type correlation, Eq. (18.2-4), employing a Reynolds number exponent n of 0.8. The experimental single-phase heat transfer data for microfin tubes obtained by Khanpara et al. (1987) shows a significant departure from the Reynolds number exponent of 0.8. Ravigururajan and Gudimeta (1995) present a correlation for microfin tube performance in the single-phase turbulent region based on a limited range of Reynolds number data for water. The Reynolds number range covered in the present flow boiling data sets exceeds this range, and their correlation scheme obtained from water data cannot be directly employed.

Table 2 shows the details of the data sets and the results from the Kandlikar and Raykoff (1997) correlation. The table includes the details of tube geometry, refrigerants used, the Reynolds number range, the constants $E'_{cb}$, $E'_{nb}$, and $n$ (obtained from their analysis), and the resulting mean errors for each data set. The ratio of the two enhancement factors, $E'_{cb}/E'_{nb}$, is also included in the table.

Figure 3 is a comparison between the predicted and experimental values of heat transfer coefficient for the R-22 and R-113 data of Khanpara et al. (1987). Over 90 percent of the data points fall between ±15 percent lines. The mean error is 5.6% for R-22 and 7.9% for R-113. The value of the Reynolds number exponent n is found to be 0.4. This constant is below the usual exponent of 0.8 found in smooth tube correlations for turbulent flow. Although the single phase data obtained by Khanpara et al. could be correlated with a Reynolds number exponent n of 1.84, the exponent obtained from their flow boiling data is 0.4. It is not possible to comment on the reasons for this from a mechanistic viewpoint, and n should be treated as a variable that represents the single phase exponent best suited in the flow boiling correlation. The single-phase heat transfer mechanism in microfin tubes is not well

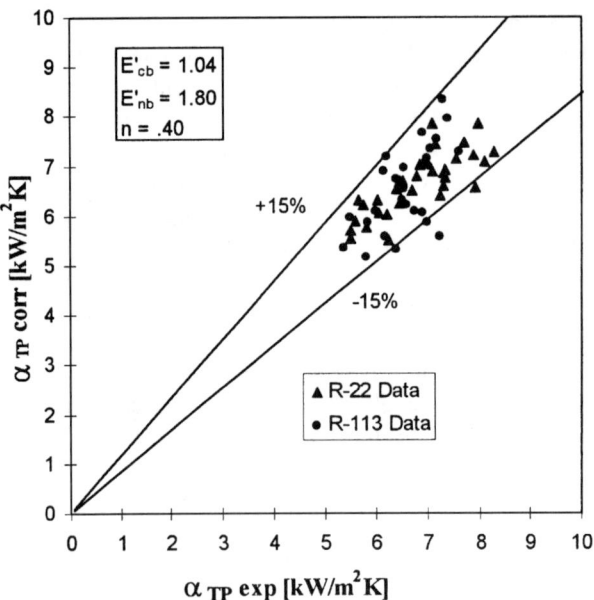

**Figure 3** Comparison of experimental data of Khanpara et al. (1987) and Kandlikar and Raykoff (1997) correlation.

Table 2  Results from Kandlikar and Raykoff (1996) correlation and comparison with experimental data sets

| Investigator | Refrigerant | Tube ID, mm | Fin Ht. mm | Helix angle | Total # Fins | Re range | $E'_{cb}$ | $E'_{nb}$ | $n$ | $E'_{cb}/E'_{nb}$ | Mean Abs error |
|---|---|---|---|---|---|---|---|---|---|---|---|
| Khanpara et al. (1987) | R-22 | 8.8 | 0.22 | 17° | 60 | 13400–25500 | 1.04 | 1.8 | 0.4 | 0.58 | 5.6% |
| | R-113 | | | | | 6200–15300 | | | | | 7.9% |
| Reid et al. (1991) | R-113 | 8.7 | 0.21 | 18° | 65 | 10300–10700 | 1.04 | 1.8 | 0.4 | 0.58 | 5.8% |
| Ha & Bergles (1993) | R-12 | 8.8 | 0.18 | 18° | 60 | 860–3500 | 1.37 | 0.658 | 0.4 | 2.10 | 10.7% |
| Murata and Hashizume (1993) | R-123 | 10.3 | 0.3 | 30 | 60 | 3500–10500 | 10.9 | 5.8 | 0.61 | 1.88 | 11.0% |
| Chamra & Webb (1995) | R-22 | 14.66 | 0.35/0.15 | 15/15 | 74/74 | 21000–33000 | 11 | 4.6 | 0.67 | 2.39 | 5.6% |
| Singh et al. (1996) | R-134a | 11.8 | 0.25 | 18° | 60 | 2630–8000 | 0.024 | 0.005 | 0.97 | 4.60 | 9.2% |

understood at this time, and further work in this area is needed to see its influence in the two-phase region.

Kandlikar and Raykoff (1997) compared the parametric trends predicted by their correlation scheme with experimental data and found that for the microfins tested, nucleate boiling is dominant in the low quality region, and convective boiling dominates in the high quality region. The dryout location is extended further downstream as compared to smooth tubes, whereas the correlation is generally applicable up to a quality of 0.8. Also shown in Table 2 are the ratio $E'_{CB}/E'_{NB}$. It is seen that for some tubes, the ratio is less than one, indicating significant nucleate boiling enhancement. Presence of nucleate boiling at preferred locations on a flat microfin surface was visually confirmed by Kandlikar and Howell (1996). For tubes tested by Ha and Bergles (1993), Murata and Hashizume (1993), Chamra and Webb (1995), and Singh et al. (1996), the ratio $E'_{CB}/E'_{NB}$ is seen to be greater than 1, indicating dominance of convective enhancement mechanism. Specific microfin profiles are believed to be responsible for these characteristics.

Another important conclusion can be drawn by comparing the data sets of Khanpara et al. (1987) and Reid et al. (1991). It can be seen that the enhancement factors and the exponent $n$ obtained for these two data sets are exactly the same. Referring to Table 2, the tubes used in these two investigations have the same inner diameter and fin height and very similar helix angle and fin pitch. This further confirms that the enhancement factors are essentially dependent on the microfin tube geometry alone.

Muzzio et al. (1998) conducted experiments with R-22 in three microfin tubes and compared their evaporation results with the Kandlikar and Raykoff (1997) correlation. One of their tubes, tube V, had geometry similar to that reported by Khanpara et al. (1987). Using constants from Khanpara et al. for $E'_{CB}$ and $E'_{NB}$ and n from Table 2, Muzzio et al. found very good agreement with their own data. Further, they observed a decreasing heat transfer coefficient trend with quality in the low quality region, confirming the enhancement in the nucleate boiling component in this region.

As the next generation enhancement devices, three dimensional microfin surfaces are being developed. A new type of grooved tube with herringbone structure is explained by Ebisu and Torikoshi (1998). Starting with a flat strip, two V-grooves of 16 degree helix angle are embossed, and the strip is then rolled into a round tube. The axial seam is induction welded, forming another V-edge. Thus, there are four V-edges. As the liquid flows in the tube, it is driven away from the forward facing V-edges, while the liquid accumulates inside the adjacent set of opposing V-edges. By aligning the forward facing V-edges to the sides of a horizontal tube, liquid can be moved to the top, forming a thicker layer as compared to a regular grooved or microfin tube. Liquid distribution patterns in a herringbone

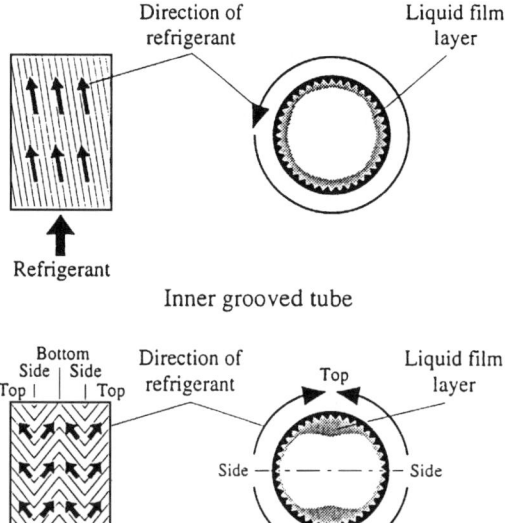

**Figure 4** Comparison of liquid distribution patterns in microfin (grooved) and grooved tubes, Ebisu et al. (1998), reproduced with permission from ASHRAE.

tube and a conventional microfin (grooved) tube are shown in Figure 4. Figure 5 shows a photograph of the herringbone tube along with a regular microfin tube.

Performance of the herringbone is considerably improved over a microfin tube. A comparison of the local heat transfer coefficients and pressure drop for the herringbone and microfin tube under similar conditions are shown in Figures 6 and 7. As expected, both heat transfer and pressure drop are higher for herringbone tubes. Similar performance improvements are obtained with herringbone tubes for in-tube condensation as well.

The choice of microfin tube geometry is strongly influenced by heat transfer enhancement, the accompanying pressure drop increase, and the cost of tubes. A life-cycle analysis needs to be carried out to determine the potential savings. In the refrigeration industry, the high volume of production and the savings in size and operating costs lead to a faster transition to augmented tubes. From a global energy conservation viewpoint, it makes sense to employ augmented surfaces in heat exchangers to reduce the resultant energy consumption.

The effect of lubricating oil on microfin tube performance was studied by Eckels et al. (1998) with mixtures of R-134a and lubricant 169 SUS penta erythritol.

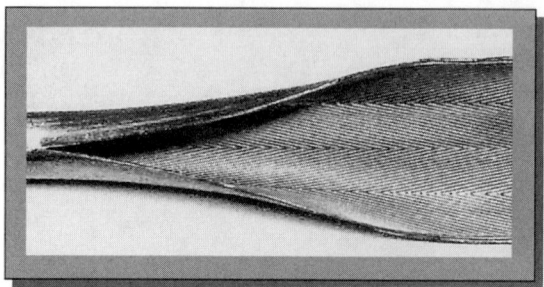
**Herringbone tube**

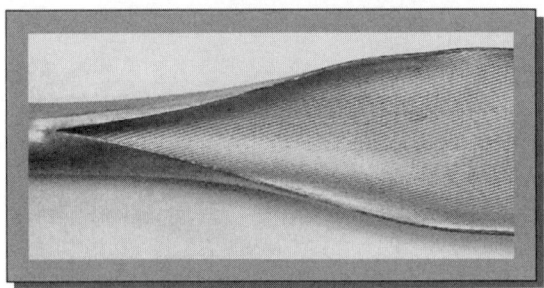
**Inner grooved tube**

**Figure 5** Photograph of Herringbone and Inner grooved tubes, Ebisu et al. (1998), reproduced with permission from ASHRAE.

Their results indicate that for lubricant mass concentrations of 1.2% and 2.4%, there was little change in heat transfer performance, while it deteriorated by up to 25% with 4.9% concentration. Pressure drop increased by 25% to 35% at concentrations 2.4% and above.

Yoshida and Matsunaga (1991) present detailed results on the effect of oil at various heat and mass fluxes. In general, the presence of oil degrades the heat transfer, but at higher heat and mass fluxes, little degradation was observed. The fin profile and the operating conditions have strong influence in determining the influence of oil, and experimental determination is recommended to determine this effect under a specific set of operating conditions.

### 18.2.2 Internal Fins

Fins provide heat transfer enhancement in single-phase flow through the increase in area associated with them. Additional surface modifications, such as louvers, are sometimes incorporated to enhance the heat transfer coefficient over the extended surfaces. Application of fins in flow boiling has been investigated by a number of

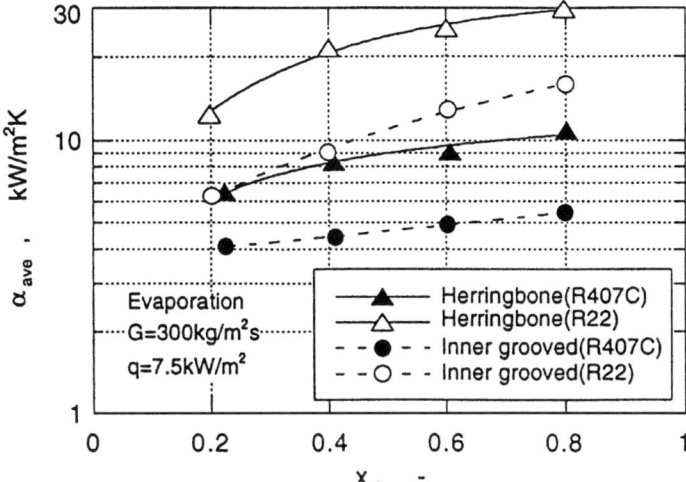

**Figure 6** Comparison of heat transfer coefficients in microfin (grooved) and Herringbone tubes, Ebisu et al. (1998), reproduced with permission from ASHRAE.

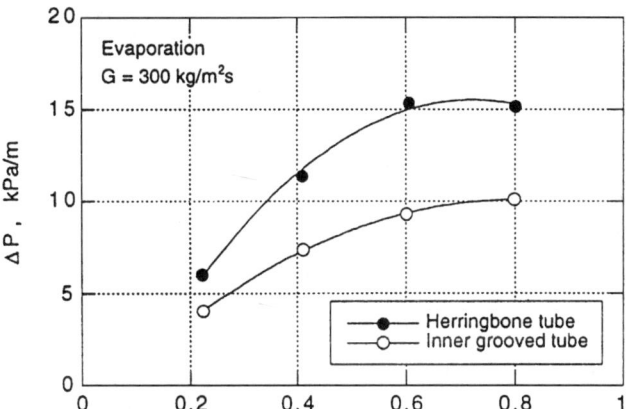

**Figure 7** Comparison of pressure drop in microfin (grooved) and Herringbone tubes, Ebisu et al. (1998), reproduced with permission from ASHRAE.

investigators. Jensen (1987) presents a comprehensive summary of investigations on internal fins, including work by Lavin and Young (1965) on integral fins, Bolling et al. (1953) on longitudinal fins, and Schlunder and Chawla (1967) on star inserts. In general, the increase in heat transfer was associated with a considerably larger increase in pressure drop with such inserts. The introduction of small fins by Rifert et al. (1975) and internal spiral fins by Grachev et al. (1977) indicated the potential of such an arrangement with significantly lower pressure drop enhancement. Ito and Kimura (1979) tested a number of grooved (microfin) surfaces and showed that while heat transfer increased, the pressure drop penalty was considerably lower than large internal fins.

### 18.2.3 Twisted Tape Inserts

Twisted tapes are inserts that are spiral strips of metal, with their width nearly equal to the tube internal diameter. These can be inserted in existing tubular heat exchangers and serve as excellent retrofit devices for augmentation. They sometimes act like fins due to contact with the wall, but augmentation in heat transfer largely comes from the induced swirl in the flow. In addition, their ability to send the liquid toward the wall causes a delay in the dryout condition to higher qualities in an evaporator. The average heat transfer coefficient in an evaporator is considerably improved over a smooth tube under complete evaporation condition. Among other studies, Jensen and Bensler (1986) tested three twisted tapes with evaporating R-113 and observed heat transfer augmentation of up to 90% over smooth tubes.

Due to their relatively low enhancement over smooth tubes as compared to the microfin tubes, the main application area of twisted tape is in extending the dryout at higher qualities. Jensen (1984, 1985) recommends the use of twisted tape only near the dryout region where benefits of twisted tapes are greatest. He also cites several concerns, such as the effect of vibration in loosely fitting twisted tapes leading to fretting wear of the tube and increased corrosion possibility.

Other inserts, such as wire mesh completely filling the tube, have been investigated in literature. Wadekar (1998) found that wire mesh inserts do not enhance heat transfer in flow boiling.

### 18.2.4 Spirally Fluted Tubes

Spirally fluted tubes provide simultaneous augmentation on both sides and are useful in applications such as chillers. As their name suggests, the flutes run spirally along the length of the tube, and the cross-section of the tube looks like a corrugated wall. MacBain et al. (1997) obtained heat transfer and pressure drop data for a horizontal fluted tube with R-134a. Augmentation over smooth tube was observed in the entire region; augmentation in the high quality region was particularly noteworthy. Flow under similar conditions in a smooth tube results in a decreasing heat transfer coefficient with quality (as predicted by the Kandlikar, [1990] correlation), but with fluted tubes, heat transfer increased with quality, resulting in significant enhancement in this region. Ability of liquid to stay longer on the fluted walls is believed to be responsible for this enhancement.

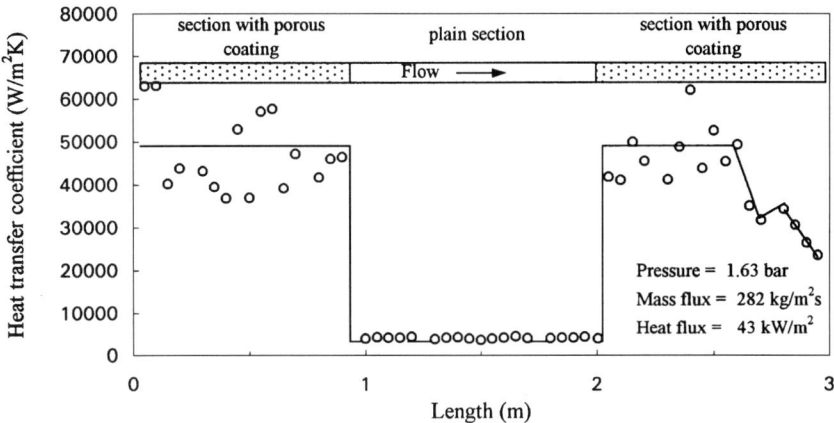

**Figure 8** Heat transfer performance of R-113 in a circular evaporator tube with porous coatings on the end sections and central uncoated section, Wadekar (1998), reproduced with permission from Gordon and Breach Science Publishers.

## 18.2.5 Porous Coated Surfaces

Porous coatings are effective in enhancing the nucleate boiling heat transfer and were employed effectively by Ammermen and You (1998) in improving subcooled flow boiling heat transfer, as discussed in Section 18.1. Wadekar (1996, 1998) reports a ten-fold increase in heat transfer coefficient with R-113 flowing in a vertical tube. The improvement was dramatically shown in a vertical evaporator tube with its top and bottom 1 m internal surface coated with a porous coating. Figure 8 shows the heat transfer coefficient along the length of the tube. The coated sections had about a ten-fold increase in heat transfer coefficient, as compared to the central uncoated section. The decrease toward the end is due to local dryout. Porous coatings provide a large number of nucleation cavities in the size range that are suitable for a specific liquid under a given set of operating conditions. Manufacturers of such coatings have developed ones specially designed for refrigerants, organic fluids, cryogenic fluids, or water by matching the particle and pore sizes to the range of cavities falling within the nucleation criterion, as given by Figure 2 in Chapter 15. The cost of these coatings is rather high and limits their widespread application in spite of highly desirable heat transfer and pressure drop characteristics.

## 18.2.6 Electrohydrodynamic Enhancement

EHD enhancement is an active method that has been applied to pool boiling for over thirty years. It has been recently applied to flow boiling in last six years. It has the advantage of being able to control the heat transfer rate by changing the applied voltage. Also, it has no moving parts, and the electric power consumption is negligible. Table 3 presents a comprehensive summary of available work in this area.

The basic principle associated with EHD enhancement in flow boiling is not clearly understood. Bryan and Sayed-Yagoobi (1997) and Salehi et al. (1997) present an explanation using the electric field equations by Pohl (1978) and Melcher (1981). The interaction of electric and flow fields in a dielectric medium results in three kinds of force fields: (a) force acting on a free charge, or Coulomb force, (b) force created by a local change of the permittivity, such as that resulting from the change of medium at the interface in an electric field, and (c) the dielectrophoretic force that results from the nonuniformity of the electric field. Thus, application of an electric field in a phase change process produces forces due to two effects: the nonuniformity of the electric field and the nonuniformity in the electric permittivity of the fluid. Nonuniformity in the electric permittivity is present due to the different permittivities of the phases. The electrical field nonuniformity can be generated with enhanced surfaces, such as microfin or corrugated tubes. Salehi et al. (1997) point to the benefits of applying EHD to enhanced tubes.

The effects of EHD on the nucleation and the two phase flow are different. The nucleate boiling at low qualities is enhanced with the application of an electric field, while it results in a deterioration of the heat transfer rate in the high quality region dominated by convective effects. Figure 9 shows the results of applying an electric field during evaporation of R-134a in a smooth tube as obtained by Bryan and Sayed-Yagoobi (1997). A five-fold enhancement is obtained at $x = 0.1$ where nucleate boiling is dominant. At higher qualities, the heat transfer rate decreases by a factor of two as the electric field is applied. The enhancement is seen to be maximum at the bottom section at low qualities, which is covered with liquid and experiences nucleate boiling.

Salehi et al. (1996) employed a helical electrode in the shape of a coiled wire inside a tube for flow boiling of R-404A. Nearly a fourfold increase was obatined at low qualities, but as quality increased beyond 0.3, the heat transfer coefficient started to decrease. Salehi et al. (1997) report similar increase with R-134a in rectangular smooth and grooved channels of 1 mm hydraulic diameter.

The destabilization of the vapor-liquid interface can lead to dramatic improvement in heat transfer rates. Since the application of EHD in some instances, such as in annular or separated flow pattern without nucleate boiling, leads to heat transfer reduction, careful research is needed to identify the specific application areas for this technique. The application of high voltage also needs to be taken into account in deciding the practicality of this technique in practical systems.

**Table 3** Data sources and comparison of EHD enhancement in smooth and microfin tubes (updated from original compilation by Bryan and Yagoobi, 1997)

| Investigator | Fluid | Tube | D mm | Electrode | $D_E$ mm | G kg/m²s | q kW/m² | x | $h_0$ kW/m²K | $h_{EHD}$ kW/m²K | $E_E(10^6)$ V/m | $E_G(10^6)$ V/m | $Q_{EHD}$ W |
|---|---|---|---|---|---|---|---|---|---|---|---|---|---|
| Yabe et al. (1992) | R-123/ R-134a | smooth fluid-heated | 10 | perforated tube | 5 | 33 & 66 (33) | 4 (4) | 0–0.9 (0.2–0.6) | 0.5–1 | 1.05–2 | 4.04 | 2.02 | N/A |
| Singh et al. (1994) | R-123 | smooth fluid-heated | 9.4 | cylinder | 3 | 50–400 (75) | 5–20 (5) | 0–0.5 (0) | 0.8 | 3.8 | 5.83 | 1.86 | 0.34 |
| Singh et al. (1994) | R-123 | smooth fluid-heated | 9.4 | cylinder | 3 | 50–400 (200) | 5–20 (5) | 0–0.5 (0) | 2.1 | 4.6 | 5.83 | 1.86 | 0.23 |
| Singh et al. (1995) | R-134a | microfin electric-heated | 12.7 | helical | 9.8 | 50–150 (50) | 5–30 (5) | 0–0.8 (0.1) | 2 | 13.9 | 2.22 | 1.84 | 0.36 |
| Salehi et al. (1996) | R-404A | microfin electric-heated | 12.7 | helical | 9.8 | 50–200 (50) | 5, 10 (10) | 0–0.8 (0.3) | 3 | 7 | 1.66 | 1.38 | 0.01 |
| Ohadi et al. (1995) | R-134a | microfin electric-heated | 12.7 | cylinder | 9.5 | 50, 100 (50) | 25 (25) | 0–0.6 (0.6) | 5 | 50 | 4.55 | 404 | 0.01 |
| Bryan and Yagoobi (1997) | R-134a | smooth fluid-heated | 14.1 | cylinder | 1.6 | 100, 300 | 10–150 | 0.005–3 0.6 (0.1) | 3 | 13.5 | N/A | N/A | N/A |

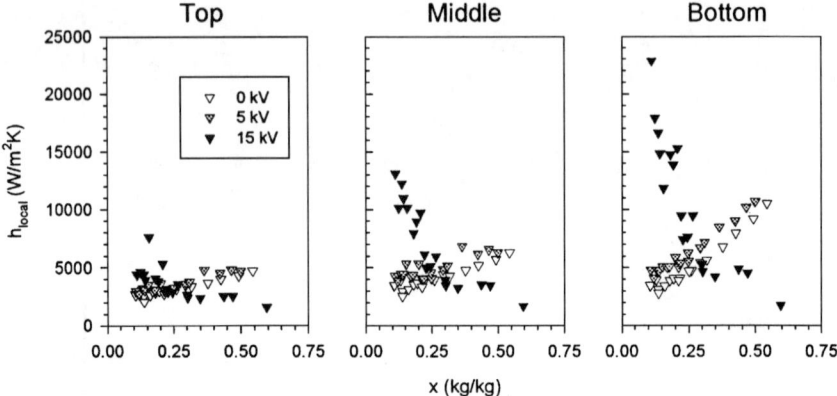

**Figure 9** Effect of EHD on local heat transfer coefficient ($h_{local}$) of R-134a in smooth 30 cm long water-heated copper tube, stratified wavy flow pattern, $G = 99.9$ kg/m$^2$s and $T_{sat} = 4.9°$C, Bryan and Sayed-Yagoobi (1998), reproduced with permission from ASME.

## 18.3 AUGMENTATION OF CHF AND POST-CHF HEAT TRANSFER

In the thermal-hydraulic design of a heat exchanger, a steam generator, or a thermal equipment, where the critical heat flux (CHF) is the limiting parameter or where the designer is faced with post-CHF heat transfer, it may be necessary to obtain a higher CHF value or better post-CHF heat transfer coefficient than that allowed by the process thermodynamic and geometry conditions. It is therefore necessary to make use of enhancement techniques in order to have a higher CHF or post-CHF heat transfer rate, for reasons similar to those in single and two-phase flow heat transfer applications (before the thermal crisis) (Bergles, 1992; Thome, 1990).

### 18.3.1 CHF Enhancement Techniques

Recent reviews of CHF enhancement techniques have been given by Boyd (1985) and Celata (1996). Among the possible techniques are passive devices, such as swirl flow (twisted tapes and helically coiled wires), extended surfaces (hypervapotron), and helical coiled tubes, and active techniques, such as electrical fields, pressure wave generation, and tangential injection. Only passive techniques will be discussed here; for active techniques, see Boyd (1985).

**18.3.1.1 Swirl flow.** Swirl flow is obtained using twisted tapes or helically coiled wires inside the flow channel to induce secondary radial and circumferential velocity components in the fluid, which obtains a better heat transfer rate and therefore a higher CHF value. A considerable increase in the pressure drop with respect to

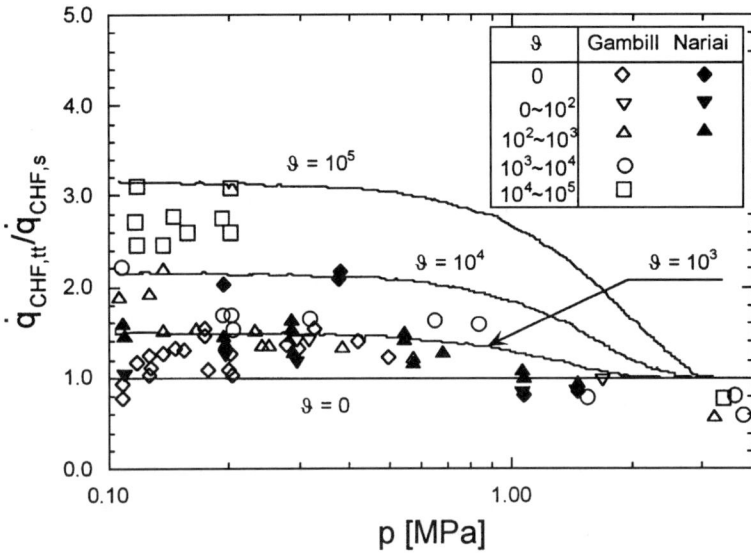

**Figure 10** Swirl flow CHF data using twisted tapes, Gambill et al. (1961), Nariai et al. (1991).

smooth tubes is observed, in general, with the use of swirl flow promoters. The use of twisted tapes as swirl flow promoters in the augmentation of the CHF in subcooled flow boiling has been studied by Achilli et al. (1993), Cardella et al. (1992), Gambill and Greene (1958), Gambill et al. (1961), and Nariai et al. (1991). An increase in the CHF, typically by a factor of 2, was generally obtained through the implementation of twisted tubes. Results by Gambill et al. (1961) and by Nariai et al. (1991) are plotted in Figure 10, where the ratio between the CHF obtained with the twisted tape and the value obtained with the smooth tube is reported, versus pressure for different values of the non-dimensional centrifugal acceleration, $\vartheta$:

$$\vartheta = \frac{a_t}{g} = \frac{\pi^2 u^2}{2gD\,\text{TTR}} \qquad (18.3\text{-}1)$$

where TTR is the twisted tape ratio and $\vartheta$ is defined as the ratio between the tangential centrifugal acceleration (due to the twisted tape) and the standard gravitational acceleration. The thermal efficiency of the twisted tape decreases as pressure increases and becomes insignificant when pressure is above 2.0 MPa. This effect is probably due to the presence of a gap between the wall and the twisted tape. In fact, the clearance allows steam trapping in the tube-tape gap (which is an increasing function of pressure) that may result in premature CHF. Cardella et al. (1992) and Achilli et al. (1993) did not find any effect of the system pressure on the thermal efficiency of the twisted tape.

A correlation for the prediction of the CHF with twisted tapes has been given by Nariai et al. (1992):

$$\frac{\dot{q}_{CHF,tt}}{\dot{q}_{CHF,st}} = \{1 + 10^{-2}\vartheta \exp[(-10^{-6}p)^2]\}^{1/6} \qquad (18.3\text{-}2)$$

with $\vartheta$ given by Eq. (18.3-1). Also, Eq. (17.1-4) can be used to predict the CHF with twisted tapes, using the resultant water velocity at the inner tube wall $u_r$, in place of u, as given by Schlosser et al. (1991):

$$\frac{u_r}{u} = \left(\frac{1+\pi^2}{4(TTR)^2}\right)^{1/2} \qquad (18.3\text{-}3)$$

The Celata et al. model (1994, 1995) presented in Section 17.1.3 can be also used to predict the CHF in subcooled flow boiling with twisted tapes.

The use of twisted tapes to enhance the CHF under saturated flow boiling conditions has been recently investigated by Lee et al. (1995). They found that in the low-quality region, the effect of the twisted tape on the CHF is negligible. In the middle-quality region, the CHF of the twisted tape inserted tube increased with mass velocity, which was contrary to the trend observed for the empty one. Besides, the CHF was found to increase by insertion of the twisted tape except for cases of very small flow rate and large twist ratio. The clearance effect was weak as compared to the subcooled region. Finally, in the high-quality region, the CHF decreased with exit quality, the decreasing rate being slower with the twisted tape than without. Also, the CHF enhancement was most remarkable in this region.

A correlation for the prediction of the CHF with twisted tape in saturated flow boiling has been proposed by Jensen (1985):

$$\frac{\dot{Q}_{tt}}{\dot{Q}_{CHF}} = (4.597 + 0.09254(TTR) + 0.004154(TTR)^2)\left(\frac{\rho_l}{\rho_g}\right)^{-0.7012}$$
$$+ 0.09012 \ln \vartheta \qquad (18.3\text{-}4)$$

with $\vartheta$ given by Eq. (18.3-1). The critical power $\dot{Q}_{CHF}$ can be obtained using a suitable correlation or model.

Helically coiled wires as swirl flow promoters have been used by Celata et al. (1993) for CHF in subcooled flow boiling. Authors used wires of spring steel having a diameter of 0.5, 0.7, and 1.0 mm and a pitch from 1.5 to 20.0 mm in 8.0 mm I.D. tubes. Results are presented in Figure 11, where an increase in the CHF up to 50% using a 1.0 mm wire at 3.5 MPa can be observed. Contrary to the twisted tape performance, where the increase in the thermal efficiency and the associate pressure drop increase are strictly inter-related, the thermal efficiency of

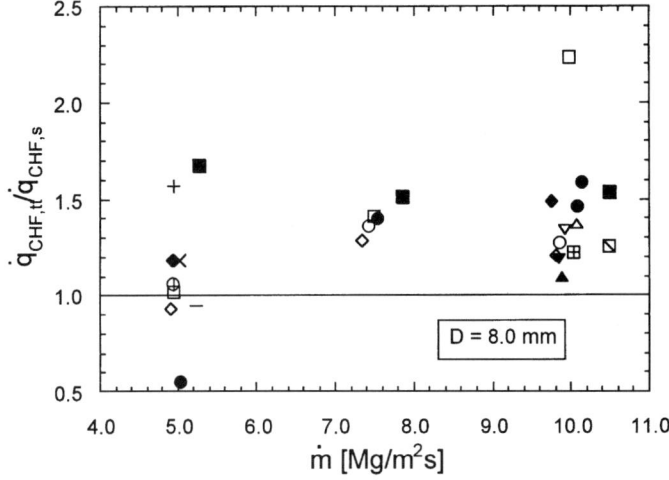

**Figure 11** Swirl flow CHF data using helically coiled wires, Celata et al. (1993).

wires is practically independent of the wire pitch, while pressure drop is inversely related to it. The latter can therefore be properly reduced, decreasing the pitch without affecting the thermal performance. The effect of the pressure on the wires efficiency is observed to be negative, in the sense that at a pressure of 5.0 MPa it drops to only 30%.

**18.3.1.2 Extended surfaces.** Kovalev (1976) investigated three different fin designs and obtained an increase up to a factor of 10 in the CHF for low velocity (0.021 to 0.14 m/s) subcooled flow in an annulus. A thorough review on the use of fins to improve the CHF is presented by Boyd (1985).

A very intriguing technique using fins (but placed perpendicular to the fluid flow in subcooled flow boiling) is the so-called "hypervapotron" technique. From a physical viewpoint, the hypervapotron effect consists of the following succession of events. The liquid inside two adjacent fins of high conductivity material and in contact with the heated wall starts boiling while the fluid bulk outside the fins is under subcooled conditions. Once the slot is full of steam, the latter undergoes a quick condensation in the subcooled liquid bulk, emptying the slots and making their replenishment with cold liquid easier. The heated wall is rewetted until the wall temperature during the uncovered phase is below the Leidenfrost temperature. The base of the fin is allowed to operate at a temperature greater than the CHF temperature, while the remaining portion operates near the temperature for the onset of stable nucleate boiling. This continuous boiling and condensation sequence (frequency between 10 and 40 Hz) allows to get a high CHF, essentially on the basis of the transport of the latent heat extracted from the heated wall during boiling and transferred to the coolant outside the fins during condensation. Cattadori et al. (1993) obtained a maximum CHF of 29.4 MW/m². A typical picture from visualized tests is reported in Figure 12.

**18.3.1.3 Helically coiled tubes.** Use of helically coiled tubes to get higher CHF values has been proposed by various researchers, such as Jensen and Bergles (1981), Berthoud and Jayanti (1990), and Kaji et al. (1995), among others.

In the coiled tube, the liquid film thickness distribution is nonuniform around the tube circumference. But, due to the secondary flow caused by centrifugal forces, the entrainment rate of liquid droplets from the inside to the outside of the coil is large, and the liquid film flows around the circumference. This may cause the dryout quality and therefore the critical heat flux to increase in the coiled tube.

### 18.3.2 Post CHF Heat transfer Enhancement Techniques

Swirl flow promoters such as twisted tapes are also an effective enhancement technique for the augmentation of heat transfer in the post-CHF region of two-phase flow. Here, the mechanism for the augmentation includes the effect of the radial velocity concentrating liquid from the center of the flow stream at the heat transfer surface. The first experiment of swirl flow post-CHF heat transfer was conducted by Bergles et al. (1971). They proposed a correlation, which is very complex, for the heat transfer coefficient:

$$\alpha = C\, \text{Re}_g^{0.8} \text{Pr}_g^{0.4} \left(\frac{T_b}{T_w}\right)^{0.32} \left(1 + 0.25 \frac{\text{Gr}_g^{0.5}}{\text{Re}_g}\right) \frac{\lambda_g}{D_h}$$

$$+ 1.1 \left(\frac{\lambda_g^3 h_{lg}^* g \theta \rho_l \rho_g}{\Delta T \eta_g (\pi/6)^{1/3}}\right)^{1/4} \left[\frac{(1-x)(6/\pi)}{x(\rho_l/\rho_g - 1) + 1}\right]^{2/3} \left(\frac{\pi}{4}\right) Z \quad (18.3\text{-}5)$$

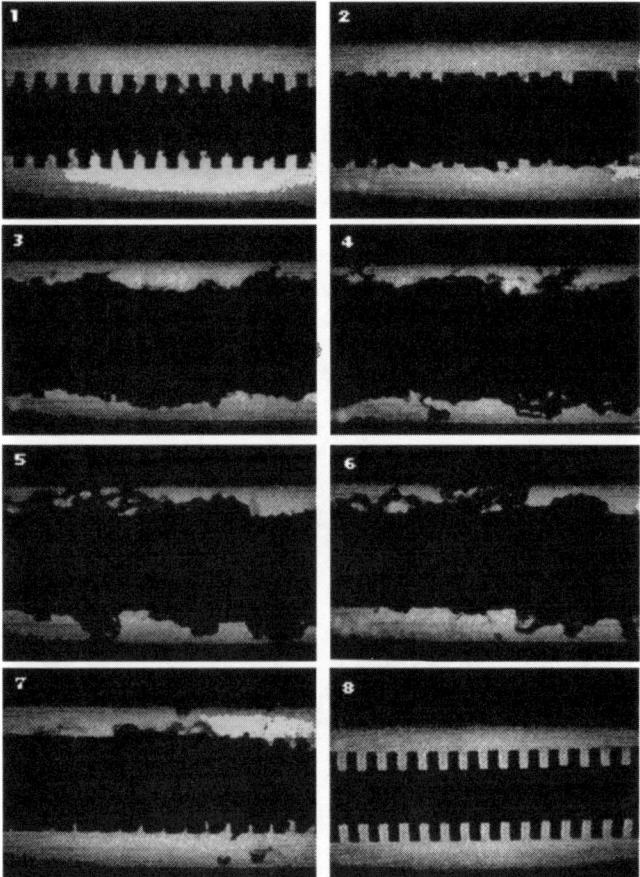

**Figure 12** Visualization of the hypervapotron effect, Cattadori et al. (1993).

where

$$\mathrm{Re}_g = \frac{\dot{m}D}{\eta_g}\left[x + (1-x)\left(\frac{\rho_g}{\rho_l}\right)\right]$$

$$C = 0.021\left[1 + \frac{0.035\pi^2}{D(\mathrm{TTR})^2(1 + \pi^2/4(\mathrm{TTR})^2}\right]$$

$$h_{lg}^* = h_{lg}\left[1 + \frac{0.35 c_{p,g}(T_w - T_s)}{h_{lg}}\right]^{-3}$$

$\mathrm{Gr}_g$ is the Grashof number of the gas phase, and Z is an empirically determined constant related to droplet size, while D is in feet. For film boiling of nitrogen at low mass velocity and at a reduced pressure of about 0.045, a value of $Z = 7$ gave satisfactory results.

More recently, swirl flow post-CHF heat transfer has been studied by Papadopoulos et al. (1991a, 1991b) and France et al. (1994).

The post-CHF heat transfer in helical coiled tubes has been studied by Chen and Zhou (1986). Here, the heat transfer coefficient in the helical coiled tube is higher than in the straight tube, also due to the action of the secondary flow and the deposition of liquid droplets in the vapor core that continuously wet the dryout location.

# REFERENCES

Achilli, A., Cattadori, G., and Gaspari, G. P. 1993 Subcooled Burnout in Uniformly and Non-Uniformly Heated Tubes. Paper C2, presented at the European Two-Phase Flow Group Meeting, Stockholm, June.

Ammerman, C. N. and You, S. M. 1998. Enhancing Small-Channel Convective Boiling Performance Using a Microporous Surface Coating. HTD-Vol. 361-3/PID-Vol. 3, *Proceedings of the ASME Heat Transfer Division—Volume 3*, ASME, pp. 467–476.

Bergles, A. E. 1964. The Influence of Flow Vibrations on Forced-Convection Heat Transfer. *Journal of Heat Transfer* 86:559–560.

Bergles, A. E. 1987. Heat Transfer Augmentation. Presented at the NATO ASI on Thermal-Hydraulic Fundamentals and Design of Two-Phase Flow Heat Exchangers, Povoa de Varzim, Portugal, July 1987. *Two-Phase Flow Heat Exchangers. Thermal-Hydraulic Fundamentals and Design*, Dordrecht, The Netherlands: Kluwer Academic Publishers, 1988, pp. 343–373.

Bergles, A. E. 1992. Heat Transfer Enhancement—Second Generation Heat Transfer Technology. *Proc. 10th UIT National Heat Transfer Conference*, Genoa, June, pp. 3–21.

Bergles, A. E., Fuller, W. D., and Hynek, S. J. 1971. Dispersed Flow Film Boiling of Nitrogen with Swirl Flow. *Int. J. Heat Mass Transfer* 14:1343–1354.

Bergles, A. E. and Newell, P. H., Jr. 1965. The Influence of Ultrasonic Vibrations on Heat Transfer to Water Flowing in Annuli. *International Journal of Heat Mass Transfer* 8:1273–1280.

Berthoud, G. and Jayanti, S. 1990. Characterization of Dryout in Helical Coils. *Int. J. Heat Mass Transfer* 33:(7):1451–1463.

Bolling, C., Donovan, W. J., and Decker, A. S. 1953. Heat Transfer to Evaporating Freon with Inner-Fin Tubing. *Refrigeration Engineering* 61:1338–1340.

Boyd, R. D. 1985. Subcooled Flow Boiling Critical Heat Flux (CHF) and Its Application to Fusion Energy Components. Part I: A Review of Fundamentals of CHF and Related Data Base. *Fusion Technology* 7:7–30.

Bryan, J. E. and Sayed-Yagoobi, J. 1997. Influence of Flow Regime, Heat Flux, and Mass Flux on Electrohydrodynamically Enhanced Convective Boiling. HTD-Vol. 351, *Proceedings of the ASME Heat Transfer Division*, ASME, pp. 187–196.

Cardella, A., Celata, G. P., Dell'Orco, G., Gaspari, G. P., Cattadori, G., and Mariani, A. 1992. Thermal Hydraulic Experiments for the NET Divertor. *Proc. 17th Symposium on Fusion Technology*, Rome, September, Volume 1, pp. 206–210.

Cattadori, G., Gaspari, G. P., Celata, G. P., Cumo, M., Mariani, A., and Zummo, G. 1993. Hypervapotron Technique in Subcooled Flow Boiling CHF. *Experimental Thermal and Fluid Science* 7:230–240.

Celata, G. P., Cumo, M., and Mariani, A. 1993. Enhancement of Water Subcooled Flow Boiling CHF in Tubes with Helically Coiled Wires. *Int. J. Heat Mass Transfer* 37(1):53–67.

Celata, G. P., Cumo, M., Mariani, A., Simoncini, M., and Zummo, G. 1994. Rationalization of Existing Mechanistic Models for the Prediction of Water Subcooled Flow Boiling Critical Heat Flux. *Int. J. Heat Mass Transfer* 37(1):347–360.

Celata, G. P. 1996. Critical Heat Flux in Water Subcooled Flow Boiling: Experimentation and Modeling. *Proc. 2nd European Thermal-Sciences Conference*, Rome, May, Volume I, pp. 27–40.

Celata, G. P., Cumo, M., Mariani, A., and Zummo, G. 1995. The Prediction of Critical Heat Flux in Water Subcooled Flow Boiling. *Int. J. Heat Mass Transfer* 38(6):1111–1119.

Chamra, L. M. and Webb, R. L. 1995. Condensation and Evaporation in Micro-Fin Tubes at Equal Saturation Temperatures. *Journal of Enhanced Heat Transfer* 3(2):219–229.

Chen, X. J. and Zhou, F. D. 1986. Forced Convection Boiling and Post Dryout Heat Transfer in Helical Coiled Tube. *Proc. 8th International Heat Transfer Conference*, San Francisco, August, 6:2221–2226.

Chiang, R. 1993. Heat Transfer and Pressure Drop During Evaporation and Condensation of R-22 in 7.5 mm and 10 mm Diameter Axial and Helical Grooved Tubes. *AIChE Symposium Series* 89(295):205–210.

Cohen, M. and Carey, V. P. 1990. A Comparison of the Flow Boiling Performance Characteristics of Partially Heated Cross-Ribbed Channels With Different Rib Geometries. *International Journal of Heat and Mass Transfer* 32(12):2459–2479.

Ebisu, T. and Torikoshi, K. 1998. Experimental Study on Evaporation and Condensation Heat Transfer Enhancement for R-407C Using Herringbone Heat Transfer Tube. *ASHRAE Transactions* 104 (2): to appear.

Eckels, S. J., Doerr, M. D., and Pate, M. B. 1998. A Comparison of the Heat Transfer and Pressure Drop Performance of R-134a-Lubricant Mixtures in Different Diameter Tubes. *ASHRAE Transactions* 104(1A):376–386.

Eckels, S. J., Pate, M. B., and Bemisderfer, C. H. 1992. Evaporation Heat Transfer Coefficients for R-22 in Micro-Fin Tubes of Different Configurations. ASME HTD-22, *Enhanced Heat Transfer*, pp. 117–125.

France, D. M., Minkowycz, W. J., and Chang, C. 1994. Analysis of Post-CHF Swirl Flow Heat Transfer. *Int. J. Heat Mass Transfer* 37(Suppl. 1):31–40.

Fujie, K., Itoh, N., Innami, T., Kimura, H., Nakayama, N., and Yanugidi, T. 1977. Heat Transfer Pipe. U.S. Patent 4,044,797 assigned to Hitachi, Ltd.

Gambill, W. R. and Greene, N. D. 1958. Boiling Burnout with Water in Vortex Flow. *Chem. Eng. Prog.* 54(10):68–76.

Gambill, W. R., Bundy, R. D., and Wansbrough, R. W. 1961. Heat Transfer, Burnout, and Pressure Drop for Water in Swirl Flow Through Tubes with Internal Twisted Tapes. *Chem. Eng. Symp. Ser.* 57(32):127–137.

Grachev, N. S., Kirillov, P. L., and Prokhorova, V. A. 1977. Heat Exchange in a Steam Generating Pipe with Internal-Ribbing. *High Temperature*: 1105–1110.

Ha, S. and Bergles, A. E. 1993. The Influence of Oil on Local Evaporation Heat Transfer Inside a Horizontal Microfin Tube. *ASHRAE Transactions* 99:1244–1255.

Ito, M. and Kimura, H. 1979. Boiling Heat Transfer and Pressure Drop in Internal Spiral-Grooved Tubes. *Bulletin of JSME* 22(171):1251–1257.

Jensen, M. K. 1985. An Evaluation of the Effect of Twisted-Tape Swirl Generators in Two-Phase Flow Heat Exchangers. *Heat Transfer Engineering* 6(4):19–30.

Jensen, M. K. 1987. Enhanced Forced Convective Vaporization and Condensation Inside Tubes. *Heat Transfer Equipment Design*. Eds. R. K. Shah, E. C. Subbarao, and R. A. Mashelkar, pp. 681–696. Washington, DC: Hemisphere Publishing Corporation.

Jensen, M. K. and Bensler, H. P. 1986. Saturated Forced-Convective Boiling Heat Transfer with Twisted-Tape Inserts. *Journal of Heat Transfer* 108:93–99.
Jensen, M. K. and Bergles, A. E. 1981. Critical Heat Flux in Helically Coiled Tubes. *Trans. ASME, Journal of Heat Transfer* 103(4):660–666.
Kaji, M., Mori, K., Nakanishi, S., Hirabayashi, K., and Ohishi, M. 1995. Dryout and Wall-Temperature Fluctuations in Helically Coiled Evaporating Tubes. *Heat Transfer—Japanese Research* 24(3):239–254.
Kandlikar, S. G. 1990. A General Correlation for Predicting the Two-Phase Flow Boiling Heat Transfer Coefficient Inside Horizontal and Vertical Tubes. *Journal of Heat Transfer* 102:219–228.
Kandlikar, S. G. 1991. A Model for Predicting the Two-Phase Flow Boiling Heat Transfer Coefficient in Augmented Tubes and Compact Evaporator Geometries. *Journal of Heat Transfer* 113:966–972.
Kandlikar, S. G. and Howell, M. L. 1996. Investigation of Nucleation and Heat Transfer for Subcooled Flow Boiling on Microfin Surfaces. *Proceedings of the 2nd European Heat Transfer/14th UIT National Conference*, Rome, Italy, Volume 1, pp. 190–200.
Kandlikar, S. G. and Raykoff, T. 1997. Predicting Flow Boiling Heat Transfer of Refrigerants in Microfin Tubes. *Enhanced Heat Transfer* 4:257–268.
Khanpara, J. C., Pate, M. B., and Bergles, A. E. 1986. Augmentation of R-113 In-Tube Evaporation in Microfin Tubes. *ASHRAE Transactions* 92(2):506–524.
Khanpara, J. C., Pate, M. B., and Bergles, A. E. 1987a. A Comparison of In-Tube Evaporation of Refrigerant R-113 in Electrically Heated Smooth and Microfin Tubes. *Advances in Enhanced Heat Transfer*, ASME HTD 68:35–46.
Khanpara, J. C., Pate, M. B., and Bergles, A. E. 1987b. Local Evaporation Heat Transfer in a Smooth Tube and a Microfin Tube Using Refrigerants 22 and 113. *Boiling and Condensation in Heat Transfer Equipment*, ASME-HTD 85:31–39.
Kovalev, S. A. 1976. Heat Transfer Crisis of Boiling of Subcooled Water on a Finned Surface Under Forced Convection Conditions. *Heat Transfer—Soviet Research* 8(4):73.
Koyama, S., Yu, J., Momoki, S., Fuji, T., and Honda, H. 1995. Forced Convective Flow Boiling Heat Transfer of Pure Refrigerants Inside a Horizontal Microfin Tube. Paper presented at the *Engineering Foundation Conference on Convective Flow Boiling*, ASME April 30–May 5, 1995, Banff, Canada.
Lavin, J. G. and Young, E. H. 1965. Heat Transfer to Evaporating Refrigerants in Two-Phase Flow. *AIChE Journal* 11:1124–1132.
Lee, S., Inone, A., and Takahashi, M. 1995. Critical Heat Flux Characteristics of R 113 Boiling Two-Phase Flow in Twisted Tape Inserted Tubes. *Heat Transfer—Japanese Research* 24(3):272–287.
Liaou, M. and di Marco, M. 1995. The Effect of Acoustic Vibration on Boiling Incipience. *Heat and Technology* 13(1):41–50.
MacBain, S. M., Bergles, A. E. and Raina, S. 1997. Heat Transfer and Pressure Drop Characteristics of Flow Boiling in a Horizontal Deep Spirally Fluted Tube. *HVAC & R Research* 3(1):65–80.
Melcher, J. R. 1981 *Continuum Electromechanics*, pp. 1–18. Cambridge, MA: MIT Press.
Murata, K. and Hashizume, K. 1993. Forced Convective Boiling of Nonazeotropic Refrigerant Mixtures Inside Horizontal Tubes. *Journal of Heat Transfer* 15:680–689.
Muzzio, A., Niro, A., and Arosio, S. 1998. Heat Transfer and Pressure Drop During Evaporation and Condensation of R-22 Inside 9.52-mm O. D. Microfin Tubes of Different Geometries. *Enhanced Heat Transfer* 5:39–52.
Nariai, H., Inasaka, F., Fujisaki, W., and Ishiguro, H. 1992. Critical Heat Flux of Subcooled Flow Boiling in Tubes with Internal Twisted Tapes. *Proc. ANS Winter Meeting* (THD), San Francisco, November, pp. 38–46.
Ohadi, M. M., Salehi, M., and Dessiatoun, S. 1995. EHD-Enhanced Convective Boiling of R-134a in Grooved Channels—Application to Compact Heat Exchangers. ASME HTD-1995 320:15–22.

Papadopoulos, P., Chang, C., France, D. M., and Minkowycz, W. J. 1991a. Mass Flux Effects in Post-CHF Swirl Heat Transfer. *Int. Comm. Heat Mass Transfer* 18:297–307.
Papadopoulos, P., France, D. M., and Minkowycz, W. J. 1991b. Heat Transfer to Dispersed Swirl Flow of High Pressure Water with Low Wall-Superheat. *Experimental Heat Transfer* 4:153–169.
Pohl, H. A. 1978. *Dielectrophoresis*. London: Cambridge University Press.
Ravigururajan, T. S. and Gudimeta, B. R. 1995. Single Phase Turbulent Flow Heat Transfer Enhancement in Micro-fin Tubes. Paper presented at the International Mechanical Engineering Congress and Exposition, Nov. 1995, ASME Book No. H01033, San Francisco.
Reid, R. S., Pate, M. B., and Bergles, A. E. 1991. A Comparison of Augmentation Techniques During In-Tube Evaporation of R-113. *Journal of Heat Transfer* 113:451–458.
Rifert, V. G., Butuzov, A. I., and Belik, D. N. 1975. Heat Transfer in Vapor Generation in a Falling Film Inside a Vertical Tube with a Finely-Finned Surface. *Heat Transfer—Soviet Research* 7(2):22–25.
Robertson, J. M. and Lovegrove, P. C. 1983. Boiling Heat Transfer With Freon 11 (R-11) in Brazed Aluminum Plate-Fin Heat Exchangers. *Transactions of ASME, Journal of Heat Transfer* 105:605–610.
Salehi, M., Ohadi, M. M., and Dessiatoun, S. 1996. The Applicability of the EHD Technique for Convective Boiling of Refrigerant Blends—Experiments with R-404A. *ASHRAE Transactions* 102(1):839–844.
Salehi, M., Ohadi, M. M., and Dessiatoun, S. 1997. EHD Enhanced Convective Boiling of R-134a in Grooved—Application to Subcompact Heat Exchangers. *Journal of Heat Transfer* 119(4):805–809.
Schlager, L. M., Pate, M. B., and Bergles, A. E. 1990. Evaporation and Condensation Heat Transfer and Pressure Drop in Horizontal 12.7 mm Microfin Tubes with Refrigerant 22. *Journal of Heat Transfer* 112:1041–1047.
Schlosser, J., Cardella, A., Massmann, P., Chappuis, P., Falter, H. D., Deschamps, P., and Deschamps, D. H. 1991. Thermal Hydraulic Tests on NET Divertor Targets Using Swirl Tubes. *Proc. ANS Winter Meeting (THD)*, San Francisco, CA, November, pp. 26–31.
Schlunder, E. U. and Chawla, J. M. 1967. Local Heat Transfer and Pressure Drop for Refrigerants Evaporating in Horizontal Internally Finned Tubes. *Proceedings International Congress on Refrigeration*, Paper 2.47.
Shinohara, Y. and Tobe, M. 1985. Development of an Improved Thermofin Tube. *Hitachi Cable Review* 4:47–50. In (Webb, 1994).
Singh, A., Ohadi, M. M., and Dessiatoun, S. 1996. Flow Boiling Heat Transfer Coefficients in a Microfin Tube. *Transactions of ASME, Journal of Heat Transfer* 118:497–499.
Singh, A., Ohadi, M. M., Dessiatoun, S., and Chu, W. 1994. In-Tube Boiling Heat Transfer Enhancement of R-123 Using the EHD Technique. *ASHRAE Transactions* 100(2):828–835.
Singh, A., Ohadi, M. M., Dessiatoun, S., and Salehi, M. 1995. In-Tube Boiling Enhancement of R-134a Utilizing the Electric Field Effect. *ASME/JSME Thermal Energy Conference* 2:215–224.
Thome, J. R. 1990. *Enhanced Boiling Heat Transfer*. Washington, D.C: Hemisphere Publishing Corp.
Thors, P. and Bogart, J 1994. In-Tube Evaporation of HCFC-22 with Enhanced Tubes. *Enhanced Heat Transfer* 1(4):365–377.
Wadekar, V. V. 1996. A Comparative Study of In-Tube Boiling on Plain and High Flux Coated Surfaces. *2nd European Thermal Sciences/14th UIT National Heat Transfer Conference*, Rome, 1:195–201.
Wadekar, V. V. 1998. Improving Industrial Heat Transfer—Compact and Not-Compact Heat Exchangers. *Journal of Enhanced Heat Transfer* 5(1):53–69.
Webb, R. L. 1994. *Principles of Enhanced Heat Transfer*. New York: John Wiley and Sons, Inc.
Yabe, A., Taketani, T., Maki, H., Takashi, K., and Nakadi, Y. 1992. Experimental Study of

Electrohydrodynamically Enhanced Evaporator for Nonazeotropic Mixtures. *ASHRAE Transactions* 98(2):455–461.

Yoshida, S. and Matsunaga, T. 1991. Influence of Oil on Heat Transfer to Refrigerant Flowing in a Horizontal, Spirally Grooved Evaporator. *Proceedings of the ASME/JSME Thermal Engineering Conference*, Eds. Lloyd, J. R. and Kurosaki, Y. Book No. 10309B, pp. 327–332.

Yoshida, S., Matsunaga, T., and Hong, H. P. 1987. Heat Transfer to Refrigerants in Horizontal Evaporator Tubes with Internal, Spiral Grooves. *Proceedings of the 1987 ASME-JSME Thermal Engineering Joint Conference* 5. Ed. P. J. Marto, pp. 165–172.

CHAPTER
# NINETEEN

## FILM CONDENSATION

### 19.1   John Rose

*University of London, London E1 4NS, United Kingdom*

### 19.2, 19.3   Haruo Uehara

*Saga University, Honjyo, Saga, Japan*

### 19.4   Shigeru Koyama

*Kyushu University, 6-1 Kasuga-koen, 816-858, Japan*

### 19.4   Tetsu Fujii

*University of East Asia, Shimonoseki 751-8503, Japan*

## 19.1  LAMINAR FILM CONDENSATION OF PURE VAPORS

### 19.1.1 Introduction

In many process applications, vapors often contain more than one molecular species, and some or all of these may condense. In this case, diffusion (with convection) in the vapor phase, leading to differences in temperature and composition between the "bulk" vapor and the vapor adjacent to the interface, is an important mechanism affecting the heat-transfer and condensation rates. Here, we shall only consider the case where one molecular species is present.

Even for the case of a pure vapor, the condensation process in an industrial condenser is extremely complex. Vapor and condensate flows are in general three-dimensional and involve effects of gravity, shear stress at the condensate surface due to vapor velocity, interface temperature difference due to non-equilibrium, and inundation, i.e., condensate from higher or upstream surfaces impinging on lower or downstream surfaces. For enhanced (profiled) surfaces (e.g., finned tubes), surface tension effects are also important. Condensate and vapor flows may be either laminar or turbulent. The condensate may form a continuous film on the surface (film condensation) or, when the surface is not wetted by the condensate, discrete droplets (dropwise condensation). Condensation may occur on external surfaces, e.g., on the outside of the tubes in a shell-and-tube condenser, or on internal surfaces, e.g., in-tube condensation. In "direct contact" condensation, liquid is brought directly into contact with the vapor at a temperature below the saturation temperature. The extent to which the condensation process is understood and the accuracy with which heat transfer coefficients can be calculated depend on the circumstances. Accurate predictions can now be made for relatively simple geometry (e.g., vertical plate or single horizontal tube) and for well-defined flow conditions.

This section is concerned with the best understood cases of laminar film condensation on vertical and horizontal plates and the horizontal tube. More complex situations are treated elsewhere. A brief discussion of interphase matter transfer is given before considering the more common case where "interface resistance" is negligible.

## 19.1.2 Interface Resistance

The fact that equilibrium conditions cannot strictly prevail at the vapor-condensate interface during condensation means that a temperature difference must occur between the vapor and condensate in the vicinity of the interface. Extrapolations to the interface of the temperature distributions in the vapor and liquid show a discontinuity, the *interface temperature drop*. The problem has been studied for many years, and it is now established that the interface temperature drop is essentially confined to a region in the vapor having a thickness of a few mean free paths of the vapor molecules. As noted by Niknejad and Rose (1981), various related theoretical approaches lead to the expression

$$m = \xi \{p_v - p_{sat}(T_s)\}/(R_g T_s)^{1/2} \tag{19.1-1}$$

where $m$ is the net condensation mass flux, $p_v$ is the vapor pressure, $p_{sat}(T_s)$ is the saturation pressure at the liquid surface temperature, $T_s$, and $R_g$ is the specific gas constant of the vapor. $\xi$ is a dimensionless quantity of order unity. Experiments and theory show that $\xi$ depends on $m$, $\xi$ *increasing* with *increasing m*, and pressure. However, as $m$ tends to zero (equilibrium), $\xi$ approaches the same value for all vapor pressures.

One of the difficulties that arises in the theory of interphase matter transfer is that it is not certain that all vapor molecules striking the liquid surface remain in the liquid phase, i.e., some molecules may be reflected. Some theoretical models incorporate a parameter $\sigma$, the *condensation coefficient*, defined as the fraction of those vapor molecules impinging on the liquid surface that remain in the liquid phase, $\sigma$ being assumed to have a constant value. In these models, $\xi_o$ (the value of $\xi$ in Eq. [19.1-1] for $m \to 0$) is a function of $\sigma$. Other approaches assume that no vapor molecules are reflected at the liquid surface when $\sigma = 1$ and $\xi_o$ is a constant. Various theoretical models lead, with $\sigma = 1$, to values of $\xi_o$ between about 0.6

and about 0.8. While earlier experimental investigations gave much lower values that were interpreted as indicating low values of $\sigma$ (down to around 0.01), more recent studies indicate a value of $\xi_o$ near 0.7, confirming the validity of theory and suggesting that $\sigma$ is equal to or near unity. The most probable explanation of the earlier low values is the presence in the vapor of non-condensing gas, leading to a significant temperature drop in the vapor that was erroneously attributed to the interface.

For condensation of a saturated vapor and for moderate departure from equilibrium at the interface when the vapor temperature $T_v \approx T_s$, Eq. (19.1-1), with the Clausius-Clapeyron equation, leads to the following expression for the interface heat-transfer coefficient $\alpha_i$:

$$\alpha_i = \xi_o h_{lg}^2 / \left( v_{lg} T_v \sqrt{R_g T_v} \right) \qquad (19.1\text{-}2)$$

where $h_{lg}$ is the specific latent heat of vaporization and $v_{lg} = v_g - v_l$, $v_g$ and $v_l$ being the specific volumes of vapor and liquid, respectively. When the vapor is treated as an ideal gas and with $v_g \gg v_l$, Eq. (19.1-2) gives:

$$\alpha_i = \xi_o p_v h_{lg}^2 / \left[ T_v (R_g T_v)^{3/2} \right] \qquad (19.1\text{-}3)$$

Equation (19.1-3) gives values of $\alpha_i$ much higher than the heat-transfer coefficient for the condensate in film condensation, except in the case of liquid metals. Therefore, the interface *resistance* is, apart from the case of liquid metals, generally negligible for practical purposes. It should be noted however that for *dropwise condensation*, when heat-transfer coefficients are very high, the interface resistance plays an important role, leading to a significant dependence of heat-transfer coefficient on vapor pressure.

### 19.1.3 Free-Convection Condensation of a Saturated Vapor

The problem of laminar film condensation (with negligible interface resistance) was first treated by Nusselt (1916) for condensation on an isothermal vertical plane surface and an isothermal horizontal tube. Nusselt's main assumptions were that the motion of the condensate is controlled solely by gravity and viscosity, that acceleration (inertia effects) in the condensate film is negligible, that heat transfer across the condensate film is by pure conduction, and that the condensate properties do not vary across the film.

For the case of free-convection condensation, Nusselt invoked the additional assumption that the shear stress from the vapor on the surface of the condensate film was negligible. For condensation on a *vertical plate* (see Figure 1), conservation of momentum in the condensate film gives

$$\eta \frac{\partial^2 u}{\partial y^2} + g \Delta \rho = 0 \qquad (19.1\text{-}4)$$

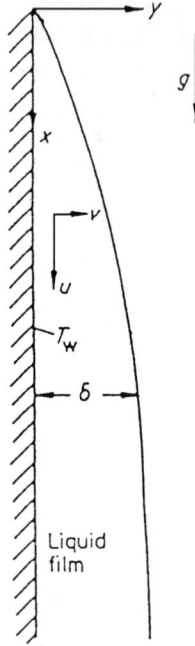

**Figure 1** Condensation on vertical plate.

where the vertical pressure gradient is taken as that in the remote vapor that has no vertical motion. In Eq. (19.1-4), $u$ is the downward velocity parallel to the plate and $y$ is measured normally outward from the plate; $\Delta\rho = \rho - \rho_g$, where $\rho$ and $\rho_g$ are the condensate and vapor densities respectively, $\eta$ is the condensate viscosity, and $g$ is the specific force of gravity.

Equation (19.1-4) is readily integrated (for constant properties) using the boundary conditions

$$u = 0 \quad \text{when } y = 0 \tag{19.1-5}$$

$$\frac{\partial u}{\partial y} = 0 \quad \text{when } y = \delta \tag{19.1-6}$$

where $\delta$ is the local condensate film thickness, to give the velocity distribution across the condensate film

$$u = \frac{g\Delta\rho}{\eta}\left(\delta y - \frac{y^2}{2}\right) \tag{19.1-7}$$

Conservation of mass in the condensate film, with local heat flux $q$ given by

$$q = m h_{lg} = \lambda \Delta T / \delta \tag{19.1-8}$$

where $\lambda$ is the condensate thermal conductivity and $\Delta T$ is the temperature drop across the condensate film, yields

$$\delta \frac{d}{dx}\left\{\int_0^\delta u\, dy\right\} = \frac{\lambda \Delta T}{\rho h_{lg}} \qquad (19.1\text{-}9)$$

where $x$ is the distance from the top of the plate.

The integral in Eq. (19.1-9) may be evaluated using Eq. (19.1-7), and for an *isothermal* surface, when $\Delta T$ is constant, Eq. (19.1-9) solved with the boundary condition

$$\delta = 0 \quad \text{at } x = 0 \qquad (19.1\text{-}10)$$

to give the local film thickness

$$\delta = \left(\frac{4\eta\lambda x \Delta T}{\rho \Delta \rho g h_{lg}}\right)^{1/4} \qquad (19.1\text{-}11)$$

The local heat-transfer coefficient $\rho/\Delta T$ is equal to $\lambda/\delta$ (see Eq. [19.1-8]) and hence is given by

$$\alpha = \left(\frac{\rho \Delta \rho g h_{lg} \lambda^3}{4\eta x \Delta T}\right)^{1/4} \qquad (19.1\text{-}12)$$

From Eq. (19.1-12), it may be seen that the local heat flux $q$ is given by

$$q = Cx^{-1/4} \qquad (19.1\text{-}13)$$

where

$$C = \left(\frac{\rho \Delta \rho g h_{lg} \lambda^3 \Delta T^3}{4\eta}\right)^{1/4} \qquad (19.1\text{-}14)$$

so that the mean heat flux for a surface of height $L$ is readily seen to be

$$\bar{q}_L = \frac{1}{L}\int_0^L q\, dx = \frac{4}{3}q_L \qquad (19.1\text{-}15)$$

where $q_L$ is the local value of $q$ at $x = L$. The mean heat-transfer coefficient for a surface of height $L$, $\bar{q}_L/\Delta T$ is then given by

$$\bar{\alpha}_L = \frac{2\sqrt{2}}{3}\left(\frac{\rho \Delta \rho g h_{lg} \lambda^3}{\eta L \Delta T}\right)^{1/4} \qquad (19.1\text{-}16)$$

and the mean Nusselt number by

$$\overline{Nu_L} = \frac{\bar{\alpha}_L L}{\lambda} = \frac{2\sqrt{2}}{3}\left(\frac{\rho \Delta \rho g h_{lg} L^3}{\eta \lambda \Delta T}\right)^{1/4} \qquad (19.1\text{-}17)$$

or

$$\overline{Nu}_L = \frac{2\sqrt{2}}{3}\left(\frac{Gr_L}{J}\right)^{1/4} \qquad (19.1\text{-}18)$$

where

$$J = \frac{\lambda \Delta T}{\eta h_{lg}} \qquad (19.1\text{-}19)$$

and

$$Gr_L = \frac{\rho \Delta \rho g L^3}{\eta^2} \qquad (19.1\text{-}20)$$

For condensation on inclined plates, the above equations hold with $g \sin \phi$ replacing $g$, where $\phi$ is the angle made by the plate with the horizontal.

For condensation on a *horizontal tube* (see Figure 2), when the condensate film is thin compared with the tube radius, a momentum balance for the condensate film at a point where the radius make an angle $\theta$ to the vertical yields

$$\eta \frac{\partial^2 u}{\partial y^2} + g \sin \theta \Delta \rho = 0 \qquad (19.1\text{-}21)$$

where $u$ is the tangential velocity and $y$ is distance measured radially from the tube surface. Equation (19.1-21), with zero velocity at the tube surface and zero

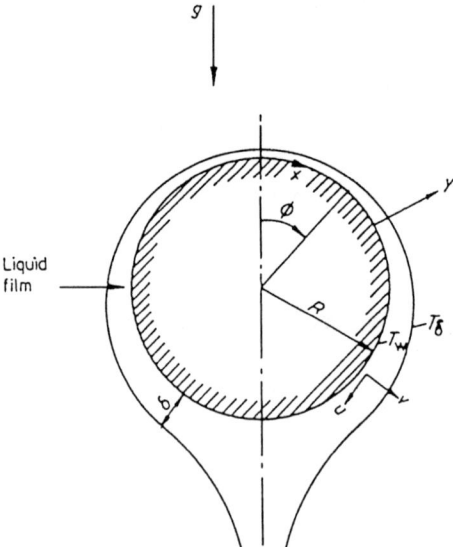

**Figure 2** Condensation on horizontal tube.

shear stress assumed at the condensate surface, gives for the tangential velocity in the condensate film

$$u = \frac{g \sin \theta}{\eta} \Delta \rho \left( \delta y - \frac{y^2}{2} \right) \qquad (19.1\text{-}22)$$

Conservation of mass with radial conduction across the condensate film yields

$$\frac{\delta}{R} \frac{d}{d\theta} \left\{ \int_0^\delta u \, dy \right\} = \frac{\lambda \Delta T}{\rho h_{lg}} \qquad (19.1\text{-}23)$$

where $R$ is the tube radius.

Equation (19.1-23), with Eq. (19.1-22), yields the following differential equation for the condensate film thickness

$$\delta \frac{d}{d\theta} (\delta^3 \sin \theta) = \frac{3}{2} \frac{\eta \lambda d \Delta T}{\rho \Delta \rho g h_{lg}} \qquad (19.1\text{-}24)$$

where $d$ is the tube diameter. Putting

$$z = \delta^4 \cdot \frac{\rho \Delta \rho g h_{lg}}{\eta \lambda d \Delta T} \qquad (19.1\text{-}25)$$

for an *isothermal* surface when $\Delta T$ is constant, Eq. (19.1-24) may be written as

$$\sin \theta \frac{dz}{d\theta} + \frac{4}{3} z \cos \theta - 2 = 0 \qquad (19.1\text{-}26)$$

By symmetry, $dz/d\theta = 0$ at $\theta = 0$, when Eq. (19.1-26) gives

$$z_{\theta=0} = 3/2 \qquad (19.1\text{-}27)$$

so that the film thickness at the top of the tube is

$$\delta_{\theta=0} = \left( \frac{3}{2} \frac{\eta \lambda d \Delta T}{\rho \Delta \rho g h_{lg}} \right)^{1/4} \qquad (19.1\text{-}28)$$

The solution of Eq. (19.1-26), subject to the condition that $z$ is finite at $\theta = 0$ or by symmetry $dz/d\theta = 0$, is

$$z = \frac{2}{\sin^{4/3} \theta} \int_0^\theta \sin^{1/3} \theta \, d\theta \qquad (19.1\text{-}29)$$

as may be readily verified by differentiation.

Using Eqs. (19.1-25) and (19.1-29), the local heat flux $q = \lambda \Delta T/\delta$ may be written as

$$q = \left\{ \frac{\rho \Delta \rho g h_{lg} \lambda^3 \Delta T^3}{\eta d} \right\}^{1/4} \left\{ \frac{2}{\sin^{4/3} \theta} \int_0^\theta \sin^{1/3} \theta \, d\theta \right\}^{-1/4} \qquad (19.1\text{-}30)$$

The mean heat flux up to angle $\theta$ is then given by

$$\bar{q}_\theta = \left\{ \frac{\rho \Delta \rho g h_{lg} \lambda^3 \, \Delta T^3}{\eta d} \right\}^{1/4} \psi(\theta) \tag{19.1-31}$$

where

$$\psi(\theta) = \frac{1}{2^{1/4}} \frac{1}{\theta} \int_0^\theta \frac{\sin^{1/3}\theta}{\left( \int_0^\theta \sin^{1/3}\theta \, d\theta \right)^{1/4}} \, d\theta \tag{19.1-32}$$

and

$$\int_0^\theta \frac{\sin^{1/3}\theta}{\left( \int_0^\theta \sin^{1/3}\theta \, d\theta \right)^{1/4}} \, d\theta = \frac{4}{3} \left\{ \int_0^\theta \sin^{1/3}\theta \, d\theta \right\}^{3/4} \tag{19.1-33}$$

so that

$$\bar{q}_\theta = \left\{ \frac{\rho \Delta \rho g h_{lg} \lambda^3 \, \Delta T^3}{\eta d} \right\}^{1/4} \frac{4}{2^{1/4} \, 3} \cdot \frac{1}{\theta} \left\{ \int_0^\theta \sin^{1/3}\theta \, d\theta \right\}^{3/4} \tag{19.1-34}$$

When $\theta = \pi$, we obtain the mean flux for the tube

$$\bar{q} = \frac{4}{2^{1/4} 3\pi} \left\{ \frac{\rho \Delta \rho g h_{lg} \lambda^3 \, \Delta T^3}{\eta d} \right\}^{1/4} \left\{ \int_0^\pi \sin^{1/3}\theta \, d\theta \right\}^{3/4} \tag{19.1-35}$$

and

$$\int_0^\pi \sin^{1/3}\theta \, d\theta = 2^{7/3} \pi^2 / [\Gamma(1/3)]^3 \tag{19.1-36}$$

where $\Gamma$ is the gamma function (see Rose, 1998). Thus

$$\bar{q} = (8/3)(2\pi)^{1/2} [\Gamma(1/3)]^{-9/4} \left\{ \frac{\rho \Delta \rho g h_{lg} \lambda^3 \, \Delta T^3}{\eta d} \right\}^{1/4}$$

$$= 0.728018 \cdots \left\{ \frac{\rho \Delta \rho g h_{lg} \lambda^3 \, \Delta T^3}{\eta d} \right\}^{1/4} \tag{19.1-37}$$

$$\bar{\alpha} = \frac{\bar{q}}{\Delta T} = 0.728018 \cdots \left\{ \frac{\rho \Delta \rho g h_{lg} \lambda^3}{\eta d \, \Delta T} \right\}^{1/4} \tag{19.1-38}$$

$$\overline{Nu} = \frac{\bar{\alpha} d}{\lambda} = 0.728018 \cdots \left\{ \frac{\rho \Delta \rho g h_{lg} d^3}{\eta \lambda \, \Delta T} \right\}^{1/4} \tag{19.1-39}$$

or

$$\overline{Nu} = 0.728018\cdots(Gr_d/J)^{1/4} \qquad (19.1\text{-}40)$$

where

$$Gr_d = \frac{\rho \Delta \rho g d^3}{\eta^2} \qquad (19.1\text{-}41)$$

Finally, it may be noted that Eq. (19.1-29) indicates that the film thickness becomes infinite at the bottom of the tube and invalidates the assumption that $\delta \ll R$. However, as the film thickness increases towards the lower part of the tube, the local heat flux becomes very small, so that the effect of erroneous values on the average heat flux and heat-transfer coefficient for the whole tube is small.

Solutions have been given for the above problems using the condition of uniform surface heat flux rather than uniform surface temperature (see Fujii et al., 1972). For the *vertical plate*, the results for the mean heat-transfer coefficient and mean Nusselt number are the same as those given by Eqs. (19.1-16) and (19.1-17), except that the average value of $\Delta T$

$$\overline{\Delta T_L} = \frac{1}{L} \int_0^L \Delta T \, dx \qquad (19.1\text{-}42)$$

replaces $\Delta T$, and the uniform heat flux replaces the average heat flux. For the horizontal tube with uniform surface heat flux, Fujii et al. (1972) give

$$\overline{Nu} = 0.695 \left\{ \frac{\rho \Delta \rho g h_{lg} d^3}{\eta \lambda \overline{\Delta T_d}} \right\}^{1/4} \qquad (19.1\text{-}43)$$

with

$$\overline{\Delta T_d} = \frac{1}{\pi} \int_0^\pi \Delta T \, d\theta \qquad (19.1\text{-}44)$$

which may be compared with Eq. (19.1-39). It should be noted that, in this case

$$\overline{\Delta T_d} = \frac{q}{\pi \lambda} \int_0^\pi \delta \, d\theta \qquad (19.1\text{-}45)$$

so that erroneous values of $\delta$ near $\theta = \pi$ when $\delta$ becomes large will have a significant effect on $\overline{\Delta T_d}$. This casts some doubt on the validity of Eq. (19.1-43).

More recently, Memory and Rose (1991) have solved the Nusselt problem for the horizontal tube using a cosine distribution of surface temperature suggested by experimental measurements. It was found that even in the most extreme case where $\Delta T$ is zero at the top of the tube, the results are the same as those given by Eqs. (19.1-37), (19.1-38), and (19.1-39) but with the mean $\overline{\Delta T_d}$ replacing the uniform $\Delta T$. The leading constant in all cases was 0.7280.

## 19.1.4 Boundary Layer Solutions

With the advent of computers, solutions have been obtained by several researchers on the basis of the boundary-layer equations for the condensate film, thereby relaxing Nusselt's approximations (neglect of inertia terms in the momentum equation, convection terms in the energy equation, and shear stress at the condensate surface). These works have been reviewed by Rose (1988). The overall conclusion is that for a wide range of conditions covering those normally occurring in practice, the simple Nusselt results are surprisingly accurate. The results of the more recent works are conveniently summarized by equations given by Chen (1961a, 1961b), which apply equally to vertical plates and horizontal tubes and to local and mean values of Nusselt number:

$$\frac{Nu}{Nu_{Nu}} = \left[\frac{1 + 0.68H + \frac{0.02}{Pr}H^2}{1 + \frac{0.85}{Pr}H - \frac{0.15}{Pr}H^2}\right]^{1/4} = \left[\frac{1 + 0.68PrJ + 0.02PrJ^2}{1 + 0.85J - 0.15PrJ^2}\right]^{1/4} \tag{19.1-46}$$

where $Nu_{Nu}$ is the Nusselt number given by the Nusselt theory, $Pr$ is the condensate Prandtl number, $J$ is defined in Eq. (19.1-19), and

$$H = \frac{c_p \Delta T}{h_{lg}} \tag{19.1-47}$$

where $c_p$ is the constant pressure specific heat capacity of the condensate. Equation (19.1-46) fitted Chen's numerical results to within 1%.

For low Prandtl number condensates (liquid metals), the normalized Nusselt number falls quite sharply with increasing $J$ but differs significantly from unity only for values of $J$ well beyond those that occur in practice. Erroneously high values of $J$ have been reported in some early works on condensation of metals, but these are due to vapor-side temperature drops (arising from the presence of non-condensing gases or interphase matter transfer resistance) being included in $\Delta T$, the temperature drop *across the condensate film*.

## 19.1.5 Forced-Convection Condensation of a Saturated Vapor

For the case of condensation with vapor flow along a *horizontal plane surface*, the condensate film flows under the influence of surface shear stress due to the flowing vapor, and gravity is not important. For the low condensation rate limit, the local surface shear stress $\tau_\delta$ is given by the result for flow without condensation

$$\frac{\tau_\delta}{\rho_v U_\infty^2} \cdot Re_x^{1/2} = 0.332 \tag{19.1-48}$$

where $U$ is the free-stream vapor velocity parallel to the surface, $\rho_v$ and $\eta_v$ are the vapor density and viscosity, respectively, $x$ is the distance from the leading edge of the plate, and

$$Re_x = U_\infty \rho_v x / \eta_v \tag{19.1-49}$$

For the high condensation rate limit and when the condensate surface velocity is much smaller than the vapor free-stream velocity, the surface shear stress is given by

$$\tau_\delta = m U_\infty \tag{19.1-50}$$

where $m$ is the condensation mass flux. In the general case, the surface shear stress is determined by simultaneous solution of the momentum equations for the vapor and condensate with appropriate conditions at the interface.

When the condensate film is treated using the Nusselt approximations, it is found that $m \propto x^{-1/2}$ (this is also true for condensation in the presence of a non-condensing gas), so that the equation given by Rose (1979)

$$\frac{c_f Re_x^{1/2}}{2} = \frac{0.747}{1 + 1.57(0.84 - B)^{1.27}} - B \tag{19.1-51}$$

where

$$c_f = \tau_\delta / 1/2 (\rho_v U_\infty^2) \tag{19.1-52}$$

$$B = (v_0 / U_\infty) Re_x^{1/2} = -(m / \rho_v U_\infty) Re_x^{1/2} \tag{19.1-53}$$

and $v_0$ is the normal (outward) vapor velocity at the condensate surface, gives the surface shear stress in the general case. It is readily seen that Eq. (19.1-51) agrees closely with Eq. (19.1-48) for zero condensation rate ($B = 0$) and with Eq. (19.1-50) for infinite condensation rate ($-B \to \infty$).

The problem of forced-convection condensation on a horizontal isothermal surface has been treated by several investigators, notably Cess (1960), Koh (1962a), and Shekriladze and Gomelauri (1966). Equation (19.1-48) leads to

$$Nu_x \tilde{Re}_x^{-1/2} = 0.436 \, G^{-1/3} \tag{19.1-54}$$

where

$$\tilde{Re}_x = U_\infty \rho x / \eta \tag{19.1-55}$$

$$G = \left(\frac{\lambda \Delta T}{\eta h_{lg}}\right) \cdot \left(\frac{\rho \eta}{\rho_v \eta_v}\right)^{1/2} \tag{19.1-56}$$

and Eq. (19.1-50), with the approximation that the vapor free-stream velocity greatly exceeds the condensate surface velocity, gives

$$Nu_x \tilde{Re}_x^{-1/2} = 0.5 \tag{19.1-57}$$

Note that $\tilde{Re}_x$ has the vapor velocity and condensate properties.

Equations (19.1-54) and (19.1-57) are both conservative, i.e., they underestimate the heat transfer coefficient. Equation (19.1-54) is more accurate when $G <$ about 1, and Eq. (19.1-57) is more accurate when $G >$ about 1. A general formula that summarizes the results quite well has been given by Rose (1988):

$$Nu_x \tilde{Re}_x^{-1/2} = 0.436 \left[ \frac{1.508}{(1+J)^{3/2}} + \frac{1}{G} \right]^{1/3} \quad (19.1\text{-}58)$$

The presence of $J$ in Eq. (19.1-58) results from non-neglect of the surface velocity of the condensate film. Since in practice $J \ll 1$, this has a marginal effect. It may be noted that Eq. (19.1-58), with $J \ll 1$, reduces to Eqs. (19.1-54) and (19.1-57) for small and large $G$, respectively. It may be seen from Eqs. (19.1-54), (19.1-57), and (19.1-58) that the local heat flux varies along the plate as $x^{-1/2}$, so that the mean Nusselt number for a plate of length $L$, $\overline{Nu_L}$, is equal to twice $Nu_L$, the local value at $x = L$.

Solutions have also been obtained for vapor downflow on a vertical plate where both gravity and vapor shear stress are included. Fujii and Uehara (1972) used an integral treatment in which the surface shear stress was obtained by matching shear stresses for the liquid and vapor on either side of the interface. Their results were approximated by

$$\overline{Nu_L} \tilde{Re}_L^{-1/2} = \left\{ 0.656(1.2 + G^{-1})^{4/3} + 0.79 F_L \right\}^{1/4} \quad (19.1\text{-}59)$$

where

$$\tilde{Re}_L = U_\infty \rho L / \eta \quad (19.1\text{-}60)$$

$$F_L = \eta h_{lg} g L / \lambda \Delta T U_\infty^2 \quad (19.1\text{-}61)$$

Shekriladze (1977) modified an earlier result of Shekriladze and Gomelauri (1966) to extend its range of validity to low condensation rates and obtained

$$\overline{Nu_L} \tilde{Re}_L^{-1/2} = \frac{\sqrt{2}}{3} K \frac{(2 + \sqrt{1 + 16 F_L K^{-4}})}{(1 + \sqrt{1 + 16 F_L K^{-4}})^{1/2}} \quad (19.1\text{-}62)$$

where

$$K = (1 + 0.66\, G^{-1})^{1/3} \quad (19.1\text{-}63)$$

$F_L$ in Eqs. (19.1-59) and (19.1-62) is sometimes written in terms of simpler dimensionless numbers,

$$F_L = Pr / Fr_L H \quad (19.1\text{-}64)$$

where $Fr_L$ is the Froude number $U_\infty^2 / gL$ and $H$ is defined in Eq. (19.1-47). This seems inappropriate here, since $c_P$ and hence $Pr$ and $H$ are not relevant to the problem. Moreover, in order that Eqs. (19.1-59) and (19.1-62) are compatible with the Nusselt free-convection solution when $F_L \to \infty$, $F_L$ should strictly be written

$$F_L = \Delta\rho \, \eta \, h_{\lg} \, g \, L / \rho \lambda \Delta T U_\infty^2 \qquad (19.1\text{-}65)$$

The solutions on which Eqs. (19.1-59) and (19.1-62) are based relate to cases for which $\Delta\rho \approx \rho$, i.e., not near the critical point. $F_L$ may be more usefully written in terms of simpler dimensionless numbers as

$$F_L = Gr_L / J \tilde{Re}_L^2 \qquad (19.1\text{-}66)$$

where $J$ and $Gr_L$ are defined in Eqs. (19.1-19) and (19.1-20), from which it is evident that $F_L$ measures the relative importance of gravity and vapor velocity.

For forced-convection condensation on a *horizontal tube*, the problem is complicated by pressure variation around the tube and, more seriously, by separation of the vapor boundary layer. By using the high condensation rate, limiting value of the surface shear stress (analogous to Eq. [19.1-50] for the flat plate), and assuming potential flow outside the vapor boundary layer so that the vapor boundary layer does not separate, Shekriladze and Gomelauri (1966) obtained solutions for vertical vapor downflow that may be closely approximated (see Rose, 1984) by

$$\overline{Nu} \tilde{Re}_d^{-1/2} = \frac{0.9 + 0.728 F_d^{1/2}}{\left(1 + 3.44 F_d^{1/2} + F_d\right)^{1/4}} \qquad (19.1\text{-}67)$$

where

$$\overline{Nu} = \bar{\alpha} d / \lambda \quad (\bar{\alpha} \text{ is the mean heat-transfer coefficient}) \qquad (19.1\text{-}68)$$
$$F_d = \Delta\rho \eta h_{\lg} g d / \rho \lambda \Delta T U_\infty^2 = Gr_d / J \tilde{Re}_d^2 \qquad (19.1\text{-}69)$$
$$\tilde{Re}_d = U_\infty \rho d / \eta \qquad (19.1\text{-}70)$$

and $Gr_d$ is defined in Eq. (19.1-41).

Equation (19.1-67) reduces to the Nusselt solution when the vapor velocity is zero. By underestimating the surface shear stress prior to separation of the vapor boundary layer and overestimating the surface shear stress thereafter, Eq. (19.1-67) is conservative for the upper part of the tube and sometimes overestimates the heat-transfer for the lower part of the tube. Equation (19.1-67) is in fair agreement with data for various fluids (see Rose, 1988).

More detailed solutions of the problem of forced convection condensation on a horizontal tube have been obtained by Gaddis (1979), Fujii et al. (1979), Fujii (1981), Lee and Rose (1982), and Honda and Fujii (1984). The results, which cannot generally be expressed as simple equations, are reviewed by Rose (1988).

### 19.1.6 Effect of Variable Properties

Viscosity, thermal conductivity, and density depend on temperature, which varies across the condensate film. In the foregoing discussion, these properties have been assumed to be uniform. When using the results given above, it is necessary to adopt appropriate mean, representative, or reference properties. Various investigators have used approximate methods or numerical variable-property solutions to obtain a "reference temperature" as a suitable mean value between the vapor and wall temperatures. Equations of the type

$$T^* = \beta T_w + (1 - \beta)T_\delta \qquad (19.1\text{-}71)$$

where $T^*$ is the reference temperature and $T_w$ and $T_\delta$ are the wall and condensate surface temperatures, respectively, have been suggested by several investigators, as discussed by Rose (1988) and Fujii (1991). The recommended values of $\beta$ differ somewhat among authors for different condensing fluids and for forced and free convection conditions.

It is clear that since the temperature dependence of the properties is different for each property and the properties play different roles in the problem, the single reference temperature concept can only be approximate. Variation in thermal conductivity and density are generally much weaker than that of viscosity, and the reference temperature is dominated by viscosity variation. Values quoted for $\beta$ are in some cases based on comparisons with solutions that include inertia and convection effects in the condensate film or sometimes when these are neglected. As discussed above, for practical purposes, inertia and convection effects are small and should not affect the value of the reference temperature significantly.

For calculating the representative viscosity, Mayhew et al. (1965) and Fujii (1991) use the approximation that reciprocal viscosity varies linearly with temperature to show that the values of $\beta$ in Eq. (19.1-71) are 3/4 for free convection condensation and 2/3 for forced convection condensation. The heat transfer coefficient and Nusselt number are not significantly different when thermal conductivity and density are obtained using these values or when taking $\beta$ to be 1/2. It is evident from the derivations that $\rho_g$ should be taken at the vapor temperature and $h_{lg}$ at the condensate surface temperature (equal to the vapor temperature for the case of a saturated vapor and with negligible interface temperature drop, as considered here).

In all cases, reference temperature values have been determined on the basis of solutions for a flat plate. However, for practical purposes, the same values are probably adequate for the horizontal tube when other uncertainties, particularly in the case of forced convection, may be more important.

## 19.2 TRANSITION AND TURBULENT FILM CONDENSATION

### 19.2.1 Transition and Turbulent Film Condensation of Body Forced Convection

**19.2.1.1 Correlations of local heat transfer coefficient.** Since Nusselt (1916) first presented a solution for laminar condensation of a saturated pure steam on an isothermal vertical plate, a number of authors have conducted the experimental and theoretical studies on the film condensation on a vertical plate and horizontal tube (Fujii and Uehara, 1972).

Recently, Uehara and Kinoshita (1994) conducted an experimental study on the body forced convection film condensation on a vertical plate (length: 2.980 m) for the vapor of CFC11, CFC113, and HCFC123. They found that the flow patterns of condensate film on a vertical plate were classified into laminar flow, sine wave flow, harmonic wave flow, and turbulent flow, as shown Figure 3. They proposed the nondimensional correlations for the local heat transfer coefficients for laminar flow, sine wave flow, harmonic wave flow, and turbulent flow as the following equations:

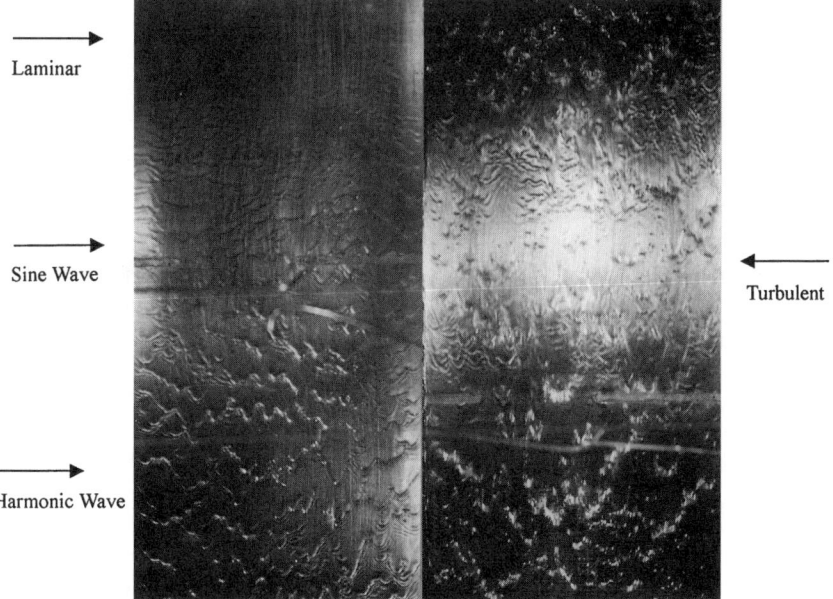

**Figure 3** Flow patterns of condensate film.

1) laminar flow

$$Nu_x = 0.707(Gr_x Pr_L/Ja)^{1/4} \qquad (19.2\text{-}1)$$

2) sine wave flow

$$Nu_x = 1.65 So^{-1/3}(Ja/Pr_L)^{1/3}(Gr_x Pr_L/Ja)^{1/3} \qquad (19.2\text{-}2)$$

3) harmonic wave flow

$$Nu_x = 0.725(Ja/Pr_L)^{1/15}(Gr_x Pr_L/Ja)^{4/15} \qquad (19.2\text{-}3)$$

4) turbulent flow

$$Nu_x = 0.043 Ja^{1/5} Gr_x^{2/5} \qquad (19.2\text{-}4)$$

Equation (19.2-1) is Nusselt's equation for laminar film condensation, where the Nusselt number $Nu_x$, Grashof number $Gr_x$, Jakov number $Ja$, and Soflata number $So$ are defined as follows:

$$Nu_x = \frac{\alpha_x x}{\lambda_L} \qquad (19.2\text{-}5)$$

$$Gr_x = \left(\frac{gx^3}{v_L^2}\right)\left(\frac{\rho_L - \rho_v}{\rho_L}\right) \qquad (19.2\text{-}6)$$

$$Ja = \frac{c_{PL}(T_{Vx} - T_{wx})}{h_{fg}} \qquad (19.2\text{-}7)$$

$$So = \left(\frac{3\sigma^3}{\rho_L^3 g v_L^4}\right)^{1/5} \qquad (19.2\text{-}8)$$

**19.2.1.2 Transition point.** The transition point from laminar flow to sine wave flow, from sine wave flow to harmonic wave flow and then to turbulent flow are expressed as the following equations:

1) Transition point from the laminar flow to sine wave flow:

$$(Gr_x Pr_L/Ja)_{LSC} = 3.83 \times 10^{-5} So^4 (Ja/Pr_L)^{-4} \qquad (19.2\text{-}9)$$

2) Transition point from the sine wave flow to harmonic flow:

$$(Gr_x Pr_L/Ja)_{SHC} = 4.39 \times 10^{-6} So^5 (Ja/Pr_L)^{-4} \qquad (19.2\text{-}10)$$

3) Transition point from the harmonic flow to turbulent flow:

$$(Gr_x Pr_L/Ja)_{HTC} = 1.59 \times 10^9 Ja^{-4} Pr_L^{5/2} \qquad (19.2\text{-}11)$$

Uehara and Kinoshita (1994) proposed the correlation of the local heat transfer coefficients for $Gr_x Pr_L/Ja \geq 4.39 \times 10^{-6} So^5 (Ja/Pr_L)^{-4}$ as the following equation:

$$Nu_x = 0.725(Ja/Pr_L)^{1/15}(Gr_x Pr_L/Ja)^{4/15}$$
$$\times \{1 + 6.25 \times 10^{-10}[Ja^2 Pr_L^{-5/4}(Gr_x Pr_L/Ja)^{1/2}]^2\}^{2/15} \quad (19.2\text{-}12)$$

### 19.2.1.3 Correlation of the local heat transfer coefficient using the relation between condensation number $Nu_x^*$ and function $f(Re_x^*, Pr_L, So)$.

Since Kirkbride (1933) showed the correlation of mean heat transfer coefficient using condensation number $Nu^*$ and film Reynolds number $Re^*$, a number of authors have shown the correlation of mean heat transfer coefficient for body forced convection film condensation on a vertical surface using $Nu^*$ and $Re^*$. The local condensation number $Nu^*$ and the film Reynolds number $Re_x^*$ are expressed by

$$Nu_x^* = \frac{\alpha_x (\nu_L^2/g)^{1/3}}{\lambda_L}\left(\frac{\rho_L}{\rho_L - \rho_V}\right)^{1/3} \quad (19.2\text{-}13)$$

$$Re_x^* = \frac{4\dot{q}x}{\mu_L L} \quad (19.2\text{-}14)$$

where

$$\dot{q}_x = \frac{1}{x}\int_0^x q_x\,dx \quad (19.2\text{-}15)$$

The local Nusselt number $Nu_x$ and the local condensation number $Nu_x^*$ for body-forced convection film condensation on a vertical plate and pure vapor can be expressed generally by

$$Nu_x = C_1 Ja^a\, Gr_x^b\, Pr_L^c\, So^d \quad (19.2\text{-}16)$$

$$Nu_x^* = C_2 Re_x^{*m}\, Pr_L^n\, So^l \quad (19.2\text{-}17)$$

The exponents m, n, l, and constant $C_2$ in Equation (19.2-17) can be expressed by using $C_1$, A, B, C, and D as

$$C_2 = \{C_1[(1+a)/4]^a\}^{\frac{1}{(1+a)}} \quad (19.2\text{-}18)$$

$$m = \frac{a}{1+a} \quad (19.2\text{-}19)$$

$$n = \frac{a+c}{1+a} \quad (19.2\text{-}20)$$

$$l = \frac{d}{1+a} \quad (19.2\text{-}21)$$

Using equations (19.2-18) to (19.2-21), we can obtain the correlation of the local condensation number on a vertical plate for laminar flow, sine wave flow, harmonic wave flow, and turbulent flow as the follows:

1) for laminar flow:
$$Nu_x^* = 1.1 Re_x^{*-1/3} \quad Re_x^* \leq 0.296 \, So \quad (19.2\text{-}22)$$

2) for sine wave flow:
$$Nu_x^* = 1.65 So^{-1/3} \quad 0.296 So \leq Re_x^* \leq 0.135 So^{4/3} \quad (19.2\text{-}23)$$

3) for harmonic wave flow:
$$Nu_x^* = 1.0 Re_x^{*-1/4} \quad 0.135 So^{4/3} \leq Re_x^* \leq 891 Pr_L^{2/5} \quad (19.2\text{-}24)$$

4) for turbulent flow:
$$Nu_x^* = 0.059 \left(Pr_L Re_x^*\right)^{1/6} \quad Re_x^* \geq 891 Pr_L^{-2/5} \quad (19.2\text{-}25)$$

Uehara and Kinoshita (1994) proposed the following equation for $Re_x^* \geq 0.135 So^{4/3}$

$$Nu_x^* = 1.0 \, Re_x^{*-1/4} \left\{1 + 4.22 \times 10^{-8} \left(Pr_L^{2/5} Re_x^*\right)^{5/2}\right\}^{1/6} \quad (19.2\text{-}26)$$

### 19.2.1.4 Correlations of the mean heat transfer coefficients for body forced convection film condensation.
Since Kirkbride first proposed the correlation of the mean heat transfer coefficient for the turbulent flow condensation on a vertical surface in 1933, many authors proposed the correlations of the mean heat transfer coefficient for body forced convection turbulent film condensation:

1) Kirkbride's equation (1933)
$$Nu_m^* = 0.007 \, Re_m^{*0.4} \quad Re_m^* > 1800 \quad (19.2\text{-}27)$$

2) Colburn's equation (1934)
$$Nu_m^* = 0.056 \, Pr_L^{1/3} Re_m^{*0.2} \quad Re_m^* \geq 1800 \quad (19.2\text{-}28)$$

3) Grigul's equation (1942)
$$Nu_m^* = 0.135 \, Re_m^{*1/3} \quad Re_m^* > 1800 \quad (19.2\text{-}29)$$

where
$$Nu_m^* = \bar{\alpha} \left(v_L^2/g\right)^{1/3} [\rho_L/(\rho_L - \rho_V)]^{1/3}/\lambda_L \quad (19.2\text{-}30)$$
$$Re_m^* = 4\bar{q} \cdot l/(\mu_L L) \quad (19.2\text{-}31)$$

Equations (19.2-27) to (19.2-29) were obtained using the experimental data of diphenyl mixture, diphenyl oxide, and water on a vertical tube.

Recently, Uehara and Kinoshita (1997) obtained the correlations of mean heat transfer coefficients for body forced convection sine wave flow, harmonic wave flow, and turbulent flow condensation on a vertical plate as follows:

(1) Correlations of Mean Heat Transfer Coefficients Using Nusselt Number $Nu_l$ and Function $f(Gr_l, Pr_L, Ja, So)$

- laminar flow

$$Nu_l = 0.943(Gr_l\, Pr_L/Ja)^{1/4} \quad Gr_l\, Pr_L/Ja \leq 1.21 \times 10^{-3} So^4 (Ja/Pr_L)^{-4}$$
(19.2-32)

- sine wave flow

$$Nu_l = 1.65 So^{-1/3}(Ja/Pr_L)^{1/3}(Gr_l\, Pr_L/Ja)^{1/3}$$
$$1.21 \times 10^{-3} So^4(Ja/Pr_L)^{-4} \leq (Gr_l Pr_L/Ja)$$
$$\leq 1.24 \times 10^{-4} So^5 (Ja/Pr_L)^{-4}$$
(19.2-33)

- harmonic wave flow

$$Nu_l = 0.906(Ja/Pr_L)^{1/15}(Gr_l Pr_L/Ja)^{4/15} 1.24 \times 10^{-4} So^5 (Ja/Pr_L)^{-4}$$
$$< (Gr_l Pr_L/Ja) < 3.21 \times 10^{10} Ja^{-4}\, Pr_{L^{5/2}}$$
(19.2-34)

- turbulent flow

$$Nu_l = 0.036 Ja^{1/5}\, Gr_l^{2/5} \quad (Gr_l Pr/Ja) \geq 3.21 \times 10^{10}\, Ja^{-4}\, Pr_L^{2/5}$$
(19.2-35)

where

$$Nu_l = \bar{\alpha} l/\lambda_L \tag{19.2-36}$$

$$Gr_l = (gl^3/v_L^2)[(\rho_L - \rho_v)/\rho_L] \tag{19.2-37}$$

Uehara and Kinoshita (1994) proposed the following correlation for $Gr_l Pr_L/Ja \geq 1.24 \times 10^{-4} So^5 (Ja/Pr_L)^{-4}$:

$$Nu_l = 0.906(Ja/Pr_L)^{1/15}(Gr_l\, Pr_L/Ja)^{4/15}$$
$$\times \left\{1 + 3.12 \times 10^{-11} \left[Ja^2\, Pr_L^{-5/4}(Gr_l\, Pr_L/Ja)^{1/2}\right]^2\right\}^{2/15} \quad (19.2\text{-}38)$$

(2) Correlation of Mean Heat Transfer Coefficient Using $Nu_m^*$ and $f(Re_m^*, Pr_L, So)$
Changing the equations (19.2-32) to (19.2-35) into the relations between $Nu_m^*$ and $f(Re_m^*, Pr_L, So)$, we can obtain the following equations.

- laminar flow

$$Nu_m^* = 1.47\,\text{Re}_m^{*-1/3} \quad \text{Re}_m^* \leq 0.707 So \qquad (19.2\text{-}39)$$

- sine wave flow

$$Nu_m^* = 1.65 So^{-1/3} \quad 0.707 So \leq \text{Re}_m^* \leq 0.329 So^{4/3} \qquad (19.2\text{-}40)$$

- harmonic wave flow

$$Nu_m^* = 1.25\,\text{Re}_m^{*-1/4} \quad 0.329 So^{4/3} \leq \text{Re}_m^* \leq 2260\,\text{Pr}_L^{-2/5} \qquad (19.2\text{-}41)$$

- turbulent flow

$$Nu_m^* = 0.050\left(\text{Pr}_L \text{Re}_m^*\right)^{1/6} \quad \text{Re}_m^* \geq 2260\,\text{Pr}_L^{-2/5} \qquad (19.2\text{-}42)$$

Uehara and Kinoshita (1997) proposed the following correlation for $\text{Re}_m^* > 0.329 So^{4/3}$:

$$Nu_m^* = 1.25\,\text{Re}_m^{*-1/4}\left\{1 + 4.10 \times 10^{-9}\left(\text{Pr}_L^{2/5}\text{Re}_m^*\right)^{5/2}\right\}^{1/6} \qquad (19.2\text{-}43)$$

Figure 4 shows the comparison of Equation (19.2-43) with experimental data obtained by Hebbard and Badger (1934), Meisenburg et al. (1935), Gregorig et al.

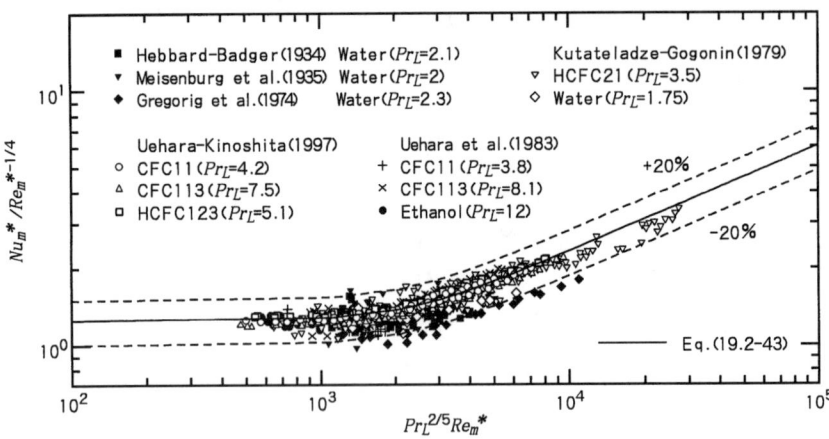

**Figure 4** Comparison of Eq.(19.2-43) with experimental data.

(1974), Kutateladze and Gogonin (1979), Uehara et al. (1983), and Uehara and Kinoshita (1997).

## 19.2.2 Theoretical Study on Transition Point and Heat Transfer of Wave Flow and Turbulent Flow

**19.2.2.1 Stability analysis of condensate film flow.** The condensate film first flows laminarly at the top portion of the surface, then changes to sine wave flow, harmonic wave flow, and finally to turbulent flow, if the length of cooling surface is long enough.

The hydrodynamic stability analysis on condensate film on a vertical plate for body forced convection has been conducted by Marshall and Lee (1973), and they have shown that a laminar condensation film is unstable and waves will appear. However, the overall effect of the condensation mass transfer tends to stabilize the film.

**19.2.2.2 Theoretical analysis of wavy film condensation.** Kapitza (1948) first conducted simple analytical treatment of heat transfer in a wavy film based on the assumption of regular sinusoidal wave and considering only heat conduction across the film. According to Kapitza's analysis, the enhanced heat transfer rate for wavy film is 21% above that for the smooth film.

Soflata (1980, 1981) proposed the correlations of the mean heat transfer coefficient for the sine wave condensation film, assuming that the waves were sinusoidal and moved with a constant velocity.

Uehara et al. (1982) analyzed the wavy film condensation using Soflat's model for wavy film and two phase boundary layer and proposed the following correlations:

$$Nu_x = (1 - \beta^2)^{-3/8} \frac{1}{\sqrt{2}} (Gr_x Pr_L / Ja)^{1/4} \qquad (19.2\text{-}44)$$

for body forced convection,

$$Nu_x = 0.45(1 - \beta^2)^{-1/2} \left\{ 1.2 + \frac{Pr_L}{RJa(1-\beta^2)^{-1/2}} \right\}^{1/3} Re_x^{1/2} \qquad (19.2\text{-}45)$$

for forced convection, and

$$Nu_x = \chi_\beta \left\{ 1 + \frac{(1-\beta^2)^{-3/2} Pr_L}{4\chi_\beta^4 Ja Fr_x} \right\}^{1/4} Re_x^{1/2} \qquad (19.2\text{-}46)$$

for combined convection, where

$$Fr_x = \frac{U_\infty^2}{gx} \tag{19.2-47}$$

$$\chi_\beta = 0.45(1-\beta^2)^{-1/2}\left\{1.2 + \frac{Pr_L(1-\beta^2)^{1/2}}{RJa}\right\}^{1/3} \tag{19.2-48}$$

$$R = \left(\frac{\rho_L \mu_L}{\rho_V \mu_V}\right)^{1/2} \tag{19.2-49}$$

$\beta$ is a dimensionless amplitude of waves and can be expressed in the following equation from the result of an analysis by Penev et al. (1973).

$$\beta = (\delta_{max} - \delta)/\delta \tag{19.2-50}$$

$$1 - \beta^2 = 0.47 We^{-0.138} \tag{19.2-51}$$

where *We* is Weber number:

$$We = u_0^2 \rho_L \delta/\sigma \tag{19.2-52}$$

$u_0$: mean (over the cross section of the film and the wavelength) film velocity
$\beta$: mean (over the wavelength) film thickness
$\beta_{max}$: film thickness in cross section corresponding to the crests of wave

Hydrodynamic and heat transfer analysis of the wavy film condensation were conducted by Hirshburg and Florshuetz (1982a, 1982b). The flow dynamics and heat transfer of the wave film condensation on a vertical plate were analyzed by solving the time-dependent Navier-Stokes and energy equations as well as the Poisson equation for the pressure with finite schemes and non-periodic boundary conditions by Stuhlträger et al. (1993,1995).

Various turbulent models for the eddy diffusivity of momentum and heat have been proposed for solving the velocity profile, film thickness, and local or mean condensation heat transfer coefficient for the body forced convection.

The main models in the turbulent film condensation without vapor flow are shown as follows:

1. The von Karman-Nikurade model, as used by Seban (1954) and Rohsenow et al. (1956)

$$\begin{aligned}\varepsilon_M/\nu &= 0 & 0 \le y^\dagger \le 5 \\ \varepsilon_M/\nu &= y^\dagger/5 - 1 & 5 \le y^\dagger \le 30 \\ \varepsilon_M/\nu &= y^\dagger/2.5 & y^\dagger < 30 \\ Pr_T &= 1 & \end{aligned} \tag{19.2-53}$$

2. The Deissler model, as used by Dukler (1960)

$$\varepsilon_M/\nu = (0.125)^2 u^\dagger y^\dagger [1 - \exp\{-(0.125)^2 u^\dagger y^\dagger\}]$$
$$= \text{Deisseler model for } y^\dagger \leq 20$$

$$\varepsilon_M/\nu = (0.4)^2 (du^\dagger/dy^\dagger)^3/(d^2 u^\dagger/dy^{\dagger 2})^2$$
$$= \text{von Karman model for } y^\dagger > 20$$

$$Pr_T = 1 \tag{19.2-54}$$

Uehara (1998) conducted the theoretical analysis for the turbulent film condensation on a vertical plate using the following basic equations, boundary conditions, and the eddy diffusivity of momentum and heat.

Basic equations:

$$\frac{\partial u}{\partial x} + \frac{\partial v}{\partial y} = 0 \tag{19.2-55}$$

$$\frac{\partial}{\partial y}\left[\left(\nu_L + \varepsilon_M\right)\frac{\partial u}{\partial y}\right] + g\left(\frac{\rho_L - \rho_V}{\rho_L}\right) = 0 \tag{19.2-56}$$

$$\frac{\partial}{\partial y}\left[(\kappa_L + \varepsilon_H)\frac{\partial T}{\partial y}\right] = 0 \tag{19.2-57}$$

Boundary conditions:

$$x = 0; \quad u = 0; \quad \delta = 0 \tag{19.2-58}$$

$$y = 0; \quad u = v = 0; \quad T = T_W \tag{19.2-59}$$

$$y = \delta \quad \frac{\partial u}{\partial y} = 0 \quad T = T_V \tag{19.2-60}$$

$$c_{PL}\rho_L(\kappa_L + \varepsilon_H)\frac{\partial T}{\partial y} = \left(\rho_L u \frac{d\delta}{dx} - \rho_L v\right)_L \tag{19.2-61}$$

$$\frac{\varepsilon_M}{\nu_L} = \frac{\varepsilon_H}{\nu_V} = 0.1 y^\dagger [1 - \exp(-0.0017 y^\dagger)] \tag{19.2-62}$$

The correlations of the local and mean heat transfer coefficient for the turbulent film condensation are proposed for $Pr_L = 0.01$–$100$.

$$Nu_x = 0.221 Pr_L^{-3/5}\left(1 + 0.905 Pr_L^{-11/8}\right)^{-2/5} Gr_x^k Ja^{3k-1} \quad \text{for } 0.01 \leq Pr_L \leq 11 \tag{19.2-63}$$

$$Nu_x = 0.032 Pr_L^{1/5} Gr_x^{2/5} Ja^{1/5} \quad \text{for } 11 \leq Pr_L \leq 100 \tag{19.2-64}$$

where

$$\kappa_l = 0.33 Pr_L^{0.08}. \tag{19.2-65}$$

Using $Nu_x^*$, $Re_x^*$, and $Pr_L$, we can obtain the following expressions:

$$Nu_x^* = 0.221^{1-p} \left(\frac{0.25}{1-p}\right)^p Pr_L^{(8p-3)/5} \times \left(1 + 0.905 Pr_L^{-11}\right)^{-2(1-p)/5} Re_x^{*p}$$

$$\text{for } 0.01 \leq Pr_L \leq 11 \quad (19.2\text{-}66)$$

$$Nu_x^* = 0.046 \, Re_x^{1/6} Pr_L^{1/3} \quad \text{for } 11 \leq Pr_L \leq 100 \tag{19.2-67}$$

where

$$p = 1 - Pr_L^{-0.08}/0.99. \tag{19.2-68}$$

The mean Nusselt number is expressed by the following equations:

$$Nu_l = \frac{0.074}{k} Pr_L^{-3/5} \left(1 + 0.905 Pr_L^{-11/8}\right)^{-2/5} Gr_l^k Ja^{3k-1} \quad \text{for } 0.01 \leq Pr \leq 11;$$

$$(19.2\text{-}69)$$

$$Nu_l = 0.027 Pr_L^{1/5} Gr_l^{2/5} Ja^{1/5} \quad \text{for } 11 \leq Pr_L \leq 100 \tag{19.2-70}$$

Using $Nu_m^*$, $Re_m^*$, we can obtain the following equations.

$$Nu_m^* = (1-p)0.221^{1-p}\left(\frac{0.25}{1-p}\right)^p Pr_L^{(8p-3)/5} \times \left(1 + 0.905 Pr_L^{-11/8}\right)^{-2(1-p)/5} Re_m^{*p}$$

$$\text{for } 0.01 \leq Pr_L \leq 11 \quad (19.2\text{-}71)$$

$$Nu_m^* = 0.038 Re_m^{*1/6} Pr_L^{1/3} \quad \text{for } 11 \leq Pr_L \leq 100 \tag{19.2-72}$$

In Figure 5, the experimental data of the local heat transfer obtained by Uehara and Kinoshita (1988, 1994) are compared with the predictions of Dukler (1960), correlations (19.2-22) to (19.2-25), and correlation (19.2-64) for $Pr_L = 1$, 5, and 10. The Uehara–Kinoshita correlations agrees very well with the experimental data, but the Dukler predictions are larger than experimental data obtained by Hebbard and Badger (1934), Meisenburg et al. (1935), Gregorig et al. (1974), Kutateladze and Gogonin (1979), Uehara et al. (1983), Uehara et al. (1988), and Uehara and Kinoshita (1997).

In Figure 6, the experimental data for the mean heat transfer coefficient are compared with correlation (19.2-39) to (19.2-42) and (19.2-71). The correlations (19.2- 39) to (19.2-42) and correlation (19.2-71) agree very well with experimental data.

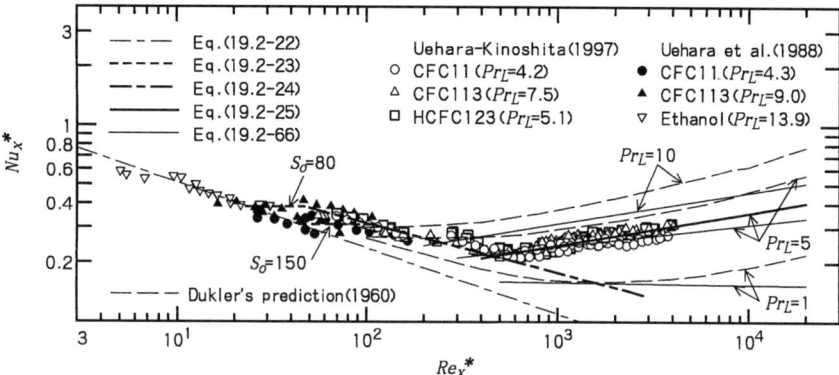

**Figure 5** Comparison of theoretical study with experimental data for local heat transfer coefficient.

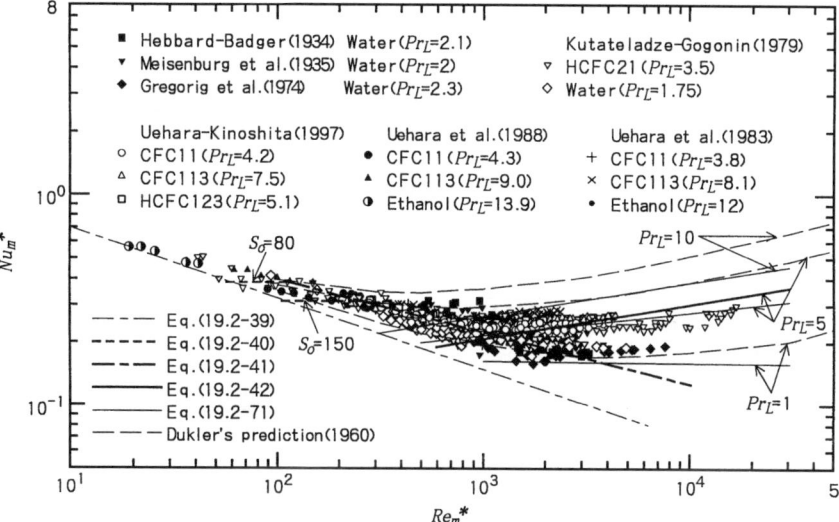

**Figure 6** Comparison of theoretical study with experimental data for mean heat transfer coefficient.

### 19.2.3 Transition and Turbulent Film Condensation of Combined and Forced Convection

**19.2.3.1 Correlation of local heat transfer coefficient.** Uehara et al. (1989) measured the local heat transfer coefficient of the forced convection coefficient of the forced convection film condensation on a vertical plate (length = 0.911 m) for the vapor of CFC11, CFC 113, and CFC123. In their experiment, the laminar and sine wave film were not observed. They proposed the correlations of the local heat transfer coefficient for the harmonic wave flow of the forced and the combined convection condensation on a vertical plate.

1) Forced convection

$$Nu_x = 2.11 \chi_{\beta H} Re_x^{1/2} \qquad (19.2\text{-}73)$$

2) Combined convection

$$Nu_x = 1.26 \chi_{\beta H} \left\{ 7.86 + \frac{Pr_L(1-\beta_H^2)^{-3/2}}{4\chi_{\beta H}^4 JaFr_x} \right\}^{1/4} Re_x^{1/2} \qquad (19.2\text{-}74)$$

where

$$\chi_{BH} = 0.45(1-\beta_H^2)^{-1/2} \left\{ 1.2 + \frac{Pr_L(1-\beta_H^2)^{1/2}}{RJa} \right\}^{1/3} \qquad (19.2\text{-}75)$$

$$1 - \beta_H^2 = 3.0 \times 10^{-2} \left(\frac{Ja}{So}\right)^{-0.533} Pr_L^{-0.35} \qquad (19.2\text{-}76)$$

Uehara et al. (1989) proposed the correlations of the local forced and combined convection turbulent film condensation on a vertical plate.

1) Forced convection

$$Nu_x = 0.125 Ja^{1/15} Pr_L^{1/3} R^{-1/2} Re_x^{4/5} \qquad (19.2\text{-}77)$$

2) Combined convection

$$Nu_x = 0.125(1 + 0.024 Ja^{1/3} Pr_L^{1/6} R^{5/4}/Fr_x)^{2/5} \times Ja^{1/15} Pr_L^{1/3} R^{-1/2} Re_x^{4/5} \qquad (19.2\text{-}78)$$

In Figure 7, the experimental data obtained by Uehara et al. (1989) were compared with the correlation (19.2-77). The correlation (19.2-77) agrees with the experimental data.

## 19.2.4 Turbulent Film Condensation of Binary Mixture on a Vertical Plate

Many researchers proposed that binary mixture is a suitable working fluid to improve the cycle thermal efficiency of the power plant and the coefficient of performance of a heat pump. However, in the condensation of binary mixture, a volatile

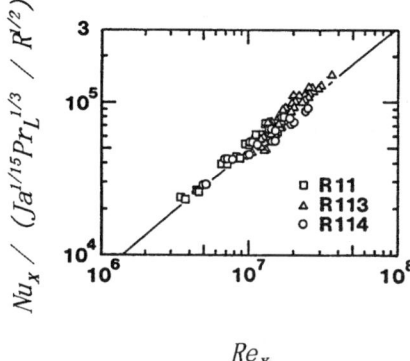

**Figure 7** Comparison of Eq. (19.2-77) with experimental data.

vapor concentrates near the vapor-liquid interface and creates diffusion layer. This fact reduces the condensation heat transfer coefficient of binary mixture. Kinoshita and Uehara (1995) measured the local heat transfer and mass transfer coefficient for the body forced convection turbulent film and vapor layer of the binary mixtures (CFC11/CFC113, HCFC123/CFC113) on a vertical plate/length 2.980 m. They proposed the following correlation for the local Sherwood number

$$Sh_x = 8.0 \times 10^{-3} \left(\frac{\rho_L}{\rho_V}\right)^{1/5} Pr_L^{-2/3} Ja_L^{4/5} R^{6/5} \{(Gr_x)_V Sc\}^{2/5} \quad (19.2\text{-}79)$$

where

$$Sh_x = \beta_x x / D \quad (19.2\text{-}80)$$

$$\beta_x = j_x / \{\rho_V (W_{Vi} - W_{V\infty})\} \quad (19.2\text{-}81)$$

$$j_x = \dot{m}_x (W_{Vi} - W_L) \quad (19.2\text{-}82)$$

$$Ja_L = c_{pL}(T_i - T_w)/L \quad (19.2\text{-}83)$$

$$(Gr_x)_V = gx^3 \omega / v_V^2 \quad (19.2\text{-}84)$$

$$\omega = \omega_W + \omega_T - \omega_W \omega_T \quad (19.2\text{-}85)$$

$$\omega_W = \frac{M_1 - M_2}{M_1 - (M_1 - M_2)W_{V\infty}}(W_{Vi} - W_{V\infty}) \quad (19.2\text{-}86)$$

$$\omega_T = (T_V - T_i)/T_V \quad (19.2\text{-}87)$$

where $\beta_x$ is the local mass transfer coefficient at the vapor-loquid interface, $j_x$ is the local diffusion mass flux of a volatile component, $W_{V\infty}$ is the mass fraction of volatile component in the bulk vapor, $W_{Vi}$ is the mass fraction of volatile component

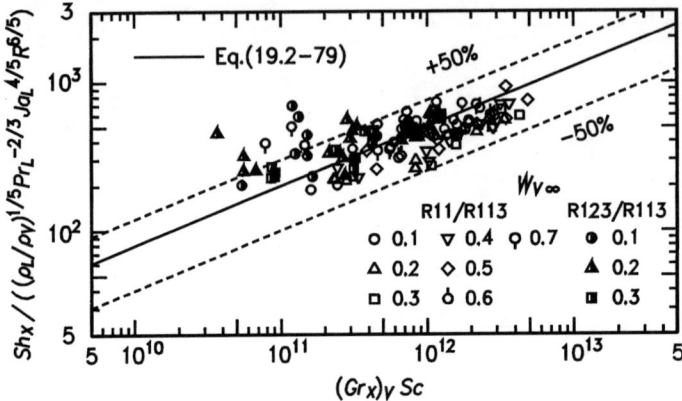

**Figure 8** Comparison of Eq. (19.2-79) with experimental data.

in the vapor at the vapor-liquid interface, $\dot{m}_x$ is local condensation mass flax, $W_L$ is a mass fraction of volatile component in the liquid, $T_i$ is the temperature at the vapor-liquid interface, $\omega$, $\omega_W$, and $\omega_T$ are parameters of buoyancy force, $M_2$ is molecular weight of volatile component, and $M_1$ is molecular weight of less volatile component.

In Figure 8, the comparison between experimental data and Equation (19.2-79) is shown. In Figure 9, the ratio of heat transfer coefficients for binary mixtures and pure vapor $(\alpha_x)_{mix}/(\alpha_x)_{pure}$ are plotted against the mass fraction of volatile component in the bulk vapor $W_{V\infty}$ with a parameter, which is temperature difference between bulk vapor and cooling surface $\Delta T \, (= T_{V\infty x} - T_{wox})$ at $x$ of 1.709 m.

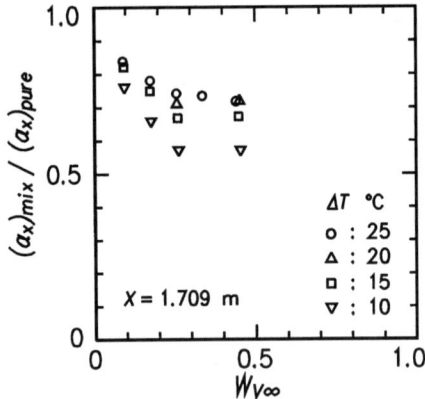

**Figure 9** $(\alpha_x)_{mix}/(\alpha_x)_{pure} \sim W_{V\infty}$.

In Figure 9, $(\alpha_x)_{mix}/(\alpha_x)_{pure}$ decrease with increasing of $W_{V\infty}$. The rate of decrease is greater as $\Delta T$ is smaller.

Uehara et al. (1995) measured the local heat transfer and local mass transfer coefficients for the forced convection turbulent film and vapor layer on a vertical plate (length = 0.913 m). They proposed the following correlations of the local Sherwood number.

$$Sh_x = 0.046 Re_{xV}^{4/5} Sc^{1/3} \qquad (19.2\text{-}88)$$

where

$$Re_{xV} = \frac{u_x x}{\nu_V}. \qquad (19.2\text{-}89)$$

## 19.3 CONDENSATION ON TUBE BANKS

The tube banks with horizontal plain tubes are employed for the large condenser, such as the steam condenser in large power plant and the fluids with high liquid thermal conductivity. It is important to predict the condensation heat transfer coefficient and pressure drop of steam through the tube banks for design of the large condenser.

### 19.3.1 Condensation of Pure Steam on Horizontal Smooth Tube Banks

Fujii et al. (1972) carried out the experiment for condensation in horizontal cross flows of low pressure saturated steam through both in line and staggered arranged tube banks of 14 mm diameter and 22 mm spacing and obtained the correlation for condensation heat transfer as follows:

$$(Nu_d)_n = K\chi \left(1 + \frac{0.276 Pr_L}{\chi^4 (Fr_d)_n Ja}\right)^{1/4} (Re_d)_n^{1/2} \qquad (19.3\text{-}1)$$

where $(Nu_d)_n$ is the mean Nusselt number of nth row of tube banks, $(Fr_d)_n$ is Froude number of nth row of tube banks for minimum flow area, $(Re_d)_n$ is Reynolds number of nth row of tube banks for maximum flow area. $(Nu_d)_n$, $(Fr_d)_n$, and $(Re_d)_n$, $Ja$, $R$, and $\chi$ are defined by following equations, respectively:

$$(Nu_d)_n = \frac{(\alpha_m)_n d_0}{\lambda_L} \qquad (19.3\text{-}2)$$

$$(Fr_d)_n = \frac{M^2}{\rho_V g d_0} \qquad (19.3\text{-}3)$$

$$(Re_d)_n = \frac{M d_0}{\rho_V \nu_L} \qquad (19.3\text{-}4)$$

$$J_a = \frac{c_{PL} \Delta T}{h_{fg}} \qquad (19.3\text{-}5)$$

$$R = \left(\frac{\rho_L \mu_L}{\rho_V \mu_V}\right)^{1/2} \qquad (19.3\text{-}6)$$

$$\chi = 0.9\left(1 + \frac{Pr_L}{R J_a}\right) \qquad (19.3\text{-}7)$$

In Equation (19.3-1), $K$ is the constant as follows:

$$K = 0.8 \quad \text{for in line} \qquad (19.3\text{-}8)$$

$$K = 1.0 \quad \text{for staggered} \qquad (19.3\text{-}9)$$

In Equation (19.3-1), $d_0$ is outer diameter of a tube and $M$ is mass flow rate of vapor through maximum flow area.

At medium to high vapor velocities, condensation in tube banks is considerably affected by the flow direction of vapor. Fujii (1981) showed the comparison of experimental data for horizontal, downward, and upward flow of low pressure steam in inline and staggered tube banks in Figure 10. In Figure 10, the Nusselt number for the downward and horizontal flow in inline and staggered tube banks

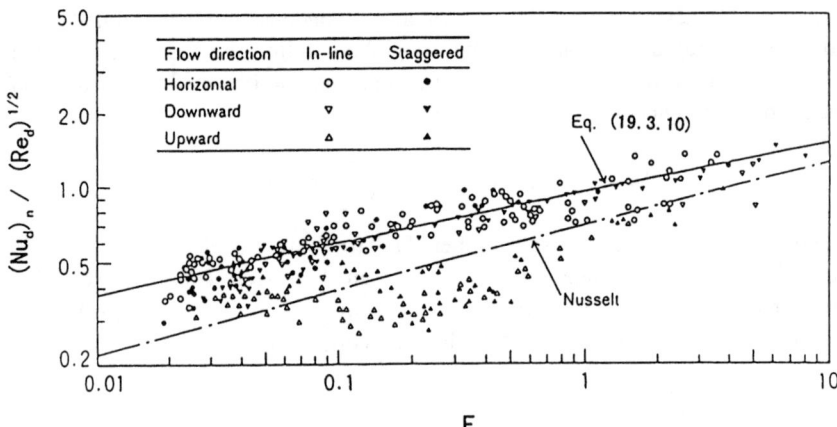

**Figure 10** Comparison of data for horizontal, downward, and upward flow of steam in in-line and staggered tube banks. (Data of Fujii, 1981).

are almost identical and are correlated well by the following equation,

$$(Nu_d)_n/(Re_d)_n^{1/2} = 0.96\{Pr/(Fr_d)_n J\}^{0.2} = 0.96 F^{0.2} \quad (19.3\text{-}10)$$

This shows that the effect of the condensate from upper tubes is small for horizontal and downward steam flow of low pressure in inline and staggered tube banks. The data for the upward flow are lower than those for the downward and horizontal flow. The difference is largest in region $0.1 < F < 1$, and the data are even lower than the prediction of the Nusselt (1916) equation, which is rewritten in terms of $(Nu_d)_n/(Re_d)_n$ and $F$ as

$$(Nu_d)_n = 0.725 \left(\frac{Gr_d Pr_L}{Ja}\right)^{1/4} \quad (19.3\text{-}11)$$

$$(Nu_d)_n/(Re_d)_n^{1/2} = 0.725 \left\{\frac{Pr_L}{(Fr_d)_n Ja}\right\}^{1/4} = 0.725 F^{1/4} \quad (19.3\text{-}12)$$

Shklover (1990) carried out a test for 11 different condensers that are characterized by the following: cooling surface in range of 30 to 9115 m$^2$; fan-type, belt-type, and combined tube arrangement; tube, diameter 14, 16, 19, 24, and 28; tube material is German Silver, brass; the number of water pass 1, 2, 4 is in the range of 0.006 and 0.002. Shklover obtained the following equation:

$$(\alpha_b)_m/\alpha_s = 19.0\pi^{0.1} Nu_s^{-0.5}(1+z/2)^{0.33} \bar{S}^{-0.15} \quad (19.3\text{-}13)$$

where $\pi$ is the dimensionless parameter and expressed by the following:

$$\pi = \frac{\rho_V (u_V)_{in}}{\rho_L g d} = \frac{\rho_V}{\rho_L} Fr_d \quad (19.3\text{-}14)$$

$(u_V)_{in}$ is inlet steam velocity, $z$ is cooling water passes, $\bar{S}$ is dimensionless parameter ($\bar{S} = S/A$), S is flow cross-section for steam in narrow section between tubes around the tube banks periphery, and $\alpha_s$ and $Nu_s$ are mean heat transfer coefficient and Nusselt's equation for a horizontal single tube, shown by

$$Nu = \frac{\alpha_s d_0}{\lambda_L} = 0.725 \left(\frac{Gr_d Pr_L}{Ja}\right)^{1/4} \quad (19.3\text{-}15)$$

Figure 11 shows experimental data for steam condensing in 7 tubes wide, and n tube deep (n = 1, 3, 6, and 12) in inline tube banks obtained by Shklover (1990).

In Figure 12, the ratio of Nusselt number for tube banks with and without tube inclination, $(Nu)_\theta/(Nu)_0$, is plotted as a function of the inclination angle $\theta$. From Figure 12, we found that the effect of tube inclination is more significant for a deeper tube bank.

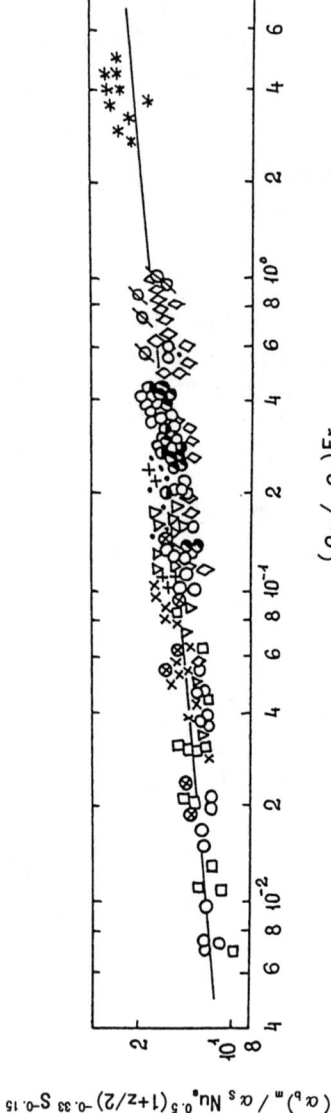

**Figure 11** Data for tube banks by Shklover (1996).

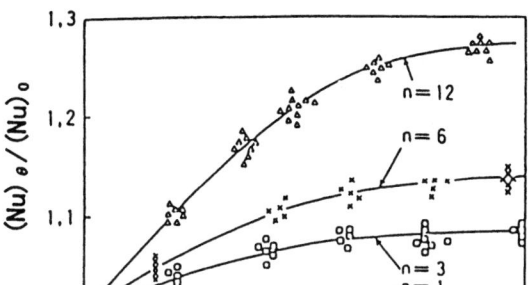

**Figure 12** Effect of the slope angle $\theta$ on the condensation heat transfer (Shklover, 1990).

### 19.3.2 Condensation of Steam-Air Mixture on Tube Banks with Horizontal Plain Tubes

Fujii and Uehara (1973) carried out the experimental study on condensation of steam-air mixture in inline and staggered arrangements with spacing to diameter ratio and obtained the following equation for the effect of the presence of air on condensation heat transfer:

$$(Nu_d)_m/(Nu_d)_0 = \exp(-5.4\phi), \quad \phi < 0.3 \qquad (19.3\text{-}16)$$

where $(Nu_d)_m$ is Nusselt number of steam-air mixture for nth row. $(Nu_d)_0$ is Nusselt number of pure steam for nth row and is calculated by using Equation 19.3-1 to 19.3-10. $\phi$ is flow rate ratio of steam-air mixture $G_m$ and air $G_a$ and is expressed by the following:

$$\phi = G_a/G_m \qquad (19.3\text{-}17)$$

Shklover (1990) carried out the experimental study for the condensation of steam-air mixture by using 8 condensers with a surface area of 1.45–935 m² and obtained the following equation for the ratio of mean heat transfer coefficient on the plain surface at steam condensation from steam-air mixture $\alpha_m$ to mean heat transfer coefficient for pure steam $\alpha_0$. The result may be described by the relation:

$$\alpha_m/\alpha_0 = 0.68\phi^{-0.04} \qquad (19.3\text{-}18)$$

where $\alpha_0$ is calculated by Equation 19.3-13 and $\phi$ is calculated by Equation 19.3-17.

### 19.3.3 Condensation of Pure Organic Vapor on Tube Banks with Horizontal Plain Tubes

For refrigerant condenser, the vapor velocity at the inlet of condenser shell is designed to be less than about 6 m/s. In this case, the effect of both the vapor shear and the condensate inundation on condensation heat transfer coefficient is very important.

Honda et al. (1988) carried out the experimental study on condensation of downward flowing R113 vapor on tube banks with horizontal plain tubes and obtained the following equations:

**Staggered tube banks**

$$(Nu_d)_n = \left[ Nu_g^4 + Nu_g^2 Nu_{sh}^2 + Nu_{sh}^4 \right]^{1/4} \tag{19.3-19}$$

where $(Nu_d)_n$ is expressed by Equation (19.3.2) and

$$Nu_g = Gr^{1/3} \left[ \left(1.2 Re_{f,g}^{-0.3}\right)^4 + \left(0.072 Re_{f,g}^{0.2}\right)^4 \right]^{1/4} \tag{19.3-20}$$

$$Nu_{sh} = 0.165 \left(\frac{P_t}{P_l}\right)^{0.7} \left[ Re_g^{-0.4} + 1.83 \left(\frac{\dot{q}_n}{\rho_G h_{LG} u_{Gn}}\right) \right]^{1/2} \times \left(\frac{\rho_G}{\rho_L}\right) \frac{Re_L Pr_L^{0.4}}{Re_{f,sh}^{0.2}} \tag{19.3-21}$$

$$Gr = g\rho_L(\rho_L - \rho_V) d_0/\eta_L^2$$

$$Re_{f,g} = 2\pi d_0 \sum_{i=1}^{(n+1)/2} \dot{q}_{2i-1}/\eta_L \eta_{Lg} \quad \text{for } n = 1, 3, 5 \cdots$$

$$Re_{f,g} = 2\pi d_0 \sum_{i=1}^{n/2} \dot{q}_{2i}/\eta_L \eta_{Lg} \quad \text{for } n = 2, 4, 6 \cdots$$

$$Re_{sh} = Re_{f,g} \quad \text{for } n = 1$$

$$Re_{f,g} = 2\pi d_0 \left(\sum_{i=1}^{n-1} \dot{q}_i d_0/P_t + \dot{q}_n\right) \Big/ \eta_{PL} h_{LG} \quad \text{for } n > 1$$

$$Re_G = \rho_V u_{Vn} d_0/\eta_V, \quad Re_{LU_{Gn}} d_0/\eta_L$$

$P_t$ is the transverse tube pitch, $P_l$ is the longitudinal tube pitch, and $u_{Gn}$ is the vapor velocity at the n-th row based on the minimum flow cross-section. For the first row, the leading coefficient on the right-hand side of Equation 19.3-21 should be replaced by 0.13.

**Inline tube bank**

$$Nu = \left(Nu_g^4 + Nu_{sh}^4\right)^{1/4} \quad (19.3\text{-}22)$$

where

$$Nu_{sh} = 0.053\left[Re_g^{-0.2} + 18.0\left(\frac{\dot{q}_n}{\rho_G h_{LG} u_{Gn}}\right)\right]^{1/2} \times \left(\frac{\rho_G}{\rho_L}\right)\frac{Re_L Pr_L^{0.4}}{Re_{f,sh}^{0.2}} \quad (19.3\text{-}23)$$

$$Re_{f,g} = 2\pi d_0 \sum_{i=1}^{n} \dot{q}_i/\eta_L h_{LG}$$

The definitions of $Nu_g$, $Re_{f,sh}$, $Re_G$, $Re_L$, and $u_{Gn}$ are the same as those for the staggered tube banks. For the first row, the leading coefficient on the right-hand side of Equation 19.3-23 should be replaced by 0.042.

### 19.3.4 Inundation of Pure Vapor on Tube Banks with Horizontal Plain Tubes

For the large condenser, the vapor flow may be downward, horizontal, and upward. For the downward flow and low velocity of vapor, the condensate inundation rate depends only on condensation rate at the upper rows. For the other film directions, it is not possible to estimate the inundation rate accurately.

Discussions on the inundation mode are given by Fujii and Uehara (1973), Fujii (1981), Marto (1984), and Honda (1997). Figure 13 shows the inundation mode that are illustrated by Honda (1997). Figure 13 (a) to (c) are the inundation mode for low vapor velocity. Condensate drains fall down at droplet for lower inundation rate (Figure 13a), then in condensate columns for medium inundation rate

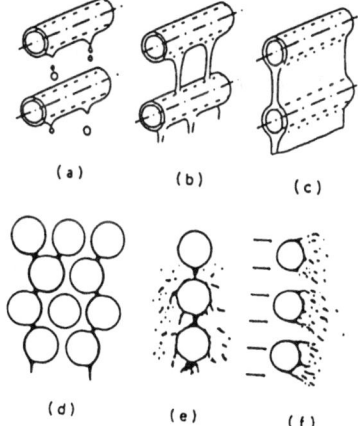

**Figure 13** Modes of condensate inundation in horizontal tube banks.

(Figure 13b), then in condensate sheet for high inundation rate (Figure 13c). Figure 13d shows the inundation mode for staggered tube banks. Figure 13e shows the inundation mode for the inline tube banks and high inundation rate and vapor velocity. The condensate impinging on the lower tube causes splashing, ripples, and turbulence on the condensate film.

For a stagnant vapor, Butterworth (1981) discusses condensate inundation. The correlation for the mean condensation heat transfer coefficient $(\alpha_m)_n$ for a vertical row of n tubes was analyzed theoretically by Nusselt (1916) for sheet mode (Figure 13c) and was obtained as the following equation:

$$(\alpha_m)_n/(\alpha_m)_1 = n^{-1/4} \qquad (19.3\text{-}24)$$

where $(\alpha_m)_1$ is the mean heat transfer coefficient for the first row and is calculated by Equation (19.3-15).

Due to the various hydrodynamic effects in the film, Equation (19.3-24) is generally recognized to underpridict the actual experimental data by about 15%. Based on the experience of operating condensers, Kern (1958) suggested an alternative to Nusselt equation.

$$\frac{(\alpha_m)_n}{(\alpha_m)_1} = n^{-1/6} \qquad (19.3\text{-}25)$$

Gunningham and Ben Boundinar (1990) carried out the experiment for the effect of condensate inundation on the condensation heat transfer plain tube and obtained the following equation:

$$\frac{(\alpha_m)_n}{(\alpha_m)_1} = n^{-0.157} \qquad (19.3\text{-}26)$$

### 19.3.5 Film Condensation of Pure Vapor on Tube Banks of Horizontal Finned Tubes

Horizontal finned tubes are commonly used in the shell and tube condensers in the refrigeration, air conditioning, and process industries due to their high heat transfer performance. Systematic, experimental, and theoretical study has been conducted for the effect of fin geometry, tube material, condensing fluid, vapor velocity, and condensate on the condensation on a finned tube. The comprehensive reviews for a finned tube were given by Webb (1988), Marto (1988), and Sukhatme (1990).

Katz and Geist (1948), Gogonin et al. (1983), Honda et al. (1991, 1992, 1994), Webb and Murawski (1990), and Murata et al. (1990) measured the row by row heat transfer coefficient for vapors condensing on the vertical columns of horizontal finned tubes.

Honda et al. (1996) measured the row by row heat transfer coefficient during condensation of HCFC123 on the staggered tube banks of four two-dimensional finned horizontal tubes.

## Table 1 Dimensions of test tubes (Honda et al. 1996)

| Tube designation | | A | B | C | D |
|---|---|---|---|---|---|
| Fin pitch | $p$(mm) | 0.96 | 0.52 | 0.50 | 0.50 |
| Fin height | $h$(mm) | 1.43 | 1.09 | 1.41 | 1.39 |
| Fin thickness at fin root | $t$(mm) | 0.45 | 0.36 | 0.17 | 0.22 |
| Radius of curvature at fin tip | $r_0$(mm) | 0.068 | 0.045 | 0.050 | 0.020 |
| | $b^a$(—) | — | — | 10 | 10 |
| Fin half tip angle | $\theta$(rad) | 0.082 | 0.062 | — | — |
| Diameter at fin tip | $d_0$(mm) | 15.60 | 15.80 | 15.60 | 15.60 |
| Tube inside diameter | (mm) | 11.21 | 12.00 | 11.40 | 11.40 |

[a] Applies to tubes C and D.

Table 1 shows dimensions of finned tubes used in experiment by Honda et al. (1996). Figure 14 depicts a horizontal cross section and close-up of finned tubes that are listed in Table 1.

Figure 15 shows the condensation number of staggered tube banks for HCFC123, obtained by Honda et al (1996).

$Nu_n$ and $Re_n$, shown in Figure 15, are defined as

$$Nu_n^* = \alpha_n \left(v_L^2/g\right)^{1/3}/\lambda_L \tag{19.3-27}$$

$$\alpha_n = (Q + Q_l)/N\pi dl\Delta T \tag{19.3-28}$$

$$Re_n^* = zW_n/N\mu_L l \tag{19.3-29}$$

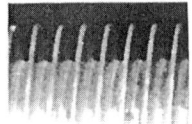
Tube A

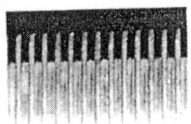
Tube B

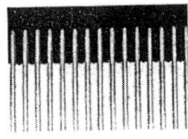
Tube C

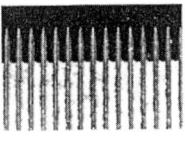
Tube D

**Figure 14** Cross section of Finned tubes (Honda et al., 1996).

**560** HANDBOOK OF PHASE CHANGE: BOILING AND CONDENSATION

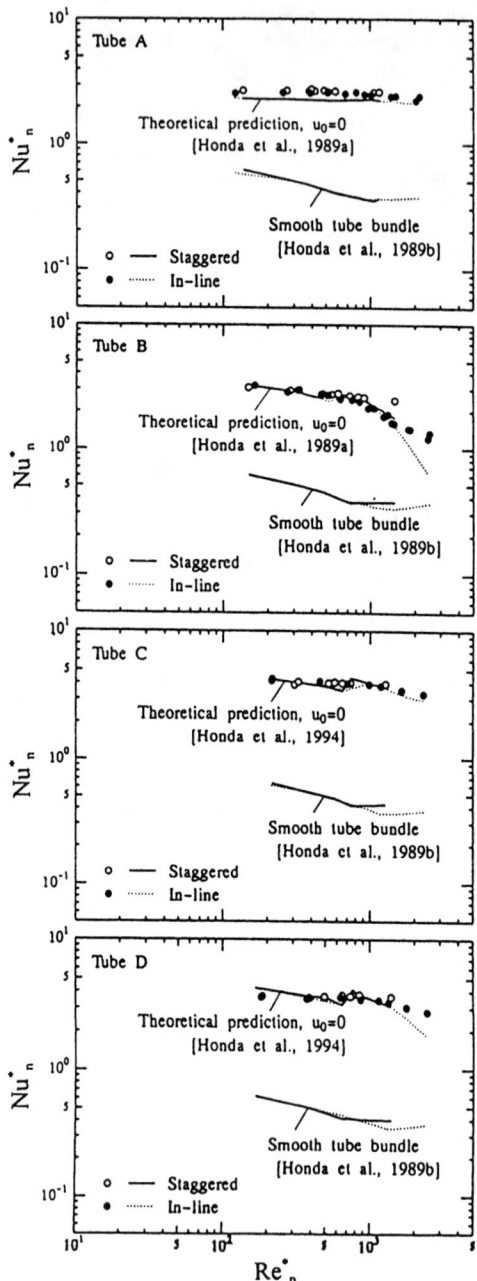

**Figure 15** Data of finned tubes (Honda et al., 1996).

where $Q$ is the heat transfer rate calculated from temperature rise and flow rate of cooling water, $Q_l$ is the heat loss to the environment, $\nu$ is the number of condensing tubes ($= 2$ or 3), $l$ is the effective length of test tube ($= 100$ mm), $\Delta T = T_s - T_{wn}$, where $T_s$ is the local saturation temperature, and $T_{wn}$ is the mean wall temperature at the fin root for a tube row.

## 19.3.6 Pressure Drop and Resistance Coefficient of Pure Steam Through Tube Banks with Horizontal Plain Tubes

Fujii et al. (1972) carried out the measurement of pressure drop and resistance coefficients of pure steam through in-line and staggered tube banks with horizontal plain tubes ($d_0 = 15$ mm, spacing $= 22$ mm).

In condensing cases, pressure drop is expressed by the following equation:

$$P_{j-1} - P_j = C_D \frac{2(\zeta(G_V)_m)^2}{(\rho_V)_m} - \left\{ \left(\frac{G_V^2}{\rho_V}\right)_{j-1} - \left(\frac{G_V^2}{\rho_V}\right)_j \right\} \quad j = 1 - N \tag{19.3-30}$$

where $P$ is the pressure (bar) at front of j tube, $G_V$ is the mass velocity of steam through maximum flow area [kg/m²s], $(\rho_V)_m$ is the arithmetic mean density of $j - 1$ and $j$, $C_D$ is the resistance coefficient, and $\zeta$ is the ratio of maximum flow area to minimum one.

In non-condensing cases, since the variation of momentum is negligibly small, Equation 19.3.28 is reduced as follows;

$$P_{j-1} - P_j = C_D \frac{2(\zeta G_V^2)_m n}{(\rho_V)_m} \tag{19.3-31}$$

In Figure 16, the resistance coefficient $C_D$ is plotted with $Re_V$ defined by the following equation:

$$Re_V = \frac{\zeta (G_V)_m d_0}{\mu_V} \tag{19.3-32}$$

In Figure 16, the double symbols denote the values for the first tube row. Figure 16 also shows the curve obtained experimentally by Bergelin et al. (1952), Kays et al. (1954), and Pierson (1959) and recommended by Fishenden and Saunders (1950) for non-condensing cases. Each of them is selected as an example having a similar spacing-to-diameter ratio (22/15).

From the data in Figure 16, we found that the $C_D$ for condensing cases for in-line arrangement is about a half of that for staggered one, $C_D$ for the first row is much larger than that for the successive ones, and $C_D$ for condensing cases is smaller than that in non-condensing ones, except for the first row.

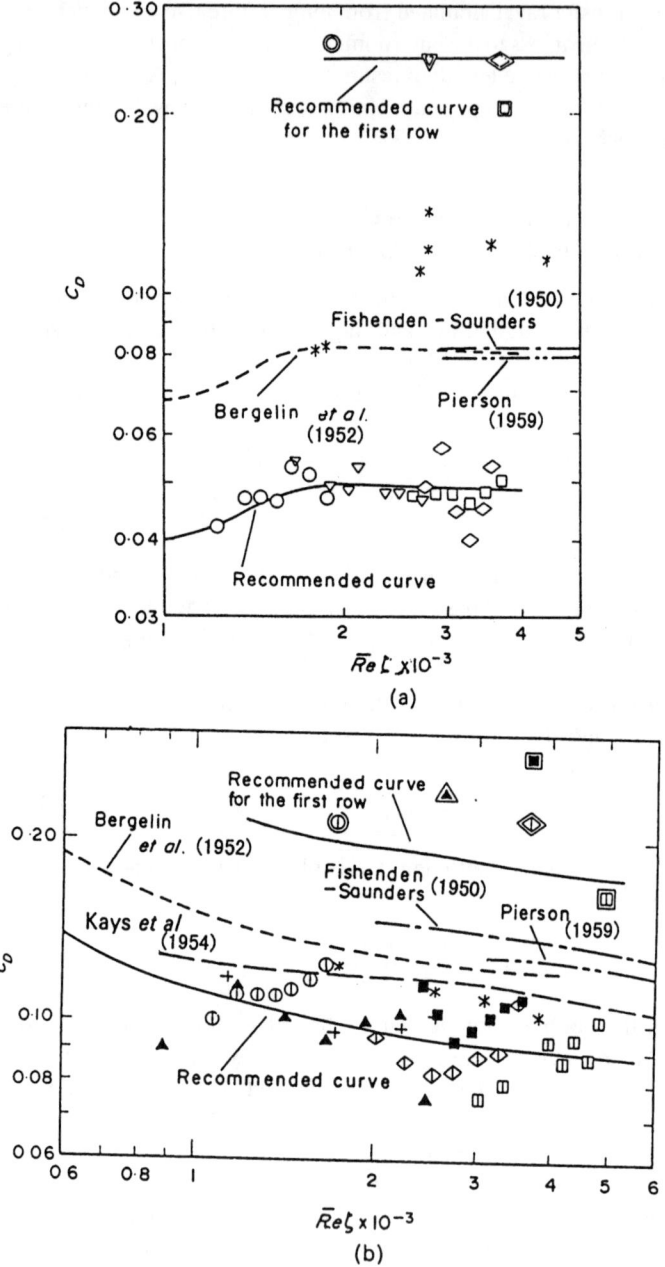

**Figure 16** Resistance coefficient through tube banks with condensation (a) inline and (b) staggered.

Zukaruskus (1972) showed the graph of $C_D$ for non-condensing gas. $C_D$ for condensation on staggered tube banks is calculated by multiplying the $C_D$ value obtained from Zukaruskus' graph with 0.75, and $C_D$ for condensation on in-line tube banks is calculated by multiplying the $C_D$ value obtained from Zukaruskus' graph with 0.4.

## 19.4 CONDENSATION OF MIXTURES

The condensation of multi-component vapor mixtures is widely encountered in chemical and food industries and is recently applied in air-conditioning/refrigeration and low-temperature-level energy utilization systems. In this section, we describe theoretical treatment on steady laminar film condensation of a multi-component vapor mixture on a flat plate in order to deepen our understanding of basic phenomena in the heat and mass transfer of the vapor mixture.

When a multi-component vapor mixture contacts a cooled solid wall with a temperature lower than the dew-point temperature of the vapor, the liquid film appears on the cooled wall, and outside the film, a boundary layer of the vapor mixture is formed. The film thickness, the boundary layer thickness, the thermodynamic state at the vapor-liquid interface, the condensation mass flux, etc., are strongly affected by the velocity of main vapor flow. When the vapor velocity is very low, the condensation characteristics are controlled by a buoyancy force due to the density difference. The former is called the *forced convection condensation*, and the latter is called the *natural convection condensation*. Condensation between these two condensation regions is called *combined forced and natural convection condensation*.

To qualitatively explain basic characteristics of the film condensation of a multi-component vapor mixture on a flat plate, we consider a binary system as an example. Figure 17a shows the distributions of temperature and vapor mass fraction in the direction normal to the cooled wall. These variations of temperature and mass fraction on a diagram of phase equilibrium are also shown in Figure 17b. In the case of the condensation of a binary vapor mixture, the less volatile component ($k = 2$) condenses more than the volatile component ($k = 1$), according to the phase equilibrium rule. Consequently, the volatile component is concentrated at the vapor-liquid interface in the vapor phase. The balance between the diffusion and convective mass transfer makes a steady mass fraction distribution in the vapor phase. At the same time, the temperature of the vapor mixture decreases from the bulk to the vapor-liquid interface because the phase equilibrium is valid at the vapor-liquid interface. In the liquid film, generally, both the temperature and mass fraction distributions are formed. The temperature drop in the condensate film is based on nearly heat conduction due to extremely thin liquid film. This mechanism is the same as in the case of condensation of a pure vapor.

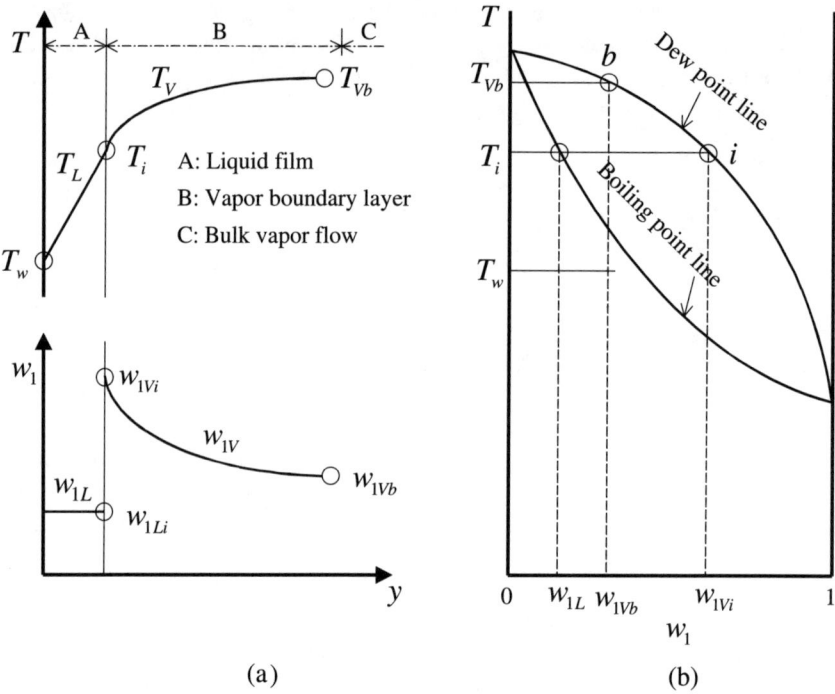

**Figure 17** Condensation of a binary vapor mixture on a vertical flat plate (a) Temperature and concentration distributions around the cooled wall (b) Phase equilibrium diagram.

The most effective method to quantitatively analyze the condensation problem of a multi-component vapor mixture is the two-phase boundary layer theory, which was established by Sparrow and Eckert (1961) for the film condensation of steam containing noncondensable gases. Based on this theory, numerous theoretical studies on the steady laminar film condensation of a multi-component vapor mixture on a flat plate have been carried out, as summarized in Table 2. Most of these studies were devoted to solving similarity solutions and demonstrated many numerical results in the form of tables and graphs. Their conclusions, however, are qualitative and lack generality. Rose (1980), Fujii et al. (1977, 1978, 1987, 1991a), and Koyama et al. (1986) proposed general correlations that can be applied to algebraically predict the condensation characteristics of binary vapor mixtures without rigorously applying the similarity solutions. The algebraic prediction method for binary vapor mixtures was extended to a multi-component condensation problem by Fujii et al. (1984, 1989) and Koyama et al. (1987a, 1987b). In the following parts, the algebraic prediction method proposed by Fujii and coworkers are introduced briefly. The numerical results of the similarity solutions and the

**Table 2** Theoretical studies of steady laminar film condensation of a multi-component vapor mixture on a flate plate

| Authors | Year | Mode | Method | Substances |
|---|---|---|---|---|
| Sparrow-Eckert | 1961 | Natural | Similarity solution | Air + $H_2O$ |
| Koh | 1962 | Forced | Similarity solution | Parametric |
| Sparrow-Lin | 1964 | Natural | Similarity solution | Air + $H_2O$ |
| Minkowycz-Sparrow | 1966 | Natural | Local similarity sol. | Air + $H_2O$ |
| Sparrow et al. | 1967 | Forced | Similarity solution | Air + $H_2O$ |
| Minkowycz-Sparrow | 1969 | Forced | Similarity solution | Air + $H_2O$ |
| Sparrow-Marashall | 1969 | Natural | Similarity solution | $CH_3OH + H_2O$ |
| Rose | 1969 | Natural | Integral method | Any gas-vapor |
| Denny et al. | 1971 | Combined | Finite difference | Air + $H_2O$ |
| Denny-Jusionis | 1972a | Combined | Finite difference | Air + ($H_2O$, $NH_3$, $C_2H_5OH$, etc.) |
| Denny-Jusionis | 1972b | Combined | Finite difference | $CH_3OH + H_2O$, $C_3H_7OH + H_2O$, etc. |
| Mori-Hijikata | 1972 | Natural | Integral method | Air + $H_2O$ |
| Hijikata-Mori | 1972 | Forced | Integral method | Air + $H_2O$ <br> Air + KCl |
| Tamir | 1973 | Natural | Integral method | $CH_3OH + H_2O$ |
| Taitel-Tamir | 1974 | Natural | Similarity solution | Air + $CH_3OH + H_2O$, $CH_3CO + CH_3OH + H_2O$ |
| Lucas | 1976 | Combined | Finite difference, Integral method | $CH_3OH + H_2O$ |
| Sage-Estrin | 1976 | Natural | Similarity solution | $Ne + N_2 + H_2O$, $N_2 + CCl_2F_2 + H_2O$, $N_2 + CH_4 + H_2O$ |
| Fujii et al. | 1977 | Forced | Similarity solution, Correlation | Air + $H_2O$ |
| Fujii et al. | 1978 | Natural | Similarity solution, Correlation | Air + $H_2O$ |
| Stephan-Laesecke | 1980 | Forced, Combined, Natural | Stagnant film theory | $CH_3OH + H_2O$, Air + $H_2O$ |
| Rose | 1980 | Forced | Correlation | Air + $H_2O$ |
| Fuji-Koyama | 1984 | Forced | Similarity solution, Correlation | Air + $CH_3OH + H_2O$ |
| Kotake | 1985 | Natural | Perturbation method | Multi-component |
| Fujii et al. | 1985 | Natural | Similarity Solution, Correlation | Air + R12 + R114 |
| Koyama et al. | 1986 | Natural | Similarity Solution, Correlation | $C_2H_5OH + H_2O$, Air + $H_2O$ |
| Fujii et al. | 1987 | Forced | Similarity Solution, Correlation | $C_2H_5OH + H_2O$, Air + $H_2O$, etc. |
| Koyama et al. | 1987a | Forced | Correlation | Multi-component |
| Koyama et al. | 1987b | Natural | Correlation | Multi-component |
| Fujii et al. | 1989 | Natural | Similarity solution | $CH_3OH + C_2H_5OH + H_2O$ |
| Fujii et al. | 1991a | Forced | Correlation | Binary vapor |

algebraic prediction method by Fujii and his coworkers are descried in detail by Fujii (1991).

### 19.4.1 Laminar Film Condensation of a Binary Vapor Mixture

We consider the steady laminar film condensation of a binary vapor mixture on a vertical flat plate, for which the vapor flows parallel and downwards. Figure 18 shows the physical model of the vapor-liquid two-phase boundary layer and the coordinate system.

Employing some relevant assumptions and the boundary layer concept, we can derive the governing equations for conservation of total mass, momentum, energy, and mass of component 1 for a binary vapor mixture; these equations are called the *two-phase boundary layer equations*. By using the similarity transformation, the governing equations can be reduced to a set of simultaneous ordinary differential equations. The details of the derivation of the two-phase boundary layer equations are described by Koh (1962), Minkowycz and Sparrow (1966), and Fujii (1991).

**19.4.1.1 Prediction method for heat and mass transfer characteristics in forced convection condensation.** Fujii et al. (1977, 1987, 1991a, 1991b) solved numerically the similarity solutions for the laminar forced convection film condensation of saturated and superheated binary vapor mixtures on a flat plate and proposed the following algebraic method to predict the heat and mass transfer characteristics.

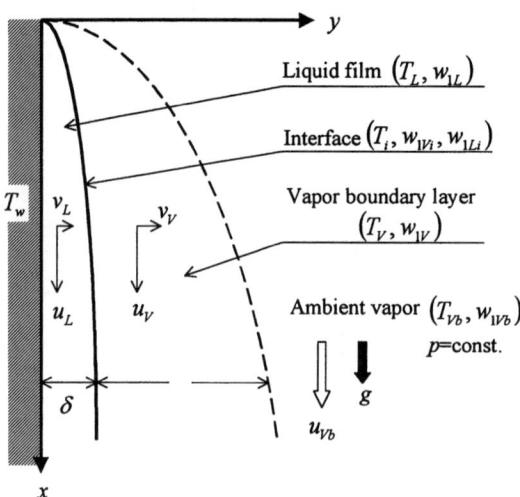

**Figure 18** Physical model and coordinate system for condensation of a binary vapor mixture.

## Heat balance at the vapor-liquid interface

$$0.433\left(1.367 - \frac{0.432}{\sqrt{2R\dot{M}_{FL}}} + \frac{1}{\sqrt{2R\dot{M}_{FL}}}\right)^{\frac{1}{2}} (1 + 0.320\, Ph^{0.87})^{-1}$$

$$= \frac{Pr_L \dot{M}_{FL}}{Ph} + C_F(Pr_V)\frac{\lambda_V}{\lambda_L}\left(\frac{\nu_L}{\nu_V}\right)^{\frac{1}{2}} \frac{T_{Vb} - T_i}{T_i - T_w}$$

$$\times \left\{1 + 2.6Pr_V^{0.66}\left[R\dot{M}_{FL}\left(1 - \frac{2}{3}c^*_{pV}(w_{1Vi} - w_{1L})\right)\right]^{1.05}\right\} \quad (19.4\text{-}1)$$

where the $\rho - \mu$ ratio $R$, the dimensionless condensation mass flux $\dot{M}_{FL}$, the phase change number $Ph$, the liquid Prandtl number $Pr_L$, the vapor Prandtl number $Pr_V$, the function of the vapor Prandtl number $C_F(Pr_V)$, and the dimensionless specific isobaric heat difference $c^*_{pV}$ are defined as

$$R = \left(\frac{\rho_L \mu_L}{\rho_V \mu_V}\right)^{\frac{1}{2}} \quad (19.4\text{-}2)$$

$$\dot{M}_{FL} = \frac{\dot{m}_x x}{\mu_L Re_{Lx}^{\frac{1}{2}}} \quad (19.4\text{-}3)$$

$$Ph = \frac{c_{pL}(T_i - T_w)}{\Delta h_{LV}} \quad (19.4\text{-}4)$$

$$Pr_L = \frac{\mu_L c_{pL}}{\lambda_L} \quad (19.4\text{-}5)$$

$$Pr_V = \frac{\mu_V c_{pV}}{\lambda_V} \quad (19.4\text{-}6)$$

$$C_F(Pr_V) = \frac{Pr_V^{\frac{1}{2}}}{(27.8 + 75.9Pr_V^{0.306} + 657Pr_V)^{\frac{1}{6}}} \quad (19.4\text{-}7)$$

$$c^*_{pV} = \frac{c_{p1V} - c_{p2V}}{c_{pV}} \quad (19.4\text{-}8)$$

In Eq. (19.4-3), the two-phase Reynolds number $Re_{Lx}$ is defined as

$$Re_{Lx} = \frac{u_{Vb} x}{\nu_L} \quad (19.4\text{-}9)$$

## Mass balance of more volatile component at the vapor-liquid interface

$$\dot{M} = \frac{C(Sc_V)}{RSc_V}\left(\frac{2.5}{1.5 + W_R}\right)^m (W_R - 1) \quad (19.4\text{-}10)$$

where the vapor Schmidt number $Sc_V$, the exponent $m$, and the ratio of concentration $W_R$ are defined as

$$Sc_V = \frac{\nu_V}{D_{12V}} \tag{19.4-11}$$

$$m = 0.5 + 0.05 Sc_V - 0.2/R^{\frac{1}{2}} \tag{19.4-12}$$

$$W_R = \frac{w_{1Vi} - w_{1L}}{w_{1Vb} - w_{1L}} \tag{19.4-13}$$

and the function of the vapor Schmidt number $C_F(Sc_V)$ is the same functional form as Eq. (19.4-7).

*Miscible condition*

$$w_{1L} = w_{1Li} = \frac{\dot{m}_{1x}}{\dot{m}_x} = \frac{\dot{m}_{1x}}{\dot{m}_{1x} + \dot{m}_{2x}} \tag{19.4-14}$$

where $\dot{m}_{kx}$ ($k = 1, 2$) is the local condensation mass flux of component $k$.

*Phase equilibrium relation at the vapor-liquid interface*

$$\left.\begin{aligned} w_{1Vi} &= W_V(T_i, p) \\ w_{1Li} &= W_L(T_i, p) \end{aligned}\right\} \tag{19.4-15}$$

When the bulk vapor condition of $(p, T_{Vb}, w_{1Vb})$ and the wall temperature $T_w$ are given as known parameters, simultaneous algebraic equations composed of Eqs. (19.4-1), (19.4-10), (19.4-14), and (19.4-15) can be solved by the following procedure: (1) guess $T_i$; (2) calculate $w_{1Vi}$ and $w_{1L}$ using the phase equilibrium relation Eq. (19.4-15) and calculate representative physical properties and dimensionless numbers $c_{pV}^*$, $Ph$, $Pr_V$, $R$, $Sc_V$ and $W_R$; (3) obtain $\dot{M}_{FL}$ from Eq. (19.4-10); (4) until the above values satisfy Eq. (19.4-1), modify the value $T_i$ and repeat calculation from steps (2) to (4); and finally (5) all physical quantities such as $T_i$, $w_{1Vi}$, $w_{1L}$, $\dot{M}_{FL}$ are obtained. Furthermore, the local condensation mass flux $\dot{m}_x$, the local condensation mass flux of more volatile component $\dot{m}_{1x}$, the local wall heat flux $q_{wx}$ and the local convective heat flux $q_{Vx}$ are calculated as

$$\dot{m}_x = \frac{\mu_L}{x} \dot{M}_{FL} Re_{Lx}^{\frac{1}{2}} \tag{19.4-16}$$

$$\dot{m}_{1x} = \dot{m}_x w_{1L} \tag{19.4-17}$$

$$q_{wx} = 0.433 \left(1.367 - \frac{0.432}{\sqrt{2R\dot{M}_{FL}}} + \frac{1}{2R\dot{M}_{FL}}\right)^{\frac{1}{2}} \frac{\lambda_L}{x}(T_i - T_w) Re_{Lx}^{\frac{1}{2}} \tag{19.4-18}$$

$$q_{Vx} = \left\{ 1 + 2.6 Pr_V^{0.66} \left[ R\dot{M}_{FL} \left( 1 - \frac{2}{3} c_{pV}^* (w_{1Vi} - w_{1L}) \right) \right]^{1.05} \right\}$$
$$\times \frac{\lambda_V (T_{Vb} - T_i)}{x} C_F(Pr_V) Re_{Vx}^{\frac{1}{2}} \qquad (19.4\text{-}19)$$

where the vapor Reynolds number $Re_{Vx}$ is defined as

$$Re_{Vx} = \frac{u_{Vb} x}{\nu_V} \qquad (19.4\text{-}20)$$

**19.4.1.2 Prediction method for heat and mass transfer characteristics in natural convection condensation.** Fujii et al. (1978) and Koyama et al. (1986) numerically solved the similarity solutions for the laminar natural convection film condensation of saturated and superheated binary vapor mixtures on a vertical flat plate. Then, they proposed the algebraic method for predicting the heat and mass transfer in natural convection condensation.

*Heat balance at the vapor-liquid interface*

$$\dot{M}_{NL}^{-\frac{1}{3}} = \frac{Pr_L \dot{M}_{NL}}{Ph} + \sqrt{2} C_N(Pr_V) \frac{\lambda_V}{\lambda_L} \left( \frac{\nu_L}{\nu_V} \right)^{\frac{1}{2}} \frac{T_{Vb} - T_i}{T_i - T_w} (\chi_i^* Pr_V)^{\frac{1}{4}}$$
$$\times \left\{ 1 + 1.25 Pr_V^{0.66} \left( \frac{R\dot{M}_{NL}}{\Omega_i^{\frac{1}{4}}} \right)^{1.17} [1 - 0.85 c_{pV}^* (w_{1Vi} - w_{1L})] \right\}$$
$$(19.4\text{-}21)$$

where the dimensionless condensation mass flux $\dot{M}_{NL}$, the function of the vapor Prandtl number $C_N(Pr_V)$, the parameter of buoyancy force $\chi_i^*$ (introduced by Tanaka, 1985) and the parameter of buoyancy force $\Omega_i$ are defined as

$$\dot{M}_{NL} = \frac{\dot{m}_x x}{\mu_L} \left( \frac{Ga_{Lx}}{4} \right)^{-\frac{1}{4}} \qquad (19.4\text{-}22)$$

$$C_N(Pr_V) = \frac{3}{4} \left( \frac{Pr_V}{2.4 + 4.9\sqrt{Pr_V} + 5 Pr_V} \right)^{\frac{1}{4}} \qquad (19.4\text{-}23)$$

$$\chi_i^* = \Omega_i + \omega_w (w_{1Vi} - w_{1Vb}) \left[ (Pr_V/Sc_V)^{\frac{1}{2}} - 1 \right] \qquad (19.4\text{-}24)$$

$$\Omega_i = \omega_T (T_{Vb} - T_i) + [1 - \omega_T (T_{Vb} - T_i)] \omega_w (w_{1Vi} - w_{1Vb}) \qquad (19.4\text{-}25)$$

In the above equations, the Galileo number $Ga_{Lx}$ and the parameters of buoyancy force due to temperature and concentration distributions in the vapor boundary layer $\omega_T$ and $\omega_w$ are defined as

$$Ga_{Lx} = \frac{gx^3}{v_L^2} \qquad (19.4\text{-}26)$$

$$\omega_T = \frac{1}{T_{Vb}} \qquad (19.4\text{-}27)$$

$$\omega_w = \frac{M_1 - M_2}{M_1 - (M_1 - M_2)w_{1Vb}} \qquad (19.4\text{-}28)$$

**Mass balance of more volatile component at the vapor-liquid interface**

$$\dot{M}_{NL} = \frac{2C_N(Sc_V)(\chi_i Sc_V)^{\frac{1}{2}}}{Sc_V R} \frac{(W_R - 1)}{(W_R + 1)^{0.5} W_R^{0.2}} \qquad (19.4\text{-}29)$$

where the function of the Schmidt number $C_N(Sc_V)$ is the same functional form as Eq. (19.4-23) and the parameter of buoyancy force $\chi_i$ introduced by Tanaka (1985) is defined as

$$\chi_i = \Omega_i + \omega_T(T_{Vb} - T_i)\left[(Sc_V/Pr_V)^{\frac{1}{2}} - 1\right] \qquad (19.4\text{-}30)$$

By solving Eqs. (19.4-21) and (19.4-29) together with the miscible condition Eq. (19.4-14) and the phase equilibrium relation Eq. (19.4-15) under a given bulk vapor condition of $(p, T_{Vb}, w_{1Vb})$ and wall temperature $T_w$, the local heat and mass transfer characteristics of binary mixture condensing on a vertical flat plate can be predicted algebraically. Then, all physical quantities, such as $T_i$, $w_{1Vi}$, $w_{1L}$, and $\dot{M}_{NL}$ are obtained. The local condensation mass flux $\dot{m}_x$, local wall heat flux $q_{wx}$, and local convective heat flux $q_{vx}$ are also calculated from the following equations.

$$\dot{m}_x = \frac{\mu_L \dot{M}_{NL}}{x}\left(\frac{Ga_{Lx}}{4}\right)^{\frac{1}{4}} \qquad (19.4\text{-}31)$$

$$q_{wx} = \frac{\lambda_L(T_i - T_w)\dot{M}_{NL}^{-\frac{1}{3}}}{x}\left(\frac{Ga_{Lx}}{4}\right)^{\frac{1}{4}} \qquad (19.4\text{-}32)$$

$$q_{Vx} = \frac{\lambda_V(T_{Vb} - T_i)}{x} C_N(Pr_V)\left(\frac{\chi_i^*}{\Omega_i}\right)^{\frac{1}{4}}(Gr_{Vx}Pr_V)^{\frac{1}{4}}$$
$$\times \left\{1 + 1.25Pr_V^{0.66}\left(\frac{R\dot{M}_{NL}}{\Omega_i^{\frac{1}{4}}}\right)^{1.17}\left[1 - 0.85c_p^*(w_{1Vi} - w_{1L})\right]\right\}$$
$$(19.4\text{-}33)$$

where the Grashof number $Gr_{Vx}$ is defined as

$$Gr_{Vx} = \frac{g\Omega_i x^3}{v_V^2} \qquad (19.4\text{-}34)$$

### 19.4.2 Laminar Film Condensation of a Multi-Component Vapor Mixture

We consider the steady laminar film condensation of an n-component vapor mixture on a vertical flat plate. The same physical model as in Subsection 19.4.1 is employed when $w_{1L}$, $w_{1Li}$, $w_{1Vi}$, $w_{1V}$, and $w_{1Vb}$ in Figure 18 are replaced by $w_{kL}$, $w_{kLi}$, $w_{kVi}$, $w_{kV}$, and $w_{kVb}$ ($k = 1, 2, \ldots, n-1$), respectively.

Toor (1964) and Stewart and Prober (1964) derived the boundary layer equations for the n-component mass transfer problem by linearizing the relevant diffusion coefficient and then showed that this problem can be treated as the combination of related binary problem by the orthogonal transformation (e.g., Wylie, 1966). Fujii and Koyama (1984) treated the two-phase boundary layer equations for the laminar forced convection film condensation of a ternary vapor mixture on a flat plate using the similarity transformation and the orthogonal transformation. Then, they proposed an algebraic method to predict the heat and mass transfer characteristics by applying the prediction method for a binary vapor mixture described in Subsection 19.4.1. Koyama et al. (1987a, 1987b) successfully extended this method to the forced and natural convection condensation problem of a multi-component vapor mixture. In their method, the governing equations for the condensation of the n-component vapor mixture are treated as (n − 1) sets of similarity solutions for the equivalent binary systems, in which the Schmidt numbers for the binary systems, $Sc_{kV}$ ($k = 1, 2, \ldots, n-1$), are determined by the orthogonal transformation of the multi-component diffusion matrix $\mathbf{A}$. The matrix $\mathbf{A}$ is defined as

$$\mathbf{A} = (a_{kl})_{n-1}^{n-1} \qquad (19.4\text{-}35)$$

where

$$a_{kl} = \frac{D_{klV}^*(w_{lVi} - w_{lVb})}{v_V(w_{kVi} - w_{kVb})} \qquad (19.4\text{-}36)$$

$$D_{klV}^* = D_{knV} - D_{klV} \qquad (19.4\text{-}37)$$

$$D_{klV} = M_k D_{klV}^M \sum_{m=1}^{n} \frac{w_{mV}}{M_m} - \frac{M_k}{M_l} \sum_{m=1}^{n} D_{kmV}^M w_{mV} \qquad (19.4\text{-}38)$$

where $D_{klV}^M$ is the diffusivity of the pair of component $k - l$ in the n-component, the value of which can be calculated by referring to text books of Hirshfelder et al.

(1954) and Bird et al. (1960). The diagonal matrix **B**, which is obtained from the matrix **A**, is given by

$$\mathbf{B} \equiv (\delta_{kl}/Sc)_{n-1}^{n-1} = \mathbf{Q}\mathbf{A}\mathbf{P} \tag{19.4-39}$$

$$\mathbf{Q} = \mathbf{P}^{-1} = (q_{kl})_{n-1}^{n-1} \tag{19.4-40}$$

$$\mathbf{P} = (p_{kl})_{n-1}^{n-1} \tag{19.4-41}$$

where $\delta_{kl}$ is the Kronecker delta and $1/Sc_{kV}$ is the eigenvalue of the matrix **A**.

In the following parts, the algebraic method proposed by Koyama et al. are described.

**19.4.2.1 Prediction method for heat and mass transfer characteristics in forced convection condensation.** Koyama et al. (1987a) proposed the following algebraic method for predicting the heat and mass transfer for the laminar forced convection film condensation of the n-component vapor mixture on a flat plate.

*Heat balance at the vapor-liquid interface*

$$0.433 \left(1.367 - \frac{0.432}{\sqrt{2R\dot{M}_{FL}}} + \frac{1}{2R\dot{M}_{FL}}\right)^{\frac{1}{2}} (1 + 0.320 Ph^{0.87})^{-1}$$

$$= \frac{Pr_L \dot{M}_{FL}}{Ph} + C_F(Pr_V) \frac{\lambda_V}{\lambda_L} \left(\frac{\nu_L}{\nu_V}\right)^{\frac{1}{2}} \frac{T_{Vb} - T_i}{T_i - T_w}$$

$$\times \left\{1 + 2.6 Pr_V^{0.66} \left[R\dot{M}_{FL}\left(1 - \frac{2}{3}\phi_i\right)\right]^{1.05}\right\} \tag{19.4-42}$$

In Eq. (19.4-41), $\phi_i$ is the function for the diffusion term, expressed as

$$\phi_i = \sum_{k=1}^{n-1} \left\{ \sum_{l=1}^{n-1} c_{pkn}^* \frac{D_{klV}^* (w_{lVi} - w_{lVb})}{\nu_V} \right.$$

$$\left. \times \left[\sum_{j=1}^{n-1} p_{lj} Sc_{jV} \left(\sum_{m=1}^{n-1} q_{jm} \frac{w_{mVi} - w_{mL}}{w_{mVi} - w_{mVb}}\right)\right]\right\} \tag{19.4-43}$$

where the dimensionless specific isobaric heat difference $c_{pknV}^*$ is defined as

$$c_{pknV}^* = \frac{c_{pkV} - c_{pnV}}{c_{pV}} \tag{19.4-44}$$

and the other dimensionless parameters are the same as in Section 19.4.1.1.

### Mass balance of component k at the vapor-liquid interface

$$\dot{M}_{FL} = \frac{C_F(Sc_{kV})}{R\,Sc_{kV}} \left(\frac{2.5}{1.5 + W_{kR}}\right)^m (W_{kR} - 1) \quad (k = 1, 2, \ldots, n-1) \tag{19.4-45}$$

where

$$\frac{1}{W_{kR}} = 1 - \frac{\sum_{l=1}^{n-1} q_{kl}}{\sum_{m=1}^{n-1} q_{km} \dfrac{w_{mVi} - w_{mL}}{w_{mVi} - w_{mVb}}} \tag{19.4-46}$$

### Miscible condition

$$w_{kL} = w_{kLi} = \frac{\dot{m}_{kx}}{\dot{m}_x} \quad (k = 1, 2, \ldots, n-1) \tag{19.4-47}$$

### Phase equilibrium relation at the vapor-liquid interface

$$\left.\begin{array}{l} w_{kVi} = W_{kV}(T_i, p, w_{1Vi}, w_{2Vi}, \ldots, w_{n-2Vi}) \\ w_{kLi} = W_{kL}(T_i, p, w_{1Vi}, w_{2Vi}, \ldots, w_{n-2Vi}) \end{array}\right\} \tag{19.4-48}$$

When the bulk vapor condition of $(p, T_{Vb}, w_{1Vb}, w_{2Vb}, \ldots, w_{n-1Vb})$ and the wall temperature $T_w$ are given as known parameters, all physical quantities, such as $T_i$, $w_{kVi}$, $w_{kL}$, and $\dot{M}_{FL}$, are obtained by simultaneously solving Eqs. (19.4-42), (19.4-45), (19.4-47), and (19.4-48). Then, in the same manner as in Section 19.4.1.1, the local condensation mass flux $\dot{m}_x$, the local condensation mass flux of the k-component $\dot{m}_{kx}$, the local wall heat flux $q_{wx}$, and the local convective heat flux $q_{Vx}$ are calculated as

$$\dot{m}_x = \frac{\mu_L}{x} \dot{M}_{FL} Re_{Lx}^{\frac{1}{2}} \tag{19.4-49}$$

$$\dot{m}_{kx} = \dot{m}_x w_{kL} \quad (k = 1, 2, \ldots, n-1) \tag{19.4-50}$$

$$q_{wx} = 0.433 \left(1.367 - \frac{0.432}{\sqrt{2R\dot{M}_{FL}}} + \frac{1}{2R\dot{M}_{FL}}\right)^{\frac{1}{2}} \frac{\lambda_L}{x}(T_i - T_w)Re_{Lx}^{\frac{1}{2}} \tag{19.4-51}$$

$$q_{Vx} = \left\{1 + 2.6Pr_V^{0.66}\left[R\dot{M}_{FL}\left(1 - \frac{2}{3}\phi_i\right)\right]^{1.05}\right\} \frac{\lambda_V(T_{Vb} - T_i)}{x} C_F(Pr_V) Re_{Vx}^{\frac{1}{2}} \tag{19.4-52}$$

### 19.4.2.2 Prediction method for heat and mass transfer characteristics in natural convection condensation.
Using the same method as for the forced convection film condensation, Koyama et al. (1987b) proposed a prediction method for the heat and mass transfer characteristics of an n-component vapor mixture condensing naturally on a vertical flat plate.

*Heat balance at the vapor-liquid interface*

$$\dot{M}_{NL}^{-\frac{1}{3}} = \frac{Pr_L \, \dot{M}_{NL}}{Ph} + \sqrt{2}\, C_N(Pr_V)\frac{\lambda_V}{\lambda_L}\left(\frac{\nu_L}{\nu_V}\right)^{\frac{1}{2}} \frac{T_{Vb} - T_i}{T_i - T_w}(\chi_i^* \, Pr_V)^{\frac{1}{4}}$$

$$\times \left\{1 + 1.25\, Pr_V^{0.66}\left(\frac{R\,\dot{M}_{NL}}{\Omega_i^{\frac{1}{4}}}\right)^{1.17}\right\} \qquad (19.4\text{-}53)$$

where

$$\chi_i^* = \Omega_i + \sum_{k=1}^{n-1}\sum_{l=1}^{n-1}\sum_{m=1}^{n-1}\omega_{wl}(w_{lVi} - w_{lVb})p_{lk}q_{km}\left[(Pr_V/Sc_{KV})^{\frac{1}{2}} - 1\right] \qquad (19.4\text{-}54)$$

$$\Omega_i = \omega_T(T_{Vb} - T_i) + [1 - \omega_T(T_{Vb} - T_i)]\sum_{k=1}^{n-1}\sum_{l=1}^{n-1}\sum_{m=1}^{n-1}\omega_{wl}(w_{lVi} - w_{lVb})p_{lk}q_{km}$$

$$(19.4\text{-}55)$$

and the other dimensionless parameters are the same as in Section 19.4.1.2. In Eqs. (19.4-54) and (19.4-55), the parameter of buoyancy force due to the concentration distribution $\omega_{wk}$ is defined as

$$\omega_{wk} = \frac{1/M_n - 1/M_k}{\sum_{l=1}^{n} w_{1Vb}/M_l} \qquad (19.4\text{-}56)$$

*Mass balance of the component k at the vapor-liquid interface*

$$\dot{M}_{NL} = \frac{2C_N(Sc_{kV})(\chi_{ki}\, Sc_{kV})^{\frac{1}{4}}}{Sc_{kV}\, R}\frac{(W_{kR} - 1)}{(W_{kR} + 1)^{0.5}\, W_{kR}^{0.2}} \quad (k = 1, 2, \ldots, n-1)$$

$$(19.4\text{-}57)$$

where

$$\chi_{ki} = \Omega_i + \omega_T(T_{Vb} - T_i)\left[(Sc_{kV}/Pr_V)^{\frac{1}{2}} - 1\right]$$

$$+ \sum_{l=1}^{n-1}\sum_{m=1}^{n-1}\sum_{p=1}^{n-1}\omega_{wm}(w_{mVi} - w_{mVb})p_{ml}q_{lp}\left[(Sc_{kV}/Sc_{lV})^{\frac{1}{2}} - 1\right] \qquad (19.4\text{-}58)$$

By simultaneously solving Eqs. (19.4-53), (19.4-57), (19.4-47), and (19.4-48) for a given mixture at a given wall temperature and a given bulk vapor condition, we can obtain all physical quantities, such as $T_i$, $w_{kVi}$, $w_{kL}$, $\dot{M}_{NL}$. Then, we can calculate the values of $\dot{m}_x$, $q_{wx}$, and $q_{Vx}$ as

$$\dot{m}_x = \frac{\mu_L \dot{M}_{NL}}{x}\left(\frac{Ga_{Lx}}{4}\right)^{\frac{1}{4}} \qquad (19.4\text{-}59)$$

$$q_{wx} = \frac{\lambda_L(T_i - T_w)\dot{M}_{NL}^{-\frac{1}{3}}}{x}\left(\frac{Ga_{Lx}}{4}\right)^{\frac{1}{4}} \qquad (19.4\text{-}60)$$

$$q_{Vx} = \frac{\lambda_V(T_{Vb} - T_i)}{x} C_N(Pr_V)\left(\frac{\chi_i^*}{\Omega_i}\right)^{\frac{1}{4}} (Gr_{Vx}Pr_V)^{\frac{1}{4}}$$

$$\times \left\{1 + 1.25 Pr_V^{0.66}\left(\frac{R\dot{M}_{NL}}{\Omega_i^{\frac{1}{4}}}\right)^{1.17}\right\}$$

$$(19.4\text{-}61)$$

### 19.4.3 Future Directions

Since Nusselt (1916) proposed the film theory for the natural convection condensation of water steam on a vertical flat plate, many researchers have investigated the condensation problem experimentally and theoretically. In the present stage, we can understand only the basic characteristics of the condensation of a multi-component mixture on a flat plate. The remaining problems to be solved are listed below:

1. The thermophysical properties of a multi-component mixture.
2. More rigorously theoretical treatment of buoyancy force due to temperature and concentration difference in a multi-component system.
3. Effect of the multi-component diffusion in the condensate film.
4. Condensation of a multi-component vapor mixture on a tube or in a tube-bank.
5. Augmentation technology of the multi-component condensation.
6. Acquisition of experimental data on the multi-component condensation.

## REFERENCES

Bergelin, O. P., Brown, G. A., and Doberstein, S. C. 1952. Heat Transfer and Fluid Friction During Flow Across Banks of Tubes—IV. *Trans. ASME* 74:953–960.

Bird, R. B., Stewart, W. E., and Lightfoot, E. N. 1960. *Transport Phenomena*. New York: John Wiley.

Butterworth, D. 1981. Inundation Without Vapor Shear. *Power Condenser Heat Transfer Technology.* Eds. P. J. Marto and R. H. Nunn. New York: Hemisphere Publishing Corporation.

Cess, R. D. 1960. Laminar Film Condensation on a Flat Plate in the Absence of Body Force. *Z Angew Math. Phys.* 11:426–433.

Chen, M. M. 1961a. An Analytical Study of Laminar Film Condensation: Part 1—Flat Plates. *Trans ASME J. Heat Transfer* 83:48–54.

Chen, M. M. 1961b. An Analytical Study of Laminar Film Condensation: Part 2—Single and Multiple Horizontal Tubes. *Trans ASME J. Heat Transfer* 83:55–60.

Colburn, A. P. 1934. Note on the Calculation of Condensation when a Portion of the Condensate Layer is in Turbulent Motion. *Trans. Am. Inst. Chem. Engrs.* 30:187–193.

Denny, V. E. and Jusionis, V. J. 1972a. Effects of Noncondensable Gas and Forced Flow on Laminar Film Condensation. *Int. J. Heat Mass Transfer* 15(2):315–326.

Denny, V. E., and Jusionis, V. J. 1972b. Effects of Forced Flow and Variable Properties of Binary Film Condensation. *Int. J. Heat Mass Transfer* 15(11):2143–2153.

Denny, V. E., Mills, A. F., and Jusionis, V. J. 1971. Laminar Film Condensation From a Steam-Air Mixture Undergoing Forced Flow Down a Vertical Surface. *Trans. ASME C, J. Heat Transfer* 93(3):297–304.

Dukler, A. E. 1960. Fluid Mechanics and Heat Transfer in Vertical Falling-Film System. *Chem. Engng. Prop. Symp. Ser.* 56:1–10.

Fishenden, H. and Saunders, O. A. 1950. *An Introduction to Heat Transfer.* London: Clarendon Press, p. 132.

Fujii, T. 1981. Vapor Shear and Condensate Inundation: An Overview. *Power Condenser Heat Transfer Technology,* Eds. P. J. Marto and R. H. Nunn, pp. 193–223. New York: Hemisphere Publishing Corporation.

Fujii, T. 1991. Theory of Laminar Film Condensation. New York: Springer-Verlag.

Fujii, T. and Koyama, S. 1984. Laminar Forced Convection Condensation of a Ternary Vapor Mixture on a Flat Plate. *Fundamentals of Phase Change: Boiling and Condensation-ASME HTD* 38:81–87.

Fujii, T. and Uehara, H. 1972. Laminar Film Condensation on a Vertical Surface. *Int. J. Heat Mass Transfer* 15:217–233.

Fujii, T. and Uehara, H. 1973. Condensation Heat Transfer. *Advance of Heat Transfer* 1:1. Yokendo, Tokyo. (in Japanese).

Fujii, T., Honda, H., and Oda, K. 1979. Condensation of Steam on a Horizontal Tube—The Influence of Oncoming Velocity and Thermal Condition at the Tube Wall. *Condensation Heat Transfer. Proc. 18th Nat. Heat Transfer Conf.* ASME, 35–43.

Fujii, T., Koyama, S., and Goto, M. 1985. Effects of Air upon Gravity Controlled Condensation of Nonazeotropic Binary Refrigerant Vapor on a Horizontal Tube. *Trans. Jpn. Soc. Mech. Eng.* 51(46B):2442–2450 (in Japanese).

Fujii, T., Koyama, S., and Watabe, M. 1987. Laminar Forced-Convection Condensation of Binary Mixtures on a Flat Plate. *Trans. Jpn. Soc. Mech. Eng.* 53(486B):541–548 (in Japanese).

Fujii, T., Koyama, S., and Watabe, M. 1989. Laminar Film Condensation of Gravity-Controlled Convection for Ternary Vapor Mixtures on a Flat Plate. *Trans. Jpn. Soc. Mech. Eng.* 55(510B):434–441 (in Japanese).

Fujii, T., Shinzato, K., and Lee, J. B. 1991a. A Proposal of a New Equation for the Mass Concentration at the Vapor-Liquid Interface in the Case of Forced-Convection Laminar Film Condensation of a Binary Vapor Mixture on a Flat Plate. *Engineering Sciences Reports, Kyushu University* 13(3):293–296.

Fujii, T., Shinzato, K., and Lee, J. B. 1991b. A Condensation of the Similarity Solution for Laminar Forced-Convection Condensation of Saturated Vapors. *Engineering Sciences Reports, Kyushu University* 13(3):305–316.

Fujii, T., Uehara, H., Hirata, K., and Oda, K. 1972. Heat Transfer and Flow Resistance in Condensation of Low Pressure Steam Flowing Through Tube Banks. *Int. J Heat Mass Transfer* 15(2):247–260.

Fujii, T., Uehara, H., Mihara, K., and Kato, T. 1977. Forced Convection Condensation in the Presence of Noncondensables—A Theoretical Treatment for Two-Phase Laminar Boundary Layer. *Reports of Research Institute of Industrial Science, Kyushu University* 66:53–80 (in Japanese).

Fujii, T., Uehara, H., Mihara, K., and Takashima, H. 1978. Body Force Convection Condensation in the Presence of Noncondensables. *Reports of Research Institute of Industrial Science, Kyushu University* 67:23–41 (in Japanese).

Fujii, T., Uehara, H., and Oda, K. 1972. Film Condensation on a Surface with Uniform Heat Flux and Body Force Convection. *Heat Transfer Jap. Res.* 4:76–83.

Gaddis, E. S. 1979. Solution of the Two-Phase Boundary-Layer Equations for Laminar Film Condensation of Vapor Flowing Perpendicular to a Horizontal Cylinder. *Int. J. Heat Mass Transfer* 22:371–382.

Gogonin, I. I., Kabov, D. A., and Sosunov, V. I. 1983. Heat Transfer in Condensation of R-12 Vapor on Bundles of Finned Tubes. *Kholodil'naya Teknika* 1:26–29.

Gregorig, R., Kern, J., and Turek, K. 1974. Improved Correlation of Film Condensation Data Based on a More Rigorous Application of Similarity Parameters. *Wärme unt Stoffübertragung* 7(1):1.

Griggul, U. 1942. Wärmeübertragung beider Kondensation mitt Turbulenten Waserhaut, *Forsch. Ing. Weser* 13:49–57.

Gunningham, J. and Ben Boudinar, M. 1990. The Effect of Condensate Inundation on the Performance of Roped Tubes. *Condenser and Condensation*: 417–429.

Hebbard, G. H. and Badger, W. L. 1934. Steam Film Heat Transfer Coefficient for Vertical Tubes. *Trans. AIChE.* 30:194–216.

Hijikata, K. and Mori, Y. 1972. Forced Convective Heat Transfer of a Gas Containing a Condensing Vapor on a Flat Plate. *Trans. Jpn. Soc. Mech. Eng.* 38(314):2630–2640 (in Japanese).

Hirshfelder, J. O., Curtiss, C. F., and Bird, R. B. 1954. Molecular Theory of Gases and Liquids. New York: John Wiley & Sons.

Hirshburg, R. I. and Florshuetz, L. W. 1982a. Laminar Wavy Film Flow. Part I: Hydrodynamic Analysis. *Trans. ASME* 104:452–458.

Hirshburg, R. I. and Florshuetz, L. W. 1982b. Laminar Wavy Film Flow. Part II: Hydrodynamic Analysis. *Trans. ASME* 104:459–464.

Honda, H. 1997. Tube Banks, Condensation Heat Transfer. In: *International Encyclopedia of Heat Mass Transfer*. Eds. G. F. Hewitt, G. L. Shires, and Y. V. Pohezhaev, pp. 1177–1181. New York: CRC Press.

Honda, H. and Fujii, T. 1984. Condensation of Flowing Vapor on a Horizontal Tube—Numerical Analysis as a Conjugate Heat Transfer Problem. *Trans. ASME, J. Heat Transfer* 106:841–848.

Honda, H., Nozu, S., and Takeda, Y. 1989a. A Theoretical Model of Film Condensation in a Bundle of Horizontal Low Finned Tubes. *Trans. ASME J Heat Transfer* 111:525–532.

Honda, H., Takamatsu, H., and Kim, K. 1994. Condensation of CFC-11 and HCFC-123 in In-Line Bundles of Horizontal Finned Tubes: Effect of Fin Geometry. *J Enhanced Heat Transfer* 1:197.

Honda, H., Takamatu, H., Takada, N., and Makishi, D. 1996. Condensation of HCFC123 in Bundles of Finned Tubes: Effect of Fin Geometry and Tube Arrangement. *Int. J. Refrig.* 19(1):1–9.

Honda, H., Uchida, B., Nozu, S., Nakata, H., and Fujii, T. 1988. Condensation of Downward Flowing R-113 Vapor on Bundles of Horizontal Smooth Tubes. *Trans. JSME* 54:1453–1460; *Heat Transfer—Jap. Res.* 18(6):31–52.

Honda, H., Uchida, B., Nozu, S., Nakata, H., and Fujii, T. 1989b. Condensation of Downward Flowing R-113 Vapors on Tube Bundles of Horizontal Smooth Tubes. *Heat Transfer—Jap. Res.* 18:131–152.

Honda, H., Uchida, B., Nozu, S., Nakata, H., and Torigoe, E. 1991. Film Condensation of R-113 on In-Line Bundles of Horizontal Finned Tubes. *Trans ASME J Heat Transfer* 113:479–486.

Honda, H., Uchida, B., Nozu, S., Torigoe, E., and Imai, S. 1992. Film Condensation of R-113 on Staggered Bundles of Horizontal Finned Tubes. *Trans ASME J Heat Transfer* 114:442–449.

Kapitza, P. L. 1948. Wavy Flow of Thin Films of Viscous Liquids. Zh. Eksoerim. *Teor. Fiz.* 18:3–18.

Kays, W. M., London, A. L., and Lo, R. K. 1954. Heat Transfer and Friction Characteristics for Gas Flow Normal to Tube Banks. *Trans. ASME* 76:387–396.

Kern, D. Q. 1958. Mathematical Development of Loading in Horizontal Condensers. *AichE. J* 4:157–160.

Kinoshita, E. and Uehara, H. 1995. Turbulent Film Condensation of Binary Mixture on a Vertical Plate. *Proc. of 4th ASME/JSME Thermal Engineering* 2:367–373.

Kirkbride, C. G. 1933. Heat Transfer by Condensing Vapor on Vertical Tube. *Trans. Am. Inst. Chem. Engrs.* 30:170–186.

Koh, J. C. Y. 1962a. Film Condensation in a Forced-Convection Boundary-Layer Flow. *Int. J. Heat Mass Transfer* 5:941–954.

Koh, J. C. Y. 1962b. Laminar Film Condensation of Condensible Gases and Gaseous Mixtures on a Flat Plate. *Proc. 4th U.S. National Congress of Applied Mechanics* 2:1327–1336.

Kotake, S. 1985. Effect of a Small Amount of Noncondensable Gas on Film Condensation. *Int. J. Heat Mass Transfer* 28(2):407–414.

Koyama, S., Goto, M., and Fujii, T. 1987a. Laminar Film Condensation of Multicomponent Mixtures on a Flat Plate-First Report, Forced Convection Condensation. *Reports of Institute of Advanced Material Study, Kyushu University* 1(1):77–83 (in Japanese).

Koyama, S., Goto, M., Watabe, M., and Fujii, T. 1987b. Laminar Film Condensation of Multicomponent Mixtures on a Flat Plate-Second Report, Gravity Controlled Condensation. *Reports of Institute of Advanced Material Study, Kyushu University* 1(1):85–89 (in Japanese).

Koyama, S., Watabe, M., and Fujii, T. 1986. The Gravity Controlled Film Condensation of Saturated and Superheated Binary Vapor Mixtures on a Vertical Plate. *Trans. Jpn. Soc. Mech. Eng.* 52(474B):827–834 (in Japanese).

Kutateladze, S. S. and Gogonin, I. I. 1979. Heat Transfer in Film Condensation of Slowly Moving Vapor. *Int. J. Heat Mass Transfer* 22(12):1593–1597.

Lee, W. C. and Rose, J. W. 1982. Film Condensation on a Horizontal Tube—Effect of Vapor Velocity. *Proc. 7th Int. Heat Transfer Conf.*, Munich, Vol. 5, 101–106.

Lucas, K. 1976. Combined Body Force and Forced Convection in Laminar Film Condensation of Mixed Vapors—Integral and Finite Difference Treatment. *Int. J. Heat Mass Transfer* 19(11):1273–1280.

Marshall, E. and Lee, C. Y. 1973. Stability of Condensate Flow down a Vertical Wall. *Int. J. Heat Transfer* 16:41–48.

Marto, P. J. 1984. Heat Transfer and Two-Phase Flow During Shell-Side Condensation. *Heat Transfer Engineering* 5:31–61.

Marto, P. J. 1988. An Evaluation of Film Condensation on Horizontal Integral Fin Tubes. *Trans ASME J Heat Transfer* 110:1287–1305.

Mayhew, Y. R., Griffiths, P. J., and Phillips, J. W. 1965. Effect of Vapor Drag on Laminar Film Condensation on a Vertical Surface. *Proc. Instn. Mech. Engnrs* 180(Pt.3J):280–287.

Meisenburg, S. J., Boarts, R. M., and Badger, W. L. 1935. The Influence of Small Concentration of Air in Steam on the Steam Film Coefficient of Heat Transfer. *AIChE. J.* 31:622–638.

Memory, S. B. and Rose, J. W. 1991. Free Convection Laminar Film Condensation on a Horizontal Tube with Variable Wall Temperature. *Int. J. Heat Mass Transfer* 34:2775–2778.

Minkowycz, W. J. and Sparrow, E. M. 1966. Condensation Heat Transfer in the Presence of Noncondensables, Interfacial Resistance, Superheating, Variable Properties, and Diffusion. *Int. J. Heat Mass Transfer* 9(10):1125–1144.

Minkowycz, W. J. and Sparrow, E. M. 1969. The Effect of Superheating on Condensation Heat Transfer in a Forced Convection Boundary Layer Flow. *Int. J. Heat Mass Transfer* 12(2):147–154.

Mori, Y. and Hijikata, K. 1972. Theoretical Study on Free Convective Condensation of a Steam Containing Noncondensable Gas on a Vertical Flat Plate. *Trans. Jpn. Soc. Mech. Eng.* 38(306):418–426 (in Japanese).
Murata, K., Abe, N., and Hashizume, K. 1996. Condensation Heat Transfer in a Bundle of Horizontal Integral-Fin Tubes. *Proc 9 th In Heat Transfer Conf* 4:259–264.
Niknejad, J. and Rose, J. W. (1981). Interphase Matter Transfer—An Experimental Study of Condensation of Mercury. *Proc. R. Soc. Lond.* A 378:305–327.
Nusselt, W. 1916. Die Oberflachenkondensation des Wasserdampfes. *Z. Vereines Deutsch. Ing.* 60(27):541–546; (28):569–575.
Penev, V., Krglov, V. S., Boyadjiev, C. H., and Vorotilin, V. P. 1972. Wavy Flow of Thin Liquids Film. *Int. J. Heat Mass Transfer* 15:1395–1406.
Pierson, O. I. 1959. Experimental Investigation of the Influence of Tube Arrangement on Convection Heat Transfer and Flow Resistance in Cross Flow of Gasses over Tube Banks. *Trans. ASME*, PRO-59-6:563–572.
Rohsenow, W. M., Webber, J. H., and Ling, A. T. 1956. Effect of Vapor Velocity on a Laminar and Turbulent-Film Condensation. *Trans. ASME* 78:1637–1643.
Rose, J. W. 1969. Condensation of a Vapor in the Presence of a Non-Condensing Gas. *Int. J. Heat Mass Transfer* 12(2):233–237.
Rose, J. W. 1979. Boundary-Layer Flow with Transpiration on an Isothermal Flat Plate. *Int. J. Heat Mass Transfer* 22:1243–1244.
Rose, J. W. 1980. Approximate Equations for Forced-Convection Condensation in the Presence of a Non-Condensing Gas on a Flat Plate and Horizontal Tube. *Int. J. Heat Mass Transfer* 23:539–546.
Rose, J. W. 1984. Effect of Pressure Gradient in Forced Convection Film Condensation on a Horizontal Tube. *Int. J. Heat Mass Transfer* 27:39–47.
Rose, J. W. 1988. Fundamentals of Condensation Heat Transfer: Laminar Film Condensation. *JSME Int. Journal, Series II* 31(3):357–375.
Rose, J. W. 1998. Condensation Heat Transfer Fundamentals. *Trans. IChemE* 76:143–152.
Sage, E. F. and Estrin, J. 1976. Film Condensation from a Ternary Mixture of Vapors upon a Vertical Surface. *Int. J. Heat and Mass Transfer* 19(3):323–333.
Seban, R. A. 1954. Remarks on Film Condensation with Turbulent Flow. *Trans. ASME* 76:299–303.
Shekriladze, I. G. and Gomelauri, V. I. 1966. Theoretical Study of Laminar Film Condensation of Flowing Vapor. *Int. J. Heat Mass Transfer* 9:581–591.
Shekriladze, I. G. 1977. Analysis of Laminar Film Condensation from a Moving Vapor. *Inzhenerno-Fizicheskii Zhurnal* 32:221–225.
Shklover, G. G. 1990. Generalized Data of Steam Condensation Computation in Horizontal Tube Bundles. *Condenser and Condensation*, 203–212.
Soflata, H. 1980. Theoretical Study of Film Wise Condensation Considering Wave Initiation. *Wärme- und Stoffubertragung* 14:201–210.
Soflata, H. 1981. Improved Theoretical Model for Wavy Film Wise Condensation. *Wärme- und Stoffubertragung* 15:117–124.
Sparrow, E. M. and Eckert, E. R. G. 1961. Effects of Superheated Vapor and Noncondensable Gases on Laminar Film Condensation. *AIChE J.* 7(3):473–477.
Sparrow, E. M. and Lin, S. H. 1964. Condensation Heat Transfer in the Presence of a Noncondensable Gas. *Trans. ASME, J. Heat Transfer C* 86(3):430–436.
Sparrow, E. M. and Marshall, E. 1969. Binary, Gravity-Flow Film Condensation. *J. Heat Transfer* 91(2):205–211.
Sparrow, E. M., Minkowycz, J. W., and Saddy, M. 1967. Forced Convection Condensation in the Presence of Noncondensables and Interfacial Resistance. *Int. J. Heat Mass Transfer* 10(12):1829–1845.

Stephan, K. and Laesecke, A. 1980. The Influence of Suction on Heat and Mass Transfer in Condensation of Mixed Vapors. *Wärme-und Stoffübertragung* 13(1/2):115–123.
Stewart, W. E. and Prober, R. 1964. Matrix Calculation of Multicomponent Mass Transfer in Isothermal Systems. *I & EC Fundament.* 3(3):224–235.
Stuhlträger, E., Miyara, A., and Uehara, H. 1995. Flow Dynamics and Heat Transfer of a Condensate Film on a Vertical Wall—II. Flow Dynamics and Heat Transfer. *Int. J. Heat Mass Transfer* 38(15):2715–2772.
Stuhlträger, E., Naridomi, Y., Miyara, A., and Uehara, H. 1993. Flow Dynamics and Heat Transfer of a Condensate Film on a Vertical Wall—I. Numerical Analysis and Flow Dynamics. *Int. J. Heat Mass Transfer* 36(6):1677–1686.
Sukhatme, S. P. 1990. Condensation on Enhanced Surface Horizontal Tube. *Proc 9th In Heat Transfer Conf:* 305–328.
Taitel, Y. and Tamir, A. 1974. Film Condensation of Multicomponent Mixtures. *Int. J. Multiphase Flow* 1(5):697–714.
Tamir, A. 1973. Condensation of Binary Mixtures of Miscible Vapors. *Int. J. Heat Mass Transfer* 16(3):683–685.
Tanaka, H. 1985. On Expression for Local Nusselt Number and Local Sherwood Number Concerning Simultaneous Heat and Mass Transfer in Free Convection from a Vertical Plate. *Reports of Research Institute of Industrial Science, Kyushu University* 78:47–52 (in Japanese).
Toor, H. L. 1964. Solution of the Linearized Equations of Multicomponent Mass Transfer: II. Matrix Methods. *AIChE J.* 10(4):460–465.
Uehara, H. and Kinoshita, E. 1994. Wave and Turbulent Film Condensation on a Vertical Surface (Correlation for Local Heat-Transfer Coefficient). *Trans. of JSME.* 60(577), 3109–3116.
Uehara, H. and Kinoshita, E. 1997. Wave and Turbulent Film Condensation on a Vertical Surface (Correlation for Average Heat-Transfer Coefficient). *Trans. JSME.*, pp. 4013–4020.
Uehara, H., Egashira, S., and Taguchi, Y. 1989. Film Condensation on a Vertical Smooth Surface in Flowing Vapor (1st Report, Flow Patterns of Condensate Film and Local Heat Transfer Coefficients). *Trans. JSME*: 450–456.
Uehara, H., Kinoshita, E., Ido, H., Sugimoto, K., and Hasegawa, H. 1995. Experimental Study on Forced Convection Turbulent Film Condensation of Binary Mixture. *Proc. Japan National Syp. Heat Transfer:* 717–718.
Uehara, H., Kinoshita, E., and Matuda, S. 1998. Theoretical Analysis of Turbulent Film Condensation on a Vertical Surface. *Trans. JSME* 64:4137–4144.
Uehara, H., Kusuda, H., Nakaoka, T., and Yamada, M. 1983. Experimental Study on Film Condensation on a Vertical Surface. *Trans. JSME* 49(439B):666–675.
Uehara, H., Nakaoka, T., Kusuda, H., and Nakashima, S. 1982. Wave Film Condensation on a Vertical Surface (Combined Convection). *Trans. JSME* 48(433):1751–1760.
Uehara, H., Nakaoka, T., Murata, K., and Egashira, S. 1988. Body Forced Convection Condensation on a Vertical Smooth Surface (1st Report, Flow Pattern of Condensate Film and Local Heat Transfer Coefficient). *Trans. JSME* 54(505B):2537–2544.
Webb, R. I. 1988. Enhancement of Film Condensation. *Int Comm Heat Mass Transfer* 15:475–507.
Webb, R. I. and Murawski, C. G. 1990. Row Effect for R-11 Condensation on Enhanced Tubes. *Trans ASME J Heat Transfer* 112:768–776.
Wylie, C. R., Jr. 1966. *Advanced Engineering Mathematics.* 3rd editon, pp. 429–492. New York: McGraw-Hill.
Zukauskas, A. 1972. *Advances in Heat Transfer, 8.* New York: Academic Press, pp. 93–161.

CHAPTER
# TWENTY

## DROPWISE CONDENSATION

**John Rose**

*University of London, London E1 4NS, United Kingdom*

**Yoshio Utaka**

*Yokohama National University, Yokohama 240-8501, Japan*

**Ichiro Tanasawa**

*Tokyo University of Agriculture and Technology, Tokyo 184-8588, Japan*

## 20.1 INTRODUCTION

Dropwise condensation occurs when a vapor condenses on a surface that is not wetted by the condensate. The condensate does not spread but forms discrete drops, as shown in Figure 1, for dropwise condensation of ethylene glycol on a copper surface promoted by trilauryl trithiophosphite. It has long been recognized that for non-metal vapors, dropwise condensation gives much higher heat-transfer coefficients than found with film condensation. For instance, the heat-transfer coefficient for dropwise condensation of steam is more than twenty times that for film condensation at atmospheric pressure.

Dropwise condensation involves a combination of several processes. Bare surface is continually exposed to vapor by coalescences between drops and by the sweeping action of the departing drops as they are removed from the surface by gravity or vapor shear stress. "Primary" drops are formed at nucleation sites on the exposed surface (typical nucleation site densities are in the range $10^7$ to $10^9$ sites/mm$^2$). The primary drops grow by condensation until coalescences occur between neighbors. The coalesced drops continue to grow, and new ones form and grow at sites exposed through coalescences. As the process continues, coalescences occur between drops of various sizes, while the largest drops continue to grow until they reach their maximum size ($r \approx 1$ mm), when they are removed from the surface. The diameter ratio between the largest and smallest drops during dropwise condensation of steam is around $10^6$.

**582** HANDBOOK OF PHASE CHANGE: BOILING AND CONDENSATION

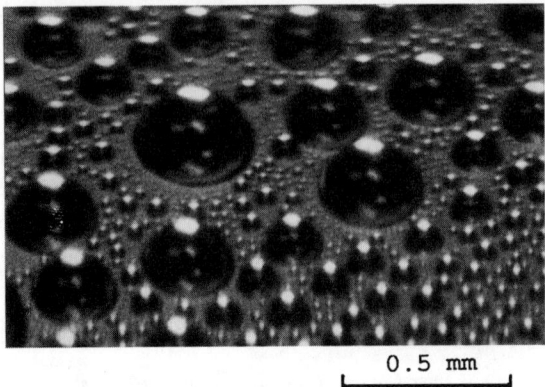

**Figure 1** Dropwise condensation (ethylene glycol at 11.5 kPa, photographed at angle 45 degrees to the copper condensing surface promoted by trilauryl trithiophosphite, Utaka et al., 1988).

Reviews of dropwise condensation heat transfer have been given by Le Fevre and Rose (1969), Tanasawa (1991), Marto (1994), and Rose (1994).

## 20.2 PROMOTION OF DROPWISE CONDENSATION

Clean metal surfaces are wetted by non-metallic liquids, and film condensation is the mode that normally occurs in practice. Non-wetting agents, known as promoters, are needed to promote dropwise condensation. Unfortunately, sufficiently reliable promoting techniques have not yet been developed, except on the laboratory scale, and dropwise condensation has not so far been used on an industrial scale to any significant extent.

Methods that have been used for promoting dropwise condensation may be classified into the following categories:

1. Application of an appropriate non-wetting agent, i.e., organic promoter, to the condenser surface before operation.
2. Injection of the non-wetting agent intermittently (or continuously) into the vapor.
3. Coating the condensing surface with a thin layer of an inorganic compound, such as metal sulfide.
4. Plating the condensing surface with chromium or a thin layer of a noble metal, such as gold.
5. Coating the condensing surface with a thin layer of an organic polymer, such as polytetrafluoroethylene (PTFE, Teflon).

Various promoters have been identified and used successfully in laboratory tests, mainly with steam. The earliest to be used were fatty acids, which must be injected intermittently into the vapor to maintain dropwise condensation for long intervals. More promising promoters are long chain hydrocarbon molecules with an active group that bonds with the metal surface to present a hydrophobic surface to the vapor. Excess promoter is washed away by the condensate to leave a mono-molecular layer of negligible thermal resistance. A typical example of this type of promoter is dioctadecyl disulphide, which has given satisfactory dropwise condensation lifetimes in laboratory investigations.

Successful industrial application of dropwise condensation has been prevented by promoter breakdown often associated with surface oxidation. PTFE provides an excellent non-wetting surface; however, it has not been found possible to produce sufficiently thin durable surface layers. A layer of thickness 0.02 to 0.03 mm offers a thermal resistance sufficient to offset the advantage of dropwise over film condensation for steam.

Dropwise condensation has frequently been observed on metal surfaces such as chromium and gold, which are very smooth, without use of a promoting agent. It seems probable, however, that non-wetting impurities were present. In experiments where great care has been taken to ensure clean conditions, film condensation has been found (see Erb, 1973; Erb and Thelen, 1966; Wilkins et al., 1973a; Woodruff and Westwater, 1979).

## 20.3 DROPWISE CONDENSATION OF STEAM

### 20.3.1 Measurements at Atmospheric Pressure

The heat-transfer coefficient of dropwise condensation of steam at a pressure near 1 atm has been measured by many researchers. Taken together, these show a considerable scatter due to the effect of noncondensing gas and the accuracy of measuring method. Heat-transfer coefficients obtainable with dropwise condensation are high and hence prone to error in measurement of the small temperature difference; they are also very susceptible to reduction by the presence in the vapor of noncondensing gas. In the absence of significant vapor velocity, very small gas concentrations lead to appreciable lowering of the heat-transfer coefficient. In more recent years, improved experimental techniques have led to reproducible and reliable experimental data; see, for instance, Le Fevre and Rose (1964, 1965) and Citakoglu and Rose (1968). At present, it can be said that the heat-transfer coefficient of dropwise condensation for steam at 1 atm, under the normal gravitational acceleration and on a vertical copper surface, is about $230 \pm 50$ kW/(m$^2$ K) in the heat flux range of 0.1–1 MW/m$^2$, provided that there is no effect of noncondensing

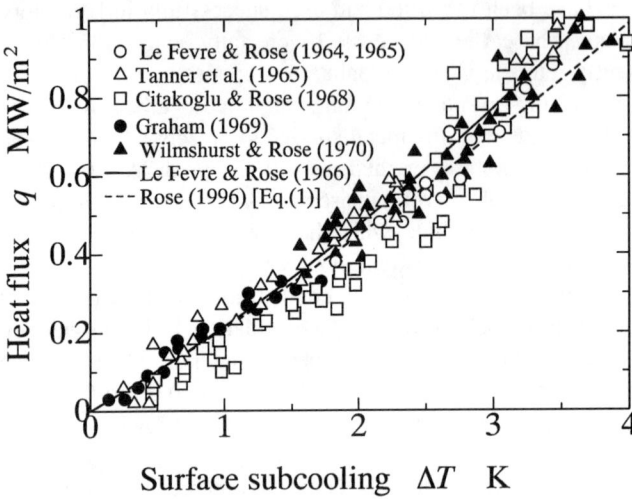

**Figure 2** Dropwise condensation of steam on copper surfaces at atmospheric pressure.

gases and the steam velocity is smaller than about 10 m/s. Relatively small differences between the more recent investigations are due to the effects of steam velocity and surface characteristics.

Figure 2 shows several representative measurements for steam at atmospheric pressure together with the theory of Le Fevre and Rose (1966) (see Section 5) and an empirical equation for steam (see Eq. [20.3-1] below). The fact that Figure 2 is not a straight line through the origin shows that the heat-transfer coefficient of dropwise condensation depends on the surface subcooling. In smaller $\Delta T$-range, the tendency of decreasing heat-transfer coefficient with decreasing surface subcooling is due to the decreasing number density of active nucleation sites on the condensing surface. In the range of moderate cooling intensity, the heat-transfer coefficient becomes nearly constant with increasing surface subcooling.

### 20.3.2 Effect of Pressure

Several sets of results are available for dropwise condensation of steam on copper condensing surfaces at pressures below 1 atm, as shown in Figure 3. All data show a tendency of decreasing heat-transfer coefficient with decreasing pressure. This is caused mainly by the increase of the interfacial resistance to mass transfer at the liquid-vapor interface at low pressure. Differences between different data sets are in part attributable to the dependence of heat-transfer coefficient on $\Delta T$, with higher heat-transfer coefficients being found at larger surface subcoolings. The solid lines

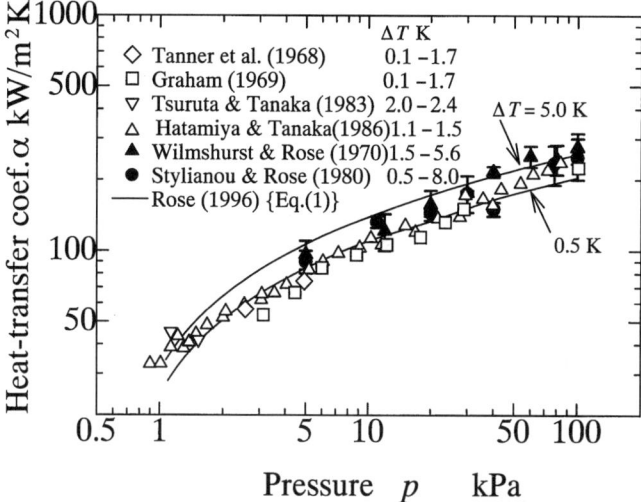

**Figure 3** Dependence of heat-transfer coefficient on pressure for steam [Note that the "error bars" indicated for the data of Wilmshurst & Rose (1970) and Stylianou & Rose (1980) are due to dependece of $\alpha$ on $\Delta T$].

are calculated by the empirical equation for steam proposed by Rose (1996);

$$\alpha/(\mathrm{kW/m^2\,K}) = T_c^{0.8}\,(5 + 0.3\,\Delta T/\mathrm{K}). \qquad (20.3\text{-}1)$$

where $T_c$ is Celsius temperature of the saturated vapor.

### 20.3.3 Effect of Departing Drop Size

The heat-transfer coefficient of dropwise condensation is dependent on the distribution of drop sizes on the surface, which in turn depends on the maximum drop diameter or the departing drop diameter. Tanasawa et al. (1976) measured the dependence of the heat-transfer coefficient for steam at atmospheric pressure on the departing drop diameter under almost constant heat flux of 600 kW/m², using gravitational, centrifugal, and vapor shear forces to change the departing drop diameter. The results are shown in Figure 4. It is seen that the heat-transfer coefficient is proportional to the departing drop diameter to the power of about $-0.3$. The range of $\Delta T$ in the measurements was quite small, so the dependence of heat-transfer coefficient on $\Delta T$ was not significant. It is very interesting to note that the theories of Le Fevre and Rose (1966) (see Rose, 1976, 1988) and Tanaka (1975a, 1975b), discussed in Section 5, lead to virtually the same result.

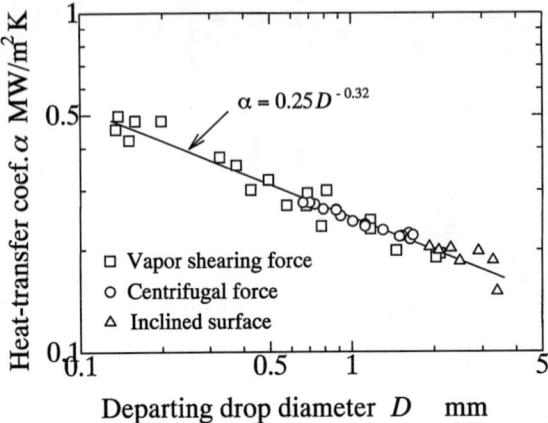

**Figure 4** Dependence of heat-transfer coefficient for steam on departing drop diameter [Tanasawa et al. (1976)].

### 20.3.4 Effect of Thermal Properties of Surface Material

In the dropwise condensation process, those parts of the surface under relatively large drops are nearly adiabatic, while the heat flux is large on those regions having very small drops. Also, drops move on the surface due to the coalescences. Hence, the temperature and the heat flux on the condensing surface must be nonuniform and fluctuating. An effect of thermal conductivity is expected due to the *constriction effect*, for which a model has been proposed by Mikic (1969). According to the Mikic theory, the heat-transfer coefficient must be lower on a poor conductive material. An effect of heat capacity (transient heat conduction) of the surface material should also arise from the unsteady nature of process. Both would be expected to lead to an effective additional resistance to heat transfer.

Figure 5 shows the experimental and theoretical results. There has been considerable controversy on this topic, not over the fact that such resistances are expected on physical grounds, but rather over their magnitudes. The measurements of Wilkins and Bromley (1973b), Hannemann and Mikic (1976a) and Tsuruta and Togashi (1989) have suggested quite a strong dependence of heat-transfer coefficient on thermal conductivity of the surface materials, while data of Stylianou and Rose (1980), who questioned the accuracy of some of the earlier measurement, and Aksan and Rose (1973) have indicated insignificant dependence. The dependencies of heat-transfer coefficient on temperature difference discussed above is also relevant, since those measurements that show low heat-transfer coefficients at low surface thermal conductivity have necessarily low $\Delta T$, while those experiments performed at higher $\Delta T$ have generally shown small or negligible effect.

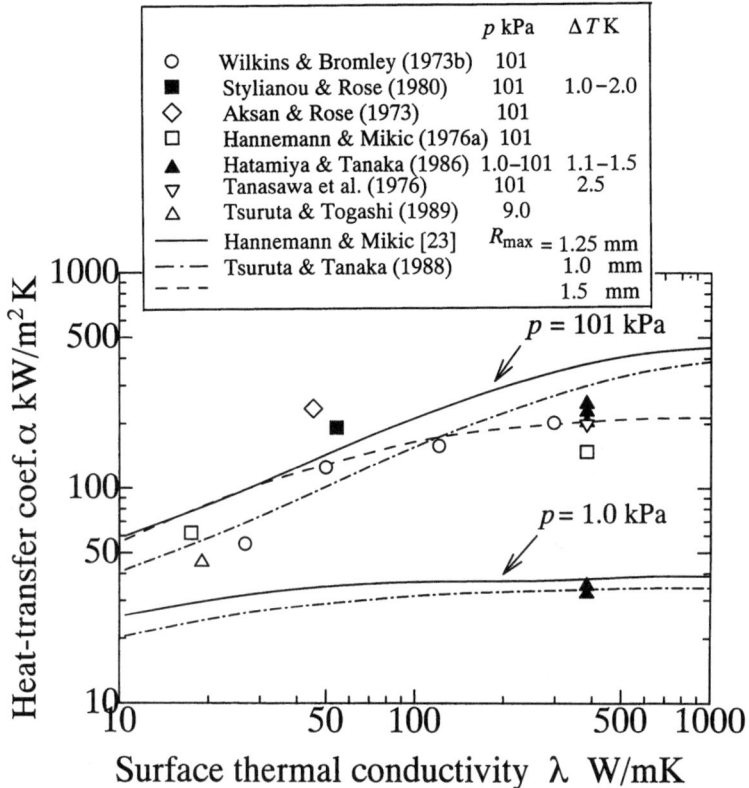

**Figure 5** Dependence of heat-transfer coefficient on thermal conductivity of surface material for steam.

A possible explanation is that at a high $\Delta T$, the condensation rate, and hence coalescence rate, are very high, and the temperature distribution on the condensing surface is effectively smoothed so that dependence on thermal properties of the surface would be small, whereas the reverse is true at low $\Delta T$, when the condensation rate and hence the rate of coalescence is relatively small.

Further accurate data are needed to resolve the question of the extent to which the dependence of heat-transfer coefficient on conductivity of surface material is affected by condensation rate. For this purpose, measurements with different condensing surface materials should be of sufficient accuracy and cover the sufficiently wide range of heat flux, which should be the same for all surfaces. Such experiments may require intensive cooling when using low conductivity test surfaces.

Theoretical studies of this problem assuming steady heat conduction have been made by Hannemann and Mikic (1976a) and Tsuruta and Tanaka (1988), which show dependent heat-transfer coefficient on thermal conductivity of the condensing material. Both models showed good agreement with data for low $\Delta T$. No dependence on heat capacity (transient heat conduction) has been established either experimentally or theoretically.

### 20.3.5 Condensation Curve

With increasing surface subcooling, it has been shown by Takeyama and Shimizu (1974) for steam and Wilmshurst and Rose (1974) for organic vapors that the heat flux in dropwise condensation has a peak value, and that the transition to film condensation occurs at high $\Delta T$. Figure 6 shows the measurements of heat flux plotted against surface subcooling ("condensation curves") for steam at atmospheric pressure by Tanasawa and Utaka (1983) and Takeyama and Shimizu (1974) using special condensing blocks to achieve large heat flux. It is thought that the latter may be subject to some inaccuracy of measurement.

It may be seen from Figure 6 that very high heat-transfer coefficients are maintained up to a very high heat flux.

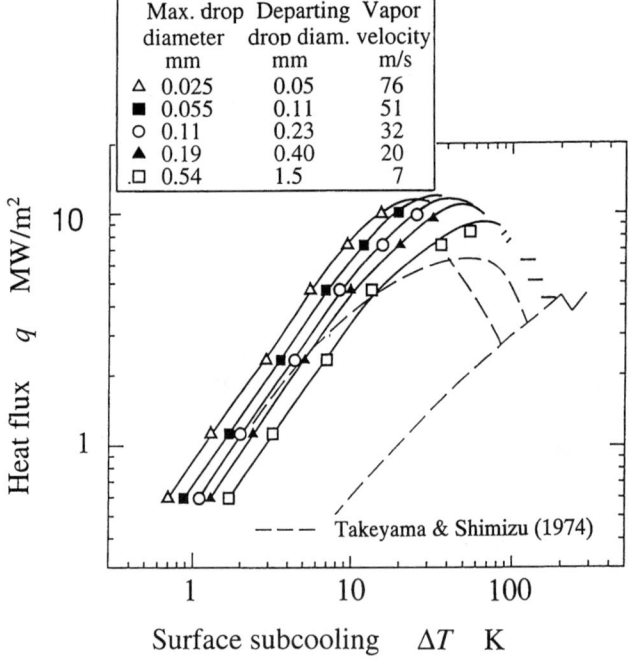

**Figure 6** Conduction curves for steam at atmospheric pressure (Tanasawa & Utaka, 1983).

## 20.4 DROPWISE CONDENSATION OF ORGANIC VAPORS

To date, most measurements have been done with steam, for which dropwise condensation can be readily promoted and maintained in the laboratory owing to the high surface tension of water. To promote and maintain dropwise condensation of other fluids is more difficult.

Experiments have been performed with several vapors. Figure 7 shows the results of Wilmshurst and Rose (1974) for aniline and nitrobenzene on a PTFE coated surface, Stylianou and Rose (1983) for ethylene glycol, and Utaka et al. (1987, 1994) for propylene glycol, ethylene glycol, and glycerol, on a copper surface using a mono-layer type promoter at reduced pressures.

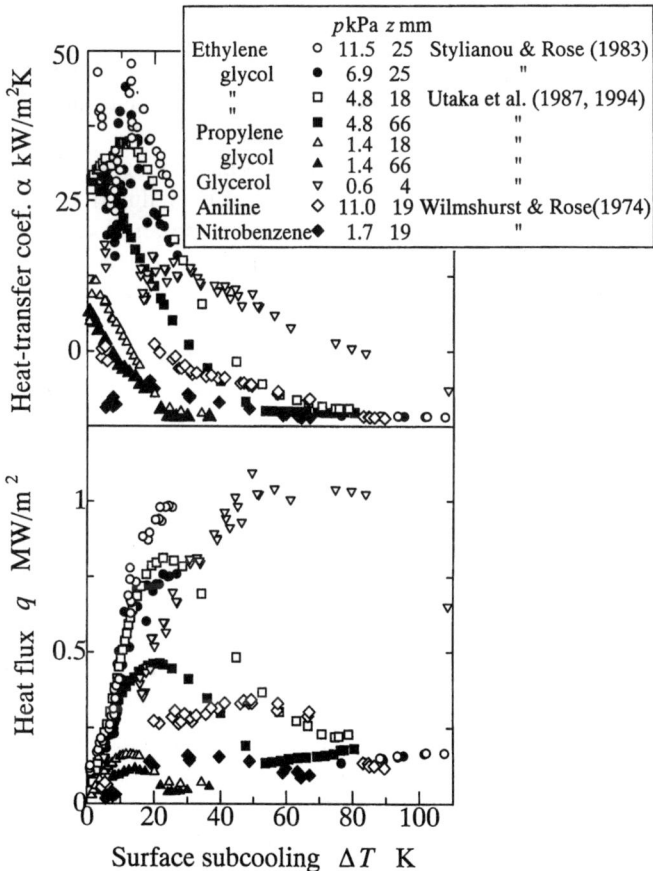

**Figure 7** Heat transfer characteristics for organic vapors.

As in the case of steam, in the moderate cooling intensity range, the heat-transfer coefficient for dropwise condensation is significantly larger than for film condensation and decreases with decreasing pressure. Quantitatively, the heat-transfer characteristics for these organic vapors differ from those for steam due to the wide range of physical properties. Mainly due to lower liquid thermal conductivity of the organic fluids, relatively low heat-transfer coefficients in comparison with steam are seen. It can also be seen that the surface subcooling ranges of ideal dropwise condensation differ widely, depending on the fluid. For a fluid of higher surface tension such as glycerol, dropwise condensation is maintained up to larger surface subcooling, compared with a lower surface tension liquid such as propylene glycol.

The peak heat fluxes are factors of 10 to 100 smaller than for steam at atmospheric pressure due to high viscosity, low surface tension, and low latent heat of condensation of these fluids. As a result, the condensation curves (peak heat-transfer coefficient) are readily obtainable without special methods to obtain intensive cooling. The peak heat flux decreases with decreasing pressure and with increasing distance from the top of the condensing surface. Typically, transition from dropwise to film condensation occurs as follows. As the cooling intensity is increased, following the range of "ideal" dropwise condensation, thin rivulets of condensate are formed, and subsequently film condensation appears lower down the surface. The condensate film extends upwards with an increase in cooling intensity until the surface is wholly covered with condensate film. Other transition modes have been observed, in some cases showing "hysteresis" as the cooling intensity is reduced. The phenomenon of transition is complicated, and various mechanisms have been suggested (see Stylianou and Rose, 1983; Takeyama and Shimizu, 1974; Utaka et al., 1988, 1990).

## 20.5 HEAT TRANSFER THEORY

### 20.5.1 Le Fevre and Rose Theory

This theory (Le Fevre and Rose, 1966), first proposed in 1966, derives the mean heat flux for dropwise condensation by combining expressions for the heat transfer through a single drop of given size and for the distribution of drop sizes. In deriving the heat transfer resistance of a single drop, the following are accounted for: (1) the influence of surface curvature on the phase equilibrium temperature, (2) the mass transfer resistance at the liquid–vapor interface, and (3) the heat conduction resistance through the drop. The relation between the heat flux through the base of a drop and the surface subcooling $\Delta T$ is given by Eq. (20.5-1) in Table 1. The distribution of drop sizes is given by Eq. (20.5-2), which expresses the fraction

## Table 1 Dropwise condensation theories

| Le Fevre (1966), Rose (1976, 1988) | | Tanaka (1975a, 1975b) | |
|---|---|---|---|
| $\Delta T = \dfrac{2\sigma}{r}\dfrac{v_l T}{h_{fg}} + \left(\dfrac{K_1 r}{\lambda} + \dfrac{K_2 v_g T}{h_{fg}^2}\dfrac{\gamma+1}{\gamma-1}\sqrt{\dfrac{RT}{2\pi}}\right)q_B$ | (20.5-1) | $\dfrac{\partial N}{\partial t} = -\dfrac{\partial(N\dot{r}_a)}{\partial t} - \int_r^{R_{\max}} 2\pi\rho[\dot{r}_a(r)+\dot{r}_a(\rho)]\Psi(r;N)N(r)N(\rho)d\rho$ $+ \pi R_{\max}^2 N(R_{\max})\dot{r}_a(R_{\max})N(r)$ | (20.5-6) |
| $f = 1-(r/R_{\max})^n$ | (20.5-2) | $\Psi(r,t;N) = \dfrac{1}{\left(1-\displaystyle\int_r^{R_{\max}}\pi\rho^2 N(\rho,t)d\rho\right)\left(1-\dfrac{r}{r_E(r,t)}\right)}$ | (20.5-7) |
| $\alpha = \dfrac{n}{R_{\max}^n \Delta T}\displaystyle\int_{R_{\min}}^{R_{\max}} \dfrac{\dfrac{\Delta T}{T} - \dfrac{2\sigma v_l}{rh_{fg}}}{\dfrac{K_1 r}{\lambda T} + \dfrac{K_2 v_g}{h_{fg}^2}\dfrac{\gamma+1}{\gamma-1}\sqrt{\dfrac{RT}{2\pi}}} r^{n-1}dr$ | (20.5-3) | $r_E(r,t) = 2\dfrac{1-\displaystyle\int_r^{R_{\max}}\pi\rho^2 N(\rho,t)d\rho}{\displaystyle\int_r^{R_{\max}} 2\pi\rho N(\rho,t)d\rho}$ | (20.5-8) |
| $R_{\min} = \dfrac{2\sigma v_g}{h_{fg}}\dfrac{T}{\Delta T}$ | (20.5-4) | $\displaystyle\int_{R_{\min}}^r \dfrac{2}{3}\pi\rho^3 \pi r[\dot{r}_a(r)+\dot{r}_a(\rho)]\Psi(\rho;N)N(\rho)d\rho = 2\pi r^2(\dot{r}_a-\dot{r}_e)$ | (20.5-9) |
| $R_{\max} = K_3\sqrt{\dfrac{\sigma}{(\rho_l-\rho_g)g}}$ | (20.5-5) | $r_E(R_{\min},t) = D$ | (20.5-10) |
| | | $\alpha R_{\max}/\lambda = 5.3(R_{\max}/D)^{0.7}$ | (20.5.11) |

of surface area $f$ covered by drops having base radius greater than $r$. (Note that, for any $n$, for $r \to 0$, $f \to 1$ and for $r \to R_{max}$, $f \to 0$). From these equations, the surface heat transfer coefficient is given by Eq. (20.5-3). The radii of the smallest viable drop $R_{min}$ and the maximum drop $R_{max}$ were taken as Eqs. (20.5-4) and (20.5-5), respectively. The dimensionless constants $K_1$, $K_2$ are shape factors, and $K_3$ arises from dimensional analysis. For dropwise condensation of steam $K_1 = 2/3$, $K_2 = 1/2$, $K_3 = 0.4$, and $n = 1/3$. The integral in Eq. (20.5-3) can be given in closed form. (See also Rose, 1988).

### 20.5.2 Tanaka's Theory

A theory proposed by Tanaka (1975a, 1975b) considers the transient change of local drop size distribution, taking into account the processes of growth and coalescence of drops.

Drops formed on the bare surface grow by direct condensation with a rate of $\dot{r}_e(r)$, but because coalescence between drops takes place at the same time, the apparent rate of growth is as an average, $\dot{r}_a(r,t)$. The number of drops per unit area having radii between $r$ and $r + dr$ is denoted as $N(r,t)dr$. Here, $t$ is the time elapsed after the area of the condensing surface was swept off by a departing drop. In such a situation, the relation of Eqs. (20.5-6)–(20.5-8) is derived for drops with radius $r$ by considering the balance between growth and loss (by coalescence and sweeping). The variable $r_E$ defined by Eq. (20.5-8) is the "equivalent diameter for coalescence" and is the measure of how closely packed the drops are. Equation (20.5-9) is derived for the volume increase of a drop with radius $r$ when the drop grows by coalescence. It may be noted that the rate of drop growth was obtained from the incorrect theory of Fatika and Katz (1949) as for $\dot{r}_e$, but the quantitative effect on the model of Tanaka is not clear. It was assumed that $r_E$ is equal to the average distance $D$ between neighboring nucleation sites as expressed by Eq. (20.5-10), and Eqs. (20.5-6) and (20.5-9) solved numerically. The relation for the heat-transfer coefficient was derived as Eq. (20.5-11).

### REFERENCES

Aksan, S. N. and Rose, J. W. 1973. Dropwise Condensation—The Effect of Thermal Properties of the Condenser Material. *Int. J. Heat Mass Transfer* 16:461–467.

Citakoglu, E. and Rose, J. W. 1968. Dropwise Condensation—Some Factors Influencing the Validity of Heat-Transfer Measurements. *Int. J. Heat Mass Transfer* 11:523–537.

Erb, R. A. 1973. Dropwise Condensation on Gold. *Gold Bull.* 6:2.

Erb, R. A. and Thelen, E. 1966. Dropwise Condensation Characteristics of Permanent Hydrophobic Systems. U.S. Off. Saline Water Res. Dev. Rep. No. 184.

Fatika, N. and Katz, D. L. 1949. Dropwise Condensation. *Chem. Eng. Prog.* 45:661–674.

Graham, C. 1969. The Limiting Heat Transfer Mechanism of Dropwise Condensation. Ph. D. Thesis, Massachusetts Institute of Technology.

Hannemann, R. J. and Mikic, B. B. 1976a. An Experimental Investigation into the Effect of Surface Thermal Conductivity on the Rate of Heat Transfer in Dropwise Condensation. *Int. J. Heat Mass Transfer* 19:1309–1317.

Hannemann, R. J. and Mikic, B. B. 1976b. An Analysis of the Effect of Surface Thermal Conductivities on the Rate of Heat Transfer in Dropwise Condensation. *Int. J. Heat Mass Transfer* 19:1299–1307.

Hatamiya, S. and Tanaka, H. 1986. A Study on the Mechanism of Dropwise Condensation. (1st Report, Measurement of Heat-Transfer Coefficient of Steam at Low Pressures). *Trans. JSME, Ser. B* 52(476):1828–1833.

Le Fevre, E. J. and Rose, J. W. 1964. Heat-Transfer Measurement During Dropwise Condensation of Steam. *Int. J. Heat Mass Transfer* 7:272–273.

Le Fevre, E. J. and Rose, J. W. 1965. An Experimental Study of Heat Transfer Study by Dropwise Condensation. *Int. J. Heat Mass Transfer* 8:1117–1133.

Le Fevre, E. J. and Rose, J. W. 1966. A Theory of Heat-Transfer by Dropwise Condensation. *Proc. 3rd Int. Heat Transfer Conf.* 2:362–375.

Le Fevre, E. J. and Rose, J. W. 1969. Dropwise Condensation. *Proc. Symp. Bicentenary of the James Watt Patent*, Univ. Glasgow, 166–191.

Marto, P. J. 1994. Vapor Condenser. *McGraw Hill Year Book of Science and Technology*, 428–431. New York: McGraw Hill.

Mikic, B. B. 1969. On Mechanism of Dropwise Condensation. *Int. J. Heat Mass Transfer* 12:1311–1323.

Rose, J. W. 1976. Further Aspects of Dropwise Condensation Theory. *Int. J. Heat Mass Transfer* 19:1363–1370.

Rose, J. W. 1988. Some Aspects of Dropwise Condensation Theory. *Int. Communications in Heat and Mass Transfer* 15:449–473.

Rose, J. W. 1994. Dropwise Condensation. *Heat Exchanger Design Update*. New York: Begell House Inc., 1–3.

Rose, J. W. 1996. Private communication.

Stylianou, S. A. and Rose, J. W. 1980. Dropwise Condensation on Surfaces Having Different Thermal Conductivities. *Trans. ASME, J. Heat Transfer* 102:477–482.

Stylianou, S. A. and Rose, J. W. 1983. Drop-to-Filmwise Condensation Transition: Heat Transfer Measurements for Ethandiol. *Int. J. Heat Mass Transfer* 26(5):747–760.

Takeyama, T. and Shimizu, S. 1974. On the Transition of Dropwise-Film Condensation. *Proc. 5th Int. Heat Transfer Conf.* 3:274–278.

Tanaka, H. 1975a. A Theoretical Study on Dropwise Condensation. *J. Heat Transfer* 97:72–78.

Tanaka, H. 1975b. Measurement of Drop-Size Distribution During Transient Dropwise Condensation. *J. Heat Transfer* 97:341–346.

Tanasawa, I., Ochiai, J., Utaka, Y., and Enya, S. 1976. Experimental Study on Dropwise Condensation (Effect of Departing Drop Size on Heat-Transfer Coefficient). *Trans. JSME* 42(361):2846–2853.

Tanasawa, I. and Utaka, Y. 1983. Measurement of Condensation Curves for Dropwise Condensation of Steam at Atmospheric Pressure. *J. Heat Transfer* 105:633–638.

Tanasawa, I. 1991. Advances in Condensation Heat Transfer. *Advances in Heat Transfer* 21:55–139.

Tanner, D. W., Pope, C. J., Potter, C. J., and West, D. 1965. Heat Transfer in Dropwise Condensation—Part I: The Effects of Heat Flux, Steam Velocity, and Non-Condensable Gas Concentration. *Int. J. Heat Mass Transfer* 8:427–436.

Tanner, D. W., Pope, C. J., Potter, C. J., and West, D. 1968. Heat Transfer in Dropwise Condensation at Low Steam Pressures in the Absence of Non-Condensable Gas. *Int. J. Heat Mass Transfer* 11:181–190.

Tsuruta, T. and Tanaka, H. 1983. Microscopic Study of Dropwise Condensation. *Trans. JSME, Ser. B* 49(446):2181–2189.

Tsuruta, T. and Tanaka, H. 1988. A Theoretical Study on Constriction Resistance in Dropwise Condensation. *Trans. JSME, Ser. B* 54:2811–2816.

Tsuruta, T. and Togashi, S. 1989. A Study on the Constriction Resistance in Dropwise Condensation, Surface Chemistry. *Trans. JSME, Ser. B* 55:2852–2860.

Utaka, Y., Kubo, R., and Ishii, K. 1994. Heat Transfer Characteristics of Condensation of Vapor on a Lyophobic Surface. *Proc. 10th Int. Heat Transfer Conf.* 3:401–406.

Utaka, Y., Saito, A., Ishikawa, H., and Yanagida, H. 1987. Transition from Dropwise Condensation to Film Condensation of Propylene Glycol, Ethylene Glycol, and Glycerol Vapors. *Proc. 2nd ASME-JSME Thermal Eng. Conf.* 4:377–384.

Utaka, Y., Saito, A., and Yanagida, H. 1988. On the Mechanism Determining the Transition Mode from Dropwise to Film Condensation. *Int. J. Heat Mass Transfer* 31(5):1113–1120.

Utaka, Y., Saito, A., and Yanagida, H. 1990. An Experimental Investigation of the Reversibility and Hysteresis of the Condensation Curves. *Int. J. Heat Mass Transfer* 33(4):649–659.

Wilkins, D. G. and Bromley, L. A. 1973b. Dropwise Condensation Phenomena. *AIChE J.* 19:839–845.

Wilkins, D. G., Bromley, L. A., and Read, S. M. 1973a. Dropwise and Filmwise Condensation of Water Vapor on Gold. *AIChE J.* 19:119–123.

Wilmshurst, R. and Rose, J. W. 1970. Dropwise Condensation—Further Heat-Transfer Measurements. *Proc. 4th Int. Heat Transfer Conf.* 6:Cs1–4.

Wilmshurst, R. and Rose, J. W. 1974. Dropwise and Filmwise Condensation of Aniline, Ethandiol, and Nitrobenzene. *Proc. 5th Int. Heat Transfer Conf.* 3:269–273.

Woodruff, D. W. and Westwater, J. W. 1979. Steam Condensation on Electroplated Gold: Effect of Plating Thickness. *Int. J. Heat Mass Transfer* 22:629–632.

CHAPTER
# TWENTY ONE

## DIRECT CONTACT CONDENSATION

**Ichiro Tanasawa**

*Tokyo University of Agriculture and Technology, Tokyo 184-8588, Japan*

**Yasuhiko H. Mori**

*Keio University, Yokohama 223-8522, Japan*

**Yoshio Utaka**

*Yokohama National University, Yokohama 240-8501, Japan*

## 21.1 INTRODUCTION

Direct contact condensation is usually considered to be a mode of condensation observed when a vapor makes direct contact with a low-temperature liquid and condenses on its surface. However, a vapor condenses onto the liquid surface even in the cases of film and dropwise condensation, neither one of which falling under the category of direct contact condensation. The essential difference between direct contact condensation and indirect condensation (i.e., film and dropwise) is that the low-temperature liquid itself acts as the only heat sink in the former, while a coolant, which flows along the other side of a condensing surface, absorbs the latent heat of condensation in the latter. Thus, in direct contact condensation, the maximum amount of condensate is limited by the heat capacity of the low-temperature liquid.

Direct contact condensation is roughly classified into two types: one is the case when the low-temperature liquid is dispersed in the bulk of vapor phase; the other is the case when the vapor, which is to be condensed, forms a dispersed phase. A typical example of the former is observed when a low-temperature liquid drop or a liquid jet falls down through a space filled with a vapor. A steam condenser invented nearly 300 years ago by Thomas Newcomen and improved later by James Watt for their steam engines employed this type of condensation. An example of the latter is the collapse of steam bubbles in a pool of subcooled water occurring in pool boiling. The collapse of bubbles is accompanied with a big noise that is heard when water is boiled in a kettle.

In both cases, the vapor and low-temperature liquid can be the same species (e.g., steam condensing on a water jet) or different species (e.g., fluorocarbon vapor condensing on the surface of water droplets). In addition, in the case of different species, the low-temperature liquid and the condensate can be either miscible or immiscible. The characteristics of direct contact condensation vary greatly, depending upon which type of condensation takes place.

Only some fundamentals of direct contact condensation are described in this chapter due to the space limitation. Articles by Sideman (1966) and Sideman and Moalem-Maron (1982) and a book edited by Kreith and Boehm (1988) are highly recommended for more detailed information.

## 21.2 CASE WHEN A LOW-TEMPERATURE LIQUID FORMS A DISPERSED PHASE

### 21.2.1 Condensation on a Liquid Jet

Hasson et al. (1964) derived asymptotic Nusselt numbers for direct contact condensation of a vapor onto (1) a cylindrical jet, (2) a sheet jet, and (3) a fan jet. The results are expressed by Eqs. (21.2-1)–(21.2-3) and shown in Figure 1.

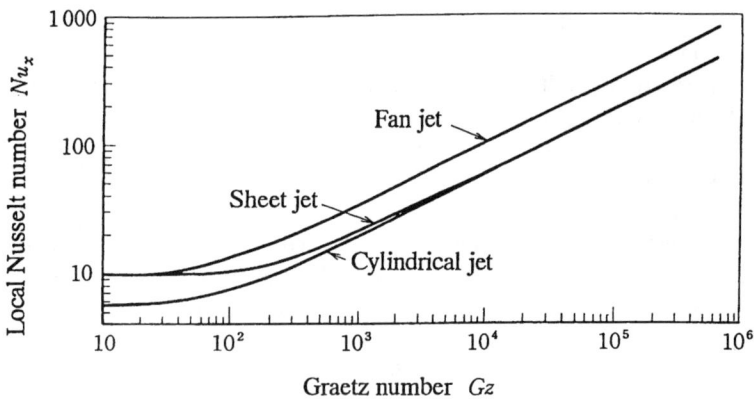

**Figure 1** Dependence of the local Nusselt number on the Graetz number in direct contact condensation on jets.

(1) *Cylindrical jet*: The asymptotic Nusselt numbers for a laminar-flow liquid jet with a constant velocity and diameter are expressed as follows:

$$Nu_x = \begin{cases} 5.784 & \text{when } Gz \to 0 \\ \dfrac{\sqrt{Gz/\pi}}{1 - (8/\sqrt{\pi Gz})} \approx \sqrt{\dfrac{Gz}{\pi}} & \text{when } Gz \to \infty \end{cases} \quad (21.2\text{-1a and b})$$

where $Nu_x$ ($= \alpha_x d_e/\lambda$) is the local Nusselt number, $\alpha_x$ is the local heat transfer coefficient at the distance $x$ from the nozzle exit, $\lambda$ is the thermal conductivity of the condensate, and $d_e$ is the equivalent diameter of the liquid jet and equal to the diameter of jet. In this case, $Gz$ ($= U d_e/(\kappa x)$) is the Graetz number, $U$ is the mean velocity of the jet, $\kappa$ is the thermal diffusivity of the condensate, and $x$ is the distance from the nozzle exit.

(2) *Sheet jet*: The asymptotic Nusselt numbers for a laminar, constant-velocity, and uniform-thickness sheet jet are expressed as follows:

$$Nu_x = \begin{cases} \pi^2 \; (= 9.780) & \text{when } Gz \to 0 \\ \dfrac{\sqrt{Gz/\pi}}{1 - (8/\sqrt{\pi Gz})} \approx \sqrt{\dfrac{Gz}{\pi}} & \text{when } Gz \to \infty \end{cases} \quad (21.2\text{-2a and b})$$

where the thickness of the liquid jet sheet is used as the equivalent diameter $d_e$.

(3) *Fan jet*: The asymptotic Nusselt numbers for the laminar, constant velocity fan jet (of which the thickness of the liquid film is inversely proportional to the distance from the nozzle exit) are expressed as follows:

$$Nu_x = \begin{cases} \pi^2 \; (= 9.780) & \text{when } Gz \to 0 \\ \dfrac{\sqrt{3Gz/\pi}}{1 - (8/\sqrt{\pi Gz})} \approx \sqrt{\dfrac{3Gz}{\pi}} & \text{when } Gz \to \infty \end{cases} \quad (21.2\text{-3a and b})$$

where twice the liquid film thickness is used as the equivalent diameter $d_e$.

### 21.2.2 Condensation on a Falling Liquid Drop

The transport of heat from the vapor to a low-temperature liquid drop is governed by the thermal resistance for condensation at the surface of the drop and the thermal resistance inside the drop. In most cases, however, the former is negligibly small when compared with the latter.

There are three models proposed for the heat transport inside the drop. They are:

(1) *Solid sphere model*, which does not take into consideration the flow inside the drop,

(2) *Circulatory flow model*, which takes into consideration the flow inside the drop, and
(3) *Complete mixing model*, which assumes that the temperature inside the drop is uniform. However, this model is not adequate in many instances.

A typical example of the solid sphere model is an analytical solution by Newman (1931) for the heat conduction in a sphere. In this solution, the change of temperature distribution in the sphere is obtained under the condition of a uniform and constant temperature at the surface (which corresponds to zero external thermal resistance). Newman's solution gives the dimensionless mixed-cup temperature $E_m [= (T_m - T_i)/(T_v - T_i)]$ inside the drop as

$$E_m = 1 - \frac{1}{\pi^2} \sum_{n=1}^{\infty} \frac{1}{n^2} \exp\left(-\frac{\pi^2 n^2 \kappa t}{r^2}\right) \qquad (21.2\text{-}4)$$

where $T_m$ is the mixed-cup temperature inside the drop, $T_i$ is the initial (uniform) temperature of the drop, $T_v$ is the vapor temperature, $\kappa$ is the thermal diffusivity of the liquid, and $r$ is the radius of the drop.

A much simplified approximation for Eq. (21.2-4) is proposed by Vermeulen (1953):

$$E_m = \sqrt{1 - \exp\left(-\frac{\pi^2 \kappa t}{r^2}\right)} \qquad (21.2\text{-}5)$$

In Figure 2, the solid line represents Eq. (21.2-4), and the circular symbols represent

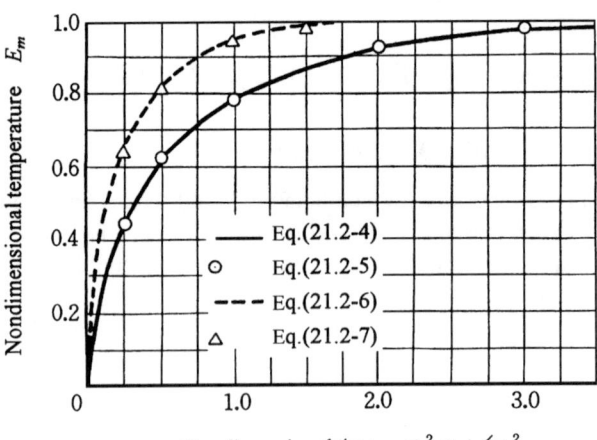

**Figure 2** Rise of the nondimensional mixed-cup temperature of a drop calculated by different models.

**Table 1** Values of the constants $A_n$ and the eigenvalues $\lambda_n$ in Eq. (21.2-6)

| $n$ | $\lambda_n$ | $A_n$ |
|---|---|---|
| 1 | 1.656 | 1.29 |
| 2 | 9.08 | 0.596 |
| 3 | 22.2 | 0.386 |
| 4 | 38.5 | 0.35 |
| 5 | 63.0 | 0.28 |
| 6 | 89.8 | 0.22 |
| 7 | 123.8 | 0.16 |

values obtained from Eq. (21.2-5), indicating that Eq. (21.2-4) gives a good approximation to Eq. (21.2-5).

A good example of the circulatory flow model is the solution obtained by Kronig and Brink (1950). They employed the Hadamard stream function and derived a solution, assuming that the stream lines and the isotherms inside the drop coincide. The expression they derived is

$$E_m = 1 - \frac{3}{8} \sum_{n=1}^{\infty} A_n^2 \exp\left(-\frac{16\lambda_n \kappa t}{r^2}\right) \qquad (21.2\text{-}6)$$

where $A_n$'s are the constants and $\lambda_n$'s are the eigenvalues shown in Table 1. Since the calculation of Eq. (21.2-6) is a little complicated, the following approximation is proposed by Calderbank and Korchinski (1956):

$$E_m = \sqrt{1 - \exp\left(-\frac{2.25\pi^2 \kappa t}{r^2}\right)} \qquad (21.2\text{-}7)$$

The broken line in Figure 2 indicates Eq. (21.2-6), whereas the triangular symbols represent the values obtained from Eq. (21.2-7).

Hijikata et al. (1984) found that a rate of condensation much higher than the one predicted by Eq. (21.2-6) is obtained when the vapor of a refrigerant CFC-113 is condensed on a drop of CFC-113. According to them, the much higher condensation rate is achieved because the stream lines and the isotherms inside the drop do not coincide with each other, and the stream lines take different paths for every circulation due to periodical deformation of the drop while falling down. Nakajima and Tanasawa (1990) obtained an even higher condensation rate for direct contact condensation of CFC-113 vapor on a falling water droplet. They observed that the condensate of CFC-113 does not cover the whole surface of the water droplet but accumulates on the top of the drop, just like a cap. A very high condensation rate is attained because most parts of the surface of the water drop are always exposed to the vapor.

## 21.3 CASE WHEN A VAPOR FORMS A DISPERSED PHASE

When a vapor is injected as discrete bubbles into a pool of subcooled liquid, direct contact condensation occurs while the bubbles are rising toward the free surface. Such form of direct contact condensation can be classified into three cases, depending on the combination of liquid and vapor and their miscibility.

Case 1: The vapor and the low-temperature liquid are the same substance.
Case 2: The vapor and the low-temperature liquid are different substances and are miscible when the vapor is condensed.
Case 3: The vapor and the low-temperature liquid are different substances and immiscible when the vapor is condensed.

Further, the case C can be subdivided into two cases, according to Mori (1985):

Case 3a: The low-temperature liquid is well wetted with the condensate, and the condensate entirely envelops the vapor bubble, forming a vapor-liquid two-phase bubble.
Case 3b: The condensate does not wet the low-temperature liquid, and a drop (or drops) of condensate detaches from the vapor bubble.

The following description applies to cases 1 and 3a.

### 21.3.1 Condensation of a Single, Pure Vapor Bubble

The vapor to be condensed is assumed to be pure, containing no non-condensable gases. Assuming a quasi-steady state established at each instant, the instantaneous heat transfer from (and the rise motion of) a bubble are expressed in terms of the Nusselt number $Nu \, (= \alpha d / \lambda_c)$ and the drag coefficient $c_d$ as

$$Nu = a_1 Pr_c^{a_2} Re^{a_3} \qquad (21.3\text{-}1)$$

$$c_d = b_1 Re^{b_2} \qquad (21.3\text{-}2)$$

respectively, where $d$ is the equivalent spherical diameter of the bubble, $\alpha$ is the heat transfer coefficient related to the nominal bubble-surface area $\pi d^2$ and to the temperature difference $\Delta T$ between the saturation temperature of the condensing substance and the temperature in the bulk of the continuous phase (i.e., the low temperature liquid), $\lambda_c$ is the thermal conductivity of the continuous phase,

$\Pr_c$ ($= \kappa_c/v_c$) is the Prandtl number of the continuous phase, Re ($= Ud/v_c$) is the Reynolds number, $\kappa_c$ and $v_c$ are the thermal diffusivity and the kinematic viscosity, respectively, of the continuous phase, $U$ is the velocity of rise of the bubble, and $a_1$, $a_2$, $a_3$, $b_1$, and $b_2$ are dimensionless numerical factors, which are evaluated later.

The time $t^*$ elapsed before the vapor bubble (or the vapor phase in the two-phase bubble) is completely condensed, and the distance $h^*$ for the bubble to rise during this time period is approximated by Eqs. (21.3-3)–(21.3-7) (Sudhoff et al., 1982):

$$\frac{\kappa_c t^*}{d_i^2} = \frac{K_t}{2 - 3E_t}\{1 - X^{(2/3) - E_t}\} \tag{21.3-3}$$

$$\frac{h^*}{d_i} = \frac{K_h}{1 + 3E_t}\{1 - X^{(1/3) + E_h}\} \tag{21.3-4}$$

where

$$E_t = a_3/(2 + b_2) \tag{21.3-5a}$$

$$E_h = (1 - a_3)/(2 + b_2) \tag{21.3-5b}$$

$$K_t = \left\{2(1 - X)a_1 Ja \Pr_c^{a_2}\left(\frac{4Ga}{3b_1}\right)^{E_t}\right\}^{-1} \tag{21.3-6a}$$

$$K_h = \left\{\{2(1 - X)a_1 Ja\}^{-1}\Pr_c^{1-a_2}\left(\frac{4Ga}{3b_1}\right)^{E_h}\right\} \tag{21.3-6b}$$

$$X = 0 \quad \text{for Case A} \tag{21.3-7a}$$

$$X = \rho_v/\rho_d \quad \text{for Case C}_1 \tag{21.3-7b}$$

where $d_i$ is the initial value of $d$, Ga ($= gd_i^3/v_c^2$) is the Galileo number, $g$ is the acceleration due to gravity, Ja ($= \rho_c c_{p,c} \rho_c \Delta T_i/(\rho_v h_{lg})$) is the Jakob numger, $\rho_c$ and $c_{p,c}$ are the mass density and the specific heat capacity, respectively, of the continuous phase, $\Delta T_i$ is the initial value of $\Delta T$ (note that $\Delta T$ varies with the rise of the bubble due to a reduction in the hydrostatic head exerted on the bubble), $h_{lg}$ is the latent heat of vaporization of the condensing substance, and $\rho_v$ and $\rho_d$ are the mass densities in the states of saturated vapor and saturated liquid, respectively, of the condensing substance. Values of the numerical factors $a_1$, $a_2$, $a_3$, $b_1$, and $b_2$ are dependent on the Reynolds number and may change, depending upon the substances of both phases and the extent to which they are contaminated (Clift et al., 1978). The values of coefficients $a_1$, $a_2$, and $a_3$ (recommended by Isenberg and Sideman, 1970) are shown in Table 2. However, as mentioned in the table,

**Table 2** Values of the constants in Eq. (21.3-1) recommended by Isenberg and Sideman (1970)

|  | $a_1$ | $a_2$ | $a_3$ | Theoretical bases for the values of constants |
|---|---|---|---|---|
| Case A | $2/\sqrt{\pi}$ | 1/2 | 1/2 | Theoretical solution for heat transfer to a sphere in potential flow |
| Case $C_1$ | $1/\sqrt{\pi}$ | 1/3 | 1/2 | Semi-empirical solution for evaporation of a drop in air flow |

these values represent only rough approximations. When the continuous phase is water and most of condensation occurs in the range $10^3 \leq Re \leq 10^4$, one may take $b_1 = 2.6$ and $b_2 = 0$ (Clift et al., 1978; Sudhoff et al., 1982).

### 21.3.2 Effect of Non-Condensable Gases

When non-condensable gases are contained in the vapor phase, the bubble (or the gas phase in the two-phase bubble) does not vanish but reaches the liquid surface retaining some amount of the vapor phase. If both the vapor and the non-condensable gases are assumed to be ideal gases and no non-condensable gases are assumed to be dissolved in the continuous phase, the fraction of the mass $\tilde{m}_v$ of vapor reaching the liquid surface is given by

$$\tilde{m}_v = \frac{p_s/p_\infty}{1 - (p_s/p_\infty)} \frac{\tilde{x}_g}{1 - \tilde{x}_g} \qquad (21.3\text{-}8)$$

where $\tilde{x}_g$ is the molar fraction of the non-condensable gases at the initiation of condensation, $p_\infty$ is the system pressure, and $p_s$ is the saturation pressure of the condensable vapor corresponding to the bulk temperature of the continuous phase. The concentration of the non-condensable gases increases as condensation proceeds and the rate of condensation is reduced. Generally speaking, $t^*$ and $h^*$ increase remarkably when the molar concentration of the non-condensable gases, $\tilde{x}_g$, is 0.005 or higher (Jacobs and Major, 1982).

### 21.3.3 Condensation on a Train of Vapor Bubbles

When the frequency of vapor injection into the continuous phase is increased, a train of bubbles (or two-phase bubbles) is formed. In such cases, the values of $t^*$ and $h^*$ become larger than the values given by Eqs. (21.3-3)–(21.3-7). Geometry of the bubble train, the rising velocity, and the temperature distribution in the liquid are all interrelated, and the numerical calculation by iteration is needed to predict $t^*$ and $h^*$ (Moalem et al., 1972).

# REFERENCES

Calderbank, P. H. and Korchinski, I. J . O . 1956. Circulation in Liquid Drops (A Heat-Transfer Study). *Chem. Eng. Sci.* 6:65.

Clift, R., Grace, J. R., and Weber, M. E. 1978. *Bubbles, Drops, and Particles*. New York: Academic Press, 171.

Hasson, D., Luss, D., and Peck, R. 1964. The Theoretical Analysis of Vapor Condensation on Laminar Liquid Jets. *Int. J. Heat Mass Transfer* 7:969.

Hijikata, K., Mori, Y., and Kawaguchi, H. 1984. Direct Contact Condensation of Vapor to Falling Cooled Droplets. *Int. J. Heat Mass Transfer* 27:1631.

Isenberg, J. and Sideman, S. 1970. Direct Contact Heat Transfer with Change of Phase: Bubble Condensation in Immiscible Liquids. *Int. J. Heat Mass Transfer* 13:997.

Jacobs, H. R. and Major, B. H. 1982. The Effect of Non-Condensable Gases on Bubble Condensation in an Immiscible Liquid. *J. Heat Mass Transfer* 104:487.

Kreith, F. and Boehm, R. F., eds. 1988. *Direct Contact Heat Transfer*. New York: Hemisphere Publishing Co.

Kronig, R. and Brink, J. C. 1950. On the Theory of Extraction from Falling Drops. *Appl. Sci. Res.* A2:142.

Moalem, D., Sideman, S., Orell, A., and Hetsroni, G. 1972. Condensation of Bubble Trains: An Approximate Solution. *Progress in Heat and Mass Transfer* 6:155.

Mori, Y. H. 1985. Classification of Configurations of Two-Phase Vapor/Liquid Bubbles in an Immiscible Liquid in Relation to Direct-Contact Evaporation and Condensation Processes. *Int. J. Multiphase Flow* 11:571.

Nakajima, H. and Tanasawa, I. 1990. Direct Contact Condensation of the Vapor of an Immiscible and Insoluble Substance on Falling Liquid Droplets. *Heat Transfer Enhancement and Energy Conservation*. Ed. Deng, S.-J., p. 335. New York: Hemisphere Publishing Co.

Newman, A. B. 1931. The Drying of Porous Solids: Diffusion Calculations. *Trans. AIChE* 27:310.

Sideman, S. 1966. Direct Contact Heat Transfer Between Immiscible Liquids. *Advances in Chemical Engineering* 6:207. New York: Academic Press.

Sideman, S. and Moalem-Maron, D. 1982. *Advances in Heat Transfer* 15:227. New York: Academic Press.

Sudholf, B., Plischke, M., and Weinspach, P.- M. 1982. Direct Contact Heat Transfer with Change of Phase—Condensation or Evaporation of a Drobble. *Ger. Chem . Eng.* 5:24.

Vermeulen, T. 1953. Theory for Irreversible and Constant-Pattern Solid Diffusion. *I&EC* 45:1664.

CHAPTER
# TWENTY TWO

## AUGMENTATION TECHNIQUES IN EXTERNAL CONDENSATION

**Hiroshi Honda**

*Kyushu University, Kasuga, Fukuoka, Japan*

**John Rose**

*University of London, London E1 4NS, United Kingdom*

Heat transfer in film condensation is controlled by the thermal resistance of the condensate film. Thus, augmentation of condensation heat transfer is achieved by either thinning the condensate film or by augmenting turbulent mixing of the condensate, thereby thinning the viscous sublayer. A number of augmentation techniques have been proposed for external condensation. Among them, those techniques that utilize the surface tension effects are commonly employed in many practical applications. Finned tubes, fluted tubes, corrugated tubes, wire wrapped tubes, and tubes sintered with metal particles are included in this category. Other augmentation techniques include attaching promoters such as non-wetting strips, drainage skirts and strips, and electric fields.

## 22.1 VERTICAL FLUTED TUBE

Vertical fluted tubes (often called grooved or finned tubes) with various flute geometries have been developed for vertical shellside condensers. In many cases, the surface area enhancement of a fluted tube as compared to a smooth tube is less than 2. Figure 1 shows the physical model of film condensation on a vertical fluted tube originally proposed by Gregorig (1954). The tube has round ridges and troughs with small dimensions. Thus, the condensate film has a convex interface at the ridge and a concave interface at the trough. Due to the surface tension effect, the liquid

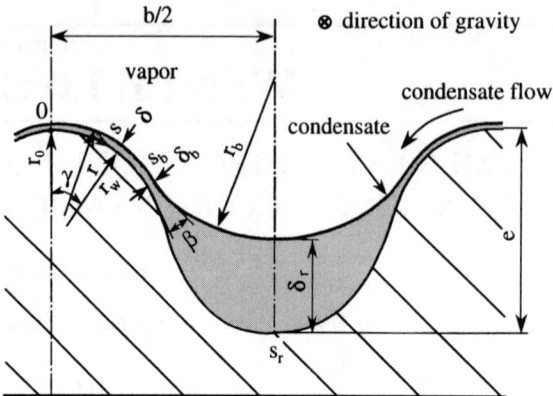

**Figure 1** Film condensation on a vertical fluted tube.

pressure at the ridge is higher than that at the trough. As a result, condensate flow directing from the ridge to the trough is induced. This results in a very thin condensate film (i.e., a very high heat transfer coefficient) near the ridge and a thick condensate film (i.e., a low heat transfer coefficient) near the trough. The condensate gathered at the trough is drained by gravity. When the trough is flat and the condensate flow rate is small, the thick film region is formed only at the corner of the trough.

Here we will consider the case shown in Figure 1. For the thin film region near the ridge, the pressure gradient along the surface of a fluted tube is given by $\partial P/\partial s = \sigma \partial(1/r)/\partial s$, where P is the liquid pressure, s is the coordinate measured along the surface from the top of the ridge, and r is the radius of curvature of the liquid-vapor interface. Assuming that the liquid film thickness $\delta$ is much smaller than the flute pitch $b$ and the flute depth $e$ and assuming the laminar flow, the basic equation for the condensate film thickness $\delta$ is obtained as follows:

$$\frac{\rho_l g}{3\nu_l} \frac{\partial \delta^3}{\partial z} - \frac{\sigma}{3\nu_l} \frac{\partial}{\partial s}\left[\frac{\partial}{\partial s}\left(\frac{1}{r}\right)\delta^3\right] = \frac{\lambda_l(T_s - T_w)}{\delta h_{lg}} \qquad (22.1\text{-}1)$$

where $z$ is the distance measured vertically downward from the top of the tube, $T_s$ is the saturation temperature, and $T_w$ is the wall temperature. The first and second terms at the left hand side of Eq. (22.1-1) denote the increments of condensate flow rate in the z- and s-directions, respectively, and the right hand side denotes the condensation mass flux. The boundary conditions at the tube top and at the ridge are

$$\delta = 0 \quad \text{at } z = 0 \qquad (22.1\text{-}2)$$

$$\partial\delta/\partial s = \partial^3\delta/\partial s^3 = 0 \quad \text{at } s = 0 \qquad (22.1\text{-}3)$$

Two other boundary conditions are derived from the condition that the thin condensate film is connected smoothly with the thick condensate film at $s = s_b$. In the thick film region, the radius of curvature of the interface $r_b$ is almost constant because the condensate pressure in the horizontal cross section is almost constant. Thus,

$$\partial \delta / \partial s = \tan \beta, \quad r = r_b \quad \text{at } s = s_b \tag{22.1-4}$$

where $\beta$ is the angle shown in Figure 1.

Assuming laminar flow, the basic equation for the condensate flow in the thick film region is written as

$$\rho_l g + \mu_l \nabla^2 w = 0 \tag{22.1-5}$$

where $w$ denotes the condensate velocity in the z-direction. The boundary conditions are

$$\partial w / \partial n = 0 \quad \text{at the liquid-vapor interface} \tag{22.1-6}$$
$$\partial w / \partial s = 0 \quad \text{at } s = s_r \tag{22.1-7}$$
$$w = \left(\rho_l g \delta_b^2 / \mu_e\right) [(y/\delta_b) - (y/\delta_b)^2/2] \quad \text{at } s = s_b \tag{22.1-8}$$

where $n$ denotes the coordinate normal to the interface and $y$ the coordinate measured vertically outward from the surface.

The variation of $s_b$ along $z$ is obtained from the relation between the heat transfer rate $Q$ in the region of $0 \sim z$ and the vertical condensate flow rate $M$ at $z$:

$$Q = h_{lg} M \tag{22.1-9}$$

Then, the average heat flux based on the projected surface area $q$ and the average heat transfer coefficient $\alpha$ are obtained from

$$q = Q(l)/bl, \quad \alpha = q/(T_s - T_w) \tag{22.1-10}$$

where $l$ is the tube length. The flutes are gradually flooded with condensate as $l$ increases. This results in a decrease in $\alpha$. Mori et al. (1981a) proposed to shorten the effective tube length by attaching condensate drainage skirts, as shown in Figure 2.

Figure 3 shows the numerical solutions of Eqs. (22.1-1)–(22.1-9) obtained by Mori and Hijikata (1984). In Figure 3, the $\alpha$ values for three kinds of fluted tubes (i.e., flat-bottomed flute, triangular flute, and wavy flute) with a very small radius of curvature $r_o$ at the ridge are plotted as a function of $b$. For all tubes, $\alpha$ increases as $b$ decreases and takes the highest value at $b = 0.5 \sim 0.6$ mm. Then it decreases with further decreasing $b$. This is due to the combined effects of the surface area increase and the decrease in the cross-sectional area of the drainage channel. The highest value of $\alpha$ is obtained by the flat bottomed flute with a relatively large drainage

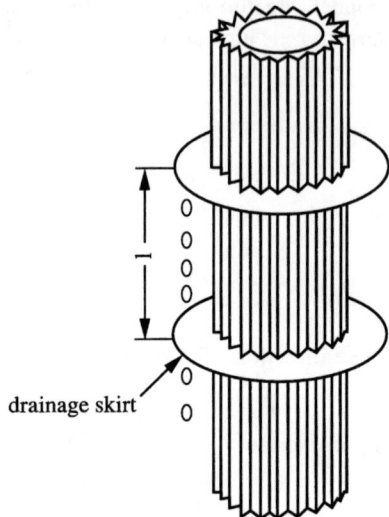

**Figure 2** Vertical fluted tube with drainage skirts.

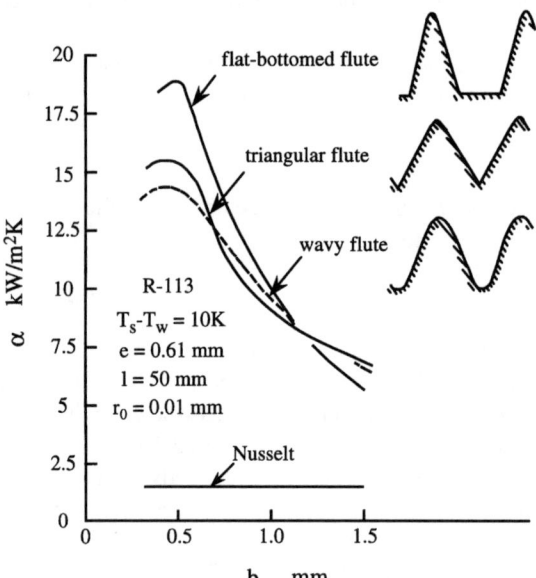

**Figure 3** Variation of average heat transfer coefficient with flute pitch.

channel. This tube shows the $\alpha$ value about 10 times as large as the prediction of the Nusselt (1916) equation for a vertical surface:

$$Nu_l = 0.943 G_l^{0.25} \tag{22.1-11}$$

where $Nu_l = \alpha l/\lambda_l$ and $G_l = \rho_l g h_{lg} l^3 / \lambda_l \nu_l (T_s - T_w)$.

On the basis of the approximate solution in which $r = r_w$ was assumed in Eq. (22.1-1), where $r_w$ is the radius of curvature of the flute surface, Adamek (1981) and Kedzierski and Webb (1990) proposed fin profiles that gave a high heat transfer performance. Honda and Fujii (1984) developed a semi-empirical expression for the average heat transfer coefficient. Adamek and Webb (1990b) developed a theoretical model of film condensation in the drainage channel.

## 22.2 HORIZONTAL FINNED TUBE

Horizontal finned tubes are commonly used to enhance shell-side condensation of refrigerants and other organic fluids with relatively low values of surface tension. The fin shapes of commercially available tubes are divided into two categories: two-dimensional fins and recently developed three-dimensional fins. In many cases, the surface area enhancement of a finned tube ranges from 2.5 to 5. A wide range of experimental data has been accumulated for both two-dimensional and three-dimensional fins. A number of theoretical models have been proposed for the two-dimensional fin tubes. A comprehensive review of relevant literature is given by Marto (1988).

Figure 4 shows examples of the fin geometry. Tubes A and B have two-dimensional fins, while tubes C to F have three-dimensional fins. It is generally

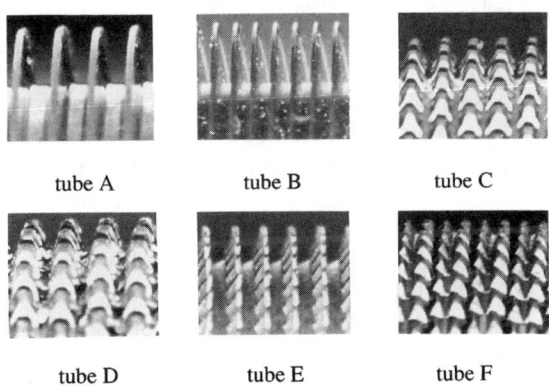

**Figure 4** Example of fin geometry.

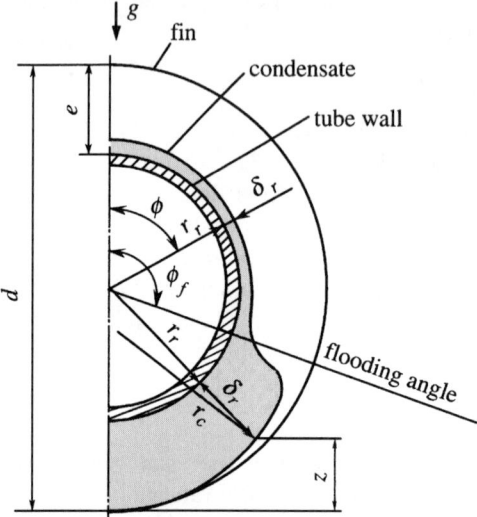

**Figure 5** Film condensation on a horizontal two-dimentional fin tube.

believed that the three-dimensional fin is superior to the two-dimensional fin because the former has more corners than the latter. However, experimental results (Honda et al., 1991; Webb and Murawski, 1990) have shown that the three dimensional fin tubes are subject to a much higher effect of condensate inundation, and the heat transfer coefficient decreases more rapidly than the two-dimensional fin tubes. This is due to the fact that the two-dimensional fins with relatively large values of fin height and fin spacing prevent the falling condensate from spreading axially, and the inter-fin space acts as a good drainage channel.

Figure 5 shows the cross-section of a horizontal two-dimensional fin tube at the mid-point between adjacent fins on which film condensation occurs. The condensate profile in the fin cross-section is basically the same as that for a vertical fluted tube shown in Figure 4. The condensate generated on the fin surface is driven by the combined effects of gravity and surface tension toward the fin root. Then, the condensate is drained circumferentially by gravity. Thus, a thin condensate film is formed on the fin surface, and a relatively thick condensate film is formed on the fin root tube surface. At the lower part of the tube, the surface tension acts to retain condensate between fins. Thus the inter-fin space at the angular portion of $\phi_f \leq \phi \leq \pi$ is almost completely flooded with condensate. For a trapezoidal fin tube with fin height $e$, fin pitch $b$, fin spacing at fin tip $c$, fin half-tip angle $\theta$, and tube diameter at fin tip $d$, the flooding angle $\phi_f$ is given by Honda et al., 1983:

$$\phi_f = \cos^{-1}(X - 1) \quad \text{for } 0 \leq X \leq 2 \qquad (22.2\text{-}1a)$$

and

$$\phi_f = 0 \quad \text{for } 2 \leq X \tag{22.2-1b}$$

where $X = \frac{4\sigma \sin\theta}{\rho_l g d c}$ for $\frac{c(1-\cos\theta)}{\sin\theta} \leq 2e$ and $X = \frac{(4\sigma/\rho_l g d e)}{1+(b/2e)^2}$ for $\frac{c(1-\cos\theta)}{\sin\theta} \geq 2e$

As seen from Eq. (22.2-1), the value of $\phi_f$ decreases as the surface tension to liquid density ratio $\sigma/\rho_l$ increases or $c$ decreases. Masuda and Rose (1987) developed a theoretical model for predicting retention near the fin roots in the unflooded part.

For the thin film region, the basic equation for the condensate film thickness is written as

$$\frac{2\rho_l g \cos\gamma}{3\nu_l d} \frac{\partial}{\partial \phi}(\delta^3 \sin\phi) + \frac{1}{3\nu_l} \frac{\partial}{\partial s}\left\{\left[\rho_l g_s - \sigma \frac{\partial}{\partial s}\left(\frac{1}{r}\right)\right]\delta^3\right\} = \frac{\lambda_l(T_s - T_w)}{\delta h_{lg}} \tag{22.2-2}$$

where $\gamma$ is the angle measured from the center of fin tip (see Figure 1). The boundary conditions are

$$\partial \delta/\partial \phi = 0 \quad \text{at } \phi = 0 \tag{22.2-3}$$

$$\partial \delta/\partial s = \partial^3 \delta/\partial s^3 = 0 \quad \text{at } s = 0 \tag{22.2-4}$$

for

$$0 \leq \phi \leq \phi_f, \quad \partial \delta/\partial s = \partial^3 \delta/\partial s^3 = 0 \quad \text{at } s = s_r \tag{22.2-5}$$

for

$$\phi_f < \phi \leq \pi, \quad \partial \delta/\partial s = \tan\beta, \quad r = r_b \quad \text{at } s = s_b \tag{22.2-6}$$

The condensate flow in the thick film region is very slow; thus, the profile of the thick condensate film is determined by the static force balance between the gravity and surface tension forces:

$$\sigma(1/r_b - 1/r_c) = \rho_l g z \tag{22.2-7}$$

where $r_b$ and $r_c$ are the radius of curvature of the interface in the fin cross-section and the tube cross-section, respectively, and $z$ is the height of the interface measured from the tube bottom (see Figure 5). When an appropriate value of $\beta(\sim\pi/6)$ is assumed, the variation of $s_r$ along $\phi$ is obtained from Eq. (22.2-7).

Figure 6 shows an example of the solution of Eqs. (22.2-3)–(22.2-7) obtained by Honda et al. (1995), where the condensate profiles at nine angular positions are

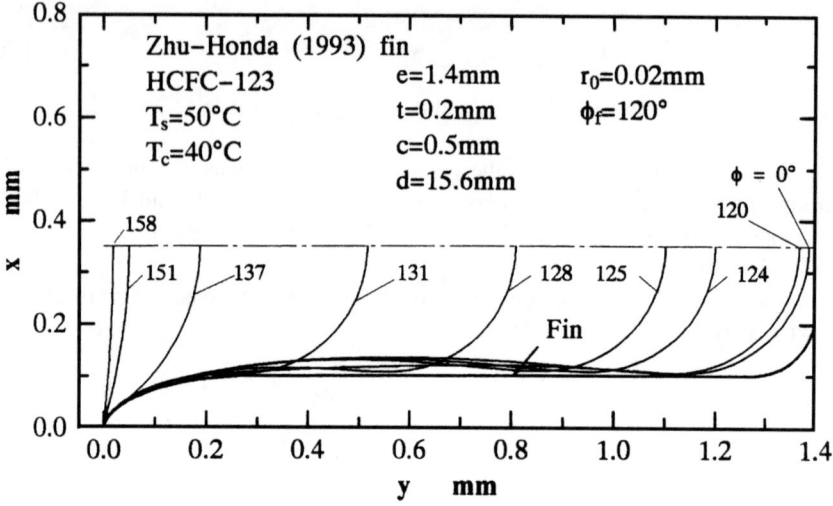

**Figure 6** Condensate profile on a horizontal two-dimensional fin tube.

plotted. In Figure 6, the Cartesian coordinates $x$ and $y$ are measured from the fin tip. It is seen from Figure 6 that the condensate profile changes very slowly in the unflooded region $0 \leq \phi \leq \phi_f$ and very rapidly after $\phi = \phi_f$ is reached.

It is practically important to identify the optimum fin profile and the optimum fin dimensions that give the highest heat transfer performance. Figure 7 shows a comparison of the heat transfer performance for eight classes of two-dimensional fin tubes with the same values of $b$, $e$, and $r_o$, where the local heat transfer coefficient at tube top $\alpha_o$ is plotted as a function of $r_o$ (Honda et al., 1995). Excepting the parabolic fin, the fin thickness at fin root $t$ is also the same. The parabolic fin and the fin profiles proposed by Gregorig (1954), Adamek (1981), Kedzierski and Webb (1990), and Zhu and Honda (see Figure 6) have a common characteristic—the curvature of the fin surface increases smoothly with increasing $s$. As expected, these fin profiles show almost the same heat transfer performance. The single-rib fin and the double-rib fin, respectively, have one and two circmferential ribs of 0.1 mm in height on the fin flank of the Zhu and Honda fin. These fin profiles yield the $\alpha_o$ values that are about 1.7 to 1.9 times as large as those for the parabolic fins.

For the two-dimensional-fin tube, a number of theoretical models have been proposed to predict the heat transfer performance. In principle, these theoretical models are based on the approximate solutions of Eqs. (22.2-3)–(22.2-7). Beatty and Katz (1948) proposed the following equation:

$$Nu_d = 0.689 G_d^{1/4} \left[ 1.3\eta \left( \frac{A_f}{A_o} \right) \left( \frac{d}{e_e} \right)^{1/4} + \left( \frac{A_r}{A_o} \right) \left( \frac{d_r}{d} \right)^{1/4} \right] \left( \frac{A}{A_{ef}} \right) \quad (22.2\text{-}8)$$

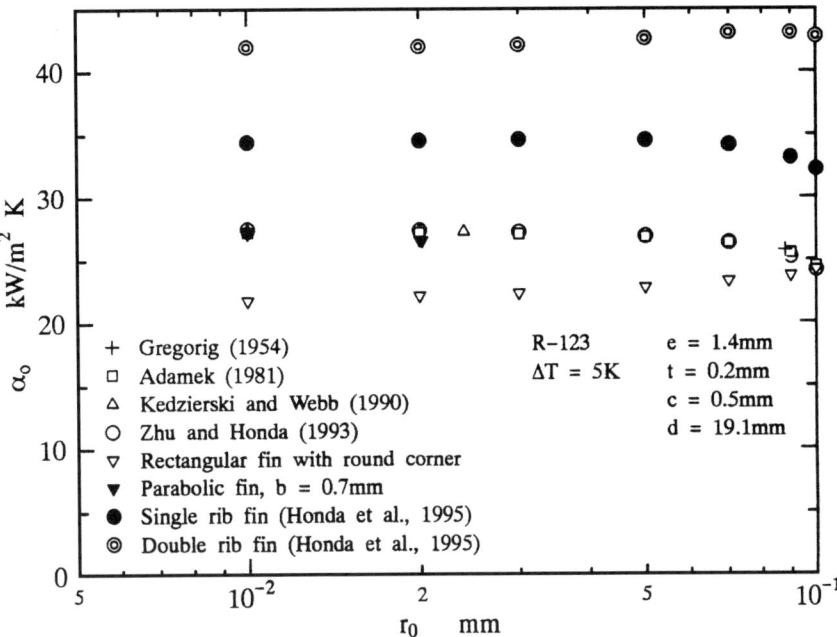

**Figure 7** Comparison of heat transfer performance for eight classes of two-dimensional fin tubes.

where $Nu_d = \alpha d/\lambda_l$, $G_d = \rho_l g h_{lg} d^3/\lambda_l \nu_l (T_s - T_{wr})$, $A = A_f + A_r$, $A_{ef} = \eta A_f + A_r$, $e_e = \pi(d^2 - d_r^2)/4d$, $\eta$ is the fin efficiency, $A_f$ is the fin surface area, $A_r$ is the fin root surface area, and $A_o$ is the nominal surface area of a smooth tube with diameter $d$. The theoretical models of Webb et al. (1985), Honda et al. (1988), Adamek and Webb (1990a), Murata and Hashizume (1992), and Rose (1994) took into account the combined effects of gravity and surface tension. In these models, the average heat transfer coefficient was expressed as a weighted average of the heat transfer coefficients for the unflooded and flooded regions. For a trapezoid-fin tube, the model of Rose (1994) is recommended because it is relatively simple and gives good agreement to available experimental data. Briggs and Rose (1994) adapted the model of Rose (1994) to account for the fin efficiency. This model can readily be used to optimize the fin dimensions.

Figure 8 shows a comparison of the measured average transfer coefficients for R-113, ethylene glycol, and water, condensing on five rectangular fin tubes with the same values of $b$ and $t$ as the theoretical predictions of the Beatty and Katz, Honda et al., and Rose models. The experimental data are due to Rose (1994). In Figure 8, the augmentation ratio $\alpha/\alpha_N$ is plotted as a function of $c$, where $\alpha_N$ is the theoretical prediction of the Nusselt (1916) equation for a horizontal tube:

$$Nu_d = 0.728 G_d^{1/4} \qquad (22.2\text{-}9)$$

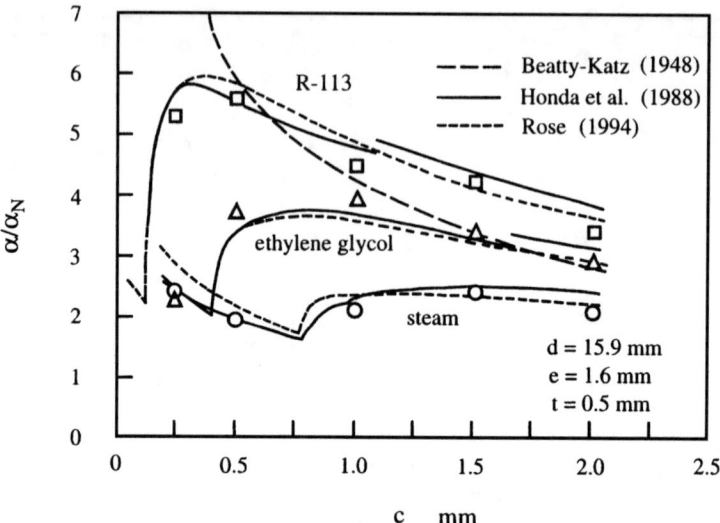

**Figure 8** Comparison of measured and predicted average heat transfer coefficients.

The $\alpha/\alpha_N$ ratio decreases in the order of R-113, ethylene glycol, and water (i.e., in the increasing order of $\sigma/\rho_l$). This is due to the decrease in $\phi_f$ as given by Eq. (22.2-1). It is also seen from Figure 8 that the optimum value of $c$ that gives the highest $\alpha/\alpha_N$ ratio increases in the increasing order of $\sigma/\rho_l$. The Beatty and Katz equation cannot predict the dependence of $\alpha/\alpha_N$ on $\sigma/\rho_l$ and $c$ observed in the experimental data. The predictions of the Honda et al. and Rose models give a good agreement with the experimental data. These models predict a minimum value of $\alpha/\alpha_N$ at a point where $X = 2$ is satisfied.

As mentioned above, the $\alpha/\alpha_N$ ratio decreases as $\sigma/\rho_l$ increases. The deleterious effect of liquid retention can be avoided by attaching a porous drainage strip at the tube bottom (Honda et al., 1983). Figure 9 compares the condensation pattern and the values of $\phi_f$ and $\alpha/\alpha_N$ for methanol condensing on horizontal two-dimensional fin tubes with and without the porous drainage strip. The tube dimensions are $d = 19.4$ mm, $b = 0.50$ mm, $e = 1.13$ mm, and $t = 0.11$ mm. The porous drainage strip has a thickness of 1.9 mm, effective pore diameter of 0.4 mm, and height of $z_p$. It is seen from Figure 9 that both $\phi_f$ and $\alpha/\alpha_N$ increase significantly by use of the porous drainage strip.

Condensation phenomena in actual shell-and-tube condensers are subject to the combined effects of vapor velocity and condensate inundation. Experimental results have shown that the effect of vapor velocity is much smaller for a finned tube than for a smooth tube. For forced convection condensation on a horizontal

 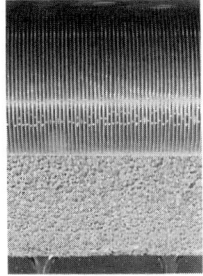

(a) without drainage strip  
$\phi_f = 1.19$ rad  
$\alpha/\alpha_N = 6.2$

(b) with drainage strip  
$z_p = 13.6$ mm  
$\phi_f = 2.14$ rad  
$\alpha/\alpha_N = 10.2$

**Figure 9** Comparison of condensation pattern between horizontal two-dimensional fin tube with and without porous drainage strip.

two-dimensional fin tube, Cavallini et al. (1996) used the following expression of the average heat transfer coefficient:

$$\alpha = \left(a_{st}^2 + a_{fc}^2\right)^{1/2} \qquad (22.2\text{-}10)$$

where $\alpha_{st}$ and $\alpha_{fc}$ are the average heat transfer coefficients for the stationary vapor condition and for the forced convection controlled condition, respectively. Honda et al. (1989) and Murata et al. (1992) proposed theoretical models of film condensation on bundles of horizontal two-dimensional fin tubes. In these models, the effect of vapor velocity was neglected.

Figure 10 compares the heat transfer characteristics during R-113 condensation on in-line bundles of six kinds of horizontal finned tubes shown in Figure 4 (Honda et al., 1991), where the condensation number $Nu_f = \alpha(g/v_l^2)^{1/3}/\lambda_l$ is plotted as a function of the film Reynolds number $Re_f$. The tube dimensions are $d = 15.8$ mm, $b = 0.5 \sim 1.0$ mm, $e = 1.0 \sim 1.43$ mm, $t = 0.11 \sim 0.45$ mm. It is seen from Figure 10 that the two-dimensional-fin tubes A and B show a much smaller decrease in $Nu_f$ with increasing $Re_f$ than the three-dimensional-fin tubes C–F. In Figure 10, experimental data for vertical fluted tubes and an electrohydrodynamically augmented vertical smooth tube are also shown. Comparison of these data reveals that the highest heat transfer performance is obtained by tube B with small values of $b$ ($= 0.5$ mm) and $t$ ($= 0.11$ mm).

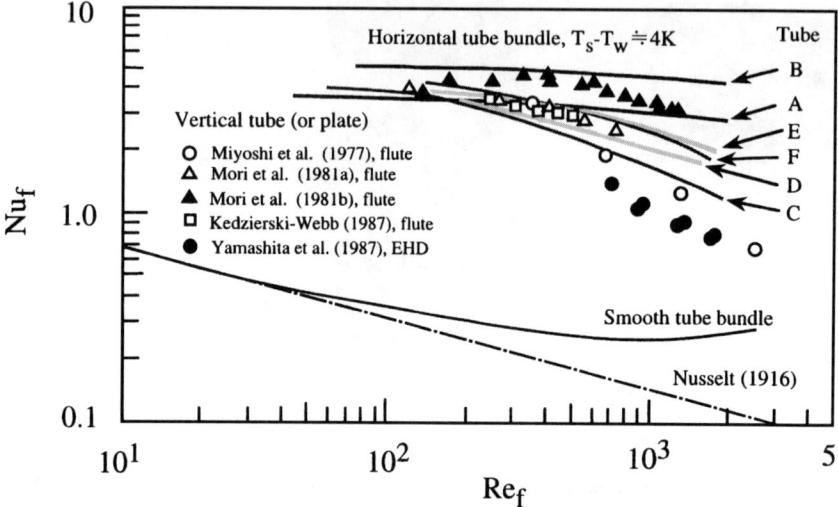

**Figure 10** Comparison of heat transfer characteristics between horizontal and vertical augmented tubes.

## 22.3 ELECTROHYDRODYNAMIC AUGMENTATION TECHNIQUE

When a high electric field is applied to a liquid-vapor system, instability of liquid-vapor interface is induced. This phenomenon can be used to augment condensation heat transfer. Figure 11 shows the physical model of the liquid-vapor system when the voltage $V$ is applied between infinite horizontal parallel plates placed in the vapor and liquid, respectively. If the elapsed time is longer than the relaxation time of electric charge in the liquid (which is about 1 ms, 10 ms, and 10 s for

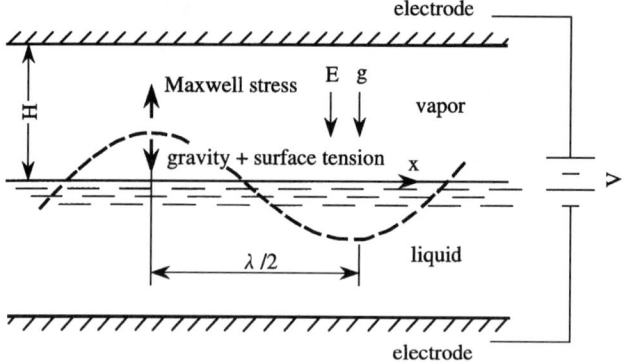

**Figure 11** Liquid-vapor interface under an electric field.

water, R-123, and R-113, respectively; Yabe, 1991), the voltage in the liquid is almost the same as that of the electrode. Thus, a uniform electric field of strength $E = V/H$ is produced in the vapor space, and the Maxwell stress $\varepsilon_v E^2/2$ acts vertically upward on the liquid-vapor interface, where $H$ is the height of the vapor space and $\varepsilon_v$ is the dielectric constant of vapor. When a small disturbance is applied to the liquid-vapor interface, the Maxwell stress acts to destabilize the interface because it is higher at the ridge than at the trough. On the other hand, the gravity and surface tension forces act to stabilize the interface. For an infinite liquid depth, the stability criterion is given by (Tanasawa, 1991):

$$\sigma k^2 - 8.85 \times 10^{-12} \varepsilon_v E^2 k \coth(kH) + (\rho_l - \rho_v)g = 0 \qquad (22.3\text{-}1)$$

where $k$ is the wave number. The critical voltage above which the interface becomes unstable depends on $H$ and the dimension of the liquid-vapor interface.

Velkoff and Miller (1965) were the first to report on the electrohydrodynamic augmentation of condensation. They tested several kinds of electrodes that were placed parallel to a vertical condensing surface. When a high voltage ($\geq 30\,\text{kV}$) was applied between the electrode and the condensing surface, the condensate film became unstable, and the condensate jet directing toward the electrode was generated. Sunada et al. (1991) used a transparent plate electrode placed parallel to a vertical condensing surface. They observed a surface granulation phenomenon of the condensate film, which was named the *EHD pseudo-dropwise condensation*. Figure 12 shows their results, where the local heat transfer coefficient $\alpha_z$ is

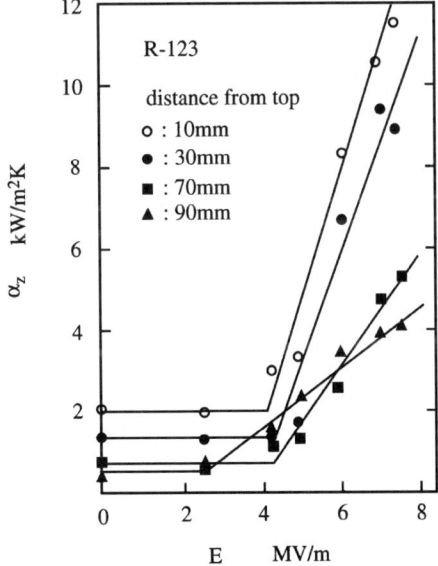

**Figure 12**  Variation of local heat transfer coefficient with electric field strength.

plotted as a function of $E$. The effect of the electric field is apparent in the region of $E > 4$ MV/m where the EHD pseudo-dropwise condensation occurred. Yamashita et al. (1991) used a combination of a lattice electrode and a helical wire electrode for a vertical shell-and-tube condenser. A comparison of their results with those for vertical fluted tubes and horizontal finned tubes is given in Figure 10.

## 22.4 OTHER TECHNIQUES

Vertical wires attached at regular intervals to a vertical tube and helical wire wrap on a horizontal tube provide a considerable condensation augmentation. The mechanism of augmentation is similar to the cases of vertical fluted tubes and horizontal finned tubes, except that the wire itself does not act as a heat transfer surface. Thomas (1967) and Fujii et al. (1987) developed semi-empirical equations of the average heat transfer coefficient for a vertical tube with attached vertical wires and a horizontal tube with a helical wire wrap, respectively.

Horizontal corrugated tubes have been tested for condensation of steam (Marto et al., 1979; Mehta and Rao, 1979). Generally, the steam side augmentation obtained by the corrugated tube is much smaller than the waterside augmentation. The maximum value of the reported augmentation ratio is about 1.4.

## REFERENCES

Adamek, T. 1981. Bestimmung der Kendensationgrössen auf Feingewellten Oberflächen zur Auslegung Optimaler Wandprofile. *Wärme und Stoffübertragung* 15:255–270.
Adamek, T. and Webb, R. L., 1990a. Prediction of Film Condensation on Horizontal Integral Fin Tubes. *Int. J. Heat Mass Transfer* 33:1721–1735.
Adamek, T. and Webb, R. L. 1990b. Prediction of Film Condensation on Vertical Finned Plates and Tubes: A Model for the Drainage Channel. *Int. J. Heat Mass Transfer* 33:1737–1749.
Beatty, K. O. and Katz, D. L. 1948. Condensation of Vapors on Outside of Finned Tubes. *Chem. Eng. Prog* 44:55–70.
Briggs, A. and Rose, J. W. 1994. Effect of Fin Efficiency on a Model for Condensation Heat Transfer on a Horizontal, Integral-Fin-Tube. *Int. J. Heat Mass Transfer* 37:457–463.
Cavallini, A., Doretti, L., Longo, G. A., and Rosetto, L. 1996. A New Model for Forced-Convection Condensation on Integral-Fin Tubes. *ASME J. Heat Transfer* 118:689–693.
Fujii, T., Wang, W. C., Koyama, S., and Shimizu, Y. 1987. Heat Transfer Enhancement for Gravity Controlled Condensation on a Horizontal Tube by Coiling a Wire. In: *Heat Transfer Science and Technology*. Washington, DC: Hemisphere, pp. 773–780.
Gregorig, R. 1954. Hautkondensation an Feingewellten Oberfl_Chen. *Z. Angew. Math. Phys.* 5:36–49.
Honda, H. and Fujii, T. 1984. Semi-Empirical Equation for Condensation Heat Transfer on Vertical Fluted Tubes. *ASME HTD* 38:99–106.
Honda, H., Nozu, S., and Mitsumori, K. 1983. Augmentation of Condensation on Horizontal Finned

Tubes by Attaching a Porous Drainage Plate. *Proc. ASME-JSME Thermal Engineering Joint Conference* 3:289–296.

Honda, H., Nozu, S., and Takeda, Y. 1989. A Theoretical Model of Film Condensation in a Bundle of Horizontal Low Finned Tubes. *ASME J. Heat Transfer* 111:525–532.

Honda, H., Nozu, S., and Uchima, B. 1988. A Generalized Prediction Method for Heat Transfer During Condensation on a Horizontal Low Finned Tube. *JSME Int. J., Ser.* 31:709–717.

Honda, H., Takamatsu, H., and Makishi, O. 1995. Numerical Analysis of Film Condensation on a Horizontal Two-Dimensional Fin Tube. In: *Heat Transfer in Condensation. Proc. Eurotherm Seminar* 47:48–54.

Honda, H., Uchima, B., Nozu, S., Nakata, H., and Torigoe, E. 1991. Film Condensation of R-113 on In-Line Bundles of Horizontal Finned Tubes. *ASME J. Heat Transfer* 113:479–486.

Kedzierski, M. A. and Webb, R. L. 1987. Experimental Measurement of Condensation on Vertical Plates with Enhanced Fins. *ASME HTD* 85:87–95.

Kedzierski, M. A. and Webb, R. L. 1990. Practical Fin Shapes for Surface-Tension-Drained Condensation. *ASME J. Heat Transfer* 112:479–485.

Marto, P. J. 1988. An Evaluation of Film Condensation on Horizontal Integral-Fin Tubes. *ASME J. Heat Transfer* 110:1287–1305.

Marto, P. J., Reilly, D. J., and Fenner, J. H. 1979. An Experimental Comparison of Enhanced Heat Transfer Condenser Tubing. In: *Advances in Enhanced Heat Transfer.* New York: ASME, pp. 1–10.

Masuda, H. and Rose, J. W. 1987. Static Configuration of Liquid Films on Horizontal Tubes with Low Radial Fins: Implications for Condensation Heat Transfer. *Proc. Roy. Soc. London*, A410:125–139.

Mehta, H. H. and Rao, M. R. 1979. Heat Transfer and Frictional Characteristics of Spirally Enhanced Tubes for Horizontal Condensers. In: *Advances in Enhanced Heat Transfer.* New York: ASME, pp. 11–22.

Miyoshi, M., Takahata, T., and Mochida, Y. 1977. Condensation Heat Transfer of Freon-11. *Proc. 14th Nat. Heat Transfer Symp. Japan*: 247–249.

Mori, Y. and Hijikata, K. 1984. Enhancement of Condensation Heat Transfer. In: *Advanced Heat Transfer* (in Japanese). Tokyo: Yokendo, pp. 216–225.

Mori, Y., Hijikata, K., Hirasawa, S., and Nakayama, W. 1981a. Optimized Performance of Condensers with Outside Condensing Surface. *ASME J. Heat Transfer* 103:96–102.

Mori, Y., Hijikata, K., and Kondo, T. 1981b. Fundamental Study of Condenser Tubes for Highest Performance. *Proc. 18th Nat. Heat Transfer Symp. Japan*: 163–165.

Murata, K. and Hashizume, K. 1992. Prediction of Condensation Heat Transfer Coefficient in Horizontal Integral-Fin Tube Bundles. *Experimental Heat Transfer* 5:115–130.

Nusselt, W. 1916. Die Oberfl.Chenkondensation des Wasserdampfes. *Zeit. Ver. Deut. Ing.* 60:541–546, 569–575.

Rose, J. W. 1994. An Approximate Equation for the Vapor-Side Heat-Transfer Coefficient for Condensation on Low-Finned Tubes. *Int. J. Heat Mass Transfer* 37:865–875.

Sunada, Y., Yabe, A., Taketani, T., and Yoshizawa, Y. 1991. Experimental Study of Pseudo-Dropwise Condensation. *Proc. ASME/JSME Thermal Eng. Joint Conf. 1991* 3:47–53.

Tanasawa, I. 1991. Advances in Condensation Heat Transfer. In: *Advances in Heat Transfer* 21:55–139.

Thomas, D. G. 1967. Enhancement of Film Condensation Rates on Vertical Tubes by Vertical Wires. *Ind. Eng. Chem. Fundamentals* 6:97–102.

Velkoff, H. R. and Miller, T. H. 1965. Condensation of Vapor on a Vertical Plate with a Transverse Electrostatic Field. *ASME J. Heat Transfer* 87:197–201.

Webb, R. L. and Murawski, C. G. 1990. Row Effect for R-11 Condensation on Enhanced Tubes. *ASME J. Heat Transfer* 112:768–776.

Webb, R. L., Rudy, T. M., and Kedzierski, M. A. 1985. Prediction of Condensation Coefficient on Horizontal Integral-Fin Tubes. *ASME J. Heat Transfer* 107:369–376.

Yabe, Y. 1991. Active Heat Transfer Enhancement by Applying Electric Fields. *Proc. ASME/JSME Thermal Eng. Joint Conf. 1991* 3:xv–xxiii.

Yamashita, K., Kumagai, M., Sekita, S., Yabe, A., Taketani, T., and Kikuchi, K. 1991. Heat Transfer Characteristics of an EHD Condenser. *Proc. ASME/JSME Thermal Eng. Joint Conf. 1991* 3:61–67.

Yamashita, K., Kumagai, M., Watanabe, Y., Kikuchi, K., Yabe, A., and Taketani, T. 1987. The Development of an EHD Condenser. *Proc. 24th Nat. Heat Transfer Symp. Japan,* pp. 170–172.

Zhu, H. and Honda, H. 1993. Optimization of Fin Geometry of a Horizontal Low-Finned Condenser Tube. *Heat Transfer—Japanese Research* 22:372–386.

CHAPTER
# TWENTY THREE

## HEAT TRANSFER AND PRESSURE DROP IN INTERNAL FLOW CONDENSATION

Shigeru Koyama
Jian Yu

*Kyushu University, Kasuga, 816-8580, Japan*

## 23.1 INTRODUCTION

The condensation inside tubes is generally classified according to the tube orientation: condensation inside vertical tube and inside horizontal tube. In a vertical tube, an annular condensate film forms on the tube surface, whereas in a horizontal tube, the flow direction is perpendicular to the gravity and makes the two-phase flow of vapor and condensate more complicated.

Figure 1 shows a condensation flow pattern in a horizontal smooth tube. The saturated vapor ($x = 1$) enters the tube and condenses as it flows through the tube. The vapor quality at the outlet is zero for complete condensation. Near the inlet of the tube, the relatively high vapor velocity causes the flow to be annular. As the vapor condenses downstream, the vapor velocity decreases, and the condensate on the top of tube flows down to the bottom of the tube, due to the effect of gravity. As a result, the condensate will accumulate at the bottom, and the vapor will take the upper space across the tube cross-section. The flow pattern changes from annular to stratified flow, and the Nusselt solution is applicable to the upper part of the tube where the condensate film is very thin. This leads to a varying heat flux distribution along the tube circumference. At very low vapor velocities, both the vapor and the condensate flow are laminar, and the slug flow is formed in the downstream region. In the case of very high vapor velocity, annular-mist flow pattern is formed, and the pressure drop along the tube increases remarkably.

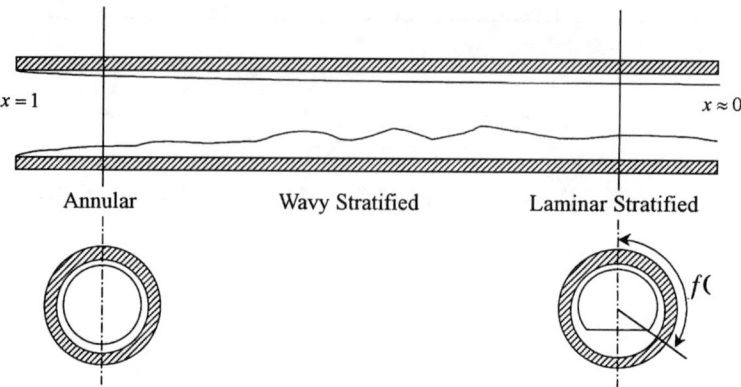

**Figure 1** Flow pattern of convective condensation in tube.

## 23.2 PRESSURE DROP

In the case of condensation in smooth tubes, the total pressure gradient along the tube, $dp/dz$, mainly comes from three parts: the momentum pressure gradient, $dp_m/dz$, the friction pressure gradient, $dp_f/dz$, and the gravitational pressure gradient, $dp_{gr}/dz$.

$$\frac{dp}{dz} = \frac{dp_m}{dz} + \frac{dp_f}{dz} + \frac{dp_{gr}}{dz} \qquad (23.2\text{-}1)$$

In the above equation, the momentum pressure gradient is usually determined based on the separated flow model, as given by the following equation:

$$\frac{dp_m}{dz} = -\frac{d}{dz}\left[\frac{G^2 x^2}{\xi \rho_V} + \frac{G^2(1-x)^2}{(1-\xi)\rho_L}\right] \qquad (23.2\text{-}2)$$

Uniform velocity profiles in the vapor and the liquid phases are assumed in deriving Eq. (23.2-2). The gravitational pressure gradient is estimated from the relative position from the tube inlet. The prediction of the friction pressure gradient is usually carried out based on the experimental results. For the horizontal tube, the Lockhart-Martinelli method is commonly employed in correlating data. In this method, the two-phase friction pressure gradient is expressed as

$$\left(\frac{dp}{dz}\right)_f = \left(\frac{dp}{dz}\right)_L \Phi_L^2 = \left(\frac{dp}{dz}\right)_V \Phi_V^2 \qquad (23.2\text{-}3)$$

where $(dp/dz)_L$ and $(dp/dz)_V$ are the friction pressure gradients of liquid-only flow and vapor-only flow, respectively. A number of researchers have correlated the two-phase multiplier $\Phi_V$ as a function of the Lockhart-Martinelli parameter, $X_{tt}$.

Soliman et al. (1968) developed their correlation from the experimental results for the two-phase flow of CFC114 as

$$\Phi_V = 1 + 2.85 X_{tt}^{0.523} \quad (23.2\text{-}4)$$

From the experimental data of CFC12 condensing in a horizontal smooth tube, Azer et al. (1972) developed the following correlation for friction pressure drop.

$$\Phi_V = 1 + 1.09 X_{tt}^{0.039} \quad (23.2\text{-}5)$$

The Zivi (1964) correlation for the void fraction was used in above two correlations.

Fujii et al. (1976) proposed a correlation considering the effects of mass flow rate and physical properties. The void fraction in their study was calculated by the Fauske (1961) equation:

$$\Phi_V = 1 + a X_{tt}^{0.2} \quad (23.2\text{-}6)$$

where

$$a = 1.24 \left( \frac{G}{\sqrt{\rho_V \rho_L}} \right)^{0.7} \quad \text{at } \frac{G}{\sqrt{\rho_V \rho_L}} \leq 1.5 \text{ m/s}$$

$$a = 1.65 \quad \text{at } \frac{G}{\sqrt{\rho_V \rho_L}} > 1.5 \text{ m/s}$$

Haraguchi et al. (1994a) modified the correlation of Fujii et al. (1976) and obtained a simple correlation for pure refrigerants HCFC22, HCFC123, and HFC134a condensing in a horizontal smooth tube. They adopted the Smith (1971) equation for predicting the void fraction:

$$\Phi_V = 1 + 0.5 \left[ \frac{G}{\sqrt{g d \rho_V (\rho_L - \rho_V)}} \right]^{0.75} X_{tt}^{0.35} \quad (23.2\text{-}7)$$

For the vertical tube, Borchman (1967) and Goodykoontz and Brown (1967) carried out many experiments using water, CFC11, and CFC113. Their results agree in certain degree with the Blasius correlation, which is usually used for the single-phase flow in tube. The friction factor $C_f$ is defined as

$$\Delta p = C_f \left( \frac{\rho_V U_{in}^2}{2} \right) \frac{l}{d} \quad (23.2\text{-}8)$$

where $U_{in}$ is the vapor inlet velocity. On the other hand, Equation (23.2-4) (Soliman et al., 1968) also agrees with the data for vertical downward condensation.

The pressure drop characteristic in microfin tube was also studied by Haraguchi et al. (1993). The microfin tube they used is 6 m long with the average inner diameter of 8.37 mm, the fin height 0.17 mm, the fin pitch 0.44 mm, the fin number

60, and the helix angle 18 deg. They tested three kinds of refrigerants, HCFC22, HCFC123, and HFC134a, in this tube, and proposed the following correlation:

$$\Phi_V = 1.1 + 1.3 \left[ \frac{G \cdot X_{tt}}{\sqrt{g \, d\rho_V(\rho_L - \rho_V)}} \right]^{0.35} \quad (23.2\text{-}9)$$

## 23.3 CONDENSATION HEAT TRANSFER OF PURE VAPORS

### 23.3.1 Turbulent Liquid Film Theory

In the turbulent liquid film, the shear stress is proportional to the velocity gradient as follows:

$$\tau = \rho_L(\nu_L + \varepsilon)\frac{du}{dy} \quad (23.3\text{-}1)$$

where $\varepsilon$ is the turbulent eddy diffusivity. Similar to the above relation, the heat flux is proportional to the temperature gradient as

$$q = -\rho_L c_{pL}(a_L + \varepsilon_h)\frac{dT}{dy} = -\rho_L c_{pL}\left(\frac{\nu_L}{Pr_L} + \varepsilon_h\right)\frac{dT}{dy} \quad (23.3\text{-}2)$$

where $\varepsilon_h$ is the eddy diffusivity for heat. The dimensionless form of Eq. (23.3-2) based on the wall heat flux $q_w$ and the wall temperature $T_w$ is derived as

$$\frac{q}{q_w} = \left(\frac{1}{Pr_L} + \frac{\varepsilon_h}{\nu_L}\right)\frac{dT^+}{dy^+} \quad (23.3\text{-}3)$$

where $T^+$ is a dimensionless temperature, expressed as

$$T^+ = \frac{\rho_L c_{pL}(T_w - T)}{q_w}\sqrt{\frac{\tau_w}{\rho_L}} \quad (23.3\text{-}4)$$

In the turbulent liquid film, $\varepsilon_h$ is usually assumed to equal to $\varepsilon$. Equation (23.3-3) is then transformed as

$$dT^+ = \frac{q/q_w}{1/Pr_L + \varepsilon/\nu_L} dy^+ \quad (23.3\text{-}5)$$

Integrating the above equation from 0 to $y_i^+$ and using Eq. (23.3-4), a relation between the temperature difference $(T_i - T_w)$ and the heat transfer coefficient $\alpha$ is obtained as

$$\alpha = \frac{\rho_L c_{pL}}{T_i^+}\sqrt{\frac{\tau_w}{\rho_L}}, \quad \frac{\alpha \mu_L}{k_L \rho_L^{1/2}} = \frac{Pr_L}{T_i^+}\sqrt{\tau_w} \quad (23.3\text{-}6)$$

where

$$T_i^+ = \int_0^{y_i^+} \frac{q/q_w}{1/Pr_L + \varepsilon/\nu_L} dy^+ \tag{23.3-7}$$

Traviss et al. (1973) applied the momentum and heat transfer analogy to the annular flow model using the von Karman universal velocity distribution in the turbulent liquid film. They assumed the temperatures in the vapor core and at liquid-vapor interface to be equal to the saturation temperature. The axial heat conduction and subcooling of the liquid film were also neglected in their study. A simple formulation for the dimensionless temperature was obtained from their analysis as

$$Re_L \leq 50, \quad T_i^+ = 0.707 Pr_L Re_L^{0.5} \tag{23.3-8}$$

$$50 < Re_L \leq 1125, \quad T_i^+ = 5Pr_L + 5\ln[1 + Pr_L(0.09636 Re_L^{0.585} - 1)] \tag{23.3-9}$$

$$Re_L > 1125, \quad T_i^+ = 5Pr_L + 5\ln(1 + 5Pr_L) + 2.5\ln\left(0.00313 Re_L^{0.812}\right) \tag{23.3-10}$$

The heat transfer coefficient can be calculated using Eqs. (23.3-8), (23.3-9), (23.3-10), (23.3-6), and the correlation of Soliman et al., Eq. (23.2-4). The final correlation of Traviss et al. (1973) is expressed as

$$Nu = 0.15 \frac{\Phi_V}{X_{tt}} \cdot \frac{Pr_L Re_L^{0.9}}{T_i^+} \tag{23.3-11}$$

Traviss et al. compared their correlation to the experimental data for R12 and R22, and recommended this general design correlation for the forced convective condensation in the range of $T_i^+$ from 0.15 to 15.

### 23.3.2 Experimental Correlation for Smooth Tube

In the high mass flux region, $G > 400$ kg/(m²s), the forced convective condensation dominates the heat transfer characteristics. The effect of gravity can be neglected. For the condensation in this region, the correlations proposed by Cavallini and Zecchin (1974) and Shah (1979) are commonly used in industry.

Cavallini and Zecchin (1974) presented a dimensionless correlation for forced convective condensation of pure saturated vapor inside tubes based on a simple hydrodynamic model of the annular flow pattern and on the momentum and heat transfer analogy. Their analysis was limited to the ranges of density ratio $\rho_L/\rho_V$ from 10 to 2000, viscosity ratio $\mu_V/\mu_L$ from 0.01 to 1, Reynolds number from 5,000 to 500,000, Prandtl number from 0.8 to 20, vapor quality from 0.1 to 0.9, thermal group $c_{pL}(T_V - T_w)/h_{lg}$ from 0.01 to 0.2, and Froude number from 15 to 4,000. From the regression analysis of the data, they found that the Nusselt number mainly depends on the Reynolds number, the Prandtl number, and quality group $1 + x((\rho_L/\rho_V)^{0.5} - 1)$. Other parameters, such as density ratio, viscosity ratio, thermal group, and the Froude number, do not influence remarkably within the ranges of parameters investigated. For 460 data points of CFC113, CFC12, and HCFC22 from 8 different sources, the analytical and experimental results agree well with their following correlation:

$$Nu = 0.0344 Re_L^{0.83}[1 + x((\rho_L/\rho_V)^{0.5} - 1)]^{0.82} Pr_L^{0.35} \qquad (23.3\text{-}12)$$

By modifying the Dittus-Boelter equation for condensation in smooth tubes, Shah (1979) proposed a very simple correlation based on 474 experimental data from many sources, covering water, R11, R12, R113, methanol, ethanol, benzene, toluene, and trichloroethylene in horizontal, vertical, and inclined tubes of diameters ranging from 7 to 40 mm.

$$Nu = 0.023 Re_L^{0.8} Pr_L^{0.4} \left[ (1-x)^{0.8} + \frac{3.8 x^{0.76}(1-x)^{0.04}}{(p_{sat}/p_c)^{0.38}} \right] \qquad (23.3\text{-}13)$$

Based on his recommendation, the Shah correlation is applicable in the range of reduced pressure from 0.002 to 0.44, saturation temperature from 21 to 310°C, vapor velocity from 3 to 300 m/s, vapor quality from 0 to 1, mass flux from 10.8 to 1599 kg/(m²s), all liquid Reynolds number over 350 for tube and over 3000 for annulus, liquid Prandtl number over 0.5, and without the limitation for heat flux. From his analysis, the mean deviation for the 474 data points was only 15.4%. Recently, Moser et al. (1998) proved the reliability of the Shah correlation using 1197 data points for six kinds of refrigerants from 18 sources. They found that the deviation of the Shah correlation is only 14.37% for all data points.

Besides, Akers et al. (1959), Boyko and Kruzhilin (1967), Azer et al. (1972), and Moser et al. (1998) also developed correlations for the condensation of pure refrigerants in horizontal smooth tube. These correlations are mainly available for the refrigerant and can predict the condensation heat transfer characteristics very well in many cases.

In the mass flux range from 100 to 400 kg/(m²s), the forced convective condensation and the gravity controlled convective condensation are of same importance. In the case of low mass flux and low vapor quality, the gravity controlled convective condensation dominates all the characteristics. For the condensation in this region, Fujii et al. (1980) proposed an empirical correlation concerning both effects. From the same consideration, Haraguchi et al. (1994b) proposed a correlation for the refrigerants using the asymptotic model. This model offers a smooth transition between the two different limiting phenomena: forced convective condensation and gravity controlled convective condensation. The result based on this model is applicable in the entire range between these two limiting phenomena. Haraguchi et al. tested three kinds of refrigerants, HCFC22, HCFC123, and HFC134a, in a horizontal smooth tube with inner diameter of 8.4 mm and developed the following correlation using their own experimental data:

$$Nu \equiv \frac{\alpha d}{\lambda_L} = \left(Nu_F^2 + Nu_B^2\right)^{1/2} \qquad (23.3\text{-}14)$$

where

$$Nu_F = 0.0152\left(1 + 0.6 Pr_L^{0.8}\right)(\Phi_V/X_{tt}) Re_{Lo}^{0.77} \qquad (23.3\text{-}15)$$

$$Nu_B = 0.725 H(\xi) \left(\frac{Ga\, Pr_L}{Ph_L}\right)^{\frac{1}{4}} \qquad (23.3\text{-}16)$$

$$H(\xi) = \xi + \{10[(1-\xi)^{0.1} - 1] + 1.7 \times 10^{-4} Re\}\sqrt{\xi}(1 - \sqrt{\xi}) \qquad (23.3\text{-}17)$$

$$Re_{Lo} = \frac{G(1-x)d}{\mu_L} \qquad (23.3\text{-}18)$$

$$Re = \frac{Gd}{\mu_L} \qquad (23.3\text{-}19)$$

$$\xi = \left[1 + \frac{\rho_V}{\rho_L}\left(\frac{1-x}{x}\right)\left(0.4 + 0.6 \sqrt{\frac{\frac{\rho_L}{\rho_V} + 0.4\frac{1-x}{x}}{1 + 0.4\frac{1-x}{x}}}\right)\right]^{-1} \qquad (23.3\text{-}20)$$

This correlation is applicable for the refrigerant condensation in a horizontal smooth tube in the range of mass flux from 90 to 400 kg/(m²s), vapor quality from 0.1 to 0.9, heat flux from 3 to 33, liquid Prandtl number from 2.5 to 4.5, Reynolds number for liquid-only flow $Re_{Lo}$ from 200 to 20,000, liquid Reynolds number $Re$ from 3000 to 30,000, and the parameter $Ga\, Pr_L/Ph_L$ from $4.8 \times 10^9$ to $9.5 \times 10^{10}$.

## 23.4 CONDENSATION HEAT TRANSFER OF BINARY MIXTURES

During the condensation of zeotropic binary vapor mixture in tubes, the compositions as well as the temperatures in the vapor and liquid phases change along the length of the tube. The mass fraction of more volatile component in the vapor core increases, and the temperature of the bulk vapor mixture decreases along the flow direction. Due to the heat and mass transfer resistance, there is a state of non-equilibrium between the phases. The phase equilibrium is only established at

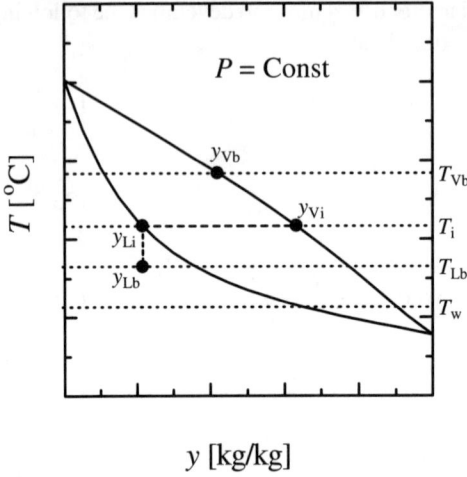

**Figure 2** Phase equilibrium diagram.

the vapor-liquid interface, as indicated in the diagram of Figure 2. For the additional mass transfer resistance in the vapor and liquid phases, the condensation heat transfer coefficient of vapor mixture would be lower than that of pure vapor. But the heat transfer characteristic in the liquid film can be considered the same as that for the condensation of pure vapor. Usually, the heat transfer resistance can be measured from the temperature distribution in a cross-section of tube, which would be the same as that in the pure vapor case. But the mass fraction distribution in a cross-section is hardly ever measured, especially for in-tube condensation. This resistance is difficult to estimate. One of the most important aspects in the prediction of heat transfer in condensation of binary mixtures is therefore to clarify the mass fraction distribution and mass transfer characteristic during the condensation process.

The pioneering work to predict simultaneous heat and mass transfer characteristics of binary vapor mixture is well established as the film theory, which is summarized by Bird et al. (1960). Combining this theory and the Nusselt theory, von Es and Heertjes (1956) analyzed their experimental data on the condensation of a binary vapor mixture (benzene/toluene) flowing downward in a vertical tube. They found that the local mass transfer coefficient was in proportion to $Re_V^{0.8} Sc_V^{1/3}$ and the local vapor-liquid interface temperature lay just below the bubble-point line. von Es and Heertjes (1962) also followed the upward condensation of a binary vapor mixture. After their studies, the main research target moved to the multi-component system, and the film theory has been applied to the design of many types of condensers for binary systems for a long time in the chemical engineering field.

In the past ten years, binary vapor mixtures have received attention again to find alternative refrigerants in heat pump/refrigeration systems, and many researchers have engaged in experimental and theoretical studies on the condensation of alternative refrigerant mixtures in tubes.

Zhang et al. (1995) proposed a non-equilibrium model of condensation in a horizontal smooth tube. They tested the condensation heat transfer characteristics of HFC32/134a and HFC32/125/134a mixtures and developed a predictive method using their model. Their predicted and experimental results on heat transfer coefficient agreed well for both mixtures. But the mass fraction distribution and the mass transfer characteristic were not clarified in their study.

Koyama et al. (1998) developed a non-equilibrium model for condensation of binary refrigerant mixtures inside horizontal smooth tubes. In their model, it is assumed that the phase equilibrium is only established at the vapor-liquid interface, while the bulk vapor and the bulk liquid are in non-equilibrium. They considered the effect of liquid subcooling on condensation heat transfer and pressure drop but neglected the effect of vapor superheat. They derived the governing equations for heat and mass transfer characteristics of refrigerant mixture in two-phase region as follows:

## Momentum Balance of Refrigerant

$$\frac{dp}{dz} = -\left(\frac{4W_{V\,in}}{\pi d^2}\right)^2 \frac{d}{dz}\left[\frac{x^2}{\xi^2 \rho_V} + \frac{(1-x)^2}{(1-\xi)^2 \rho_L}\right] + \frac{dp_f}{dz} \quad (23.4\text{-}1)$$

The void fraction $\xi$ and the frictional pressure change $dp_f/dz$ are calculated using Eqs. (23.3-20) and (23.2-7), respectively.

## Heat Balance of Refrigerant

$$q_w = -\frac{W_{V\,in}}{\pi d}\frac{d}{dz}\{xh_{Vb} + (1-x)h_{Lb}\} = \alpha_L(T_i - T_w) \quad (23.4\text{-}2)$$

The liquid film heat transfer coefficient $\alpha_L$ is calculated using Eq. (23.3-14).

## Mass Balance of More Volatile Component in Vapor Core

$$\dot{m}_1 = -\frac{W_{V\,in}}{\pi d}\frac{d}{dz}(xy_{1b}) = -\frac{W_{V\,in}}{\pi d}\frac{y_{1i}\,dx}{dz} - \beta_V(y_{1i} - y_{1b}) \quad (23.4\text{-}3)$$

The vapor mass transfer coefficient $\beta_V$ is calculated using the correlation proposed by Koyama et al. (1998) as follows:

$$Sh_V = \frac{\beta_V d}{\rho_V D} = 0.023\sqrt{\xi}\,\Phi_V^2 Re_V^{0.8} Sc_V^{1/3} \qquad (23.4\text{-}4)$$

## Mass Balance of More Volatile Component in Liquid Film

$$\dot{m}_1 = \frac{W_{V\,in}}{\pi d}\frac{d}{dz}\{(1-x)x_{1b}\} = -\frac{W_{V\,in}\,x_{1i}}{\pi d}\frac{dx}{dz} + \beta_L(x_{1i} - x_{1b}) \qquad (23.4\text{-}5)$$

From the assumption $\beta_L \to \infty$, the following relation is reduced from Eq. (23.4-5):

$$x_{1b} = x_{1i} \qquad (23.4\text{-}6)$$

## Relation Between Vapor Quality and Mass Fraction

$$x = (y_{1b\,in} - x_{1b})/(y_{1b} - x_{1b}) \qquad (23.4\text{-}7)$$

where $y_{1b\,in}$ is the bulk mass fraction of more volatile component at the refrigerant inlet.

The local values of vapor quality and the thermodynamic states of refrigerant bulk vapor, vapor-liquid interface, bulk liquid, and wall heat flux were obtained by solving Eqs. (23.4-1) to (23.4-7), starting with the conditions of refrigerant vapor at the inlet of the condenser and the wall temperature distribution along the tube. The detailed calculation procedure was described by Koyama et al. (1998).

Using their method, Koyama et al. obtained the local heat transfer and pressure drop characteristics, as well as the local mass fraction distribution and the mass transfer characteristics during the condensation process. Figures 3, 4 and 5 show some of their results. It is found in Figure 4 that the vapor diffusion mass flux of more volatile component at the vapor-liquid interface ($\dot{m}\cdot y_{1i} - \dot{m}_1$) decreases in the refrigerant flow direction, while the liquid mass flux of that ($\dot{m}_1 - \dot{m}\cdot x_{1i}$) increases in the refrigerant flow direction. This reveals that the mass transfer rate is controlled by the diffusion in the vapor side at the beginning point of condensation, and the diffusion in the liquid side increases gradually as the condensation proceeds. Figure 5 shows that the values of $y_{1b}$, $y_{1i}$, and $x_{1i}$ ($= x_{1b}$) increase in the downstream section. It is also shown that $\xi$ ($= \dot{m}_1/\dot{m}$) coincides with $x_{1b}$ at the beginning point of condensation and approaches to $y_{1b}$ in downstream region. This trend of $\xi$ corresponds to the mass transfer characteristics shown in Figure 4.

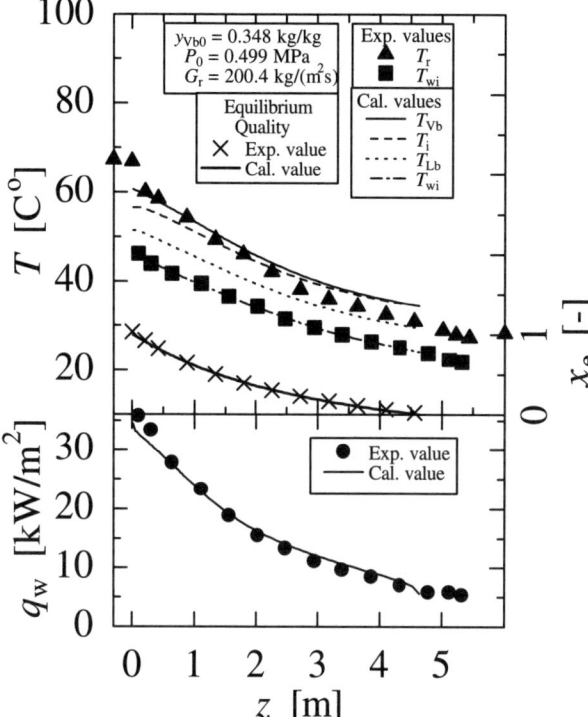

**Figure 3** Distributions of temperatures, heat flux and vapor quality along tube axis (HFC134a/HCFC123).

For the condensation of binary mixtures inside a microfin tube, Koyama et al. (1999) extended the same model as for the smooth tube to calculate the local values of vapor quality, the thermodynamic states of refrigerant bulk vapor, vapor-liquid interface and bulk liquid, and wall heat flux. In this case, the correlations for heat transfer coefficient in liquid film and pressure drop are changed to those for microfin tubes proposed by Yu and Koyama (1998) and Haraguchi et al. (1993).

Condensation of binary mixtures in enhanced tubes has been experimentally studied by Kedzierski and Kim (1998) for twisted tape inserts for single-component refrigerants and their zeotropic and azeotropic mixtures. Kedzierski and Goncalves (1999) present local convective condensation measurements for R410A (R32/R125, 50/50% mass) and pure refrigerants in a micro-fin tube. Both heat transfer and pressure drop measurements are provided. The heat transfer degradation associated with R410A was shown to be relatively small and believed to be mostly due to nonlinear property effects.

**632** HANDBOOK OF PHASE CHANGE: BOILING AND CONDENSATION

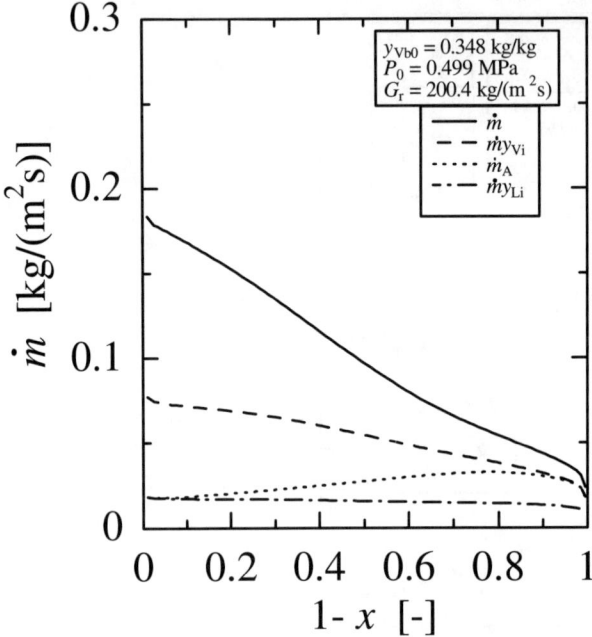

**Figure 4** Distribution of condensate rate along tube axis (HFC134a/HCFC123).

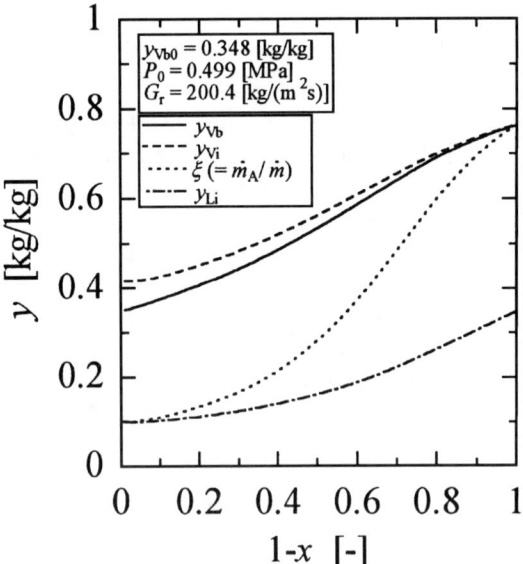

**Figure 5** Distribution of mass fraction along tube axis (HFC134a/HCFC123).

## 23.5 CONDENSATION HEAT TRANSFER OF MULTI-COMPONENT MIXTURES

Multicomponent mixtures are encountered in many chemical and process industries. The search for alternative refrigerants has resulted in a ternary refrigerant mixture R407C, composed of 23wt%HFC32, 25wt%HFC125 and 52wt%HFC134a as a possible candidate for replacing R22, which has been widely used in air-conditioning and refrigeration systems until now.

In the case of multi-component mixture condensation, the treatment of the mass transfer is very complicated due to the coupling effect between components. Schrodt (1973) applied the film theory to a ternary system (methanol/water/air) condensing in a vertical tube. In his theory, the ternary system was treated as the combination of two pseudo-binary systems. Toor (1964) developed the linearized method to analyze the multi-component mass transfer program. His method treats the multi-component mass transfer equations as the combination of equivalent binary mass transfer equations by using the orthogonal matrix transformation, based on the assumption that the multi-component diffusivity matrix and the other physical properties are constant. In the treatment of the multi-component diffusivity matrix, Krishna and Standart (1976) developed a more rigorous method to solve the multi-component mass transfer problem. Based on the film theory, Webb and Sardesai (1981) compared these three multi-component mass transfer models with the experimental data on the condensation of two different ternary vapor mixtures in a vertical smooth tube. Their comparisons showed that these models were applicable to predict the total condensation rate, but they recommended Toor's linearized model and the Krishna-Standart model.

Koyama and Lee (1998) extended the non-equilibrium model for the condensation of binary refrigerant mixture in a horizontal smooth tube (Koyama et al., 1998) to multi-component refrigerant mixtures. The assumptions used in this section are the same as those in Section 23.4. The governing equations for heat and mass transfer characteristics in the two-phase region are derived as:

### Momentum Balance of Refrigerant

$$\frac{dp}{dz} = -\left(\frac{4W_{V\text{in}}}{\pi d^2}\right)^2 \frac{d}{dz}\left[\frac{x^2}{\xi^2 \rho_V} + \frac{(1-x)^2}{(1-\xi)^2 \rho_L}\right] + \frac{dp_f}{dz} \qquad (23.5\text{-}1)$$

The void fraction $\xi$ and the frictional pressure change $dp_f/dz$ are calculated using Eqs. (23.3-20) and (23.2-7), respectively.

## Heat Balance of Refrigerant

$$q_w = -\frac{W_{V\text{in}}}{\pi d}\frac{d}{dz}\{xh_{Vb} + (1-x)h_{Lb}\} = \alpha_L(T_i - T_w) \tag{23.5-2}$$

The liquid film heat transfer coefficient $\alpha_L$ is calculated using Eq. (23.3-14), which was developed from the condensation of pure refrigerants in horizontal smooth tube, as mentioned in Section 23.3-2.

## Mass Balance of Component $k (k = 1, 2, \ldots, n-1)$ in Vapor Core

$$\dot{m}_k = -\frac{W_{V\text{in}}}{\pi d}\frac{d}{dz}(xy_{kb}) = -\frac{W_{V\text{in}}\, y_{ki}}{\pi d}\frac{dx}{dz} - \beta_{kV}(y_{ki} - y_{kb}) \tag{23.5-3}$$

The vapor mass transfer coefficient $\beta_{kV}$ is calculated using the following equation:

$$Sh_V = \frac{\beta_{kV} d}{\rho_V D^*_{kk}} = 0.023\sqrt{\xi}\,\Phi_V^2 Re_V^{0.8} Sc_{kV}^{1/3} \tag{23.5-4}$$

where

$$Re_V = \frac{Gxd}{\mu_V}, \quad Sc_{kV} = \frac{\mu_V}{\rho_V D^*_{kk}}, \quad D^*_{kj} = D_{kn} - D_{kj} \tag{23.5-5,6,7}$$

$$D_{kj} = M_K D_{kj}^M \left(\sum_{m=1}^{n}\frac{y_{mb}}{M_m}\right) - \frac{M_k}{M_j}\left(\sum_{m=1}^{n} D_{km}^M y_{mb}\right) \tag{23.5-8}$$

## Mass Balance of Component $k (k = 1, 2, \ldots, n-1)$ in Liquid Film

$$\dot{m}_k = \frac{W_{V\text{in}}}{\pi d}\frac{d}{dz}\{(1-x)x_{kb}\} = -\frac{W_{V\text{in}} x_{ki}}{\pi d}\frac{dx}{dz} + \beta_{kL}(x_{ki} - x_{kb}) \tag{23.5-9}$$

From the assumption $\beta_{kL} \to \infty$, the following relation is reduced from the above equation:

$$x_{kb} = x_{ki} \tag{23.5-10}$$

## Relation Between Vapor Quality and Mass Fraction

$$x = (y_{kb\text{ in}} - x_{kb})/(y_{kb} - x_{kb}) \tag{23.5-11}$$

where $y_{kb\text{in}}$ is the bulk mass fraction at the refrigerant inlet.

The details of the calculation method is given by Koyama and Lee (1998). From their calculation of the condensation of ternary zeotropic refrigerant mixtures composed of HFC32/HFC125/HFC134a, including R407C, the local values of vapor quality, thermodynamic states at bulk vapor, vapor-liquid interface and bulk liquid, mass flux, etc., were obtained for a constant wall temperature and constant wall heat flux conditions.

The above prediction method can be easily extended to the condensation in microfin tube by using the correlations of heat transfer coefficient in liquid film and pressure drop for the corresponding tube.

## 23.6 FUTURE RESEARCH NEEDS

During the past 30 years, the research on condensation heat transfer inside tubes has made considerable progress. Many investigators have carried out experimental and theoretical studies in this field. The condensation heat transfer and pressure drop characteristics in the smooth tube can be predicted reasonably well from equipment designers' viewpoint. Some of the areas where further research is warranted are listed here:

1. The effect of superheated vapor on condensation heat transfer in tube.
2. Heat transfer characteristics in low mass flux region.
3. Mass transfer characteristics in the liquid phase.
4. Augmentation technology for in-tube condensation and appropriate predictive methods.
5. Development of simple and reliable prediction correlation for vapor mixtures in general design practice.

## REFERENCES

Akers, W. W., Deans, H. A., and Crosser, O. K. 1959. Condensation Heat Transfer Within Horizontal Tubes. *Chem. Eng. Prog. Symp. Ser.* 29:171–176.

Azer, N. Z., Abis, L. V., and Soliman, H. M. 1972. Local Heat Transfer Coefficients During Annular Flow Condensation. *ASHRAE Trans.* 78(2):135–143.

Bird, R. B., Stewart, W. E., and Lightfoot, E. N. 1960. *Transport Phenomena*. John Wiley & Sons, Inc.

Borchman, J. 1967. Heat Transfer of High Velocity Vapors Condensing in Annuli. *ASHRAE Trans.* 73.

Boyko, L. D. and Kruzhilin, G. N. 1967. Heat Transfer and Hydraulic Resistance During Condensation of Steam in a Horizontal Tube and in a Bundle of Tubes. *Int. J. Heat Mass Transfer* 10(3):361–373.

Cavallini, A. and Zecchin, R. 1974. A Dimensionless Correlation for Heat Transfer in Forced Convection Condensation. *Proc. 5th Int. Heat Transfer Conference* 3:309–313.

Fauske, H. K. 1961. Critical Two-Phase Steam Water Flows. *Proc. of Heat Transfer & Fluid Mech. Inst.*, Stanford, CA: Stanford Univ. Press, pp. 79–89.

Fujii, T., Honda, H., Nagata, S., Fujii, M., and Nozu, S. 1976. Condensation of R11 in Horizontal Tube (1st Report: Flow Pattern and Pressure Drop). *Trans. JSME (B)* 42(363):3541–3550 (in Japanese).

Fujii, T., Honda, H., and Nozu, S. 1980. Condensation of Fluorocarbon Refrigerants Inside a Horizontal Tube (Proposals of Semi-Empirical Expressions for the Local Heat Transfer Coefficient and Interfacial Friction Factor). *Refrigeration* 55(627):3–20 (in Japanese).

Goodykoontz, J. H. and Brown, W. F. 1967. Local Heat Transfer and Pressure Distributions for Freon-113 Condensing in Downflow in a Vertical Tube. NASA TN D-3952.

Haraguchi, H., Koyama, S., Esaki, J., and Fujii, T. 1993. Condensation Heat Transfer of Refrigerants HFC134a, HCFC123, and HCFC22 in a Horizontal Smooth Tube and a Horizontal Microfin Tube. *Proc. 30th National Heat Transfer Symp. of Japan*, Yokohama, pp. 343–345 (in Japanese).

Haraguchi, H., Koyama, S., and Fujii, T. 1994a. Condensation of Refrigerants HCFC22, HFC134a, and HCFC123 in a Horizontal Smooth Tube (1st Report, Proposal of Empirical Expressions for the Local Frictional Pressure Drop). *Trans. JSME (B)* 60(574):239–244 (in Japanese).

Haraguchi, H., Koyama, S., and Fujii, T. 1994b. Condensation of Refrigerants HCFC22, HFC134a, and HCFC123 in a Horizontal Smooth Tube (2nd Report, Proposal of Empirical Expressions for the Local Heat Transfer Coefficient). *Trans. JSME (B)* 60(574):245–252 (in Japanese).

Hayashi, T. 1998. Enhanced Condensation Heat Transfer of Refrigerant HFC134a in Horizontal Tubes. Master Thesis, Kyushu University, 1998 (in Japanese).

Kedzierski, M. A. and Goncalves, J. M. 1999. Horizontal Convective Condensation of Alternative Refrigerants Within a Micro-Fin Tube. *Journal of Enhanced Heat Transfer* 6(1).

Kedzierski, M. A. and Kim, M. S. 1998. Convective Boiling and Condensation Heat Transfer with a Twisted-Tape Insert for R12, R22, R152a, R134a, R290, R32/R134a, R32/R152a, R290/R134a, and R134a/600a. *Thermal Science and Engineering* 6(1):113–122.

Koyama, S. and Lee, S. M. 1998. A Prediction Model for Condensation of Ternary Refrigerant Mixtures Inside a Horizontal Smooth Tube. *Proceedings of 11st Int. Heat Transfer Conference* 6:427–432, Aug. 23–28, Korea.

Koyama, S., Yu, J., and Ishibashi, A. 1998. Condensation of Binary Refrigerant Mixtures in a Horizontal Smooth Tube. *Thermal Science & Engineering* 6(1):123–129.

Koyama, S., Yu, J., and Ishibashi, A. 1999. Heat and Mass Transfer of Binary Refrigerant Mixtures Condensation in a Horizontal Microfin Tube. *Proceedings of 5th ASME/JSME Thermal Engineering Joint Conference*, March 15–19, San Diego.

Krishna, R. and Standart, G. L. 1976. A Multicomponent Film Model Incorporating a General Matrix Method of Solution to the Maxwell-Stefan Equations. *AIChE J.* 2(2):383–389.

Moser, K. W., Webb, R. L., and Na, B. 1998. A New Equivalent Reynolds Number Model for Condensation in Smooth Tubes. *ASME Trans., J. Heat Transfer* 120(2):410–417.

Schrodt, J. T. 1973. Simultaneous Heat and Mass Transfer from Multicomponent Condensing Vapor-Gas Systems. *AIChE J.* 19(4):753–759.

Shah, M. M. 1979. A General Correlation for Heat Transfer During Film Condensation Inside Pipes. *Int. J. Heat and Mass Transfer* 22:547–556.

Smith, S. L. 1971. Void Fraction in Two-Phase Flow: A Correlation Based Upon an Equal Velocity Heated Model. *Heat and Fluid Flow* 1(1):22–39.

Soliman, M., Shuster, J. R., and Berenson, P. J. 1968. A General Heat Transfer Correlation for Annular Flow Condensation. *ASME Trans., J. Heat Transfer*, 90(2):267–276.

Toor, H. L. 1964. Solution of the Linearized Equation of Multicomponent Mass Transfer: II. Matrix Methods. *AIChE J.* 10(4):460–465.

Traviss, D. P., Rohsenow, W. M., and Baron, A.B. 1973. Forced Convection Condensation Inside Tubes: A Heat Transfer Equation for Condenser Design. *ASHRAE Trans.* 79(1):157–165.

von Es, J. P. and Heertjes, P. M. 1956. On the Condensation of a Vapor of a Binary Mixture in a Vertical Tube. *Chemical Engineering Science* 5:217–225.

von Es, J. P. and Heertjes, P. M. 1962. The Condensation of a Vapor of a Binary Mixture. *British Chemical Engineering* 8:580–586.

Webb, D. R. and Sardesai, R. G. 1981. Verification of Multicomponent Mass Transfer Models for Condensation Inside a Vertical Tube. *Int. J. Multiphase Flow* 7(3):507–520.

Yu, J. and Koyama, S. 1998. Condensation Heat Transfer of Pure Refrigerants in Microfin Tubes. *Proceedings of the 1998 Int. Refrig. Conf. at Purdue*, pp. 325–330.

Zhang, L., Hihara, E., Saito, T., Oh, J. T., and Ijima, H. 1995. A Theoretical Model for Predicting the Boiling and Condensation Heat Transfer of Ternary Mixture Inside a Horizontal Smooth Tube. *Proceeding of Thermal Engineering Conference*, 95, JSME, pp. 94–96 (in Japanese).

Zivi, S. M. 1964. Estimation of Steady-State Steam Void-Fraction by Means of the Principle of Minimum Entropy Production. *ASME Trans., J. Heat Transfer* 86:247–252.

CHAPTER
# TWENTY FOUR

## AUGMENTATION TECHNIQUES AND CONDENSATION INSIDE ADVANCED GEOMETRIES

**24.1   Moo Hwan Kim**

*Pohang University of Science and Technology, Pohang, Korea 790-784*

**24.2   Vijayaraghavan Srinivasan**

*Praxair, Inc., Tonawanda, NY 14150-7891. USA*

**24.2   Ramesh K. Shah**

*Delphi Harrison Thermal Systems, GM, Lockport, NY 14094-1896. USA*

## 24.1  AUGMENTATION TECHNIQUES IN INTERNAL FLOW GEOMETRIES

This section considers augmentation techniques for internal forced flows. Augmentation techniques used in external condensation are generally applicable to condensation inside tubes, but stratification of the flow by gravity needs to be considered at low vapor velocities in horizontal tubes. During the last several decades, many augmentation techniques inside tubes have been tested and established. Recently, the use of non-azeotropic refrigerant mixtures (NARMs) has resulted in lower heat transfer coefficients compared to when pure refrigerants are used. Special attention has been paid to improving the condensation heat transfer coefficient of NARMs in the refrigeration industry. These techniques include the use of inserts and internal fins. A special type of tube called *micro-fin tube* was developed in the late 1970's and is currently widely used in industry. The tubing cost and pressure drop must be considered when selecting enhanced condensation heat transfer techniques.

### 24.1.1  Fundamentals

Condensation heat transfer augmentation in enhanced geometries occurs due to three reasons. First, mixing becomes more efficient due to recirculation and vortex shedding when inserts and fins are present. Second, the wetted perimeter increases greatly while the cross sectional area of the flow passage decreases. In addition to that, the curvature of the enhanced geometries causes the surface tension force to become comparable to the inertia force (the 'Gregorig effect'). For micro-fins, the surface tension force can be dominant due to the small radius of curvature. Third, spirally grooved micro-fin tubes also make the annular film more uniform along the tube circumference.

The basic concept behind enhanced condensation heat transfer is to reduce the condensate film thickness. When fins are attached to the inner walls of the tube or when inserts are installed, the flow path becomes longer than for a plain tube, resulting in an increase in heat transfer.

The main difference between inserts and internal fins is that inserts can affect the entire flow field, while internal fins can only affect the flow near the wall. Inserts work better when the heat transfer resistance is more or less evenly distributed throughout the flow cross section. On the other hand, internal fins are more effective if the heat transfer resistance is concentrated near the walls. For condensate films, internal fins may be more effective if the film is thin and turbulent, while inserts may be more effective if the condensate film is thick and laminar. However, the pressure drop penalties associated with the enhancement in heat transfer must be considered.

### 24.1.2 Inserts

Royal and Bergles (1976) tested the effects of tube inclination, twisted tape inserts, and internally finned tubes on condensation heat transfer with low-pressure steam. Their results showed that the internally finned tubes were most effective in augmenting heat transfer. Royal and Bergles (1978) also investigated the augmentation of horizontal in-tube condensation by means of twisted tape inserts and internally finned tubes. The twisted tape inserts were found to increase the average heat transfer coefficients by as much as 30% above smooth tube values. Internally finned tubes increased the average heat transfer coefficients by 150% when compared to the smooth tube.

Luu and Bergles (1979) performed an experiment on augmentation of in-tube condensation of R113 with twisted tape inserts and internally finned tubes. They found that twisted tapes increased the heat transfer coefficient and pressure drop by about 30% and 250% over smooth tubes, respectively, while internally finned tubes increased the heat transfer coefficient by 120% over smooth tubes with a modest increase in pressure drop. Azer and Said (1974) investigated the heat transfer coefficient during condensation in a smooth tube, a tube with inner fins, and a tube with static mixer inserts. Their results showed that heat transfer coefficient increased above that for the smooth tube by 130–150% for the inner finned tube and about 120% for the tube with mixer inserts. Lin et al. (1980) tested static in-line mixer (called Kenix mixer) inserts using R-113. The maximum ratio of the heat transfer coefficients with mixers to those without mixers was 185%, but the pressure drop penalty of about 400% was felt to be too high.

Generally speaking, the film thickness is small in tubes during condensation, so inserts may not be appropriate to maximize film condensation heat transfer. Inserts may be more economical than inner finned tubes, however, and may be used to an advantage when thick laminar films are present.

### 24.1.3 Internal Fins

Several types of internal fins have been used to increase the surface area and promote heat transfer in fluid flows. Vrable et al. (1974) studied in-tube condensation of R-12 in horizontal internally finned tubes. The condensation heat transfer coefficient based on the smooth bore area increased by about 200%. They proposed the following correlation for condensation heat transfer coefficients inside internally finned tubes:

$$\frac{\alpha D_h}{\lambda_l} = 0.0075 \mathrm{Re}_{eq}^{0.8} \mathrm{Pr}^{0.33} p_r \qquad (24.1\text{-}1)$$

where

$$\mathrm{Re}_{eq} = (2\dot{m} D_h/\eta_l)[x(\rho_l/\rho_g)^{0.5} + (1-x)] \qquad (24.1\text{-}2)$$

and $p_r$ = reduced pressure, $p/p_{cr}$. They developed this correlation from the smooth tube correlation of Cavallini and Zecchin (1974) by replacing the conventional hydraulic diameter $D_h$ by twice its value. Reisbig (1974) obtained similar results using R-12 containing some oil. As mentioned in Section 24.1.2, Royal and Bergles (1976, 1978) and Luu and Bergles (1979) investigated the condensation heat transfer and pressure drop in internally finned tubes as well as tubes with twisted tape inserts. Their results indicated that the internally finned tubes were better than twisted tape inserts for condensation heat transfer and pressure drop. A review of their results is given by Webb (1994).

Royal and Bergles (1978) developed the following correlation by modifying the smooth tube correlation of Akers et al. (1959) with the correction factor $(b^2/WD_i)$, where $b$ is fin height and $W$ is the channel width between internal fins. They developed a correlation for condensation heat transfer coefficients from their steam condensation data inside horizontal tubes with straight and spiral fins, as follows:

$$\frac{\alpha D_h}{\lambda_l} = 0.0265 \mathrm{Re}_{eq}^{0.8} \mathrm{Pr}^{0.33}[1 + 160(b^2/WD_i)^{1.91}] \qquad (24.1\text{-}3)$$

where

$$\mathrm{Re}_{eq} = \frac{\dot{m}_{eq} D_h}{\eta_l} \quad \text{and} \quad \dot{m}_{eq} = \dot{m}[(1-x) + x(\rho_l/\rho_g)^{0.5}] \quad (24.1\text{-}4)$$

Luu and Bergles (1979) suggested a correlation from their data of R-113 condensed inside internally finned tubes, as follows:

$$\frac{\alpha D_h}{\lambda_l} = 0.024 \mathrm{Re}^{0.8} \mathrm{Pr}^{0.8} \left[ [(\rho/\rho_m)_{in}^{0.5} + (\rho/\rho_m)_{out}^{0.5}]/2 \right] (b^2/WD_i)^{-0.22} \quad (24.1\text{-}5)$$

where

$$\mathrm{Re} = \frac{\dot{m} D_h}{\eta_l} \quad \text{and} \quad \rho/\rho_m = 1 + x(\rho_l/\rho_g - 1) \quad (24.1\text{-}6)$$

This correlation was obtained by modifying the smooth tube correlation of Boyko and Kruzhilin (1967) by the correction factor $(b^2/WD_i)^{-0.22}$.

Said and Azer (1983), Kaushik and Azer (1988, 1989, 1990), and Sur and Azer (1991a) suggested correlations and analytical models for condensation heat transfer and pressure drop in internally finned tubes.

Hitachi has developed a 'micro-fin tube' that is widely used in the air-conditioning industry. This is discussed below.

### 24.1.4 Micro-Fin Tubes

Since the original micro-fin tube (Hitachi Thermofin™ Tube) was first developed by Fujii et al. (1977), many improved versions have been developed. Table 1 shows the specifications of the micro-fin tubes developed in Hitachi Cable, Ltd.

Figure 1 shows the cross sectional shapes of micro-fin tubes developed in Hitachi Cable, Ltd. Figure 2 summarizes the development of the micro-fin tubes in Hitachi Cable, Ltd. As shown in these figures, the micro-fin shows better performance with increasing fin height and helix angle for both evaporation and condensation, with one exception—that Thermofin-HEX-C does not enhance the performance for condensation against Thermofin-EX. Webb (1994) summarized the chronological improvements in the Hitachi Thermofin™ Tube, citing Yasuda et al.(1990).

Hitachi researchers varied the fin height, spiral angle (helix angle), and fin apex angle of the original Thermofin™ Tube (enhancement in heat transfer coefficient of 180% over plain tubes), resulting in an enhancement in heat transfer coefficient of 310% for the HEX-C during condensation for a given mass velocity.

Because there are so many parameters that affect the heat transfer and pressure drop performance (e.g., spiral angle [helix angle], fin height, apex angle, mass velocity, and mass quality), few experiments and analysis have been systematically performed.

## Table 1 Specifications of the micro-fin tubes developed in Hitachi Cable, Ltd. (from Yasuda et al., 1990)

|  | Plain tube | Thermo fin | Thermo fin-EX | Thermofin -HEX | | Thermofin-HEX-C | |
|---|---|---|---|---|---|---|---|
| Outer diameter $D_o$ [mm] | 9.52 | 9.52 | 9.52 | 9.52 | 7.94 | 9.52 | 7.94 |
| Mean wall thickness $t_{avg}$ [mm] | 0.30 | 0.37 | 0.36 | 0.36 | 0.36 | 0.39 | 0.36 |
| Weight per length [gm/mm] | 78 | 95 | 93 | 93 | 77 | 99 | 77 |
| Bottom wall thickness $t_w$ [mm] | — | 0.30 | 0.30 | 0.30 | 0.30 | 0.30 | 0.30 |
| Groove depth $H_f$ [mm] | — | 0.15 | 0.20 | 0.20 | 0.20 | 0.25 | 0.20 |
| Number of grooves [n] | — | 65 | 60 | 60 | 50 | 60 | 50 |
| Helix angle $\beta$ [deg.] | — | 25 | 18 | 18 | 18 | 30 | 30 |
| Apex angle [deg.] | — | 90 | 53 | 40 | 40 | 40 | 40 |
| Increasing ratio of inner surface area | 1 | 1.28 | 1.51 | 1.60 | 1.61 | 1.75 | 1.61 |

One of the most interesting parameters is the fin helix angle. Shinohara and Tobe (1985) showed that the condensation heat transfer coefficient for the Thermofin-EX gradually increases as the helix angle increases from 7 to 30. Khanpara (1986) tested a smooth tube and nine micro-fin tubes, resulting in enhancements in condensation heat transfer coefficients of 150–310% for R-113 and 160–175% for R-22 over the smooth tube at the mass velocities of 150–600 kg/(m²s). Shinohara et al. (1987) showed that the R-22 condensation coefficient in a 9.5 mm O.D. tube increases 20% as the helix angle is increased from 10 to 35. Schlager et al. (1990a) tested three micro-fin tubes having helix angles of 15, 18, and 25, but the tubes were not in same fin heights. Table 2 shows the tested tubes (12.7 mm tubes) of their study.

Figure 3 shows the condensation heat transfer results for smooth and micro-fin tubes. By their results, the highest condensation coefficient was obtained by the tube having the highest fin height and 18° helix angle, i.e., Micro-fin 1.

In a recent study, Yang et al. (1995) developed a new-type of three dimensional inner microfin tubes. For R-11 at inlet pressures of $p_{in} = 147$–265 kPa and condensate mass flux ranging from 33 to 153 kg/m²s, the average heat transfer coefficient was seen to increase by up to 140% over that of two dimensional micro-fin tube. Figures 4 and 5 are the schematics of a 2-D tube and a 3-D tube.

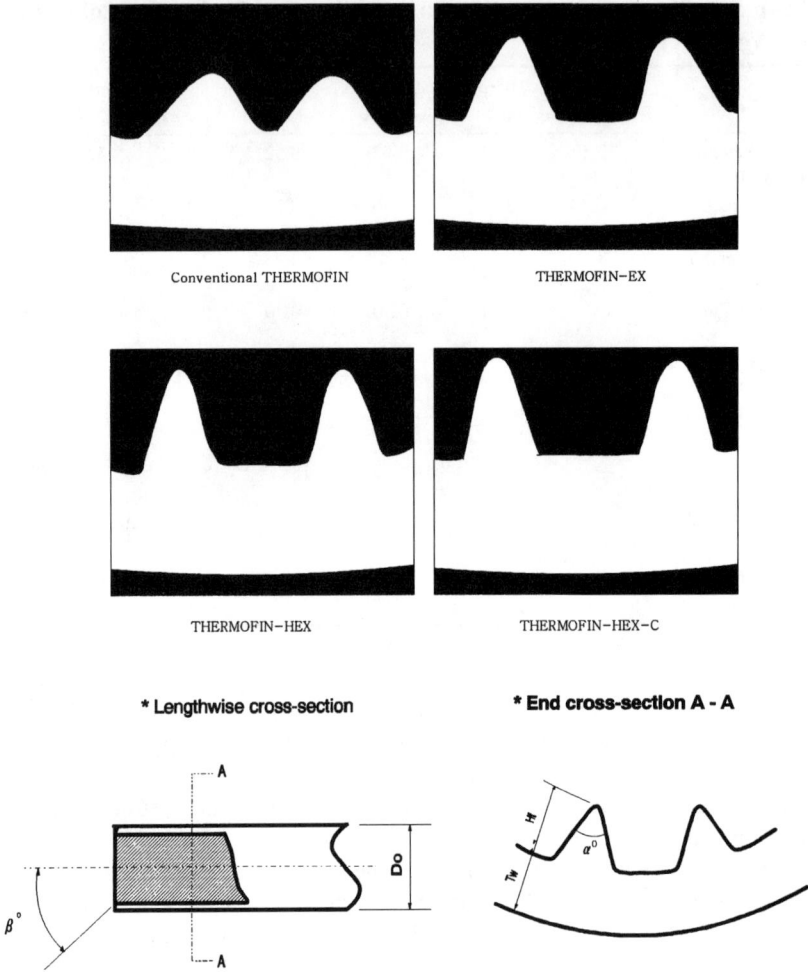

**Figure 1** Cross sectional shapes of micro-fin tubes developed in Hitachi Cable, Ltd. (From Yasuda et al., 1990; reproduced with permission).

Figure 6 shows one of their results. In spite of the somewhat questionable decreasing trends of the average heat transfer coefficients against the mass flux, it is worthwhile to note the enhancement of the 3-D tube from the 2-D tube is quite high.

It is speculated that the three most important factors that affect the enhancement of condensation in micro-fin tubes are the area increase, secondary flow effects (enhancing flow mixing) by fins, and surface tension effects from fin curvatures. When the condensate film is thin or the mass quality is large, the surface tension forces will dominate, and the fin shape becomes very important. When the

**Table 2  Dimension of the tubes tested in Schlager et al. (1990a)**

|  | Smooth | Micro-fin 1 | Micro-fin 2 | Micro-fin 3 |
|---|---|---|---|---|
| $D_o$ (mm) | 12.7 | 12.7 | 12.7 | 12.7 |
| $D_{i,max}$ (mm) | 10.9 | 11.7 | 11.7 | 11.7 |
| wall thickness (mm) | 0.90 | 0.50 | 0.50 | 0.50 |
| fin height (mm) | — | 0.30 | 0.20 | 0.15 |
| number of fins | — | 60 | 70 | 60 |
| helix angle (deg) | — | 18 | 15 | 25 |

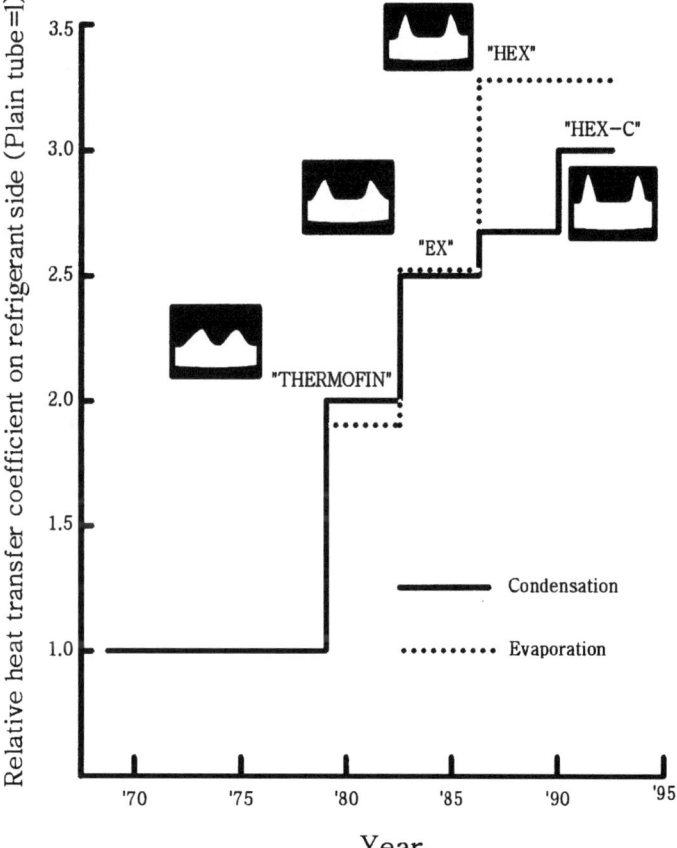

**Figure 2**  Development of the micro-fin tubes in Hitachi Cable, Ltd. (From Yasuda et al., 1990; reproduced with permission).

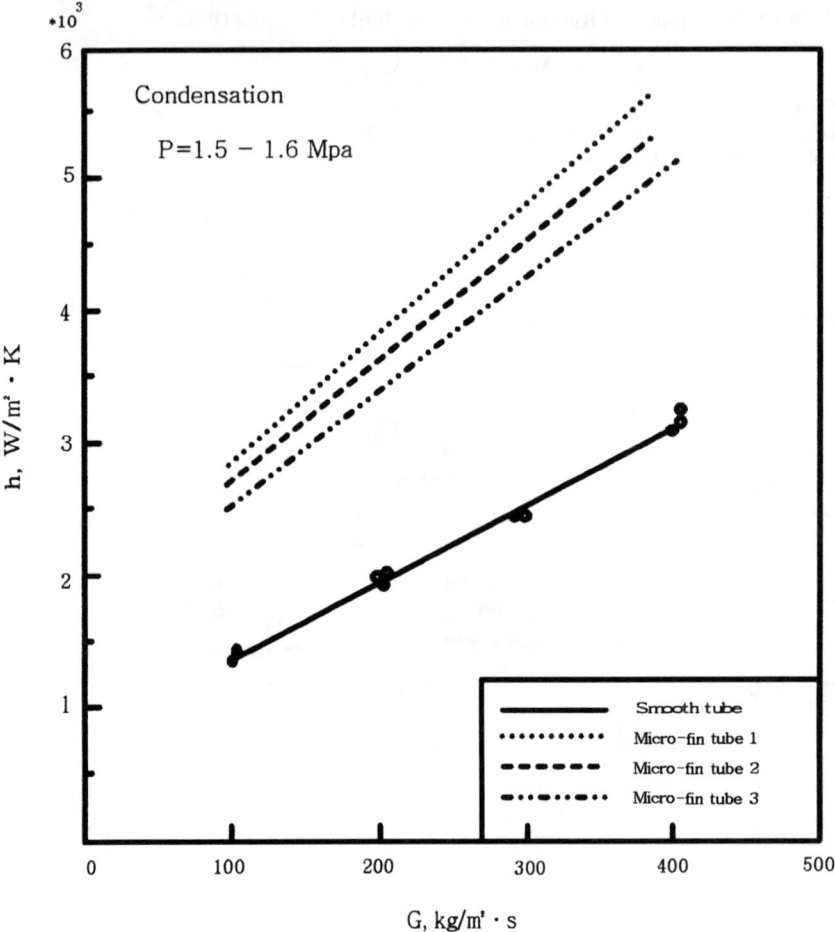

**Figure 3** Condensation heat transfer results for smooth and micro-fin tubes as a function of mass flux. (From Schlager et al., 1990a; reproduced with permission).

condensate film is thick enough to cover the micro-fins, surface tension effects disappear and the secondary flow effects of the film disturbance by the fins dominate. Systematic parametric studies are needed to obtain a fundamental understanding of the mechanisms by which heat transfer is enhanced during condensation in micro-fin tubes.

## 24.1.5 Oil Effects on Convective Condensation

Oil flows through the components of an air conditioning system, including the evaporator and condenser. Pate (1988) reports that the oil fraction ranges from

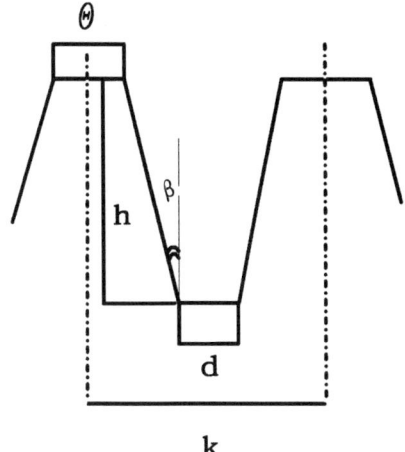

Figure 4  Schematic diagram of a 2-D tube used by Yang et al. (1995).

about 0.5% to 2.0% when an oil separator is present, and up to 5% or higher without an oil separator.

Tichy et al. (1985) investigated the effect of oil on condensation heat transfer and reported that the heat transfer coefficient was reduced relative to oil free systems by 10% for oil concentrations of 2% and by 23% for oil concentrations of 5%. Pressure drop was observed to increase only slightly with oil concentration. They proposed the following empirical correlation based on the Shah's correlation (1979):

$$\frac{\alpha D_i}{\lambda_l} = \left[0.023 \text{Re}_l^{0.8} \text{Pr}_l^{0.4}\right] \left[(1-x)^{0.8} + \frac{3.8 x^{0.76}(1-x)^{0.04}}{\text{Pr}^{0.38}}\right]$$
$$\times [0.88 + (\text{Re}_{l,ref}/\text{Re}_l)^{1.99}] e^{-5.0\omega} \quad (24.1\text{-}7)$$

where $\text{Re}_l$ = Reynolds number based on liquid, $\text{Re}_{l,ref}$ = reference Reynolds number = 3650, and $\omega$ = mass fraction of oil.

The correlation results are shown in Figure 7.

Schlager et al. (1987) surveyed oil effects on condensation heat transfer and found that oil always degrades the heat transfer. Schlager et al. (1988) investigated

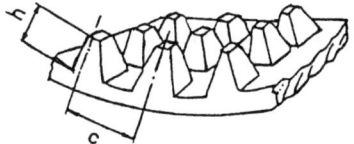

Figure 5  Schematic diagram of a 3-D tube used by Yang et al. (1995).

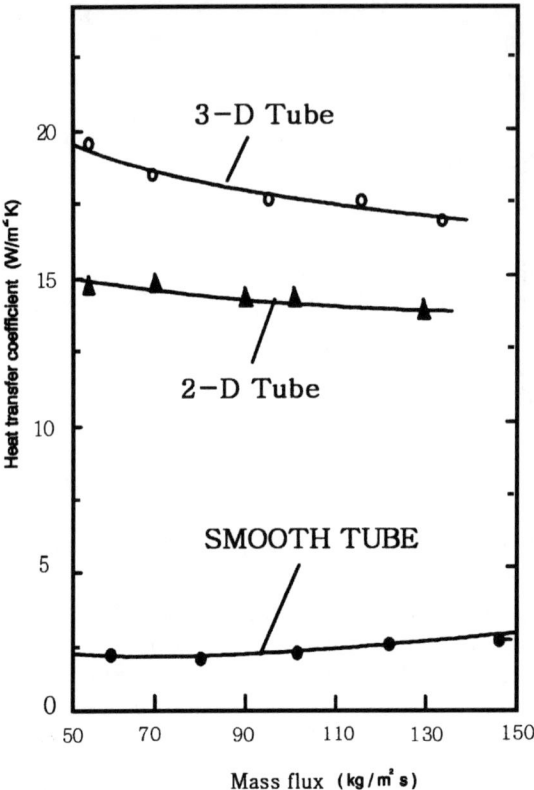

**Figure 6** Comparison of the average heat transfer coefficients of the 3-D tube, 2-D tube, and the smooth tube used by Yang et al. (1995).

the condensation of R-22 and a 150SUS naphthenic oil mixture and found a 13% decrease in heat transfer with a 5% lubricant content. Schlager et al. (1990b) also developed design equations for the oil effects on condensation heat transfer in smooth, microfin, and low fin tubes with the concentration variation of up to 5 wt.% of 150-SUS and 300-SUS oil. The mass flux ranged from 125 to 400 kg/m²s. The condensing temperature was 41°C. The mass quality ranged from 15 to 85%. They presented the following correlation for the enhancement factor for a microfin tube over a smooth tube performance:

$$EF = (\eta_{lr}/\eta_{lm})^{0.47} \quad \text{or} \quad EF = e^{-0.32\omega} \qquad (24.1\text{-}8)$$

where the subscripts $lr$ means liquid phase of pure refrigerant, $lm$ means liquid phase of the refrigerant/oil mixture, and $\omega$ means the mass fraction of oil. $EF$ is defined as the ratio of heat transfer when refrigerant-oil mixture was used to heat transfer when pure refrigerant was used.

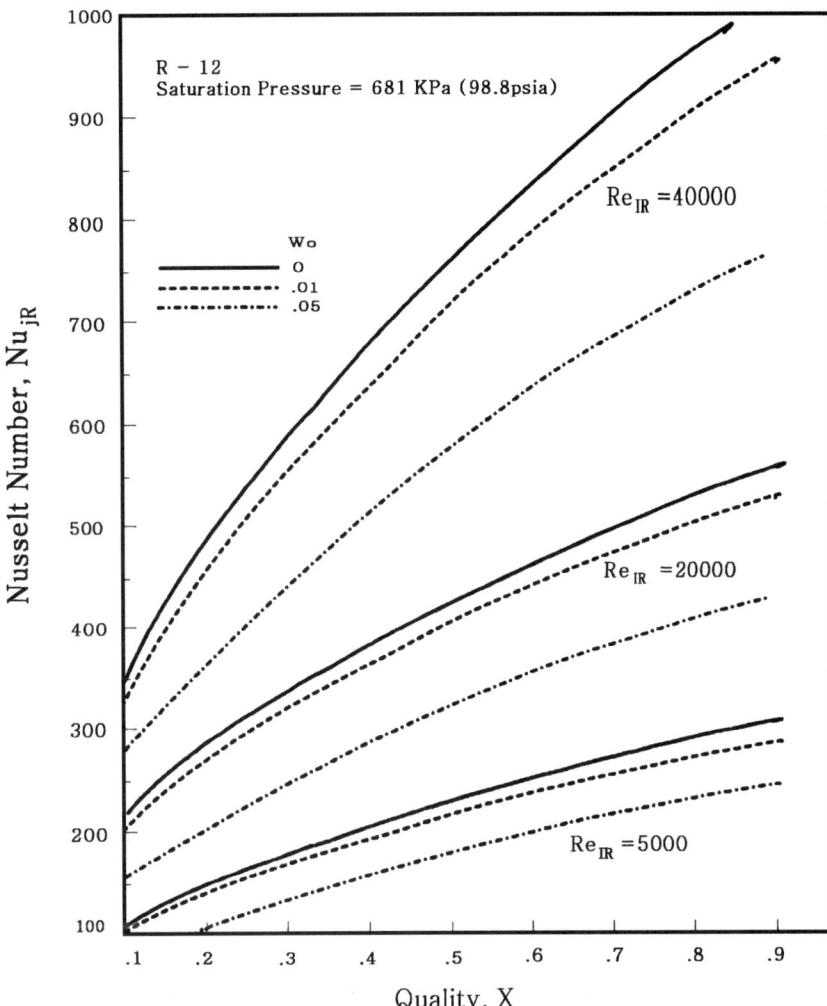

**Figure 7** Correlation results for various Reynolds numbers and oil fractions (From Tichy et al., 1985; reproduced with permission).

Sur and Azer (1991b) showed that the presence of 1.2%, 2.8%, and 4.0% 150-SUS naphthenic oil reduced heat transfer coefficients by 7%, 12%, and 16%, respectively, compared with pure R-113. Eckels and Pate (1991) reported a rough 10% degradation in heat transfer for R-12 and a 5% 150SUS naphthenic oil mixture, but no significant effect of 165SUS PAG oil on heat transfer coefficient of R-134a.

Shao and Granryd (1995) report that the heat transfer coefficient in the case of oil contained refrigerant is strongly dependent on the definition of the saturation

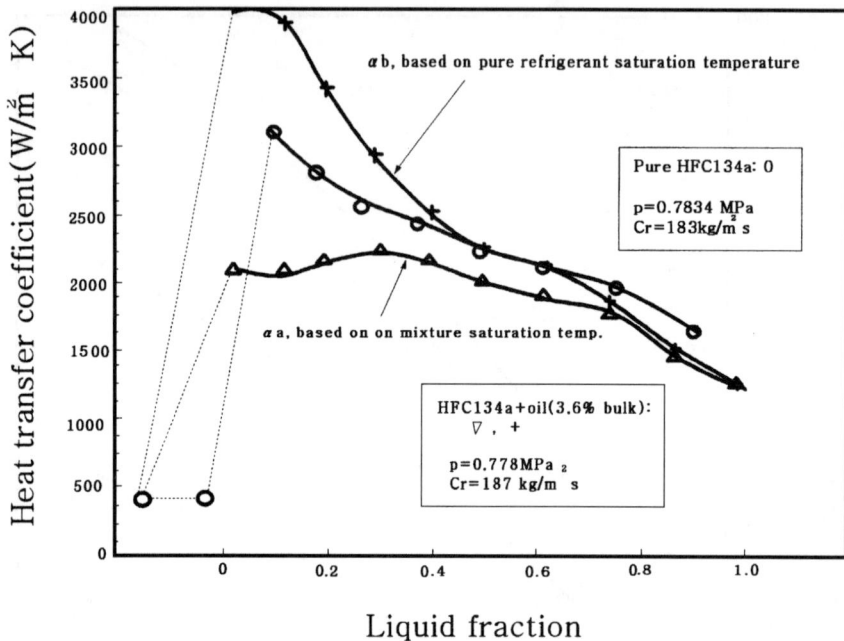

**Figure 8** Typical profiles of local heat transfer coefficient along the condenser for pure R-133a and oil/R-134a mixture. (From Shao and Granryd, 1995.)

temperature. The typical profiles of local heat transfer coefficients along the condenser is shown in Figure 8.

From the result, the condensation heat transfer coefficients based on the mixture saturation temperature of oil-refrigerant mixture are reduced by an average 10–20% depending on oil concentrations, compared with pure refrigerant.

Unlike evaporation heat transfer, where the effects of oil are unclear, it is generally accepted that heat transfer degrades with increasing oil fraction during condensation. The available data for condenser design are still not sufficient, however. Also, the physical mechanisms by which heat transfer degradation occurs are still not understood. In the case of evaporation heat transfer, Thome (1995) explains for the trends of oil effect on heat transfer during flow boiling according to five categories:

(1) thermodynamic effects on heat transfer coefficient
(2) local physical properties of refrigerant/oil mixture
(3) influence of oil on the nucleate boiling process in flow boiling
(4) influence of oil on convective contribution to flow boiling
(5) mass transfer effects on the evaporation process.

It is suggested that for condensation, the following effects of oil should be checked:

(1) influence of oil on convective contribution to condensation: the change in viscosity of refrigerant/oil mixtures by addition of oil results in a decrease in Reynolds number and an increase of Prandtl number.
(2) influence of oil on Gregorig effects: when the surface tension of the oil is much different from that of the refrigerant, the surface tension effects on condensation should be included.
(3) the definition of saturation temperature: pure refrigerant saturation temperature or refrigerant/oil mixture saturation temperature.

## 24.1.6 Convective Condensation of Non-Azeotropic Refrigerant Mixtures

As a non-azeotropic refrigerant mixture condenses, the less volatile (the component with the higher condensing temperature) condenses first, then forms a concentration boundary layer both in the vapor and the liquid region adjacent to the condensing interface. This boundary layer can be regarded as thermal resistance to condensation heat transfer. The condensing temperature of the mixture becomes lower as condensation proceeds, and this change of temperature is referred to as *temperature gliding*. It can be advantageous for the performance of counterflow heat exchangers in refrigeration and heat pump cycle when the gliding temperature is well matched to the heat source or sink temperature difference between the inlet and the outlet.

Chlorofluorocarbons (CFCs) and hydrochlorofluorocarbons (HCFCs) have been rapidly replaced by alternative refrigerants due to concerns regarding ozone depletion and global warming. Some refrigerant mixtures have been suggested as potential candidates for replacing R-22. Relatively little research regarding phase change heat transfer of refrigerant mixtures has been performed, but this is changing.

Bokhanovskiy (1980) performed a condensation experiment on a non-azeotropic mixture of R-22 and R-12 and obtained the average heat transfer coefficient as a function of heat flux. Four regions of heat transfer characteristics were observed, and the mass transfer effects were especially prominent in the low heat flux region.

Tandon et al. (1985, 1986) proposed the following condensation heat transfer correlation for an R-22/R-12 mixture:

$$\frac{\alpha_m L}{\lambda_l} = 2.82 \text{Pr}^{1/3} \left( \frac{h_{lg}}{c_p \Delta T} \right)^{0.365} \text{Re}_g^{0.146} \qquad (24.1\text{-}9)$$

This correlation, however, does not take into account the composition of the binary mixture.

Mochizuki et al. (1988) measured the temperatures of the local wall, cooling water, and vapor along the tube axis, and obtained the local condensation heat transfer coefficients of a R-113/R-11 refrigerant mixture flowing in the inner tube and cooling water in the annulus space in a counterflow direction. The following empirical correlation was suggested:

$$\frac{\alpha_m x}{\lambda_l} = 0.38 \left(\frac{x}{D}\right)^{-0.4} H^{-0.6} R^{-0.8} \text{Pr}^{0.8} \text{Re}_l^{0.8} \qquad (24.1\text{-}10)$$

where H is $c_p \Delta T / h_{lg}$ and R is $(\rho_l/\rho_g)^{1/2}(\eta_l/\eta_g)^{1/2}$.

Koyama et al. (1988, 1991) carried out the experiment for the condensation of the R-22/R-114 mixture in both the compressor and the pump systems. The local heat transfer coefficients were obtained by using a condensing apparatus consisting of 12 test sections. Also, they modeled mass transfer on the vapor side and could accurately predict the mixture condensation heat transfer in smooth and micro-fin tubes.

Torikoshi and Ebisu (1993) confirmed that the heat transfer degrades when using a non-azeotropic mixture of R-32/R-134a (30:70 wt.%), and they also reported that pressure drop of the binary mixture could be calculated using the ideal mixing rule.

Shizuya et al. (1995) investigated the condensation heat transfer of four single components, R-22, R-142b, R-114, and R-123, and their mixtures condensing in 7mm ID smooth and grooved tubes. Figure 9 presents some of their results. They

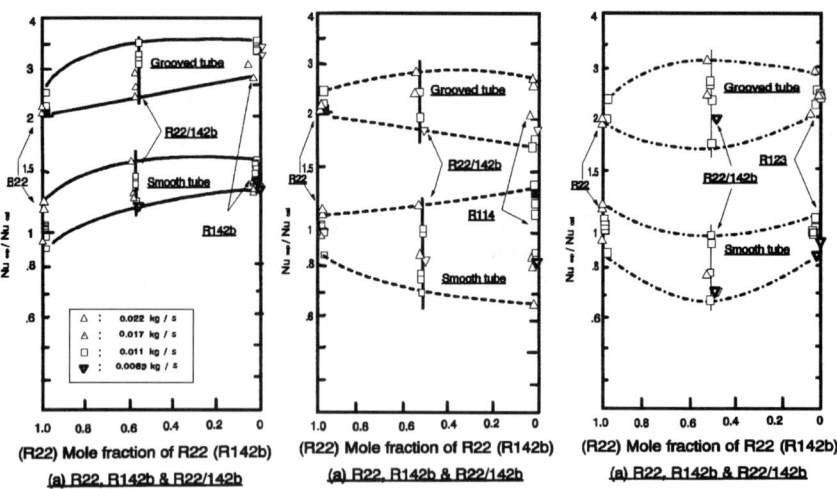

**Figure 9** Comparison of heat transfer performance in annular flow regime (From Shizuya et al., 1995; reproduced with permission).

found that heat transfer is reduced when using refrigerant mixtures in cases where the boiling temperatures of their components differ greatly. Also, heat transfer appears to improve for refrigerant mixtures by grooving the tube inner surfaces, which also compensates to a considerable degree the performance reduction associated with mixtures.

It is difficult to use the limited information in the open literature to design condensers using non-azeotropic mixtures, especially since the mechanisms by which reductions in heat transfer occur are not well understood.

## 24.2 CONDENSATION IN COMPACT HEAT EXCHANGERS

### 24.2.1 Introduction

In a condenser, the process stream (single component or multicomponent with or without noncondensable gases) is condensed to a liquid with or without desuperheating and/or subcooling. Compact condensers are a special class of heat exchangers that have low hydraulic diameters or a heat transfer surface area density greater than 400 $m^2/m^3$ on the condensation or liquid side and/or greater than 700 $m^2/m^3$ on the gas side. The coolant stream in a two-fluid condenser can be a gas, a single-phase liquid, or a vaporizing liquid. In this chapter, only filmwise condensation is considered, since it is difficult to maintain dropwise condensation in industrial applications. Depending on the condenser design, condensation may take place inside or outside a circular tube or inside a noncircular, plain, or enhanced passage. In some cases, matrix type (plate-fin) surface may be employed to enhance condensation. A general classification of condensers is presented in Figure 10. While tubular condensers have been historically used in power,

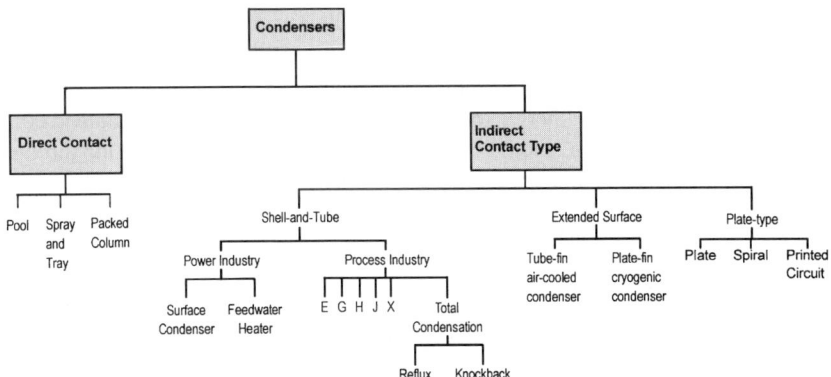

**Figure 10** Classification of condensers.

process, and refrigeration/air-conditioning industries since early 1900s, compact extended surface condensers are more commonly used in automotive and aerospace air-conditioning, and cryogenic processing systems are used for air separation. Other applications of compact condensers are: condensation of refrigerant mixtures, condensation of binary and multicomponent mixtures, condensation in new energy conversion systems, micro-gravity condensation in space applications, heat rejection unit in space vehicles, and vent condenser for power plant condensers.

Some common constructions of compact condensers are: (1) individually finned round tubes with smooth or micro-finned surface inside to enhance condensation heat transfer, (2) continuous flat fins (plain or maybe with waves, louvers, or other enhancements) on round or flat tubes (with or without flow interruptions inside to enhance condensation), (3) plate-fin heat exchangers that use corrugated fins such as perforated, wavy, or serrated fins (offset strip fins) brazed to partition sheets, and (4) plate-and-frame heat exchangers with corrugated flow passages. Other compact condenser constructions are welded plate (stacked plate), spiral plate, printed circuit, and dimple plate (welded, pressure bonded) heat exchangers. The flow passage geometries in most compact condensers are usually noncircular in cross section or have small diameter circular tubes. The flow arrangement can be single-pass, conventional multipass, or serpentine. The flow passage orientation for condensing stream can be horizontal, vertical, or inclined. The major advantages of compact condensers are small volume and packaging, low mass, lower total cost (including installation), modular design approach, and the flexibility of selecting flow passage geometry, ultra-high performance, and close temperature approaches. The single most important problem with compact condensers is potential fouling in small size passages for a fouling fluid. The use of compact condensers is increasing in power, process, and other industries due to the above advantages in niche applications where fouling can be managed. In addition to a heat transfer device, compact plate-fin condensers are being used as heat and mass transfer devices, such as in distillation columns (Panchal, 1993). Generally, multicomponent condensers are mass transfer devices.

In this chapter, the following topics are addressed: compact condenser types and their applications, distinctive features of condensation through enhanced noncircular passages, modeling methods employed for analyzing condensation through noncircular passages, predictive methods for friction and heat transfer, fin efficiency calculations, and design methodology.

## 24.2.2 Compact Condenser Types

The configurations of compact condensers depend primarily on the coolants used and specific applications. Table 3 summarizes the coolant media, principal applications, and typical configurations of condensers used in such applications.

**Table 3  Compact condenser types, applications, and coolants**

| Coolant | Applications | Typical configurations |
|---|---|---|
| Single-phase gas | a. Automotive, Aerospace<br>b. Chemical Process Systems | Tube-fin (circular tubes) and plate-fin (flattened enhanced tubes) heat exchanger. |
| Single-phase liquid | a. Condensation of ammonia vapor in Energy Conversion Systems.<br>b. Chemical/process systems-vapor condensers.<br>c. Industrial refrigeration. | Plate-and-frame heat exchanger<br>Plate-fin heat exchanger<br>Printed circuit heat exchanger |
| Boiling (or vaporizing) liquid | Cryogenic heat exchangers | Plate-fin heat exchanger |

**24.2.2.1 Tube-fin type.** Tube (or plate)-fin type compact condensers that primarily use gas as a coolant can be found in automotive and aerospace applications. Similarly, condensation of overhead vapors from distillation columns use gas streams in the process as a coolant. The use of air as a coolant is also found in condensers employed in refrigeration and air-conditioning applications, where compact heat exchangers are used.

The low values of the heat transfer coefficient $\alpha$ normally associated with gas flows necessitates the use of fins on the gas side. Typical designs are shown in Figures 11a and 11b. A circular tube and flat fin construction is used in most non-automotive applications, i.e., copper tubes and aluminum wavy or louvered fins. The flat or continuous fins are also sometimes referred to as *plate fins*. The tube can be flattened to give a rectangular or oval flow cross section. The tubes can have micro-finned surface inside the tubes to enhance condensation heat transfer (see Figure 12). In most condensers, fans are used for flowing air over the fins and tubes. Centrifugal fans are used when the air flows over the condenser through a duct; propeller fans are used with condensers installed outdoors. In a multipass condenser, the air and refrigerant flow in such a way as to have overall cross-counterflow arrangement for a higher exchanger effectiveness and performance.

**24.2.2.2 Plate-and-frame and printed circuit exchangers.** Plate-and-frame and the printed circuit compact heat exchangers are used on those applications having liquid as a coolant. However, high pressure drops encountered in two-phase flows in the narrow passages in such exchangers restrict their widespread use. Some of the favorable application areas include: (1) steam heating of liquids (with condensing steam) such as in the pasteurization of milk, (2) condensing of refrigerants using water as a coolant, and (3) in chemical process systems. A review of the applications of plate-and-frame exchangers for condensing duty is given by Kumar (1983). A

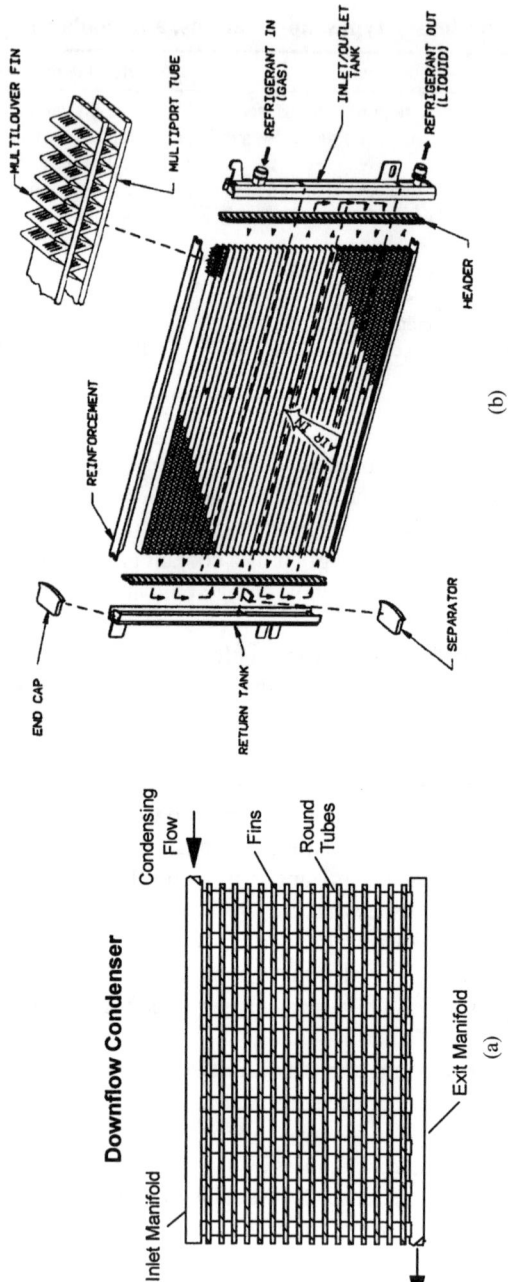

Figure 11 Compact condensers: (a) round tube and flat fin construction, (b) flat tube and corrugated fin construction (courtesy of Delphi Harrison Thermal Systems).

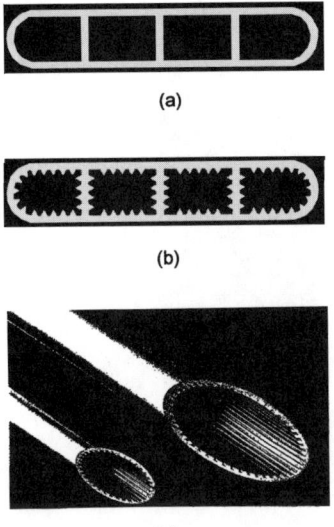

**Figure 12** Enhanced tubes used in compact condensers: (a) plain tube, (b) micro-fin tube, (c) inner-grooved tubes.

typical compact printed circuit condenser is shown in Figure 13. Printed circuit heat exchangers are used in off-shore platforms where compactness becomes an important consideration.

**24.2.2.3 Plate-fin type.** These heat exchangers are used primarily as evaporators/condensers. Boiling liquid oxygen condenses nitrogen vapor in a main condenser/reboiler of a cryogenic air separation plant. Such a heat exchanger operates at very low $\Delta T$ (effective temperature difference). Plate-fin heat exchangers (Figure 14) with a variety of fin-types (see Figure 15) have been designed for these applications. Condensation takes place vertically downward along the plate-fin passages. The *corrugated* fin surface in a plate-fin heat exchanger is also referred to as a *matrix-type* surface.

**24.2.2.4 Flow geometry and orientations.** Compact condensers used in applications described above typically have the following flow geometry and orientation for the condensing side passages of the heat exchanger:

- Condensation inside a round tube with or without microfins, oriented vertically (downward condensation) or horizontally.
- Condensation inside a small hydraulic diameter flattened extruded tube with and without microfins (see Figure 12).

**658** HANDBOOK OF PHASE CHANGE: BOILING AND CONDENSATION

**Figure 13** Printed circuit heat exchanger.

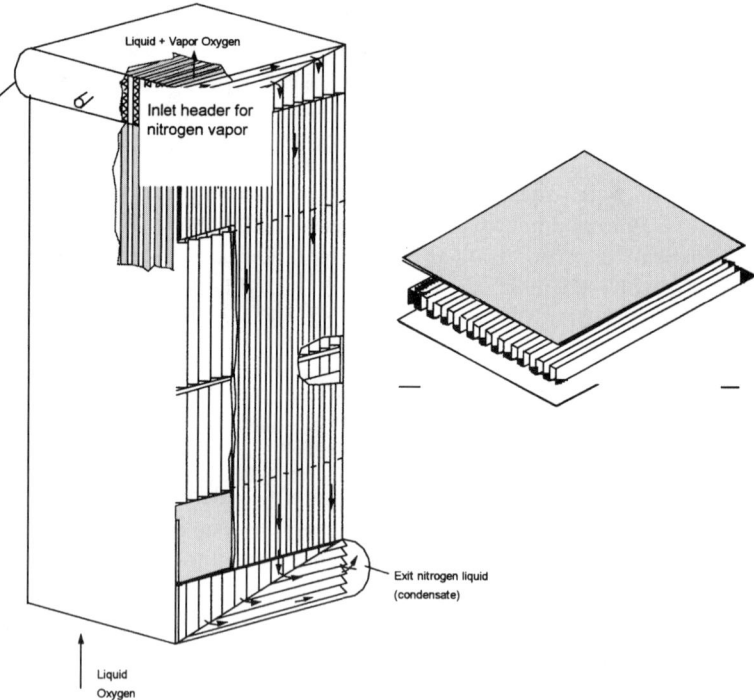

**Figure 14** Plate-fin condenser for a cryogenic application with nitrogen condensing and oxygen boiling.

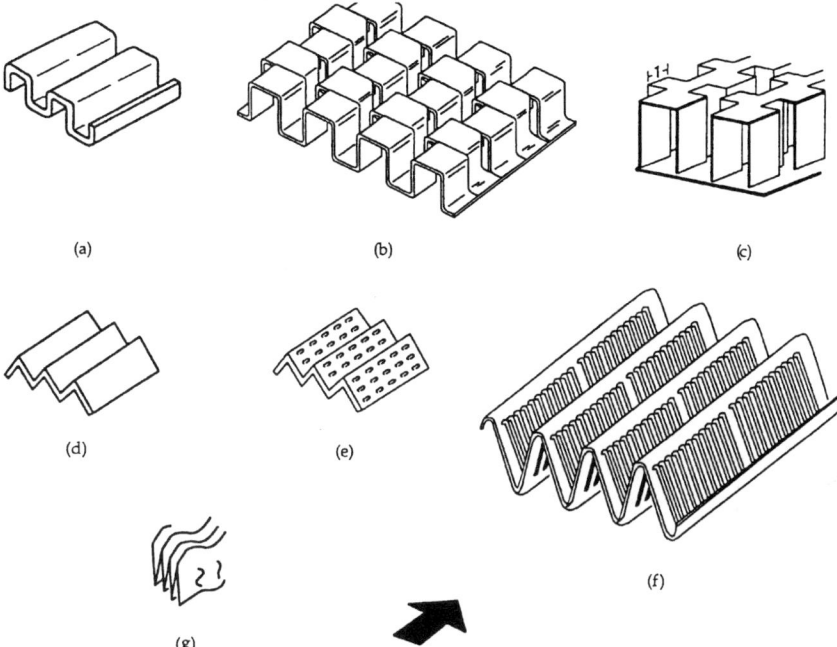

**Figure 15** Examples of plate-fin surface. (a) Rectangular (plain); (b) rectangular (offset); (c) offset strip; (d) triangular (perforated); (f) louvred; (g) wavy (Polley, 1991).

- Condensation inside a flow passage formed in-between corrugated plates, as shown in Figure 16. The flow is predominantly vertical.
- Condensation in a plate-fin passage. The fins can be plain, perforated, wavy, or serrated. The flow orientation is predominantly vertical downward. However, in reflux condensers, the vapor flows upward countercurrent to the condensate draining downward.

### 24.2.3 Important Flow Characteristics of Condensation in Compact Passages

The small channel dimensions, low mass flux values, and noncircular geometries influence the flow characteristics in a compact condenser. Table 4 shows the ranges of the mass flux G, Reynolds number Re for liquid and vapor phases, Weber number We (a ratio of inertia force to surface tension force) for liquid and vapor phases, Bond number Bo (a ratio of gravity force to surface tension force), and hydraulic diameter of some compact condensers. Data for shell-and-tube heat exchangers

## Table 4  Flow parameters in compact condensers

| Condenser Type | Application | Range of G kg/m²s | $Re_l$ | $Re_v$ | $We_l$ | $We_v$ | Bo | $D_h$ mm |
|---|---|---|---|---|---|---|---|---|
| Plate-fin | Cryogenic main condensers (nitrogen) | 15–50 | 0–1000 | 0–12,000 | 0–0.75 | 0–25 | 1.0–10.0 | 1.5–3.0 |
| Flat tube and corrugated fin | Automotive A/C condensers (R-134a refrigerant) | 10–120 | 0–1000 | 0–12,000 | 0–1.0 | 0–50 | 0.6–20.0 | 1.0–3.0 |
| Plate-and-frame | Energy conversion devices/chemical process systems | 2–40 | 0–1200 | 0–30,000 | 0–0.60 | 0–450 | 3.0–12.0 | 2.0–8.0 |
| Printed circuit | Chemical process systems | 2–20 | 0–600 | 0–15,000 | 0–0.30 | 0–200 | 3.0–12.0 | 1.2–1.5 |
| Shell-and-tube | Powerplant (steam-water) | 20–500 | 0–20,000 | 0–50,000 | 0–100 | 0–5000 | 3.0–85.0 | 12.7–25.4 |

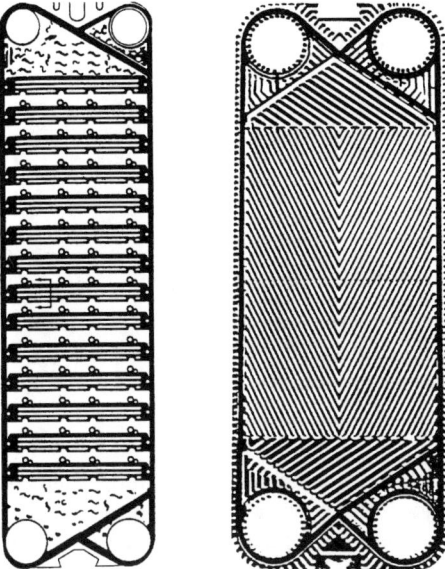

**Figure 16** Corrugated Surfaces (Plate-and-Frame Heat Exchanger).

are also provided for comparison purpose; the larger G values are for small power plant condensers that typically use shell-and-tube condensers.

As seen from Table 3, the hydraulic diameter (or the length scale) of a compact heat exchanger flow passage is roughly an order of magnitude less than that for a circular tube in conventional shell-and-tube heat exchangers. The smaller length scale increases the $L/D_h$ ratio and therefore could increase the resultant pressure drop. In order to meet the specified pressure drop constraint, the mass flux G is reduced in these passages. Thus, it is a common practice to design compact condensers with low mass flux values.

In Table 3, the Weber numbers for the liquid and the vapor phase are shown for compact heat exchangers. The low liquid Weber numbers in the operating regime of the condenser suggest that the surface tension force dominates at low qualities. At high qualities and in the vapor phase, the inertia force tends to dominate over the surface tension force. The Bond number at certain operating regimes of the heat exchanger shows that both the gravity and surface tension force have equal influence.

Flow patterns in small noncircular passages were studied by Wambsganss et al. (1993), Tran et al. (1993), and Robertson et al. (1986). It is important to note that flow patterns are strongly influenced by the small channel dimensions that

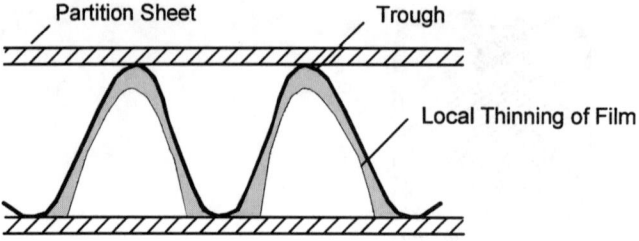

**Figure 17** Condensation in the trough region of the fin.

precludes a straightforward extension of the large diameter circular tube studies. The studies also indicate that the flow conditions at which transition occurs for compact heat exchanger passages are significantly different from those for round tube passages.

Surface tension plays an important role by enhancing the two-phase flow heat transfer characteristics in compact condensers having small hydraulic diameter flow passages. It also produces the Gregorig effect, where the condensate is drawn into corners of the flow passages, thereby bringing down the film thickness (just outside of the trough region, as shown in Figure 17) and increasing the heat transfer coefficient. Hirasawa et al. (1980) have also shown that the surface tension force through the condensate in the trough region induces a strong suction flow near the side surface of a fin, tending to produce a region of very thin liquid film as shown in Figure 17, thus enhancing the condensation heat transfer coefficient. Hirasawa et al. (1980) have shown that the Nusselt number was increased by a factor of 3 due to the surface tension effect for one finned surface that they had investigated! The study was done on a single finned passage.

Additional features, such as nonuniformity in the core flow and liquid shedding in the core flow at fin interruptions, are important for condensation in interrupted passages, such as in offset strip fin (serrated fin) channels. Nonuniformity of the core flow is found to alter the entrainment and deposition, which in turn changes the distribution of the liquid inventory over the perimeter of the passage. Carey (1993) has covered these aspects in more detail for adiabatic two-phase flow.

In addition to the above features, the analysis of two-phase flow inside compact condensers using finned passages becomes more complex due to the primary and secondary surfaces being at different temperatures and having significant variations in heat transfer coefficients.

### 24.2.4 Modeling and Predictive Methods for Heat Transfer

Methods used for predicting heat transfer rates are slightly different for the two common flow orientations (horizontal flow and cocurrent vertical downflow) in compact condenser flow passages due to the dominance of one of the condensation mechanisms (i.e., gravity, shear, and surface tension). Most of the predictive methods for complex flow geometries are based on experimental correlations and are described below.

### 24.2.4.1 Condensation heat transfer in vertical downflow

***Circular plain tubes*** Two principal approaches have been used to predict internal convective condensation. In the first approach, an analytical model for the condensate film is derived that is based on the idealization that the flow pattern is annular (shear dominated flow). In this method, the Nusselt number is correlated for convective transport across the liquid film in terms of the Martinelli parameter X, the Reynolds number $Re_l$ for the liquid flowing alone, and the liquid Prandtl number $Pr_l$.

$$Nu = f(X, Re_l, Pr_l) \qquad (24.2\text{-}1)$$

In this approach, the shear at the liquid-vapor interface is linked to the transport of heat across the liquid film. A number of investigators have followed this approach for predicting the condensation heat transfer coefficient for a circular tube. For example, the correlations proposed by Akers et al. (1959), Soliman et al. (1968), and Traviss et al. (1973) adopt the above approach.

In the absence of interfacial shear, the condensation heat transfer coefficient is predicted by considering falling film flow (gravity dominated flow). The method proposed by Chun and Seban (1971) analyzes the falling film using the Nusselt theory. However, this method allows for the enhancement caused by waviness of the liquid film, and this is correlated as a function of the Reynolds number $Re_l$.

For vertical downflow in a circular tube, Chen et al. (1987) have combined the results of previous works of other investigators, such as Chun and Seban (1971) and Soliman et al. (1968), and proposed a comprehensive correlation for predicting condensation heat transfer coefficient. Their correlation considers the presence as well as the absence of vapor shear (i.e., annular and falling film flow). Chen et al. assumed the following functional form for the Nusselt number:

$$Nu = [(Nu_{ZS})^{n1} + (Nu_S)^{n1}]^{1/n1} \qquad (24.2\text{-}2)$$

with

$$Nu_{ZS} = [(Nu_{lw})^{n2} + (Nu_t)^{n2}]^{1/n2} \qquad (24.2\text{-}3)$$

where

$\text{Nu}_{ZS}$ = zero-shear Nusselt number
$\text{Nu}_S$ = Nusselt number predicted with a vapor shear model
$\text{Nu}_{lw}$ = Nusselt number for wavy-laminar flow
$\text{Nu}_t$ = Nusselt number for turbulent film flow

Using the data of several previous workers, Chen et al. found the values of $n_1 = 2$ and $n_2 = 6$ as the best fit for all the data compiled in their study.

In another approach, simple empirical relations have been developed that more directly correlate condensation heat transfer experimental data. For example, the work done by Boyko and Kruzhilin (1966) on condensation follows this approach. The condensation heat transfer coefficient is given by

$$\alpha_{con} = \alpha_{lo} \left[ 1 - x \left( \frac{\rho_l}{\rho_v} - 1 \right) \right]^{1/2} \quad (24.2\text{-}4)$$

where $\alpha_{lo}$ is the single-phase heat transfer coefficient for the total flow as liquid flow.

***Circular tubes with microfins*** Condensation inside circular tubes is enhanced by a number of techniques that include twisted-tape inserts, longitudinal fins, wire-coil inserts, and microfins. However, in compact condensers, microfin tubes are predominantly used. For example: microfin tubes are used in automotive condensers and residential air-conditioners. Condensing coefficients in microfin tubes are two to three times higher than that of a plain tube at the same mass velocity (Yasuda et al., 1990). In a recent study, Chamra et al. (1996) have compared condensation heat transfer for different micro-groove geometries. Experimental friction and heat transfer data for R-22 are presented. However, it is surprising to note that no theoretical models or correlations have been proposed for the microfin tube in spite of its widespread use.

***Rectangular/flat tubes (with or without microfins)*** Flat tubes of Figure 12a are exclusively used in automotive condensers. The tubes contain webs between the flat surfaces that provide structural rigidity and pressure containment. These tubes are usually made of aluminum and are extruded. It is possible to extrude a smooth or a micro-finned inside surface.

Condensation performance of flat extruded aluminum tubes was studied by Yang and Webb (1995a). The tubes used in their study contained three internal webs that separate the flow into four separate channels. Two internal geometries were tested: one had a plain inner surface and the other had microfins (0.2 mm high). The tubes outside dimensions used in their study were 16 mm (width) ×

3 mm (high) × 0.5 mm (wall thickness). R-12 fluid was used in their tests. The data of Yang and Webb show that the condensation heat transfer coefficient increases with the heat flux to the 0.20 power. Even though this is contrary to the results from the Nusselt theory, where the heat transfer coefficient $\alpha$ is proportional to $q^{-1/3}$, the authors show that this increase in $\alpha$ is caused by the combined effects of vapor shear and momentum. The authors also show that surface tension drainage forces provide an additional enhancement at x > 0.5, which is additive to the effect produced by vapor shear. Even though no correlation is proposed, the following observation will be of help to designers: for the plain surface, at low mass velocities (up to 400 kg/m²s), the Akers (1959) correlation for circular plain tubes, which takes into account the effect of vapor shear, predicts the condensation coefficient well. However, at high mass velocities, the experimental data are 10–20% lower than those predicted by the Akers correlation.

In the Akers method, an equivalent all liquid mass velocity ($G_{eq}$) is introduced that permits data for condensation within a tube to be correlated by the usual single-phase heat transfer correlation. The liquid mass velocity $G_{eq}$ is defined such that it has the same wall shear stress as the actual two-phase flow. By this method, the effective mass flux $G_{eq}$ is obtained as

$$G_{eq} = G \left\{ (1-x) + x \left( \frac{\rho_l}{\rho_v} \right)^{1/2} \right\} \qquad (24.2\text{-}5)$$

where x is the vapor fraction and G is the actual mass flux. The condensation heat transfer coefficient is predicted using the single-phase heat transfer correlation (such as Gneilinski or Dittus-Boelter) using $G_{eq}$ as the mass velocity.

***Plate-and-frame heat exchanger*** One of the most important configurations in a compact condenser is the plate type heat exchanger. This configuration is useful in situations where the coolant is a liquid and the pressure drop on the condensing side is not a severe constraint. However, there are only a few studies in the literature for condensation in plate heat exchangers. Experimental data for condensation in plate heat exchangers were obtained by Tovazhnyanski and Kapustenko (1984) for steam, Uehara and Nakaoka (1988) for ammonia, and Kumar (1983) and Chopard et al. (1992) for refrigerants. The experimental data of these investigators covered a wide range of the Reynolds number and different corrugation angles ranging from 30 to 60°. The authors correlated the data using the same approach that is used for circular tubes. However, in plate heat exchangers, the transition from a gravity-controlled regime to a shear-dominated regime is assumed to occur at $Re_v$ between 350 and 800 (Thonon and Chopard, 1996). The actual value depends on the corrugation angle.

In the gravity-controlled regime, Thonon and Chopard (1996) recommend the use of the Nusselt equation for a plain surface. Therefore, in order to account for the effect of plate corrugations, the Nusselt value is multiplied with an enhancement factor that is obtained from single-phase data (a ratio of heat transfer coefficients in the corrugated surface to a plain surface at the same Re). In the shear-dominated regime, the Akers (1959) method is recommended by Kumar (1983) for calculating the condensation heat transfer coefficient. The effective liquid mass flux, as described previously in Eq. (24.2-5) for microfin flat tubes, is determined first. The single-phase flow relationships (for the corrugation geometry) are then used to calculate the heat transfer coefficient corresponding to the effective liquid mass flux.

***Plate-fin heat exchanger***  Plate-fin heat exchangers for condensing duties are extensively used in the cryogenic air separation plants. Gopin et al. (1976) performed tests on plain fins with very low vapor inlet velocities ($\sim 0.3$ m/s). Their data were in agreement with Nusselt's prediction for vertical plates. At higher vapor velocities, vapor shear does affect the magnitude of the heat transfer coefficient. In a recent study, Clarke (1992), investigated the heat transfer characteristics of downflow condensation in a serrated fin (offset strip fin) under conditions similar to those used in industrial cryogenic process plants. Clarke found that an approach similar to that of Chen et al. (1987) (see Eq. [24.2-2]) described above gave better results for serrated fin channels. He recommends the use of Boyko and Kruzhilin (1967) correlation for calculating $Nu_s$ (with vapor shear effects) and the Chun and Seban (1971) correlation for determining $Nu_{ZS}$ (zero-shear Nusselt number).

**24.2.4.2 Condensation heat transfer in horizontal flow.** The prediction of heat transfer for internal convective condensation in horizontal tubes is different at low and high vapor velocities. Gravity force dominates at low vapor velocities. Therefore, the condensate that forms on the upper portion of the tube drains and collects at the bottom region of the tube. This stratified flow is generally observed at low heat flux and vapor velocities. In view of flow stratification, heat transfer at the bottom of the tube where the liquid drains and collects is much less when compared to the upper portion, where a thin film exists. Correlations in the literature for predicting heat transfer for the stratified flow conditions in a circular tube may be summarized in terms of the following equation:

$$\alpha = 0.725 K_1 \left[ \frac{k_l^3 (\rho_l - \rho_g) g h_{lv} K_2}{\mu_l D_h (t_s - t_w)} \right]^{1/4} \quad (24.2\text{-}6)$$

where $\alpha$ is the local heat transfer coefficient for the condensate film. The parameter $K_1$ is a correction factor that takes into account the collection of liquid in the bottom of the tube where no condensation occurs. Various authors provide the value of $K_1$ as a function of $\theta$ where $\theta$ is the angle subtended by the liquid surface formed by condensate retention. Chato (1962), for example, suggested a value of $\theta = 120°$ and

$K_1$ becomes 0.78. Chato found that his data for R-113 agreed well with the above equation with $K_1 = 0.78$. The parameter $K_2$ takes into account liquid subcooling. $K_2$ is determined using the method described by Chato. A typical value of $K_2$ is 1.15. However, note that by setting $K_1$ and $K_2 = 1$, Eq. (24.2-6) becomes Nusselt's original equation for condensation outside of a horizontal tube.

At higher vapor velocities, the liquid film gets evenly distributed around the tube and the annular flow gets established. When the condensate film is evenly distributed around the tube, many of the heat transfer models for vertical tubes may be used for horizontal tubes, such as the correlation of Akers (1959) or Traviss et al. (1973).

Equations discussed above are summarized in Table 5.

## 24.2.5 Two-Phase Pressure Gradient in Condensing Flow

The need for accurate methods for predicting pressure drop in compact condensers cannot be overemphasized because it affects both the fluid pumping power and condensation heat transfer (since the saturation temperature changes with the saturation pressure). In heat exchangers with high thermal effectivenesses, such as the cryogenic main condenser/reboiler, the pressure drop across the condensing channel of a brazed aluminum plate-fin heat exchanger has an important effect on the economics of the process. Typically, in a main condenser of an air separation plant, a one psi (7 kPa) increase in pressure drop can result in a 0.5 to 1.0% increase in the compressor power, which places a significant cost penalty. For example, typical compressor power required is $10^4$ kW for a 1000 tons/day oxygen plant; hence, a 7 kPa (1 psi) increase in pressure drop can have a significant impact on annual electric cost. The pressure loss in a main condenser can range from 3.5 to 14.0 kPa (0.5 to 2 psi).

Two-phase pressure drop in condensing flow is calculated by integrating the local pressure gradient over the length of the flow channel. The local pressure gradient in turn is computed in terms of the frictional, momentum, and gravitational components. For flow in a horizontal passage, the gravitational component of pressure drop is absent. The frictional component is traditionally evaluated from empirical correlations. Many of these correlations, such as that of Chisholm (1983), are derived from adiabatic two-phase flow or boiling data. Several investigators have also calculated pressure losses based on flow patterns.

**A circular tube.** For two-phase flow through circular tubes, a one-dimensional momentum balance yields the following expression for the local two-phase pressure gradient (see Soliman et al. [1968]):

$$\frac{dp}{dz} = (\rho_v \gamma + (1-\gamma)\rho_l)g + \frac{d}{dz}\left[\dot{m}^2\left\{\frac{(1-x)^2}{\rho_l(1-\lambda)} + \frac{x^2}{\rho_v \gamma}\right\}\right] + \frac{\tau_w}{r_h} \quad (24.2\text{-}7)$$

**Table 5 Heat Transfer Correlation for Condensation in Compact HX Surfaces**

| Type of compact HX surface | Flow orientation | Flow regime | Recommended method | Comments |
|---|---|---|---|---|
| 1. Circular plain tube inside | Vertical downflow | All | $\mathrm{Nu} = \left[(\mathrm{Nu}_{ZS})^{n_1} + (\mathrm{Nu}_S)^{n_1}\right]^{1/n_1}$<br><br>$\mathrm{Nu}_{ZS} = \left[(\mathrm{Nu}_{lw})^{n_2} + (\mathrm{Nu}_t)^{n_2}\right]^{n_2}$<br><br>where $\mathrm{Nu}_{lw}$ and $\mathrm{Nu}_t$ are given by Chun and Seban (1971) and $n_1 = 2$; $n_2 = 6$<br><br>$\mathrm{Nu}_{lw} = 0.822((\mathrm{Re}_l)^{-0.22}\left(\dfrac{gD_h^3\rho_l^2}{\mu_l^2}\right)^{1/3}$ for $\mathrm{Re}_l \leq 300$<br><br>and for all other values of $\mathrm{Re}_l$<br><br>$\mathrm{Nu}_t = 3.8 \times 10^{-3}(\mathrm{Re}_l)^{0.4}(\mathrm{Pr}_l)^{0.65}\left(\dfrac{gD_h^3\rho_l^2}{\mu_l^2}\right)^{1/3}$<br><br>For finding $\mathrm{Nu}_S$, determine the heat transfer coefficient using Eq. (24.2-4). Alternatively, determine $\alpha$ from the Ditus-Boelter equation using the mass velocity given by Eq. (24.2-5). | $\mathrm{Nu}_{ZS}$ is the zero-shear Nusselt number.<br><br>$\mathrm{Nu}_S$ is the Nusselt number due to vapor shear.<br><br>$\mathrm{Nu}_{lw}$ is the Nusselt number of laminar, wavy film.<br><br>$\mathrm{Nu}_t$ is the Nusselt number of turbulent film. |
| 2. Circular plain tube inside | Horizontal | Stratified | Use Eq. (24.2-6). | |
| | | Annular | Determine the heat transfer coefficient using Eq. (24.2-4). Alternatively, determine $\alpha$ from the Dittus-Boelter equation using the mass velocity given by Eq. (24.2-5). | |
| 3. Rectangular flat tubes | Horizontal/vertical downflow | All | Determine $\alpha$ from the Dittus-Boelter equation using the mass velocity given by Eq. (24.2-5). | |

| | | | |
|---|---|---|---|
| 4. Rectangular flat tubes with microfins | Horizontal/vertical downflow | All | Use manufacturer's data. For typical microfin geometries, the enhancement in heat transfer including the surface area enhancement ranges from a factor of 1.6 to 2.2 over a plain surface. In the absence of manufacturer's data, and for obtaining a rough estimate, determine $\alpha$ as for plain rectangular tubes and multiply by a factor of 1.5 |
| 5. Corrugated plates | Vertical | Gravity controlled $Re_v < 800$ | Use Nusselt's equation for condensation on a flat vertical plate and multiply by an enhancement factor that is obtained from manufacturer's single-phase data (a ratio of heat transfer coefficient in the corrugated surface to a plain surface at the same $Re_v$) |
| 6. Corrugated plates | Vertical/horizontal | Shear-dominated regime $Re_v > 800$ | Use Eq. (24.2-5) to determine $G_{eq}$ (effective liquid mass flux). Use single-phase relationships (for the corrugation geometry) to calculate the heat transfer coefficient corresponding to the equivalent liquid flux. |
| 7. Plate-fin geometry | Vertical downflow | All | $Nu = \left[Nu_{BK}^{n_1} + Nu_{ZS}^{n_1}\right]$<br>$n_1 = 6$<br>$Nu_{BK}$ = Nusselt number from Boyko-Kruzhilin. Eq. (24.2-4)<br>$Nu_{ZS}$ = Nusselt number for Chun-Seban (See #1 above) |

The three terms on the right-hand side of the above equation are the gravitational, momentum[1], and frictional components of the *local* pressure gradient, respectively. The total pressure drop is obtained by integrating the local pressure gradient over the entire length of the tube. Computation of the gravitational and momentum components of Eq. (24.2-7) requires knowledge of the void fraction $\gamma$. The correlations for $\gamma$ available in the literature are specific to the flow geometry in question. For round tubes, the void fraction $\gamma$ has generally been correlated with either the Martinelli parameter X (defined as $\{(dp/dz)_l/(dp/dz)_v\}^{1/2}$, where the subscripts l and v represent the liquid and vapor phases) or the two-phase frictional multiplier $\phi_l$. For example, Wallis (1970) calculated the void fraction $\gamma$ from $\phi_l$ for round tubes using a separated cylinder model for all flow orientations (horizontal, vertical up or down) as follows:

$$\gamma = 1 - \frac{1}{\phi_l} \qquad (24.2\text{-}8)$$

where $\phi_l$ is the friction multiplier defined as

$$\phi_l = \left[\frac{(dp/dz)_{fr}}{(dp/dz)_l}\right]^{1/2} \qquad (24.2\text{-}9)$$

where the subscript fr corresponds to the frictional component of the two-phase pressure drop and the subscript l denotes the frictional pressure gradient that would result if the liquid flowed alone through the channel at a mass flux equal to $G(1-x)$. The friction multiplier $\phi_v$ is defined similarly by replacing the subscripts l to v in Eq. (24.2-9). The frictional component of the two-phase pressure drop, represented by the last term of Eq. (24.2-7), is predicted by using appropriate correlations for one of the frictional multipliers, $\phi_l$ or $\phi_v$.

In most compact heat exchanger applications, $\phi_l$ is determined by the following Chisholm (1983) correlation based on an elementary separated flow model.

$$\phi_l^2 = 1 + \frac{C}{X} + \frac{1}{X^2} \qquad (24.2\text{-}10)$$

The factor C is a constant dependent on the state of flow of the phases (liquid and vapor) alone in the flow passage (t = turbulent, v = laminar), and X is the Martinelli parameter. This form of correlation has been found particularly useful because the value of C can be adjusted to give a best fit to a given set of data. The values of C given by Chisholm for a circular tube are given in Table 6.

---

[1] Conservatively, the momentum effect (pressure recovery due to deceleration) is neglected in condensation. This is because one does not get the ideal pressure recovery, perhaps due to the thickening of condensate film as a result of an adverse pressure gradient.

**Table 6 Values of C in Eq. (24.2-10), Chisholm (1983)**

| Liquid | Vapor | Abbreviation | C |
|---|---|---|---|
| turbulent | turbulent | tt | 20.00 |
| viscous | turbulent | vt | 12.00 |
| turbulent | viscous | tv | 10.00 |
| viscous | viscous | vv | 5.00 |

**Rectangular flattened tubes with or without microfins.** Wambsganss et al. (1991) in a recent study for horizontal two-phase adiabatic flow in a rectangular passage (19.05 × 3.18 mm) developed a modified version of the Chisholm correlation in which the C factor was made a function of the Martinelli parameter X and the Reynolds number $Re_{lo} (= GD_h/\mu_l)$ for the mixture flowing as a liquid.

$$C = f(X, Re_{lo}) = aX^b \qquad (24.2\text{-}11)$$

where

$$a = f(Re_{lo}) = -2.44 + 0.00939 Re_{lo} \qquad (24.2\text{-}12)$$

$$b = f(Re_{lo}) = -0.938 + 0.00432 Re_{lo} \qquad (24.2\text{-}13)$$

Equations (24.2-12) and (24.2-13) are valid for $Re_{lo} < 2000$ and $X < 1.0$. The authors point out that the application of the above correlation to smaller channels results in an improvement over the Chisholm correlation.

Recently, Yang and Webb (1995b) measured pressure drop for R-12 flowing in both rectangular plain and microfin tubes that are used in automotive condensers. The flow condition was adiabatic. They found that the Chisholm correlation did not predict the experimental data well. The authors tried only constant values of C and found that no single value of C correlated the data well. However, the equivalent mass velocity concept proposed by Akers et al. (1959) provided a very good correlation of their data. Both the plain and microfin tube data were correlated within ±20% by a single curve. Their correlation is given by

$$\frac{f}{f_l} = 0.435 Re_{eq}^{0.12} \qquad (24.2\text{-}14)$$

where $f_l$ is the single-phase friction factor for the liquid phase flowing alone (generally determined experimentally) and $Re_{eq}$ is based on $G_{eq}$, calculated from Eq. (24.2-5).

**Plate-and-frame heat exchanger.** Kumar (1983) has suggested section-wise calculation of the pressure drop by splitting the plate into several zones. The mean vapor fraction or quality in each zone is determined from heat transfer calculations.

The single-phase friction factor for the liquid flowing alone is determined using appropriate correlations for the plate geometry. The two-phase friction multiplier as a function of the Martinelli parameter X is then determined by Chisholm's correlation [Eq. (24.2-10)]. It is also relevant to note that Arman and Rabas (1995) used the void fraction correlation developed by Premoli et al. (1971) for predicting pressure drop in downflow condensation inside a chevron passage.

**Plate-fin heat exchanger.** Much of the work done on predicting the pressure drop for vertical downflow condensation in serrated and plain plate-fin passages remains industrial proprietary information. The correlation approach for predicting pressure losses is discussed by Robertson et al. (1986). It is found that the frictional component of the pressure drop in compact condenser passages is predicted using the same basic approach as that for the smooth round tubes (for example, the Chisholm type correlation). However, the round tube correlation cannot be directly applied to the rectangular passages. As shown in Eq. (24.2-11), $\phi_l$ is found to depend both on X and $Re_{lo}$ (and therefore mass flux G). Hence, there is a need to take into account the mass flux dependency in the correlation for $\phi_l$, particularly for rectangular passages as shown in Eqs. (24.2-12) and (24.2-13).

## 24.2.6 Fin Efficiency Calculations in Compact Condensers

Design calculations for compact condensers that use extended surfaces (for example, tube-fin or plate-fin heat exchangers) must take into account the fin efficiency. This is usually done by using the fin efficiency procedure developed for the single-phase flow, where generally constant heat transfer coefficient $\alpha$ is employed. Srinivasan and Shah (1997) have shown that the use of single-phase fin efficiency formulas for condensing applications, while very convenient, could result in a significant error for certain flow and geometry conditions. The appropriateness of using the fin efficiency formulas for constant $\alpha$ has been shown to depend on a parameter $F_1/F_2^4$. The parameters $F_1$ and $F_2$ depend on flow conditions and the fin geometry, and are defined in the Nomenclature. Small values of $F_1/F_2^4$ yield high fin efficiency values, and therefore constant $\alpha$ fin efficiency formulas are accurate. However, for condensing applications where $F_1/F_2^4 > 1000$, errors can be as large as 15%; thus, a numerical solution becomes necessary provided that the local $\alpha$ distribution is known. Condensation on fins depends on the fin orientation with respect to the prime surface. Available fin efficiency formulas are provided in Table 7 for different finned tube configurations.

For plain, serrated and other corrugated plate-fin geometries, use the single-phase fin efficiency formula with $\alpha_{avg} = \alpha_{experiment}$ after ensuring that the

## AUGMENTATION TECHNIQUES AND CONDENSATION INSIDE ADVANCED GEOMETRIES

**Table 7  Fin Efficiency Formulas for Different Fin Orientations**

| Fin type and orientation | Applicable fin efficiency equation | Range of validity/Comments |
|---|---|---|
| 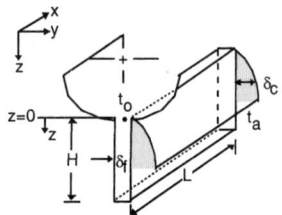<br>Rectangular longitudinal fin attached to a pipe from above. | $\eta_f = \tanh(mH)/mH$<br>where for a rectangular fin:<br>$m^2 = 2\alpha_{ave}/k_f\delta_f$<br>$\alpha_{ave} = 2^{3/2}k_l F_1^{3/4}/3H$ | $F_1/F_2^4 \leq 100$<br>For values greater than 100, solve for fin efficiency using numerical techniques. |
| 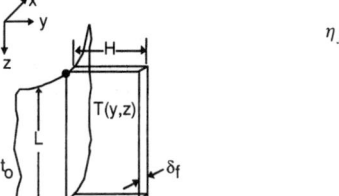<br>Rectangular longitudinal fin attached to a pipe from beneath. | Use equations above. | $F_1/F_2^4 \leq 0.01$<br>For values between 0.01 and 1.0 numerical solutions are available (see Srinivasan and Shah, 1997).<br>For values greater than 1.0 solve for the fin efficiency numerically. |
| 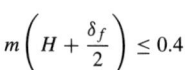<br>Rectangular fins laterally attached to a vertical surface. | $\eta_f = 1.1008 \left[\dfrac{F_2^4}{F_1}\dfrac{L}{H}\right]^{1/8}$ | $\left(\dfrac{F_1}{F_2^4}\right)\left(\dfrac{H}{L}\right) \geq 100$<br>For other values, use numerical solutions. |
| 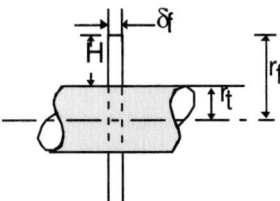<br>Rectangular radial fin attached to a horizontal pipe. | $\eta_f = \dfrac{\tanh[m(H+\delta_f/2)]}{m(H+\delta_f/2)}$ | $m\left(H+\dfrac{\delta_f}{2}\right) \leq 0.4$<br>For other values, use a more rigorous approach (refer to Srinivasan and Shah, 1997). |

single-phase value of $\eta_f$ is greater than 80%; in order to optimize the use of fin material, it is a general practice to have $\eta_f > 80\%$.

### 24.2.7 Condenser Design Methodology

There are two basic thermal design problems: rating and sizing. In the rating problem, the geometry and the size of the heat exchanger are given as input. Entering fluid conditions are known. In this case, the heat transfer rate and pressure drops on each fluid side of the heat exchanger are predicted. In a sizing problem, the heat transfer rate and pressure drops are specified, and the size and geometry of the exchanger are to be determined; normally, pressure drop limits are specified for each fluid stream. Due to the design complexity and too many unknown parameters, the current industrial practice for a sizing problem is to assume some specific size for selected heat transfer surfaces and do the rating calculations as outlined in the following paragraph. If the computed performance does not match the specifications, the size of the condenser is modified and the rating calculations are performed again iteratively on the size until the specified and computed heat duty and pressure drops match within acceptable limits.

Condenser design methodology depends upon whether or not the coolant side thermal resistance $(1/\eta_f \alpha A)_c$ is controlling (i.e., has percentage-wise a high value). If it is controlling, a large variation in heat transfer coefficients during the condensation has a negligible effect on the overall UA; in that case, the single-phase $\varepsilon$-NTU or MTD method can be used for the determination of heat transfer rate of the condenser by considering a constant value of $\alpha$ on the condensation side. However, when the coolant side thermal resistance is *not* controlling, the $\varepsilon$- NTU or MTD method cannot be used for reasonably accurate calculations. This is because there can be a large variation in heat transfer coefficients from inlet to outlet of a condenser (desuperheating to subcooling conditions). In this case, each pass (or each "tube," depending upon the flow arrangement) of the condenser is divided into a number of segments, and mass, momentum, and energy balance and rate equations are applied to each segment to compute outlet temperatures, qualities, and pressures for known or assumed inlet conditions. For such calculations, based on local conditions for each phase, the flow regime is predicted; accordingly, a flow regime based appropriate correlation is used to determine the heat transfer coefficient and friction factor for each segment. Local fin efficiency is also computed once the heat transfer coefficient is known. Such stepwise calculations are performed either by a marching or iterative procedure, depending upon the exchanger flow arrangement and the number of passes, to determine the outlet conditions. Variations in local $\alpha$, $\Delta T$, fluid properties, velocity effects, or different flow regimes, on one or both fluid sides of the condenser, can be taken into account in such calculations.

## 24.2.8 Concluding Remarks

This chapter dealt with condensation in compact heat exchanger surfaces. Condensers using compact surfaces belong to one of the following major category —noncircular ducts, microfin surface, corrugated surface, or plate-fin geometry. Based on a comprehensive review of the available literature, methods for calculating the heat transfer coefficient and pressure drop are enumerated. Fin efficiency formulas for some fin geometries and their orientations have also been outlined. Overall methodology of design and analysis of compact condensers is summarized. Thus, while the available information for designing compact condensers is presented in this chapter, the lack of information in many areas provide challenges to the researchers to advance the frontiers of compact condenser theory and analysis.

## REFERENCES

Akers, W. W., Deans, H. A., and Crosser, O. K. 1959. Condensation Heat Transfer Within Horizontal Tubes. *Chem. Eng. Prog. Symp. Ser. 55*, 29:171–176.

Arman, B. and Rabas, T. J. 1995. *Condensation Analysis for Plate-Frame Heat Exchangers*. HTD Vol. 314, Eds. V. Sernas, R. D. Boyd, and M. K. Jensen. New York: ASME, pp. 97–104.

Azer, N. Z. and Said, S. A. 1974. Augmentation of Condensation Heat Transfer by Internally Finned Tubes and Twisted Tape Inserts. *Advances in Enhanced Heat Transfer, ASME, Proc. 18th Nat. Heat Transfer Conf.*, San Diego, pp. 33–38.

Bokhanovskiy, Y. G. 1980. Heat Transfer from Freon-12, Freon-22, and Their Mixtures in a Coiled-Tube Condenser. *Heat Transfer—Soviet Research* 12(4):43–45.

Boyko, L. D. and Kruzhilin, G. N. 1967. Heat Transfer and Hydraulic Resistance During Condensation of Steam in a Horizontal Tube and in a Bundle of Tubes. *Int. J. Heat Mass Transfer* 10:361–373.

Carey, V. P. 1993. Two-Phase Flow in Small-Scale Ribbed and Finned Passages for Compact Evaporators and Condensers. *Nucl. Engg. Design* 141:249–268.

Cavallini, A. and Zecchin, R. 1974. A Dimensionless Correlation for Heat Transfer in Forced Convection Condensation. *Proc. 5th Int. Heat Transfer Conf.* 3:309–313.

Chamra, L. M., Webb, R. L., and Randlett, M. R. 1996. Advanced Microfin Tubes for Condensation. *Int. J. Heat Mass Transfer* 39:1839–1846.

Chato, J. C. 1962. Laminar Condensation Inside Horizontal and Inclined Tubes. *ASHRAE* 4(2):52.

Chen, S. L., Gerner, F. M., and Tien, C. L. 1987. General Film Condensation Correlations. *Exp. Heat Transfer* 1:93–107.

Chisholm, D. 1983. *Two-Phase Flow in Pipelines and Heat Exchanger*. London: George Godwin.

Chopard, F., Marvillet, C., and Pantaloni, J. 1992. Assessment of Heat Transfer Performance of Rectangular Channel Geometries: Implication on Refrigerant Evaporator and Condenser Design. *Proc. First European Conf. Th. Sciences.*, IChemE 129(1):79–87.

Chun, K. R. and Seban, R. A. 1971. Heat Transfer to Evaporating Liquid Films. *ASME J. Heat Transfer* 93:391–396.

Clarke, R. H. 1992. The Condensation Heat Transfer Characteristics of Liquid Nitrogen in Serrated, Plate-Fin Passages. Paper presented (not published) at the Third U.K. National Heat Transfer Conference, Birmingham, U.K.

Eckels, S. J. and Pate, M. B. 1991. In-Tube Evaporation and Condensation of Refrigerant-Lubricant Mixtures of HFC134a and CFC12. *ASHRAE Trans.* 97(2):62–70.

Fujii, K., Itoh, N., Innami, T., Kimura, H., Nakayama, N., and Yanugidi, T. 1977. Heat Transfer Pipe. *U.S. Patent* 4,044,797, assigned to Hitachi, Ltd.

Gopin, S. R., Usynkin, I. P., and Aver'yanov, I. G. 1976. Heat Transfer in Condensation of Freons on Finned Surfaces. *Heat Transfer—Sov. Res.* 8(6):114–120.

Hirasawa, S., Hijikata, K., Mori, Y., and Nakayama, W. 1980. Effect of Surface Tension on Condensate Motion in Laminar Film Condensation (Study of Liquid Film in a Small Trough). *Int. J. Heat Mass Transfer* 23:471–478.

Kaushik, N. and Azer, N. Z. 1988. A General Heat Transfer Correlation for Condensation Inside Internally Finned Tubes. *ASHRAE Trans.* 94(2):261–279.

Kaushik, N. and Azer, N. Z. 1989. An Analytical Heat Transfer Prediction Model for Condensation Inside Longitudinally Internally Finned Tubes. *ASHRAE Trans.* 95(2):516–523.

Kaushik, N. and Azer, N. Z. 1990. A General Pressure Drop Correlation for Condensation Inside Internally Finned Tubes. *ASHRAE Trans.* 96(1):242–255.

Khanpara, J. C. 1986. Augmentation of In-Tube Evaporation and Condensation with Micro-Fin Tubes Using Refrigerants R-113 and R-22. Ph.D. Thesis, Iowa State University.

Koyama, S., Gao, L., Kumamura, N., and Fujii, T. 1991. An Experimental Study of Condensation of Non-Azeotropic Refrigerant Mixtures HCFC22+CFC114 Inside a Horizontal Smooth Tube. *JSME Trans.* 57(538):2032–2038.

Koyama, S., Miyara, A., Fujii, T., Takamatsu, H., and Yonemoto, K. 1988. Condensation of Refrigerant Mixtures R22+R114 Inside a Horizontal Tube. *JSME Trans.* 54(502):1447–1452.

Kumar, H. 1983. Condensation Duties in Plate Heat Exchangers. Condensers in Theory and Practice. *IChemE Symp. Ser.* 75:478–486.

Lin, S. T., Azer, N. S., and Fan, L. T. 1980. Heat Transfer and Pressure Drop During Condensation Inside Horizontal Tubes with Static Mixer Inserts. *ASHRAE Trans.* 82(2):649–651.

Luu, M. and Bergles, A. E. 1979. Experimental Study of the Augmentation of In-Tube Condensation of R113. *ASHRAE Trans.* 85(2):132–145.

Mochizuki, S., Inoue, T., and Tominage, M. 1988. Condensation of Non-Azeotropic Binary Mixtures in a Horizontal Tube. *JSME Trans.* 54(503):1796–1801.

Panchal, C. B. 1993. Compact Heat Exchangers for Condensation Applications: Yesterday, Today, and Tomorrow. In: *Condensation and Condenser Design*. Eds. J. Taborek, J. Rose, and I. Tanasawa, pp. 303–316. New York: Engineering Science Foundation and ASME publication.

Pate, M. B. 1988. Design Considerations for Air-Conditioning Evaporator and Condenser Coils. In: *Two-Phase Flow Heat Exchangers*. Klauber Academic Publishers, pp. 849–884.

Premoli, A., Francesco, D., and Prina, A. 1971. A Dimensionless Correlation for Determining the Density of Two-Phase Mixtures. *La Thermotecnia* 25(17).

Reisbig, R. L. 1974. Condensation Heat Transfer Augmentation Inside Splined Tubes. *AIAA/ASME Thermophysics Conference*, Boston, Paper 74-HT-7.

Robertson, J. M., Blundell, N., and Clarke, R. H. 1986. The Condensing Characteristics of Nitrogen in Plain, Brazed Aluminum, Plate-Fin Heat Exchanger Passages. *Heat Transfer 1986, Proc. 8th Int. Heat Transfer Conf.* 4:1719–1724. Washington, DC: Hemisphere.

Royal, J. H. and Bergles, A. E. 1976. Experimental Study of the Augmentation of Horizontal In-Tube Condensation. *ASHRAE Trans.* 82:919–931.

Royal, J. H. and Bergles, A. E. 1978. Augmentation of Horizontal In-Tube Condensation by Means of Twisted Tape Inserts and Internally Finned Tubes. *J. Heat Transfer* 100:17–23.

Said, S. A. and Azer, N. Z. 1983. Heat Transfer and Pressure Drop During Condensation Inside Horizontal Finned Tubes. *ASHRAE Trans.* 89(1):114–134.

Schlager, L. M., Pate, M. B., and Bergles, A. E. 1987. A Survey of Refrigerant Heat Transfer and Pressure Drop Emphasizing Oil Effects and In-Tube Augmentation. *ASHRAE Trans.* 93(1).

Schlager, L. M., Pate, M. B., and Bergles, A. E. 1988. Evaporation and Condensation of Refrigerant-Oil Mixtures in a Smooth Tube and Micro-Fin Tube. *ASHRAE Trans.* 94(1):149–166.

Schlager, L. M., Pate, M. B., and Bergles, A. E. 1990a. Evaporation and Condensation Heat Transfer and Pressure Drop in Horizontal, 12.7 mm Micro-Fin Tubes with Refrigerant 22. *J. Heat Transfer* 112:1041–1047.

Schlager, L. M., Pate, M. B., and Bergles, A. E. 1990b. Performance Predictions of Refrigerant-Oil Mixtures in Smooth and Internally Finned Tubes—Part II: Design Equations. *ASHRAE Trans.* 96(1):170–182.

Shah, M. M. 1979. A General Correlation for Heat Transfer During Film Condensation Inside Pipes. *Int. J. of Heat and Mass Transfer* 22:547–556.

Shao, D. W. and Granryd, E. 1995. Heat Transfer and Pressure Drop of HFC134a-Oil Mixtures in a Horizontal Condensing Tube. *Int. J. Refrig.* 18(8):524–533.

Shinohara, Y. and Tobe, M. 1985. Development of an Improved Thermofin Tube. *Hitachi Cable Review* 4:47–50.

Shinohara, Y., Oizumi, K., Itoh, Y., and Hori, M. 1987. Heat Transfer Tubes with Grooved Inner Surface. U.S. Patent 4,658,892.

Shizuya, M., Itoh, M., and Hijikata, K. 1995. Condensation of Non-Azeotropic Binary Refrigerant Mixtures Including R22 as a More Volatile Component Inside a Horizontal Tube. *J. Heat Transfer* 117(2):538–543.

Soliman, M., Schuster, J. R., and Berenson, P. J. 1968. A General Heat Transfer Correlation for Annular Flow Condensation. *ASME J. Heat Transfer* 90:267–276.

Srinivasan, V. and Shah, R. K. 1997. Fin Efficiency of Extended Surfaces in Two-Phase Flow. *Int. J. Heat and Fluid Flow* 18:419–429.

Sur, B. and Azer, N. Z. 1991a. An Analytical Pressure Drop Prediction Model for Condensation Inside Longitudinally Internally Finned Tubes. *ASHRAE Trans.* 97(2):54–61.

Sur, B. and Azer, N. Z. 1991b. Effect of Oil on Heat Transfer and Pressure Drop During Condensation of Refrigerant-113 Inside Smooth and Internally Finned Tubes. *ASHRAE Trans.* 97(1):365–373.

Tandon, T. N., Varma, H. K., and Gupta, C. P. 1985. Prediction of Flow Patterns During Condensation of Binary Mixtures in a Horizontal Tube. *ASME Trans.* 107:424–430.

Tandon, T. N., Varma, H. K., and Gupta, C. P. 1986. Generalized Correlation for Condensation of Binary Mixtures Inside a Horizontal Tube. *Int. J. Refrig.* 9:134–136.

Thome, J. R. 1995. Flow Boiling of Refrigerant-Oil Mixtures: A Current Review. *Convective Flow Boiling Conference*, Paper VI-6.

Thonon, B. and Chopard, F. 1996. Condensation in Plate Exchangers: Assessment of a General Design Method. *Heat Transfer in Condensation*. Eds. C. Marvillet and R. Vidil, pp. 10–17. Paris: Elsevier.

Tichy, J. A., Macedon, N. A., and Duval, W. W. B. 1985. An Experimental Investigation of Heat Transfer in Forced Convection Condensation of Oil-Refrigerant Mixtures. *ASHRAE Trans.* 91(1A):297–308.

Torikoshi, K. and Ebisu, T. 1993. Heat Transfer and Pressure Drop Characteristics of R-134a, R-32, and a Mixture of R-32/R-134A Inside a Horizontal Tube. *ASHRAE Trans. Research* 99:90–96.

Tovazhnyanski, L. L. and Kapustenko, P. A. 1984. Intensification of Heat and Mass Transfer in Channels of Plate Condensers. *Chem. Eng. Communication* 31:351–366.

Tran, T. N., Wambsganss, W. M., France, D. M., and Jendrzejczyk, J. A. 1993. Boiling Heat Transfer in a Small, Horizontal, Rectangular Channel. *AIChE Symp. Ser. No. 295* 89:253–261.

Traviss, D. P., Rohsenow, W. M., and Baron, A. B. 1973. Forced Convection Condensation in Tubes: A Heat Transfer Correlation for Condenser Design. *ASHRAE Trans.* 79(I):157–165.

Uehara, H. and Nakaoka, T. 1988. Performance Test of a Shell and Plate Type Condenser for OTEC. *Experimental Thermal and Fluid Science* 1:275–281.

Vrable, D. A., Yang, W. J., and Clark, J. A. 1974. Condensation of Refrigerant-12 Inside Horizontal Tubes with Internal Axial Fins. *Proc. 5th International Heat Transfer Conference* 3:250–254.

Wambsganss, M. W., France, D. M., Jendrzejczyk, J. A., and Tran, T. N. 1993. Boiling Heat Transfer in a Horizontal Small-Diameter Tube. *ASME J. Heat Transfer.* 115:963–972.

Wambsganss, M. W., Jendrzejczyk, J. A., and France, D. M. 1991. Two-Phase Flow Patterns and Transitions in a Small, Horizontal Rectangular Channel. *Int. J. Multiphase Flow* 17(3):327–342.

Webb, R. L. 1994. *Principles of Enhanced Heat Transfer.* New York: John Wiley & Sons, Inc.

Yang, C. Y. and Webb, R. L. 1995a. Condensation of R-12 in Small Hydraulic Diameter Extruded Aluminum Tubes with and Without Micro-Fins. *Int. J. Heat Mass Transfer* 39:791–800.

Yang, C. Y. and Webb, R. L. 1995b. Friction Pressure Drop of R-12 in Small Hydraulic Diameter Extruded Aluminum Tubes with and Without Micro-Fins. *Int. J. Heat Mass Transfer* 39:801–809.

Yang, D. Xin, M. D., and Huang, S. M. 1995. Experiment for Condensing Heat Transfer Performance in Horizontal Three Dimensional Inner Microfin Tubes. *Two-Phase Flow Modeling and Experimentation.*

Yasuda, K., Ohizumi, K., Hori M., and Kawamata, O. 1990. Development of Condensing Thermofin-HEX-C Tube. *Hitachi Cable Review* 9:27–30.

CHAPTER
# TWENTY FIVE

## INSTRUMENTATION IN BOILING AND CONDENSATION STUDIES

**Jean-Marc Delhaye**

*Commissariat à l'Energie Atomique, Grenoble, 38054 Grenoble Cedex 9, France*

**25.8    David B. R. Kenning**

*Oxford University, Oxford, United Kingdom*

**25.4.3    Nobuyuki Takenaka**

*Kobe University, Kobe, 657-8501 Japan*

Three decades ago, an in-depth review on two-phase flow instrumentation was edited by Letourneau and Bergles (1969), including already 368 references. Since then, interest in two-phase flow and heat transfer by scientists and engineers has continued to increase. The upcoming sophisticated computer codes that study and predict two-phase flow and heat transfer in complex geometries and/or transient regimes has not decreased the need for measurements but rather has enhanced it. Consequently, a great deal of effort has been spent on gas-liquid measuring techniques for almost thirty years now. Two categories of publications have been generated: (1) papers for the specialists in instrumentation, such as the communications contained in the 746-page book edited by Delhaye and Cognet (1984), or in the proceedings of the OECD/CSNI meeting on advanced instrumentation and measurements techniques in two-phase flow (1997), and (2) publications for potential users, such as the Handbook of Multiphase Systems (edited by Hetsroni [1982]), which provides selection charts and guidelines for choosing a measuring technique, or the paper by Brand et al. (1993).

Apart from the problems encountered in any measuring method used in single phase flow, further difficulties appear when attempting to measure quantities in two-phase flow. The majority of these difficulties are related to the presence of the two phases, but others are due to the conditions of flow confinement. These difficulties are exemplified in the introduction to the paper by Jones and Delhaye (1976).

Despite these difficulties, several techniques can be used to measure practical or fundamental parameters with a fair degree of accuracy. The purpose of the following is to present the principles of a few methods that can be considered as well-established and particularly adapted to industrial conditions.

## 25.1 BASIC DEFINITIONS

Given the fluctuating character of two-phase flows, a complete and rational presentation of the describing parameters requires the use of phase density functions and averaging operators (Delhaye et al., 1981). However, the limited scope of this review only needs simple (though accurate) definitions of the quantities to be measured. Among them, void fractions, specific areas, and quality are peculiar two-phase flow parameters, the definitions of which are given here.

### 25.1.1 Void Fractions

*Void fraction* is a term that has several meanings. For this reason, its use should be avoided and replaced by the specific name of the quantity dealt with, i.e., *local* void fraction, *line* void fraction, *area* void fraction, or *volumetric* void fraction.

Consider a two-phase mixture flowing in a tube (Figure 1). During time interval $T$, a given point $M$ is alternately surrounded by the gas phase (subscript $G$) and the liquid phase (subscript $L$). Denoting respectively by $T_G$ and $T_L$ the cumulated residence-times of the gas and liquid phases within the time interval $T$, we can

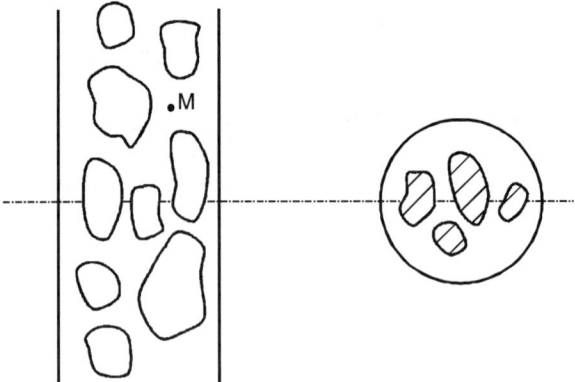

**Figure 1** Two-phase mixture flowing in a pipe.

define the *local void fraction* $\alpha_G$ as the ratio of the gas residence-time $T_G$ to the time interval T:

$$\alpha_G \triangleq \frac{T_G}{T} \equiv \frac{T_G}{T_G + T_L} \qquad (25.1\text{-}1)$$

where $\triangleq$ is the definition symbol. It is of the utmost importance to acknowledge that $\alpha_G$ is a local quantity, dependent on $M$ and defined over a certain time interval $T$, the extent of which being chosen according to the flow fluctuations (Delhaye and Achard, 1977).

Consider now a particular chord or diameter of the pipe at a given time. This segment is discontinuously occupied by the gas and liquid phases (see Figure 1). Denoting respectively by $L_G$ and $L_L$ the cumulated lengths of the segments occupied by the gas and liquid phases over the chord or diameter considered, we can define the *instantaneous line void fraction* $R_{G1}$ as the ratio of the length $L_G$ occupied by the gas phase to the total length $L$:

$$R_{G1} \triangleq \frac{L_G}{L} \equiv \frac{L_G}{L_G + L_L} \qquad (25.1\text{-}2)$$

where subscript 1 refers to a line void fraction.

Finally, consider a particular cross section of the pipe at a given time. This cross section is discontinuously occupied by the gas and liquid phases. Denoting respectively by $A_G$ and $A_L$ the cumulated cross-sectional areas occupied by the gas and liquid phases within the cross section considered, we can define the *instantaneous area void fraction* $R_{G2}$ as the ratio of the area $A_G$ occupied by the gas phase to the pipe cross-sectional area $A$:

$$R_{G2} \triangleq \frac{A_G}{A} \equiv \frac{A_G}{A_G + A_L} \qquad (25.1\text{-}3)$$

where subscript 2 refers to an area void fraction.

Instantaneous line or area void fractions are instantaneous space-fractions for the gas phase that depend on time and the segment or cross section considered. There exist fundamental identities that relate the time-averages of space void fractions to space-averages of the local void fraction. They read (Delhaye et al., 1981):

$$\bar{R}_{G1} \triangleq \frac{1}{T} \int_T R_{G1}\, dt \equiv \frac{1}{L} \int_L \alpha_G\, dL \qquad (25.1\text{-}4)$$

$$\bar{R}_{G2} \triangleq \frac{1}{T} \int_T R_{G2}\, dt \equiv \frac{1}{A} \int_L \alpha_G\, dA \qquad (25.1\text{-}5)$$

As we will see in the next section, equation [25.1-4] enables probe measurements of local void fractions to be tallied with radiation attenuation measurements of line void fractions.

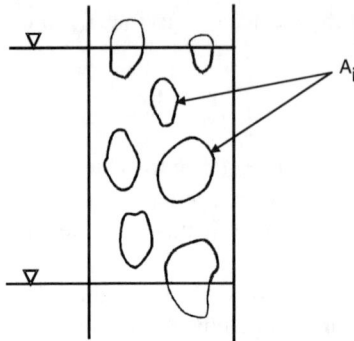

**Figure 2** Control volume V used in the definition of the volumetric interfacial area.

### 25.1.2 Volumetric Interfacial Area

Given are a pipe, a fixed control volume V limited by the pipe wall, and two cross-sectional planes located a certain distance apart (see Figure 2).

At a given time, the cumulated area of the interfaces enclosed within volume V is denoted by $A_i$. The *volumetric interfacial area* $\Gamma$ is an instantaneous quantity defined on volume $V$ by the following relation:

$$\Gamma \triangleq \frac{A_i}{V} \qquad (25.1\text{-}6)$$

The connection between this volumetric interfacial area and the kinematics of the interfaces contained within volume V can be found in the book by Delhaye et al. (1981).

### 25.1.3 Quality

The *quality* x of a two-phase mixture flowing in a pipe is defined as the ratio of the gas mass flow rate $M_G$ to the total mass rate $M$ of the mixture:

$$x \triangleq \frac{M_G}{M} \equiv \frac{M_G}{M_G + M_L} \qquad (25.1\text{-}7)$$

## 25.2 LOCAL VOID FRACTION MEASUREMENTS

### 25.2.1 Electrical Probes

The first requirement to be met when using an electrical probe in two-phase flow is that one phase has a significantly different electrical conductivity from the other. Consequently, variations in conductance permit the measurements of the local void fraction and the arrival frequency of the bubbles at a given point in a continuous, conducting fluid. By using a double probe, a transit velocity can be measured,

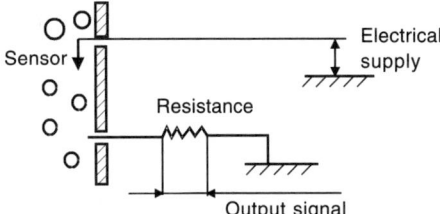

**Figure 3** Electrical diagram of a resistive probe.

but one has to be very careful when giving physical significance to this velocity (Delhaye and Achard, 1977; Galaup, 1975).

Figure 3 shows the classical electrical diagram of a resistive probe, while Figure 4 displays a typical probe geometry. Impedance changes due to the passage of bubbles at the tip of the probe produce a fluctuation in the output signal. One of the principal features that differentiate the electrical circuits shown in Figure 3 is the type of electrical supply. *Direct current supply* requires low voltages in order to reduce electrochemical phenomena on the sensor. Resultant electronics may become troublesome, and sensors may still sustain alteration due to electrochemical deposits at low flows. When *an alternating current supply* is used, phase changes are detected by amplitude modulation of the alternating output signal. This technique has been used by several investigators to eliminate the electrochemical phenomena on the sensor. When high speed flows are investigated, the required supply frequency can be very high (e.g., 1 MHz), and much trouble occurs with the electronics. Galaup (1975) used a supply frequency lower than the frequency of the physical phenomenon, eliminating electrochemical effects and providing pseudo DC operation in each half wave.

According to the way that the sensor is energized, the ideal output signal of a resistive probe is either a binary wave sequence or a sequence of bursts of constant amplitude oscillations separated by zero voltage zones. Actually, the output signal is misshapen with respect to the ideal signal due to the interface deformations.

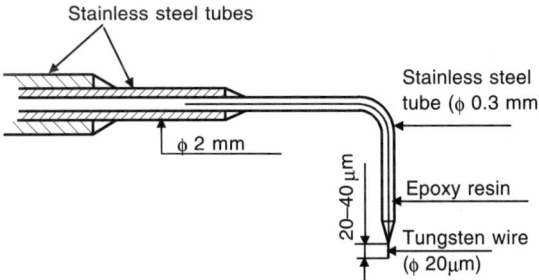

**Figure 4** Miniature probe geometry (Lecroart and Porte, 1971).

The true signal is generally transformed into a binary sequence with the help of a trigger level. Galaup (1975) used a level adjustment based upon a comparison between the integrated void profile and the line void fraction obtained with a $\gamma$-ray absorption method.

The electrical probe described in Figure 4 does not work in dispersed droplet flow due to the impossibility of having a continuous electrical path in the liquid phase between the two electrodes. Reimann and John (1978) provided local void fraction data in steam-water flow at pressure up to 100 bar obtained with a high frequency probe. This probe is made of a coaxial wire energized by a 100 to 300 MHz current. A standing wave reflector senses the differential voltage between the forward and reflected waves, which is a function of the nature of the medium surrounding the tip of the probe.

### 25.2.2 Optical Probes

An optical probe is sensitive to the change in the refractive index of the surrounding medium and is thus responsive to interfacial passages enabling measurements of local void fraction and interface passage frequencies to be obtained even in a non-conducting fluid. By using two sensors and a cross-correlation method, some information may be obtained on a transit velocity (Galaup, 1975).

General reviews on the optical probe method can be found in Cartellier (1990) and Cartellier and Achard (1991). Recent advances are proposed in the papers by Cartellier et al. (1996), Cartellier (1997), and Garnier (1997). Measurements of local quantities in two-phase flows with optical probes have been extensively made for more than 25 years. Different kinds of flow have been investigated, such as R114 boiling flows simulating PWR steam generator conditions (Bouchter et al., 1990), air-water bubbly flow in a vertical pipe (Grossetête, 1995a, 1995b), and R12 boiling flows simulating PWR core conditions (Cubizolles, 1996; Garnier, 1997).

**25.2.2.1 U-shaped optical probe.** A tiny optical sensor was proposed by Danel and Delhaye (1971) and developed by Galaup (1975). This probe consists of a single optical fiber, 40 $\mu$m in diameter. The overall configuration is shown in Figure 5. The active element of the probe is obtained by bending the fiber into

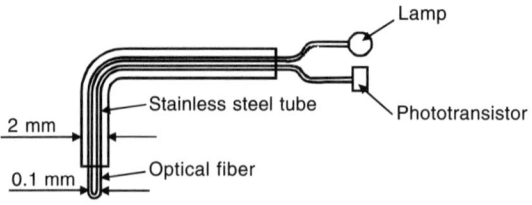

**Figure 5** U-shaped fiber optical sensor (Danel and Delhaye, 1971).

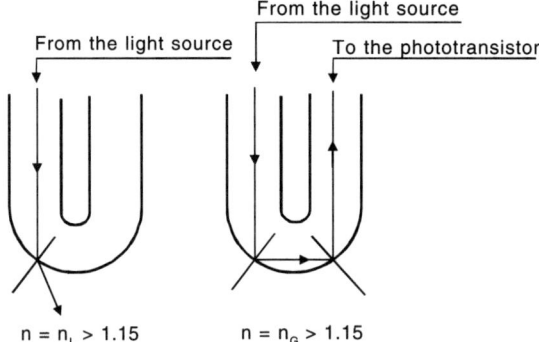

**Figure 6** Active part of the U-shaped fiber optical sensor (Danel and Delhaye, 1971).

a U-shape. The entire fiber, except for the U-shaped bend, is protected inside a stainless steel tube, 2 mm in diameter. The active part of the probe, as shown in Figure 6, has a characteristic size of 0.1 mm.

Signal analysis is accomplished through an adjustable threshold, which enables the signal to be transformed into a binary signal. Consequently, the local void fraction is a function of this threshold, which is adjusted and then held fixed during a traverse in order to obtain agreement between the profile average and a $\gamma$-ray measurement of the line void fraction. Experimental results for void profiles in Freon two-phase flow with phase change and in air-water flow are given by Galaup (1975). Miniaturized U-shaped optical probes were used by Charlot et al. (1978) to determine local void fraction profiles in a four-rod bundle cooled by a vaporizing freon flow. Figure 7 shows some typical void profiles obtained in the central subchannel of the bundle.

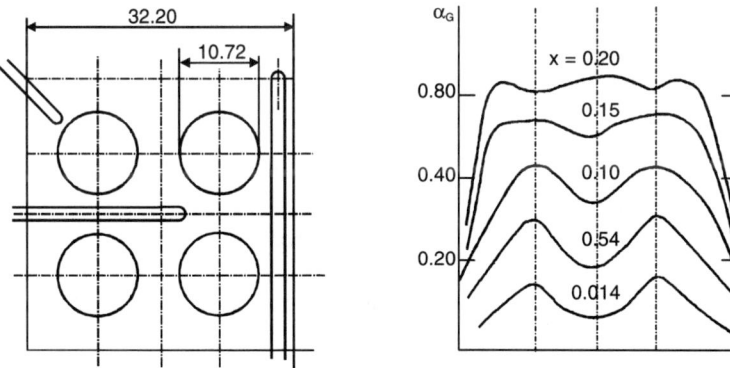

**Figure 7** Local void fraction profiles in the central subchannel of a four rod bundle. Freon-freon vapor flow (23.3 bar; 80°C; 50 g cm$^{-2}$s$^{-1}$), Charlot et al. (1978).

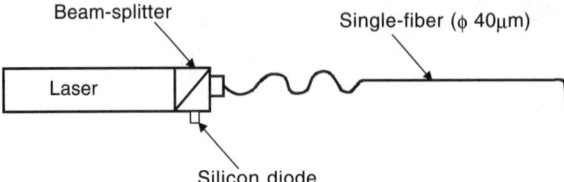
**Figure 8** Single-fiber optical probe (Danel et al., 1984).

**25.2.2.2 Single fiber optical probe.** The interest given to finely dispersed bubbly or droplet flow has brought about the development of single fiber optical probes (Danel et al., 1984; Delhaye, 1983). The optical fiber has a diameter of 40 $\mu$m, and its extremity can be cut into a hemispherical or slender profile adapted to each individual problem. The sensitive part of the sensor can be less than 10 $\mu$m in diameter and the rise-time of the signal during the passage of an interface less than 0.4 $\mu$m (See Figure 8).

In 1983, Delhaye et al. reported the very first reliability tests of an optical probe that was especially designed to withstand high pressures and temperatures (180 bar and 360°C). These reliability tests were performed in an autoclave filled with water. They showed that the proposed design enabled an optical probe to be immersed in demineralized water at 180 bar and 360°C during more than a hundred hours, the sapphire needle that was used as the sensor tip did not dissolve, and the junction between the sapphire needle and the probe metallic sheath ensured a perfect seal between the inside of the probe and its environment. The optical components were not destroyed and their functions were not altered despite the high temperature surrounding. However, the probes suffered from two major drawbacks: the fabrication was not regular and the design was not appropriate for probes bent at a right-angle. A few years ago, a new design was tested that seemed to overcome these hindrances. Moreover, this new design could be directly adapted to single fiber probe. Reliability tests were performed and showed that such probes could withstand immersion in demineralized water at 200 bar and 400°C during more than 100 hours.

The advantages of optical probes are numerous and well known:

- Contrary to the case of resistivity probes, it is not necessary that one of the phases possesses properties of known connexity.
- It is not necessary that one of the phases be electrically conducting.
- Their response is very rapid (less than 1 $\mu$s for single fiber probe).
- They can be used over a large range of temperature and pressure, due to the use of special components and design.
- The transparency of the fluids does not come into play.
- The spatial resolution is very good (less than 10 $\mu$m for single fiber probes).

## 25.3 LINE VOID FRACTION MEASUREMENTS

### 25.3.1 The Photon Attenuation Technique

A beam of monochromatic, collimated photons of incident intensity $I_O$ traversing a substance of thickness e and density $\rho$ has an emerging intensity I given by the following exponential absorption law:

$$I = I_O \exp\left[-\left(\frac{\mu}{\rho}\right)\rho e\right] \qquad (25.3\text{-}1)$$

The quantity $\frac{\mu}{\rho}$ is the specific absorption coefficient of the material. This coefficient generally decreases piecewise with the energy of the photons and is independent of the physical state of the substance (solid, liquid, or gas). Tables giving the values of this coefficient for different materials can be found in McMaster et al. (1969), Storm and Israel (1970), and Stukenbroeker et al. (1970). Figure 9 shows the mass absorption coefficient $\frac{\mu}{\rho}$ as a function of the incident beam energy for water.

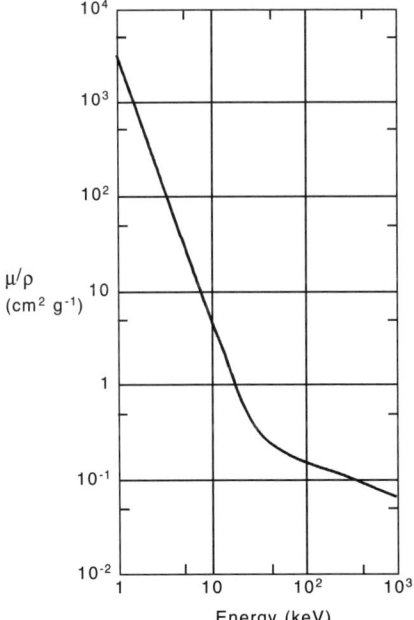

**Figure 9**  Mass absorption coefficient of water as a function of the incident beam energy.

## 25.3.2 The Line Void Fraction Determination

When a collimated beam is used, the radiation is absorbed by the wall, and the two phases in a series mode. At any given time, the attenuation of the beam is given by the following relation:

$$I = I_O \exp(-\mu_p e_p) \exp[-\mu_L(1 - R_{G1})d] \exp[-\mu_G R_{G1} d] \quad (25.3\text{-}2)$$

where $e_p$ is the total wall thickness, $d$ the distance between the walls, and $\mu_p$, $\mu_G$, $\mu_L$ are the absorption coefficients of the wall, gas, and liquid.

(i) For *low pressure gas-liquid flows at ambient temperature* (Galaup, 1975), it is only necessary to measure intensities $I_G$ and $I_L$ corresponding respectively to the channel filled with gas and that filled with liquid. The *instantaneous* line void fraction is then easily obtained, provided $I_O$ is a constant:

(ii)

$$R_{G1} = \frac{\ln(I/I_L)}{\ln(I_G/I_L)} \quad (25.3\text{-}3)$$

(iii) *For high-pressure steam-water flows*, it is usually impossible to measure $I_G$ by filling up the pipe with steam. However, we have:

$$\frac{\mu_L}{\rho_L} = \frac{\mu_G}{\rho_G} \quad (25.3\text{-}4)$$

and a calibration in conditions as close as possible to experimental conditions will be necessary (Martin, 1969, 1972; Réocreux, 1974).

## 25.3.3 Errors due to Fluctuating Voids

In steady-state two-phase flow, the emerging intensity $I$ (in photons/s) is generally measured over a certain period $\theta$ (10 s to 1 min); consequently, the measurement actually gives the number $N$ of emerging photons counted over the time interval $\theta$,

$$N \triangleq \int_{t-\frac{\theta}{2}}^{t+\frac{\theta}{2}} I \, dt \quad \text{(in photons)} \quad (25.3\text{-}5)$$

Since the average of an exponential is not equal to the exponential of the average, the measurement does not give in fact the void fraction $\bar{R}_G$ averaged over the time interval $\theta$. This error can be considerable for highly fluctuating flows. The deviation can range from 0.05 for churn-flow up to 0.20 for slug flow. However, the measurement of time-averaged void fractions in fluctuating flows can be handled by one of the following method.

(i) The averaged void fraction $\bar{R}_G$ can be determined from the probability density function of the instantaneous void fraction $R_G$ obtained for a very short counting time (e.g., 0.05 s). This technique has been reported in a series of papers by Hancox et al. (1972), Harms and Laratta (1973), and Laratta and Harms (1974).
(ii) Levert and Helminski (1973) used a dual energy method based on the differential absorption of radiation energy.
(iii) Log amplifiers were used by Jones (1973) to linearize the instantaneous signal. The only requirement is that the response time of the amplifier should be smaller than the lower period of the physical fluctuations.
(iv) For a homogeneous bubbly or droplet flow, Ohba (1980) proposed an implicit relation between the void fraction and the intensities $I$, $I_G$, and $I_L$. However, the results are close to those obtained from Eq. (25.3-3), provided that the contrast remains lower than 100.

## 25.3.4 Choice of Radiation

A radiation is characterized by its *energy spectrum* and its *intensity*. The *contrast* is defined by the relationship

$$c \triangleq \frac{I_G}{I_L} \quad (25.3\text{-}6)$$

where $I_G$ and $I_L$ correspond respectively to the channel filled with gas and filled with liquid. For gas-liquid flow at low pressure,

$$c = \exp(\mu_L d) \quad (25.3\text{-}7)$$

The greater the contrast, the higher the sensitivity of the measurement. To increase the contrast, the mass absorption coefficient $\frac{\mu_L}{\rho_L}$ must be increased, therefore decreasing the energy (Figure 9).

On the other hand, the *photon emission fluctuation* leads to the following statistical relationship:

$$\frac{\Delta N}{N} = \left(\frac{1}{N}\right)^{1/2} \quad (25.3\text{-}8)$$

where $N$ is the number of photons counted. For purposes of accuracy, $N$ must be sufficiently high. As a result, either the counting time $\theta$ or the emerging intensity $I$ must therefore be sufficiently high. Consequently, if the incident intensity $I_O$ is fixed, the mass absorption coefficient must be decreased and thus the energy increased.

Constraints due to the contrast and to the photon emission fluctuations have indeed opposite effects on the choice of the photon energy and of the source intensity. In this respect, X-rays have beam intensity $10^3$ to $10^4$ times higher than $\gamma$-rays.

The photon beam must be *monochromatic* for the exponential absorption law (Eq. 25.3-2) to be applicable. On that account, $\gamma$-ray emission is more monochromatic than X-ray bremsstrahlung emission. However, filters or electronic discriminators can be used to select or detect only those photons with energy in a certain band.

The *stability* of the source with time is another important parameter of measurement accuracy, and $\gamma$-rays are to be preferred to X-rays due to their rather long half-lives of the principal sources. However, certain methods can be used to avoid the inconvenience of X-ray generator drifts and/or fluctuations (Du Bousquet, 1969; Jones, 1973; Lahey, 1977; Nyer, 1969; Solésio, 1978).

### 25.3.5 Radiation Detection

The emerging intensity $I$ is measured with a scintillator coupled to a photomultiplier supplied with correctly stabilized high-voltage. Generally, a pre-time method is used, in which the pulses are counted during a predetermined time. Xenon ionization chambers seem to be more stable than photomultipliers.

### 25.3.6 Examples

**25.3.6.1 Steady-state steam-water flow at high pressure.** Martin (1969, 1972) measured the line void fraction at high pressure (up to 140 bar) in a rectangular channel (50 × 2.8 mm) simulating a sub-channel of a nuclear reactor plate-type fuel element. The test section consisted of two vertical plates heated by Joulean effect and was enclosed in a thick casing drilled with holes, allowing a horizontal X-ray beam to pass through the two 0.5 mm thick lateral sides (see Figure 10). This X-ray beam, 2 mm in height and 0.05 mm in width, scanned the test cross section in a movement parallel to the heated plates. The line void fraction $\bar{R}_{G1}$ of the upward steam-water flow was measured every 0.025 mm with a position accuracy of about 0.005 mm despite the severe experimental conditions, (i.e., fluid pressure: 140 bar; fluid temperature: 335°C; ambient temperature: 50°C). Typical distributions of the line void fraction $\bar{R}_{G1}$ are given in Figure 10.

**25.3.6.2 Liquid film thickness measurements.** The thickness of a wavy liquid film flowing down an inclined plane was measured by Solésio et al. (1978) by means of an X-ray absorption technique (see Figure 11). The film thickness, with an average value of about one millimeter, was determined each millisecond with a precision finer than 0.050 mm. Figure 11 shows the film thickness versus time when 35 Hz waves are generated at the free surface of the liquid film. The continuous line represents the signal obtained by means of the X-ray absorption technique, whereas the dashed line represents the signal obtained by means of a conductivity

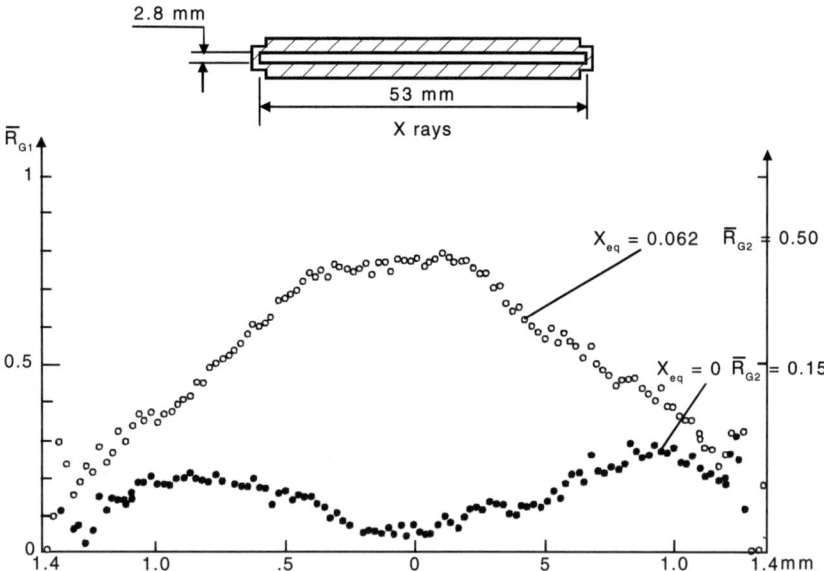

**Figure 10** Line void fractions $\bar{R}_{G1}$ in steady-state steam-water flow at high pressure (Martin, 1969, 1972). Pressure: 80 bar; heat flux density, 100 W cm$^{-2}$; mass velocity: 220 g cm$^{-2}$s$^{-1}$; $x_{eq}$: equilibrium quality.

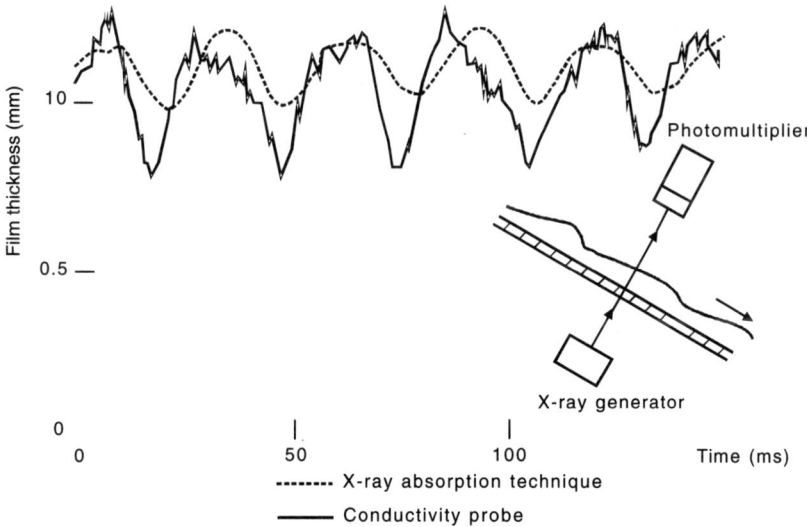

**Figure 11** Instantaneous liquid height (Solésio et al., 1978).

probe, which measures the liquid conductance between two electrodes mounted flush with the wall.

### 25.3.7 Design Parameters of an X-ray Densitometer

Due to the constant use of this measuring technique, Fournier and Jeandey (1984) developed a computer program simulating the behavior of an X-ray beam from its emission to its detection. This program is able to optimize the major design parameters of an experimental setup by taking into account all possible sources of uncertainty, such as void fluctuations, Compton scattering, beam hardening, system drifts, positioning, and statistical uncertainty. The input data of the program are the thickness and the material of the walls traversed by the beam, the components of the two-phase flow, and the characteristics of the detector (either the absorbing substance with its thickness or a detector with its efficiency). In addition, tables of absorption coefficients have been stored in the program for a wide range of chemical elements likely to be found on the beam path. The program enables the user to choose the best value for the tube high-voltage and to select filters to minimize the uncertainty.

## 25.4 AREA VOID FRACTION MEASUREMENTS

### 25.4.1 Photon Attenuation Techniques

**25.4.1.1 One-shot technique.** In the *one-shot technique* (Charléty, 1971; Gardner et al., 1970; Nyer, 1969), the radiation crossed the whole of the tube cross section containing the two-phase mixture. The beam height must be small compared with the tube diameter in order to restrict the measurement to a given cross section. Calibration with lucite mockups are generally necessary due to the lack of a specific absorption law. A positive appraisal of the one-shot technique was given by Besset (1979). He showed that the accuracy $\Delta R_{G2}$ could be better than $\pm 0.05$ for area void fractions ranging from 0 to 0.80.

**25.4.1.2 Single beam densitometer.** The *time-averaged* area void fraction $\bar{R}_{G2}$ can be determined from a profile of time-averaged chordal void fraction $\bar{R}_{G1}$. In a pipe of circular cross section, we have:

$$\bar{R}_{G2} = \frac{1}{\pi R^2} \int_{y=-R}^{y=+R} 2\sqrt{R^2 - y^2}\, \bar{R}_{G1}(y)\, dy \qquad (25.4\text{-}1)$$

where $R$ is the pipe radius and $y$ the distance from the axis of the pipe to the photon beam. Note that if the flow is axisymmetric, the local void fraction $\alpha_G$ is a solution

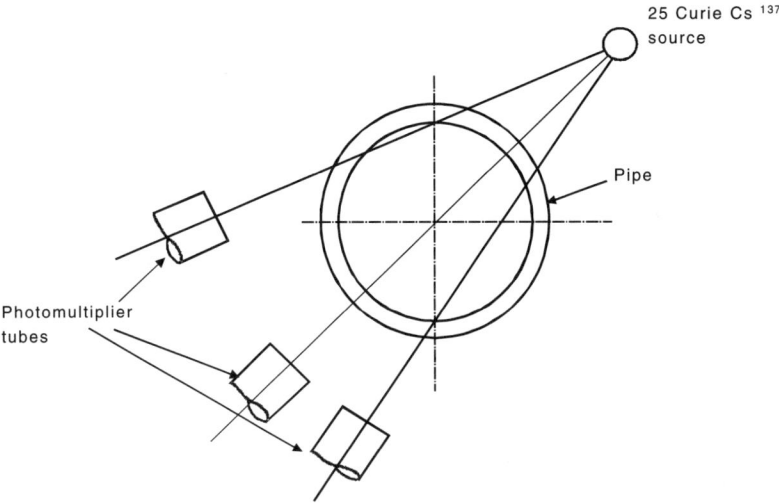

**Figure 12** Three-beam gamma densitometer (Banerjee et al., 1978).

of the following Abel integral equation:

$$\int_Y^R \frac{r\alpha_G(r)}{\sqrt{r^2 - y^2}} dr = \bar{R}_{G1}(y)\sqrt{R^2 - y^2} \qquad (25.4\text{-}2)$$

where $r$ is the radial coordinate.

**25.4.1.3 Multibeam densitometers.** The *multibeam gamma densitometer* has been used for many years by laboratories involved in water reactor safety studies. Figure 12 shows a schematic of the three-beam densitometer used by Banerjee and Jolly (1978). A 25 Ci cesium 137 source provides three $\gamma$-ray beams that are directed through the pipe in the same cross section plane. The beams are attenuated according to the line void fractions, and the measurement of the attenuation of each beam can be used to determine the area void fraction $R_{G2}$. This technique requires a model connecting the area void fraction, the flow pattern, and the three measured line void fractions.

Several laboratories have used multibeam densitometers for measuring area void fractions in transient two-phase flow. However, the size of the standard scintillators has limited the number of beams to around ten. The development of medical X-ray tomography equipment removed this constraint and void fractions measurements were made with up to 31 beams (Jeandey, 1982). The equipment used by Jeandey consisted of a 140 kV electrostatic generator supplying the high-voltage of an X-ray tube. A flat, fan-shaped beam of X-rays covered the whole cross section of the test conduit and impinged onto a series of 31 anti-Compton collimators.

Each collimator was followed by a xenon ionization chamber. The test conduit was a vertical cylindrical tube, 20 mm in diameter, followed by a divergent with a diameter of 60 mm. The conduit walls traversed by the X-ray beam were stainless steel, 1.5 mm thick. The pressure was 100 bar and the temperature 300°C. The spatial resolution of each beam within the test section was $1 \times 1$ mm$^2$.

### 25.4.2 Impedance Void Meters

Impedance void meters have proved to be sufficiently adequate for measuring area void fractions in a wide range of circumstances, especially in the study of void fraction waves. The most effective meters use flush-mounted electrodes at the pipe wall; two versions of these meters have been used so far. In the first version, a fixed electrical field is created between two electrodes, whereas in the second version, a rotating electrical field is created between three pairs of electrodes that are energized sequentially (Merilo et al., 1977; Snell et al., 1978). The advantage of the six electrode sensor is that its signal is less affected by the spatial distribution of the void fraction than that delivered by a two electrode sensor. An improved development of the six electrode sensor was reported by Tournaire (1985, 1986, 1987) and Delhaye et al. (1987) in connection with an experimental investigation of void fraction waves. It appears that impedance void meters are reliable, fairly accurate, and not too expensive. However, they require walls that are not electrically conducting.

An advanced theoretical modeling of the impedance void meter can be found in Lemonnier et al. (1991), whereas practical applications are presented in de Cachard (1989) and de Cachard and Delhaye (1996) for air-lift pumping systems in Hervieu (1994), Veneau (1995), and Hervieu and Veneau (1996) for liquefied propane flashing flow, and in Mi et al. (1997), Seleghim (1996), and Hervieu and Seleghim (1997) for flow regime identification.

Several attempts have been made to use impedance tomography in heterogeneous media (Williams and Beck, 1995). However, it has been proved that impedance tomography could not provide the local value of the void fraction with sufficient accuracy (Lemonnier, 1995; Lemonnier and Peytraud, 1995, 1996, 1997; Peytraud, 1995).

### 25.4.3 Neutron Scattering and Radiography Techniques

X-ray attenuation techniques are not suitable for void fraction measurements in metallic piping when the void fraction is larger than 0.8. This is due to the fact that a small change in the liquid fraction is concealed by the absorption of the X-ray beam by the metallic wall. On the contrary, neutron scattering is a very sensitive technique in this case. For a stainless-steel tube 12 mm in diameter, the best choice found by

Freitas (1981) was the backward scattering of thermal neutrons. A neutron beam produced by a nuclear reactor was collimated in a conduit filled with helium to avoid scattering or attenuation by humidity. A bismuth shield was installed to stop the $\gamma$-rays. A boron-lined proportional detector was used to count the scattered neutrons. A 2.2 contrast ratio was obtained for void fractions ranging from 0.8 to 1.0.

Recently, significant improvements were reported in the use of neutron radiography in two phase flow (Mishima and Hibiki, 1997; Takenaka et al., 1997).

Applications of neutron radiography have also been proposed for many nondestructive examinations, since the attenuation characteristics of neutron rays in materials are much different from those of X-rays and gamma-rays, i.e., an image difficult to be visualized by X-rays or gamma-rays may possibly be visualized by neutron rays.

Figure 13 shows the mass attenuation coefficients of X-rays by a solid line and those of neutron rays by symbols against atomic numbers. The mass attenuation coefficients of X-rays increase with increasing the atomic number. Therefore, X-rays are suitable to see an object made of high atomic number elements through that of low atomic number elements. However, the mass attenuation coefficient of thermal neutron rays greatly depend on the elements. Since the mass attenuation coefficient of neutron rays of water is higher than those of metals like aluminum and the elements of stainless steel, neutron radiography is suitable for the visualization of water two-phase flow in a metallic vessel or tube. It is also low for low melting metals, like lead, bismuth, and tin; therefore, these liquid metals flow can be also visualized by neutron radiography.

Neutrons produced in a nuclear reactor or generated by nuclear interaction in an accelerator are thermalized in a moderator. A parallel beam is obtained by a collimator and the beam is irradiated to the test object. Neutrons are not visible or sensible to films for optical rays and X-rays; therefore, the neutron image of the object is converted to the other radioactive rays image, which is sensible to the films in film methods. It is also converted to the optical image by a scintillation converter in real-time methods and recorded by a high-sensitivity camera, like a Silicon Intensified Target (SIT) tube camera to make movies. An image intensifier is often used for high-speed movies. A cooled Charged Couple Device (CCD) camera is used for high resolution and high dynamic range still imaging. More details on neutron radiography and its applications can be found in Domanus (1992).

Figure 14 shows photographs of a gas lighter taken by the film method using optical rays, thermal neutron rays, and X-rays to show the difference of the attenuation characteristics (Hiraoka, 1995; Yoneda et al., 1990). The surface of the gas lighter was covered with a metallic plate, lighter contained parts made from metals, plastic resins, and the oil. The oil and the structure made of the plastic resins can be seen by neutron-rays. The oil inside the metallic tank was not visible, but metallic pipes and springs were visible by X-rays.

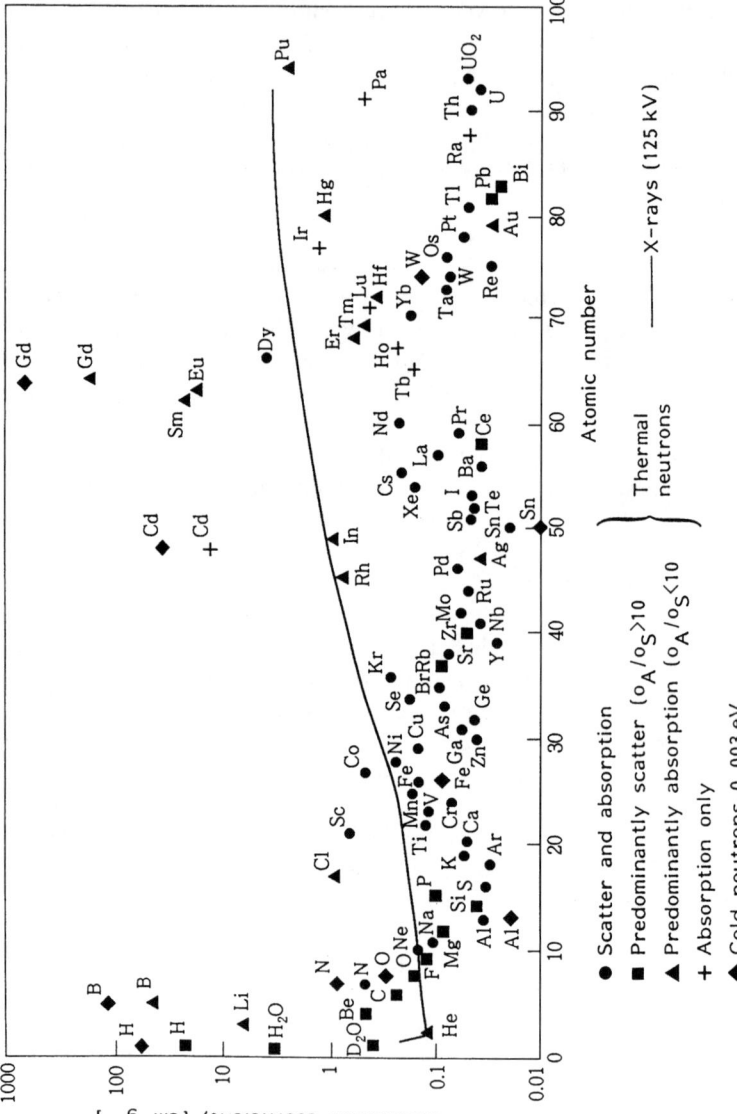

**Figure 13** Mass attenuation coefficients of neutron and X-rays.

INSTRUMENTATION IN BOILING AND CONDENSATION STUDIES **697**

(a)

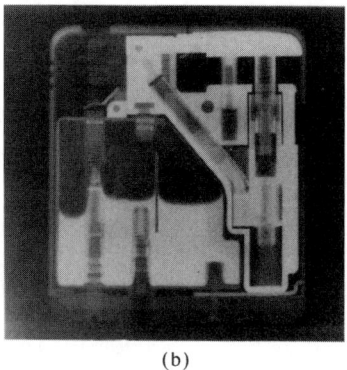
(b)

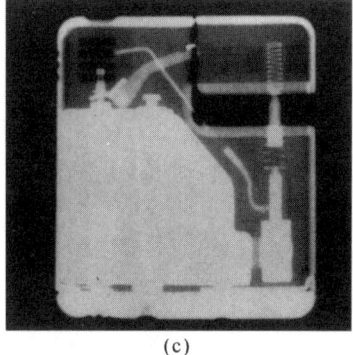
(c)

**Figure 14** Photographs of a gas lighter by optical, thermal neutron, and X-rays: (a) optical rays, (b) thermal neutron rays, (c) X-rays.

Visualization and measurement of various two-phase flows by neutron radiography were reported using reactor and accelerator based systems. Typical results of the applications are shown below.

Costigan & Wade (1984) reported visualization of inverted annular flow using a reactor system at Harwell. Water inverted annular flow was clearly visualized as shown in Figure 15 in a stainless steel tube 12.2 mm in O.D. and 9.25 mm in I.D. heated up to 600°C. Inverted annular flow was also visualized by Takenaka et al. (1990) using an accelerator based system at Sumitomo Heavy Ind. Consecutive pictures of the rewetting process of inverted annular flow with and without a twisted tape were shown in Figure 16. A twisted tape made from stainless steel was inserted in a stainless steel tube 20 mm in inner diameter and 1 mm in thickness heated up to 500°C. The tape was not visible without water but was seen when the water followed the tape.

**698** HANDBOOK OF PHASE CHANGE: BOILING AND CONDENSATION

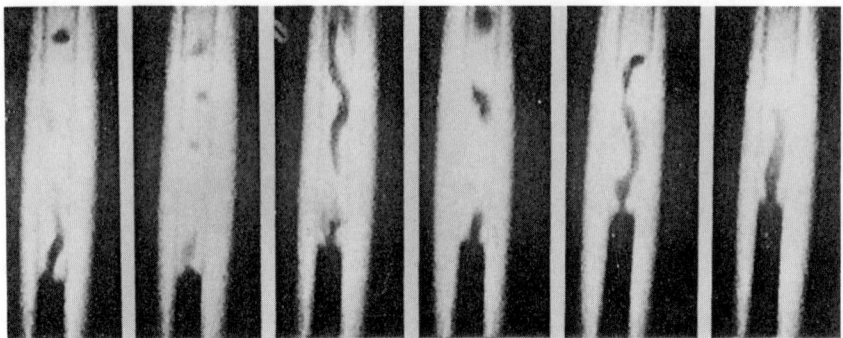

**Figure 15** Flow visualization of inverted annular flow.

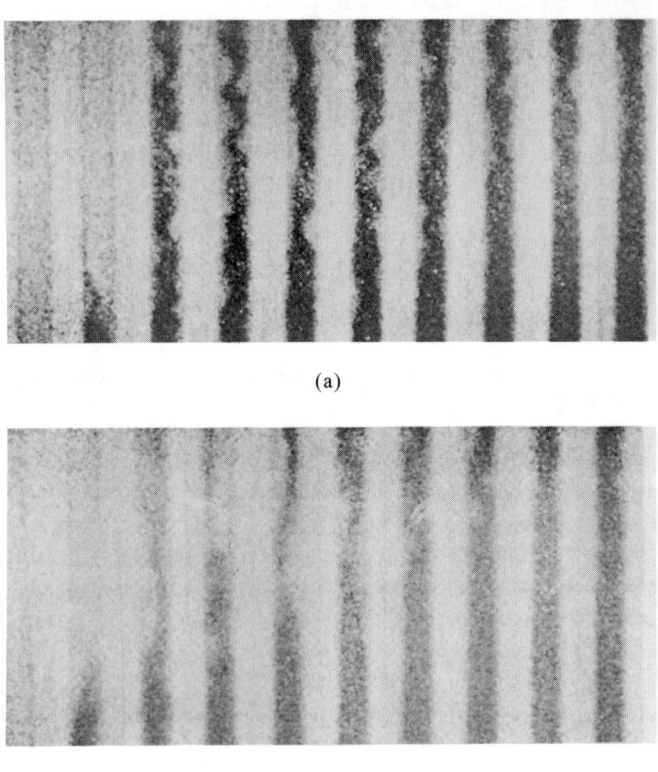

(a)

(b)

**Figure 16** Flow visualization of inverted annular flow with and without a twisted tape.

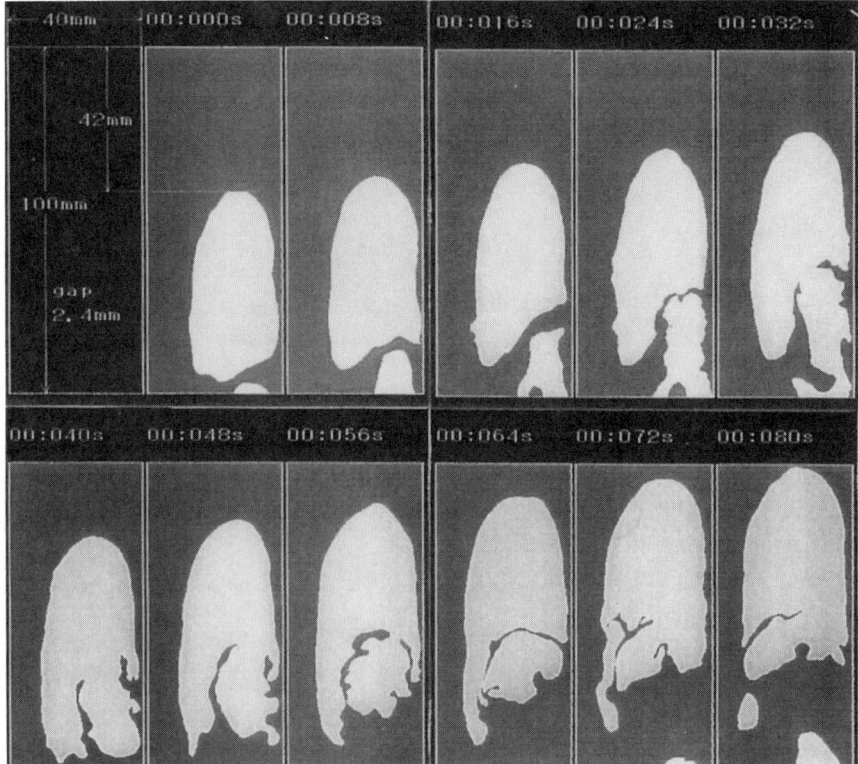

**Figure 17** High speed visualization of air-water two-phase flow.

High speed visualization of air-water two-phase flow in a narrow gap made of aluminum plates was carried out by Hibiki et al. (1995) using a neutron radiography system at Japanese Research Reactor 3 Modified (JRR-3M) of the Japan Atomic Energy Research Institute. Slug flow was clearly visualized in 250 frames/second, as shown in Figure 17. It was reported that the visualization with 1000 frames/second would be possible by the present neutron radiography systems using image intensifier systems.

Behaviors of water vapor bubbles in a lead-bismuth-tin alloy were observed using a high speed neutron radiography system at JRR-3M by Nishi et al. (1996). The melting point of the alloy was 95°C. Water was injected through a nozzle into the alloy in a rectangular vessel 25 mm in thickness. Vaporization of water in the molten metal by liquid-liquid direct contact heat transfer was observed in 500 frames/second, as shown in Figure 18.

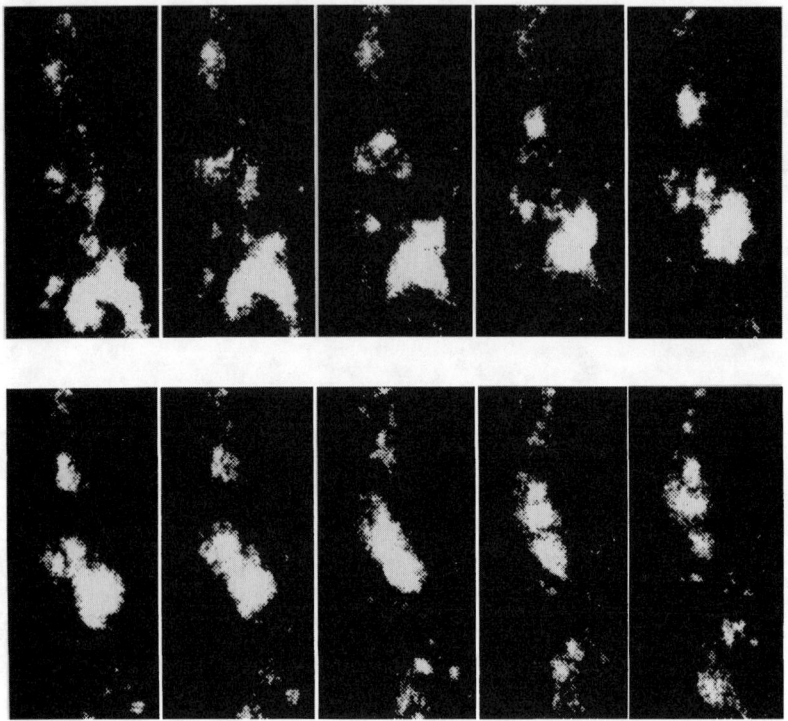

**Figure 18** High speed visualization of water vapor bubbles in molten lead-bismuth-tin alloy generated by liquid-liquid heat transfer.

A high resolution and high dynamic range cooled CCD camera system at JRR-3M was used by Takenaka et al. (1996) for three-dimensional void fraction measurement of a steady two-phase flow by a neutron radiography CT method. Air-water two-phase flow was visualized in a 4 × 4 rod bundle made of aluminum tube, 10 mm outer diameter and supported with stainless steel spacers. The two-phase flow behavior around the spacer in a rod bundle is important to study for the safety considerations of water cooled nuclear reactors. Figures 19a and 19b show the projection image of the rod bundle around the spacer by neutron radiography with the cooled CCD camera with and without two-phase flow. The rod bundle was rotated with an angle of 0.72 degrees, and 250 projections were taken for the CT reconstruction. The spatial resolution was estimated as 0.18 mm. Examples of the void fraction distributions were shown in Figures 20a, 20b, and 20c upstream, inside, and downstream of the spacer, respectively. Water fraction was plotted at 320 × 320 points in each figure. The effects of the spacer on the void fraction distribution were clearly shown. The distributions for 1018 cross-sections could

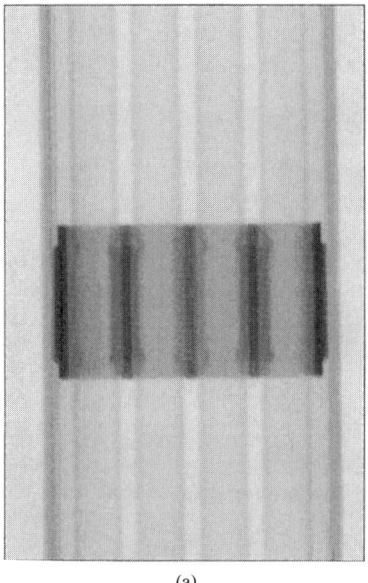 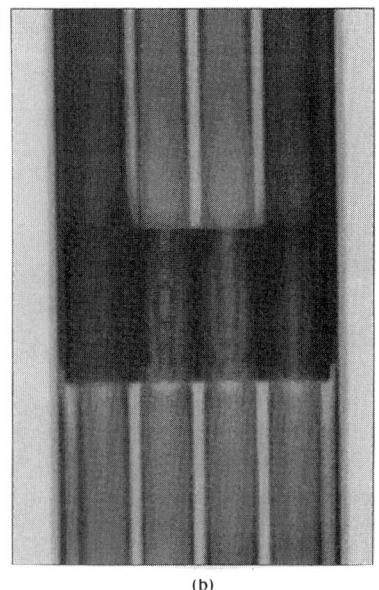

(a) (b)

**Figure 19** Visualization of a rod bundle with a cooled CCD camera (a) without two-phase flow and (b) with two-phase flow.

be obtained if the CT reconstructions were carried out for every slice, i.e., the void fraction measurement at more than one hundred million points could be conducted by this method. It was reported that the spatial resolution up to 0.1 mm would be possible.

It has been reported that two-phase flow in a metallic tube or container and liquid metal flow were successfully visualized and measured in high speed or high spatial resolution by neutron radiography. Recently, movable neutron sources using a small accelerator have been developed. More applications of neutron radiography to the experimental studies on heat transfer in phase change were expected.

## 25.5 MASS FLOW RATE MEASUREMENTS

The need for transient mass flow rates measurements appeared in the blowdown studies performed for a better understanding of the loss of coolant accident of water reactors. A number of devices have been proposed so far and are amply described in the book by Hewitt (1978). Among them, the combination of a Venturi and a turbine flowmeter seems extremely promising. Its advantages lie in its mechanical reliability and simple use.

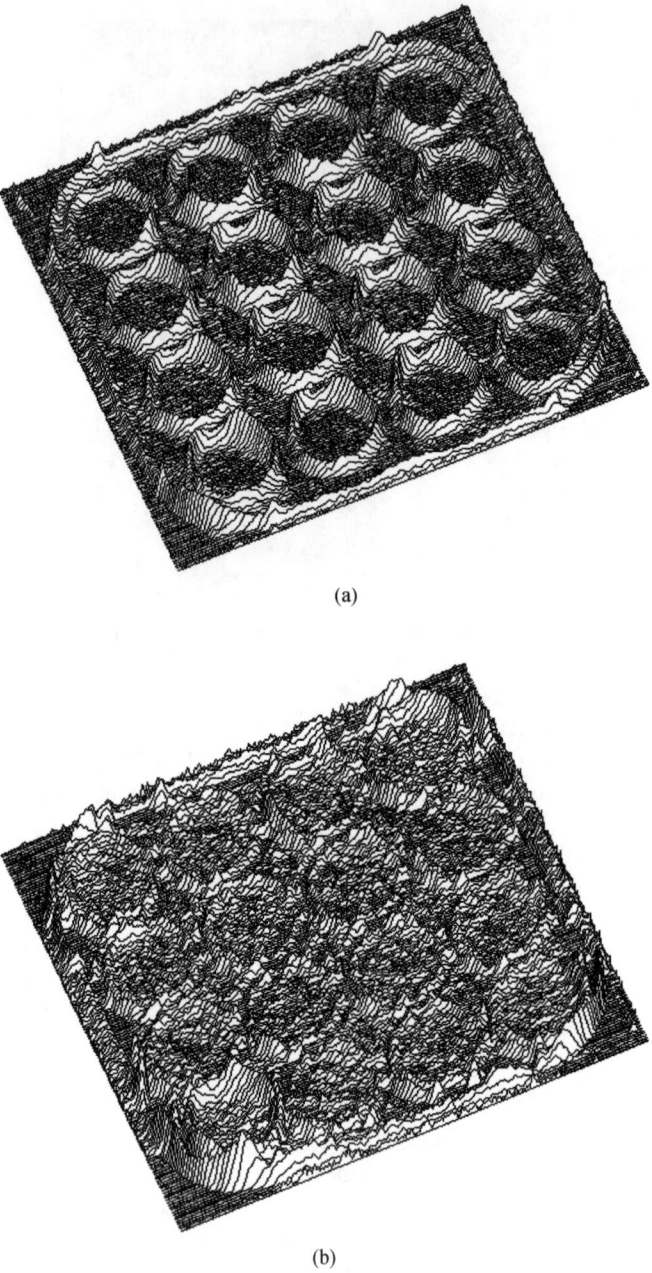

(a)

(b)

**Figure 20** Three-dimensional void fraction distribution of air-water two-phase flow in a rod bundle around a spacer (a) upstream of the spacer, (b) inside the spacer, and (c) downstream of the spacer.

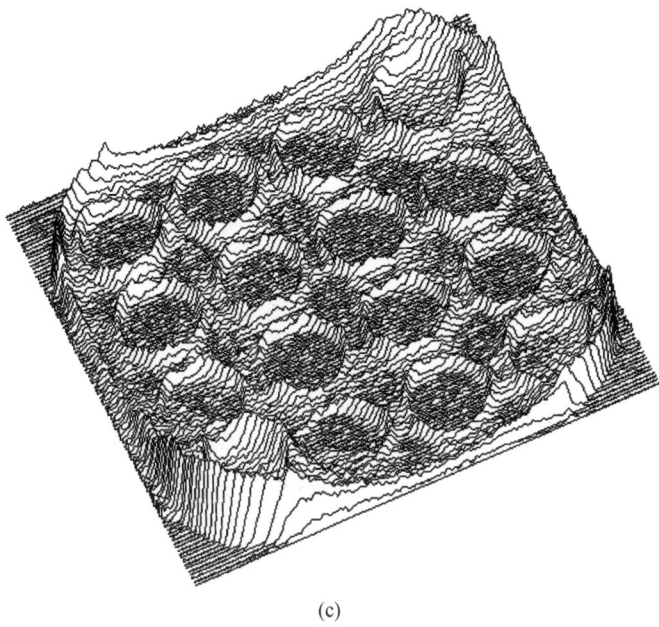

(c)

**Figure 20** (*Continued*).

However, an accurate and definite modeling of the response of each instrument in transient two-phase flows still has to be achieved. In the following, we will successively examine the behavior of the Venturi meter and turbine flowmeter in two-phase gas-liquid flow. Then we will indicate how to use the two instruments to determine the mass flow rate and the quality of a two-phase mixture.

### 25.5.1 The Venturi Tube in Two-phase Flow

At high pressure, the more extensive results seem to have been obtained by Frank et al. (1977), who carried out an experimental program on an argon-water loop running between 18 and 83 bar. The results are fairly well correlated by the following equations:

$$\Delta p = K_v \frac{M^2}{\rho_v} \qquad (25.5\text{-}1)$$

$$\frac{1}{\rho_v} \triangleq \frac{x^2}{R_v \rho_G} + \frac{(1-x)^2}{(1-R_v)\rho_L} \qquad (25.5\text{-}2)$$

where $K_v$ is a dimensional constant determined in single-phase liquid flow. The quantity $R_v$ is a fictitious void fraction determined in terms of the quality $x$ and

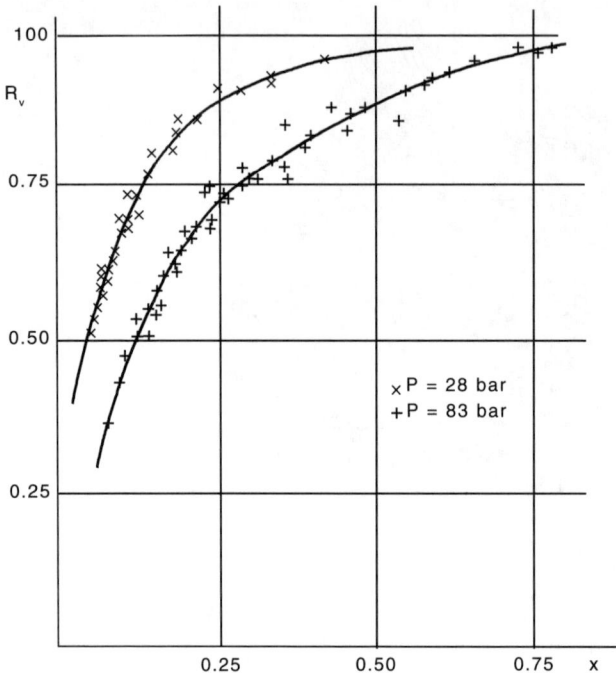

**Figure 21** Calibration curve used for the Venturi (Frank et al., 1977).

the pressure by means of a calibration on an argon-water loop. An example of such a calibration curve is given in Figure 21. The correlation was tested for the following parameter ranges: argon-water pressure from 18 to 83 bar, steam-water equivalent pressure from 40 to 140 bar, quality from .03 to .75, void fraction from .3 to .99, and mass flow rate from .10 to .80 kg s$^{-1}$.

In a *vertical* Venturi tube, the pressure difference $\Delta p$ must take into account the hydrostatic pressure difference between the upstream and throat pressure taps. If $\rho$ denotes the two-phase mixture density and h the distance between the pressure taps, we thus have

(i) for an *upward* vertical flow:

$$\Delta p \triangleq (p_{upstream} - p_{throat}) - \rho g h \tag{25.5-3}$$

(ii) for a *downward* vertical flow:

$$\Delta p \triangleq (p_{upstream} - p_{throat}) - \rho g h \tag{25.5-4}$$

At low pressure, Boyer and Lemonnier (1996) developed a model to predict the velocity and pressure distributions along a venturi for air-water and oil-water dispersed two-phase flow. The venturi was a part of a multiphase flow meter specially designed for petroleum engineering (Boyer, 1996).

### 25.5.2 The Turbine Flowmeter in Two-Phase Flow

In *single-phase flow*, one can define a flow coefficient $C$ and a rotation Reynolds number $N$ by the following relations:

$$C \triangleq \frac{Q}{n d^3} \quad (25.5\text{-}5)$$

$$N \triangleq \frac{d D^2}{\nu} \quad (25.5\text{-}6)$$

where $Q$ is the volumetric flow rate, $n$ is the rotational frequency, $D$ is the pipe diameter, and $\nu$ is the kinematic viscosity of the fluid. Hochreiter (1958) has shown that the flow coefficient $C$ is a function of the rotation Reynolds number $N$. However, the flow coefficient appears to be a constant for $N > 2000$ and in this case, the rotational frequency $n$ is proportional to the volumetric flow rate. Introducing the mass flow rate $M$ and the fluid density $\rho_T$, we thus obtain:

$$n = K_T \frac{M}{\rho_T} \quad (25.5\text{-}7)$$

where $K$ is a dimensional calibration constant.

With respect to *two-phase flow*, the same type of formula as Eq. [25.5-7] has been looked for, relating the rotational frequency, the total mass flow rate $M$ of the mixture, and a two-phase density $\rho_T$, and using the dimensional calibration constant $K_T$ determined for single-phase liquid flow.

The models encountered in the literature are based on an analysis of the different forces acting on the turbine blades. There exist primarily two models: the first one was proposed by Popper (1961a, 1961b) and tested by Rouhani (1964), and the second one was given by Aya (1975). These two models give results that are practically equivalent.

The force balance written by Popper (1961a) leads to the following relation:

$$n = K_R A \langle W_L \rangle \frac{(1 - R_{G2})\rho_L + R_{G2}\rho_G \gamma^2}{(1 - R_{G2})\rho_L + R_{G2}\rho_G \gamma} \quad (25.5\text{-}8)$$

where $A$ is the pipe cross section area, $\langle W_L \rangle$ is the area-averaged velocity of the liquid phase, $R_{G2}$ is the area void fraction, $\rho_G$ and $\rho_L$ are the gas and liquid densities, respectively, and $\gamma$ is the slip ratio defined by:

$$\gamma \triangleq \frac{\langle W_G \rangle}{\langle W_L \rangle} \quad (25.5\text{-}9)$$

where $\langle W_G \rangle$ is the area-averaged velocity of the gas phase. If the true quality is denoted by $x$, Eq. (25.5-8) becomes:

$$n = K_T A \langle W_L \rangle [1 + x(\gamma - 1)] \tag{25.5-10}$$

Comparing Eqs. (25.5-7) and (25.5-10) and taking account of the following equation:

$$(1 - x) M = (1 - R_{G2}) \rho_L \langle W_L \rangle A \tag{25.5-11}$$

we obtain an expression for the equivalent density:

$$\frac{1}{\rho_T} \triangleq \frac{(1-x)^2}{(1-R_{G2})\rho_L} + \frac{x^2}{R_{G2}\rho_G} \tag{25.5-12}$$

This equivalent density was also found by Rouhani (1964), who started from a different expression of the forces acting on the turbine blades. It agrees fairly well with the experimental results obtained by Rouhani in steam water flows with a pipe diameter of 6 mm, a pressure from 10 to 50 bar, a mass velocity from 516 to 1,850 kg m$^{-2}$s$^{-1}$, a quality $x$ from .0015 to .36, and a void fraction $R_{G2}$ from .01 to 0.90.

Frank et al. (1977) used the same equivalent density, but based on a fictitious void fraction $R_T$ determined as a function of the quality and the pressure by a calibration on an argon-water loop. An example of a calibration curve is given in Figure 22. The tests carried out by Frank et al. (1977) were obtained for a pressure from 18 to 38 bar (equivalent to steam-water flow pressures between 40 and 140 bar), a pipe diameter of 27 mm, a quality from .03 to .75, a void fraction from .30 to .99, and a mass flow rate from .10 to .80 kg s$^{-1}$.

Aya (1975) used a different expression for the force balance on the turbine blades. He obtained the following equation:

$$n = K_T A \langle W_L \rangle \frac{\gamma + \left[ \frac{(1-R_{G2})\rho_L}{R_{G2}\rho_G} \right]^{1/2}}{1 + \left[ \frac{(1-R_{G2})\rho_L}{R_{G2}\rho_G} \right]^{1/2}} \tag{25.5-13}$$

The equivalent density to be used in Eq. [25.5-7] was then given by:

$$\frac{1}{\rho_T} = \frac{x}{R_{G2}\rho_G + \sqrt{R_{G2}(1-R_{G2})\rho_G\rho_L}} + \frac{1-x}{(1-R_{G2})\rho_L + \sqrt{R_{G2}(1-R_{G2})\rho_G\rho_L}} \tag{25.5-14}$$

Experiments by Barnerjee and Jolly (1978) have shown that this equation could be slightly better than Rouhani's equation (25.5-12) in steam-water flows for a

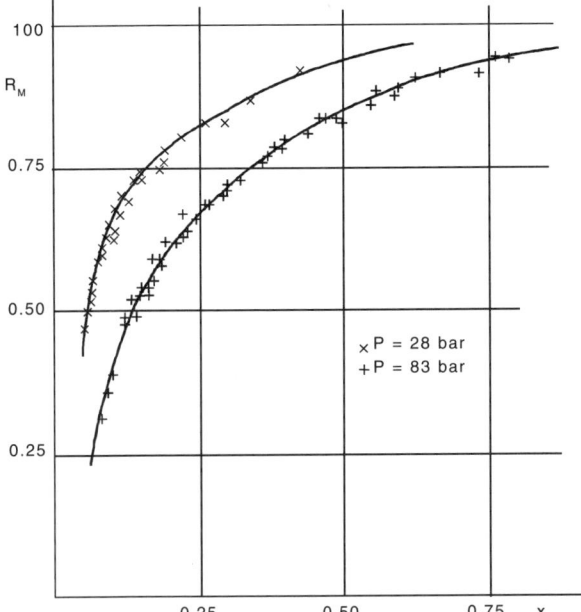

**Figure 22** Calibration curve used for the determination of the equivalent density in Eq. (25.5-2) (Frank et al., 1977).

pressure from 37 to 54 bar, a pipe diameter of 38.1, 49.2, or 73.7 mm, a liquid mass flow rate from 0 to 22.2 kg s$^{-1}$, and a steam mass flow rate from 0 to 3.9 kg s$^{-1}$.

These models constitute exploratory investigations that have to be supplemented by a more rigourous and detailed analysis of the turbine flowmeter in steady-state and transient two-phase flow. Steps in this direction were made by MPR Associates (1978) and Kamath and Lahey (1980).

### 25.5.3 The Determination of the Mass Flow Rates of Both Phases

In *steady-state flow*, the Venturi-turbine combination can be used to determine both the mass flow rate $M$ and the quality $x$. The first method proposed by Frank et al. (1977) consisted of the following procedure:

- Determination of $K_v$ and $K_T$ from single phase flow calibrations
- Determination of the $R_v(x, p)$ and $R_T(x, p)$ curves from two-phase flow calibrations

- Modeling of the hydrostatic term in Eq. (25.5-3) or (25.5-15) by the homogeneous model:

$$\frac{1}{\rho} = \frac{x}{\rho_G} + \frac{1-x}{\rho_L} \qquad (25.5\text{-}15)$$

- Pressure and temperature measurements
- Venturi differential pressure ($p_{upstream} - p_{throat}$) and turbine rotational frequency $n$ measurements
- Iterative solution for Eqs. (25.5-1, 2, 7 and 12) and curves of Figures 21 and 22.

A slightly different method was proposed by Frank et al. (1980). Instead of using calibration curves $R_v(x, p)$, the authors transformed the void fractions $R$ into slip ratios $\gamma$ by the relation:

$$\gamma = \frac{x}{1-x} + \frac{1-R}{R}\frac{\rho_L}{\rho_G} \qquad (25.5\text{-}16)$$

Then, they determined the calibration curbes for the Venturi tube and the turbine meter in terms of the slip ratios versus the density ratio $\frac{\rho_G}{\rho_L}$. This measuring technique was developed for the French Phebus reactor safety experiments and tested in steady state steam water flow for pressures of 30 and 90 bar, mass flow rates of .5 and 5 kg/s, a quality of .02 and .80, and a pipe diameter of 66.7 mm.

In transient two-phase flow, it seems that the Venturi-turbine combination does not provide consistent results due to the time lags introduced by both instruments. For this reason, Bonneton (1980) preferred to use the Venturi tube or the turbine meter separately. The densities $\rho_v$ and $\rho_t$ were determined by means of a single beam gamma densitometer. The mass flow rate was then computed directly from Eq. (25.5-1) or (25.5-7) and the quality from Eq. (23.5-15), that is, by assuming a homogeneous two-phase flow. Bonneton concluded that the turbine-densitometer combination was well adapted to the early stage of a blowdown experiment, whereas the Venturi-densitometer combination was more convenient during the end of the blowdown.

Turbines had to be specially designed at CEA/Grenoble to withstand the extremely severe hydrometric conditions of a blowdown test. John et al. (1984) report on the testing of mass flow rate measuring spool-piece involving two drag bodies, two local and one full flow turbines, and a two-beam gamma densitometer in transient steam-water flow. The mass flow rates determined by different combinations of the spool-piece components were compared with the reference mass flow rate measured with the KfK True Mass Flow Meter.

## 25.6 VOLUMETRIC INTERFACIAL AREA MEASUREMENTS

Consider a two-phase mixture flowing in a pipe and a control volume limited by two cross-sectional planes and the pipe wall. The volumetric interfacial area is defined as the interfacial area enclosed in the control volume divided by the measure of the control volume. The area is then an instantaneous quantity defined over a volume. Conversely, the local interfacial area at a given point is defined as the sum of the reciprocals of the speeds of displacement of the interfaces passing through the point, divided by the time interval that is considered. The local interfacial area is then a local quantity defined over a time interval. One can show that the time-average of the volumetric interfacial area is identical to the volume-average of the local interfacial area (Delhaye, 1976; Delhaye and Achard, 1977, 1978; Ishii, 1987).

### 25.6.1 Visible Light Attenuation Technique

In steady state two-phase flows, several techniques can be used to measure the time-averaged volumetric interfacial area (Veteau, 1979). Among these methods, the visible light attenuation technique is particularly interesting since it can be used in transient bubbly or droplet flow to measure the instantaneous interfacial area of a swarm of bubbles or droplet, 0.1 to several millimeter in diameter.

The experimental setup is represented in Figure 23. The light source $S$ gives a parallel light beam by means of lens $L_1$. A photoreceiver located near the source $S$

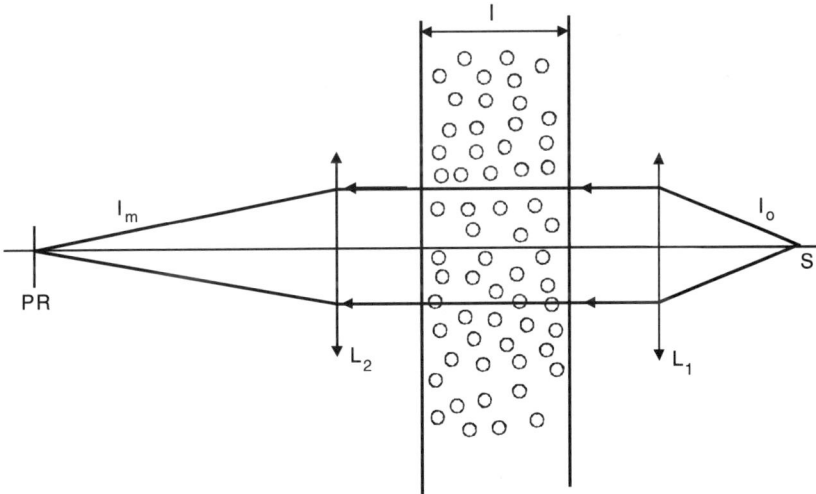

**Figure 23** Experimental set up for interfacial area measurements by the visible light attenuation technique.

measures the intensity $I_o$ of the incident light beam. A second photoreceiver PR is located at the focal point of lens $L_2$ and measures the intensity $I_m$ of the attenuated light beam.

Such a device has been used for a long time to measure interfacial areas in pipes and in stirred tanks, and a critical appraisal of the previous works can be found in the report by Veteau (1979).

**25.6.1.1 Optically dilute suspensions.** If the two-phase flow is sufficiently dilute, the effect of the multiple reflections in the mixture can be neglected. Boll and Sliepcevich (1956) showed experimentally that this condition was verified if

$$\ln(I_o/I_m) < 3 \qquad (25.6\text{-}1)$$

and

$$\theta < 1.4°C \qquad (25.6\text{-}2)$$

where $\theta$ denotes the half-angle under which the optical center of lens $L_2$ sees the photoreceiver. (Figure 15). If the constraints [25.6-1] and [25.6-2] are met, an exponential model enables the volumetric interfacial area to be determined from the incident and measured intensities (Veteau, 1979):

$$\Gamma = \frac{2}{R_i l} L_n \frac{I_o}{I_m} \qquad (25.6\text{-}3)$$

where l is the length of the optical path within the two-phase mixture and $R_i$ is a coefficient that depends on $\theta$. For visible light and particle diameters larger than 0.1 mm, $R_i$ is close to 0.5 if $\theta < 1.4°$ (Veteau, 1979).

As a result we obtain:

$$\Gamma = \frac{4}{l} L_n \frac{I_o}{I_m} \qquad (25.6\text{-}4)$$

Such a device permits the determination of the probability density function of the volumetric interfacial area in a steady-state two-phase flow (see Figure 24). The smaller the diameter of the bubbles, the better the approximation given by Eq. [25.6-4]. The finite volume of the bubbles was taken into account by Ohba et al. (1978), who obtained the following relation:

$$\frac{I_o}{I_m} = \left[1 - \frac{1}{4}\left(\pi D_A^2\right)^{1/3} \Gamma^{2/3}\right]^{-\left(\frac{\Gamma}{\pi D_A^2}\right)^{1/3}} \qquad (25.6\text{-}5)$$

where $D_A$ is the equivalent diameter based on the interfacial area. Several experiments have shown that Eq. (25.6-4) is valid for bubble diameters up to 2 or 3 mm, whereas Eq. (25.6-5) can be used for bubble diameters up to 5 mm. However

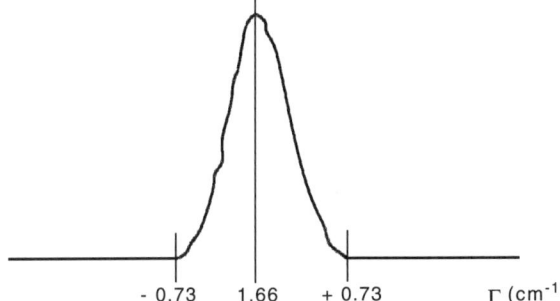

**Figure 24** Typical probability density function of the volumetric interfacial area in a steady-state air-water bubble flow. Void fraction: 0.10; Averaged volumetric interfacial area: 1.66 cm$^{-1}$.

Ohba's model seems very difficult to use because it requires the knowledge of the bubble size distribution to determine $D_A$.

**25.6.1.2 Optically dense suspensions.** Due to the occurrence of multiple reflections, an independent bubble model leads to interfacial area values that are lower than the actual ones. If the light impinging onto the photoreceiver comes from multiple reflections, the modeling is difficult, and the few tentatives (Landau et al., 1977) have not yet been confirmed experimentally.

### 25.6.2 Ultrasonic Attenuation Technique

For bubbly flows, the ultrasonic technique as described by Jones et al. (1986), Delhaye (1986), and Bensler et al. (1987) looked very promising due to its simplicity and versatility. It compares fairly well with the photographic technique or the light attenuation technique.

The single scattering theory used by Bensler et al. (1991) was replaced by a multiple scattering theory by Boyer (1996) to allow higher void fractions to be determined. The ultrasonic technique was also successfully applied in steam-water flow at 25 MPa and 500°C by Melnikov (1996).

## 25.7 MEASUREMENTS OF OTHER QUANTITIES OF INTEREST

### 25.7.1 Heat Transfer Coefficient

In blowdown studies, the internal wall heat flux and temperature are calculated from the measured value of the external wall temperature with a vanishing heat flux condition on this external wall. This is an inverse transient conduction calculation that is very sensitive to fluctuations in the measured temperature. Practical solutions to this problem can be found in Bonneton (1980), and a thorough presentation of this important issue is given in the books by Beck et al. (1985) and Alifanov et al. (1995).

### 25.7.2 Wall Shear Stress

Souhar and Cognet (1984) and Cognet et al. (1984), as well as Nakoryakov et al. (1984), measured the wall shear stress in two-phase flow by means of the diffusion-controlled electrolysis technique. They used a double sensor that enables the direction of the wall shear stress to be determined. This is particularly important in slug flow, where the liquid film surrounding the gas plug moves downward.

### 25.7.3 Local Specific Area

Following the first extensive investigation on interfacial area measurements (Veteau, 1981; Veteau and Charlot, 1981), the multisensor probe was thoroughly employed by Kataoka et al. (1985, 1986) and Grossetête (1995a, 1995b) in air-water bubbly and slug flows. A recent survey on the local measurement of interfacial area by means of multiple probes can be found in Ishii (1995).

### 25.7.4 Liquid Velocity in Bubbly Flow

Marié (1983) showed that laser Doppler anemometry could measure the statistical properties of the turbulence of the liquid phase in a bubbly flow. The results were in good agreement with those obtained by hot film anemometry. In a subsequent paper, Marié and Lance (1984) gave the value of the void fraction beyond which laser Doppler anemometry cannot be used. This critical value is a function of the thickness of the bubbly flow traversed by the light beams. It decreases from 0.3 for a thickness of 20 mm to 0.02 for a thickness of 450 mm.

Recently Ellingsen et al. (1996) strongly recommended the simultaneous use of hot film anemometry and laser Doppler anemometry to increase the reliability of the measurement of the liquid phase turbulence characteristics.

### 25.7.5 Local Temperatures in Boiling Flows

Although the classical microthermocouple had contributed to a large extent to the understanding of the local structure of two-phase flow with phase of change, it had not provided any reliable statistical information on the distribution of the temperature between the liquid and vapor phases.

The work done by Delhaye et al. (1973) was based on the possibility of separating the liquid temperature from the steam temperature and determining the local void fraction. An insulated 20 $\mu$m thermocouple was used as both a temperature sensor and an electrical phase indicator. As a result, separate histograms of liquid and steam temperatures could be obtained.

The absence of a phase indicator does not preclude the statistical analysis of the temperature signal but makes it less precise. In 1978, Afgan & Jovic used a conditional sampling to analyze the structure of the boundary layer occurring in forced convective local boiling.

## 25.8 LIQUID CRYSTAL THERMOGRAPHY IN BOILING

Bubble growth and displacement during boiling cause spatial and temporal variations in wall heat flux that, in turn, cause variations in the temperature of a wall of finite thermal diffusivity. Measurements of these variations can be used to test models of the heat transfer processes in boiling. Detailed measurements of spatially-varying fields require an optical method, the options being liquid crystal thermography and radiation thermography. The availability of high-speed color video cameras currently gives the advantage to liquid crystal thermography, but this could be changed by the development of high-speed infrared cameras. Because bubbles obscure the boiling surface, and boiling is in any case sensitive to the physicochemical state of the surface, boiling experiments with liquid crystal thermography must be performed on a thin metal plate heated by ripple-free direct electric current, with the liquid crystal applied as a thin layer on the rear adiabatic surface of the plate. The thickness of the plate has to be a compromise: too thick and the heating current has to be very large, and the high-frequency components of the interfacial temperature signal are attenuated before they reach the back of the plate; too thin and the dynamic boiling processes under investigation are modified by the limited local thermal capacity of the plate and the constraint on lateral conduction. Numerical computer models (Golobic et al., 1996; Sadasivan et al., 1995) are essential to transfer the experimental findings for these special conditions to more general conditions of boiling on thick walls.

Over a limited temperature range, thermochromic liquid crystals develop a Grandjean structure of helically stacked layers of molecules that reflect incident white light selectively at a wavelength (color) that depends on temperature, changing from red at the lower end of the colorplay range to blue at the upper end. The optically-active Grandjean texture coexists with a focal conic structure that impedes the transmission of light. The upper end of the colorplay range is defined by melting of these structures. During recooling into the colorplay range, the focal conic structure is preferentially formed, partially obscuring the colorplay. Full brightness of the display can only be restored by the application of mechanical stress or by cooling below the colorplay range and reheating: this limits the usefulness of liquid crystal thermography for studying some boiling processes, such as quenching from film to nucleate boiling.

Materials are available commercially with colorplay, commencing at 0°C to over 100°C and with colorplay ranges of 1 K to over 20 K. The changes in color are not distributed uniformly so the range for quantitative measurements may be significantly smaller than the manufacturer's stated range. The requirement to preselect the measuring range by purchasing a particular liquid crystal is a limitation in boiling due to the need to relate the range to the saturation temperature: it is an advantage to be able to control the system pressure, but this introduces the practical problem of designing against pressure differences across the thin boiling plate.

For quantitative analysis of transient events, the colorplay is recorded by high-speed color video camera; selected frames are then converted to a suitable format for computer analysis. The color-temperature dependence is conveniently expressed as a relationship between Hue H (a nonlinear function of the Red-Green-Blue signal ratios) and temperature, which eliminates the influence of the intensity of illumination. H(T) must be determined by a combined calibration of the liquid crystal and the recording system. The characteristics of liquid crystals change rapidly with exposure to UV light and slowly with exposure to high temperatures, so regular in situ calibration is desirable. Color also depends on the angles of illumination and viewing, which can be incorporated in the calibration. The resolution of temperature is limited by noise in the video signal, generated during recording and/or replay. For an analogue camera recording onto video tape at 200 frames/s, typical resolution of temperature is around 0.3 K for a liquid crystal with a working range of 10 K, achieved by averaging 10 replays and spatial filtering to reduce noise. No work has yet been reported with newer cameras with direct digital image storage at up to 1000 frames/s, which may lead to improved accuracy at the price of reduced recording time.

Liquid crystals are sold either in the form of microcapsules (about 20 $\mu$m in diameter) or as unencapsulated grease, to be applied as a thin layer over a very thin layer of chemically-compatible nonreflective black paint. The water-based paint supplied by liquid-crystal manufacturers does not always bond well at the high wall temperatures of interest in boiling. Cellulose paint can be used, but it must be baked for a long period to remove all traces of solvent. Encapsulated liquid crystal mixed with a binder is applied as a layer about 20 $\mu$m thick; unencapsulated material must be spread in a layer at least 10 $\mu$m thick and then covered by a protective layer of polyester film typically 25 $\mu$m thick. If the color recording system contains polarizing elements such as beam-splitters, care must be taken to select a polyester film that is optically inactive. Unencapsulated liquid crystal is cheaper, gives brighter colors, and can be spread in a thinner layer, but it is vulnerable to attack by moisture or solvents. The frequency response of the temperature measurements is limited by the time required to diffuse changes through the combined thickness of the plate and the layer of liquid crystal. The time constant $L^2/\alpha$

for conduction through the plate is about 2 ms for 0.1 mm thick stainless steel or 0.5 mm thick copper. Liquid crystals have thermal conductivities of around 0.2 W/mK and thermal diffusivities of around $10^{-7}$ m²/s, so the time constant is about 4 ms for a 20 $\mu$m layer and 1ms for a 10 $\mu$m layer. For the combined system, the best that can be expected is a time constant of about 5 ms, too slow to capture some fast events such as bubble growth under highly subcooled conditions, but fast enough to provide useful information about many boiling phenomena.

The spatial resolution of temperature is ultimately limited by the grain size of encapsulated material or the layer thickness of unencapsulated material, so a resolution of better than 0.1 mm is achievable. However, resolution is also limited by the number of pixels in the digitized image (and therefore by the chosen size of the field of view) and by spatial filtering to reduce signal noise. Noise is a serious limitation on the accuracy of calculations of local heat fluxes from the time derivative of wall temperature in a local heat balance. Filtering in the time domain cannot be used due to the limited frequency response of the measuring system and the low camera speed in relation to boiling events.

As yet there have been few studies of boiling by liquid crystal thermography. The pioneering study of pool nucleate boiling by Raad and Myers (1971), followed by Marto et al. (1976) studying nucleate boiling in thin liquid layers, used narrow range (2–3 K) liquid crystal on 0.025 mm thick stainless steel with the colorplay recorded by still or 64 frame/s cine photography and interpreted by eye. Watwe and Hollingsworth (1994) investigated the interaction of natural and bubble-induced convective motion in an enclosure with the regimes of nucleate boiling of R11 on a 0.076 mm thick nickel alloy plate. They used liquid crystal with a range of 5 K spread over a 90 mm diameter circle on the back of the plate. The colorplay was recorded by video camera at normal speed and interpreted qualitatively. Quantitative wall temperature data were obtained separately from a thin-film thermometer. The liquid crystal enabled them to follow the development of fronts between boiling and nonboiling patches with increasing heat flux and the sweeping of the surface by thermal waves driven by oscillations in the overall flow pattern in the pool. The identification of large-scale patterns such as these would be very difficult by any method other than liquid crystal thermography. Oka et al. (1992) studied pool boiling of n-pentane under microgravity on a 5 $\mu$m thick titanium plate, using liquid crystal with a range of 12 K and videorecording at normal speed. They used a mirror to obtain simultaneous recordings of the liquid crystal and a side view of the bubbles on the other side of the plate. They converted color to temperature quantitatively to obtain wall temperature distributions and spatial averages. They identified flow regimes and, at low heat flux, cool rings coinciding with the peripheries of rather stable bubbles sliding slowly over the surface. Kenning and Yan (1996) analyzed pool nucleate boiling of water on 0.125 mm thick stainless steel with unencapsulated liquid crystal having a colorplay range of 20 K, with simultaneous video recording at 200 frames/s of the colorplay and bubble motion. They analyzed the intensive heat transfer under large bubbles and identified nucleation sites and mechanisms of interaction leading to intermittent activity that may be chaotic (Ellepola and Kenning, 1996 ; Ellepola et al., 1996). Yan and Kenning (1995) and Yan et al. (1995, 1997) also measured the changes in wall temperature caused by steam and air bubbles sliding under an inclined plate in saturated and subcooled water. The experiments with steam bubbles were run at low wall superheats of 3 to 4 K to eliminate local nucleation and isolate convective effects, pushing the resolution of temperature change to the limit. Consequently, signal noise had a relatively large effect on the calculations of heat flux. Local patterns could be distinguished for single bubbles but were unclear for swarms of bubbles.

Zeng and Klausner (1993) used liquid crystal qualitatively to study nucleation in forced convection boiling. Aligoodarz and Kenning (1995) and Aligoodarz et al. (1998) applied the quantitative method with video recording at 200 Hz in an exploratory study of flow boiling in a narrow channel of rectangular cross-section 2 mm × 1 mm, which pushed the method to its limits in respect to temporal and spatial resolution. A long, narrow channel is poorly matched to the shape of a video frame, and optical development is required in order to make better use of the available pixels. Many opportunities remain to exploit liquid crystal thermography in boiling research, e.g., for in-tube boiling, following some development of the technique for surfaces of large curvature.

For applications to boiling heat transfer research, liquid crystal thermography suffers from practical difficulties and limited frequency response. Nevertheless, the rather small number of studies that have employed this technique have shown that it provides insight into the physical mechanisms of boiling that would be difficult to obtain in any other way: spatial variations during the onset of boiling, the existence of large-scale coherent thermal disturbances, interactions between bubbles and nucleation sites, and local variations in heat transfer. Experiments are limited to boiling on thin, electrically-heated walls, but the information obtained should be applicable more widely, with due caution, primarily through the validation of large computer models that include calculations of wall temperature variations.

## 25.9 CONCLUDING REMARKS

### 25.9.1 High-Speed Video Cameras

Visualization is the first diagnostic tool that must be used when two-phase flow systems are investigated. New equipment has appeared on the market during the past few years that has had an important impact on research efficiency. High-speed video cameras are easy to operate, and the recorded sequences can be displayed immediately after the experiment. Frame-rates reach 200 fps for color cameras and 12,000 fps for black and white cameras. A good reference on this experimental technique is the book by Miquel (1985).

### 25.9.2 Examples of Instrumentation Issues

The content of the previous pages is rather optimistic. However, reality is not so nice. Scientists and engineers are constantly consulted to solve exotic problems whose solutions often require ingenuity, skill, time, and money. Here are some examples of measurements that have not yet received definite solutions: area void fraction in helium II two-phase flow (Grimaud, 1997), flow rate and quality in hydrogen near critical pressures, quality in a subchannel of a LMFBR subassembly, local concentration of a noncondensable gas near a wall onto which steam condenses, position of the liquid-solid interface within a solidifying or melting drop, interfacial area in nondispersed flows, liquid film thickness close to the dryout point in a heated tube, area void fraction in 400 mm diameter pipes lying on the sea bottom, nucleation rates in crystallizers, bubble detection in oil wells, detection of the onset of nucleate boiling detection in a rod bundle, etc.

## REFERENCES

Afgan, N. and Jovic, L. A. 1978. Intermittent Phenomena in the Boiling Two-Phase Boundary Layer. *Int. J. Heat Mass Transfer* 31:427–434.

Alifanov, O. M., Artyukhin, E. A., and Rumyantsev, S. V. 1995. *Extreme Methods for Solving Ill-Posed Problems with Applications to Inverse Heat Transfer Problems*. New York: Begell House.

Aligoodarz, M. R. and Kenning, D. B. R. 1995a. Flow Boiling in a Narrow Channel. *Proc. Engineering Foundation Conference on Convective Flow Boiling*, Banff, April 29–May 5. New York: ASME, 311–316.

Aligoodarz, M. R. and Kenning, D. B. R. 1995b. Vapor Bubble Behavior in a Single Narrow Channel. *Transactions 4th UK National Conference on Heat Transfer*, Manchester, September 26–27, 273–276.

Aligoodarz, M. R., Yan, Y., and Kenning, D. B. R. 1998. Wall Temperature and Pressure Variations During Flow Boiling in Narrow Channels. *Proceedings 11th Int. Heat Transfer Conference*, Kyongju, 2:225–230. Philadelphia: Taylor and Francis.

Aya, I. 1975. A Model to Calculate Mass Flow Rate and Other Quantities of Two-Phase Flow in a Pipe with a Densitometer, a Drag Disk, and a Turbine Meter. ORLN-TM-4759.

Banerjee, S. and Jolly, O. P. 1978. Analysis of Steady-State Steam-Water Mass Velocity Measurements. Interim report submitted to EG & G, INEL.

Banerjee, S., Heidrick, T. R., Saltvold, J. R., and Flemons, R. S. 1978. Measurement of Void Fraction and Mass Velocity in Transient Two-Phase Flow. *Transient Two-Phase Flow, Proceedings of the CSNI Specialists Meeting*. Eds. August 3-4, 1976, Toronto. Eds. Banerjee, S and Weaver, K.R., AECL 2:789–832.

Beck, J. V., Blackwell, B., and St. Clair, C. R. Jr. 1985. *Inverse Heat Conduction, III—Posed Problems*. New York: John Wiley & Sons, Inc.

Bensler, H. P., Delhaye, J. M., and Favreau, C. 1987. Measurement of Interfacial Area in Bubbly Flows by Means of an Ultrasonic Technique. *ANS Proceedings, 1987 National Heat Transfer Conference*, Aug. 9–12. Lagrange Park, IL: ANS, 240–246.

Bensler, H. P., Delhaye, J. M., and Favreau, C. 1991. Determination of the Volumetric Interfacial Area, Volumetric Void Fraction, and Sauter Mean Diameter in Bubbly Flow by Means of Ultrasound Attenuation. *Experimental Heat Transfer, Fluid Mechanics, and Thermodynamics 1991*. Eds. Keffer, J. F., Shah, R. K., and Ganic, E. N., pp. 1096–1104. Elsevier.

Besset, G. 1979. Etude Expérimentale de L'Ébullition Périodique de L'Eau dans un Canal Chauffant Vertical à la Pression Atmosphérique. Thèse de Docteur Ingénieur, Université Scientifique et Médicale et Institut National Polytechnique de Grenoble.

Boll, R. H. and Sliepcevich, C. M. 1956. Evaluation of Errors of Optical Origin Arising in the Size Analysis of a Dispersion by Light Transmission. *J. Opt. Soc. Am. 46* 3:200.

Bonneton, M. 1980. Contribution à L'Étude des Coefficients de Transferts de Chaleur Lors de la Décompression d'un Tube Chauffant Refroidi par de L'Eau. Thèse de Docteur Ingénieur, Institut National Polytechnique et Université Scientifique et Médicale de Grenoble.

Bouchter, J. C., Gouirand, J. M., Haquet, J. F., and Ivars, J. F. 1990. Application of Advanced Optical Probes Instrumentation in Steam Generator Tube Bundles. *Advances in Gas-Liquid Flows—1990*. Eds. Kim, J. H., Rohatgi, U. S., and Hashemi, A. pp. 147–155. FED-Volume 99, HTD-Volume 155. ASME.

Boyer, C. 1996. Etude d'un Procédé de Mesure des Débits d'un Écoulement Triphasique de Type Eau-Huile-Gaz. Thèse de Doctorat, Institut National Polytechnique de Grenoble.

Boyer, C. and Lemonnier, H. 1996. Design of a Flow Metering Process for Two-Phase Dispersed Flows. *Int. J. Multiphase Flow* 22(4):713–732.

Brand, B., Emmerling, R., Fischer, C. H., Gaul, H. P., and Umminger, K. 1993. Two-Phase Flow Instrumentation. *Nuclear Engineering and Design* 145:113–130.

Cartellier, A. 1990. Optical Probes for Local Void Fraction Measurements: Characterization of Performance. *Rev. Sci. Instrum.* 61(2):874–886.

Cartellier, A. 1997. Measurement of Gas Phase Characteristics Using New Monofiber Optical Probes and Real Time Signal Processing. *Proceedings of the OECD/CSNI Specialist Meeting on Advanced Instrumentation and Measurement Techniques*, March 17–20, 1997, Santa Barbara.

Cartellier, A. and Achard, J. L. 1991. Local Phase Detection Probes in Fluid/Fluid Two-Phase Flows. *Rev. Sci. Instrum.* 62(2):270–303.

Charléty, P. 1971. Ebullition du Sodium en Convection Forcée. Thèse de Docteur Ingénieur, Faculté des Sciences, Université de Grenoble.

Charlot, R., Oulmann, T., and Ricque, R. 1978. Boucle Frénésie. Détermination du Taux de Vide et du Type D'Écoulement au Moyen de Sondes Optiques dans une Grappe à Quatre Barreaux Chauffants. *Compte Rendu D'Essais TT/SETRE/78-9-B/RC, TO, RR*.

Cognet, G., Lebouché, M., and Souhar, M. 1984. Wall Shear Measurements by Electrochemical Probe for Gas-Liquid Two-Phase Flow in Vertical Duct. *AICHE Journal* 30(2):338–341.

Costigan, G. and Wade, C. D. 1984. Visualization of the Reflooding of a Vertical Tube by Dynamic Neutron Radiography. *Int. Workshop on Fundamental Aspects of Post-dryout Heat Transfer*, Salt Lake City, USA, 2–101.

Cubizolles, G. 1996. Etude Stéréologique de la Topologie des Écoulements Diphasiques à Haute Pression. Thèse de Doctorat, Ecole Centrale, Lyon.

Danel, F. and Delhaye, J. M. 1971. Sonde Optique pour Mesure du Taux de Présence Local en Écoulement Diphasique. *Mesures-Régulation-Automatisme*, Août-Septembre: 99–101.

Danel, F., Vermeille, H., Guilloud, J. C., Jacquet, A., and Delhaye, J. M. 1984. High-Speed Multiple Spark Cameras for Gas-Liquid Two-Phase Flow Studies. *Measuring Techniques in Gas-Liquid Two-Phase Flows*. Eds. Delhaye, J. M. and Cognet, G., pp. 67–89. Berlin: Springer-Verlag.

de Cachard, F. 1989. Etude Théorique et Expérimentale des Instabilités des Systèmes de Pompage par Air-Lift. Thèse de Doctorat, Institut National Polytechnique de Grenoble.

de Cachard, F. and Delhaye, J. M. 1996. A Slug-Churn Flow Model for Small-Diameter Airlift Pump. *Int. J. Multiphase Flow* 22(4):627–649.

Delhaye, J. M. 1976. Sur les Surfaces Volumiques Locale et Intégrale en Écoulement Diphasique, *CRAS*, Série A 282:243–246.

Delhaye, J. M. 1983. Two-Phase Pipe Flow. *International Chemical Engineering* 23(3):385–410.

Delhaye, J. M. 1986. Recent Advances in Two-Phase Flow Instrumentation. *Heat Transfer 1986*, Volume 1. Eds. Tien, C. L., Carey, V. P., and Ferrell, J. K., pp. 215–226. New York: Hemisphere.

Delhaye, J. M. and Achard, J. L. 1977. On the Use of Averaging Operators in Two-Phase Flow Modeling. *Thermal and Hydraulic Aspects of Nuclear Reactor Safety, Vol. 1: Light Water Reactors*. Eds. Jones, O. C. and Bankoff, S. G., pp. 289–332. New York: ASME.

Delhaye, J. M., and Achard, J. L. 1978. On the Averaging Operators Introduced in Two-Phase Flow Modeling, *Transient Two-Phase Flow, Proceedings of the CSNI Specialists Meeting*. Eds. Banerjee, S. and Weaver, K. R. August 3–4, 1976, Toronto. AECL 1:5–84.

Delhaye, J. M. and Cognet, G. eds. 1984. *Measuring Techniques in Gas-Liquid Two-Phase Flows*. Berlin: Springer-Verlag.

Delhaye, J. M., Charlot, R., Danel, F., and Arnault, J. 1983. An Optical Probe for Interface Detection at High Pressure (180 Bar) and High Temperature (360°C). *Thermal-Hydraulics of Nuclear Reactors*, Volume 2. Ed. Merilo, M., pp. 1427–1430. Lagrange Park, IL: ANS.

Delhaye, J. M., Faveau, C., Saiz-Jabardo, J. M., and Tournaire, A. 1987. Experimental Investigation on the Performance of Impedance Sensors with Two and Six Electrodes for Area-Averaged Void Fraction Measurements. *ANS Proceedings, 1987 National Heat Transfer Conference*. pp. 234–239. New York: ANS.

Delhaye, J. M., Giot, M., and Riethmuller, M. L. eds. 1981. *Thermohydraulics of Two-Phase Systems for Industrial Design and Nuclear Engineering*. New York: McGraw Hill.

Delhaye, J. M., Séméria, R., and Flamand, J. C. 1973. Void Fraction, Vapor, and Liquid Temperatures: Local Measurements in Two-Phase Flow Using a Micro Thermocouple. *J. Heat Transfer* 95(3):365–370.

Domanus, J. C., ed. 1992. *Practical Neutron Radiography*. Kluwer Acad. Pub.

Du Bousquet, J. L. 1969. Etude du Mélange Entre Deux Sous-Canaux d'un Élément Combustible Nucléaire à Grappe. Thèse de Docteur Ingénieur, Faculté des Sciences, Université de Grenoble.

Ellepola, J. H. and Kenning, D. B. R. 1996. Nucleation Site Interactions in Pool Boiling. *Proc. 2nd European Thermal-Sciences and 14th UIT National Heat Transfer Conference*, Rome, May 29–31; 3:1669–1675.

Ellepola, J. H., McSharry, P. E., and Kenning, D. B. R. 1996. Is Nucleate Boiling Chaotic? (And Who Cares?). *Proceedings Eurotherm Seminar No. 48: Pool Boiling*. Paderborn, 1996, pp. 17–24. September 18–20. Pisa: Edizioni ETS.

Ellingsen, K., Risso, F., Roig, V., and Suzanne, C. 1996. Improvements of Velocity Measurements in Bubbly Flows by Comparison of Simultaneous Hot-Film and Laser Doppler Anemometry Signals. 1997 ASME Fluids Engineering Division Summer Meeting, ASME.

Fournier, T., and Jeandey, C. 1984. Optimization of an Experimental Setup for Void Fraction Determination by the X-Ray Attenuation Technique. *Measuring Techniques in Gas-Liquid Two-Phase Flows*. Eds. Delhaye, J. M. and Cognet, G. pp. 199–228. Berlin: Springer-Verlag.

Frank, R., Mazars, J., and Ricque, R. 1977. Determination of Mass Flow Rate and Quality Using a Turbine Meter and a Venturi. *Heat and Fluid Flow in Water Reactor Safety*. pp. 63–68. London: The Institution of Mech. Engrs.

Frank, R., Reimann, J., and John, H. 1980. Mass Flow Rate and Quality Measurements with a Venturi Nozzle and a Turbine Meter in Steam-Water Flow. European Two-Phase Flow Group Meeting, Glasgow.

Freitas, R. L. 1981. Hydrodynamique des Écoulements Eau-Vapeur dans la Zone Remouillée d'un Tube Chauffant en Renoyage. Thèse de Docteur Ingénieur, Institut National Polytechnique et Université Scientifique et Médicale de Grenoble.

Galaup, J. P. 1975. Contribution à L'Étude des Méthodes de Mesure en Écoulement Diphasique, Thèse de Docteur Ingénieur, Université Scientifique et Médicale de Grenoble, Institut National Polytechnique de Grenoble.

Gardner, R. P., Bean, R. H., and Ferrel, J. L. 1970. On the Gamma-Ray One-Shot-Collimator Measurement of Two-Phase Flow Void Fraction. *Nuclear Applications and Technology* 8:88–94.

Garnier, J. 1997. Measurement of Local Flow Pattern in Boiling R12 Simulating PWR Conditions with Multiple Optical Probes. *Proceedings of the OECD/CSNI Specialist Meeting on Advanced Instrumentation and Measurement Techniques*, March 17–20, 1997, Santa Barbara.

Golobic, I., Pavlovic, E., Strgar, S., Kenning, D. B. R., and Yan, Y. 1996. Wall Temperature Variations During Bubble Growth on a Thin Plate: Computations and Experiments. Eurotherm Seminar No.48 on Pool Boiling, Paderborn, 1996, pp. 25–32. Pisa: Edizioni ETS.

Grimaud, L. 1997. Thermohydraulique de L'Hélium II Diphasique en Circulation Forcée. Thèse de Doctorat, Institut National Polytechnique de Grenoble.

Grossetête, C. 1995a. Caractérisation Expérimentale et Simulations de L'Évolution d'un Écoulement à Bulles Ascendant dans une Conduite Verticale. Thèse de Doctorat, Ecole Centrale, Paris.

Grossetête, C. 1995b. Experimental Investigation and Preliminary Numerical Simulations of Void Profile Development in a Vertical Cylindrical Pipe. *Sec. Int. Conference on Multiphase Flow, ICMF'95*. Eds. Serizawa, A., Fukano, T., and Bataille, J. IF1/1–10.

Hancox, W. T., Forrest, C. F., and Harms, A. A. 1972. Void Determination in Two-Phase System Employing Neutron Transmission. ASME Paper 72-HT-2.

Harms, A. A. and Laratta, F. A. 1973. The Dynamic-Bias in Radiation Interrogation of Two-Phase Flow. *Int. J. Heat Mass Transfer* 16:1459–1465.

Hervieu, E. 1994. Débitmétrie d'un Écoulement Diphasique de Propane. *La Houille Blanche* 7:121–127.

Hervieu, E. and Seleghim Jr., P. 1997. An Objective Indicator for Two-Phase Flow Pattern Transition. *Proceedings of the OECD/CSNI Specialist Meeting on Advanced Instrumentation and Measurement Techniques*, 1997, Santa Barbara.

Hervieu, E. and Veneau, T. 1996. Experimental Determination of the Droplet Size and Velocity Distributions at the Exit of the Bottom Discharge Pipe of a Liquefied Propane Storage Tank During a Blowdown. *J. Loss Prev. Process Ind.* 9(6):413–425.

Hetsroni, G., ed. 1982. *Handbook of Multiphase Systems*. McGraw-Hill Book Company.

Hewitt, G. E. 1978. *Measurement of Two-Phase Flow Parameters*. New York: Academic Press.

Hibiki, T., Mishima, K., and Matsubayashi, M. 1995. Application of High-Frame-Rate Neutron Radiography with a Steady Thermal Neutron Beam to Two-Phase Flow Measurements in a Metallic Rectangular Duct. *Nucl. Technol.* 110:422–435.

Hiraoka, E., ed. 1995. *Collected Neutron Radiographs in Japan*. Nihon Hihakai Kennsa Kyokai (in Japanese).

Hochreiter, H. M. 1958. Dimensionless Correlation of Coefficients of Turbine-Type Flowmeters. *Trans. ASME*, 1369.

Ishii, M. 1987. Interfacial Area Modeling. *Multiphase Science and Technology*, Volume 3. Eds. Hewitt, G. F., Delhaye, J. M., and Zuber, N. Washington, DC: Hemisphere; Berlin: Springer-Verlag.
Ishii, M. 1995. Local Measurement of Interfacial Area in Two-Phase Flow. *Annual Review of Heat Transfer*, Volume 6. Ed. Tien, C. L., pp. 271–321. New York: Begell House.
Jeandey, C. 1982. Multibeam X-ray Densitometer for Flow Pattern and Void Fraction Determination in Steam-Water Mixtures. *Measurement in Polyphase Flows*. Eds. Hedrick, T. R. & Patel, B. R. pp. 19–28. New York: ASME, G 00209.
John, H., Reimann, J., Eisele, G., Ohlmer, E., and Schultze, W. 1984. Test of a Mass Flow Rate Measuring Spool Piece Involving Drag Body, Gamma Densitometer, Local Flow Turbines, and Full Flow Turbine in Transient Two-Phase Flow. *Mass Flow Measurements*. Eds. Heidrick, T. R. and Reimer, R. M., pp. 113–121. New York: ASME.
Jones, O. C. 1973. Statistical Considerations in Heterogeneous, Two-Phase Flowing System. Ph. D. Thesis, Rensselaer Polytechnic Institute, Troy, N.Y.
Jones, O. C. and Delhaye, J. M. 1976. Transient and Statistical Measurement Techniques for Two-Phase Flows: A Critical Review. *Int. J. Multiphase Flow* 3:89–116.
Jones, S. W., Amblard, A., and Favreau, D. 1986. Interaction of an Ultrasonic Wave with a Bubbly Mixture. *Experiments in Fluids* 4(6):341–349.
Kamath, P. S. and Lahey, R. T. 1980. A Turbine-Meter Evaluation Model for Two-Phase Transients. *J. Heat Transfer* 102:9–13.
Kataoka, I., Ishii, M., and Serizawa, A. 1985. Interfacial Area in Two-Phase Flow: Formulation and Measurement. *Multiphase Flow and Heat Transfer*. Eds. Dhir, V. K., Chen, J. C., and Jones, O. C., pp. 131–140. ASME G 00304.
Kataoka, I., Ishii, M., and Serizawa, A. 1986. Local Formulation and Measurements of Interfacial Area Concentration in Two-Phase Flow. *Int. J. Multiphase Flow* 12(4):505–529.
Kenning, D. B. R. and Yan, Y. 1996. Pool Boiling Heat Transfer on a Thin Plate: Features Revealed by Liquid Crystal Thermography. *Int. J. Heat Mass Transfer* 39:3117–3137.
Lahey, R. T. 1977. Two-Phase Flow Phenomena in Nuclear Reactor Technology. Quarterly Progress Report, March 1–May 31, 1977. Contract (49-24)-0301 prepared for the USNRC by Dept. Of Nuclear Engineering, Rensselaer Polytechnic Institute, Troy, N.Y.
Landau, J., Boyle, J., Gomaa, H. G., and Al Tawell, A. M. 1977. Comparison of Methods for Measuring Interfacial Areas in Gas-Liquid Dispersion. *Can. J. Chem. Engng.* 55:13.
Laratta, F. A. and Harms, A. A. 1974. A Reduced Formula for the Dynamic-Bias in Radiation Interrogation of Two-Phase Flow. *Int. J. Heat Mass Transfer* 17:464.
Lecroart, H. and Porte, R. 1971. Electrical Probes for Study of Two-Phase Flow at High Velocity. *International Symposium on Two-Phase System*, Haifa, Israel.
Lemonnier, H. 1995. Multiphase Instrumentation: The Keystone of Multidimensional Multiphase Flow Modeling. Invited lecture. *Two-Phase Flow Modelling and Instrumentation*, Volume 1. Eds. Celata, G. P. and Shah, R. K., Eds, Edizioni ETS, Pisa, Italy, 23–30.
Lemonnier, H., Nakach, R., Favreau, C., and Selmer-Olsen, S. 1991. Sensitivity Analysis of an Impedance Void Meter to the Void Distribution in Annular Flow: A Theoretical Study. *Nuclear Engineering and Design* 126(1):105–112.
Lemonnier, H. and Peytraud, J. F. 1995. A New Algorithm for Impedance Imaging of Two-Phase Flows. *Proc. ASME Forum on Measurement Techniques in Multiphase Flows*, San Francisco, Nov. 12–17.
Lemonnier, H. and Peytraud, J. F. 1996. Techniques Tomographiques en Écoulement Diphasique. *La Houille Blanche* 1–2:86–97.
Lemonnier, H. and Peytraud, J. F. 1997. Is 2D Impedance Tomography a Reliable Technique for

Two-Phase Flow? *Proceedings of the OECD/CSNI Specialist Meeting on Advanced Instrumentation and Measurement Techniques*, 1997, Santa Barbara.

Letourneau, B. W. and Bergles, A. E. eds. 1969. Two-Phase Flow Instrumentation. *Proceedings of a Session at the 11th National Heat Transfer Conference*, Minneapolis, MI, Aug. 3–6.

Levert, F. E. and Helminski, E. 1973. A Dual-Energy Method for Measuring Void Fraction in Flowing Medium. *Nuclear Technology* 19:58–60.

Marié, J. L. 1983. Investigation of Two-Phase Bubbly Flows Using Laser Doppler Anemometry. *PhysicoChemical Hydrodynamics* 4(2):103–118.

Marié, J. L. and Lance, M. 1984. Turbulence Measurements in Two-Phase Bubbly Flows Using Laser Doppler Anemometry. *Measuring Techniques in Gas-Liquid Two-Phase Flows*. Eds. Delhaye, J. M. and Cognet, G., pp. 141–148. Berlin: Springer-Verlag.

Martin, R. 1969. Mesure du Taux de Vide à Haute Pression Dans un Canal Chauffant. CEA-R 3781.

Martin, R. 1972. Measurements of the Local Void Fraction at High Pressure in a Heating Channel. *Nuclear Science and Engineering* 48:125–138.

Marto, P. J., MacKenzie, D. K., and Rivers, A. D. 1976. Nucleate Boiling in Thin Liquid Films. Solar and Nuclear Heat Transfer. *AIChE Symposium Series No. 164*, Volume 73:228–235.

McMaster, W. H., Kerr del Grande, N., Mallett, J. H., and Hubbell, J. H. 1969. Compilation of X-Ray Cross Section. Report UCRL-50174, Sect. II, Rev. 1, Lawrence Radiation Lab.

Melnikov, V. I. 1996. Two-Phase Flows Diagnostics by Acoustical Probing Method. $2^{nd}$ *European Thermal-Sciences and 14th UIT National Heat Transfer Conference*. Eds. Celata, G. P., Di Marco, P. and Mariani, A., pp. 1057–1062. Pisa: Edizioni ETS.

Merilo, M., Dechene, R. L., and Cichowlas, W. M. 1977. Void Fraction Measurement with a Rotating Field Conductance Gauge. *Journal of Heat Transfer* 99:330–332.

Mi, Y., Li, M., Xiao, Z., Tsoukalas, L. H., and Ishii, M. 1997. Impedance Void-Meter and Neural Networks for Vertical Two-Phase Flows. *Proceedings of the OECD/CSNI Specialist Meeting on Advanced Instrumentation and Measurement Techniques*, 1997, Santa Barbara.

Miquel, J. C. 1985. L'Observation en Vidéo Rapide de 500 à 25000 ts$^{-1}$ ou en Cinéma Grande Vitesse. Technique et Documentation, Lavoisier (Paris).

Mishima, K. and Hibiki, T. 1997. Development of High-Frame Rate Neutron Radiography and Quantitative Measurement Method for Multiphase Flow Research. *Proceedings of the OECD/CSNI Specialist Meeting on Advanced Instrumentation and Measurement Techniques*, 1997, Santa Barbara.

MPR Associates, Inc. 1978. Spatial Dependence of Turbine Meter Response in Two-Phase Flow, NUREG/CP-0006. *Proceedings of the US Nuclear Regulatory Commission Review Group Meeting on Two-Phase Flow Instrumentation*. Rensselaer Polytechnic Institute, Troy, N.Y., March 13–14 1978, paper I-16.

Nakoryakov, V. Y., Kashinskiy, O. N., and Koz'menko, B. K. 1984. The Electrochemical Method for Study of Turbulence in Two-Phase Flow. *Fluid Mechanics—Soviet Research* 13(3):11–22.

Nishi, Y., Kinoshita, I., Furuya, M., Takenaka, N., Matsubayashi, M., and Tsuruno, M. 1997. Application of Neutron Radiography to Visualization of Direct Contact Heat Exchanger Between Water and Low Melting Point Alloy. In: *Fifth World Conference on Neutron Radiography*. DGZfp, 548–555.

Nyer, M. 1969. Etude des Phénomènes Thermiques et Hydrauliques Accompagnant une Excursion Rapide de Puissance sur un Canal Chauffant. CEA-R 3497.

Ohba, K. 1980. Relationship Between Radiation Transmittivity and Void Fraction in Two-Phase Dispersed Flow. *Technol. Rep. Osaka Univ.* 30(1517–1550):245–254.

Ohba, K., Itoh, T., and Yuhara, T. 1978. Light Attenuation Technique for Void Fraction Measurement in Two-Phase Bubbly Flow—Part III. Effects of Some Parameters on Accuracy of Measurements. *Technology Reports of the Osaka University* 28 1450:507–516.

Oka, T., Abe,Y., Mori, Y. H., and Nagashima, A. 1992. Observational Study of Pool Boiling Under Microgravity. *JSME Int. J., Series II* 35:280–286.

Peytraud, J. F. 1995. Etude de la Tomographie Électrique pour la Mesure du Taux de Vide Local en Écoulements Diphasiques. Thèse de Doctorat, Institut National Polytechnique de Grenoble.

Popper, G. F. 1961a. In-Core Instrumentation for the Measurement of Hydrodynamic Parameters in Water Cooled Reactors. Advanced course in in-core instrumentation for water-cooled reactors at Institut for Atomenergi, Kjeller, Norway, 1, Section V.IV.B, V.32–V.39.

Popper, G. F. 1961b. Proceedings of the Power Reactor In-Core Instrumentation Meeting. Washington D.C., April 28–29, 1960. TID-7598, Instruments Reactor Technology, 37–47.

Proceedings of the OECD/CSNI Specialist Meeting on Advanced Instrumentation and Measurement Techniques, 1997, Santa Barbara.

Raad, T. and Myers, J. E. 1971. Nucleation Studies in Pool Boiling on Thin Plates Using Liquid Crystals. *AIChE Journal* 17:1260–1261.

Reimann, J. and John, H. 1978. Measurements of the Phase Distribution in Horizontal Air-Water and Steam-Water Flow, *CSNI Specialists Meeting on Transient Two-Phase Flow*. June 12–14, 1978, Paris.

Réocreux, M. 1974. Contribution à L'Étude des Débits Critiques en Écoulement Diphasique Eau-Vapeur. Thèse de Doctorat ès Sciences, Université Scientifique et Médicale de Grenoble.

Rouhani, Z. 1964. Application of the Turbine Type Flowmeters in the Measurement of Steam Quality and Void. Symposium on In-Core Instrumentation. Oslo, June 1964, USAEC-CONF-640607.

Sadasivan, P., Unal, C., and Nelson, R. A. 1995. Nonlinear Aspects of High Heat Flux Nucleate Boiling. *J. Heat Transfer* 117:981–987.

Seleghim, P., Jr. 1996. Caractérisation des Changements de Configuration d'un Écoulement Diphasique Horizontal par L'Application de Méthodes D'Analyse Temps-Fréquence. Thèse de Doctorat, Institut National Polytechnique de Grenoble, Spécialité: Mécanique.

Snell, C. C., Dechene, R. L., and Newton, R. E. 1978. Two-Phase Relative Volume Fraction Measurement with a Rotating Field Conductance Gauge. *Measurements in Polyphase Flows*. Ed. Stock, D. E., pp. 21–24. New York: ASME.

Solésio, J. N. 1978. Mesure de L'Épaisseur Locale Instantanée d'un Film Liquide Ruisselant sur une Paroi. Examen des Méthodes Existantes. Mise en Oeuvre d'une Technique Basée sur L'Absorption de Rayons X. CEA-R4925.

Solésio, J. N., Flamand, J. C., and Delhaye, J. M. 1978. Liquid Film Thickness Measurements by Means of an X-Ray Absorption Technique. *Topics in Two-Phase Heat Transfer and Flow*, Ed. Bankoff, S. G., pp. 193–198. New York: ASME.

Souhar, M. and Cognet, G. 1984. Wall Shear Stress Measurement by Electrochemical Probes in Two-Phase Flow—Bubble and Slug Regimes. *Measuring Techniques in Gas-Liquid Two-Phase Flows*. Eds. Delhaye, J. M. and Cognet, G., pp. 723–744. Berlin: Springer-Verlag.

Storm, E. and Israel, H. I. 1970. Photon Crosssections from 1 keV to 100 MeV for Elements $Z = 1$ to $Z = 100$, Nuclear Data Tables, A7, 565–681.

Stukenbroeker, G. L., Bonilla, C. F., and Peterson, R. W. 1970. The Use of Lead as a Shielding Material. *Nuclear Engineering and Design*, 13, I, 3.145.

Takenaka, N., Asano, H., Fujii, T., and Matsubayashi, M. 1997. Three-Dimensional Void Fraction Measurement of Steady Two-Phase Flow by Neutron Radiography. *Proceedings of the OECD/CSNI Specialist Meeting on Advanced Instrumentation and Measurement Techniques*, 1997, Santa Barbara.

Takenaka, N., Asano, H., Fujii, T., Wada, T., Matsubayashi, M., and Tsuruno, A. 1996. Three-Dimensional Measurement of Steady Air-Water Two-Phase Flow in a Rod Bundle by Neutron Radiography. *Proc. Japan-US Seminar on Two-Phase Flow Dynamics*, July 1996, Fukuoka, Japan, 331–337.

Takenaka, N., Fujii, T., Akagawa, K., Ono, A., Sonoda, K., Nishizaki, K., and Asano, H. 1990. Application of Neutron Radiography to Visualization of Multiphase Flows. *Flow Meas. Instrum.* 1:149–156.

Tournaire, A. 1985. Détection des Perturbations de Taux de Vide dans un Écoulement Diphasique en Conduite Cylindrique. Optimisation de la Méthode par Sonde à Impédance. CEA-R-55323.

Tournaire, A. 1986. Dependence of the Instantaneous Response of Impedance Probes on the Local Distribution of the Void Fraction in a Pipe. *Int. J. Multiphase Flow* 12(6):1019–1024.

Tournaire, A. 1987. Détection et Étude des Ondes de Taux de Vide en Écoulement Diphasique à Bulles Jusqu'à la Transition Bulles-Bouchons. Thèse de Docteur Ingénieur, Institut National Polytechnique et Université Scientifique et Médicale de Grenoble.

Veneau, T. 1995. Etude Expérimentale et Modélisation de la Décompression d'un Réservoir de Propane. Thèse de Doctorat, Institut National Polytechnique de Grenoble.

Veteau, J. M. 1979. Mesure des Aires Interfaciales dans les Écoulements Diphasiques. CEA-R-5005.

Veteau, J. M. 1981. Contribution à L'Étude des Techniques de Mesure de L'Aire Interfaciale dans les Écoulements à Bulles. Thèse de Docteur ès Sciences, Université Scientifique et Médicale et Institut National Polytechnique de Grenoble.

Veteau, J. M. and Charlot, R. 1981. Interfacial Area Measurements in Two-Phase Bubbly Flows: Comparison Between the Light Attenuation Technique and a Local Method. European Two-Phase Flow Group Meeting, Eindhoven (The Netherlands), June 2–5.

Watwe, A. A. and Hollingsworth, D. K. 1994. Liquid Crystal Images of Surface Temperature During Incipient Boiling. *Experimental Thermal and Fluid Science* 9:22–33.

Williams, R. A. and Beck, M. S., eds. 1995. *Process Tomography—Principles, Techniques, and Applications*. Butterworth-Heinemann.

Yan, Y. and Kenning, D. B. R. 1995. Flow Boiling in Bubbly Flow. *Proc. Engineering Foundation Conference on Convective Flow Boiling*, Banff, April 29–May 5, 293–298. New York: ASME.

Yan, Y., Grant, I., Kenning, D. B. R., and Cornwell, K. 1995. Heat Transfer to Sliding Bubbles Under Plane and Curved Surfaces. *Transactions 4th UK National Conference on Heat Transfer*, Manchester, 1995, September 26–27, pp. 295–300. London: IMechE.

Yan, Y., Kenning, D. B. R., and Cornwell, K. 1997. Sliding and Sticking Bubbles Under Inclined Plane and Curved Surfaces. *Int. J. Refrigeration* 20:583–591.

Yoneda, K., Kawai, T., Fujine, S., Uturo, M., Ikeda, Y., Yokoi, M., and Kobayashi, H. 1990. Cold Neutron Hole in KUR and Its Radiography Tests. *Proc. 1st. Int. Top. Meet. on Neutron Radiography System Design and Characterization*, Ontario, Canada, 32–42.

Zeng, L. Z. and Klausner, J. F. 1993. Nucleation Site Density in Forced Convection Boiling. *J. Heat Transfer*, 115:215–221.

# CONVERSION FACTORS FOR COMMONLY USED QUANTITIES

(Reprinted from Introduction to Thermal Sciences by Satish G. Kandlikar)

| Physical quantity | British units | SI units | Multiply by British → SI | Multiply by SI → British |
|---|---|---|---|---|
| *Basic Quantities* | | | | |
| *Area | ft$^2$ | m$^2$ | 0.0929 | 10.7639 |
| *Force | lbf | N | 4.4482 | 0.22481 |
| *Length | ft | m | 0.3048 | 3.28084 |
| *Mass | lbm | kg | 0.45359 | 2.20462 |
| *Density | lbm/ft$^3$ | kg/m$^3$ | 16.018 | 0.062428 |
| *Pressure or Stress | lbf/ft$^2$ | N/m$^2$ (Pa) | $0.99284 \times 10^6$ | $1.00721 \times 10^{-6}$ |
| | lbf/in$^2$ | N/m$^2$ (Pa) | 6894.73 | $0.14504 \times 10^{-3}$ |
| *Time | h | s | 3600 | $0.27778 \times 10^{-3}$ |
| *Volume | ft$^3$ | m$^3$ | 0.028317 | 35.31448 |
| *Mass flow rate | lb/h | kg/s | $1.26 \times 10^{-4}$ | 7936.7 |
| | lb/min | kg/s | $7.56 \times 10^{-3}$ | 132.28 |
| *Volume flow rate | ft$^3$/h | m$^3$/s | $7.8658 \times 10^{-6}$ | $0.127133 \times 10^{-6}$ |
| | ft$^3$/min, CFM | m$^3$/s | $4.7195 \times 10^{-4}$ | 2118.87 |
| *Energy related* | | | | |
| Energy | Btu | J | 1055.042 | $9.4783 \times 10^{-4}$ |
| Specific energy | Btu/lb$_m$ | J/kg | 2326.122 | $4.299 \times 10^{-4}$ |
| Power | Btu/hr | W | .2930712 | 3.41214 |
| *Heat transfer related* | | | | |
| *heat flux | Bth/h ft$^2$ | W/m$^2$ | 3.154 | 0.31706 |
| *heat transfer coefficient | Btu/h ft$^2$ °F | W/m$^2$ °C | 5.67859 | 0.1761 |
| *specific heat | Btu/lbm °F | W/m$^2$ °C | 4186.8 | $0.238846 \times 10^{-3}$ |
| *thermal conductivity | Btu/h ft °F | W/m °C | 1.731 | 0.5779 |
| *viscosity | lbm/h ft | kg/m s | $0.4134 \times 10^{-3}$ | 2418.9 |

# CONVERSION FACTORS IN DIFFERENT UNITS

(Reprinted from Introduction to Thermal Sciences by Satish G. Kandlikar)

### (a) Length

|     | m | cm | mm | $\mu$m | ft | in |
|-----|---|----|----|----|----|----|
| m   | 1 | 100 | 1000 | $1 \times 10^6$ | 3.28084 | 39.37 |
| cm  | 0.01 | 1 | 10 | $10 \times 10^3$ | $32.8084 \times 10^{-3}$ | 0.3937 |
| mm  | 0.001 | 0.1 | 1 | 1000 | $3.28084 \times 10^{-3}$ | 0.03937 |
| $\mu$m | $1 \times 10^{-6}$ | $0.1 \times 10^{-3}$ | 0.001 | 1 | $3.28084 \times 10^{-6}$ | $39.37 \times 10^{-6}$ |
| ft  | 0.3048 | 30.48 | $0.3048 \times 10^3$ | $0.3048 \times 10^6$ | 1 | 12 |
| in  | 0.0254 | 2.54 | 25.4 | $25.4 \times 10^3$ | 0.083333 | 1 |

### (b) Area

|     | $m^2$ | $cm^2$ | $mm^2$ | $ft^2$ | $in^2$ |
|-----|-------|--------|--------|--------|--------|
| $m^2$  | 1 | $10 \times 10^3$ | $1 \times 10^6$ | 10.7639 | 1550 |
| $cm^2$ | $0.1 \times 10^{-3}$ | 1 | $0.1 \times 10^3$ | 0.00107639 | 0.155 |
| $mm^2$ | $1 \times 10^{-6}$ | 0.001 | 1 | $10.7639 \times 10^{-6}$ | 0.00155 |
| $ft^2$ | 0.929 | 929 | $92.9 \times 10^3$ | 1 | 144 |
| $in^2$ | $0.64516 \times 10^{-3}$ | 6.4516 | $0.64516 \times 10^3$ | 0.006944 | 1 |

### (c) Pressure

|     | $N/m^2$ (Pa) | bar | atm | mm Hg | $lb_f/in^2$ (psi) |
|-----|--------------|-----|-----|-------|-------------------|
| $N/m^2$ | 1 | $10 \times 10^{-6}$ | $9.8692 \times 10^{-6}$ | 0.0075006 | $0.145036 \times 10^{-3}$ |
| bar     | $0.1 \times 10^6$ | 1 | 0.98692 | 750.06 | 14.5038 |
| atm     | $0.101325 \times 10^6$ | 1.01325 | 1 | 760 | 14.696 |
| mm Hg   | 133.32237 | $1.33323 \times 10^{-6}$ | 0.00131579 | 1 | 0.0193368 |
| $lb_f/in^2$ | $0.894745 \times 10^6$ | 0.06894745 | 0.0680457 | 51.71475 | 1 |

### (d) Energy

|     | J | Btu | ft·$lb_f$ |
|-----|---|-----|-----------|
| J   | 1 | $9.4783 \times 10^{-4}$ | .73756 |
| Btu | 1055.042 | 1 | 778.156 |
| ft·$lb_f$ | 1.35582 | $1.2851 \times 10_{-3}$ | 1 |

(Continued)

**(Continued)**

### (e) Thermal Conductivity

|  | W/m·°C | W/cm·°C | W/in·°F | Btu/h·ft$^2$·°F |
|---|---|---|---|---|
| W/m·°C | 1 | 0.01 | 0.0254 | 0.5779 |
| W/cm·°C | 100 | 1 | 2.54 | 57.79 |
| W/in·°F | 39.37008 | 0.3937008 | 1 | 22.75197 |
| Btu/h·ft$^2$·°F | 1.731 | 0.01731 | 0.04397 | 1 |

### (f) Heat Transfer Coefficient

|  | W/m$^2$·°C | W/cm$^2$·°C | W/in$^2$·°C | Btu/h·ft·°F |
|---|---|---|---|---|
| W/m$^2$·°C | 1 | $0.1 \times 10^{-3}$ | $0.64516 \times 10^{-3}$ | 0.1761 |
| W/cm$^2$·°C | $10 \times 10^3$ | 1 | 6.4516 | 1761 |
| W/in$^2$·°F | 1550 | 0.155 | 1 | 272.9854 |
| Btu/h·ft·°F | 5.678 | $0.5678 \times 10^{-3}$ | 0.0036632 | 1 |

### (g) Heat Flux

|  | W/m$^2$ | W/cm$^2$ | W/in$^2$ | Btu/h·ft$^2$ |
|---|---|---|---|---|
| W/m$^2$ | 1 | $0.1 \times 10^{-3}$ | $0.64516 \times 10^{-3}$ | 0.3170 |
| W/cm$^2$ | $10 \times 10^3$ | 1 | 6.4516 | 3170 |
| W/in$^2$ | 1550 | 0.155 | 1 | 491.351 |
| Btu/h·ft$^2$ | 3.154 | $0.3154 \times 10^{-3}$ | 0.0020348 | 1 |

### (h) Viscosity

|  | N s/m$^2$, (Poiseuille) | Poise | Centipoise | lb/h ft |
|---|---|---|---|---|
| N·s/m$^2$ | 1 | 10 | 1000 | 2420 |
| Poise | 0.1 | 1 | 100 | 242 |
| Centipoise | 0.001 | 0.01 | 1 | 2.42 |
| lb$_{in}$/h·ft | $0.4134 \times 10^{-3}$ | 0.004134 | 0.4134 | 1 |

# INDEX

Acceleration pressure gradient, 201, 297, 425
Active nucleation site density, 89, 94
Active stabilization, 182
Activity coefficient, 27, 30
Advanced geometries, 403
Advancing contact angle, 184, 190
Annular flow, 67, 201, 207, 223
Annular-dispersed flow, 212, 289
Annular-slug flow, 416
Antoine equation, 7
Archimedes number, 328
Augmentation
  external condensation, 605
    EHD
      horizontal finned tube, 609
      optimum fin dimensions, 612
      trapezoid-fin tube, 613
      two-dimensional fin tube, 612, 615
      vertical fluted tube, 605
  external flow boiling, 331, 359
    CHF, 361
    macro-structured surfaces, 360
    micro-structured surfaces, 360
    radial and rectangular grooves, 360
  flow boiling, 495
    CHF
      extended surfaces, 515
      helically coiled tube, 516
      helically coiled wire, 514
      swirl flow, 512
      techniques, 512
    post-CHF, 516
    saturated, 498
      EHD, 509
      internal fins, 506
      microfin tubes, 498
      porous coating, 509
      spirally fluted tubes, 508
      twisted tapes, 508
    subcooled, 495
      EHD, 496
      hysteresis, 496
      porous coating, 496
      vibrations, 498
  internal condensation, 621, 639
    fundamentals, 639
    inserts, 640
    internal fins, 641
    microfin tubes, 642, 664
    rectangular/flat tubes, 664
  pool boiling, 121, *see* enhancement
Average concentration in boundary layer, 102
Azeotrope, 22

Binary mixture, 22
  condensation, 627, 651

Binary mixture (contd.)
  critical heat flux, 447, 468
  flow boiling, 428
    model, 428
  external, multicomponent, 571
  laminar film condensation, 566
  pool boiling, 99
Boiling crisis, 67
Boiling curve, 64
Bond number, 45
Bubble
  departure, 86
  diameter at departure, 93
  dynamics, 85, 86
    subcooled flow, 372
  growth time, 88
  nucleation, 125
  radius, 9
  release frequency, 88, 93
  shape, 123
Bubble growth
  diffusion controlled, 100
  suppression factor, 300
Bubble point temperature, 21
Bubble-slug transition, 208, 239
Bubbly flow, 200, 289
Burnout heat flux, 67, 145

Capillary
  constant, 45
  length, 42
  pressure, 44, 45
Cassie-Baxter equation, 47
Cavity
  conical, 80
  diameter, 83
  minimum wall superheat, 83
  mouth angle, 84, 91
  mouth radius, 80
Chaos, 274
Chemical heterogeneity, 43
Chemical potential, 6
Churn flow, 206, 223
Churn-annular transition, 210
Clausius-Clapeyron Equation, 6
Combination rule, 33
Compact heat exchangers
  boiling, 412
    confinement number, 414

  flooding, 414
  flow regimes, 415
  heat transfer correlations, 416
  plate heat exchangers, 412
  pressure drop, 424
  printed circuit heat exchangers, 412
condensers, 653
  cryogenic application, 658
  fin efficiency, 671
  flow characteristics, 659
  flow geometry, 657
  flow parameters, 656
  modeling, 662
  plate-and-frame, 655, 665
  plate-fin, 657
  printed circuit heat exchangers, 655
  tube-fin type, 655
  types, 654
Composite surface, 47
Compressibility factor, 3, 12
  vapor phase, 27
Computational fluid dynamics models, 203
Condensation
  augmentation techniques, 605
  compact heat exchangers, 653
  direct contact, 595
  falling liquid drop, 597
  liquid jet, 596
  non-condensable gases, 602
  train of vapor bubbles, 602
  vapor bubble, 600
dropwise, 581
  condensation curves, 588
  departing drop size effect, 585
  heat transfer theory, 590
  organic vapors, 589
  pressure effect, 584
  promotion, 582
  steam, 583
  surface material properties, 586
internal, 621
  augmentation, 639
  binary mixtures, 627
  circular tubes with microfins, 664
  compact condensers, 653
  horizontal flow, 666
  non-azeotropic refrigerant mixtures, 651
  oil effect, 646
  pressure drop, 622

pressure gradient, 667
pure vapors, 624
smooth tube correlations, 625
turbulent liquid film, 624
vertical tubes, 663
laminar film, external, 523
binary mixture, 566
boundary layer solutions, 532
forced convection, 532
horizontal surface, 533
horizontal tube, 535
vertical, 534
multicomponent mixture, 571
saturated vapor, 525
variable properties, 536
vertical plate, 531
liquid jet, 596
mixtures, 563
internal multicomponent, 633
non-condensable gases, 564
oil effect, 649
shell and tube condensers, 614
transition, 537, 538
theoretical analysis, 543
tube banks, horizontal smooth, 551
inundation, 557
pressure drop, 561
pure organic vapor, 556
pure steam, 551
steam-air mixtures, 555
tube banks, horizontal finned, 558
pure vapor, 558
turbulent film, 537
binary mixtures, 548
body forced convection, 540
combined, 547
correlations, 537
transition point, 538
Condensation coefficient, 56
Condensation curves, 588
Condensation number, 539
Condenser design methodology, 672
Confined bubble flow, 416
Contact angle, 42, 57, 73, 84, 187
advancing, 43, 184, 373
apparent, 48
critical heat flux, 147
dynamic, 43, 50
effective, 42

equilibrium, 46
flow boiling, 373
hysteresis, 43, 48–49, 185
metastable, 43
receding, 43, 49, 184, 373
reentrant, 122, 125
retreating, 184
Contact instability, 50
Contact line, 42
critical speed, 51
Coulomb force, 135
Critical boiling point, 181
Critical cavity size, 371
Critical heat flux
external flow boiling, 336
augmentation, 361
flow boiling, 217, 443
saturated, 459
binary mixtures, 468
correlations, 465
diameter effect, 462
dryout, 474
heat flux distribution effect, 465
heated length effect, 462
mass flux effect, 461
models, 470
neural network, 469
non-uniform heat flux, 469
orientation effect, 464
parametric trends, 460
pressure effect, 461
subcooling effect, 460
wall thickness effect, 465
subcooled, 444
binary mixtures, 447
correlations, 453
diameter effect, 447
dissolved gas effect, 452
heat flux distribution effect, 452
heated length effect, 450
mass flux effect, 445
models, 455–456
orientation effect, 445
parametric trends, 445
pressure effect, 447
subcooling effect, 445
wall material effect, 451
wall thickness effect, 451

Critical heat flux (*contd.*)
  impinging jets, 336
    free surface
      circular, 336
      effect of subcooling, 338
      multiple, 337
      single-jet, 336
      wall jet, 340
    submerged impinging jet, 341
    submerged wall jet, 341
  mechanistic models, 151
  mixtures, 161
  non-condensables, 158
  pool boiling, 65, 145
    factors affecting, 145
      contact angle, 147
      heater capacity, 148
      heater orientation, 150
      surface roughness, 146
      surface wettability, 147
    subcooled pool boiling, 158
    vapor escape path instability model, 151
Critical length, 152
Critical point, 5
Critical two-phase flow, 279
Critical wavelength, 153
Cross coefficients, 33

Degrees of freedom, 17
Densitometer
  single-beam, 692
  multiple beam, 693
  x-ray, 692
Density wave oscillation, 263, 268
Departing drop size, 585
Departure bubble diameter, 93
Departure from nucleate boiling, DNB, 67
Dielectrophoretic force, 135
Diffusion coefficient, 37, 105, 434
Diffusion resistance, 161
Direct contact condensation, 595,
  *see* Condensation
Dispersed bubbly flow, 211, 212
Dispersed flow, 200
Distributed parameter model, 269
Dried-up mode, 131
Drift flux model, 229, 270, 296
Drift velocity, 296
Dryout, 474

Dynamic model, 121

EHD, 123, 134, 496, 509, 616
Electric field, 133
Electrical body force, 135
Electrical probes, 680
Electrical resistance probes, 155
Electrodynamic equations, 135
Electrophoretic force, 135
Enhanced surfaces for pool boiling, 125, 138
  structured surfaces, 127
Enhancement mechanism
  pool boiling, 122
Enhancement techniques
  pool boiling, 121
    active methods, 123
    EHD, 123
    passive methods, 123
    reentrant cavities, 125
    structured surfaces, 128
    vibration, 133
Equation of state, 2
  Benedict-Webb-Rubin equation, 4, 34
  ideal gas equation, 3
  Peng-Robinson equation, 4
  Redlich-Kwong equation, 4, 33
  two-constant equations, 5, 32
  van der Waals equation, 4
  virial equation, 3
Equilibrium
  metastable, 8
  state, 18
  thermodynamic, 1
  two-phase, 7
  vapor-liquid thermal, 82
Equilibrium criteria, 1
Equilibrium critical flow model, 280
Eötvös number, 45
Excess properties, 30
External flow boiling, 331

F-factor, 303
Falling film, 342
  convective heat transfer, 345
  film thickness, 343
  liquid film flow, 342
  minimum wetting rate, 349
Falling film boiling, 354
  dynamic pressure fluctuations, 358

INDEX **733**

entrainment, 354
local dryout, 357
saturated boiling length
Falling film evaporation, 350
  heat transfer, 351
  minimum wetting rate, 352
Feedback system, 269
Fiber optical probe, 686
Film boiling, 66, 478
  analytical models, 180
  cleanliness, 188
  coating, 187
  external, 311
  flow, 478
  foam limit model, 180
  heater size effect, 189
  horizontal cylinder, 178
  horizontal flat plate, 180
  horizontal wire, 178
  inclined surface, 176
  liquid-solid contact, 180
  monolayer, 180
  phenomenological models, 191
  radiation, 169, 173
  roughness effect, 189
  saturated, 313
  sphere, 179
  stability limits, 183
  subcooling effect, 189
  subcooled liquid, 173, 179
  Taylor instability, 66, 68
  transient, 179
  transient experiments, 186
  vertical surfaces, 170
Film condensation, *see* Condensation
Flow boiling
  advanced geometries, 403
  binary mixtures, 429, 468
  circular tubes, 367
    saturated, 386
    subcooled, 368
  compact heat exchangers, 412
  critical heat flux, 217, 443
  internal, 66
  liquid-deficient region, 480
  map, 392, 394
  mechanisms, 395
  microgravity, 435
  narrow channels, 403

post-CHF region, 217
shell-side, 300
Flow condensation, *see* Condensation
Flow film boiling, 313
  external
    correlation, 320
    governing equations, 315
    local similarity transformation, 315
    separation point, 317
    sphere, 313, 326
    stagnation region, 313
    subcooled, 313
    uniform heat flux model, 316
    wake region, 317
Flow instability, 261, 263
Flow orientation, 297
Flow pattern map, 207, 238
  annular channel, 238
  flat channel, 239
  Mandhane, 213
  narrow channel, 239
  rectangular channel, 238, 239
  Taitel-Dukler, 214
  triangular channel, 238
  tube bundles, 289
  upward flow, 238
Flow patterns, 200, 206
  compact evaporators, 415
  condensation, 215
  evaporation, 215
  fin effect, 241, 248, 253
  flat narrow channel, 243
  horizontal tube, 211
  inclined tubes, 215
  orientation effect, 248
  saturated flow boiling, 387
  vertical downflow, 210
  vertical upflow, 206
Flow regimes in flow boiling, 68
Flow separation point, 312
Fluid-surface parameter, 390
Free-surface impinging jets, 332
  circular, 332
  planar, 333
  Friction factor, 224
  two-phase, 225
Friction pressure drop
  subcooled, 383
Frictional pressure gradient, 201, 297, 424

# 734  INDEX

Fugacity coefficient, 6
  mixtures, 11, 15
Fully developed boiling, 369
Fully developed nucleate boiling, 72, 75
  free surface jets, 334

Gaertner's first transition, 72
Gamma ray absorption, 155
Gibbs function, 5
  mixture, 15
  molar, 6
  molar excess, 30
  partial molar, 12, 15
  quasi, 21
Gibbs phase rule, 17
Gravitational pressure gradient, 201, 297, 425
Grooved tubes, *see* Microfin tubes
Growth time, 88

Heat pipe, 408
Heat sink, 407
Henry-Fauske model, 282
Homogeneous equilibrium model, 281
Homogeneous model, 202, 220, 397
Homogeneous nucleation, 79
Hovering period, 153
Hydrostatic pressure gradient, 425
Hysteresis, 65
  film boiling, 183, 184
  pool boiling, 130
Ideal mixtures, 26, 28
Impinging jets, 331
  configurations, 332
  critical heat flux, 336
  incipience of nucleate boiling, 334
  two-phase, 404

Inception superheat, 81
Incipient superheat, 81, 84–85
Inserts, condensation, 640
Instrumentation, 679
  heat transfer coefficient, 711
  interfacial area, 709
    ultrasonic attenuation, 711
  liquid crystal thermography, 713
  liquid velocity, 712
  local temperature, 712
  mass flow rate, 701

  venturi tube, 703
  turbine, 705
  void fraction
    electrical probes, 682
    fiber optical probe, 686
    high speed video camera, 716
    impedance, 694
    line, 688
    neutron scattering, 694
    photon attenuation technique, 687, 692
    optical probes, 684
    radiation, 689
    radiography, 694
    x-ray densitometer, 692
  wall shear stress, 712
Interfacial area, 682
  measurement, 709
Interface concentration, 103
Interfacial tension, 44
  liquid-gas, 46
  solid-gas, 46
  solid-liquid, 46
Intermittent flow, 201, 289
Internal fins
  flow boiling, 506
  internal condensation, 641
Instability
  liquid-vapor interface, 176
  macroscopic saw-tooth, 43
  oscillatory, 268
  vapor nuclei, 84
Interaction parameter, binary, 33
Interface resistance, 524
Inundation, 557
Inverse annular flow boiling, 68
Isolated bubble flow, 415

Jet impingement, *see* Impinging jets

Kelvin-Helmholtz instability, 153
Kettle reboiler, 286

Laminar film condensation, 523
Laplace transform, 268
Ledinegg instability, 263
Leonard-Jones potential, 53
Linear stability analysis, 269
Liquid contact time, 190
Liquid cooling, 408

INDEX  **735**

Liquid crystal thermography, 713
Liquid-deficient region, 480
Liquid droplet, 53
Liquid jet–condensation, 596
Liquid-vapor interface, 9, 53, 136, 160, 176
Local assumption, 419
Lockhart-Martinelli curves, 226, 397
Lockhart-Martinelli parameter, 297, 385, 399
Loss-of-coolant accidents, 170
Low-fin tube, 127
Lumped parameter model, 266

Macrolayer dry-out model, 152
Macrolayer thickness measurement, 155, 157
Marangoni convection, 160
Marangoni number, 162
Margules equation, 31
Martinelli parameter, 214
Mass flow rate measurement, 701
Maximum heat flux, 435
Mechanical stability, 9
Mechanistic models, CHF, 151
Micro-bubble emission boiling, 159
Microchannel cooling, 404, 408, 411
Microelectronic equipment cooling, 403
Microfin tubes
   boiling, 498
      correlations, 500
      oil effect, 505
      three dimensional, 504
      condensation, 642
Microgravity
   flow boiling, 435
Microlayer
   evaporation, 93
   thickness, 137
Minimum film boiling point, 181
Minimum heat flux point, 180
Mist cooling, 363
Mixing rule for mixtures, 32
Mixtures
   ideal, 26
   mixing rule, 32
   multicomponent, 24
   non-ideal, 29
   phase equilibrium diagrams, 17, 28
Moderate diffusion induced suppression, 431
Molecular effusion, 154, 160

Multicomponent mixtures, 24
Multiphase flow, 223

Near-azeotropic region, 431
Negative damping, 268
Net vapor generation, 369
Neural network, 469
Neutron scattering, 694
Non-ideal mixtures, 29
Non-linear dynamics, 274
Non-linear oscillation, 266
Non-wetting agent, 582
Nucleate boiling, 71
   fully developed, 72, 75
   heat transfer, 93
   surface roughness effect, 74
   surface wettability effect, 75
Nucleation criterion, 64, 379
Nucleation site density, 89
Nyquist method, 273

Onset of nucleate boiling, ONB, 64
   subcooled flow, 369
Onset of significant void, 369
Optical probes, 155, 682, 687
Optimum fin dimensions, 612

P-v-T relationship, 2
Pade approximation, 268
Parachor, 39
Partial boiling, 375
Partial dryout, 416
Partial nucleate boiling, 65
Passive stabilization, 182
Perforated fin, 427
Phase equilibrium
   diagrams for mixtures, 17
   mixtures, 16, 28
   multicomponent, 13
Phenomenological models
   film models, 191
Photographic observation, 155
Photon attenuation technique, 687
Plug flow, 206, 212
Pool boiling, 63
   binary mixtures, 99
   critical heat flux, 65
   film boiling, 66
   heat transfer coefficient, 66

# 736 INDEX

Pool boiling (*contd.*)
  hysteresis, 65, 130
  mixtures, 99
    heat transfer coefficient, 104
  natural convection, 64
  nucleate boiling, 71
    aging, 76
    binary mixtures, 99
      pseudo-single component heat transfer coefficient, 101
    cavities, 76
    correlations, 95
    corrosion, 76
    electric field effect, 136
    enhancement techniques, 121
    enhancement mechanisms, 122
    fully developed, 65, 67, 72, 75
    gravity effect, 78
    heater geometry effect, 76
    liquid subcooling effect, 77
    metal ions, 76
    multicomponent, 99
    pressure effect, 77
    reference heat flux, 77
    reference heat transfer coefficient, 77
    saturated pool boiling, 96
    surface condition effect, 95
    surface contamination, 76
    surface roughness effect, 74
    surface wettability effect, 75
    surfactant effect, 106
  nucleation characteristics, 79
  partial nucleate boiling, 65
  transition boiling, 66
Porous coating, 496, 509
Post CHF heat transfer, 477
Pressure drop, 266
  compact condensers, 622
  compact evaporator, 424
  internal flow condensation, 622
  condensation, 622
  condensation on tube banks, 561
  overall, 297
  saturated flow boiling, 396
  subcooled flow, 384
Pressure drop multipliers, 226
Pressure drop oscillation, 263, 264
Property changes on mixing, 24

Quality
  actual, 232
  definition, 682
  thermodynamic, 393
Quenching, 79, 133, 181

Radiation in film boiling, 169, 173
Radiography, 694
Raoult's law, 28
Rayleigh-Taylor instability, 153
Reactor cooling, 181
Reduced pressure, 98
Residence time, 267
Rogue sites, 370
Roughness effect
  contact angle, 42
  critical heat flux, pool boiling, 146

Saturated film boiling, 313
Saturated flow boiling, 386
  critical heat flux, 459
  flow boiling map, 392, 394
  flow patterns, 387
  fluid-surface parameter, 390, 391
  heat transfer, 387
  mechanisms, 395
  post-dryout region, 396
  pressure drop, 396
  rectangular geometry, 395
  wetted wall region, 387
Semi-slug flow, 213
Separated flow, 201
Separated flow model, 202, 222, 226, 229
Serrated fin, 427
Severe diffusion induced suppression, 432
Shell-side, 285
Significant void flow region, 369
Single-phase friction pressure drop, 250
Single-phase pressure gradient, 224
Slip flow model, 281
Slug-annular flow transition, 239
Slug-churn transition, 209
Slug flow, 206, 212, 223
Solid-liquid-vapor interactions, 52
  direct simulation, 53
  Leonard-Jones potential, 53
  Monte Carlo technique, 53
Spinodal, liquid and vapor, 9
Spirally fluted tube, 508

INDEX 737

Spray flow, 289
Spray cooling, 363
Stability criterion
　simplified, 274
Stability limits in film boiling, 182
Stratified flow, 201, 211
Stratified-slug transition, 215
Stratified-wavy flow, 212
Structured surfaces, 127
Subcooled flow boiling, 231, 368
　bubble dynamics, 372
　flow boiling map, 392, 394
　fully developed, 369, 374
　　location, 379
　heat transfer, 374
　onset of nucleate boiling, 369, 370
　onset of significant void, 369
　partial boiling, 375, 380
　pressure drop, 384
　regions, 368
　significant void flow, 369, 381
　void fraction, 383
　word of caution, 383
Subcooled region, 266
Submerged jets, 333
Subsurface tunnels, 131
Suction-evaporation mode, 131
Superficial velocities, 218, 296
Suppression factor, 423
　mass diffusion induced, 104, 431
Surface characteristics, 89
Surface roughness, 90
Surface tension, 37, 42
　aqueous mixtures, 38
　non-aqueous mixtures, 39
Surfactant, 106

Taylor instability, 66
Thermal layer
　reformation, 86
　thickness, 83
Thermodynamic equilibrium quality, 393
Thermodynamic non-equilibrium, 481
Thermodynamic properties
　extensive, 13
　intensive, 17
　partial molar, 13
　pure substances, 34
　mixtures, 25, 34

Thick film region, 611
Tie line, 21
Transient boiling, 78
Transient film boiling, 179
Transient heat transfer coefficient, 78
Transition boiling, 66, 181
Transitional film boiling curve, 184
Transport properties, 35
Trapezoid-fin tube, 613
Tube bundle, 285, 300
　in-line, 288
　staggered, 288
Turbulent film condensation, 537
Twisted tapes
　boiling, 508
Two-dimensional fin tube, 612, 615
Two-fluid model, 202
Two-mode boiling, 183
Two-phase
　cross-flow, 285
　density, 219
　enthalpy, 219
　friction multiplier, 251, 297, 303
　friction pressure drop, 252, 285, 297
　　fin effect, 253
　quality, 219
　Reynolds number, 225
　viscosity, 225
Two-phase boundary layer equations, 169
Two-phase flow
　component non-equilibrium, 200
　computational fluid dynamics models, 203
　density, 219
　enthalpy, 219
　flow patterns, 200
　hydrodynamic non-equilibrium, 199
　narrow channels, 233
　non-circular channels, 233
　non-equilibrium effects, 198
　phenomenological models, 203, 222
　quality, 219
　thermodynamic non-equilibrium, 199
Two-phase pressure drop, 249
　channel orientation effect, 251
　channel size effect, 251
　Chisholm and Laird correlation, 251
　condensing flow, 667
　　circular tube, 667
　　plate-fin heat exchanger, 672

Two-phase pressure drop (*contd.*)
    plate-frame heat exchanger, 672
    rectangular/flat tube, 671
    fluid property effect, 251
    Lockhart-Martinelli correlation, 249
    shell-side, 297

van der Pol equation, 266
van Laar equation, 31
Vapor explosions, 170
Vapor-film unit model, 175
Vapor pressure
    equation, 7
    spherical interface, 10
Vapor stem merging model, 154
Virial coefficients, 3
Void fraction
    area, 692
    air-water, 293
    CHF, 155
    definitions, 680
    homogeneous, 228
    instantaneous area, 681
    instantaneous line, 681
    measurement, 682
    steam-water, 295
    subcooled flow, 383
    tube bundles, 289, 291
    two-phase flow, 219, 228, 270
Void wave, 264
Volume fraction of vapor, 230

Waiting period, 88
Waiting time, 88
    binary mixtures, 106
Wake region, 312
Wave motion, 174
Wavy film condensation, 543
Wettability, 147, 180, 187
Wetting
    complete, 46
    partial, 46
Wilson equation, 31, 32
Wispy annular flow, 206, 207

X-ray densitometer, 692

Young-Dupre equation, 46
Young-Laplace equation, 44
Young's equation, 46

Zaloudek model, 282